Student Solutions Manual

DANIEL S. MILLER Niagara County Community College

Blitzer

COLLEGE ALGEBRA FOURTH EDITION

PEARSON
Prentice
Hall

Upper Saddle River, NJ 07458

Editor-in-Chief: Sally Yagan
Acquisitions Editor: Adam Jaworski
Project Manager: Dawn Murrin
Executive Managing Editor: Kathleen Schiaparelli
Assistant Managing Editor: Karen Bosch
Production Editor: Jenelle J. Woodrup
Supplement Cover Manager: Paul Gourhan
Supplement Cover Designer: Christopher Kossa
Manufacturing Buyer: Ilene Kahn
Manufacturing Manager: Alexis Heydt-Long

© 2007 Pearson Education, Inc.
Pearson Prentice Hall
Pearson Education, Inc.
Upper Saddle River, NJ 07458

Pearson Prentice Hall™ is a trademark of Pearson Education, Inc.

The author and publisher of this book have used their best efforts in preparing this book. These efforts include the development, research, and testing of the theories and programs to determine their effectiveness. The author and publisher make no warranty of any kind, expressed or implied, with regard to these programs or the documentation contained in this book. The author and publisher shall not be liable in any event for incidental or consequential damages in connection with, or arising out of, the furnishing, performance, or use of these programs.

Printed in the United States of America

10 9 8 7 6 5 4 3 2 1

ISBN 0-13-195364-8

Pearson Education Ltd., *London*
Pearson Education Australia Pty. Ltd., *Sydney*
Pearson Education Singapore, Pte. Ltd.
Pearson Education North Asia Ltd., *Hong Kong*
Pearson Education Canada, Inc., *Toronto*
Pearson Educación de Mexico, S.A. de C.V.
Pearson Education—Japan, *Tokyo*
Pearson Education Malaysia, Pte. Ltd.

Table of Contents

Chapter P

Section P.1

Check Point Exercises

1. $8 + 6(x-3)^2 = 8 + 6(13-3)^2$

$\qquad = 8 + 6(10)^2$

$\qquad = 8 + 6(100)$

$\qquad = 8 + 600$

$\qquad = 608$

2. The year 2000 is 40 years after 1960.

$P = 0.72x^2 + 9.4x + 783$

$\quad = 0.72(40)^2 + 9.4(40) + 783$

$\quad = 0.72(1600) + 376 + 783$

$\quad = 1152 + 376 + 783$

$\quad = 2311$

The equation's value of 2311 models the data in the bar graph quite well.

3. The elements common to $\{3, 4, 5, 6, 7\}$ and $\{3, 7, 8, 9\}$ are 3 and 7.

$\{3, 4, 5, 6, 7\} \cap \{3, 7, 8, 9\} = \{3, 7\}$

4. The union is the set containing all the elements of either set.

$\{3, 4, 5, 6, 7\} \cup \{3, 7, 8, 9\} = \{3, 4, 5, 6, 7, 8, 9\}$

5. $\left\{ -9,\ -1.3,\ 0,\ 0.\overline{3},\ \dfrac{\pi}{2},\ \sqrt{9},\ \sqrt{10} \right\}$

   a. Natural numbers: $\sqrt{9}$ because $\sqrt{9} = 3$

   b. Whole numbers: $0,\ \sqrt{9}$

   c. Integers: $-9,\ 0,\ \sqrt{9}$

   d. Rational numbers: $-9,\ -1.3,\ 0,\ 0.\overline{3},\ \sqrt{9}$

   e. Irrational numbers: $\dfrac{\pi}{2},\ \sqrt{10}$

   f. Real numbers:

$\qquad \left\{ -9,\ -1.3,\ 0,\ 0.\overline{3},\ \dfrac{\pi}{2},\ \sqrt{9},\ \sqrt{10} \right\}$

6.   **a.** $\left| 1 - \sqrt{2} \right|$

Because $\sqrt{2} \approx 1.4$, the number inside the absolute value bars is negative. The absolute value of x when $x < 0$ is $-x$. Thus,

$\left| 1 - \sqrt{2} \right| = -\left(1 - \sqrt{2}\right) = \sqrt{2} - 1$

  b. $\left| \pi - 3 \right|$

Because $\pi \approx 3.14$, the number inside the absolute value bars is positive. The absolute value of a positive number is the number itself. Thus,

$\left| \pi - 3 \right| = \pi - 3$.

  c. $\dfrac{|x|}{x}$

Because $x > 0$, $|x| = x$.

Thus, $\dfrac{|x|}{x} = \dfrac{x}{x} = 1$

7. $|-4 - (5)| = |-9| = 9$

The distance between -4 and 5 is 9.

8. $7(4x^2 + 3x) + 2(5x^2 + x)$

$\quad = 7(4x^2 + 3x) + 2(5x^2 + x)$

$\quad = 28x^2 + 21x + 10x^2 + 2x$

$\quad = 38x^2 + 23x$

9. $6 + 4[7 - (x-2)]$

$\quad = 6 + 4[7 - x + 2)]$

$\quad = 6 + 4[9 - x]$

$\quad = 6 + 36 - 4x$

$\quad = 42 - 4x$

Exercise Set P.1

1. $7 + 5(10) = 7 + 50 = 57$

3. $6(3) - 8 = 18 - 8 = 10$

5. $8^2 + 3(8) = 64 + 24 = 88$

7. $7^2 - 6(7) + 3 = 49 - 42 + 3 = 7 + 3 = 10$

1

9. $4 + 5(9-7)^3 = 4 + 5(2)^3$
$$= 4 + 5(8) = 4 + 40 = 44$$

11. $8^2 - 3(8-2) = 64 - 3(6)$
$$= 64 - 18 = 46$$

13. $\dfrac{5(x+2)}{2x-14} = \dfrac{5(10+2)}{2(10)-14}$
$$= \dfrac{5(12)}{6}$$
$$= 5 \cdot 2$$
$$= 10$$

15. $\dfrac{2x+3y}{x+1}; x = -2, y = 4$
$$= \dfrac{2(-2)+3(4)}{-2+1} = \dfrac{-4+12}{-1} = \dfrac{8}{-1} = -8$$

17. $C = \dfrac{5}{9}(50-32) = \dfrac{5}{9}(18) = 10$
$10°C$ is equivalent to $50°F$.

19. $h = 4 + 60t - 16t^2 = 4 + 60(2) - 16(2)^2$
$$= 4 + 120 - 16(4) = 4 + 120 - 64$$
$$= 124 - 64 = 60$$
Two seconds after it is kicked, the ball's height is 60 feet.

21. $\{1,2,3,4\} \cap \{2,4,5\} = \{2,4\}$

23. $\{s,e,t\} \cap \{t,e,s\} = \{s,e,t\}$

25. $\{1,3,5,7\} \cap \{2,4,6,8,10\} = \{\ \}$
The empty set is also denoted by $\varnothing$.

27. $\{a,b,c,d\} \cap \varnothing = \varnothing$

29. $\{1,2,3,4\} \cup \{2,4,5\} = \{1,2,3,4,5\}$

31. $\{1,3,5,7\} \cup \{2,4,6,8,10\}$
$$= \{1,2,3,4,5,6,7,8,10\}$$

33. $\{a,e,i,o,u\} \cup \varnothing = \{a,e,i,o,u\}$

35. **a.** $\sqrt{100}$

 b. $0, \sqrt{100}$

 c. $-9, 0, \sqrt{100}$

 d. $-9, -\dfrac{4}{5}, 0, 0.25, 9.2, \sqrt{100}$

 e. $\sqrt{3}$

 f. $-9, -\dfrac{4}{5}, 0, 0.25, \sqrt{3}, 9.2, \sqrt{100}$

37. **a.** $\sqrt{64}$

 b. $0, \sqrt{64}$

 c. $-11, 0, \sqrt{64}$

 d. $-11, -\dfrac{5}{6}, 0, 0.75, \sqrt{64}$

 e. $\sqrt{5}, \pi$

 f. $-11, -\dfrac{5}{6}, 0, 0.75, \sqrt{5}, \pi, \sqrt{64}$

39. 0

41. Answers may vary.

43. True; -13 is to the left of -2 on the number line.

45. True; 4 is to the right of -7 on the number line.

47. True; $-\pi = -\pi$

49. True; 0 is to the right of -6 on the number line.

51. $|300| = 300$

53. $|12 - \pi| = 12 - \pi$

55. $\left|\sqrt{2} - 5\right| = 5 - \sqrt{2}$

57. $\dfrac{-3}{|-3|} = \dfrac{-3}{3} = -1$

59. $\big||-3| - |-7|\big| = |3 - 7| = |-4| = 4$

61. $|x + y| = |2 + (-5)| = |-3| = 3$

63. $|x| + |y| = |2| + |-5| = 2 + 5 = 7$

65. $\dfrac{y}{|y|} = \dfrac{-5}{|-5|} = \dfrac{-5}{5} = -1$

67. The distance is $|2 - 17| = |-15| = 15$.

69. The distance is $|-2 - 5| = |-7| = 7$.

71. The distance is
$|-19 - (-4)| = |-19 + 4| = |-15| = 15$.

73. The distance is
$|-3.6 - (-1.4)| = |-3.6 + 1.4| = |-2.2| = 2.2$.

75. $6 + (-4) = (-4) + 6$; commutative property of addition

77. $6 + (2 + 7) = (6 + 2) + 7$; associative property of addition

79. $(2 + 3) + (4 + 5) = (4 + 5) + (2 + 3)$; commutative property of addition

81. $2(-8 + 6) = -16 + 12$; distributive property of multiplication over addition

83. $\dfrac{1}{x+3}(x+3) = 1; x \neq -3$, inverse property of multiplication

85. $5(3x + 4) - 4 = 5 \cdot 3x + 5 \cdot 4 - 4$
$= 15x + 20 - 4$
$= 15x + 16$

87. $5(3x - 2) + 12x = 5 \cdot 3x - 5 \cdot 2 + 12x$
$= 15x - 10 + 12x$
$= 27x - 10$

89. $7(3y - 5) + 2(4y + 3)$
$= 7 \cdot 3y - 7 \cdot 5 + 2 \cdot 4y + 2 \cdot 3$
$= 21y - 35 + 8y + 6$
$= 29y - 29$

91. $5(3y - 2) - (7y + 2) = 15y - 10 - 7y - 2$
$= 8y - 12$

93. $7 - 4[3 - (4y - 5)] = 7 - 4[3 - 4y + 5]$
$= 7 - 4[8 - 4y]$
$= 7 - 32 + 16y$
$= 16y - 25$

95. $8x^2 + 4 - [6(x^2 - 2) + 5]$
$= 18x^2 + 4 - [6x^2 - 12 + 5]$
$= 18x^2 + 4 - [6x^2 - 7]$
$= 18x^2 + 4 - 6x^2 + 7$
$= 18x^2 - 6x^2 + 4 + 7$
$= (18 - 6)x^2 + 11 = 12x^2 + 11$

97. $-(-14x) = 14x$

99. $-(2x - 3y - 6) = -2x + 3y + 6$

101. $\dfrac{1}{3}(3x) + [(4y) + (-4y)] = x + 0$
$= x$

103. $|-6| \; \square \; |-3|$
$6 \; \square \; 3$
$6 > 3$
Since $6 > 3$, $|-6| > |-3|$.

105. $\left|\dfrac{3}{5}\right| \; \square \; |-0.6|$
$|0.6| \; \square \; |-0.6|$
$0.6 \; \square \; 0.6$
$0.6 = 0.6$
Since $0.6 = 0.6$, $\left|\dfrac{3}{5}\right| = |-0.6|$.

107. $\dfrac{30}{40} - \dfrac{3}{4} \; \square \; \dfrac{14}{15} \cdot \dfrac{15}{14}$
$\dfrac{30}{40} - \dfrac{30}{40} \; \square \; \dfrac{14}{\cancel{15}} \cdot \dfrac{\cancel{15}}{\cancel{14}}$
$0 \; \square \; 1$
$0 < 1$
Since $0 < 1$, $\dfrac{30}{40} - \dfrac{3}{4} < \dfrac{14}{15} \cdot \dfrac{15}{14}$.

109. $\dfrac{8}{13} \div \dfrac{8}{13} \;\square\; |-1|$

$\dfrac{8}{13} \cdot \dfrac{13}{8} \;\square\; 1$

$1 \;\square\; 1$

$1 = 1$

Since $1 = 1$, $\dfrac{8}{13} \div \dfrac{8}{13} = |-1|$.

111. $x - (x + 4) = x - x - 4 = -4$

113. $6(-5x) = -30x$

115. $5x - 2x = 3x$

117. $8x - (3x + 6) = 8x - 3x - 6 = 5x - 6$

119. $N = 17x^2 - 65.4x + 302.2$
$= 17(4)^2 - 65.4(4) + 302.2$
$= 17(16) - 261.6 + 302.2$
$= 272 - 261.6 + 302.2$
≈ 313
The formula models the graph's data very well.

121. $N = 17x^2 - 65.4x + 302.2$
$= 17(6)^2 - 65.4(6) + 302.2$
$= 17(36) - 392.4 + 302.2$
$= 612 - 392.4 + 302.2$
≈ 522
The formula predicts that there will be 522 U.S. billionaires in 2006.

123. Model 1: $N = -2.04x + 10.24$
$= -2.04(0) + 10.24$
$= 10.24$
Model 2: $N = 0.04x^2 - 3.6x + 11$
$= 0.04(0)^2 - 3.6(0) + 11$
$= 11$
Model 3: $N = 0.76x^3 - 4x^2 + 1.8x + 10.5$
$= 0.76(0)^3 - 4(0)^2 + 1.8(0) + 10.5$
$= 10.5$
Model 3 was the best model for 1999.

125. Model 1: $N = -2.04x + 10.24$
$= -2.04(4) + 10.24$
$= 2.08$
Model 2: $N = 0.04x^2 - 3.6x + 11$
$= 0.04(4)^2 - 3.6(4) + 11$
$= -2.76$

Model 3: $N = 0.76x^3 - 4x^2 + 1.8x + 10.5$
$= 0.76(4)^3 - 4(4)^2 + 1.8(4) + 10.5$
$= 2.34$
Model 3 was the best model for 2003.

126. Model 1: $N = -2.04x + 10.24$
$= -2.04(4) + 10.24$
$= 2.08$
Model 2: $N = 0.04x^2 - 3.6x + 11$
$= 0.04(4)^2 - 3.6(4) + 11$
$= -2.76$
Model 3: $N = 0.76x^3 - 4x^2 + 1.8x + 10.5$
$= 0.76(4)^3 - 4(4)^2 + 1.8(4) + 10.5$
$= 2.34$
Model breakdown occurs for model 2 in 2003 as shown by the negative result.

127. a. $0.05x + 0.12(10,000 - x)$
$= 0.05x + 1200 - 0.12x$
$= 1200 - 0.07x$

b. $1200 - 0.07x = 1200 - 0.07(6000)$
$= \$780$

141. a. False; x has a coefficient of 1.

b. False; $5 + 3(x - 4) = 5 + 3x - 12 = 3x - 7$

c. False; $-x - x = -2x$.

d. True; $x - 0.02(x + 200)$
$= x - 0.02x - 4$
$= x - 0.02x - 0.02(200)$
$= 0.98x - 4$

(d) is true.

143. $-\pi > -3.5$

145. a. $x = 100$

$$\frac{0.5x + 5000}{100}$$
$$= \frac{5050}{100}$$
$$= \$50.50$$

$x = 1000$

$$\frac{0.5(1000) + 5000}{1000}$$
$$= \frac{5500}{1000}$$
$$= \$5.50$$

$x = 10,000$

$$\frac{0.5(10,000) + 5000}{10,000}$$
$$= \frac{10000}{10000}$$
$$= \$1$$

b. No, they would need make 10,000 clocks for the cost to be \$1 so they can add \$.50.

Section P.2

Check Point Exercises

1. a. $3^3 3^2 = 3^{3+2} = 3^5$ or 243

b. $\left(4x^3y^4\right)\left(10x^2y^6\right) = 4 \cdot 10 \cdot x^3 \cdot x^2 \cdot y^4 \cdot y^6$
$$= 40x^{3+2} \cdot y^{4+6}$$
$$= 40x^5 \cdot y^{10}$$

2. a. $\dfrac{(-3)^6}{(-3)^3} = (-3)^3 = -27$

b. $\dfrac{27x^{14}y^8}{3x^3y^5} = \dfrac{27}{3} \cdot \dfrac{x^{14}}{x^3} \cdot \dfrac{y^8}{y^5} = 9x^{14-3}y^{8-5} = 9x^{11}y^3$

3. a. $5^{-2} = \dfrac{1}{5^2} = \dfrac{1}{25}$

b. $(-3)^{-3} = \dfrac{1}{(-3)^3} = \dfrac{1}{-27} = -\dfrac{1}{27}$

c. $\dfrac{1}{4^{-2}} = \dfrac{1}{\frac{1}{4^2}} = 1 \cdot \dfrac{4^2}{1} = 4^2 = 16$

d. $3x^{-6}y^4 = 3 \cdot \dfrac{1}{x^6} \cdot y^4 = \dfrac{3y^4}{x^6}$

4. a. $\left(3^3\right)^2 = 3^{3 \cdot 2} = 3^6$ or 729

b. $\left(y^7\right)^{-2} = y^{7(-2)} = y^{-14} = \dfrac{1}{y^{14}}$

c. $\left(b^{-3}\right)^{-4} = b^{-3(-4)} = b^{12}$

5. $(-4x)^3 = (-4)^3(x)^3 = -64x^3$

6. a. $\left(-\dfrac{2}{y}\right)^5 = \dfrac{(-2)^5}{y^5} = \dfrac{-32}{y^5}$

b. $\left(\dfrac{x^5}{3}\right)^3 = \dfrac{\left(x^5\right)^3}{3^3} = \dfrac{x^{15}}{27}$

7. a. $\left(2x^3y^6\right)^4 = (2)^4\left(x^3\right)^4\left(y^6\right)^4 = 16x^{12}y^{24}$

b. $\left(-6x^2y^5\right)\left(3xy^3\right)$
$$= (-6) \cdot 3 \cdot x^2 \cdot x \cdot y^5 \cdot y^3$$
$$= -18x^3y^8$$

c. $\dfrac{100x^{12}y^2}{20x^{16}y^{-4}} = \left(\dfrac{100}{20}\right)\left(\dfrac{x^{12}}{x^{16}}\right)\left(\dfrac{y^2}{y^{-4}}\right)$
$$= 5x^{12-16}y^{2-(-4)}$$
$$= 5x^{-4}y^6$$
$$= \dfrac{5y^6}{x^4}$$

5

d. $\left(\dfrac{5x}{y^4}\right)^{-2} = \dfrac{(5)^{-2}(x)^{-2}}{(y^4)^{-2}}$

$\qquad = \dfrac{(5)^{-2}(x)^{-2}}{(y^4)^{-2}}$

$\qquad = \dfrac{5^{-2}x^{-2}}{y^{-8}}$

$\qquad = \dfrac{y^8}{5^2 x^2}$

$\qquad = \dfrac{y^8}{25x^2}$

8. a. $-2.6\times10^9 = -2,600,000,000$

b. $3.017\times10^{-6} = 0.000003017$

9. a. $5,210,000,000 = 5.21\times10^9$

b. $-0.00000006893 = -6.893\times10^{-8}$

10. $410\times10^7 = \left(4.1\times10^2\right)\times10^7$

$\qquad = 4.1\times\left(10^2\times10^7\right)$

$\qquad = 4.1\times10^9$

11 a. $\left(7.1\times10^5\right)\left(5\times10^{-7}\right)$

$\qquad = 7.1\cdot5\times10^5\cdot10^{-7}$

$\qquad = 35.5\times10^{-2}$

$\qquad = \left(3.55\times10^1\right)\times10^{-2}$

$\qquad = 3.55\times\left(10^1\times10^{-2}\right)$

$\qquad = 3.55\times10^{-1}$

b. $\dfrac{1.2\times10^6}{3\times10^{-3}} = \dfrac{1.2}{3}\cdot\dfrac{10^6}{10^{-3}}$

$\qquad = 0.4\times10^{6-(-3)}$

$\qquad = 0.4\times10^9$

$\qquad = 4\times10^8$

12. $\dfrac{2.02\times10^{12}}{2.88\times10^8} = \dfrac{2.02}{2.88}\cdot\dfrac{10^{12}}{10^8}$

$\qquad \approx 0.7014\times10^4$

$\qquad \approx 7014$

The per capita tax was \$7014 in 2002.

Exercise Set P.2

1. $5^2\cdot2 = (5\cdot5)\cdot2 = 25\cdot2 = 50$

3. $(-2)^6 = (-2)(-2)(-2)(-2)(-2)(-2) = 64$

5. $-2^6 = -2\cdot2\cdot2\cdot2\cdot2\cdot2 = -64$

7. $(-3)^0 = 1$

9. $-3^0 = -1$

11. $4^{-3} = \dfrac{1}{4^3} = \dfrac{1}{4\cdot4\cdot4} = \dfrac{1}{64}$

13. $2^2\cdot2^3 = 2^{2+3} = 2^5 = 2\cdot2\cdot2\cdot2\cdot2 = 32$

15. $(2^2)^3 = 2^{2\cdot3} = 2^6 = 2\cdot2\cdot2\cdot2\cdot2\cdot2 = 64$

17. $\dfrac{2^8}{2^4} = 2^{8-4} = 2^4 = 2\cdot2\cdot2\cdot2 = 16$

19. $3^{-3}\cdot3 = 3^{-3+1} = 3^{-2} = \dfrac{1}{3^2} = \dfrac{1}{3\cdot3} = \dfrac{1}{9}$

21. $\dfrac{2^3}{2^7} = 2^{3-7} = 2^{-4} = \dfrac{1}{2^4} = \dfrac{1}{2\cdot2\cdot2\cdot2} = \dfrac{1}{16}$

23. $x^{-2}y = \dfrac{1}{x^2}\cdot y = \dfrac{y}{x^2}$

25. $x^0 y^5 = 1\cdot y^5 = y^5$

27. $x^3\cdot x^7 = x^{3+7} = x^{10}$

29. $x^{-5}\cdot x^{10} = x^{-5+10} = x^5$

31. $(x^3)^7 = x^{3\cdot7} = x^{21}$

33. $(x^{-5})^3 = x^{-5\cdot3} = x^{-15} = \dfrac{1}{x^{15}}$

35. $\dfrac{x^{14}}{x^7} = x^{14-7} = x^7$

37. $\dfrac{x^{14}}{x^{-7}} = x^{14-(-7)} = x^{14+7} = x^{21}$

39. $(8x^3)^2 = 8^2(x^3)^2 = 8^2 x^{3\cdot2} = 64x^6$

41. $\left(-\dfrac{4}{x}\right)^3 = \dfrac{(-4)^3}{x^3} = -\dfrac{64}{x^3}$

43. $(-3x^2 y^5)^2 = (-3)^2 (x^2)^2 \cdot (y^5)^2$
$$= 9x^{2 \cdot 2} y^{5 \cdot 2}$$
$$= 9x^4 y^{10}$$

45. $(3x^4)(2x^7) = 3 \cdot 2x^4 \cdot x^7 = 6x^{4+7} = 6x^{11}$

47. $(-9x^3 y)(-2x^6 y^4) = (-9)(-2)x^3 x^6 y y^4$
$$= 18x^{3+6} y^{1+4}$$
$$= 18x^9 y^5$$

49. $\dfrac{8x^{20}}{2x^4} = \left(\dfrac{8}{2}\right)\left(\dfrac{x^{20}}{x^4}\right) = 4x^{20-4} = 4x^{16}$

51. $\dfrac{25a^{13} \cdot b^4}{-5a^2 \cdot b^3} = \left(\dfrac{25}{-5}\right)\left(\dfrac{a^{13}}{a^2}\right)\left(\dfrac{b^4}{b^3}\right)$
$$= -5a^{13-2} b^{4-3}$$
$$= -5a^{11} b$$

53. $\dfrac{14b^7}{7b^{14}} = \left(\dfrac{14}{7}\right)\left(\dfrac{b^7}{b^{14}}\right) = 2 \cdot b^{7-14} = 2b^{-7} = \dfrac{2}{b^7}$

55. $(4x^3)^{-2} = (4^{-2})(x^3)^{-2}$
$$= 4^{-2} x^{-6}$$
$$= \dfrac{1}{4^2 x^6}$$
$$= \dfrac{1}{16x^6}$$

57. $\dfrac{24x^3 \cdot y^5}{32x^7 y^{-9}} = \dfrac{3}{4} x^{3-7} y^{5-(-9)}$
$$= \dfrac{3}{4} x^{-4} y^{14}$$
$$= \dfrac{3y^{14}}{4x^4}$$

59. $\left(\dfrac{5x^3}{y}\right)^{-2} = \dfrac{5^{-2} x^{-6}}{y^{-2}} = \dfrac{y^2}{25x^6}$

61. $\left(\dfrac{-15a^4 b^2}{5a^{10} b^{-3}}\right)^3$
$$= \left(\dfrac{-3b^{2-(-3)}}{a^{10-4}}\right)^3$$
$$= \left(\dfrac{-3b^5}{a^6}\right)^3$$
$$= \dfrac{-27b^{15}}{a^{18}}$$

63. $\left(\dfrac{3a^{-5} b^2}{12a^3 b^{-4}}\right)^0 = 1$

64. $\left(\dfrac{4a^{-5} b^3}{12a^3 b^{-5}}\right)^0 = 1$

65. $3.8 \times 10^2 = 380$

67. $6 \times 10^{-4} = 0.0006$

69. $-7.16 \times 10^6 = -7,160,000$

71. $7.9 \times 10^{-1} = 0.79$

73. $-4.15 \times 10^{-3} = -0.00415$

75. $-6.00001 \times 10^{10} = -60,000,100,000$

77. $32,000 = 3.2 \times 10^4$

79. $638,000,000,000,000,000$
$$= 6.38 \times 10^{17}$$

81. $-5716 = -5.716 \times 10^3$

83. $0.0027 = 2.7 \times 10^{-3}$

85. $-0.00000000504 = -5.04 \times 10^{-9}$

87. $(3 \times 10^4)(2.1 \times 10^3)$
$$= (3 \times 2.1)(10^4 \times 10^3)$$
$$= 6.3 \times 10^{4+3} = 6.3 \times 10^7$$

89. $(1.6 \times 10^{15})(4 \times 10^{-11})$
$$= (1.6 \times 4)(10^{15} \times 10^{-11})$$
$$= 6.4 \times 10^{15+(-11)} = 6.4 \times 10^4$$

91. $\left(6.1\times10^{-8}\right)\left(2\times10^{-4}\right)$

$=\left(6.1\times2\right)\left(10^{-8}\times10^{-4}\right)$

$=12.2\times10^{-8+(-4)}$

$=12.2\times10^{-12}=1.22\times10^{-11}$

93. $\left(4.3\times10^{8}\right)\left(6.2\times10^{4}\right)$

$=\left(4.3\times6.2\right)\left(10^{8}\times10^{4}\right)$

$=26.66\times10^{8+4}$

$=26.66\times10^{12}$

$=2.666\times10^{13}\approx2.67\times10^{13}$

95. $\dfrac{8.4\times10^{8}}{4\times10^{5}}=\dfrac{8.4}{4}\times\dfrac{10^{8}}{10^{5}}$

$=2.1\times10^{8-5}=2.1\times10^{3}$

97. $\dfrac{3.6\times10^{4}}{9\times10^{-2}}=\dfrac{3.6}{9}\times\dfrac{10^{4}}{10^{-2}}$

$=0.4\times10^{4-(-2)}$

$=0.4\times10^{6}=4\times10^{5}$

99. $\dfrac{4.8\times10^{-2}}{2.4\times10^{6}}=\dfrac{4.8}{2.4}\times\dfrac{10^{-2}}{10^{6}}$

$=2\times10^{-2-6}=2\times10^{-8}$

101. $\dfrac{2.4\times10^{-2}}{4.8\times10^{-6}}=\dfrac{2.4}{4.8}\times\dfrac{10^{-2}}{10^{-6}}$

$=0.5\times10^{-2-(-6)}$

$=0.5\times10^{4}=5\times10^{3}$

103. $\dfrac{480,000,000,000}{0.00012}=\dfrac{4.8\times10^{11}}{1.2\times10^{-4}}$

$=\dfrac{4.8}{1.2}\times\dfrac{10^{11}}{10^{-4}}$

$=4\times10^{11-(-4)}$

$=4\times10^{15}$

105. $\dfrac{0.00072\times0.003}{0.00024}$

$=\dfrac{\left(7.2\times10^{-4}\right)\left(3\times10^{-3}\right)}{2.4\times10^{-4}}$

$=\dfrac{7.2\times3}{2.4}\times\dfrac{10^{-4}\cdot10^{-3}}{10^{-4}}=9\times10^{-3}$

107. $\dfrac{\left(x^{-2}y\right)^{-3}}{\left(x^{2}y^{-1}\right)^{3}}=\dfrac{x^{6}y^{-3}}{x^{6}y^{-3}}$

$=x^{6-6}y^{-3-(-3)}=x^{0}y^{0}=1$

109. $\left(2x^{-3}yz^{-6}\right)\left(2x\right)^{-5}=2x^{-3}yz^{-6}\cdot2^{-5}x^{.-5}$

$=2^{-4}x^{-8}yz^{-6}=\dfrac{y}{2^{4}x^{8}z^{6}}=\dfrac{y}{16x^{8}z^{6}}$

111. $\left(\dfrac{x^{3}y^{4}z^{5}}{x^{-3}y^{-4}z^{-5}}\right)^{-2}=\left(x^{6}y^{8}z^{10}\right)^{-2}$

$=x^{-12}y^{-16}z^{-20}=\dfrac{1}{x^{12}y^{16}z^{20}}$

113. $\dfrac{\left(2^{-1}x^{-2}y^{-1}\right)^{-2}\left(2x^{-4}y^{3}\right)^{-2}\left(16x^{-3}y^{3}\right)^{0}}{\left(2x^{-3}y^{-5}\right)^{2}}$

$=\dfrac{\left(2^{2}x^{2}y^{2}\right)\left(2^{-2}x^{8}y^{-6}\right)\left(1\right)}{\left(2^{2}x^{-6}y^{-10}\right)}$

$=\dfrac{x^{18}y^{6}}{4}$

115. $62.6\text{ million}=62.6\times10^{6}=6.26\times10^{7}$

So, 6.26×10^{7} people will be 65 and over in 2025.

117. $131.2-34.9=96.3$

$96.3\text{ million}=96.3\times10^{6}=9.63\times10^{7}$ There will be 9.63×10^{7} more people 65 and over in the year 2100 than in 2000.

119. $20\text{ billion}=2\times10^{10}$

$\dfrac{2\times10^{10}}{2.92\times10^{8}}=\dfrac{2}{2.92}\times\dfrac{10^{10}}{10^{8}}$

$\approx0.6849\times10^{10-8}$

$=0.6849\times10^{2}$

$=6.849\times10^{1}\approx68$

The average American consumes about 68 hotdogs each year.

121. $8\text{ billion}=8\times10^{9}$

$\dfrac{8\times10^{9}}{3.2\times10^{7}}=\dfrac{8}{3.2}\times\dfrac{10^{9}}{10^{7}}$

$=2.5\times10^{9-7}$

$=2.5\times10^{2}=250$

$2.5\times10^{2}=250$ chickens are raised for food each second in the U.S.

123. $\dfrac{6.8 \times 10^{12}}{2.9 \times 10^{8}} = \dfrac{6.8}{2.9} \cdot \dfrac{10^{12}}{10^{8}}$

$\approx 2.3448 \times 10^{4}$

$\approx 23,448$

If the national debt was divided evenly among every individual in the U.S., each citizen would have to pay \$23,448.

133. a. False, $4^{-2} = \dfrac{1}{16} > 4^{-3} = \dfrac{1}{64}$

    b. True, $5^{-2} = \dfrac{1}{25} > 2^{-5} = \dfrac{1}{32}$

    c. False, $16 = (-2)^{4} \neq 2^{-4} = \dfrac{1}{16}$

    d. False. $\begin{aligned} 5^{2} \cdot 5^{-2} &= 5^{2-2} = 5^{0} = 1 \\ 2^{5} \cdot 2^{-5} &= 2^{5-5} = 2^{0} = 1 \end{aligned}$

        1 is not greater than 1

135. $b^{A} = MN, b^{C} = M, b^{D} = N$

$b^{A} = b^{C} b^{D}$

$A = C + D$

Section P.3

Check Point Exercises

1. a. $\sqrt{81} = 9$

    b. $-\sqrt{9} = -3$

    c. $\sqrt{\dfrac{1}{25}} = \dfrac{1}{5}$

    d. $\sqrt{36 + 64} = \sqrt{100} = 10$

    e. $\sqrt{36} + \sqrt{64} = 6 + 8 = 14$

2. a. $\sqrt{75} = \sqrt{25 \cdot 3} = \sqrt{25}\sqrt{3} = 5\sqrt{3}$

    b. $\sqrt{5x} \cdot \sqrt{10x} = \sqrt{5x \cdot 10x}$

$= \sqrt{50x^{2}}$

$= \sqrt{25 \cdot 2x^{2}}$

$= \sqrt{25x^{2}} \cdot \sqrt{2}$

$= 5x\sqrt{2}$

3. a. $\sqrt{\dfrac{25}{16}} = \dfrac{\sqrt{25}}{\sqrt{16}} = \dfrac{5}{4}$

    b. $\dfrac{\sqrt{150x^{3}}}{\sqrt{2x}} = \sqrt{\dfrac{150x^{3}}{2x}}$

$= \sqrt{75x^{2}}$

$= \sqrt{25x^{2}} \cdot \sqrt{3}$

$= 5x\sqrt{3}$

4. a. $8\sqrt{13} + 9\sqrt{13} = (8 + 9)\sqrt{3}$

$= 17\sqrt{13}$

    b. $\sqrt{17x} - 20\sqrt{17x}$

$= 1\sqrt{17x} - 20\sqrt{17x}$

$= (1 - 20)\sqrt{17x}$

$= -19\sqrt{17x}$

5. a. $5\sqrt{27} + \sqrt{12}$

$= 5\sqrt{9 \cdot 3} + \sqrt{4 \cdot 3}$

$= 5 \cdot 3\sqrt{3} + 2\sqrt{3}$

$= 15\sqrt{3} + 2\sqrt{3}$

$= (15 + 2)\sqrt{3}$

$= 17\sqrt{3}$

    b. $6\sqrt{18x} - 4\sqrt{8x}$

$= 6\sqrt{9 \cdot 2x} - 4\sqrt{4 \cdot 2x}$

$= 6 \cdot 3\sqrt{2x} - 4 \cdot 2\sqrt{2x}$

$= 18\sqrt{2x} - 8\sqrt{2x}$

$= (18 - 8)\sqrt{2x}$

$= 10\sqrt{2x}$

6. a. If we multiply numerator and denominator by $\sqrt{3}$, the denominator becomes $\sqrt{3} \cdot \sqrt{3} = \sqrt{9} = 3$. Therefore, multiply by 1, choosing $\dfrac{\sqrt{3}}{\sqrt{3}}$ for 1.

$\dfrac{5}{\sqrt{3}} = \dfrac{5}{\sqrt{3}} \cdot \dfrac{\sqrt{3}}{\sqrt{3}} = \dfrac{5\sqrt{3}}{\sqrt{9}} = \dfrac{5\sqrt{3}}{3}$

9

b. The *smallest* number that will produce a perfect square in the denominator of $\dfrac{6}{\sqrt{12}}$ is $\sqrt{3}$ because $\sqrt{12} \cdot \sqrt{3} = \sqrt{36} = 6$. So multiply by 1, choosing $\dfrac{\sqrt{3}}{\sqrt{3}}$ for 1.

$$\frac{6}{\sqrt{12}} = \frac{6}{\sqrt{12}} \cdot \frac{\sqrt{3}}{\sqrt{3}} = \frac{6\sqrt{3}}{\sqrt{36}} = \frac{6\sqrt{3}}{6} = \sqrt{3}$$

7. Multiply by $\dfrac{4-\sqrt{5}}{4-\sqrt{5}}$.

$$\frac{8}{4+\sqrt{5}} = \frac{8}{4+\sqrt{5}} \cdot \frac{4-\sqrt{5}}{4-\sqrt{5}}$$

$$= \frac{8(4-\sqrt{5})}{4^2 - (\sqrt{5})^2}$$

$$= \frac{8(4-\sqrt{5})}{16-5}$$

$$= \frac{8(4-\sqrt{5})}{11} \text{ or } \frac{32-8\sqrt{5}}{11}$$

8. **a.** $\sqrt[3]{40} = \sqrt[3]{8 \cdot 5} = \sqrt[3]{8} \cdot \sqrt[3]{5} = 2\sqrt[3]{5}$

b. $\sqrt[5]{8} \cdot \sqrt[5]{8} = \sqrt[5]{64} = \sqrt[5]{32} \cdot \sqrt[5]{2} = 2\sqrt[5]{2}$

c. $\sqrt[3]{\dfrac{125}{27}} = \dfrac{\sqrt[3]{125}}{\sqrt[3]{27}} = \dfrac{5}{3}$

9. $3\sqrt[3]{81} - 4\sqrt[3]{3}$

$$= 3\sqrt[3]{27 \cdot 3} - 4\sqrt[3]{3}$$

$$= 3 \cdot 3\sqrt[3]{3} - 4\sqrt[3]{3}$$

$$= 9\sqrt[3]{3} - 4\sqrt[3]{3}$$

$$= (9-4)\sqrt[3]{3}$$

$$= 5\sqrt[3]{3}$$

10. **a.** $25^{\frac{1}{2}} = \sqrt{25} = 5$

b. $8^{\frac{1}{3}} = \sqrt[3]{8} = 2$

c. $-81^{\frac{1}{4}} = -\sqrt[4]{81} = -3$

d. $(-8)^{\frac{1}{3}} = \sqrt[3]{-8} = -2$

e. $27^{-\frac{1}{3}} = \dfrac{1}{27^{\frac{1}{3}}} = \dfrac{1}{\sqrt[3]{27}} = \dfrac{1}{3}$

11. **a.** $27^{\frac{4}{3}} = \left(\sqrt[3]{27}\right)^4 = (3)^4 = 81$

b. $4^{\frac{3}{2}} = \left(\sqrt[2]{4}\right)^3 = (2)^3 = 8$

c. $32^{-\frac{2}{5}} = \dfrac{1}{32^{\frac{2}{5}}} = \dfrac{1}{\left(\sqrt[5]{32}\right)^2} = \dfrac{1}{2^2} = \dfrac{1}{4}$

12. **a.** $\left(2x^{4/3}\right)\left(5x^{8/3}\right)$

$$= 2 \cdot 5 x^{4/3} \cdot x^{8/3}$$

$$= 10x^{(4/3)+(8/3)}$$

$$= 10x^{12/3}$$

$$= 10x^4$$

b. $\dfrac{20x^4}{5x^{\frac{1}{2}}} = \left(\dfrac{20}{5}\right)\left(\dfrac{x^4}{x^{\frac{1}{2}}}\right)$

$$= 4x^{4-(\frac{1}{2})}$$

$$= 4x^{(\frac{8}{2})-(\frac{1}{2})}$$

$$= 4x^{\frac{7}{2}}$$

13. $\sqrt[6]{x^3} = x^{\frac{3}{6}} = x^{\frac{1}{2}} = \sqrt{x}$

Exercise Set P.3

1. $\sqrt{36} = \sqrt{6^2} = 6$

3. $-\sqrt{36} = -\sqrt{6^2} = -6$

5. $\sqrt{-36}$, The square root of a negative number is not real.

7. $\sqrt{25-16} = \sqrt{9} = 3$

9. $\sqrt{25} - \sqrt{16} = 5 - 4 = 1$

11. $\sqrt{(-13)^2} = \sqrt{169} = 13$

13. $\sqrt{50} = \sqrt{25 \cdot 2} = \sqrt{25}\sqrt{2} = 5\sqrt{2}$

15. $\sqrt{45x^2} = \sqrt{9x^2 \cdot 5}$
$= \sqrt{9x^2}\sqrt{5}$
$= \sqrt{9}\sqrt{x^2}\sqrt{5}$
$= 3|x|\sqrt{5}$

17. $\sqrt{2x} \cdot \sqrt{6x} = \sqrt{2x \cdot 6x}$
$= \sqrt{12x^2}$
$= \sqrt{4x^2} \cdot \sqrt{3}$
$= 2x\sqrt{3}$

19. $\sqrt{x^3} = \sqrt{x^2} \cdot \sqrt{x} = x\sqrt{x}$

21. $\sqrt{2x^2} \cdot \sqrt{6x} = \sqrt{2x^2 \cdot 6x}$
$= \sqrt{12x^3}$
$= \sqrt{4x^2} \cdot \sqrt{3x}$
$= 2x\sqrt{3x}$

23. $\sqrt{\dfrac{1}{81}} = \dfrac{\sqrt{1}}{\sqrt{81}} = \dfrac{1}{9}$

25. $\sqrt{\dfrac{49}{16}} = \dfrac{\sqrt{49}}{\sqrt{16}} = \dfrac{7}{4}$

27. $\dfrac{\sqrt{48x^3}}{\sqrt{3x}} = \sqrt{\dfrac{48x^3}{3x}} = \sqrt{16x^2} = 4x$

29. $\dfrac{\sqrt{150x^4}}{\sqrt{3x}} = \sqrt{\dfrac{150x^4}{3x}}$
$= \sqrt{50x^3}$
$= \sqrt{25x^2} \cdot \sqrt{2x}$
$= 5x\sqrt{2x}$

31. $\dfrac{\sqrt{200x^3}}{\sqrt{10x^{-1}}}$
$= \sqrt{\dfrac{200x^3}{10x^{-1}}}$
$= \sqrt{20x^{3-(-1)}}$
$= \sqrt{20x^4}$
$= \sqrt{4 \cdot 5x^4}$
$= 2x^2\sqrt{5}$

33. $7\sqrt{3} + 6\sqrt{3} = (7+6)\sqrt{3} = 13\sqrt{3}$

35. $6\sqrt{17x} - 8\sqrt{17x} = (6-8)\sqrt{17x} = -2\sqrt{17x}$

37. $\sqrt{8} + 3\sqrt{2} = \sqrt{4 \cdot 2} + 3\sqrt{2}$
$= 2\sqrt{2} + 3\sqrt{2}$
$= (2+3)\sqrt{2}$
$= 5\sqrt{2}$

39. $\sqrt{50x} - \sqrt{8x} = \sqrt{25 \cdot 2x} - \sqrt{4 \cdot 2x}$
$= 5\sqrt{2x} - 2\sqrt{2x}$
$= (5-2)\sqrt{2x}$
$= 3\sqrt{2x}$

41. $3\sqrt{18} + 5\sqrt{50} = 3\sqrt{9 \cdot 2} + 5\sqrt{25 \cdot 2}$
$= 3 \cdot 3\sqrt{2} + 5 \cdot 5\sqrt{2}$
$= 9\sqrt{2} + 25\sqrt{2}$
$= (9+25)\sqrt{2}$
$= 34\sqrt{2}$

43. $3\sqrt{8} - \sqrt{32} + 3\sqrt{72} - \sqrt{75}$
$= 3\sqrt{4 \cdot 2} - \sqrt{16 \cdot 2} + 3\sqrt{36 \cdot 2} - \sqrt{25 \cdot 3}$
$= 3 \cdot 2\sqrt{2} - 4\sqrt{2} + 3 \cdot 6\sqrt{2} - 5\sqrt{3}$
$= 6\sqrt{2} - 4\sqrt{2} + 18\sqrt{2} - 5\sqrt{3}$
$= 20\sqrt{2} - 5\sqrt{3}$

45. $\dfrac{1}{\sqrt{7}} = \dfrac{1}{\sqrt{7}} \cdot \dfrac{\sqrt{7}}{\sqrt{7}} = \dfrac{\sqrt{7}}{7}$

47. $\dfrac{\sqrt{2}}{\sqrt{5}} = \dfrac{\sqrt{2}}{\sqrt{5}} \cdot \dfrac{\sqrt{5}}{\sqrt{5}} = \dfrac{\sqrt{10}}{5}$

49. $\dfrac{13}{3+\sqrt{11}} = \dfrac{13}{3+\sqrt{11}} \cdot \dfrac{3-\sqrt{11}}{3-\sqrt{11}}$
$= \dfrac{13(3-\sqrt{11})}{3^2 - (\sqrt{11})^2}$
$= \dfrac{13(3-\sqrt{11})}{9-11}$
$= \dfrac{13(3-\sqrt{11})}{-2}$

51.
$$\frac{7}{\sqrt{5}-2} = \frac{7}{\sqrt{5}-2} \cdot \frac{\sqrt{5}+2}{\sqrt{5}+2}$$
$$= \frac{7(\sqrt{5}+2)}{(\sqrt{5})^2 - 2^2}$$
$$= \frac{7(\sqrt{5}+2)}{5-4}$$
$$= 7(\sqrt{5}+2)$$

53.
$$\frac{6}{\sqrt{5}+\sqrt{3}} = \frac{6}{\sqrt{5}+\sqrt{3}} \cdot \frac{\sqrt{5}-\sqrt{3}}{\sqrt{5}-\sqrt{3}}$$
$$= \frac{6(\sqrt{5}-\sqrt{3})}{(\sqrt{5})^2 - (\sqrt{3})^2}$$
$$= \frac{6(\sqrt{5}-\sqrt{3})}{5-3}$$
$$= \frac{6(\sqrt{5}-\sqrt{3})}{2}$$
$$= 3(\sqrt{5}-\sqrt{3})$$

55. $\sqrt[3]{125} = \sqrt[3]{5^3} = 5$

57. $\sqrt[3]{-8} = \sqrt[3]{(-2)^3} = -2$

59. $\sqrt[4]{-16}$ is not a real number.

61. $\sqrt[4]{(-3)^4} = |-3| = 3$

63. $\sqrt[5]{(-3)^5} = -3$

65. $\sqrt[5]{-\frac{1}{32}} = \sqrt[5]{-\frac{1}{2^5}} = -\frac{1}{2}$

67. $\sqrt[3]{32} = \sqrt[3]{8 \cdot 4} = \sqrt[3]{8}\sqrt[3]{4} = 2 \cdot \sqrt[3]{4}$

69. $\sqrt[3]{x^4} = \sqrt[3]{x^3 \cdot x} = x \cdot \sqrt[3]{x}$

71. $\sqrt[3]{9} \cdot \sqrt[3]{6} = \sqrt[3]{54} = \sqrt[3]{27 \cdot 2} = \sqrt[3]{27}\sqrt[3]{2} = 3\sqrt[3]{2}$

73. $\frac{\sqrt[5]{64x^6}}{\sqrt[5]{2x}} = \sqrt[5]{\frac{64x^6}{2x}} = \sqrt[5]{32x^5} = 2x$

75. $4\sqrt[5]{2} + 3\sqrt[5]{2} = 7\sqrt[5]{2}$

77.
$$5\sqrt[3]{16} + \sqrt[3]{54} = 5\sqrt[3]{8 \cdot 2} + \sqrt[3]{27 \cdot 2}$$
$$= 5 \cdot 2\sqrt[3]{2} + 3\sqrt[3]{2}$$
$$= 10\sqrt[3]{2} + 3\sqrt[3]{2}$$
$$= 13\sqrt[3]{2}$$

79.
$$\sqrt[3]{54xy^3} - y\sqrt[3]{128x}$$
$$= \sqrt[3]{27 \cdot 2xy^3} - y\sqrt[3]{64 \cdot 2x}$$
$$= 3y\sqrt[3]{2x} - 4y\sqrt[3]{2x}$$
$$= -y\sqrt[3]{2x}$$

81. $\sqrt{2} + \sqrt[3]{8} = \sqrt{2} + 2$

83. $36^{1/2} = \sqrt{36} = 6$

85. $8^{1/3} = \sqrt[3]{8} = 2$

87. $125^{2/3} = \left(\sqrt[3]{125}\right)^2 = 5^2 = 25$

89. $32^{-4/5} = \frac{1}{32^{4/5}} = \frac{1}{2^4} = \frac{1}{16}$

91.
$$\left(7x^{1/3}\right)\left(2x^{1/4}\right) = 7 \cdot 2x^{1/3} \cdot x^{1/4}$$
$$= 14 \cdot x^{1/3+1/4}$$
$$= 14x^{7/12}$$

93.
$$\frac{20x^{1/2}}{5x^{1/4}} = \left(\frac{20}{5}\right)\left(\frac{x^{1/2}}{x^{1/4}}\right)$$
$$= 4 \cdot x^{1/2-1/4}$$
$$= 4x^{1/4}$$

95. $\left(x^{2/3}\right)^3 = x^{2/3 \cdot 3} = x^2$

97. $(25x^4 y^6)^{1/2} = 25^{1/2} x^{4 \cdot 1/2} y^{6 \cdot 1/2} = 5x^2 |y|^3$

99.
$$\frac{\left(3y^{\frac{1}{4}}\right)^3}{y^{\frac{1}{12}}} = \frac{27y^{\frac{3}{4}}}{y^{\frac{1}{12}}} = 27y^{\frac{3}{4}-\frac{1}{12}}$$
$$= 27y^{\frac{8}{12}} = 27y^{\frac{2}{3}}$$

101. $\sqrt[4]{5^2} = 5^{2/4} = 5^{1/2} = \sqrt{5}$

103. $\sqrt[3]{x^6} = x^{6/3} = x^2$

105. $\sqrt[6]{x^4} = \sqrt[6/2]{x^{4/2}} = \sqrt[3]{x^2}$

107. $\sqrt[9]{x^6 y^3} = x^{\frac{6}{9}} y^{\frac{3}{9}} = x^{\frac{2}{3}} y^{\frac{1}{3}} = \sqrt[3]{x^2 y}$

109. $\sqrt[3]{\sqrt[4]{16} + \sqrt{625}} = \sqrt[3]{2 + 25} = \sqrt[3]{27} = 3$

111. $\left(49 x^{-2} y^4\right)^{-1/2} \left(xy^{1/2}\right)$

$= (49)^{-1/2} \left(x^{-2}\right)^{-1/2} \left(y^4\right)^{-1/2} \left(xy^{1/2}\right)$

$= \dfrac{1}{49^{1/2}} x^{(-2)(-1/2)} y^{(4)(-1/2)} \left(xy^{1/2}\right)$

$= \dfrac{1}{7} x^1 y^{-2} \cdot xy^{1/2} = \dfrac{1}{7} x^{1+1} y^{-2+(1/2)}$

$= \dfrac{1}{7} x^2 y^{-3/2} = \dfrac{x^2}{7 y^{3/2}}$

113. $\left(\dfrac{x^{-5/4} y^{1/3}}{x^{-3/4}}\right)^{-6} = \left(x^{(-5/4)-(-3/4)} y^{1/3}\right)^{-6}$

$= \left(x^{-2/4} y^{1/3}\right)^{-6} = x^{(-2/4)(-6)} y^{(1/3)(-6)}$

$= x^3 y^{-2} = \dfrac{x^3}{y^2}$

115. $d(x) = \sqrt{\dfrac{3x}{2}}$

$d(72) = \sqrt{\dfrac{3(72)}{2}}$

$= \sqrt{3(36)}$

$= \sqrt{3} \cdot \sqrt{36}$

$= 6\sqrt{3} \approx 10.4 \text{ miles}$

A passenger on the pool deck can see roughly 10.4 miles.

117. $v = \sqrt{20L}; L = 245$

$v = \sqrt{20 \cdot 245} = \sqrt{4900} = 70$

The motorist was traveling 70 miles per hour, so he was speeding.

119. $\dfrac{7\sqrt{2 \cdot 2 \cdot 3}}{6} = \dfrac{7 \cdot 2\sqrt{3}}{6} = \dfrac{14\sqrt{3}}{6} = \dfrac{7}{3}\sqrt{3}$

121. a. $C = 35.74 + 0.6215t - 35.74\sqrt[25]{v^4} + 0.4275t\sqrt[25]{v^4}$

$C = 35.74 + 0.6215t - 35.74 v^{\frac{4}{25}} + 0.4275 t v^{\frac{4}{25}}$

b. $C = 35.74 + 0.6215(25) - 35.74(30)^{\frac{4}{25}} + 0.4275(25)(30)^{\frac{4}{25}}$

$\approx 8° \text{ F}$

123. $P = 2l + 2w$

$= 2\left(2\sqrt{20}\right) + 2\left(\sqrt{125}\right)$

$= 4\sqrt{20} + 2\sqrt{125}$

$= 4\sqrt{4 \cdot 5} + 2\sqrt{25 \cdot 5}$

$= 4 \cdot 2\sqrt{5} + 2 \cdot 5\sqrt{5}$

$= 8\sqrt{5} + 10\sqrt{5}$

$= (8 + 10)\sqrt{5} = 18\sqrt{5}$

The perimeter is $18\sqrt{5}$ feet.

$A = lw = 2\sqrt{20} \cdot \sqrt{125}$

$= 2\sqrt{20 \cdot 125} = 2\sqrt{2500}$

$= 2 \cdot 50 = 100$

The area is 100 square feet.

133. a. false; $(-8)^{\frac{1}{3}} = \sqrt[3]{-8} = -2$ is real.

    b. false; $\sqrt{x^2 + y^2} \ne x + y$

    c. false; $(8)^{-\frac{1}{3}} = \dfrac{1}{(8)^{\frac{1}{3}}} = \dfrac{1}{\sqrt[3]{8}} = \dfrac{1}{2}$

    d. true; $2^{\frac{1}{2}} \cdot 2^{\frac{1}{2}} = 2^{\frac{1}{2}+\frac{1}{2}} = 2^1 = 2$

135. $\sqrt{25 x^{14}} = 5x^7$

137. a. $3^{\frac{1}{2}} \boxed{>} 3^{\frac{1}{3}}$

    Calculator Check: $1.7321 > 1.4422$

    b. $\sqrt{7} + \sqrt{18} \boxed{>} \sqrt{7+18}$

    Calculator Check: $6.8884 > 5$

Section P.4

Check Point Exercises

1. a. $(-17x^3 + 4x^2 - 11x - 5) + (16x^3 - 3x^2 + 3x - 15)$
$= (-17x^3 + 16x^3) + (4x^2 - 3x^2) + (-11x + 3x) + (-5 - 15)$
$= -x^3 + x^2 - 8x - 20$

    b. $(13x^3 - 9x^2 - 7x + 1) - (-7x^3 + 2x^2 - 5x + 9)$
$= (13x^3 - 9x^2 - 7x + 1) + (7x^3 - 2x^2 + 5x - 9)$
$= (13x^3 + 7x^3) + (-9x^2 - 2x^2) + (-7x + 5x) + (1 - 9)$
$= 20x^3 - 11x^2 - 2x - 8$

2. $(5x - 2)(3x^2 - 5x + 4)$
$= 5x(3x^2 - 5x + 4) - 2(3x^2 - 5x + 4)$
$= 5x \cdot 3x^2 - 5x \cdot 5x + 5x \cdot 4 - 2 \cdot 3x^2 + 2 \cdot 5x - 2 \cdot 4$
$= 15x^3 - 25x^2 + 20x - 6x^2 + 10x - 8$
$= 15x^3 - 31x^2 + 30x - 8$

3. $(7x - 5)(4x - 3) = 7x \cdot 4x + 7x(-3) + (-5)4x + (-5)(-3)$
$= 28x^2 - 21x - 20x + 15$
$= 28x^2 - 41x + 15$

4. a. Use the special-product formula shown.
$(A + B)(A - B) = A^2 - B^2$
$(7x + 8)(7x - 8) = (7x)^2 - (8)^2$
$= 49x^2 - 64$

    b. Use the special-product formula shown.
$(A + B)(A - B) = A^2 - B^2$
$(2y^3 - 5)(2y^3 + 5) = (2y^3 + 5)(2y^3 - 5) = (2y^3)^2 - (5)^2 = 4y^6 - 25$

5.   **a.**   Use the special-product formula shown.

$$(A+B)^2 = A^2 + 2AB + B^2$$
$$(x+10)^2 = x^2 + 2(x)(10) + 10^2$$
$$= x^2 + 20x + 100$$

     b.   Use the special-product formula shown.

$$(A+B)^2 = A^2 + 2AB + B^2$$
$$(5x+4)^2 = (5x)^2 + 2(5x)(4) + 4^2$$
$$= 25x^2 + 40x + 16$$

6.   **a.**   Use the special-product formula shown.

$$(A-B)^2 = A^2 - 2AB + B^2$$
$$(x-9)^2 = x^2 - 2(x)(9) + 9^2$$
$$= x^2 - 18x + 81$$

     b.   Use the special-product formula shown.

$$(A-B)^2 = A^2 - 2AB + B^2$$
$$(7x-3)^2 = (7x)^2 - 2(7x)(3) + 3^2$$
$$= 49x^2 - 42x + 9$$

7. $(x^3 - 4x^2y + 5xy^2 - y^3) - (x^3 - 6x^2y + y^3)$
$$= (x^3 - 4x^2y + 5xy^2 - y^3) + (-x^3 + 6x^2y - y^3)$$
$$= (x^3 - x^3) + (-4x^2y + 6x^2y) + (5xy^2) + (-y^3 - y^3)$$
$$= 2x^2y + 5xy^2 - 2y^3$$

8.   **a.** $(7x-6y)(3x-y) = (7x)(3x) + (7x)(-y) + (-6y)(3x) + (-6y)(-y)$
$$= 21x^2 - 7xy - 18xy + 6y^2$$
$$= 21x^2 - 25xy + 6y^2$$

     b. $(2x+4y)^2 = (2x)^2 + 2(2x)(4y) + (4y)^2$
$$= 4x^2 + 16xy + 16y^2$$

Exercise Set P.4

1.   Yes; $2x + 3x^2 - 5 = 3x^2 + 2x - 5$

3.   No; The form of a polynomial involves addition and subtraction, not division.

5. $3x^2$ has degree 2
      $-5x$ has degree 1
      4 has degree 0
      $3x^2 - 5x + 4$ has degree 2.

7. x^2 has degree 2
$-4x^3$ has degree 3
$9x$ has degree 1
$-12x^4$ has degree 4
63 has degree 0
$x^2 - 4x^3 + 9x - 12x^4 + 63$ has degree 4.

9. $(-6x^3 + 5x^2 - 8x + 9) + (17x^3 + 2x^2 - 4x - 13) = (-6x^3 + 17x^3) + (5x^2 + 2x^2) + (-8x - 4x) + (9 - 13)$
$$= 11x^3 + 7x^2 - 12x - 4$$

The degree is 3.

11. $(17x^3 - 5x^2 + 4x - 3) - (5x^3 - 9x^2 - 8x + 11) = (17x^3 - 5x^2 + 4x - 3) + (-5x^3 + 9x^2 + 8x - 11)$
$$= (17x^3 - 5x^3) + (-5x^2 + 9x^2) + (4x + 8x) + (-3 - 11)$$
$$= 12x^3 + 4x^2 + 12x - 14$$

The degree is 3.

13. $(5x^2 - 7x - 8) + (2x^2 - 3x + 7) - (x^2 - 4x - 3) = (5x^2 - 7x - 8) + (2x^2 - 3x + 7) + (-x^2 + 4x + 3)$
$$= (5x^2 + 2x^2 - x^2) + (-7x - 3x + 4x) + (-8 + 7 + 3)$$
$$= 6x^2 - 6x + 2$$

The degree is 2.

15. $(x+1)(x^2 - x + 1) = x(x^2) - x \cdot x + x \cdot 1 + 1(x^2) - 1 \cdot x + 1 \cdot 1$
$$= x^3 - x^2 + x + x^2 - x + 1$$
$$= x^3 + 1$$

17. $(2x-3)(x^2 - 3x + 5) = (2x)(x^2) + (2x)(-3x) + (2x)(5) + (-3)(x^2) + (-3)(-3x) + (-3)(5)$
$$= 2x^3 - 6x^2 + 10x - 3x^2 + 9x - 15$$
$$= 2x^3 - 9x^2 + 19x - 15$$

19. $(x+7)(x+3) = x^2 + 3x + 7x + 21 = x^2 + 10x + 21$

21. $(x-5)(x+3) = x^2 + 3x - 5x - 15 = x^2 - 2x - 15$

23. $(3x+5)(2x+1) = (3x)(2x) + 3x(1) + 5(2x) + 5 = 6x^2 + 3x + 10x + 5 = 6x^2 + 13x + 5$

25. $(2x-3)(5x+3) = (2x)(5x) + (2x)(3) + (-3)(5x) + (-3)(3) = 10x^2 + 6x - 15x - 9 = 10x^2 - 9x - 9$

27. $(5x^2 - 4)(3x^2 - 7) = (5x^2)(3x^2) + (5x^2)(-7) + (-4)(3x^2) + (-4)(-7) = 15x^4 - 35x^2 - 12x^2 + 28 = 15x^4 - 47x^2 + 28$

29. $(8x^3 + 3)(x^2 - 5) = (8x^3)(x^2) + (8x^3)(-5) + (3)(x^2) + (3)(-5) = 8x^5 - 40x^3 + 3x^2 - 15$

31. $(x+3)(x-3) = x^2 - 3^2 = x^2 - 9$

33. $(3x+2)(3x-2) = (3x)^2 - 2^2 = 9x^2 - 4$

35. $(5-7x)(5+7x) = 5^2 - (7x)^2 = 25 - 49x^2$

37. $(4x^2 + 5x)(4x^2 - 5x) = (4x^2)^2 - (5x)^2 = 16x^4 - 25x^2$

39. $\left(1-y^5\right)\left(1+y^5\right) = (1)^2 - \left(y^5\right)^2 = 1 - y^{10}$

41. $(x+2)^2 = x^2 + 2 \cdot x \cdot 2 + 2^2 = x^2 + 4x + 4$

43. $(2x+3)^2 = (2x)^2 + 2(2x)(3) + 3^2 = 4x^2 + 12x + 9$

45. $(x-3)^2 = x^2 - 2 \cdot x \cdot 3 + 3^2 = x^2 - 6x + 9$

47. $(4x^2 - 1)^2 = (4x^2)^2 - 2(4x^2)(1) + 1^2 = 16x^4 - 8x^2 + 1$

49. $(7-2x)^2 = 7^2 - 2(7)(2x) + (2x)^2 = 49 - 28x + 4x^2 = 4x^2 - 28x + 49$

51. $(x+1)^3 = x^3 + 3 \cdot x^2 \cdot 1 + 3x \cdot 1^2 + 1^3 = x^3 + 3x^2 + 3x + 1$

53. $(2x+3)^3 = (2x)^3 + 3 \cdot (2x)^2 \cdot 3 + 3(2x) \cdot 3^2 + 3^3 = 8x^3 + 36x^2 + 54x + 27$

55. $(x-3)^3 = x^3 - 3 \cdot x^3 \cdot 3 + 3 \cdot x \cdot 3^2 - 3^3 = x^3 - 9x^2 + 27x - 27$

57. $(3x-4)^3 = (3x)^3 - 3(3x)^2 \cdot 4 + 3(3x) \cdot 4^2 - 4^3 = 27x^3 - 108x^2 + 144x - 64$

59. $(5x^2 y - 3xy) + (2x^2 y - xy) = (5x^2 y + 2x^2 y) + (-3xy - xy)$
$$= (5+2)x^2 y + (-3-1)xy$$
$$= 7x^2 y - 4xy \text{ is of degree 3.}$$

61. $(4x^2 y + 8xy + 11) + (-2x^2 y + 5xy + 2) = (4x^2 y - 2x^2 y) + (8xy + 5xy) + (11+2)$
$$= (4-2)x^2 y + (8+5)xy + 13$$
$$= 2x^2 y + 13xy + 13 \text{ is of degree 3.}$$

63. $(x^3 + 7xy - 5y^2) - (6x^3 - xy + 4y^2) = (x^3 + 7xy - 5y^2)$
$$= (x^3 - 6x^3) + (7xy + xy) + (-5y^2 - 4y^2)$$
$$= (1-6)x^3 + (7+1)xy + (-5-4)y^2$$
$$= -5x^3 + 8xy - 9y^2 \text{ is of degree 3.}$$

65. $(3x^4 y^2 + 5x^3 y - 3y) - (2x^4 y^2 - 3x^3 y - 4y + 6x) = (3x^4 y^2 + 5x^3 y - 3y) + (-2x^4 y^2 + 3x^3 y + 4y - 6x)$
$$= (3x^4 y^2 - 2x^4 y^2) + (5x^3 y + 3x^3 y) + (-3y + 4y) - 6x$$
$$= (3-2)x^4 y^2 + (5+3)x^3 y + (-3+4)y - 6x$$
$$= x^4 y^2 + 8x^3 y + y - 6x \text{ is of degree 6.}$$

67. $(x+5y)(7x+3y) = x(7x) + x(3y) + (5y)(7x) + (5y)(3y)$
$$= 7x^2 + 3xy + 35xy + 15y^2$$
$$= 7x^2 + 38xy + 15y^2$$

69. $(x-3y)(2x+7y) = x(2x) + x(7y) + (-3y)(2x) + (-3y)(7y)$
$$= 2x^2 + 7xy - 6xy - 21y^2$$
$$= 2x^2 + xy - 21y^2$$

71. $(3xy-1)(5xy+2) = (3xy)(5xy)+(3xy)(2)+(-1)(5xy)+(-1)(2)$
$$= 15x^2y^2+6xy-5xy-2$$
$$= 15x^2y^2+xy-2$$

73. $(7x+5y)^2 = (7x)^2+2(7x)(5y)+(5y)^2 = 49x^2+70xy+25y^2$

75. $(x^2y^2-3)^2 = (x^2y^2)^2-2(x^2y^2)(3)+3^2 = x^4y^4-6x^2y^2+9$

77. $(x-y)(x^2+xy+y^2) = x(x^2)+x(xy)+x(y^2)+(-y)(x^2)+(-y)(xy)+(-y)(y^2)$
$$= x^3+x^2y+xy^2-x^2y-xy^2-y^3$$
$$= x^3-y^3$$

79. $(3x+5y)(3x-5y) = (3x)^2-(5y)^2 = 9x^2-25y^2$

81. $\left(7xy^2-10y\right)\left(7xy^2+10y\right) = \left(7xy^2\right)^2-\left(10y\right)^2 = 49x^2y^4-100y^2$

83. $(3x+4y)^2-(3x-4y)^2 = \left[(3x)^2+2(3x)(4y)+(4y)^2\right]-\left[(3x)^2-2(3x)(4y)+(4y)^2\right]$
$$= \left(9x^2+24xy+16y^2\right)-\left(9x^2-24xy+16y^2\right)$$
$$= 9x^2+24xy+16y^2-9x^2+24xy-16y^2$$
$$= 48xy$$

85. $(5x-7)(3x-2)-(4x-5)(6x-1)$
$$= \left[15x^2-10x-21x+14\right]-\left[24x^2-4x-30x+5\right]$$
$$= \left(15x^2-31x+14\right)-\left(24x^2-34x+5\right)$$
$$= 15x^2-31x+14-24x^2+34x-5$$
$$= -9x^2+3x+9$$

87. $(2x+5)(2x-5)\left(4x^2+25\right)$
$$= \left[(2x)^2-5^2\right]\left(4x^2+25\right)$$
$$= \left(4x^2-25\right)\left(4x^2+25\right)$$
$$= \left(4x^2\right)^2-(25)^2$$
$$= 16x^4-625$$

89. $\dfrac{(2x-7)^5}{(2x-7)^3} = (2x-7)^{5-3}$
$$= (2x-7)^2$$
$$= (2x)^2-2(2x)(7)+(7)^2$$
$$= 4x^2-28x+49$$

92. Model 2 is not a polynomial model

93. Model 1:

$N = 1.8x + 5.1$

$N = 1.8(2) + 5.1$

$N = 8.7$

Model 2:

$N = 5.6(1.2)^x$

$N = 5.6(1.2)^2$

$N = 8.064$

Model 3:

$N = 0.17x^2 + 0.95x + 5.68$

$N = 0.17(2)^2 + 0.95(2) + 5.68$

$N = 8.26$

Model 4:

$N = 0.09x^2 + 0.01x^3 + 1.1x + 5.64$

$N = 0.09(2)^2 + 0.01(2)^3 + 1.1(2) + 5.64$

$N = 8.28$

Model 1 best describes the data in 2000.

95. Model 3 is the model of degree 2.

$N = 0.17x^2 + 0.95x + 5.68$

$N = 0.17(5)^2 + 0.95(5) + 5.68$

$N = 14.68$

Model 3 best describes the data in 2003 very well.

97.
$$x(8 - 2x)(10 - 2x) = x(80 - 36x + 4x^2)$$
$$= 80x - 36x^2 + 4x^3$$
$$= 4x^3 - 36x^2 + 80x$$

99.
$$(x+9)(x+3) - (x+5)(x+1)$$
$$= x^2 + 12x + 27 - (x^2 + 6x + 5)$$
$$= x^2 + 12x + 27 - x^2 - 6x - 5$$
$$= 6x + 22$$

109.
$$[(7x+5)+4y][(7x+5)-4y] = (7x+5)^2 - 4y^2$$
$$= (7x)^2 + 2(7x)(5) + 5^2 - 16y^2$$
$$= 49x^2 + 70x + 25 - 16y^2$$

111. $(x^n + 2)(x^n - 2) - (x^n - 3)^2$
$$(x^n + 2)(x^n - 2) - (x^n - 3)^2$$
$$= (x^{2n} - 4) - (x^{2n} - 6x^n + 9)$$
$$= x^{2n} - 4 - x^{2n} + 6x^n - 9$$
$$= 6x^n - 13$$

Mid Chapter P Check Point

1. $(3x+5)(4x-7) = (3x)(4x) + (3x)(-7) + (5)(4x) + (5)(-7)$
$$= 12x^2 - 21x + 20x - 35$$
$$= 12x^2 - x - 35$$

2. $(3x+5) - (4x-7) = 3x + 5 - 4x + 7$
$$= 3x - 4x + 5 + 7$$
$$= -x + 12$$

3. $\sqrt{6} + 9\sqrt{6} = 10\sqrt{6}$

4. $3\sqrt{12} - \sqrt{27} = 3 \cdot 2\sqrt{3} - 3\sqrt{3} = 6\sqrt{3} - 3\sqrt{3} = 3\sqrt{3}$

5. $7x + 3[9 - (2x-6)] = 7x + 3[9 - 2x + 6] = 7x + 3[15 - 2x] = 7x + 45 - 6x = x + 45$

6. $(8x-3)^2 = (8x)^2 - 2(8x)(3) + (3)^2 = 64x^2 - 48x + 9$

7. $\left(x^{\frac{1}{3}}y^{-\frac{1}{2}}\right)^6 = x^{\frac{1}{3}\cdot 6}y^{-\frac{1}{2}\cdot 6} = x^2 y^{-3} = \dfrac{x^2}{y^3}$

8. $\left(\dfrac{2}{7}\right)^0 - 32^{-\frac{2}{5}} = 1 - \dfrac{1}{\left(\sqrt[5]{32}\right)^2} = 1 - \dfrac{1}{(2)^2} = 1 - \dfrac{1}{4} = \dfrac{3}{4}$

9. $(2x-5) - (x^2 - 3x + 1) = 2x - 5 - x^2 + 3x - 1 = -x^2 + 5x - 6$

10. $(2x-5)(x^2 - 3x + 1) = 2x(x^2 - 3x + 1) - 5(x^2 - 3x + 1)$
$$= 2x(x^2 - 3x + 1) - 5(x^2 - 3x + 1)$$
$$= 2x^3 - 6x^2 + 2x - 5x^2 + 15x - 5$$
$$= 2x^3 - 6x^2 - 5x^2 + 2x + 15x - 5$$
$$= 2x^3 - 11x^2 + 17x - 5$$

11. $x^3 + x^3 - x^3 \cdot x^3 = 2x^3 - x^6 = -x^6 + 2x^3$

12. $(9a - 10b)(2a + b) = (9a)(2a) + (9a)(b) + (-10b)(2a) + (-10b)(b)$
$$= (9a)(2a) + (9a)(b) + (-10b)(2a) + (-10b)(b)$$
$$= 18a^2 + 9ab - 20ab - 10b^2$$
$$= 18a^2 - 11ab - 10b^2$$

13. $\{a,c,d,e\} \cup \{c,d,f,h\} = \{a,c,d,e,f,h\}$

14. $\{a,c,d,e\} \cap \{c,d,f,h\} = \{c,d\}$

15. $\left(3x^2y^3 - xy + 4y^2\right) - \left(-2x^2y^3 - 3xy + 5y^2\right) = 3x^2y^3 - xy + 4y^2 + 2x^2y^3 + 3xy - 5y^2$
$$= 3x^2y^3 - xy + 4y^2 + 2x^2y^3 + 3xy - 5y^2$$
$$= 3x^2y^3 + 2x^2y^3 - xy + 3xy + 4y^2 - 5y^2$$
$$= 5x^2y^3 + 2xy - y^2$$

16. $\dfrac{24x^2y^{13}}{-2x^5y^{-2}} = -12x^{2-5}y^{13-(-2)} = -12x^{-3}y^{15} = -\dfrac{12y^{15}}{x^3}$

17. $\left(\dfrac{1}{3}x^{-5}y^4\right)\left(18x^{-2}y^{-1}\right) = 6x^{-5-2}y^{4-1} = \dfrac{6y^3}{x^7}$

18. $\sqrt[12]{x^4} = x^{\frac{4}{12}} = \left|x^{\frac{1}{3}}\right| = \left|\sqrt[3]{x}\right|$

19. $\dfrac{24 \times 10^3}{2 \times 10^6} = \dfrac{24}{2} \cdot \dfrac{10^3}{10^6} = 12 \times 10^{-3} = \left(1.2 \times 10^1\right) \times 10^{-3} = 1.2 \times \left(10^1 \times 10^{-3}\right) = 1.2 \times 10^{-2}$

20. $\dfrac{\sqrt[3]{32}}{\sqrt[3]{2}} = \sqrt[3]{\dfrac{32}{2}} = \sqrt[3]{16} = \sqrt[3]{2^4} = 2\sqrt[3]{2}$

21. $(x^3 + 2)(x^3 - 2) = x^6 - 4$

22. $(x^2 + 2)^2 = (x^2)^2 + 2(x^2)(2) + (2)^2 = x^4 + 4x^2 + 4$

23. $\sqrt{50} \cdot \sqrt{6} = 5\sqrt{2} \cdot \sqrt{6} = 5\sqrt{2 \cdot 6} = 5\sqrt{12} = 5 \cdot 2\sqrt{3} = 10\sqrt{3}$

24. $\dfrac{11}{7 - \sqrt{3}} = \dfrac{11}{7 - \sqrt{3}} \cdot \dfrac{7 + \sqrt{3}}{7 + \sqrt{3}} = \dfrac{77 + 11\sqrt{3}}{49 - 3} = \dfrac{77 + 11\sqrt{3}}{46}$

25. $\dfrac{11}{\sqrt{3}} = \dfrac{11}{\sqrt{3}} \cdot \dfrac{\sqrt{3}}{\sqrt{3}} = \dfrac{11\sqrt{3}}{3}$

26. $\left\{ -11, \ -\dfrac{3}{7}, \ 0, \ 0.45, \ \sqrt{25} \right\}$

27. Since $2 - \sqrt{13} < 0$ then $\left| 2 - \sqrt{13} \right| = \sqrt{13} - 2$

28. Since $x < 0$ then $|x| = -x$. Thus $x^2 |x| = -x^2 x = -x^3$

29. $120 \cdot 2.9 \times 10^8 = 348 \times 10^8 = 3.48 \times 10^2 \times 10^8 = 3.48 \times 10^{10}$

The total annual spending on ice cream is $\$3.48 \times 10^{10}$

30. $\dfrac{3 \times 10^{10}}{7.5 \times 10^9} = \dfrac{3}{7.5} \cdot \dfrac{10^{10}}{10^9} = 0.4 \times 10 = 4$

A human brain has 4 times as many neurons as a gorilla brain.

31. **a.**   Model 1:

$D = 236(1.5)^x$

$D = 236(1.5)^2$

$D = 531$

Model 2:

$D = 127x + 239$

$D = 127(2) + 239$

$D = 493$

Model 3:

$D = -54x^2 + 234x + 220$

$D = -54(2)^2 + 234(2) + 220$

$D = 472$

Model 3 best describes the data in 2004.

b.   Model 2 is the polynomial of degree 1:

$D = 127x + 239$

$D = 127(6) + 239$

$D = 1001$

Model 2 predicts Americans will spend 1001 million dollars on online dating in 2008.

Section P.5

Check Point Exercises

1. **a.** $10x^3 - 4x^2$
    $= 2x^2(5x) - 2x^2(2)$
    $= 2x^2(5x - 2)$

    b. $2x(x-7) + 3(x-7)$
    $= (x-7)(2x+3)$

2. $x^3 + 5x^2 - 2x - 10$
    $= (x^3 + 5x^2) - (2x + 10)$
    $= x^2(x+5) - 2(x+5)$
    $= (x+5)(x^2 - 2)$

3. **a.** Find two numbers whose product is 40 and whose sum is 13. The required integers are 8 and 5. Thus,
    $x^2 + 13x + 40 = (x+5)(x+8)$ or $(x+8)(x+5)$

    b. Find two numbers whose product is –14 and whose sum is –5. The required integers are –7 and 2. Thus,
    $x^2 - 5x - 14 = (x-7)(x+2)$ or $(x+2)(x-7)$.

4. Find two First terms whose product is $6x^2$.
    $6x^2 + 19x - 7 = (6x\quad)(x\quad)$
    $6x^2 + 19x - 7 = (3x\quad)(2x\quad)$

    Find two Last terms whose product is –7.
    The possible factors are $1(-7)$ and $-1(7)$.

    Try various combinations of these factors to find the factorization in which the sum of the Outside and Inside products is $19x$.

Possible Factors of $6x^2 + 19x - 7$	Sum of Outside and Inside Products (Should Equal $19x$)
$(6x+1)(x-7)$	$-42x + x = -41x$
$(6x-7)(x+1)$	$6x - 7x = -x$
$(6x-1)(x+7)$	$42x - x = 41x$
$(6x+7)(x-1)$	$-6x + 7x = x$
$(3x+1)(2x-7)$	$-21x + 2x = -19x$
$(3x-7)(2x+1)$	$3x - 14x = -11x$
$(3x-1)(2x+7)$	$21x - 2x = 19x$
$(3x+7)(2x-1)$	$-3x + 14x = 11x$

Thus, $6x^2 + 19x - 7 = (3x-1)(2x+7)$ or $(2x+7)(3x-1)$.

5. Find two First terms whose product is $3x^2$.

$$3x^2 - 13xy + 4y^2 = (3x \quad)(x \quad)$$

Find two Last terms whose product is $4y^2$.

The possible factors are $(2y)(2y)$, $(-2y)(-2y)$, $(4y)(y)$, and $(-4y)(-y)$.

Try various combinations of these factors to find the factorization in which the sum of the Outside and Inside products is $-13xy$.

$$3x^2 - 13xy + y^2 = (3x - y)(x - 4y) \text{ or } (x - 4y)(3x - y).$$

6. Express each term as the square of some monomial. Then use the formula for factoring $A^2 - B^2$.

a. $x^2 - 81 = x^2 - 9^2 = (x+9)(x-9)$

b. $36x^2 - 25 = (6x)^2 - 5^2 = (6x+5)(6x-5)$

7. Express $81x^4 - 16$ as the difference of two squares and use the formula for factoring $A^2 - B^2$.

$$81x^4 - 16 = (9x^2)^2 - 4^2 = (9x^2 + 4)(9x^2 - 4)$$

The factor $9x^2 - 4$ is the difference of two squares and can be factored. Express $9x^2 - 4$ as the difference of two squares and again use the formula for factoring $A^2 - B^2$.

$$(9x^2 + 4)(9x^2 - 4) = (9x^2 + 4)\left[(3x)^2 - 2^2\right] = (9x^2 + 4)(3x+2)(3x-2)$$

Thus, factored completely,

$$81x^4 - 16 = (9x^2 + 4)(3x+2)(3x-2).$$

8. **a.** $x^2 + 14x + 49 = x^2 + 2 \cdot x \cdot 7 + 7^2 = (x+7)^2$

b. Since $16x^2 = (4x)^2$ and $49 = 7^2$, check to see if the middle term can be expressed as twice the product of $4x$ and 7. Since $2 \cdot 4x \cdot 7 = 56x$, $16x^2 - 56x + 49$ is a perfect square trinomial. Thus,

$$16x^2 - 56x + 49 = (4x)^2 - 2 \cdot 4x \cdot 7 + 7^2$$
$$= (4x-7)^2$$

9. **a.** $= x^3 + 1^3$

$= (x+1)(x^2 - x \cdot 1 + 1^2)$

$= (x+1)(x^2 - x + 1)$

b. $-8 = (5x)^3 - 2^3$

$= (5x-2)\left[(5x)^2 + (5x)(2) + 2^2\right]$

$= (5x-2)(25x^2 + 10x + 4)$

10. Factor out the greatest common factor.

$$3x^3 - 30x^2 + 75x = 3x\left(x^2 - 10x + 25\right)$$

Factor the perfect square trinomial.

$$3x\left(x^2 - 10x + 25\right) = 3x\left(x-5\right)^2$$

11. Reorder to write as a difference of squares.

$$x^2 - 36a^2 + 20x + 100$$
$$= x^2 + 20x + 100 - 36a^2$$
$$= \left(x^2 + 20x + 100\right) - 36a^2$$
$$= \left(x+10\right)^2 - 36a^2$$
$$= (x+10+6a)(x+10-6a)$$

12. $x(x-1)^{-\frac{1}{2}}+(x-1)^{\frac{1}{2}}$

$$=(x-1)^{-\frac{1}{2}}\left[x+(x-1)^{\frac{1}{2}-(-\frac{1}{2})}\right]$$

$$=(x-1)^{-\frac{1}{2}}\left[x+(x-1)\right]$$

$$=(x-1)^{-\frac{1}{2}}(2x-1)$$

$$=\frac{(2x-1)}{(x-1)^{\frac{1}{2}}}$$

Exercise Set P.5

1. $18x+27=9\cdot 2x+9\cdot 3=9(2x+3)$

3. $3x^2+6x=3x\cdot x+3x\cdot 2=3x(x+2)$

5. $9x^4-18x^3+27x^2$
$$=9x^2(x^2)+9x^2(-2x)+9x^2(3)$$
$$=9x^2(x^2-2x+3)$$

7. $x(x+5)+3(x+5)=(x+5)(x+3)$

9. $x^2(x-3)+12(x-3)=(x-3)(x^2+12)$

11. $x^3-2x^2+5x-10=x^2(x-2)+5(x-2)$
$$=(x^2+5)(x-2)$$

13. $x^3-x^2+2x-2=x^2(x-1)+2(x-1)$
$$=(x-1)(x^2+2)$$

15. $3x^3-2x^2-6x+4=x^2(3x-2)-2(3x-2)$
$$=(3x-2)(x^2-2)$$

17. $x^2+5x+6=(x+2)(x+3)$

19. $x^2-2x-15=(x-5)(x+3)$

21. $x^2-8x+15=(x-5)(x-3)$

23. $3x^2-x-2=(3x+2)(x-1)$

25. $3x^2-25x-28=(3x-28)(x+1)$

27. $6x^2-11x+4=(2x-1)(3x-4)$

29. $4x^2+16x+15=(2x+3)(2x+5)$

31. $9x^2-9x+2=(3x-1)(3x-2)$

33. $20x^2+27x-8=(5x+8)(4x-1)$

35. $2x^2+3xy+y^2=(2x+y)(x+y)$

37. $6x^2-5xy-6y^2=(3x+2y)(2x-3y)$

39. $x^2-100=x^2-10^2=(x+10)(x-10)$

41. $36x^2-49=(6x)^2-7^2=(6x+7)(6x-7)$

43. $9x^2-25y^2=(3x)^2-(5y)^2$
$$=(3x+5y)(3x-5y)$$

45. $x^4-16=(x^2)^2-4^2$
$$=(x^2+4)(x^2-4)$$
$$=(x^2+4)(x+2)(x-2)$$

47. $16x^4-81=(4x^2)^2-9^2$
$$=(4x^2+9)(4x^2-9)$$
$$=(4x^2+9)[(2x)^2-3^2]$$
$$=(4x^2+9)(2x+3)(2x-3)$$

49. $x^2+2x+1=x^2+2\cdot x\cdot 1+1^2=(x+1)^2$

51. $x^2-14x+49=x^2-2\cdot x\cdot 7+7^2$
$$=(x-7)^2$$

53. $4x^2+4x+1=(2x)^2+2\cdot 2x\cdot 1+1^2$
$$=(2x+1)^2$$

55. $9x^2-6x+1=(3x)^2-2\cdot 3x\cdot 1+1^2$
$$=(3x-1)^2$$

57. $x^3+27=x^3+3^3$
$$=(x+3)(x^2-x\cdot 3+3^2)$$
$$=(x+3)(x^2-3x+9)$$

59. $x^3-64=x^3-4^3$
$$=(x-4)(x^2+x\cdot 4+4^2)$$
$$=(x-4)(x^2+4x+16)$$

61. $8x^3-1=(2x)^3-1^3$
$$=(2x-1)[(2x)^2+(2x)(1)+1^2]$$
$$=(2x-1)(4x^2+2x+1)$$

63. $64x^3 + 27 = (4x)^3 + 3^3$
$$= (4x+3)[(4x)^2 - (4x)(3) + 3^2]$$
$$= (4x+3)(16x^2 - 12x + 9)$$

65. $3x^3 - 3x = 3x(x^2 - 1) = 3x(x+1)(x-1)$

67. $4x^2 - 4x - 24 = 4(x^2 - x - 6)$
$$= 4(x+2)(x-3)$$

69. $2x^4 - 162 = 2(x^4 - 81)$
$$= 2[(x^2)^2 - 9^2]$$
$$= 2(x^2 + 9)(x^2 - 9)$$
$$= 2(x^2 + 9)(x^2 - 3^2)$$
$$= 2(x^2 + 9)(x+3)(x-3)$$

71. $x^3 + 2x^2 - 9x - 18 = (x^3 + 2x^2) - (9x + 18)$
$$= x^2(x+2) - 9(x+2)$$
$$= (x^2 - 9)(x+2)$$
$$= (x^2 - 3^2)(x+2)$$
$$= (x-3)(x+3)(x+2)$$

73. $2x^2 - 2x - 112 = 2(x^2 - x - 56) = 2(x-8)(x+7)$

75. $x^3 - 4x = x(x^2 - 4)$
$$= x(x^2 - 2^2)$$
$$= x(x-2)(x+2)$$

77. $x^2 + 64$ is prime.

79. $x^3 + 2x^2 - 4x - 8 = (x^3 + 2x^2) + (-4x - 8)$
$$= x^2(x+2) - 4(x+2) = (x^2 - 4)(x+2) = (x^2 - 2^2)(x+2) = (x-2)(x+2)(x+2) = (x-2)(x+2)^2$$

81. $y^5 - 81y$
$$= y(y^4 - 81) = y[(y^2)^2 - 9^2] = y(y^2 + 9)(y^2 - 9) = y(y^2 + 9)(y^2 - 3^2) = y(y^2 + 9)(y+3)(y-3)$$

83. $20y^4 - 45y^2 = 5y^2(4y^2 - 9) = 5y^2[(2y)^2 - 3^2] = 5y^2(2y+3)(2y-3)$

85. $x^2 - 12x + 36 - 49y^2$
$$= (x^2 - 12x + 36) - 49y^2 = (x-6)^2 - 49y^2 = (x-6+7y)(x-6-7y)$$

87. $9b^2x - 16y - 16x + 9b^2y$
$$= (9b^2x + 9b^2y) + (-16x - 16y) = 9b^2(x+y) - 16(x+y) = (x+y)(9b^2 - 16) = (x+y)(3b+4)(3b-4)$$

89. $x^2y - 16y + 32 - 2x^2$
$$= (x^2y - 16y) + (-2x^2 + 32) = y(x^2 - 16) - 2(x^2 - 16) = (x^2 - 16)(y-2) = (x+4)(x-4)(y-2)$$

91. $2x^3 - 8a^2x + 24x^2 + 72x$
$$= 2x(x^2 - 4a^2 + 12x + 36) = 2x[(x^2 + 12x + 36) - 4a^2] = 2x[(x+6)^2 - 4a^2] = 2x(x+6-2a)(x+6+2a)$$

93. $x^{\frac{3}{2}} - x^{\frac{1}{2}} = x^{\frac{1}{2}}\left(x^{\frac{3}{2}-\frac{1}{2}}\right) - 1 = x^{\frac{1}{2}}(x-1)$

95. $4x^{-\frac{2}{3}} + 8x^{\frac{1}{3}} = 4x^{-\frac{2}{3}}\left(1 + 2x^{\frac{1}{3}-\left(-\frac{2}{3}\right)}\right) = 4x^{-\frac{2}{3}}(1+2x) = \dfrac{4(1+2x)}{x^{\frac{2}{3}}}$

97. $(x+3)^{\frac{1}{2}} - (x+3)^{\frac{3}{2}} = (x+3)^{\frac{1}{2}}\left[1 - (x+3)^{\frac{3}{2}-\frac{1}{2}}\right] = (x+3)^{\frac{1}{2}}[1-(x+3)] = (x+3)^{\frac{1}{2}}(-x-2) = -(x+3)^{\frac{1}{2}}(x+2)$

99. $(x+5)^{-\frac{1}{2}}-(x+5)^{-\frac{3}{2}}=(x+5)^{-\frac{3}{2}}\left[(x+5)^{-\frac{1}{2}-\left(-\frac{3}{2}\right)}-1\right]=(x+5)^{-\frac{3}{2}}\left[(x+5)-1\right]=(x+5)^{-\frac{3}{2}}(x+4)=\dfrac{x+4}{(x+5)^{\frac{3}{2}}}$

101. $(4x-1)^{\frac{1}{2}}-\dfrac{1}{3}(4x-1)^{\frac{3}{2}}$

$=(4x-1)^{\frac{1}{2}}\left[1-\dfrac{1}{3}(4x-1)^{\frac{3}{2}-\frac{1}{2}}\right]=(4x-1)^{\frac{1}{2}}\left[1-\dfrac{1}{3}(4x-1)\right]=(4x-1)^{\frac{1}{2}}\left[1-\dfrac{4}{3}x+\dfrac{1}{3}\right]$

$=(4x-1)^{\frac{1}{2}}\left(\dfrac{4}{3}-\dfrac{4}{3}x\right)=(4x-1)^{\frac{1}{2}}\dfrac{4}{3}(1-x)=\dfrac{-4(4x-1)(x-1)}{3}$

103. $10x^2(x+1)-7x(x+1)-6(x+1)=(x+1)(10x^2-7x-6)=(x+1)(5x-6)(2x+1)$

105. $6x^4+35x^2-6=(x^2+6)(6x^2-1)$

107. $y^7+y=y(y^6+1)=y\left[(y^2)^3+1^3\right]=y(y^2+1)(y^4-y^2+1)$

109. $x^4-5x^2y^2+4y^4=(x^2-4y^2)(x^2-y^2)=(x+2y)(x-2y)(x+y)(x-y)$

111. $(x-y)^4-4(x-y)^2$

$=(x-y)^2\left((x-y)^2-4\right)=(x-y)^2\left((x-y)+2\right)\left((x-y)-2\right)=(x-y)^2(x-y+2)(x-y-2)$

113. $2x^2-7xy^2+3y^4=(2x-y^2)(x-3y^2)$

115. a. $(x-0.4x)-0.4(x-0.4x)=(x-0.4x)(1-0.4)=(0.6x)(0.6)=0.36x$

b. No, the computer is selling at 36% of its original price.

117. a. $(3x)^2-4\cdot2^2=9x^2-16$

b. $9x^2-16=(3x+4)(3x-4)$

119. a. $x(x+y)-y(x+y)$

b. $x(x+y)-y(x+y)=(x+y)(x-y)$

121. $V_{\text{shaded}}=V_{\text{outside}}-V_{\text{inside}}$

$=a\cdot a\cdot4a-b\cdot b\cdot4a$

$=4a^3-4ab^2$

$=4a(a^2-b^2)$

$=4a(a+b)(a-b)$

131. $x^{2n} + 6x^n + 8 = (x^n + 4)(x^n + 2)$

133. $x^4 - y^4 - 2x^3 y + 2xy^3$
$$= (x^4 - y^4) + (-2x^3 y + 2xy^3)$$
$$= (x^2 - y^2)(x^2 + y^2) - 2xy(x^2 - y^2)$$
$$= (x^2 - y^2)(x^2 + y^2 - 2xy)$$
$$= (x - y)(x + y)(x^2 - 2xy + y^2)$$
$$= (x - y)(x + y)(x - y)^2$$
$$= (x - y)^3 (x + y)$$

135. $x^2 + bx + 15$, $b = 16, -16, 8$ or -8

Section P.6

Check Point Exercises

1.   **a.**   The denominator would equal zero if $x = -5$, so -5 must be excluded from the domain.

      b. $x^2 - 36 = (x + 6)(x - 6)$
          The denominator would equal zero if $x = -6$ or $x = 6$, so -6 and 6 must both must be excluded from the domain.

2.   **a.**
$$\frac{x^3 + 3x^2}{x + 3} = \frac{x^2(x + 3)}{x + 3}$$
$$= \frac{x^2(x + 3)}{x + 3}$$
$$= x^2, \ x \neq -3$$
      Because the denominator is $x + 3$, $x \neq -3$

      b.
$$\frac{x^2 - 1}{x^2 + 2x + 1} = \frac{(x - 1)(x + 1)}{(x + 1)(x + 1)}$$
$$= \frac{x - 1}{x + 1}, x \neq -1$$
      Because the denominator is $(x + 1)(x + 1), x \neq -1$

3.
$$\frac{x + 3}{x^2 - 4} \cdot \frac{x^2 - x - 6}{x^2 + 6x + 9}$$
$$= \frac{x + 3}{(x + 2)(x - 2)} \cdot \frac{(x - 3)(x + 2)}{(x + 3)(x + 3)}$$
$$= \frac{x + 3}{(x + 2)(x - 2)} \cdot \frac{(x - 3)(x + 2)}{(x + 3)(x + 3)}$$
$$= \frac{x - 3}{(x - 2)(x + 3)}, \ x \neq -2, \ x \neq 2, \ x \neq -3$$

Because the denominator has factors of $x + 2$, $x - 2$, and $x + 3$, $x \neq -2$, $x \neq 2$, and $x \neq -3$.

4. $\dfrac{x^2-2x+1}{x^3+x} \div \dfrac{x^2+x-2}{3x^2+3}$

$= \dfrac{x^2-2x+1}{x^3+x} \cdot \dfrac{3x^2+3}{x^2+x-2}$

$= \dfrac{(x-1)(x-1)}{x(x^2+1)} \cdot \dfrac{3(x^2+1)}{(x+2)(x-1)}$

$= \dfrac{3(x-1)}{x(x+2)}, \ x \neq 0, \ x \neq -2, \ x \neq 1$

5. $\dfrac{x}{x+1} - \dfrac{3x+2}{x+1} = \dfrac{x-3x-2}{x+1}$

$= \dfrac{-2x-2}{x+1}$

$= \dfrac{-2(x+1)}{x+1}$

$= -2, x \neq -1$

6. $\dfrac{3}{x+1} + \dfrac{5}{x-1}$

$= \dfrac{3x(x-1)+5(x+1)}{(x+1)(x-1)}$

$= \dfrac{3x-3+5x+5}{(x+1)(x-1)}$

$= \dfrac{8x+2}{(x+1)(x-1)}$

$= \dfrac{2(4x+1)}{(x+1)(x-1)}$

$= \dfrac{2(4x+1)}{(x+1)(x-1)}, \ x \neq -1 \text{ and } x \neq 1.$

7.   Factor each denominator completely.

$x^2-6x+9 = (x-3)^2$

$x^2-9 = (x+3)(x-3)$

List the factors of the first denominator.

$x-3, \ x-3$

Add any unlisted factors from the second denominator.

$x-3, \ x-3, \ x+3$

The least common denominator is the product of all factors in the final list.

$(x-3)(x-3)(x+3)$ or $(x-3)^2(x+3)$ is the least common denominator.

8. Find the least common denominator.

$x^2 - 10x + 25 = (x-5)^2$

$2x - 10 = 2(x-5)$

The least common denominator is $2(x-5)(x-5)$.
Write all rational expressions in terms of the least common denominator.

$$\frac{x}{x^2 - 10x + 25} - \frac{x-4}{2x-10}$$

$$= \frac{x}{(x-5)(x-5)} - \frac{x-4}{2(x-5)}$$

$$= \frac{2x}{2(x-5)(x-5)} - \frac{(x-4)(x-5)}{2(x-5)(x-5)}$$

Add numerators, putting this sum over the least common denominator.

$$= \frac{2x - (x-4)(x-5)}{2(x-5)(x-5)}$$

$$= \frac{2x - (x^2 - 5x - 4x + 20)}{2(x-5)(x-5)}$$

$$= \frac{2x - x^2 + 5x + 4x - 20}{2(x-5)(x-5)}$$

$$= \frac{2x - x^2 + 5x + 4x - 20}{2(x-5)(x-5)}$$

$$= \frac{-x^2 + 11x - 20}{2(x-5)(x-5)}$$

$$= \frac{-x^2 + 11x - 20}{2(x-5)^2}, \; x \neq 5$$

9.

$$\frac{\dfrac{1}{x} - \dfrac{3}{2}}{\dfrac{1}{x} + \dfrac{3}{4}} = \frac{\dfrac{2}{2x} - \dfrac{3x}{2x}}{\dfrac{4}{4x} + \dfrac{3x}{4x}}, \; x \neq 0$$

$$= \frac{\dfrac{2-3x}{2x}}{\dfrac{4+3x}{4x}}, \; x \neq \frac{-4}{3}$$

$$= \frac{2-3x}{2x} \div \frac{4+3x}{4x}$$

$$= \frac{2-3x}{2x} \cdot \frac{4x}{4+3x}$$

$$= \frac{2-3x}{4+3x} \cdot \frac{4}{2}$$

$$= \frac{2-3x}{4+3x} \cdot \frac{2}{1}$$

$$= \frac{2(2-3x)}{4+3x}, \; x \neq 0 \; and \; x \neq \frac{-4}{3}$$

10. Multiply each of the three terms, $\dfrac{1}{x+7}$, $\dfrac{1}{x}$, and

7 by the least common denominator of $x(x+7)$.

$$\frac{\dfrac{1}{x+7} - \dfrac{1}{x}}{7} = \frac{x(x+7)\left(\dfrac{1}{x+7}\right) - x(x+7)\left(\dfrac{1}{x}\right)}{7x(x+7)}$$

$$= \frac{x - (x+7)}{7x(x+7)}$$

$$= \frac{-7}{7x(x+7)}$$

$$= -\frac{1}{x(x+7)}, \; x \neq 0, \; x \neq -7$$

Exercise Set P.6

1. $\dfrac{7}{x-3}, x \neq 3$

3. $\dfrac{x+5}{x^2-25} = \dfrac{x+5}{(x+5)(x-5)}, x \neq 5, -5$

5. $\dfrac{x-1}{x^2+11x+10} = \dfrac{x-1}{(x+1)(x+10)}, x \neq -1, -10$

7. $\dfrac{3x-9}{x^2-6x+9} = \dfrac{3(x-3)}{(x-3)(x-3)}$

$\qquad = \dfrac{3}{x-3}, x \neq 3$

9. $\dfrac{x^2-12x+36}{4x-24} = \dfrac{(x-6)(x-6)}{4(x-6)} = \dfrac{x-6}{4}.$

$\quad x \neq 6$

11. $\dfrac{y^2+7y-18}{y^2-3y+2} = \dfrac{(y+9)(y-2)}{(y-2)(y-1)} = \dfrac{y+9}{y-1},$

$\quad y \neq 1, 2$

13. $\dfrac{x^2+12x+36}{x^2-36} = \dfrac{(x+6)^2}{(x+6)(x-6)} = \dfrac{x+6}{x-6},$

$\quad x \neq 6, -6$

15. $\dfrac{x-2}{3x+9} \cdot \dfrac{2x+6}{2x-4} = \dfrac{x-2}{3(x+3)} \cdot \dfrac{2(x+3)}{2(x-2)}$

$\qquad = \dfrac{2}{6} = \dfrac{1}{3}, x \neq 2, -3$

17. $\dfrac{x^2-9}{x^2} \cdot \dfrac{x^2-3x}{x^2+x-12}$

$\quad = \dfrac{(x-3)(x+3)}{x^2} \cdot \dfrac{x(x-3)}{(x+4)(x-3)}$

$\quad = \dfrac{(x-3)(x+3)}{x(x+4)}, x \neq 0, -4, 3$

19. $\dfrac{x^2-5x+6}{x^2-2x-3} \cdot \dfrac{x^2-1}{x^2-4}$

$\quad = \dfrac{(x-3)(x-2)}{(x-3)(x+1)} \cdot \dfrac{(x+1)(x-1)}{(x-2)(x+2)}$

$\quad = \dfrac{x-1}{x+2}, x \neq -2, -1, 2, 3$

21. $\dfrac{x^3-8}{x^2-4} \cdot \dfrac{x+2}{3x} = \dfrac{(x-2)(x^2+2x+4)}{(x-2)(x+2)} \cdot \dfrac{x+2}{3x}$

$\qquad = \dfrac{x^2+2x+4}{3x}, x \neq -2, 0, 2$

23. $\dfrac{x+1}{3} \div \dfrac{3x+3}{7} = \dfrac{x+1}{3} \div \dfrac{3(x+1)}{7}$

$\qquad\qquad\qquad = \dfrac{x+1}{3} \cdot \dfrac{7}{3(x+1)}$

$\qquad\qquad\qquad = \dfrac{7}{9}, x \neq -1$

25. $\dfrac{x^2-4}{x} \div \dfrac{x+2}{x-2} = \dfrac{(x-2)(x+2)}{x} \cdot \dfrac{x-2}{x+2}$

$\qquad\qquad\qquad = \dfrac{(x-2)^2}{x}; x \neq 0, -2, 2$

27. $\dfrac{\dfrac{4x^2+10}{x-3} \div \dfrac{6x^2+15}{x^2-9}}{}$

$\quad = \dfrac{2(2x^2+5)}{x-3} \div \dfrac{3(2x^2+5)}{(x-3)(x+3)}$

$\quad = \dfrac{2(2x^2+5)}{x-3} \cdot \dfrac{(x-3)(x+3)}{3(2x^2+5)}$

$\quad = \dfrac{2(x+3)}{3}, x \neq 3, -3$

29. $\dfrac{x^2-25}{2x-2} \div \dfrac{x^2+10x+25}{x^2+4x-5}$

$\quad = \dfrac{(x-5)(x+5)}{2(x-1)} \div \dfrac{(x+5)^2}{(x+5)(x-1)}$

$\quad = \dfrac{(x-5)(x+5)}{2(x-1)} \cdot \dfrac{(x+5)(x-1)}{(x+5)^2}$

$\quad = \dfrac{x-5}{2}, x \neq 1, -5$

31. $\dfrac{x^2+x-12}{x^2+x-30} \cdot \dfrac{x^2+5x+6}{x^2-2x-3} \div \dfrac{x+3}{x^2+7x+6}$

$\quad = \dfrac{(x+4)(x-3)}{(x+6)(x-5)} \cdot \dfrac{(x+2)(x+3)}{(x+1)(x-3)} \cdot \dfrac{(x+6)(x+1)}{x+3}$

$\quad = \dfrac{(x+4)(x+2)}{x-5}$

$\quad x \neq -6, -3, -1, 3, 5$

33. $\dfrac{4x+1}{6x+5} + \dfrac{8x+9}{6x+5} = \dfrac{4x+1+8x+9}{6x+5}$

$$= \dfrac{12x+10}{6x+5}$$

$$= \dfrac{2(6x+5)}{6x+5} = 2, x \neq -\dfrac{5}{6}$$

35. $\dfrac{x^2-2x}{x^2+3x} + \dfrac{x^2+x}{x^2+3x} = \dfrac{x^2-2x+x^2+x}{x^2+3x}$

$$= \dfrac{2x^2-x}{x^2+3x}$$

$$= \dfrac{x(2x-1)}{x(x+3)}$$

$$= \dfrac{2x-1}{x+3}, x \neq 0, -3$$

37. $\dfrac{4x-10}{x-2} - \dfrac{x-4}{x-2} = \dfrac{4x-10-(x-4)}{x-2}$

$$= \dfrac{4x-10-x+4}{x-2}$$

$$= \dfrac{3x-6}{x-2}$$

$$= \dfrac{3(x-2)}{x-2}$$

$$= 3, x \neq 2$$

39. $\dfrac{x^2+3x}{x^2+x-12} - \dfrac{x^2-12}{x^2+x-12}$

$$= \dfrac{x^2+3x-(x^2-12)}{x^2+x-12}$$

$$= \dfrac{x^2+3x-x^2+12}{x^2+x-12}$$

$$= \dfrac{3x+12}{x^2+x-12}$$

$$= \dfrac{3(x+4)}{(x+4)(x-3)}$$

$$= \dfrac{3}{x-3}, x \neq 3, -4$$

41. $\dfrac{3}{x+4} + \dfrac{6}{x+5} = \dfrac{3(x+5)+6(x+4)}{(x+4)(x+5)}$

$$= \dfrac{3x+15+6x+24}{(x+4)(x+5)}$$

$$= \dfrac{9x+39}{(x+4)(x+5)}, x \neq -4, -5$$

43. $\dfrac{3}{x+1} - \dfrac{3}{x} = \dfrac{3x-3(x+1)}{x(x+1)}$

$$= \dfrac{3x-3x-3}{x(x+1)} = -\dfrac{3}{x(x+1)}, x \neq -1, 0$$

45. $\dfrac{2x}{x+2} + \dfrac{x+2}{x-2} = \dfrac{2x(x-2)+(x+2)(x+2)}{(x+2)(x-2)}$

$$= \dfrac{2x^2-4x+x^2+4x+4}{(x+2)(x-2)}$$

$$= \dfrac{3x^2+4}{(x+2)(x-2)}, x \neq -2, 2$$

47. $\dfrac{x+5}{x-5} + \dfrac{x-5}{x+5}$

$$= \dfrac{(x+5)(x+5)+(x-5)(x-5)}{(x-5)(x+5)}$$

$$= \dfrac{x^2+10x+25+x^2-10x+25}{(x-5)(x+5)}$$

$$= \dfrac{2x^2+50}{(x-5)(x+5)}, x \neq -5, 5$$

49. $\dfrac{4}{x^2+6x+9} + \dfrac{4}{x+3} = \dfrac{4}{(x+3)^2} + \dfrac{4}{x+3}$

$$= \dfrac{4+4(x+3)}{(x+3)^2} = \dfrac{4+4x+12}{(x+3)^2} = \dfrac{4x+16}{(x+3)^2},$$

$$x \neq -3$$

51. $\dfrac{3x}{x^2+3x-10} - \dfrac{2x}{x^2+x-6}$

$$= \dfrac{3x}{(x+5)(x-2)} - \dfrac{2x}{(x+3)(x-2)}$$

$$= \dfrac{3x(x+3)-2x(x+5)}{(x+5)(x-2)(x+3)}$$

$$= \dfrac{3x^2+9x-2x^2-10x}{(x+5)(x-2)(x+3)}$$

$$= \dfrac{x^2-x}{(x+5)(x-2)(x+3)}, x \neq -5, 2, -3$$

53. $\dfrac{4x^2+x-6}{x^2+3x+2}-\dfrac{3x}{x+1}+\dfrac{5}{x+2}$

$=\dfrac{4x^2+x-6}{(x+1)(x+2)}+\dfrac{-3x}{x+1}+\dfrac{5}{x+2}$

$=\dfrac{4x^2+x-5}{(x+1)(x+2)}+\dfrac{-3x(x+2)}{(x+1)(x+2)}+\dfrac{5(x+1)}{(x+1)(x+2)}$

$=\dfrac{4x^2+x-6-3x^2-6x+5x+5}{(x+1)(x+2)}$

$=\dfrac{x^2-1}{(x+1)(x+2)}$

$=\dfrac{(x-1)(x+1)}{(x+1)(x+2)}$

$=\dfrac{x-1}{x+2};x\neq-2,-1$

55. $\dfrac{\frac{x}{3}-1}{x-3}=\dfrac{3\left[\frac{x}{3}-1\right]}{3[x-3]}=\dfrac{x-3}{3(x-3)}=\dfrac{1}{3},\ x\neq3$

57. $\dfrac{1+\frac{1}{x}}{3-\frac{1}{x}}=\dfrac{x\left[1+\frac{1}{x}\right]}{x\left[3-\frac{1}{x}\right]}=\dfrac{x+1}{3x-1},x\neq0,\dfrac{1}{3}$

59. $\dfrac{\frac{1}{x}+\frac{1}{y}}{x+y}=\dfrac{xy\left[\frac{1}{x}+\frac{1}{y}\right]}{xy[x+y]}=\dfrac{y+x}{xy(x+y)}=\dfrac{1}{xy},$

$x\neq0,y\neq0,x\neq-y$

61. $\dfrac{x-\frac{x}{x+3}}{x+2}=\dfrac{(x+3)\left[x-\frac{x}{x+3}\right]}{(x+3)(x+2)}=\dfrac{x(x+3)-x}{(x+3)(x+2)}$

$=\dfrac{x^2+3x-x}{(x+3)(x+2)}=\dfrac{x^2+2x}{(x+3)(x+2)}$

$=\dfrac{x(x+2)}{(x+3)(x+2)}=\dfrac{x}{x+3},\ x\neq-2,-3$

63. $\dfrac{\frac{3}{x-2}-\frac{4}{x+2}}{\frac{7}{x^2-4}}=\dfrac{\frac{3}{x-2}-\frac{4}{x+2}}{\frac{7}{(x-2)(x+2)}}$

$=\dfrac{\left[\frac{3}{x-2}-\frac{4}{x+2}\right](x-2)(x+2)}{\left[\frac{7}{(x-2)(x+2)}\right](x-2)(x+2)}$

$=\dfrac{3(x+2)-4(x-2)}{7}$

$=\dfrac{3x+6-4x+8}{7}=\dfrac{-x+14}{7}$

$=-\dfrac{x-14}{7}\quad x\neq-2,2$

65. $\dfrac{\frac{1}{x+1}}{\frac{1}{x^2-2x-3}+\frac{1}{x-3}}=\dfrac{\frac{1}{x+1}}{\frac{1}{(x+1)(x-3)}+\frac{1}{x-3}}$

$=\dfrac{\frac{(x+1)(x-3)}{x+1}}{\frac{(x+1)(x-3)}{(x+1)(x-3)}+\frac{(x+1)(x-3)}{x-3}}$

$=\dfrac{x-3}{1+x+1}$

$=\dfrac{x-3}{x+2}\quad x\neq-2,-1,3$

67. $\dfrac{\frac{1}{(x+h)^2}-\frac{1}{x^2}}{h}=\dfrac{\frac{x^2(x+h)^2}{(x+h)^2}-\frac{x^2(x+h)^2}{x^2}}{hx^2(x+h)^2}$

$=\dfrac{x^2-(x+h)^2}{hx^2(x+h)^2}$

$=\dfrac{x^2-(x^2+2hx+h^2)}{hx^2(x+h)^2}$

$=\dfrac{x^2-x^2-2hx-h^2}{hx^2(x+h)^2}$

$=\dfrac{-2hx-h^2}{hx^2(x+h)^2}$

$=\dfrac{-h(2x+h)}{hx^2(x+h)^2}$

$=-\dfrac{(2x+h)}{x^2(x+h)^2}$

69. $\left(\dfrac{2x+3}{x+1} \cdot \dfrac{x^2+4x-5}{2x^2+x-3}\right) - \dfrac{2}{x+2} = \left(\dfrac{\cancel{(2x+3)}}{x+1} \cdot \dfrac{(x+5)\cancel{(x-1)}}{\cancel{(2x+3)}\cancel{(x-1)}}\right) - \dfrac{2}{x+2} = \dfrac{x+5}{x+1} - \dfrac{2}{x+2}$

$= \dfrac{(x+5)(x+2)}{(x+1)(x+2)} - \dfrac{2(x+1)}{(x+1)(x+2)} = \dfrac{(x+5)(x+2)-2(x+1)}{(x+1)(x+2)} = \dfrac{x^2+2x+5x+10-2x-2}{(x+1)(x+2)} = \dfrac{x^2+5x+8}{(x+1)(x+2)}$

71. $\left(2-\dfrac{6}{x+1}\right)\left(1+\dfrac{3}{x-2}\right) = \left(\dfrac{2(x+1)}{(x+1)} - \dfrac{6}{(x+1)}\right)\left(\dfrac{(x-2)}{(x-2)} + \dfrac{3}{(x-2)}\right)$

$= \left(\dfrac{2x+2-6}{x+1}\right)\left(\dfrac{x-2+3}{x-2}\right) = \left(\dfrac{2x-4}{x+1}\right)\left(\dfrac{x+1}{x-2}\right) = \dfrac{2\cancel{(x-2)}\cancel{(x+1)}}{\cancel{(x+1)}\cancel{(x-2)}} = 2$

73. $\dfrac{y^{-1}-(y+5)^{-1}}{5} = \dfrac{\dfrac{1}{y} - \dfrac{1}{y+5}}{5}$

LCD $= y(y+5)$

$\dfrac{\dfrac{1}{y} - \dfrac{1}{y+5}}{5} = \dfrac{y(y+5)\left(\dfrac{1}{y} - \dfrac{1}{y+5}\right)}{y(y+5)(5)} = \dfrac{y+5-y}{5y(y+5)} = \dfrac{5}{5y(y+5)} = \dfrac{1}{y(y+5)}$

75. $\left(\dfrac{1}{a^3-b^3} \cdot \dfrac{ac+ad-bc-bd}{1}\right) - \dfrac{c-d}{a^2+ab+b^2} = \left(\dfrac{1}{(a-b)(a^2+ab+b^2)} \cdot \dfrac{a(c+d)-b(c+d)}{1}\right) - \dfrac{c-d}{a^2+ab+b^2}$

$= \left(\dfrac{1}{\cancel{(a-b)}(a^2+ab+b^2)} \cdot \dfrac{(c+d)\cancel{(a-b)}}{1}\right) - \dfrac{c-d}{a^2+ab+b^2} = \dfrac{c+d}{a^2+ab+b^2} - \dfrac{c-d}{a^2+bd+b^2}$

$= \dfrac{c+d-c+d}{a^2+ab+b^2} = \dfrac{2d}{a^2+ab+b^2}$

77. **a.** $\dfrac{130x}{100-x}$ is equal to

1. $\dfrac{130\cdot40}{100-40} = \dfrac{130\cdot40}{60} = 86.67$,

    when $x=40$

2. $\dfrac{130\cdot80}{100-80} = \dfrac{130\cdot80}{20} = 520$,

    when $x=80$

3. $\dfrac{130\cdot90}{100-90} = \dfrac{130\cdot90}{10} = 1170$,

    when $x=90$

It costs \$86,670,000 to inoculate 40% of the population against this strain of flu, and \$520,000,000 to inoculate 80% of the population, and \$1,170,000,000 to inoculate 90% of the population.

b. For $x=100$, the function is not defined.

c. As x approaches 100, the value of the function increases rapidly. So it costs an astronomical amount of money to inoculate almost all of the people, and it is impossible to inoculate 100% of the population.

33

79. a. The crime rate is the number of crimes per person. Thus the rational expression is the number of crimes divided by the total population
$$\frac{-0.3t+14}{3.6t+260}$$

b. $\dfrac{-0.3t+14}{3.6t+260} = \dfrac{-0.3(8)+14}{3.6(8)+260} \approx 0.04$

The crime rate in 2002 was 0.04.
That is 4000 per 100,000 people.

c. The rational expression models the crime rate in 2002 fairly well.

81. $P = 2L + 2W$
$$= 2\left(\frac{x}{x+3}\right) + 2\left(\frac{x}{x-4}\right)$$
$$= \frac{2x}{x+3} + \frac{2x}{x+4}$$
$$= \frac{2x(x+4)}{(x+3)(x+4)} + \frac{2x(x+}{(x+3)(}$$
$$= \frac{2x^2+8x+2x^2+6x}{(x+3)(x+4)}$$
$$= \frac{4x^2+14x}{(x+3)(x+4)}$$

97.
$$\frac{1}{x^n-1} - \frac{1}{x^n+1} - \frac{1}{x^{2n}-1}$$
$$= \frac{x^n+1}{x^{2n}-1} - \frac{x^n-1}{x^{2n}-1} - \frac{1}{x^{2n}-1}$$
$$= \frac{x^n+1-x^n+1-1}{x^{2n}-1}$$
$$= \frac{1}{x^{2n}-1}$$

99. $(x-y)^{-1} + (x-y)^{-2} = \dfrac{1}{(x-y)} + \dfrac{1}{(x-y)^2} = \dfrac{(x-y)}{(x-y)(x-y)} + \dfrac{1}{(x-y)^2} = \dfrac{x-y+1}{(x-y)^2}$

Chapter P Review Exercises

1. $3+6(x-2)^3 = 3+6(4-2)^3$
$$= 3+6(2)^3$$
$$= 3+6(8)$$
$$= 3+48$$
$$= 51$$

2. $x^2-5(x-y) = 6^2-5(6-2)$
$$= 36-5(4)$$
$$= 36-20$$
$$= 16$$

3. $S = 0.015x^2+x+10$
$$S = 0.015(60)^2+(60)+10$$
$$= 0.015(3600)+60+10$$
$$= 54+60+10$$
$$= 124$$

4. $A = \{a,b,c\} \quad B = \{a,c,d,e\}$
$$\{a,b,c\} \cap \{a,c,d,e\} = \{a,c\}$$

5. $A = \{a,b,c\} \quad B = \{a,c,d,e\}$
$$\{a,b,c\} \cup \{a,c,d,e\} = \{a,b,c,d,e\}$$

6. $A = \{a, b, c\}$ $C = \{a, d, f, g\}$
$\{a, b, c\} \cup \{a, d, f, g\} = \{a, b, c, d, f, g\}$

7. $A = \{a, b, c\}$ $C = \{a, d, f, g\}$
$\{a, d, f, g\} \cap \{a, b, c\} = \{a\}$

8. a. $\sqrt{81}$

    b. $0, \sqrt{81}$

    c. $-17, 0, \sqrt{81}$

    d. $-17, -\dfrac{9}{13}, 0, 0.75, \sqrt{81}$

    e. $\sqrt{2}, \pi$

    f. $-17, -\dfrac{9}{13}, 0, 0.75, \sqrt{2}, \pi, \sqrt{81}$

9. $|-103| = 103$

10. $|\sqrt{2} - 1| = \sqrt{2} - 1$

11. $|3 - \sqrt{17}| = \sqrt{17} - 3$ since $\sqrt{17}$ is greater than 3.

12. $|4 - (-17)| = |4 + 17| = |21| = 21$

13. $3 + 17 = 17 + 3$;
commutative property of addition.

14. $(6 \cdot 3) \cdot 9 = 6 \cdot (3 \cdot 9)$;
associative property of multiplication.

15. $\sqrt{3}(\sqrt{5} + \sqrt{3}) = \sqrt{15} + 3$;
distributive property of multiplication over addition.

16. $(6 \cdot 9) \cdot 2 = 2 \cdot (6 \cdot 9)$;
commutative property of multiplication.

17. $\sqrt{3}(\sqrt{5} + \sqrt{3}) = (\sqrt{5} + \sqrt{3})\sqrt{3}$;
commutative property of multiplication.

18. $(3 \cdot 7) + (4 \cdot 7) = (4 \cdot 7) + (3 \cdot 7)$;
commutative property of addition.

19. $5(2x - 3) + 7x = 10x - 15 + 7x = 17x - 15$

20. $\dfrac{1}{5}(5x) + [(3y) + (-3y)] - (-x) = x + [0] + x = 2x$

21. $3(4y - 5) - (7y + 2) = 12y - 15 - 7y - 2 = 5y - 17$

22. $8 - 2[3 - (5x - 1)] = 8 - 2[3 - 5x + 1]$
$= 8 - 2[4 - 5x]$
$= 8 - 8 + 10x$
$= 10x$

23. $E = 10x + 166$
$E = 10(20) + 166 = 366$

$E = 0.04x^2 + 9.2x + 169$
$E = 0.04(20)^2 + 9.2(20) + 169 = 369$
The actual number was 368 so the better formula was $E = 0.04x^2 + 9.2x + 169$.

24. $(-3)^3(-2)^2 = (-27) \cdot (4) = -108$

25. $2^{-4} + 4^{-1} = \dfrac{1}{2^4} + \dfrac{1}{4}$
$= \dfrac{1}{16} + \dfrac{1}{4}$
$= \dfrac{1}{16} + \dfrac{4}{16}$
$= \dfrac{5}{16}$

26. $5^{-3} \cdot 5 = 5^{-3}5^1 = 5^{-3+1} = 5^{-2} = \dfrac{1}{5^2} = \dfrac{1}{25}$

27. $\dfrac{3^3}{3^6} = 3^{3-6} = 3^{-3} = \dfrac{1}{3^3} = \dfrac{1}{27}$

28. $(-2x^4 y^3)^3 = (-2)^3(x^4)^3(y^3)^3$
$= (-2)^3 x^{4 \cdot 3} y^{3 \cdot 3}$
$= -8x^{12} y^9$

29. $(-5x^3 y^2)(-2x^{-11} y^{-2})$
$= (-5)(-2)x^3 x^{-11} y^2 y^{-2}$
$= 10 \cdot x^{3-11} y^{2-2}$
$= 10x^{-8} y^0$
$= \dfrac{10}{x^8}$

30. $(2x^3)^{-4} = (2)^{-4}(x^3)^{-4}$

$\qquad = 2^{-4}x^{-12}$

$\qquad = \dfrac{1}{2^4 x^{12}}$

$\qquad = \dfrac{1}{16x^{12}}$

31. $\dfrac{7x^5 y^6}{28x^{15} y^{-2}} = \left(\dfrac{7}{28}\right)(x^{5-15})(y^{6-(-2)})$

$\qquad = \dfrac{1}{4}x^{-10}y^8$

$\qquad = \dfrac{y^8}{4x^{10}}$

32. $3.74 \times 10^4 = 37{,}400$

33. $7.45 \times 10^{-5} = 0.0000745$

34. $3{,}590{,}000 = 3.59 \times 10^6$

35. $0.00725 = 7.25 \times 10^{-3}$

36. $(3 \times 10^3)(1.3 \times 10^2) = (3 \times 1.3) \times (10^3 \times 10^2)$

$\qquad = 3.9 \times 10^5$

$\qquad = 390{,}000$

37. $\dfrac{6.9 \times 10^3}{3 \times 10^5} = \left(\dfrac{6.9}{3}\right) \times 10^{3-5}$

$\qquad = 2.3 \times 10^{-2}$

$\qquad = 0.023$

38. $\dfrac{10^9}{10^6} = 10^{9-6} = 10^3$

It would take 10^3 or 1000 years to accumulate $1 billion.

39. $(2.9 \times 10^8) \times 150$

$\qquad = (2.9 \times 10^8) \times (1.5 \times 10^2)$

$\qquad = (2.9 \times 1.5) \times (10^8 \times 10^2)$

$\qquad = 4.35 \times 10^{10}$

The total annual spending on movies is 4.35×10^{10}.

40. $\sqrt{300} = \sqrt{100 \cdot 3} = \sqrt{100} \cdot \sqrt{3} = 10\sqrt{3}$

41. $\sqrt{12x^2} = \sqrt{4x^2 \cdot 3} = \sqrt{4x^2} \cdot \sqrt{3} = 2|x|\sqrt{3}$

42. $\sqrt{10x} \cdot \sqrt{2x} = \sqrt{20x^2}$

$\qquad = \sqrt{4x^2} \cdot \sqrt{5}$

$\qquad = 2x\sqrt{5}$

43. $\sqrt{r^3} = \sqrt{r^2} \cdot \sqrt{r} = r\sqrt{r}$

44. $\sqrt{\dfrac{121}{4}} = \dfrac{\sqrt{121}}{\sqrt{4}} = \dfrac{11}{2}$

45. $\dfrac{\sqrt{96x^3}}{\sqrt{2x}} = \sqrt{\dfrac{96x^3}{2x}}$

$\qquad = \sqrt{48x^2}$

$\qquad = \sqrt{16x^2} \cdot \sqrt{3}$

$\qquad = 4x\sqrt{3}$

46. $7\sqrt{5} + 13\sqrt{5} = (7+13)\sqrt{5} = 20\sqrt{5}$

47. $2\sqrt{50} + 3\sqrt{8} = 2\sqrt{25 \cdot 2} + 3\sqrt{4 \cdot 2}$

$\qquad = 2 \cdot 5\sqrt{2} + 3 \cdot 2\sqrt{2}$

$\qquad = 10\sqrt{2} + 6\sqrt{2}$

$\qquad = 16\sqrt{2}$

48. $4\sqrt{72} - 2\sqrt{48} = 4\sqrt{36 \cdot 2} - 2\sqrt{16 \cdot 3}$

$\qquad = 4 \cdot 6\sqrt{2} - 2 \cdot 4\sqrt{3}$

$\qquad = 24\sqrt{2} - 8\sqrt{3}$

49. $\dfrac{30}{\sqrt{5}} = \dfrac{30}{\sqrt{5}} \cdot \dfrac{\sqrt{5}}{\sqrt{5}} = \dfrac{30\sqrt{5}}{5} = 6\sqrt{5}$

50. $\dfrac{\sqrt{2}}{\sqrt{3}} = \dfrac{\sqrt{2}}{\sqrt{3}} \cdot \dfrac{\sqrt{3}}{\sqrt{3}} = \dfrac{\sqrt{6}}{3}$

51. $\dfrac{5}{6+\sqrt{3}} = \dfrac{5}{6+\sqrt{3}} \cdot \dfrac{6-\sqrt{3}}{6-\sqrt{3}}$

$\qquad = \dfrac{5(6-\sqrt{3})}{36-3}$

$\qquad = \dfrac{5(6-\sqrt{3})}{33}$

52.
$$\frac{14}{\sqrt{7}-\sqrt{5}} = \frac{14}{\sqrt{7}-\sqrt{5}} \cdot \frac{\sqrt{7}+\sqrt{5}}{\sqrt{7}+\sqrt{5}}$$
$$= \frac{14(\sqrt{7}+\sqrt{5})}{7-5}$$
$$= \frac{14(\sqrt{7}+\sqrt{5})}{2}$$
$$= 7(\sqrt{7}+\sqrt{5})$$

53. $\sqrt[3]{125} = 5$

54. $\sqrt[5]{-32} = -2$

55. $\sqrt[4]{-125}$ is not a real number.

56. $\sqrt[4]{(-5)^4} = \sqrt[4]{625} = \sqrt[4]{5^4} = 5$

57. $\sqrt[3]{81} = \sqrt[3]{27 \cdot 3} = \sqrt[3]{27} \cdot \sqrt[3]{3} = 3\sqrt[3]{3}$

58. $\sqrt[3]{y^5} = \sqrt[3]{y^3 y^2} = y\sqrt[3]{y^2}$

59. $\sqrt[4]{8} \cdot \sqrt[4]{10} = \sqrt[4]{80} = \sqrt[4]{16 \cdot 5} = \sqrt[4]{16} \cdot \sqrt[4]{5} = 2\sqrt[4]{5}$

61.
$$4\sqrt[3]{16} + 5\sqrt[3]{2} = 4\sqrt[3]{8 \cdot 2} + 5\sqrt[3]{2}$$
$$= 4 \cdot 2\sqrt[3]{2} + 5\sqrt[3]{2}$$
$$= 8\sqrt[3]{2} + 5\sqrt[3]{2}$$
$$= 13\sqrt[3]{2}$$

61.
$$\frac{\sqrt[4]{32x^5}}{\sqrt[4]{16x}} = \sqrt[4]{\frac{32x^5}{16x}} = \sqrt[4]{2x^4} = x\sqrt[4]{2}$$

62. $16^{1/2} = \sqrt{16} = 4$

63. $25^{-1/2} = \frac{1}{25^{1/2}} = \frac{1}{\sqrt{25}} = \frac{1}{5}$

64. $125^{1/3} = \sqrt[3]{125} = 5$

65. $27^{-1/3} = \frac{1}{27^{1/3}} = \frac{1}{\sqrt[3]{27}} = \frac{1}{3}$

66. $64^{2/3} = (\sqrt[3]{64})^2 = 4^2 = 16$

67. $27^{-4/3} = \frac{1}{27^{4/3}} = \frac{1}{(\sqrt[3]{27})^4} = \frac{1}{3^4} = \frac{1}{81}$

68. $(5x^{2/3})(4x^{1/4}) = 5 \cdot 4x^{2/3+1/4} = 20x^{11/12}$

69. $\frac{15x^{3/4}}{5x^{1/2}} = \left(\frac{15}{5}\right)x^{3/4-1/2} = 3x^{1/4}$

70.
$$(125 \cdot x^6)^{2/3} = (\sqrt[3]{125x^6})^2$$
$$= (5x^2)^2$$
$$= 25x^4$$

71. $\sqrt[6]{y^3} = (y^3)^{1/6} = y^{3 \cdot 1/6} = y^{1/2} = \sqrt{y}$

72. $(-6x^3 + 7x^2 - 9x + 3) + (14x^3 + 3x^2 - 11x - 7) = (-6x^3 + 14x^3) + (7x^2 + 3x^2) + (-9x - 11x) + (3 - 7)$
$$= 8x^3 + 10x^2 - 20x - 4$$
The degree is 3.

73. $(13x^4 - 8x^3 + 2x^2) - (5x^4 - 3x^3 + 2x^2 - 6) = (13x^4 - 8x^3 + 2x^2) + (-5x^4 + 3x^3 - 2x^2 + 6)$
$$= (13x^4 - 5x^4) + (-8x^3 + 3x^3) + (2x^2 - 2x^2) + 6$$
$$= 8x^4 - 5x^3 + 6$$
The degree is 4.

74. $(3x - 2)(4x^2 + 3x - 5) = (3x)(4x^2) + (3x)(3x) + (3x)(-5) + (-2)(4x^2) + (-2)(3x) + (-2)(-5)$
$$= 12x^3 + 9x^2 - 15x - 8x^2 - 6x + 10$$
$$= 12x^3 + x^2 - 21x + 10$$

75. $(3x - 5)(2x + 1) = (3x)(2x) + (3x)(1) + (-5)(2x) + (-5)(1)$
$$= 6x^2 + 3x - 10x - 5$$
$$= 6x^2 - 7x - 5$$

76. $(4x + 5)(4x - 5) = (4x^2) - 5^2 = 16x^2 - 25$

77. $(2x + 5)^2 = (2x)^2 + 2(2x) \cdot 5 + 5^2 = 4x^2 + 20x + 25$

78. $(3x - 4)^2 = (3x)^2 - 2(3x) \cdot 4 + (-4)^2 = 9x^2 - 24x + 16$

79. $(2x + 1)^3 = (2x)^3 + 3(2x)^2(1) + 3(2x)(1)^2 + 1^3 = 8x^3 + 12x^2 + 6x + 1$

80. $(5x - 2)^3 = (5x)^3 - 3(5x)^2(2) + 3(5x)(2)^2 - 2^3 = 125x^3 - 150x^2 + 60x - 8$

81. $(7x^2 - 8xy + y^2) + (-8x^2 - 9xy - 4y^2) = (7x^2 - 8x^2) + (-8xy - 9xy) + (y^2 - 4y^2)$
$$= -x^2 - 17xy - 3y^2$$
The degree is 2.

82. $(13x^3y^2 - 5x^2y - 9x^2) - (-11x^3y^2 - 6x^2y + 3x^2 - 4)$
$$= (13x^3y^2 - 5x^2y - 9x^2) + (11x^3y^2 + 6x^2y - 3x^2 + 4)$$
$$= (13x^3y^2 + 11x^3y^2) + (-5x^2y + 6x^2y) + (-9x^2 - 3x^2) + 4$$
$$= 24x^3y^2 + x^2y - 12x^2 + 4$$
The degree is 5.

83. $(x + 7y)(3x - 5y) = x(3x) + (x)(-5y) + (7y)(3x) + (7y)(-5y)$
$$= 3x^2 - 5xy + 21xy - 35y^2$$
$$= 3x^2 + 16xy - 35y^2$$

84. $(3x - 5y)^2 = (3x)^2 - 2(3x)(5y) + (-5y)^2$
$$= 9x^2 - 30xy + 25y^2$$

85. $(3x^2 + 2y)^2 = (3x^2)^2 + 2(3x^2)(2y) + (2y)^2$
$$= 9x^4 + 12x^2y + 4y^2$$

86. $(7x + 4y)(7x - 4y) = (7x)^2 - (4y)^2$
$$= 49x^2 - 16y^2$$

87. $(a - b)(a^2 + ab + b^2)$
$$= a(a^2) + a(ab) + a(b^2) + (-b)(a^2)$$
$$+ (-b)(ab) + (-b)(b^2)$$
$$= a^3 + a^2b + ab^2 - a^2b - ab^2 - b^3$$
$$= a^3 - b^3$$

88. $15x^3 + 3x^2 = 3x^2 \cdot 5x + 3x^2 \cdot 1$
$$= 3x^2(5x + 1)$$

89. $x^2 - 11x + 28 = (x - 4)(x - 7)$

90. $15x^2 - x - 2 = (3x + 1)(5x - 2)$

91. $64 - x^2 = 8^2 - x^2 = (8 - x)(8 + x)$

92. $x^2 + 16$ is prime.

93. $3x^4 - 9x^3 - 30x^2 = 3x^2(x^2 - 3x - 10)$
$$= 3x^2(x - 5)(x + 2)$$

94. $20x^7 - 36x^3 = 4x^3(5x^4 - 9)$

95. $x^3 - 3x^2 - 9x + 27 = x^2(x - 3) - 9(x - 3)$
$$= (x^2 - 9)(x - 3)$$
$$= (x + 3)(x - 3)(x - 3)$$
$$= (x + 3)(x - 3)^2$$

96. $16x^2 - 40x + 25 = (4x - 5)(4x - 5)$
$$= (4x - 5)^2$$

97. $x^4 - 16 = (x^2)^2 - 4^2$
$$= (x^2 + 4)(x^2 - 4)$$
$$= (x^2 + 4)(x + 2)(x - 2)$$

98. $y^3 - 8 = y^3 - 2^3 = (y - 2)(y^2 + 2y + 4)$

99. $x^3 + 64 = x^3 + 4^3 = (x + 4)(x^2 - 4x + 16)$

100. $3x^4 - 12x^2 = 3x^2(x^2 - 4)$
$$= 3x^2(x - 2)(x + 2)$$

101. $27x^3 - 125 = (3x)^3 - 5^3$
$$= (3x - 5)[(3x)^2 + (3x)(5) + 5^2]$$
$$= (3x - 5)(9x^2 + 15x + 25)$$

102. $x^5 - x = x(x^4 - 1)$
$$= x(x^2 - 1)(x^2 + 1)$$
$$= x(x - 1)(x + 1)(x^2 + 1)$$

103. $x^3 + 5x^2 - 2x - 10 = x^2(x + 5) - 2(x + 5)$
$$= (x^2 - 2)(x + 5)$$

104. $x^2 + 18x + 81 - y^2 = (x^2 + 18x + 81) - y^2$
$$= (x + 9)^2 - y^2$$
$$= (x + 9 - y)(x + 9 + y)$$

105. $16x^{-\frac{3}{4}} + 32x^{\frac{1}{4}} = 16x^{-\frac{3}{4}}\left(1 + 2x^{\frac{1}{4} - \left(-\frac{3}{4}\right)}\right)$
$$= 16x^{-\frac{3}{4}}(1 + 2x)$$
$$= \frac{(1 + 2x)}{16x^{\frac{3}{4}}}$$

106.
$$\left(x^2 - 4\right)\left(x^2 + 3\right)^{\frac{1}{2}} - \left(x^2 - 4\right)^2\left(x^2 + 3\right)^{\frac{3}{2}}$$
$$= \left(x^2 - 4\right)\left(x^2 + 3\right)^{\frac{1}{2}}\left[1 - \left(x^2 - 4\right)\left(x^2 + 3\right)\right]$$
$$= (x - 2)(x + 2)\left(x^2 + 3\right)^{\frac{1}{2}}\left[1 - (x - 2)(x + 2)\left(x^2 + 3\right)\right]$$
$$= (x - 2)(x + 2)(x^2 + 3)^{\frac{1}{2}}(-x^4 + x^2 + 13)$$

107. $12x^{-\frac{1}{2}} + 6x^{-\frac{3}{2}} = 6x^{-\frac{3}{2}}(2x + 1) = \dfrac{6(2x + 1)}{x^{\frac{3}{2}}}$

108. $\dfrac{x^3 + 2x^2}{x + 2} = \dfrac{x^2(x + 2)}{x + 2} = x^2, \ x \neq -2$

109. $\dfrac{x^2 + 3x - 18}{x^2 - 36} = \dfrac{(x + 6)(x - 3)}{(x + 6)(x - 6)} = \dfrac{x - 3}{x - 6}$,
$$x \neq -6, 6$$

110. $\dfrac{x^2 + 2x}{x^2 + 4x + 4} = \dfrac{x(x + 2)}{(x + 2)^2} = \dfrac{x}{x + 2}$,
$$x \neq -2$$

111. $\dfrac{x^2+6x+9}{x^2-4} \cdot \dfrac{x+3}{x-2} = \dfrac{(x+3)^2}{(x-2)(x+2)} \cdot \dfrac{x+3}{x-2}$

$\qquad = \dfrac{(x+3)^3}{(x-2)^2(x+2)},$

$\qquad x \neq 2, -2$

112. $\dfrac{6x+2}{x^2-1} \div \dfrac{3x^2+x}{x-1}$

$\qquad = \dfrac{2(3x+1)}{(x-1)(x+1)} \div \dfrac{x(3x+1)}{x-1}$

$\qquad = \dfrac{2(3x+1)}{(x-1)(x+1)} \cdot \dfrac{x-1}{x(3x+1)}$

$\qquad = \dfrac{2}{x(x+1)},$

$\qquad x \neq 0, 1, -1, -\dfrac{1}{3}$

113. $\dfrac{x^2-5x-24}{x^2-x-12} \div \dfrac{x^2-10x+16}{x^2+x-6}$

$\qquad = \dfrac{(x-8)(x+3)}{(x-4)(x+3)} \div \dfrac{(x-2)(x-8)}{(x+3)(x-2)}$

$\qquad = \dfrac{x-8}{x-4} \cdot \dfrac{x+3}{x-8}$

$\qquad = \dfrac{x+3}{x-4},$

$\qquad x \neq -3, 4, 2, 8$

114. $\dfrac{2x-7}{x^2-9} - \dfrac{x-10}{x^2-9} = \dfrac{2x-7-(x-10)}{x^2-9}$

$\qquad = \dfrac{x+3}{(x+3)(x-3)}$

$\qquad = \dfrac{1}{x-3},$

$\qquad x \neq 3, -3$

115. $\dfrac{3x}{x+2} + \dfrac{x}{x-2} = \dfrac{3x}{x+2} \cdot \dfrac{x-2}{x-2} + \dfrac{x}{x-2} \cdot \dfrac{x+2}{x+2}$

$\qquad = \dfrac{3x^2-6x+x^2+2x}{(x+2)(x-2)}$

$\qquad = \dfrac{4x^2-4x}{(x+2)(x-2)}$

$\qquad = \dfrac{4x(x-1)}{(x+2)(x-2)},$

$\qquad x \neq 2, -2$

116. $\dfrac{x}{x^2-9} + \dfrac{x-1}{x^2-5x+6}$

$\qquad = \dfrac{x}{(x-3)(x+3)} + \dfrac{x-1}{(x-2)(x-3)}$

$\qquad = \dfrac{x}{(x-3)(x+3)} \cdot \dfrac{x-2}{x-2} + \dfrac{x-1}{(x-2)(x-3)} \cdot \dfrac{x+3}{x+3}$

$\qquad = \dfrac{x(x-2)+(x-1)(x+3)}{(x-3)(x+3)(x-2)}$

$\qquad = \dfrac{x^2-2x+x^2+2x-3}{(x-3)(x+3)(x-2)}$

$\qquad = \dfrac{2x^2-3}{(x-3)(x+3)(x-2)}$

$\qquad x \neq 3, -3, 2$

117. $\dfrac{4x-1}{2x^2+5x-3} - \dfrac{x+3}{6x^2+x-2}$

$\qquad = \dfrac{4x-1}{(2x-1)(x+3)} - \dfrac{x+3}{(2x-1)(3x+2)}$

$\qquad = \dfrac{4x-1}{(2x-1)(x+3)} \cdot \dfrac{3x+2}{3x+2}$

$\qquad \quad - \dfrac{x+3}{(2x-1)(3x+2)} \cdot \dfrac{x+3}{x+3}$

$\qquad = \dfrac{12x^2+8x-3x-2-x^2-6x-9}{(2x-1)(x+3)(3x+2)}$

$\qquad = \dfrac{11x^2-x-11}{(2x-1)(x+3)(3x+2)},$

$\qquad x \neq \dfrac{1}{2}, -3, -\dfrac{2}{3}$

118. $\dfrac{\dfrac{1}{x}-\dfrac{1}{2}}{\dfrac{1}{3}-\dfrac{x}{6}} = \dfrac{\dfrac{1}{x}-\dfrac{1}{2}}{\dfrac{1}{3}-\dfrac{x}{6}} \cdot \dfrac{6x}{6x}$

$\qquad = \dfrac{6-3x}{2x-x^2}$

$\qquad = \dfrac{-3(x-2)}{-x(x-2)}$

$\qquad = \dfrac{3}{x},$

$\qquad x \neq 0, 2$

119.
$$\frac{3+\frac{12}{x}}{1-\frac{16}{x^2}} = \frac{3+\frac{12}{x}}{1-\frac{16}{x^2}} \cdot \frac{x^2}{x^2}$$
$$= \frac{3x^2+12x}{x^2-16}$$
$$= \frac{3x(x+4)}{(x+4)(x-4)}$$
$$= \frac{3x}{x-4},$$
$$x \neq 0, 4, -4$$

120.
$$\frac{3-\frac{1}{x+3}}{3+\frac{1}{x+3}} = \frac{3-\frac{1}{x+3}}{3+\frac{1}{x+3}} \cdot \frac{x+3}{x+3}$$
$$= \frac{3(x+3)-1}{3(x+3)+1}$$
$$= \frac{3x+9-1}{3x+9+1}$$
$$= \frac{3x+8}{3x+10},$$
$$x \neq -3, -\frac{10}{3}$$

Chapter P Test

1. $5(2x^2-6x)-(4x^2-3x) = 10x^2-30x-4x^2+3x$
$$= 6x^2-27x$$

2. $7+2[3(x+1)-2(3x-1)]$
$$= 7+2[3x+3-6x+2]$$
$$= 7+2[-3x+5]$$
$$= 7-6x+10$$
$$= -6x+17$$

3. $\{1,2,5\}\cap\{5,a\} = \{5\}$

4. $\{1,2,5\}\cup\{5,a\} = \{1,2,5,a\}$

5. $(2x^2y^3-xy+y^2)-(-4x^2y^3-5xy-y^2)$
$$= 2x^2y^3-xy+y^2+4x^2y^3+5xy+y^2$$
$$= 2x^2y^3+4x^2y^3-xy+5xy+y^2+y^2$$
$$= 6x^2y^3+4xy+2y^2$$

6. $\frac{30x^3y^4}{6x^9y^{-4}} = 5x^{3-9}y^{4-(-4)} = 5x^{-6}y^8 = \frac{5y^8}{x^6}$

7. $\sqrt{6r}\cdot\sqrt{3r} = \sqrt{18r^2} = \sqrt{9r^2}\cdot\sqrt{2} = 3r\sqrt{2}$

8. $4\sqrt{50}-3\sqrt{18} = 4\sqrt{25\cdot2}-3\sqrt{9\cdot2}$
$$= 4\cdot5\sqrt{2}-3\cdot3\sqrt{2}$$
$$= 20\sqrt{2}-9\sqrt{2}$$
$$= 11\sqrt{2}$$

9. $\frac{3}{5+\sqrt{2}} = \frac{3}{5+\sqrt{2}}\cdot\frac{5-\sqrt{2}}{5-\sqrt{2}}$
$$= \frac{3(5-\sqrt{2})}{25-2}$$
$$= \frac{3(5-\sqrt{2})}{23}$$

10. $\sqrt[3]{16x^4} = \sqrt[3]{8x^3\cdot2x}$
$$= \sqrt[3]{8x^3}\cdot\sqrt[3]{2x}$$
$$= 2x\sqrt[3]{2x}$$

11. $\frac{x^2+2x-3}{x^2-3x+2} = \frac{(x+3)(x-1)}{(x-2)(x-1)} = \frac{x+3}{x-2},$
$$x \neq 2, 1$$

12. $\frac{5\times10^{-6}}{20\times10^{-8}} = \frac{5}{20}\cdot\frac{10^{-6}}{10^{-8}} = 0.25\times10^2 = 2.5\times10^1$

13. $(2x-5)(x^2-4x+3)$
$$= 2x^3-8x^2+6x-5x^2+20x-15$$
$$= 2x^3-13x^2+26x-15$$

14. $(5x+3y)^2 = (5x)^2+2(5x)(3y)+(3y)^2$
$$= 25x^2+30xy+9y^2$$

15. $\frac{2x+8}{x-3}\div\frac{x^2+5x+4}{x^2-9}$
$$= \frac{2(x+4)}{x-3}\div\frac{(x+1)(x+4)}{(x-3)(x+3)}$$
$$= \frac{2(x+4)}{x-3}\cdot\frac{(x-3)(x+3)}{(x+1)(x+4)}$$
$$= \frac{2(x+3)}{x+1},$$
$$x \neq 3, -1, -4, -3$$

16. $\dfrac{x}{x+3}+\dfrac{5}{x-3}$

$=\dfrac{x}{x+3}\cdot\dfrac{x-3}{x-3}+\dfrac{5}{x-3}\cdot\dfrac{x+3}{x+3}$

$=\dfrac{x(x-3)+5(x+3)}{(x+3)(x-3)}$

$=\dfrac{x^2-3x+5x+15}{(x+3)(x-3)}$

$=\dfrac{x^2+2x+15}{(x+3)(x-3)},x\neq 3,-3$

17. $\dfrac{2x+3}{x^2-7x+12}-\dfrac{2}{x-3}$

$=\dfrac{2x+3}{(x-3)(x-4)}-\dfrac{2}{x-3}$

$=\dfrac{2x+3}{(x-3)(x-4)}-\dfrac{2}{x-3}\cdot\dfrac{x-4}{x-4}$

$=\dfrac{2x+3-2(x-4)}{(x-3)(x-4)}$

$=\dfrac{2x+3-2(x-4)}{(x-3)(x-4)}$

$=\dfrac{2x+3-2x+8}{(x-3)(x-4)}$

$=\dfrac{11}{(x-3)(x-4)},$

$x\neq 3,4$

18. $\dfrac{\dfrac{1}{x}-\dfrac{1}{3}}{\dfrac{1}{x}}=\dfrac{\dfrac{1}{x}-\dfrac{1}{3}}{\dfrac{1}{x}}\cdot\dfrac{3x}{3x}=\dfrac{3-x}{3},$

$x\neq 0$

19. $x^2-9x+18=(x-3)(x-6)$

20. $x^3+2x^2+3x+6=x^2(x+2)+3(x+2)$

$\qquad\qquad\qquad\quad=(x^2+3)(x+2)$

21. $25x^2-9=(5x)^2-3^2=(5x-3)(5x+3)$

22. $36x^2-84x+49=(6x)^2-2(6x)\cdot7+7^2$

$\qquad\qquad\qquad\quad=(6x-7)^2$

23. $y^3-125=y^3-5^3=(y-5)(y^2+5y+25)$

24. $(x^2+10x+25)-9y^2$

$=(x+5)^2-9y^2$

$=(x+5-3y)(x+5+3y)$

25. $x(x+3)^{-\frac{3}{5}}+(x+3)^{\frac{2}{5}}$

$=(x+3)^{-\frac{3}{5}}\left[x+(x+3)\right]$

$=(x+3)^{-\frac{3}{5}}(2x+3)=\dfrac{2x+3}{(x+3)^{\frac{3}{5}}}$

26. $-7,-\dfrac{4}{5},0,0.25,\sqrt{4},\dfrac{22}{7}$ are rational numbers.

27. $3(2+5)=3(5+2)$;
commutative property of addition

28. $6(7+4)=6\cdot7+6\cdot4$
distributive property of multiplication over
addition

29. $0.00076=7.6\times10^{-4}$

30. $27^{-\frac{5}{3}}=\dfrac{1}{27^{\frac{5}{3}}}=\dfrac{1}{\left(\sqrt[3]{27}\right)^5}=\dfrac{1}{(3)^5}=\dfrac{1}{243}$

31. $2\left(6.3\times10^9\right)=12.6\times10^9=1.26\times10^{10}$

32. a. Model 2 describes data for men and Model
1 describes data for women.

b. $E=0.18t+65$
$E=0.18(50)+65$
$\quad=74$
The model predicts that the life expectancy
for men in 2000 was 74 years. This fits the
data in the graph fairly well.

Chapter 1

Section 1.1

Check Point Exercises

1.

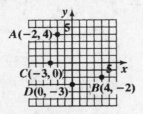

2.

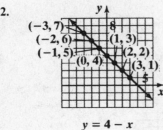

$$y = 4 - x$$

$x = -3, y = 7$

$x = -2, y = 6$

$x = -1, y = 5$

$x = 0, y = 4$

$x = 1, y = 3$

$x = 2, y = 2$

$x = 3, y = 1$

3.

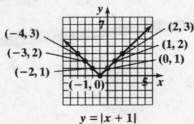

$$y = |x + 1|$$

$x = -4, y = 3$

$x = -3, y = 2$

$x = -2, y = 1$

$x = -1, y = 0$

$x = 0, y = 1$

$x = 1, y = 2$

$x = 2, y = 3$

4. The meaning of a $[-100, 100, 50]$ by $[-100, 100, 10]$ viewing rectangle is as follows:

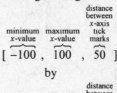

by

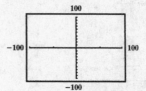

5. a. The graph crosses the x-axis at $(-3, 0)$. Thus, the x-intercept is -3. The graph crosses the y-axis at $(0, 5)$. Thus, the y-intercept is 5.

b. The graph does not cross the x-axis. Thus, there is no x-intercept. The graph crosses the y-axis at $(0, 4)$. Thus, the y-intercept is 4.

c. The graph crosses the x- and y-axes at the origin $(0, 0)$. Thus, the x-intercept is 0 and the y-intercept is 0.

6. The number of federal prisoners sentenced for drug offenses in 2003 is about 57% of 159,275. This can be estimated by finding 60% of 160,000.

$N \approx 60\%$ of $160,000$

$= 0.60 \times 160,000$

$= 96,000$

43

Exercise Set 1.1

1.

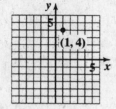

3.

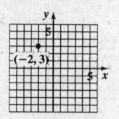

5.

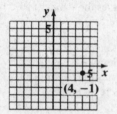

7.

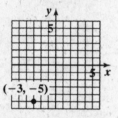

9.

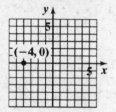

11.

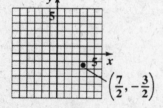

13.

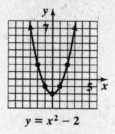

$$y = x^2 - 2$$

$x = -3, y = 7$

$x = -2, y = 2$

$x = -1, y = -1$

$x = 0, y = -2$

$x = 1, y = -1$

$x = 2, y = 2$

$x = 3, y = 7$

15.

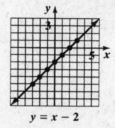

$$y = x - 2$$

$x = -3, y = -5$

$x = -2, y = -4$

$x = -1, y = -3$

$x = 0, y = -2$

$x = 1, y = -1$

$x = 2, y = 0$

$x = 3, y = 1$

17.

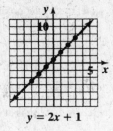

$$y = 2x + 1$$

$x = -3, y = -5$
$x = -2, y = -3$
$x = -1, y = -1$
$x = 0, y = 1$
$x = 1, y = 3$
$x = 2, y = 5$
$x = 3, y = 7$

21.

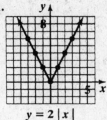

$$y = 2\,|x|$$

$x = -3, y = 6$
$x = -2, y = 4$
$x = -1, y = 2$
$x = 0, y = 0$
$x = 1, y = 2$
$x = 2, y = 4$
$x = 3, y = 6$

19.

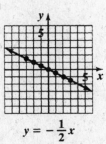

$$y = -\frac{1}{2}x$$

$x = -3, y = \dfrac{3}{2}$

$x = -2, y = 1$

$x = -1, y = \dfrac{1}{2}$

$x = 0, y = 0$

$x = 1, y = -\dfrac{1}{2}$

$x = 2, y = -1$

$x = 3, y = -\dfrac{3}{2}$

23.

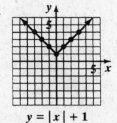

$$y = |x| + 1$$

$x = -3, y = 4$
$x = -2, y = 3$
$x = -1, y = 2$
$x = 0, y = 1$
$x = 1, y = 2$
$x = 2, y = 3$
$x = 3, y = 4$

45

25.

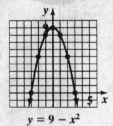

$$y = 9 - x^2$$

$x = -3, y = 0$
$x = -2, y = 5$
$x = -1, y = 8$
$x = 0, y = 9$
$x = 1, y = 8$
$x = 2, y = 5$
$x = 3, y = 0$

27.

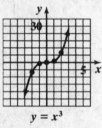

$$y = x^3$$

$x = -3, y = -27$
$x = -2, y = -8$
$x = -1, y = 1$
$x = 0, y = 0$
$x = 1, y = 1$
$x = 2, y = 8$
$x = 3, y = 27$

29. (c) x-axis tick marks –5, –4, –3, –2, –1, 0, 1, 2, 3, 4, 5; y-axis tick marks are the same.

31. (b); x-axis tick marks –20, –10, 0, 10, 20, 30, 40, 50, 60, 70, 80; y-axis tick marks –30, –20, –10, 0, 10, 20, 30, 40, 50, 60, 70

33. The equation that corresponds to Y_2 in the table is (c), $y_2 = 2 - x$. We can tell because all of the points $(-3, 5)$, $(-2, 4)$, $(-1, 3)$, $(0, 2)$, $(1, 1)$, $(2, 0)$, and $(3, -1)$ are on the line $y = 2 - x$, but all are not on any of the others.

35. No. It passes through the point $(0, 2)$.

37. $(2, 0)$

39. The graphs of Y_1 and Y_2 intersect at the points $(-2, 4)$ and $(1, 1)$.

41. **a.** 2; The graph intersects the x-axis at (2, 0).

    b. –4; The graph intersects the y-axis at (0,–4).

43. **a.** 1, –2; The graph intersects the x-axis at (1, 0) and (–2, 0).

    b. 2; The graph intersects the y-axis at (0, 2).

45. **a.** –1; The graph intersects the x-axis at (–1, 0).

    b. none; The graph does not intersect the y-axis.

47.

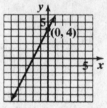

$$y = 2x + 4$$

49.

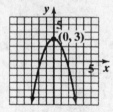

$$y = 3 - x^2$$

51.

x	(x, y)
-3	$(-3, 5)$
-2	$(-2, 5)$
-1	$(-1, 5)$
0	$(0, 5)$
1	$(1, 5)$
2	$(2, 5)$
3	$(3, 5)$

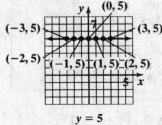

$$y = 5$$

53.

x	(x, y)
-2	$\left(-2, -\dfrac{1}{2}\right)$
-1	$(-1, -1)$
$-\dfrac{1}{2}$	$\left(-\dfrac{1}{2}, -2\right)$
$-\dfrac{1}{3}$	$\left(-\dfrac{1}{3}, -3\right)$
$\dfrac{1}{3}$	$\left(\dfrac{1}{3}, 3\right)$
$\dfrac{1}{2}$	$\left(\dfrac{1}{2}, 2\right)$
1	$(1, 1)$
2	$\left(2, \dfrac{1}{2}\right)$

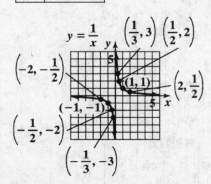

55. There were approximately 65 democracies in 1989.

57. The number of democracies increased at the greatest rate between 1989 and 1993.

59. There were 49 democracies in 1977.

61. $R = 165 - 0.75A; \quad A = 40$

$R - 165 - 0.75A = 165 - 0.75(40)$

$\qquad = 165 - 30 = 135$

The desirable heart rate during exercise for a 40-year old man is 135 beats per minute. This corresponds to the point (40, 135) on the blue graph.

63. a. At birth we have $x = 0$.

$y = 2.9\sqrt{x} + 36$

$\quad = 2.9\sqrt{0} + 36$

$\quad = 2.9(0) + 36$

$\quad = 36$

According to the model, the head circumference at birth is 36 cm.

b. At 9 months we have $x = 9$.

$y = 2.9\sqrt{x} + 36$

$\quad = 2.9\sqrt{9} + 36$

$\quad = 2.9(3) + 36$

$\quad = 44.7$

According to the model, the head circumference at 9 months is 44.7 cm.

c. At 14 months we have $x = 14$.

$y = 2.9\sqrt{x} + 36$

$\quad = 2.9\sqrt{14} + 36$

$\quad \approx 46.9$

According to the model, the head circumference at 14 months is roughly 46.9 cm.

d. The model describes healthy children.

47

71. $y = 45.48x^2 - 334.35x + 1237.9$

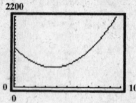

The discharges decreased from 1990 to 1994, but started to increase after 1994. The policy was not a success.

73. (a)

75. (b)

77. (b)

Section 1.2

Check Point Exercises

1.
$$4x + 5 = 29$$
$$4x + 5 - 5 = 29 - 5$$
$$4x = 24$$
$$\frac{4x}{4} = \frac{24}{4}$$
$$x = 6$$
Check:
$$4x + 5 = 29$$
$$4(6) + 5 = 29$$
$$24 + 5 = 29$$
$$29 = 29 \text{ true}$$
The solution set is $\{6\}$.

2.
$$4(2x + 1) - 29 = 3(2x - 5)$$
$$8x + 4 - 29 = 6x - 15$$
$$8x - 25 = 6x - 15$$
$$8x - 25 - 6x = 6x - 15 - 6x$$
$$2x - 25 = -15$$
$$2x - 25 + 25 = -15 + 25$$
$$2x = 10$$
$$\frac{2x}{2} = \frac{10}{2}$$
$$x = 5$$

Check:
$$4(2x + 1) - 29 = 3(2x - 5)$$
$$4[2(5) + 1] - 29 = 3[2(5) - 5]$$
$$4[10 + 1] - 29 = 3[10 - 5]$$
$$4[11] - 29 = 3[5]$$
$$44 - 29 = 15$$
$$15 = 15 \text{ true}$$
The solution set is $\{5\}$.

3.
$$\frac{x-3}{4} = \frac{5}{14} - \frac{x+5}{7}$$
$$28 \cdot \frac{x-3}{4} = 28\left(\frac{5}{14} - \frac{x+5}{7}\right)$$
$$7(x-3) = 2(5) - 4(x+5)$$
$$7x - 21 = 10 - 4x - 20$$
$$7x - 21 = -4x - 10$$
$$7x + 4x = -10 + 21$$
$$11x = 11$$
$$\frac{11x}{11} = \frac{11}{11}$$
$$x = 1$$
Check:
$$\frac{x-3}{4} = \frac{5}{14} - \frac{x+5}{7}$$
$$\frac{1-3}{4} = \frac{5}{14} - \frac{1+5}{7}$$
$$\frac{-2}{4} = \frac{5}{14} - \frac{6}{7}$$
$$-\frac{1}{2} = -\frac{1}{2}$$
The solution set is $\{1\}$.

4.
$$\frac{5}{2x} = \frac{17}{18} - \frac{1}{3x}, \ x \neq 0$$
$$18x \cdot \frac{5}{2x} = 18x\left(\frac{17}{18} - \frac{1}{3x}\right)$$
$$18 \cdot \frac{5}{2x} = 18x \cdot \frac{17}{18} - 18x \cdot \frac{1}{3x}$$
$$45 = 17x - 6$$
$$45 + 6 = 17x - 6 + 6$$
$$51 = 17x$$
$$\frac{51}{17} = \frac{17x}{17}$$
$$3 = x$$
The solution set is $\{3\}$.

5.
$$\frac{x}{x-2}=\frac{2}{x-2}-\frac{2}{3}, \quad x\neq 2$$

$$3(x-2)\cdot\frac{x}{x-2}=3(x-2)\left[\frac{2}{x-2}-\frac{2}{3}\right]$$

$$3(x-2)\cdot\frac{x}{x-2}=(3x-2)\cdot\frac{2}{x-2}-3(x-2)\cdot\frac{2}{3}$$

$$3x=6-(x-2)\cdot 2$$

$$3x=6-2(x-2)$$

$$3x=6-2x+4$$

$$3x=10-2x$$

$$3x+2x=10-2x+2x$$

$$5x=10$$

$$\frac{5x}{5}=\frac{10}{5}$$

$$x=2$$

The solution set is the empty set, $\varnothing$.

6. Set $y_1=y_2$.

$$\frac{1}{x+4}+\frac{1}{x-4}=\frac{22}{x^2-16}$$

$$\frac{1}{x+4}+\frac{1}{x-4}=\frac{22}{(x+4)(x-4)}$$

$$\frac{(x+4)(x-4)}{x+4}+\frac{(x+4)(x-4)}{x-4}=\frac{22(x+4)(x-4)}{(x+4)(x-4)}$$

$$(x-4)+(x+4)=22$$

$$x-4+x+4=22$$

$$2x=22$$

$$x=11$$

Check:

$$\frac{1}{x+4}+\frac{1}{x-4}=\frac{22}{x^2-16}$$

$$\frac{1}{11+4}+\frac{1}{11-4}=\frac{22}{11^2-16}$$

$$\frac{1}{15}+\frac{1}{7}=\frac{22}{105}$$

$$\frac{22}{105}=\frac{22}{105}\quad\text{true}$$

7.
$$4x-7=4(x-1)+3$$
$$4x-7=4(x-1)+3$$
$$4x-7=4x-4+3$$
$$4x-7=4x-1$$
$$-7=-1$$

The original equation is equivalent to the statement $-7=-1$, which is false for every value of x. The solution set is the empty set, $\varnothing$. The equation is an inconsistent equation.

Exercise Set 1.2

1. $7x-5=72$
$$7x=77$$
$$x=11$$
Check:
$$7x-5=72$$
$$7(11)-5=72$$
$$77-5=72$$
$$72=72$$
The solution set is $\{11\}$.

3. $11x-(6x-5)=40$
$$11x-6x+5=40$$
$$5x+5=40$$
$$5x=35$$
$$x=7$$
The solution set is $\{7\}$.

Check:
$$11x-(6x-5)=40$$
$$11(7)-[6(7)-5]=40$$
$$77-(42-5)=40$$
$$77-(37)=40$$
$$40=40$$

5. $2x-7=6+x$
$$x-7=6$$
$$x=13$$
The solution set is $\{13\}$.

Check:
$$2(13)-7=6+13$$
$$26-7=19$$
$$19=19$$

7. $7x+4=x+16$
$$6x+4=16$$
$$6x=12$$
$$x=2$$
The solution set is $\{2\}$.

Check:
$$7(2)+4=2+16$$
$$14+4=18$$
$$18=18$$

49

9. $3(x-2)+7 = 2(x+5)$

$3x-6+7 = 2x+10$

$3x+1 = 2x+10$

$x+1 = 10$

$x = 9$

The solution set is $\{9\}$.

Check:

$3(9-2)+7 = 2(9+5)$

$3(7)+7 = 2(14)$

$21+7 = 28$

$28 = 28$

11. $3(x-4)-4(x-3) = x+3-(x-2)$

$3x-12-4x+12 = x+3-x+2$

$-x = 5$

$x = -5$

The solution set is $\{-5\}$.

Check:

$3(-5-4)-4(-5-3) = -5+3-(-5-2)$

$3(-9)-4(-8) = -2-(-7)$

$-27+32 = -2+7$

$5 = 5$

15. $25 - [2+5y-3(y+2)] \quad = -3(2y-5)-[5(y-1)-3y+3]$

$25 - [2+5y-3y-6] \quad = -6y+15-[5y-5-3y+3]$

$25 - [2y-4] \quad\quad\quad = -6y+15-[2y-2]$

$25 - 2y+4 \quad\quad\quad\; = -6y+15-2y+2$

$-2y+29 \quad\quad\quad = -8y+17$

$6y \quad\quad\quad\quad = -12$

$y \quad\quad\quad\quad = -2$

The solution set is $\{-2\}$.

Check:

$25-[2+5y-3(y+2)] = -3(2y-5)-[5(y-1)-3y+3]$

$25-[2+5(-2)-3(-2+2)] = -3[2(-2)-5]-[5(-2-1)-3(-2)+3]$

$25-[2-10-3(0)] = -3[-4-5]-[5(-3)+6+3]$

$25-[-8] = -3(-9)-[-15+9]$

$25+8 = 27-(-6)$

$33 = 27+6$

$33 = 33$

13. $16 = 3(x-1)-(x-7)$

$16 = 3x-3-x+7$

$16 = 2x+4$

$12 = 2x$

$6 = x$

The solution set is $\{6\}$.

Check:

$16 = 3(6-1)-(6-7)$

$16 = 3(5)-(-1)$

$16 = 15+1$

$16 = 16$

17. $\dfrac{x}{3} = \dfrac{x}{2} - 2$

$6\left[\dfrac{x}{3} = \dfrac{x}{2} - 2\right]$

$2x = 3x - 12$

$12 = 3x - 2x$

$x = 12$

The solution set is $\{12\}$.

19. $20 - \dfrac{x}{3} = \dfrac{x}{2}$

$6\left[20 - \dfrac{x}{3} = \dfrac{x}{2}\right]$

$120 - 2x = 3x$

$120 = 3x + 2x$

$120 = 5x$

$x = \dfrac{120}{5}$

$x = 24$

The solution set is $\{24\}$.

21. $\dfrac{3x}{5} = \dfrac{2x}{3} + 1$

$15\left[\dfrac{3x}{5} = \dfrac{2x}{3} + 1\right]$

$9x = 10x + 15$

$9x - 10x = 15$

$-x = 15$

$x = -15$

The solution set is $\{-15\}$.

23. $\dfrac{3x}{5} - x = \dfrac{x}{10} - \dfrac{5}{2}$

$10\left[\dfrac{3x}{5} - x = \dfrac{x}{10} - \dfrac{5}{2}\right]$

$6x - 10x = x - 25$

$-4x - x = -25$

$-5x = -25$

$x = 5$

The solution set is $\{5\}$.

25. $\dfrac{x+3}{6} = \dfrac{3}{8} + \dfrac{x-5}{4}$

$24\left[\dfrac{x+3}{6} = \dfrac{3}{8} + \dfrac{x-5}{4}\right]$

$4x + 12 = 9 + 6x - 30$

$4x - 6x = -21 - 12$

$-2x = -33$

$x = \dfrac{33}{2}$

The solution set is $\left\{\dfrac{33}{2}\right\}$.

27. $\dfrac{x}{4} = 2 + \dfrac{x-3}{3}$

$12\left[\dfrac{x}{4} = 2 + \dfrac{x-3}{3}\right]$

$3x = 24 + 4x - 12$

$3x - 4x = 12$

$-x = 12$

$x = -12$

The solution set is $\{-12\}$.

29. $\dfrac{x+1}{3} = 5 - \dfrac{x+2}{7}$

$21\left[\dfrac{x+1}{3} = 5 - \dfrac{x+2}{7}\right]$

$7x + 7 = 105 - 3x - 6$

$7x + 3x = 99 - 7$

$10x = 92$

$x = \dfrac{92}{10}$

$x = \dfrac{46}{5}$

The solution set is $\left\{\dfrac{46}{5}\right\}$.

31. a. $\dfrac{4}{x} = \dfrac{5}{2x} + 3 \ (x \neq 0)$

b. $\dfrac{4}{x} = \dfrac{5}{2x} + 3$

$8 = 5 + 6x$

$3 = 6x$

$\dfrac{1}{2} = x$

The solution set is $\left\{\dfrac{1}{2}\right\}$.

33. a. $\dfrac{2}{x}+3=\dfrac{5}{2x}+\dfrac{13}{4}\ (x\ne 0)$

b. $\dfrac{2}{x}+3=\dfrac{5}{2x}+\dfrac{13}{4}$

$8+12x=10+13x$

$-x=2$

$x=-2$

The solution set is $\{-2\}$.

35. a. $\dfrac{2}{3x}+\dfrac{1}{4}=\dfrac{11}{6x}-\dfrac{1}{3}\ (x\ne 0)$

b. $\dfrac{2}{3x}+\dfrac{1}{4}=\dfrac{11}{6x}-\dfrac{1}{3}$

$8+3x=22-4x$

$7x=14$

$x=2$

The solution set is $\{2\}$.

37. a. $\dfrac{x-2}{2x}+1=\dfrac{x+1}{x}\quad (x\ne 0)$

b. $\dfrac{x-2}{2x}+1=\dfrac{x+1}{x}$

$x-2+2x=2x+2$

$x-2=2$

$x=4$

The solution set is $\{4\}$.

39. a. $\dfrac{1}{x-1}+5=\dfrac{11}{x-1}\ (x\ne 1)$

b. $\dfrac{1}{x-1}+5=\dfrac{11}{x-1}$

$1+5(x-1)=11$

$1+5x-5=11$

$5x-4=11$

$5x=15$

$x=3$

The solution set is $\{3\}$.

41. a. $\dfrac{8x}{x+1}=4-\dfrac{8}{x+1}\ (x\ne -1)$

b. $\dfrac{8x}{x+1}=4-\dfrac{8}{x+1}$

$8x=4(x+1)-8$

$8x=4x+4-8$

$4x=-4$

$x=-1\Rightarrow$ no solution

The solution set is the empty set, $\varnothing$.

43. a. $\dfrac{3}{2x-2}+\dfrac{1}{2}=\dfrac{2}{x-1}\ (x\ne 1)$

b. $\dfrac{3}{2x-2}+\dfrac{1}{2}=\dfrac{2}{x-1}$

$\dfrac{3}{2(x-1)}+\dfrac{1}{2}=\dfrac{2}{x-1}$

$3+1(x-1)=4$

$3+x-1=4$

$x=2$

The solution set is $\{2\}$.

45. a. $\dfrac{3}{x+2}+\dfrac{2}{x-2}=\dfrac{8}{(x+2)(x-2)};(x\ne -2,2)$

b. $\dfrac{3}{x+2}+\dfrac{2}{x-2}=\dfrac{8}{(x+2)(x-2)}$

$(x\ne 2,x\ne -2)$

$3(x-2)+2(x+2)=8$

$3x-6+2x+4=8$

$5x=10$

$x=2\Rightarrow$ no solution

The solution set is the empty set, $\varnothing$.

47. a. $\dfrac{2}{x+1}-\dfrac{1}{x-1}=\dfrac{2x}{x^2-1}\ (x\ne 1,x\ne -1)$

b.

$\dfrac{2}{x+1}-\dfrac{1}{x-1}=\dfrac{2x}{x^2-1}$

$\dfrac{2}{x+1}-\dfrac{1}{x-1}=\dfrac{2x}{(x+1)(x-1)}$

$2(x-1)-1(x+1)=2x$

$2x-2-x-1=2x$

$-x=3$

$x=-3$

The solution set is $\{-3\}$.

49. a. $\dfrac{1}{x-4}-\dfrac{5}{x+2}=\dfrac{6}{(x-4)(x+2)}; (x\neq-2,4)$

b.
$$\frac{1}{x-4}-\frac{5}{x+2}=\frac{6}{x^2-2x-8}$$
$$\frac{1}{x-4}-\frac{5}{x+2}=\frac{6}{(x-4)(x+2)}$$
$$(x\neq 4, x\neq-2)$$
$$1(x+2)-5(x-4)=6$$
$$x+2-5x+20=6$$
$$-4x=-16$$
$$x=4\Rightarrow \text{ no solution}$$
The solution set is the empty set, $\varnothing$.

51. Set $y_1=y_2$.
$$5(2x-8)-2=5(x-3)+3$$
$$10x-40-2=5x-15+3$$
$$10x-42=5x-12$$
$$10x-5x=-12+42$$
$$5x=30$$
$$x=6$$
The solution set is $\{6\}$.

53. Set $y_1-y_2=1$.
$$\frac{x-3}{5}-\frac{x-5}{4}=1$$
$$20\cdot\frac{x-3}{5}-20\cdot\frac{x-5}{4}=20\cdot 1$$
$$4(x-3)-5(x-5)=20$$
$$4x-12-5x+25=20$$
$$-x+13=20$$
$$-x=7$$
$$x=-7$$
The solution set is $\{-7\}$.

55. Set $y_1+y_2=y_3$.
$$\frac{5}{x+4}+\frac{3}{x+3}=\frac{12x+19}{x^2+7x+12}$$
$$\frac{5}{x+4}+\frac{3}{x+3}=\frac{12x+19}{(x+4)(x+3)}$$
$$(x+4)(x+3)\left(\frac{5}{x+4}+\frac{3}{x+3}\right)=(x+4)(x+3)\frac{12x+19}{(x+4)(x+3)}$$
$$5(x+3)+3(x+4)=12x+19$$
$$5x+15+3x+12=12x+19$$
$$8x+27=12x+19$$
$$-4x=-8$$
$$x=2$$
The solution set is $\{2\}$.

57.
$$0=4[x-(3-x)]-7(x+1)$$
$$0=4[x-3+x]-7x-7$$
$$0=4[2x-3]-7x-7$$
$$0=8x-12-7x-7$$
$$0=x-19$$
$$-x=-19$$
$$x=19$$
The solution set is $\{19\}$.

59.
$$0 = \frac{x+6}{3x-12} - \frac{5}{x-4} - \frac{2}{3}$$
$$0 = \frac{x+6}{3(x-4)} - \frac{5}{x-4} - \frac{2}{3}$$
$$3(x-4)\cdot 0 = 3(x-4)\left(\frac{x+6}{3(x-4)} - \frac{5}{x-4} - \frac{2}{3}\right)$$
$$0 = \frac{3(x-4)(x+6)}{3(x-4)} - \frac{5\cdot 3(x-4)}{x-4} - \frac{2\cdot 3(x-4)}{3}$$
$$0 = (x+6) - 15 - 2(x-4)$$
$$0 = x+6-15-2x+8$$
$$0 = -x-1$$
$$x = -1$$
The solution set is $\{-1\}$.

61. $4(x-7) = 4x-28$
$4x-28 = 4x-28$
The given equation is an identity.

63. $2x+3 = 2x-3$
$3 = -3$
The given equation is an inconsistent equation.

65. $4x+5x = 8x$
$9x = 8x$
$x = 0$
The given equation is a conditional equation.

67. $\frac{2x}{x-3} = \frac{6}{x-3} + 4$
$2x = 6 + 4(x-3)$
$2x = 6 + 4x - 12$
$-2x = -6$
$x = 3 \Rightarrow$ no solution
The given equation is an inconsistent equation.

69. $\frac{x+5}{2} - 4 = \frac{2x-1}{3}$
$3(x+5) - 24 = 2(2x-1)$
$3x+15-24 = 4x-2$
$-x = 7$
$x = -7$
The solution set is $\{-7\}$.
The given equation is a conditional equation.

71. $\frac{2}{x-2} = 3 + \frac{x}{x-2}$
$2 = 3(x-2) + x$
$2 = 3x-6+x$
$-4x = -8$
$x = 2 \Rightarrow$ no solution
The solution set is the empty set, $\varnothing$.
The given equation is an inconsistent equation.

73. $8x - (3x+2) + 10 = 3x$
$8x-3x-2+10 = 3x$
$2x = -8$
$x = -4$
The solution set is $\{-4\}$.
The given equation is a conditional equation.

75. $\frac{2}{x} + \frac{1}{2} = \frac{3}{4}$
$8 + 2x = 3x$
$-x = -8$
$x = 8$
The solution set is $\{8\}$.
The given equation is a conditional equation.

77. $\frac{4}{x-2} + \frac{3}{x+5} = \frac{7}{(x+5)(x-2)}$
$4(x+5) + 3(x-2) = 7$
$4x+20+3x-6 = 7$
$7x = -7$
$x = -1$
The solution set is $\{-1\}$.
The given equation is a conditional equation.

79.
$$\frac{4x}{x+3} - \frac{12}{x-3} = \frac{4x^2+36}{x^2-9}; x \neq 3, -3$$
$$4x(x-3) - 12(x+3) = 4x^2 + 36$$
$$4x^2 - 12x - 12x - 36 = 4x^2 + 36$$
$$4x^2 - 24x - 36 = 4x^2 + 36$$
$$-24x - 36 = 36$$
$$-24x = 72$$
$$x = -3 \quad \text{No solution}$$
The solution set is { }.
The given equation is an inconsistent equation.

81. The equation is $3(x-4) = 3(2-2x)$, and the solution is $x = 2$.

83. The equation is $-3(x-3) = 5(2-x)$, and the solution is $x = 0.5$.

85. Solve: $4(x-2) + 2 = 4x - 2(2-x)$
$$4x - 8 + 2 = 4x - 4 + 2x$$
$$4x - 6 = 6x - 4$$
$$-2x - 6 = -4$$
$$-2x = 2$$
$$x = -1$$
Now, evaluate $x^2 - x$ for $x = -1$:
$$x^2 - x = (-1)^2 - (-1)$$
$$= 1 - (-1) = 1 + 1 = 2$$

87. Solve for x: $\frac{3(x+3)}{5} = 2x + 6$
$$3(x+3) = 5(2x+6)$$
$$3x + 9 = 10x + 30$$
$$-7x + 9 = 30$$
$$-7x = 21$$
$$x = -3$$
Solve for y: $-2y - 10 = 5y + 18$
$$-7y - 10 = 18$$
$$-7y = 28$$
$$y = -4$$

Now, evaluate $x^2 - (xy - y)$ for $x = -3$ and $y = -4$:
$$x^2 - (xy - y)$$
$$= (-3)^2 - [-3(-4) - (-4)]$$
$$= (-3)^2 - [12 - (-4)]$$
$$= 9 - (12 + 4) = 9 - 16 = -7$$

89.
$$\left[(3+6)^2 \div 3\right] \cdot 4 = -54x$$
$$(9^2 \div 3) \cdot 4 = -54x$$
$$(81 \div 3) \cdot 4 = -54x$$
$$27 \cdot 4 = -54x$$
$$108 = -54x$$
$$-2 = x$$
The solution set is $\{-2\}$.

91.
$$5 - 12x = 8 - 7x - \left[6 \div 3(2+5^3) + 5x\right]$$
$$5 - 12x = 8 - 7x - \left[6 \div 3(2+125) + 5x\right]$$
$$5 - 12x = 8 - 7x - \left[6 \div 3 \cdot 127 + 5x\right]$$
$$5 - 12x = 8 - 7x - \left[2 \cdot 127 + 5x\right]$$
$$5 - 12x = 8 - 7x - \left[254 + 5x\right]$$
$$5 - 12x = 8 - 7x - 254 - 5x$$
$$5 - 12x = -12x - 246$$
$$5 = -246$$
The final statement is a contradiction, so the equation has no solution. The solution set is $\varnothing$.

93.
$$0.7x + 0.4(20) = 0.5(x+20)$$
$$0.7x + 8 = 0.5x + 10$$
$$0.2x + 8 = 10$$
$$0.2x = 2$$
$$x = 10$$
The solution set is $\{10\}$.

95. $4x+13-\left\{2x-\left[4(x-3)-5\right]\right\}=2(x-6)$

$4x+13-\left\{2x-\left[4x-12-5\right]\right\}=2x-12$

$4x+13-\left\{2x-\left[4x-17\right]\right\}=2x-12$

$4x+13-\left\{2x-4x+17\right\}=2x-12$

$4x+13-\left\{-2x+17\right\}=2x-12$

$4x+13+2x-17=2x-12$

$6x-4=2x-12$

$4x-4=-12$

$4x=-8$

$x=-2$

The solution set is $\left\{-2\right\}$.

97. Let T = 4421. Then

$4421=165x+2771$

$1650=165x$

$10=x$

Tuition will be $4421 ten years after 1996, which is the school year ending 2006.

99. $D=\dfrac{1}{9}N+\dfrac{26}{9}; \quad D=\dfrac{7}{2}$

$\dfrac{7}{2}=\dfrac{1}{9}N+\dfrac{26}{9}$

$18\left(\dfrac{7}{2}\right)=18\left(\dfrac{1}{9}N+\dfrac{26}{9}\right)$

$63=2N+52$

$11=2N$

$\dfrac{11}{2}=\dfrac{2N}{2}$

$5.5=N$

If the high-humor group averages a level of depression of 3.5 in response to a negative life event, the intensity of that event would be 5.5. The solution is the point along the horizontal axis where the graph for the high-humor group has a value of 3.5 on the vertical axis. This corresponds to the point $(5.5, 3.5)$ on the high-humor graph.

101. $C=\dfrac{DA}{A+12}; C=500, D=1000$

$500=\dfrac{1000A}{A+12}$

$(A+12)\cdot 500=(A+12)\left(\dfrac{1000A}{A+12}\right)$

$500A+6000=1000A$

$6000=500A$

$12=A$

The child's age is 12 years old.

103. The solution is the point (12, 500) on the blue graph.

105. No, because the graphs cross, neither formula gives a consistently smaller dosage.

107. 11 learning trials; represented by the point $(11, 0.95)$ on the graph.

109.
$$C=\dfrac{x+0.1(500)}{x+500}$$

$$0.28=\dfrac{x+0.1(500)}{x+500}$$

$$0.28(x+500)=x+0.1(500)$$

$$0.28x+140=x+50$$

$$-0.72x=-90$$

$$\dfrac{-0.72x}{-0.72}=\dfrac{-90}{-0.72}$$

$$x=125$$

125 liters of pure peroxide must be added.

120. $\{3\}$

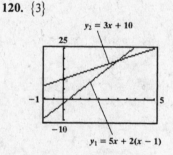

121. $\{5\}$

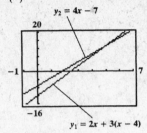

$y_2 = 4x - 7$

$y_1 = 2x + 3(x - 4)$

123. $\{-5\}$

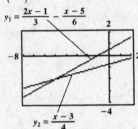

$y_1 = \dfrac{2x - 1}{3} - \dfrac{x - 5}{6}$

$y_2 = \dfrac{x - 3}{4}$

125. Answers may vary.

127. $\dfrac{4x - b}{x - 5} = 3$

$4x - b = 3(x - 5)$

The solution set will be $\varnothing$ if $x = 5$.

$4(5) - b = 3(5 - 5)$

$20 - b = 0$

$20 = b$

$b = 20$

Section 1.3

Check Point Exercises

1. Let x = the number of football injuries
Let $x + 0.6$ = the number of basketball injuries
Let $x + 0.3$ = the number of bicycling injuries

$x + (x + 0.6) + (x + 0.3) = 3.9$

$x + x + 0.6 + x + 0.3 = 3.9$

$3x + 0.9 = 3.9$

$3x = 3$

$x = 1$

$x = 1$

$x + 0.6 = 1 + 0.6 = 1.6$

$x + 0.3 = 1 + 0.3 = 1.3$

In 2004 there were 1 million football injuries, 1.6 million basketball injuries, and 1.3 million bicycling injuries.

2. Let x = the number of years after 2004 that it will take until Americans will purchase 79.9 million gallons of organic milk.

$40.7 + 5.6x = 79.9$

$5.6x = 79.9 - 40.7$

$5.6x = 39.2$

$x = \dfrac{39.2}{5.6}$

$x = 7$

Americans will purchase 79.9 million gallons of organic milk 7 years after 2004, or 2011.

3. Let x = the number of minutes at which the costs of the two plans are the same.

$$\underbrace{15 + 0.08x}_{\text{Plan A}} = \underbrace{3 + 0.12x}_{\text{Plan B}}$$

$15 + 0.08x - 15 = 3 + 0.12x - 15$

$0.08x = 0.12x - 12$

$0.08x - 0.12x = 0.12x - 12 - 0.12x$

$-0.04x = -12$

$\dfrac{-0.04x}{-0.04} = \dfrac{-12}{-0.04}$

$x = 300$

The two plans are the same at 300 minutes.

4. Let x = the computer's price before the reduction.

$x - 0.30x = 840$

$0.70x = 840$

$x = \dfrac{840}{0.70}$

$x = 1200$

Before the reduction the computer's price was $1200.

5. Let x = the amount invested at 9%.
Let $5000 - x$ = the amount invested at 11%.

$0.09x + 0.11(5000 - x) = 487$

$0.09x + 550 - 0.11x = 487$

$-0.02x + 550 = 487$

$-0.02x = -63$

$x = \dfrac{-63}{-0.02}$

$x = 3150$

$5000 - x = 1850$

$3150 was invested at 9% and $1850 was invested at 11%.

6. Let x = the width of the court.
Let $x + 44$ = the length of the court.
$$2l + 2w = P$$
$$2(x + 44) + 2x = 288$$
$$2x + 88 + 2x = 288$$
$$4x + 88 = 288$$
$$4x = 200$$
$$x = \frac{200}{4}$$
$$x = 50$$
$$x + 44 = 94$$
The dimensions of the court are 50 by 94.

7.
$$2l + 2w = P$$
$$2l + 2w - 2l = P - 2l$$
$$2w = P - 2l$$
$$\frac{2w}{2} = \frac{P - 2l}{2}$$
$$w = \frac{P - 2l}{2}$$

8.
$$P = C + MC$$
$$P = C(1 + M)$$
$$\frac{P}{1 + M} = \frac{C(1 + M)}{1 + M}$$
$$\frac{P}{1 + M} = C$$
$$C = \frac{P}{1 + M}$$

Exercise Set 1.3

1. Let x = the number
$$5x - 4 = 26$$
$$5x = 30$$
$$x = 6$$
The number is 6.

3. Let x = the number
$$x - 0.20x = 20$$
$$0.80x = 20$$
$$x = 25$$
The number is 25.

5. Let x = the number
$$0.60x + x = 192$$
$$1.6x = 192$$
$$x = 120$$
The number is 120.

7. Let x = the number
$$0.70x = 224$$
$$x = 320$$
The number is 320.

9. Let x = the number
$x + 26$ = the other number
$$x + (x + 26) = 64$$
$$x + x + 26 = 64$$
$$2x + 26 = 64$$
$$2x = 38$$
$$x = 19$$
If $x = 19$, then $x + 26 = 45$.
The numbers are 19 and 45.

11.
$$y_1 - y_2 = 2$$
$$(13x - 4) - (5x + 10) = 2$$
$$13x - 4 - 5x - 10 = 2$$
$$8x - 14 = 2$$
$$8x = 16$$
$$\frac{8x}{8} = \frac{16}{8}$$
$$x = 2$$

13.
$$y_1 = 8y_2 + 14$$
$$10(2x - 1) = 8(2x + 1) + 14$$
$$20x - 10 = 16x + 8 + 14$$
$$20x - 10 = 16x + 22$$
$$4x = 32$$
$$\frac{4x}{4} = \frac{32}{4}$$
$$x = 8$$

15.
$$3y_1 - 5y_2 = y_3 - 22$$
$$3(2x + 6) - 5(x + 8) = (x) - 22$$
$$6x + 18 - 5x - 40 = x - 22$$
$$x - 22 = x - 22$$
$$x - x = -22 + 22$$
$$0 = 0$$
The solution set is the set of all real numbers.

17.
$$3y_1 + 4y_2 = 4y_3$$

$$3\left(\frac{1}{x}\right) + 4\left(\frac{1}{2x}\right) = 4\left(\frac{1}{x-1}\right)$$

$$\frac{3}{x} + \frac{2}{x} = \frac{4}{x-1}$$

$$\frac{5}{x} = \frac{4}{x-1}$$

$$\frac{5x(x-1)}{x} = \frac{4x(x-1)}{x-1}$$

$$5(x-1) = 4x$$

$$5x - 5 = 4x$$

$$x = 5$$

19. Let x = the number of births (in thousands)
Let $x - 229$ = the number of deaths (in thousands).

$$x + (x - 229) = 521$$

$$x + x - 229 = 521$$

$$2x - 229 = 521$$

$$2x - 229 + 229 = 521 + 229$$

$$2x = 750$$

$$\frac{2x}{2} = \frac{750}{2}$$

$$x = 375$$

There are 375 thousand births and
$375 - 229 = 146$ thousand deaths each day.

21. Let x = the number of Internet users in China.
$x + 10$ = the number of Internet users in Japan.
$x + 123$ = the number of Internet users in the
United States.

$$x + (x + 10) + (x + 123) = 271$$

$$3x + 133 = 271$$

$$3x = 138$$

$$x = 46$$

If $x = 46$, then $x + 10 = 56$ and $x + 123 = 169$.
Thus, there are 46 million Internet users in
China, 56 million Internet users in Japan, and
169 Internet users in the United States.

23. Let x = the percentage of Conservatives.
Let $2x + 4.4$ = the percentage of Liberals.

$$x + (2x + 4.4) = 57.2$$

$$x + 2x + 4.4 = 57.2$$

$$3x + 4.4 = 57.2$$

$$3x + 4.4 - 4.4 = 57.2 - 4.4$$

$$3x = 52.8$$

$$\frac{3x}{3} = \frac{52.8}{3}$$

$$x = 17.6$$

$$2x + 4.4 = 39.6$$

The percentage of Conservatives is 17.6% and
the percentage of Liberals is 39.6%

25. Let L = the life expectancy of an American man.
y = the number of years after 1900.

$$L = 55 + 0.2y$$

$$85 = 55 + 0.2y$$

$$30 = 0.2y$$

$$150 = y$$

The life expectancy will be 85 years in the year
$1900 + 150 = 2050$.

27. a. $y = 1.7x + 39.8$

b. $1.7x + 39.8 = 44.9 + 8.5$
$1.7x + 39.8 = 53.4$

$$1.7x = 13.6$$

$$\frac{1.7x}{1.7} = \frac{13.6}{1.7}$$

$$x = 8$$

The number of Americans without health
insurance will exceed 44.9 million by 8.5
million 8 years after 2000, or 2008.

c.

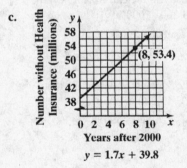

$$y = 1.7x + 39.8$$

29. Let v = the car's value.
     y = the number of years (after 2003).
     $$v = 80,500 - 8705y$$
     $$19,565 = 80,500 - 8705y$$
     $$-60,935 = -8705y$$
     $$7 = y$$
     The car's value will be $19,565 after 7 years.

31. Let x = the number of months.
     The cost for Club A: $25x + 40$
     The cost for Club B: $30x + 15$
     $$25x + 40 = 30x + 15$$
     $$-5x + 40 = 15$$
     $$-5x = -25$$
     $$x = 5$$
     The total cost for the clubs will be the same at 5 months. The cost will be
     $25(5) + 40 = 30(5) + 15 = \$165$

33. Let x = the number of uses.
     Cost without coupon book: $1.25x$
     Cost with coupon book: $15 + 0.75x$
     $$1.25x = 15 + 0.75x$$
     $$0.50x = 15$$
     $$x = 30$$
     The bus must be used 30 times in a month for the costs to be equal.

35. a. Let x = the number of years (after 2005).
         College A's enrollment: $13,300 + 1000x$

         College B's enrollment: $26,800 - 500x$
         $$13,300 + 1000x = 26,800 - 500x$$
         $$13,300 + 1500x = 26,800$$
         $$1500x = 13,500$$
         $$x = 9$$
         The two colleges will have the same enrollment in the year $2005 + 9 = 2014$.
         That year the enrollments will be
         $13,300 + 1000(9)$
         $= 26,800 - 500(9)$
         $= 22,300$ students

     b. Check points to determine that
         $y_1 = 13,300 + 1000x$ and
         $y_2 = 26,800 - 500x$.

37. Let x = the cost of the television set.
     $$x - 0.20x = 336$$
     $$0.80x = 336$$
     $$x = 420$$
     The television set's price is $420.

39. Let x = the nightly cost
     $$x + 0.08x = 162$$
     $$1.08x = 162$$
     $$x = 150$$
     The nightly cost is $150.

41. Let x = the annual salary for men whose highest educational attainment is a high school degree.
     $$x + 0.22x = 44,000$$
     $$1.22x = 44,000$$
     $$x \approx 36,000$$
     The annual salary for men whose highest educational attainment is a high school degree is about $36,000.

43. Let c = the dealer's cost
     $$584 = c + 0.25c$$
     $$584 = 1.25c$$
     $$467.20 = c$$
     The dealer's cost is $467.20.

45. Let x = the amount invested at 6%.
     Let $7000 - x$ = the amount invested at 8%.
     $$0.06x + 0.08(7000 - x) = 520$$
     $$0.06x + 560 - 0.08x = 520$$
     $$-0.02x + 560 = 520$$
     $$-0.02x = -40$$
     $$x = \frac{-40}{-0.02}$$
     $$x = 2000$$
     $$7000 - x = 5000$$
     $2000 was invested at 6% and $5000 was invested at 8%.

47. Let x = amount invested at 12%
     $8000 - x$ = amount invested at 5% loss
     $$.12x - .05(8000 - x) = 620$$
     $$.12x - 400 + .05x = 620$$
     $$.17x = 1020$$
     $$x = 6000$$
     $$8000 - x = 2000$$
     $6000 at 12%, $2000 at 5% loss

49. Let w = the width of the field
Let $2w$ = the length of the field
$P = 2(\text{length}) + 2(\text{width})$
$300 = 2(2w) + 2(w)$
$300 = 4w + 2w$
$300 = 6w$
$50 = w$
If $w = 50$, then $2w = 100$. Thus, the dimensions are 50 yards by 100 yards.

51. Let w = the width of the field
Let $2w + 6$ = the length of the field
$228 = 6w + 12$
$216 = 6w$
$36 = w$
If $w = 36$, then $2w + 6 = 2(36) + 6 = 78$. Thus, the dimensions are 36 feet by 78 feet.

53. Let x = the width of the frame.
Total length: $16 + 2x$
Total width: $12 + 2x$
$P = 2(\text{length}) + 2(\text{width})$
$72 = 2(16 + 2x) + 2(12 + 2x)$
$72 = 32 + 4x + 24 + 4x$
$72 = 8x + 56$
$16 = 8x$
$2 = x$
The width of the frame is 2 inches.

55. Let x = number of hours
$35x$ = labor cost
$35x + 63 = 448$
$35x = 385$
$x = 11$
It took 11 hours.

57. Let x = inches over 5 feet
$100 + 5x = 135$
$5x = 35$
$x = 7$
A height of 5 feet 7 inches corresponds to 135 pounds.

59. Let x = the weight of unpeeled bananas.
$\dfrac{7}{8}x$ = weight of peeled bananas

$x = \dfrac{7}{8}x + \dfrac{7}{8}$

$\dfrac{1}{8}x = \dfrac{7}{8}$

$x = 7$
The banana with peel weighs 7 ounces.

61. $A = lw$

$w = \dfrac{A}{l}$

area of rectangle

63. $A = \dfrac{1}{2}bh$

$2A = bh$

$b = \dfrac{2A}{h}$;

area of triangle

65. $I = Prt$

$P = \dfrac{I}{rt}$;

interest

67. $E = mc^2$

$m = \dfrac{E}{c^2}$;

Einstein's equation

69. $T = D + pm$

$T - D = pm$

$\dfrac{T - D}{m} = \dfrac{pm}{m}$

$\dfrac{T - D}{m} = p$

total of payment

71. $A = \dfrac{1}{2}h(a + b)$

$2A = h(a + b)$

$\dfrac{2A}{h} = a + b$

$\dfrac{2A}{h} - b = a$

area of trapezoid

73.
$$S = P + Prt$$
$$S - P = Prt$$
$$\frac{S - P}{Pt} = r;$$
interest

75.
$$B = \frac{F}{S - V}$$
$$B(S - V) = F$$
$$S - V = \frac{F}{B}$$
$$S = \frac{F}{B} + V$$

77.
$$IR + Ir = E$$
$$I(R + r) = E$$
$$I = \frac{E}{R + r}$$
electric current

79.
$$\frac{1}{p} + \frac{1}{q} = \frac{1}{f}$$
$$qf + pf = pq$$
$$f(q + p) = pq$$
$$f = \frac{pq}{p + q}$$
thin lens equation

89. a.
$$F = 30 + 5x$$
$$F = 7.5x$$

b.

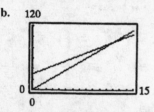

c. Calculator shows the graphs to intersect at $(12, 90)$; the two options both cost \$90 when 12 hours court time is used per month.

d.
$$30 + 5x = 7.5x$$
$$30 = 2.5x$$
$$x = 12$$
Rent the court 12 hours per month.

91. Let x = original price
$x - 0.4x = 0.6x$ = price after first reduction
$0.6x - 0.4(0.6x)$ = price after second reduction
$$0.6x - 0.24x = 72$$
$$0.36x = 72$$
$$x = 200$$
The original price was \$200.

93. Let x = correct answers
$26 - x$ = incorrect answers
$$8x - 5(26 - x) = 0$$
$$8x - 130 + 5x = 0$$
$$13x - 130 = 0$$
$$13x = 130$$
$$x = 10$$
10 problems were solved correctly.

95. Let x = the number of plants originally stolen
After passing the first security guard, the thief
has: $x - \left(\dfrac{1}{2}x + 2\right) = x - \dfrac{1}{2}x - 2 = \dfrac{1}{2}x - 2$

After passing the second security guard, the thief
has: $\dfrac{1}{2}x - 2 - \left(\dfrac{\frac{1}{2}x - 2}{2} + 2\right) = \dfrac{1}{4}x - 3$

After passing the third security guard, the thief
has: $\dfrac{1}{4}x - 3 - \left(\dfrac{\frac{1}{4}x - 3}{2} + 2\right) = \dfrac{1}{8}x - \dfrac{7}{2}$

Thus, $\dfrac{1}{8}x - \dfrac{7}{2} = 1$
$$x - 28 = 8$$
$$x = 36$$
The thief stole 36 plants.

Section 1.4

Check Point Exercises

1. **a.** $(5 - 2i) + (3 + 3i)$
$= 5 - 2i + 3 + 3i$
$= (5 + 3) + (-2 + 3)i$
$= 8 + i$

b. $(2 + 6i) - (12 - i)$
$= 2 + 6i - 12 + i$
$= (2 - 12) + (6 + 1)i$
$= -10 + 7i$

2. **a.** $7i(2 - 9i) = 7i(2) - 7i(9i$
$= 14i - 63i^2$
$= 14i - 63(-1)$
$= 63 + 14i$

b. $(5 + 4i)(6 - 7i) = 30 - 35i + 24i - 28i^2$
$= 30 - 35i + 24i - 28(-1)$
$= 30 + 28 - 35i + 24i$
$= 58 - 11i$

3. $\dfrac{5 + 4i}{4 - i} = \dfrac{5 + 4i}{4 - i} \cdot \dfrac{4 + i}{4 + i}$
$= \dfrac{20 + 5i + 16i + 4i^2}{16 + 4i - 4i - i^2}$
$= \dfrac{20 + 21i - 4}{16 + 1}$
$= \dfrac{16 + 21i}{17}$
$= \dfrac{16}{17} + \dfrac{21}{17}i$

4. **a.** $\sqrt{-27} + \sqrt{-48} = i\sqrt{27} + i\sqrt{48}$
$= i\sqrt{9 \cdot 3} + i\sqrt{16 \cdot 3}$
$= 3i\sqrt{3} + 4i\sqrt{3}$
$= 7i\sqrt{3}$

b. $(-2 + \sqrt{-3})^2 = (-2 + i\sqrt{3})^2$
$= (-2)^2 + 2(-2)(i\sqrt{3}) + (i\sqrt{3})^2$
$= 4 - 4i\sqrt{3} + 3i^2$
$= 4 - 4i\sqrt{3} + 3(-1)$
$= 1 - 4i\sqrt{3}$

c. $\dfrac{-14 + \sqrt{-12}}{2} = \dfrac{-14 + i\sqrt{12}}{2}$
$= \dfrac{-14 + 2i\sqrt{3}}{2}$
$= \dfrac{-14}{2} + \dfrac{2i\sqrt{3}}{2}$
$= -7 + i\sqrt{3}$

Exercise Set 1.4

1. $(7 + 2i) + (1 - 4i) = 7 + 2i + 1 - 4i$
$= 7 + 1 + 2i - 4i$
$= 8 - 2i$

3. $(3 + 2i) - (5 - 7i) = 3 - 5 + 2i + 7i$
$= 3 + 2i - 5 + 7i$
$= -2 + 9i$

5. $6 - (-5 + 4i) - (-13 - i) = 6 + 5 - 4i + 13 + i$
$= 24 - 3i$

7. $8i - (14 - 9i) = 8i - 14 + 9i$
$= -14 + 8i + 9i$
$= -14 + 17i$

9. $-3i(7i - 5) = -21i^2 + 15i$
$= -21(-1) + 15i$
$= 21 + 15i$

11. $(-5 + 4i)(3 + i) = -15 - 5i + 12i + 4i^2$
$= -15 + 7i - 4$
$= -19 + 7i$

13. $(7 - 5i)(-2 - 3i) = -14 - 21i + 10i + 15i^2$
$= -14 - 15 - 11i$
$= -29 - 11i$

15. $(3 + 5i)(3 - 5i)$

17. $(-5 + i)(-5 - i) = 25 + 5i - 5i - i^2$
$= 25 + 1$
$= 26$

19. $(2 + 3i)^2 = 4 + 12i + 9i^2$
$= 4 + 12i - 9$
$= -5 + 12i$

21.
$$\frac{2}{3-i} = \frac{2}{3-i} \cdot \frac{3+i}{3+i}$$
$$= \frac{2(3+i)}{9+1}$$
$$= \frac{2(3+i)}{10}$$
$$= \frac{3+i}{5}$$
$$= \frac{3}{5} + \frac{1}{5}i$$

23. $\dfrac{2i}{1+i} = \dfrac{2i}{1+i} \cdot \dfrac{1-i}{1-i} = \dfrac{2i-2i^2}{1+1} = \dfrac{2+2i}{2} = 1+i$

25.
$$\frac{8i}{4-3i} = \frac{8i}{4-3i} \cdot \frac{4+3i}{4+3i}$$
$$= \frac{32i + 24i^2}{16+9}$$
$$= \frac{-24+32i}{25}$$
$$= -\frac{24}{25} + \frac{32}{25}i$$

27.
$$\frac{2+3i}{2+i} = \frac{2+3i}{2+i} \cdot \frac{2-i}{2-i}$$
$$= \frac{4+4i-3i^2}{4+1}$$
$$= \frac{7+4i}{5}$$
$$= \frac{7}{5} + \frac{4}{5}i$$

29. $\sqrt{-64} - \sqrt{-25} = i\sqrt{64} - i\sqrt{25}$
$$= 8i - 5i = 3i$$

31. $5\sqrt{-16} + 3\sqrt{-81} = 5(4i) + 3(9i)$
$$= 20i + 27i = 47i$$

33. $\left(-2 + \sqrt{-4}\right)^2 = \left(-2 + 2i\right)^2$
$$= 4 - 8i + 4i^2$$
$$= 4 - 8i - 4$$
$$= -8i$$

35. $\left(-3 - \sqrt{-7}\right)^2 = \left(-3 - i\sqrt{7}\right)^2$
$$= 9 + 6i\sqrt{7} + i^2(7)$$
$$= 9 - 7 + 6i\sqrt{7}$$
$$= 2 + 6i\sqrt{7}$$

37.
$$\frac{-8 + \sqrt{-32}}{24} = \frac{-8 + i\sqrt{32}}{24}$$
$$= \frac{-8 + i\sqrt{16 \cdot 2}}{24}$$
$$= \frac{-8 + 4i\sqrt{2}}{24}$$
$$= -\frac{1}{3} + \frac{\sqrt{2}}{6}i$$

39.
$$\frac{-6 - \sqrt{-12}}{48} = \frac{-6 - i\sqrt{12}}{48}$$
$$= \frac{-6 - i\sqrt{4 \cdot 3}}{48}$$
$$= \frac{-6 - 2i\sqrt{3}}{48}$$
$$= -\frac{1}{8} - \frac{\sqrt{3}}{24}i$$

41. $\sqrt{-8}\left(\sqrt{-3} - \sqrt{5}\right) = i\sqrt{8}(i\sqrt{3} - \sqrt{5})$
$$= 2i\sqrt{2}\left(i\sqrt{3} - \sqrt{5}\right)$$
$$= -2\sqrt{6} - 2i\sqrt{10}$$

43. $\left(3\sqrt{-5}\right)\left(-4\sqrt{-12}\right) = \left(3i\sqrt{5}\right)\left(-8i\sqrt{3}\right)$
$$= -24i^2\sqrt{15}$$
$$= 24\sqrt{15}$$

45. $(2-3i)(1-i) - (3-i)(3+i)$
$$= \left(2 - 2i - 3i + 3i^2\right) - \left(3^2 - i^2\right)$$
$$= 2 - 5i + 3i^2 - 9 + i^2$$
$$= -7 - 5i + 4i^2$$
$$= -7 - 5i + 4(-1)$$
$$= -11 - 5i$$

47. $(2+i)^2 - (3-i)^2$
$= (4 + 4i + i^2) - (9 - 6i + i^2)$
$= 4 + 4i + i^2 - 9 + 6i - i^2$
$= -5 + 10i$

49. $5\sqrt{-16} + 3\sqrt{-81}$
$= 5\sqrt{16}\sqrt{-1} + 3\sqrt{81}\sqrt{-1}$
$= 5 \cdot 4i + 3 \cdot 9i$
$= 20i + 27i$
$= 47i$ or $0 + 47i$

51. $f(x) = x^2 - 2x + 2$
$f(1+i) = (1+i)^2 - 2(1+i) + 2$
$= 1 + 2i + i^2 - 2 - 2i + 2$
$= 1 + i^2$
$= 1 - 1$
$= 0$

53. $f(x) = \dfrac{x^2 + 19}{2 - x}$
$f(3i) = \dfrac{(3i)^2 + 19}{2 - 3i}$
$= \dfrac{9i^2 + 19}{2 - 3i}$
$= \dfrac{-9 + 19}{2 - 3i}$
$= \dfrac{10}{2 - 3i}$
$= \dfrac{10}{2 - 3i} \cdot \dfrac{2 + 3i}{2 + 3i}$
$= \dfrac{20 + 30i}{4 - 9i^2}$
$= \dfrac{20 + 30i}{4 + 9}$
$= \dfrac{20 + 30i}{13}$
$= \dfrac{20}{13} + \dfrac{30}{13}i$

55. $E = IR = (4 - 5i)(3 + 7i)$
$= 12 + 28i - 15i - 35i^2$
$= 12 + 13i - 35(-1)$
$= 12 + 35 + 13i = 47 + 13i$
The voltage of the circuit is
$(47 + 13i)$ volts.

57. Sum:
$(5 + i\sqrt{15}) + (5 - i\sqrt{15})$
$= 5 + i\sqrt{15} + 5 - i\sqrt{15}$
$= 5 + 5$
$= 10$
Product:
$(5 + i\sqrt{15})(5 - i\sqrt{15})$
$= 25 - 5i\sqrt{15} + 5i\sqrt{15} - 15i^2$
$= 25 + 15$
$= 40$

67. a. False; all irrational numbers are complex numbers.

b. False; $(3 + 7i)(3 - 7i) = 9 + 49 = 58$ is a real number.

c. False; $\dfrac{7 + 3i}{5 + 3i} = \dfrac{7 + 3i}{5 + 3i} \cdot \dfrac{5 - 3i}{5 - 3i}$
$= \dfrac{44 - 6i}{34} = \dfrac{22}{17} - \dfrac{3}{17}i$

d. True;
$(x + yi)(x - yi) = x^2 - (yi)^2 = x^2 + y^2$

(d) is true.

69. $\dfrac{1+i}{1+2i} + \dfrac{1-i}{1-2i}$
$= \dfrac{(1+i)(1-2i)}{(1+2i)(1-2i)} + \dfrac{(1-i)(1+2i)}{(1+2i)(1-2i)}$
$= \dfrac{(1+i)(1-2i) + (1-i)(1+2i)}{(1+2i)(1-2i)}$
$= \dfrac{1 - 2i + i - 2i^2 + 1 + 2i - i - 2i^2}{1 - 4i^2}$
$= \dfrac{1 - 2i + i + 2 + 1 + 2i - i + 2}{1 + 4}$
$= \dfrac{6}{5}$
$= \dfrac{6}{5} + 0i$

Section 1.5

Check Point Exercises

1. **a.** $3x^2 - 9x = 0$
   $3x(x-3) = 0$
   $3x = 0$ or $x - 3 = 0$
   $x = 0$ $x = 3$
   The solution set is $\{0, 3\}$.

   b. $2x^2 + x = 1$
   $2x^2 + x - 1 = 0$
   $(2x-1)(x+1) = 0$
   $2x - 1 = 0$ or $x + 1 = 0$
   $2x = 1$ $x = -1$
   $x = \dfrac{1}{2}$
   The solution set is $\left\{-1, \dfrac{1}{2}\right\}$.

2. **a.** $3x^2 = 21$
   $\dfrac{3x^2}{3} = \dfrac{21}{3}$
   $x^2 = 7$
   $x = \pm\sqrt{7}$
   The solution set is $\left\{-\sqrt{7}, \sqrt{7}\right\}$.

   b. $5x^2 + 45 = 0$
   $5x^2 = -45$
   $x^2 = -9$
   $x = \pm\sqrt{-9}$
   $x = \pm 3i$

   c. $(x+5)^2 = 11$
   $x + 5 = \pm\sqrt{11}$
   $x = -5 \pm \sqrt{11}$
   The solution set is $\left\{-5+\sqrt{11}, -5-\sqrt{11}\right\}$.

3. **a.**   The coefficient of the x-term is 6. Half of
   6 is 3, and 3^2 is 9.
   9 should be added to the binomial.
   $x^2 + 6x + 9 = (x+3)^2$

b.   The coefficient of the x-term is -5. Half of
   -5 is $-\dfrac{5}{2}$, and $\left(-\dfrac{5}{2}\right)^2$ is $\dfrac{25}{4}$.
   $\dfrac{25}{4}$ should be added to the binomial.
   $x^2 - 5x + \dfrac{25}{4} = \left(x-\dfrac{5}{2}\right)^2$

c.   The coefficient of the x-term is $\dfrac{2}{3}$. Half of
   $\dfrac{2}{3}$ is $\dfrac{1}{3}$, and $\left(\dfrac{1}{3}\right)^2$ is $\dfrac{1}{9}$.
   $\dfrac{1}{9}$ should be added to the binomial.
   $x^2 + \dfrac{2}{3}x + \dfrac{1}{9} = \left(x+\dfrac{1}{3}\right)^2$

4. $x^2 + 4x - 1 = 0$
   $x^2 + 4x \quad = 1$
   $x^2 + 4x + 4 = 1 + 4$
   $(x+2)^2 = 5$
   $x + 2 = \pm\sqrt{5}$
   $x = -2 \pm \sqrt{5}$

5. $2x^2 + 3x - 4 = 0$
   $x^2 + \dfrac{3}{2}x - 2 = 0$
   $x^2 + \dfrac{3}{2}x \quad = 2$
   $x^2 + \dfrac{3}{2}x + \dfrac{9}{16} = 2 + \dfrac{9}{16}$
   $\left(x+\dfrac{3}{4}\right)^2 = \dfrac{41}{16}$
   $x + \dfrac{3}{4} = \pm\sqrt{\dfrac{41}{16}}$
   $x + \dfrac{3}{4} = \pm\dfrac{\sqrt{41}}{4}$
   $x = -\dfrac{3}{4} \pm \dfrac{\sqrt{41}}{4}$
   $x = \dfrac{-3 \pm \sqrt{41}}{4}$

6. $2x^2 + 2x - 1 = 0$

$a = 2, b = 2, c = -1$

$x = \dfrac{-b \pm \sqrt{b^2 - 4ac}}{2a}$

$\quad = \dfrac{-2 \pm \sqrt{2^2 - 4(2)(-1)}}{2(2)}$

$\quad = \dfrac{-2 \pm \sqrt{4 + 8}}{4}$

$\quad = \dfrac{-2 \pm \sqrt{12}}{4}$

$\quad = \dfrac{-2 \pm 2\sqrt{3}}{4}$

$\quad = \dfrac{2(-1 \pm \sqrt{3})}{4}$

$\quad = \dfrac{-1 \pm \sqrt{3}}{2}$

The solution set is $\left\{ \dfrac{-1+\sqrt{3}}{2}, \dfrac{-1-\sqrt{3}}{2} \right\}$.

7. $x^2 - 2x + 2 = 0$

$a = 1, b = -2, c = 2$

$x = \dfrac{-b \pm \sqrt{b^2 - 4ac}}{2a}$

$x = \dfrac{-(-2) \pm \sqrt{(-2)^2 - 4(1)(2)}}{2(1)}$

$x = \dfrac{2 \pm \sqrt{4 - 8}}{2}$

$x = \dfrac{2 \pm \sqrt{-4}}{2}$

$x = \dfrac{2 \pm 2i}{2}$

$x = 1 \pm i$

The solution set is $\{1 + i, 1 - i\}$.

8. a. $a = 1, \quad b = 6, \quad c = 9$

$b^2 - 4ac = (6)^2 - 4(1)(9)$

$\qquad\quad = 36 - 36$

$\qquad\quad = 0$

Since $b^2 - 4ac = 0$, the equation has one real solution.

b. $a = 2, \quad b = -7, \quad c = -4$

$b^2 - 4ac = (-7)^2 - 4(2)(-4)$

$\qquad\quad = 49 + 32$

$\qquad\quad = 81$

Since $b^2 - 4ac > 0$, the equation has two real solutions. Since 81 is a perfect square, the two solutions are rational.

c. $a = 3, \quad b = -2, \quad c = 4$

$b^2 - 4ac = (-2)^2 - 4(3)(4)$

$\qquad\quad = 4 - 48$

$\qquad\quad = -44$

Since $b^2 - 4ac < 0$, the equation has two imaginary solutions that are complex conjugates.

9. $P = 0.01A^2 + 0.05A + 107$

$115 = 0.01A^2 + 0.05A + 107$

$\quad 0 = 0.01A^2 + 0.05A - 8$

$a = 0.01, \quad b = 0.05, \quad c = -8$

$A = \dfrac{-b \pm \sqrt{b^2 - 4ac}}{2a}$

$A = \dfrac{-(0.05) \pm \sqrt{(0.05)^2 - 4(0.01)(-8)}}{2(0.01)}$

$A = \dfrac{-0.05 \pm \sqrt{0.3225}}{0.02}$

$A \approx \dfrac{-0.05 + \sqrt{0.3225}}{0.02} \qquad A \approx \dfrac{-0.05 - \sqrt{0.3225}}{0.02}$

$A \approx 26 \qquad\qquad\qquad A \approx -31$

Age cannot be negative, reject the negative answer.

Thus, a woman whose normal systolic blood pressure is 115 mm Hg is 26 years old.

10. $w^2 + 9^2 = 15^2$

$w^2 + 81 = 225$

$\quad w^2 = 144$

$\quad w = \pm\sqrt{144}$

$\quad w = \pm 12$

The width of the television is 12 inches.

Exercise Set 1.5

1. $x^2 - 3x - 10 = 0$
$(x+2)(x-5) = 0$
$x+2=0$ or $x-5=0$
$x=-2$ or $x=5$
The solution set is $\{-2, 5\}$.

3. $x^2 = 8x - 15$
$x^2 - 8x + 15 = 0$
$(x-3)(x-5) = 0$
$x-3=0$ or $x-5=0$
$x=3$ or $x=5$
The solution set is $\{3, 5\}$.

5. $6x^2 + 11x - 10 = 0$
$(2x+5)(3x-2) = 0$
$2x+5=0$ or $3x-2=0$
$2x=-5$ $3x=2$
$x=-\dfrac{5}{2}$ or $x=\dfrac{2}{3}$
The solution set is $\left\{-\dfrac{5}{2}, \dfrac{2}{3}\right\}$.

7. $3x^2 - 2x = 8$
$3x^2 - 2x - 8 = 0$
$(3x+4)(x-2) = 0$
$3x+4=0$ or $x-2=0$
$3x=-4$
$x=-\dfrac{4}{3}$ or $x=2$
The solution set is $\left\{-\dfrac{4}{3}, 2\right\}$.

9. $3x^2 + 12x = 0$
$3x(x+4) = 0$
$3x=0$ or $x+4=0$
$x=0$ or $x=-4$
The solution set is $\{-4, 0\}$.

11. $2x(x-3) = 5x^2 - 7x$
$2x^2 - 6x - 5x^2 + 7x = 0$
$-3x^2 + x = 0$
$x(-3x+1) = 0$
$x=0$ or $-3x+1=0$
$-3x=-1$
$x=\dfrac{1}{3}$
The solution set is $\left\{0, \dfrac{1}{3}\right\}$.

13. $7 - 7x = (3x+2)(x-1)$
$7 - 7x = 3x^2 - x - 2$
$7 - 7x - 3x^2 + x + 2 = 0$
$-3x^2 - 6x + 9 = 0$
$-3(x+3)(x-1) = 0$
$x+3=0$ or $x-1=0$
$x=-3$ or $x=1$
The solution set is $\{-3, 1\}$.

15. $3x^2 = 27$
$x^2 = 9$
$x = \pm\sqrt{9} = \pm 3$
The solution set is $\{-3, 3\}$.

17. $5x^2 + 1 = 51$
$5x^2 = 50$
$x^2 = 10$
$x = \pm\sqrt{10}$
The solution set is $\left\{-\sqrt{10}, \sqrt{10}\right\}$.

19. $2x^2 - 5 = -55$
$2x^2 = -50$
$x^2 = -25$
$x = \pm\sqrt{-25} = \pm 5i$
The solution set is $\{5i, -5i\}$.

21. $(x+2)^2 = 25$
$x+2 = \pm\sqrt{25}$
$x+2 = \pm 5$
$x = -2 \pm 5$
$x=-2+5$ or $x=-2-5$
$x=3$ $x=-7$
The solution set is $\{-7, 3\}$.

23. $3(x-4)^2 = 15$

$(x-4)^2 = 5$

$x-4 = \pm\sqrt{5}$

$x = 4 \pm \sqrt{5}$

The solution set is $\left\{4+\sqrt{5}, 4-\sqrt{5}\right\}$.

25. $(x+3)^2 = -16$

$x+3 = \pm\sqrt{-16}$

$x+3 = \pm 4i$

$x = -3 \pm 4i$

The solution set is $\left\{-3+4i, -3-4i\right\}$.

27. $(x-3)^2 = -5$

$x-3 = \pm\sqrt{-5}$

$x-3 = \pm i\sqrt{5}$

$x = 3 \pm i\sqrt{5}$

The solution set is $\left\{3+i\sqrt{5}, 3-i\sqrt{5}\right\}$.

29. $(3x+2)^2 = 9$

$3x+2 = \pm\sqrt{9} = \pm 3$

$3x+2 = -3 \quad \text{or} \quad 3x+2 = 3$

$3x = -5 \qquad\qquad 3x = 1$

$x = -\dfrac{5}{3} \quad \text{or} \quad x = \dfrac{1}{3}$

The solution set is $\left\{-\dfrac{5}{3}, \dfrac{1}{3}\right\}$.

31. $(5x-1)^2 = 7$

$5x-1 = \pm\sqrt{7}$

$5x = 1 \pm \sqrt{7}$

$x = \dfrac{1 \pm \sqrt{7}}{5}$

The solution set is $\left\{\dfrac{1-\sqrt{7}}{5}, \dfrac{1+\sqrt{7}}{5}\right\}$.

33. $(3x-4)^2 = 8$

$3x-4 = \pm\sqrt{8} = \pm 2\sqrt{2}$

$3x = 4 \pm 2\sqrt{2}$

$x = \dfrac{4 \pm 2\sqrt{2}}{3}$

The solution set is $\left\{\dfrac{4-2\sqrt{2}}{3}, \dfrac{4+2\sqrt{2}}{3}\right\}$.

35. $x^2 + 12x$

$\left(\dfrac{12}{2}\right)^2 = 6^2 = 36$

$x^2 + 12x + 36 = (x+6)^2$

37. $x^2 - 10x$

$\left(\dfrac{10}{2}\right)^2 = 5^2 = 25$

$x^2 - 10x + 25 = (x-5)^2$

39. $x^2 + 3x$

$\left(\dfrac{3}{2}\right)^2 = \dfrac{9}{4}$

$x^2 + 3x + \dfrac{9}{4} = \left(x + \dfrac{3}{2}\right)^2$

41. $x^2 - 7x$

$\left(\dfrac{7}{2}\right)^2 = \dfrac{49}{4}$

$x^2 - 7x + \dfrac{49}{4} = \left(x - \dfrac{7}{2}\right)^2$

43. $x^2 - \dfrac{2}{3}x$

$\left(\dfrac{\frac{2}{3}}{2}\right)^2 = \left(\dfrac{1}{3}\right)^2 = \dfrac{1}{9}$

$x^2 - \dfrac{2}{3}x + \dfrac{1}{9} = \left(x - \dfrac{1}{3}\right)^2$

45. $x^2 - \dfrac{1}{3}x$

$\left(\dfrac{\frac{1}{3}}{2}\right)^2 = \left(\dfrac{1}{6}\right)^2 = \dfrac{1}{36}$

$x^2 - \dfrac{1}{3}x + \dfrac{1}{36} = \left(x - \dfrac{1}{6}\right)^2$

47.
$$x^2 + 6x = 7$$
$$x^2 + 6x + 9 = 7 + 9$$
$$(x+3)^2 = 16$$
$$x + 3 = \pm 4$$
$$x = -3 \pm 4$$
The solution set is $\{-7, 1\}$.

49.
$$x^2 - 2x = 2$$
$$x^2 - 2x + 1 = 2 + 1$$
$$(x-1)^2 = 3$$
$$x - 1 = \pm\sqrt{3}$$
$$x = 1 \pm \sqrt{3}$$
The solution set is $\left\{1 + \sqrt{3}, 1 - \sqrt{3}\right\}$.

51.
$$x^2 - 6x - 11 = 0$$
$$x^2 - 6x = 11$$
$$x^2 - 6x + 9 = 11 + 9$$
$$(x-3)^2 = 20$$
$$x - 3 = \pm\sqrt{20}$$
$$x = 3 \pm 2\sqrt{5}$$
The solution set is $\left\{3 + 2\sqrt{5}, 3 - 2\sqrt{5}\right\}$.

53.
$$x^2 + 4x + 1 = 0$$
$$x^2 + 4x = -1$$
$$x^2 + 4x + 4 = -1 + 4$$
$$(x+2)^2 = 3$$
$$x + 2 = \pm\sqrt{3}$$
$$x = -2 \pm \sqrt{3}$$
The solution set is $\left\{-2 + \sqrt{3}, -2 - \sqrt{3}\right\}$.

55.
$$x^2 - 5x + 6 = 0$$
$$x^2 - 5x = -6$$
$$x^2 - 5x + \frac{25}{4} = -6 + \frac{25}{4}$$
$$\left(x - \frac{5}{2}\right)^2 = \frac{1}{4}$$
$$x - \frac{5}{2} = \pm\sqrt{\frac{1}{4}}$$
$$x - \frac{5}{2} = \pm\frac{1}{2}$$
$$x = \frac{5}{2} \pm \frac{1}{2}$$
$$x = \frac{5}{2} + \frac{1}{2} \quad \text{or} \quad x = \frac{5}{2} - \frac{1}{2}$$
$$x = 3 \qquad\qquad x = 2$$
The solution set is $\{2, 3\}$.

57.
$$x^2 + 3x - 1 = 0$$
$$x^2 + 3x = 1$$
$$x^2 + 3x + \frac{9}{4} = 1 + \frac{9}{4}$$
$$\left(x + \frac{3}{2}\right)^2 = \frac{13}{4}$$
$$x + \frac{3}{2} = \pm\frac{\sqrt{13}}{2}$$
$$x = \frac{-3 \pm \sqrt{13}}{2}$$
The solution set is $\left\{\dfrac{-3 + \sqrt{13}}{2}, \dfrac{-3 - \sqrt{13}}{2}\right\}$.

59. $2x^2 - 7x + 3 = 0$

$$x^2 - \frac{7}{2}x + \frac{3}{2} = 0$$

$$x^2 - \frac{7}{2}x = \frac{-3}{2}$$

$$x^2 - \frac{7}{2}x + \frac{49}{16} = -\frac{3}{2} + \frac{49}{16}$$

$$\left(x - \frac{7}{4}\right)^2 = \frac{25}{16}$$

$$x - \frac{7}{4} = \pm\frac{5}{4}$$

$$x = \frac{7}{4} \pm \frac{5}{4}$$

The solution set is $\left\{\frac{1}{2}, 3\right\}$.

61. $4x^2 - 4x - 1 = 0$

$$4x^2 - 4x - 1 = 0$$

$$x^2 - x - \frac{1}{4} = 0$$

$$x^2 - x = \frac{1}{4}$$

$$x^2 - x + \frac{1}{4} = \frac{1}{4} + \frac{1}{4}$$

$$\left(x - \frac{1}{2}\right)^2 = \frac{2}{4}$$

$$x - \frac{1}{2} = \frac{\pm\sqrt{2}}{2}$$

$$x = \frac{1 \pm \sqrt{2}}{2}$$

The solution set is $\left\{\frac{1+\sqrt{2}}{2}, \frac{1-\sqrt{2}}{2}\right\}$.

63. $3x^2 - 2x - 2 = 0$

$$x^2 - \frac{2}{3}x - \frac{2}{3} = 0$$

$$x^2 - \frac{2}{3}x = \frac{2}{3}$$

$$x^2 - \frac{2}{3}x + \frac{1}{9} = \frac{2}{3} + \frac{1}{9}$$

$$\left(x - \frac{1}{3}\right)^2 = \frac{7}{9}$$

$$x - \frac{1}{3} = \frac{\pm\sqrt{7}}{3}$$

$$x = \frac{1 \pm \sqrt{7}}{3}$$

The solution set is $\left\{\frac{1+\sqrt{7}}{3}, \frac{1-\sqrt{7}}{3}\right\}$.

65. $x^2 + 8x + 15 = 0$

$$x = \frac{-8 \pm \sqrt{8^2 - 4(1)(15)}}{2(1)}$$

$$x = \frac{-8 \pm \sqrt{64 - 60}}{2}$$

$$x = \frac{-8 \pm \sqrt{4}}{2}$$

$$x = \frac{-8 \pm 2}{2}$$

The solution set is $\{-5, -3\}$.

67. $x^2 + 5x + 3 = 0$

$$x = \frac{-5 \pm \sqrt{5^2 - 4(1)(3)}}{2(1)}$$

$$x = \frac{-5 \pm \sqrt{25 - 12}}{2}$$

$$x = \frac{-5 \pm \sqrt{13}}{2}$$

The solution set is $\left\{\frac{-5+\sqrt{13}}{2}, \frac{-5-\sqrt{13}}{2}\right\}$.

69. $3x^2 - 3x - 4 = 0$

$$x = \frac{3 \pm \sqrt{(-3)^2 - 4(3)(-4)}}{2(3)}$$

$$x = \frac{3 \pm \sqrt{9 + 48}}{6}$$

$$x = \frac{3 \pm \sqrt{57}}{6}$$

The solution set is $\left\{ \frac{3 + \sqrt{57}}{6}, \frac{3 - \sqrt{57}}{6} \right\}$

71. $4x^2 = 2x + 7$

$4x^2 - 2x - 7 = 0$

$$x = \frac{2 \pm \sqrt{(-2)^2 - 4(4)(-7)}}{2(4)}$$

$$x = \frac{2 \pm \sqrt{4 + 112}}{8}$$

$$x = \frac{2 \pm \sqrt{116}}{8}$$

$$x = \frac{2 \pm 2\sqrt{29}}{8}$$

$$x = \frac{1 \pm \sqrt{29}}{4}$$

The solution set is $\left\{ \frac{1 + \sqrt{29}}{4}, \frac{1 - \sqrt{29}}{4} \right\}$.

73. $x^2 - 6x + 10 = 0$

$$x = \frac{6 \pm \sqrt{(-6)^2 - 4(1)(10)}}{2(1)}$$

$$x = \frac{6 \pm \sqrt{36 - 40}}{2}$$

$$x = \frac{6 \pm \sqrt{-4}}{2}$$

$$x = \frac{6 \pm 2i}{2}$$

$$x = 3 \pm i$$

The solution set is $\{3 + i, 3 - i\}$.

75. $x^2 - 4x - 5 = 0$

$(-4)^2 - 4(1)(-5)$

$= 16 + 20$

$= 36$; 2 unequal real solutions

77. $2x^2 - 11x + 3 = 0$

$(-11)^2 - 4(2)(3)$

$= 121 - 24$

$= 97$; 2 unequal real solutions

79. $x^2 - 2x + 1 = 0$

$(-2)^2 - 4(1)(1)$

$= 4 - 4$

$= 0$; 1 real solution

81. $x^2 - 3x - 7 = 0$

$(-3)^2 - 4(1)(-7)$

$= 9 + 28$

$= 37$; 2 unequal real solutions

83.

$$2x^2 - x = 1$$

$$2x^2 - x - 1 = 0$$

$$(2x + 1)(x - 1) = 0$$

$$2x + 1 = 0 \text{ or } x - 1 = 0$$

$$2x = -1$$

$$x = -\frac{1}{2} \text{ or } x = 1$$

The solution set is $\left\{ -\frac{1}{2}, 1 \right\}$.

85. $5x^2 + 2 = 11x$

$$5x^2 - 11x + 2 = 0$$

$$(5x - 1)(x - 2) = 0$$

$$5x - 1 = 0 \text{ or } x - 2 = 0$$

$$5x = 1$$

$$x = \frac{1}{5} \text{ or } x = 2$$

The solution set is $\left\{ \frac{1}{5}, 2 \right\}$.

87. $3x^2 = 60$

$x^2 = 20$

$x = \pm\sqrt{20}$

$x = \pm 2\sqrt{5}$

The solution set is $\left\{ -2\sqrt{5}, 2\sqrt{5} \right\}$.

89. $x^2 - 2x = 1$

$x^2 - 2x + 1 = 1 + 1$

$(x-1)^2 = 2$

$x - 1 = \pm\sqrt{2}$

$x = 1 \pm \sqrt{2}$

The solution set is $\left\{1 + \sqrt{2}, 1 - \sqrt{2}\right\}$.

91. $(2x+3)(x+4) = 1$

$2x^2 + 8x + 3x + 12 = 1$

$2x^2 + 11x + 11 = 0$

$x = \dfrac{-11 \pm \sqrt{11^2 - 4(2)(11)}}{2(2)}$

$x = \dfrac{-11 \pm \sqrt{121 - 88}}{4}$

$x = \dfrac{-11 \pm \sqrt{33}}{4}$

The solution set is $\left\{\dfrac{-11 + \sqrt{33}}{4}, \dfrac{-11 - \sqrt{33}}{4}\right\}$.

93. $(3x-4)^2 = 16$

$3x - 4 = \pm\sqrt{16}$

$3x - 4 = \pm 4$

$3x = 4 \pm 4$

$3x = 8$ or $3x = 0$

$x = \dfrac{8}{3}$ or $x = 0$

The solution set is $\left\{0, \dfrac{8}{3}\right\}$.

95. $3x^2 - 12x + 12 = 0$

$x^2 - 4x + 4 = 0$

$(x-2)(x-2) = 0$

$x - 2 = 0$

$x = 2$

The solution set is $\{2\}$.

97. $4x^2 - 16 = 0$

$4x^2 = 16$

$x^2 = 4$

$x = \pm 2$

The solution set is $\{-2, 2\}$.

99. $x^2 - 6x + 13 = 0$

$x^2 - 6x = -13$

$x^2 - 6x + 9 = -13 + 9$

$(x-3)^2 = -4$

$x - 3 = \pm 2i$

$x = 3 \pm 2i$

The solution set is $\{3 + 2i, 3 - 2i\}$.

101. $x^2 = 4x - 7$

$x^2 - 4x = -7$

$x^2 - 4x + 4 = -7 + 4$

$(x-2)^2 = -3$

$x - 2 = \pm i\sqrt{3}$

$x = 2 \pm i\sqrt{3}$

The solution set is $\left\{2 + i\sqrt{3}, 2 - i\sqrt{3}\right\}$.

103. $2x^2 - 7x = 0$

$x(2x - 7) = 0$

$x = 0$ or $2x - 7 = 0$

$2x = 7$

$x = 0$ or $x = \dfrac{7}{2}$

The solution set is $\left\{0, \dfrac{7}{2}\right\}$.

105. $\dfrac{1}{x} + \dfrac{1}{x+2} = \dfrac{1}{3}; x \neq 0, -2$

$$3x + 6 + 3x = x^2 + 2x$$

$$0 = x^2 - 4x - 6$$

$$x = \dfrac{-(-4) \pm \sqrt{(-4)^2 - 4(1)(-6)}}{2(1)}$$

$$x = \dfrac{4 \pm \sqrt{16 + 24}}{2}$$

$$x = \dfrac{4 \pm \sqrt{40}}{2}$$

$$x = \dfrac{4 \pm 2\sqrt{10}}{2}$$

$$x = 2 \pm \sqrt{10}$$

The solution set is $\{2 + \sqrt{10},\ 2 - \sqrt{10}\}$.

107. $\dfrac{2x}{x-3} + \dfrac{6}{x+3} = \dfrac{-28}{x^2 - 9}; x \neq 3, -3$

$$2x(x+3) + 6(x-3) = -28$$

$$2x^2 + 6x + 6x - 18 = -28$$

$$2x^2 + 12x + 10 = 0$$

$$x^2 + 6x + 5 = 0$$

$$(x+1)(x+5) = 0$$

The solution set is $\{-5,\ -1\}$.

109. $x^2 - 4x - 5 = 0$

$$(x+1)(x-5) = 0$$

$x+1 = 0 \qquad x-5 = 0$
$\qquad\qquad$ or
$\quad x = -1 \qquad\qquad x = 5$

This equation matches graph (d).

111. $0 = -(x+1)^2 + 4$

$$(x+1)^2 = 4$$

$$x+1 = \pm 2$$

$$x = -1 \pm 2$$

$$x = -3, \quad x = 1$$

This equation matches graph (f).

113. $x^2 - 2x + 2 = 0$

$a = 1, \quad b = -2, \quad c = 2$

$$x = \dfrac{-b \pm \sqrt{b^2 - 4ac}}{2a}$$

$$x = \dfrac{-(-2) \pm \sqrt{(-2)^2 - 4(1)(2)}}{2(1)}$$

$$x = \dfrac{2 \pm \sqrt{-4}}{2}$$

$$x = \dfrac{2 \pm 2i}{2}$$

$$x = 1 \pm i$$

This equation has no real roots. Thus, its equation has no x-intercepts. This equation matches graph (b).

115. $y = 2x^2 - 3x$

$$2 = 2x^2 - 3x$$

$$0 = 2x^2 - 3x - 2$$

$$0 = (2x+1)(x-2)$$

$$x = -\dfrac{1}{2}, \quad x = 2$$

117. $y_1 y_2 = 14$

$$(x-1)(x+4) = 14$$

$$x^2 + 3x - 4 = 14$$

$$x^2 + 3x - 18 = 0$$

$$(x+6)(x-3) = 0$$

$$x = -6, \quad x = 3$$

74

119.
$$y_1 + y_2 = 1$$

$$\frac{2x}{x+2} + \frac{3}{x+4} = 1$$

$$(x+2)(x+4)\left(\frac{2x}{x+2} + \frac{3}{x+4}\right) = 1(x+2)(x+4)$$

$$\frac{2x(x+2)(x+4)}{x+2} + \frac{3(x+2)(x+4)}{x+4} = (x+2)(x+4)$$

$$2x(x+4) + 3(x+2) = (x+2)(x+4)$$

$$2x^2 + 8x + 3x + 6 = x^2 + 6x + 8$$

$$x^2 + 5x - 2 = 0$$

$$x = \frac{-b \pm \sqrt{b^2 - 4ac}}{2a}$$

$$x = \frac{-(5) \pm \sqrt{(5)^2 - 4(1)(-2)}}{2(1)}$$

$$x = \frac{-5 \pm \sqrt{33}}{2}$$

The solution set is $\left\{\dfrac{-5+\sqrt{33}}{2}, \dfrac{-5-\sqrt{33}}{2}\right\}$.

121.
$$y_1 - y_2 = 0$$

$$(2x^2 + 5x - 4) - (-x^2 + 15x - 10) = 0$$

$$2x^2 + 5x - 4 + x^2 - 15x + 10 = 0$$

$$3x^2 - 10x + 6 = 0$$

$$x = \frac{-b \pm \sqrt{b^2 - 4ac}}{2a}$$

$$x = \frac{-(-10) \pm \sqrt{(-10)^2 - 4(3)(6)}}{2(3)}$$

$$x = \frac{10 \pm \sqrt{28}}{6}$$

$$x = \frac{10 \pm 2\sqrt{7}}{6}$$

$$x = \frac{5 \pm \sqrt{7}}{3}$$

The solution set is $\left\{\dfrac{5+\sqrt{7}}{3}, \dfrac{5-\sqrt{7}}{3}\right\}$.

123. Values that make the denominator zero must be excluded.

$$2x^2 + 4x - 9 = 0$$

$$x = \frac{-b \pm \sqrt{b^2 - 4ac}}{2a}$$

$$x = \frac{-(4) \pm \sqrt{(4)^2 - 4(2)(-9)}}{2(2)}$$

$$x = \frac{-4 \pm \sqrt{88}}{4}$$

$$x = \frac{-4 \pm 2\sqrt{22}}{4}$$

$$x = \frac{-2 \pm \sqrt{22}}{2}$$

125. $x^2 - (6 + 2x) = 0$

$x^2 - 2x - 6 = 0$

Apply the quadratic formula.

$a = 1 \quad b = -2 \quad c = -6$

$x = \dfrac{-(-2) \pm \sqrt{(-2)^2 - 4(1)(-6)}}{2(1)}$

$= \dfrac{2 \pm \sqrt{4 - (-24)}}{2}$

$= \dfrac{2 \pm \sqrt{28}}{2}$

$= \dfrac{2 \pm \sqrt{4 \cdot 7}}{2} = \dfrac{2 \pm 2\sqrt{7}}{2} = 1 \pm \sqrt{7}$

We disregard $1 - \sqrt{7}$ because it is negative, and we are looking for a positive number.

Thus, the number is $1 + \sqrt{7}$.

127.

$\dfrac{1}{x^2 - 3x + 2} = \dfrac{1}{x + 2} + \dfrac{5}{x^2 - 4}$

$\dfrac{1}{(x - 1)(x - 2)} = \dfrac{1}{x + 2} + \dfrac{5}{(x + 2)(x - 2)}$

Multiply both sides of the equation by the least common denominator, $(x - 1)(x - 2)(x + 2)$. This results in the following:

$x + 2 = (x - 1)(x - 2) + 5(x - 1)$

$x + 2 = x^2 - 2x - x + 2 + 5x - 5$

$x + 2 = x^2 + 2x - 3$

$0 = x^2 + x - 5$

Apply the quadratic formula:

$a = 1 \quad b = 1 \quad c = -5$.

$x = \dfrac{-1 \pm \sqrt{1^2 - 4(1)(-5)}}{2(1)} = \dfrac{-1 \pm \sqrt{1 - (-20)}}{2}$

$= \dfrac{-1 \pm \sqrt{21}}{2}$

The solutions are $\dfrac{-1 \pm \sqrt{21}}{2}$, and the solution set is

$\left\{ \dfrac{-1 \pm \sqrt{21}}{2} \right\}$.

129. $\sqrt{2}x^2 + 3x - 2\sqrt{2} = 0$

Apply the quadratic formula:

$a = \sqrt{2} \quad b = 3 \quad c = -2\sqrt{2}$

$x = \dfrac{-3 \pm \sqrt{3^2 - 4(\sqrt{2})(-2\sqrt{2})}}{2(\sqrt{2})}$

$= \dfrac{-3 \pm \sqrt{9 - (-16)}}{2\sqrt{2}}$

$= \dfrac{-3 \pm \sqrt{25}}{2\sqrt{2}} = \dfrac{-3 \pm 5}{2\sqrt{2}}$

Evaluate the expression to obtain two solutions.

$x = \dfrac{-3 - 5}{2\sqrt{2}} \qquad \text{or} \qquad x = \dfrac{-3 + 5}{2\sqrt{2}}$

$= \dfrac{-8}{2\sqrt{2}} \cdot \dfrac{\sqrt{2}}{\sqrt{2}} \qquad\qquad = \dfrac{2}{2\sqrt{2}} \cdot \dfrac{\sqrt{2}}{\sqrt{2}}$

$= \dfrac{-8\sqrt{2}}{4} \qquad\qquad\qquad = \dfrac{2\sqrt{2}}{4}$

$= -2\sqrt{2} \qquad\qquad\qquad = \dfrac{\sqrt{2}}{2}$

The solutions are $-2\sqrt{2}$ and $\dfrac{\sqrt{2}}{2}$, and the solution

set is $\left\{ -2\sqrt{2}, \dfrac{\sqrt{2}}{2} \right\}$.

131. $f(x) = 0.013x^2 - 1.19x + 28.24$

$3 = 0.013x^2 - 1.19x + 28.24$

$0 = 0.013x^2 - 1.19x + 25.24$

Apply the quadratic formula:

$a = 0.013 \quad b = -1.19 \quad c = 25.24$

$x = \dfrac{-(-1.19) \pm \sqrt{(-1.19)^2 - 4(0.013)(25.24)}}{2(0.013)}$

$= \dfrac{1.19 \pm \sqrt{1.4161 - 1.31248}}{0.026}$

$= \dfrac{1.19 \pm \sqrt{0.10362}}{0.026}$

$\approx \dfrac{1.19 \pm 0.32190}{0.026}$

$\approx 58.15 \text{ or } 33.39$

The solutions are approximately 33.39 and 58.15. Thus, 33 year olds and 58 year olds are expected to be in 3 fatal crashes per 100 million miles driven. The function models the actual data well.

133. Let $y_1 = -0.01x^2 + 0.7x + 6.1$

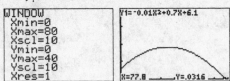

Using the TRACE feature, we find that the height of the shot put is approximately 0 feet when the distance is 77.8 feet. Graph (b) shows the shot' path.

135. Ignoring the thickness of the panel, we essentially need to find the diameter of the rectangular opening.

$$a^2 + b^2 = c^2$$
$$4^2 + 8^2 = c^2$$
$$16 + 64 = c^2$$
$$80 = c^2$$
$$c = \pm\sqrt{80} = \pm 4\sqrt{5}$$

Since we are looking for a length, we discard the negative solution. The solution is $4\sqrt{5} \approx 8.9$ and we conclude that a panel that is about 8.9 feet long is the longest that can be taken through the door diagonally.

137. $15^2 + x^2 = 20^2$
$$225 + x^2 = 400$$
$$x^2 = 175$$
$$x \approx \pm 13.23$$
13.23
The ladder reaches 13.23 feet up.

139. Let w = the width
Let $w + 3$ = the length

Area = lw
$$54 = (w + 3)w$$
$$54 = w^2 + 3w$$
$$0 = w^2 + 3w - 54$$
$$0 = (w + 9)(w - 6)$$
Apply the zero product principle.
$$w + 9 = 0 \qquad w - 6 = 0$$
$$w = -9 \qquad w = 6$$
The solution set is $\{-9, 6\}$. Disregard –9 because we can't have a negative length measurement. The width is 6 feet and the length is $6 + 3 = 9$ feet.

141. Let x = the length of the side of the original square
Let $x + 3$ = the length of the side of the new, larger square
$$(x + 3)^2 = 64$$
$$x^2 + 6x + 9 = 64$$
$$x^2 + 6x - 55 = 0$$
$$(x + 11)(x - 5) = 0$$
Apply the zero product principle.
$$x + 11 = 0 \qquad x - 5 = 0$$
$$x = -11 \qquad x = 5$$
The solution set is $\{-11, 5\}$. Disregard –11 because we can't have a negative length measurement. This means that x, the length of the side of the original square, is 5 inches.

143. Let x = the width of the path
$$(20 + 2x)(10 + 2x) = 600$$
$$200 + 40x + 20x + 4x^2 = 600$$
$$200 + 60x + 4x^2 = 600$$
$$4x^2 + 60x + 200 = 600$$
$$4x^2 + 60x - 400 = 0$$
$$4(x^2 + 15x - 100) = 0$$
$$4(x + 20)(x - 5) = 0$$
Apply the zero product principle.
$$4(x + 20) = 0 \qquad x - 5 = 0$$
$$x + 20 = 0 \qquad x = 5$$
$$x = -20$$
The solution set is $\{-20, 5\}$. Disregard –20 because we can't have a negative width measurement. The width of the path is 5 meters.

145. $x(x)(2) = 200$
$$2x^2 = 200$$
$$x^2 = 100$$
$$x = \pm 10$$
The length and width are 10 inches.

147. $x(20-2x)=13$

$20x-2x^2=13$

$0=2x^2-20x+13$

$x=\dfrac{-(-20)\pm\sqrt{(-20)^2-4(2)(13)}}{2(2)}$

$x=\dfrac{20\pm\sqrt{296}}{4}$

$x=\dfrac{10\pm17.2}{4}$

$x=9.3,0.7$

9.3 in and 0.7 in

161. $(x+3)(x-5)=0$

$x^2-5x+3x-15=0$

$x^2-2x-15=0$

163. The dimensions of the pool are 12 meters by 8 meters. With the tile, the dimensions will be $12+2x$ meters by $8+2x$ meters. If we take the area of the pool with the tile and subtract the area of the pool without the tile, we are left with the area of the tile only.

$(12+2x)(8+2x)-12(8)=120$

$\cancel{96}+24x+16x+4x^2-\cancel{96}=120$

$4x^2+40x-120=0$

$x^2+10x-30=0$

$a=1\qquad b=10\qquad c=-30$

$x=\dfrac{-10\pm\sqrt{10^2-4(1)(-30)}}{2(1)}$

$=\dfrac{-10\pm\sqrt{100+120}}{2}$

$=\dfrac{-10\pm\sqrt{220}}{2}\approx\dfrac{-10\pm14.8}{2}$

Evaluate the expression to obtain two solutions.

$x=\dfrac{-10+14.8}{2}\quad$ or $\quad x=\dfrac{-10-14.8}{2}$

$x=\dfrac{4.8}{2}\qquad\qquad x=\dfrac{-24.8}{2}$

$x=2.4\qquad\qquad x=-12.4$

We disregard –12.4 because we can't have a negative width measurement. The solution is 2.4 and we conclude that the width of the uniform tile border is 2.4 meters. This is more than the 2-meter requirement, so the tile meets the zoning laws.

Mid-Chapter 1 Check Point

1. $-5+3(x+5)=2(3x-4)$

$-5+3x+15=6x-8$

$3x+10=6x-8$

$-3x=-18$

$\dfrac{-3x}{-3}=\dfrac{-18}{-3}$

$x=6$

The solution set is $\{6\}$.

2. $5x^2-2x=7$

$5x^2-2x-7=0$

$(5x-7)(x+1)=0$

$5x-7=0\quad$ or $\quad x+1=0$

$5x=7\qquad\qquad x=-1$

$x=\dfrac{7}{5}$

The solution set is $\left\{-1,\dfrac{7}{5}\right\}$.

3. $\dfrac{x-3}{5}-1=\dfrac{x-5}{4}$

$20\left(\dfrac{x-3}{5}-1\right)=20\left(\dfrac{x-5}{4}\right)$

$\dfrac{20(x-3)}{5}-20(1)=\dfrac{20(x-5)}{4}$

$4(x-3)-20=5(x-5)$

$4x-12-20=5x-25$

$4x-32=5x-25$

$-x=7$

$x=-7$

The solution set is $\{-7\}$.

78

4. $3x^2 - 6x - 2 = 0$

$$x = \frac{-b \pm \sqrt{b^2 - 4ac}}{2a}$$

$$x = \frac{-(-6) \pm \sqrt{(-6)^2 - 4(3)(-2)}}{2(3)}$$

$$x = \frac{6 \pm \sqrt{60}}{6}$$

$$x = \frac{6 \pm 2\sqrt{15}}{6}$$

$$x = \frac{3 \pm \sqrt{15}}{3}$$

The solution set is $\left\{ \dfrac{3+\sqrt{15}}{3}, \dfrac{3-\sqrt{15}}{3} \right\}$.

5. $4x - 2(1-x) = 3(2x+1) - 5$

$$4x - 2(1-x) = 3(2x+1) - 5$$
$$4x - 2 + 2x = 6x + 3 - 5$$
$$6x - 2 = 6x - 2$$
$$0 = 0$$

The solution set is all real numbers.

6. $5x^2 + 1 = 37$

$$5x^2 = 36$$

$$\frac{5x^2}{5} = \frac{36}{5}$$

$$x^2 = \frac{36}{5}$$

$$x = \pm\sqrt{\frac{36}{5}}$$

$$x = \pm\frac{6}{\sqrt{5}}$$

$$x = \pm\frac{6}{\sqrt{5}} \cdot \frac{\sqrt{5}}{\sqrt{5}}$$

$$x = \pm\frac{6\sqrt{5}}{5}$$

The solution set is $\left\{ -\dfrac{6\sqrt{5}}{5}, \dfrac{6\sqrt{5}}{5} \right\}$.

7. $x(2x - 3) = -4$

$$2x^2 - 3x = -4$$
$$2x^2 - 3x + 4 = 0$$

$$x = \frac{-b \pm \sqrt{b^2 - 4ac}}{2a}$$

$$x = \frac{-(-3) \pm \sqrt{(-3)^2 - 4(2)(4)}}{2(2)}$$

$$x = \frac{3 \pm \sqrt{-23}}{4}$$

$$x = \frac{3 \pm i\sqrt{23}}{4}$$

The solution set is $\left\{ \dfrac{3+i\sqrt{23}}{4}, \dfrac{3-i\sqrt{23}}{4} \right\}$.

8.

$$\frac{3x}{4} - \frac{x}{3} + 1 = \frac{4x}{5} - \frac{3}{20}$$

$$\frac{3x}{4} - \frac{x}{3} + 1 = \frac{4x}{5} - \frac{3}{20}$$

$$60\left(\frac{3x}{4} - \frac{x}{3} + 1 \right) = 60\left(\frac{4x}{5} - \frac{3}{20} \right)$$

$$\frac{60(3x)}{4} - \frac{60x}{3} + 60(1) = \frac{60(4x)}{5} - \frac{60(3)}{20}$$

$$45x - 20x + 60 = 48x - 9$$
$$25x + 60 = 48x - 9$$
$$-23x = -69$$

$$\frac{-23x}{-23} = \frac{-69}{-23}$$

$$x = 3$$

The solution set is $\{3\}$.

9. $(x + 3)^2 = 24$

$$x + 3 = \pm\sqrt{24}$$
$$x = -3 \pm 2\sqrt{6}$$

The solution set is $\left\{ -3 + 2\sqrt{6}, -3 - 2\sqrt{6} \right\}$.

10.

$$\frac{1}{x^2} - \frac{4}{x} + 1 = 0$$

$$x^2\left(\frac{1}{x^2} - \frac{4}{x} + 1\right) = x^2(0)$$

$$\frac{x^2}{x^2} - \frac{4x^2}{x} + x^2 = 0$$

$$1 - 4x + x^2 = 0$$

$$x^2 - 4x + 1 = 0$$

$$x = \frac{-b \pm \sqrt{b^2 - 4ac}}{2a}$$

$$x = \frac{-(-4) \pm \sqrt{(-4)^2 - 4(1)(1)}}{2(1)}$$

$$x = \frac{4 \pm \sqrt{12}}{2}$$

$$x = \frac{4 \pm 2\sqrt{3}}{2}$$

$$x = 2 \pm \sqrt{3}$$

The solution set is $\left\{2 + \sqrt{3}, 2 - \sqrt{3}\right\}$.

11.
$$3x + 1 - (x - 5) = 2x - 4$$
$$2x + 6 = 2x - 4$$
$$6 = -4$$
The solution set is $\varnothing$.

12.

$$\frac{2x}{x^2 + 6x + 8} = \frac{x}{x+4} - \frac{2}{x+2}, \quad x \neq -2, x \neq -4$$

$$\frac{2x}{(x+4)(x+2)} = \frac{x}{x+4} - \frac{2}{x+2}$$

$$\frac{2x(x+4)(x+2)}{(x+4)(x+2)} = (x+4)(x+2)\left(\frac{x}{x+4} - \frac{2}{x+2}\right)$$

$$2x = \frac{x(x+4)(x+2)}{x+4} - \frac{2(x+4)(x+2)}{x+2}$$

$$2x = x(x+2) - 2(x+4)$$

$$2x = x^2 + 2x - 2x - 8$$

$$0 = x^2 - 2x - 8$$

$$0 = (x+2)(x-4)$$

$$x + 2 = 0 \quad \text{or} \quad x - 4 = 0$$
$$x = -2 \qquad\qquad x = 4$$

-2 must be rejected.

The solution set is $\{4\}$.

13. Let $y = 0$.

$$0 = x^2 + 6x + 2$$

$$x = \frac{-b \pm \sqrt{b^2 - 4ac}}{2a}$$

$$x = \frac{-(6) \pm \sqrt{(6)^2 - 4(1)(2)}}{2(1)}$$

$$x = \frac{-6 \pm \sqrt{28}}{2}$$

$$x = \frac{-6 \pm 2\sqrt{7}}{2}$$

$$x = -3 \pm \sqrt{7}$$

x-intercepts: $-3 + \sqrt{7}$ and $-3 - \sqrt{7}$.

14. Let $y = 0$.

$$0 = 4(x + 1) - 3x - (6 - x)$$

$$0 = 4x + 4 - 3x - 6 + x$$

$$0 = 2x - 2$$

$$-2x = -2$$

$$x = 1$$

x-intercept: 1.

15. Let $y = 0$.

$$0 = 2x^2 + 26$$

$$-2x^2 = 26$$

$$x^2 = -13$$

$$x = \pm\sqrt{-13}$$

$$x = \pm i\sqrt{13}$$

There are no x-intercepts.

16. Let $y = 0$.

$$0 = \frac{x^2}{3} + \frac{x}{2} - \frac{2}{3}$$

$$6(0) = 6\left(\frac{x^2}{3} + \frac{x}{2} - \frac{2}{3}\right)$$

$$0 = \frac{6 \cdot x^2}{3} + \frac{6 \cdot x}{2} - \frac{6 \cdot 2}{3}$$

$$0 = 2x^2 + 3x - 4$$

$$x = \frac{-b \pm \sqrt{b^2 - 4ac}}{2a}$$

$$x = \frac{-(3) \pm \sqrt{(3)^2 - 4(2)(-4)}}{2(2)}$$

$$x = \frac{-3 \pm \sqrt{41}}{4}$$

x-intercepts: $\dfrac{-3 + \sqrt{41}}{4}$ and $\dfrac{-3 - \sqrt{41}}{4}$.

17. Let $y = 0$.

$$0 = x^2 - 5x + 8$$

$$x = \frac{-b \pm \sqrt{b^2 - 4ac}}{2a}$$

$$x = \frac{-(-5) \pm \sqrt{(-5)^2 - 4(1)(8)}}{2(1)}$$

$$x = \frac{5 \pm \sqrt{-7}}{2}$$

$$x = \frac{5 \pm i\sqrt{7}}{2}$$

There are no x-intercepts.

18.

$$y_1 = y_2$$

$$3(2x - 5) - 2(4x + 1) = -5(x + 3) - 2$$

$$6x - 15 - 8x - 2 = -5x - 15 - 2$$

$$-2x - 17 = -5x - 17$$

$$3x = 0$$

$$x = 0$$

The solution set is $\{0\}$.

19.
$$y_1 y_2 = 10$$
$$(2x+3)(x+2) = 10$$
$$2x^2 + 7x + 6 = 10$$
$$2x^2 + 7x - 4 = 0$$
$$(2x-1)(x+4) = 0$$
$$2x - 1 = 0 \quad \text{or} \quad x + 4 = 0$$
$$x = \frac{1}{2} \qquad\qquad x = -4$$

The solution set is $\left\{-4, \dfrac{1}{2}\right\}$.

20.　$x^2 + 10x - 3 = 0$
$$x^2 + 10x \quad = 3$$

Since $b = 10$, we add $\left(\dfrac{10}{2}\right)^2 = 5^2 = 25$.

$$x^2 + 10x + 25 = 3 + 25$$
$$(x+5)^2 = 28$$

Apply the square root principle:
$$x + 5 = \pm\sqrt{28}$$
$$x + 5 = \pm\sqrt{4 \cdot 7} = \pm 2\sqrt{7}$$
$$x = -5 \pm 2\sqrt{7}$$

The solutions are $-5 \pm 2\sqrt{7}$, and the solution set is $\left\{-5 \pm 2\sqrt{7}\right\}$.

21.　　$2x^2 + 5x + 4 = 0$
$$a = 2 \quad b = 5 \quad c = 4$$
$$b^2 - 4ac = 5^2 - 4(2)(4)$$
$$= 25 - 32 = -7$$

Since the discriminant is negative, there are no real solutions. There are two imaginary solutions that are complex conjugates.

22.　　$10x(x+4) = 15x - 15$
$$10x^2 + 40x = 15x - 15$$
$$10x^2 - 25x + 15 = 0$$
$$a = 10 \quad b = -25 \quad c = 15$$
$$b^2 - 4ac = (-25)^2 - 4(10)(15)$$
$$= 625 - 600 = 25$$

Since the discriminant is positive and a perfect square, there are two rational solutions.

23.

x	(x, y)
-2	-5
-1	-3
0	-1
1	1
2	3

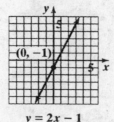

$$y = 2x - 1$$

24.

x	(x, y)
-3	-2
-2	-1
-1	0
0	1
1	0
2	-1
3	-2

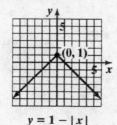

$$y = 1 - |x|$$

25.

x	(x, y)
-2	6
-1	3
0	2
1	3
2	6

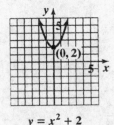

$$y = x^2 + 2$$

26.
$$L = a + (n-1)d$$
$$L = a + dn - d$$
$$-dn = a - d - L$$
$$\frac{-dn}{-d} = \frac{a}{-d} - \frac{d}{-d} - \frac{L}{-d}$$
$$n = -\frac{a}{d} + 1 + \frac{L}{d}$$
$$n = \frac{L}{d} - \frac{a}{d} + 1$$
$$n = \frac{L-a}{d} + 1$$

27.
$$A = 2lw + 2lh + 2wh$$
$$-2lw - 2lh = 2wh - A$$
$$l(-2w - 2h) = 2wh - A$$
$$l = \frac{2wh - A}{-2w - 2h}$$
$$l = \frac{A - 2wh}{2w + 2h}$$

28.
$$f = \frac{f_1 f_2}{f_1 + f_2}$$
$$(f_1 + f_2)(f) = (f_1 + f_2)\frac{f_1 f_2}{f_1 + f_2}$$
$$f_1 f + f_2 f = f_1 f_2$$
$$f_1 f - f_1 f_2 = -f_2 f$$
$$f_1(f - f_2) = -f_2 f$$
$$f_1 = \frac{-f_2 f}{f - f_2}$$
$$f_1 = \frac{f f_2}{f - f_2}$$

29. Let x = the defense budget of Japan in billions
Let $x + 4$ = the defense budget of Russia in billions
Let $x + 251$ = the defense budget of U.S. in billions
$$x + (x+4) + (x+251) = 375$$
$$3x + 255 = 375$$
$$3x = 120$$
$$x = 40$$
$$x + 4 = 44$$
$$x + 251 = 291$$
The defense budget of Japan is $40 billion, of Russia $44 billion, and of the U.S. $291 billion.

30. Let x = the number of months it takes for the average female infant to weigh 16 pounds
$$7 + 1.5x = 16$$
$$1.5x = 9$$
$$\frac{1.5x}{1.5} = \frac{9}{1.5}$$
$$x = 6$$
It takes 6 months for the average female infant to weigh 16 pounds.

31. Let x = the amount invested at 8%.
Let $25,000 - x$ = the amount invested at 9%.
$$0.08x + 0.09(25,000 - x) = 2135$$
$$0.08x + 2250 - 0.09x = 2135$$
$$-0.01x + 2250 = 2135$$
$$-0.01x = -115$$
$$x = \frac{-115}{-0.01}$$
$$x = 11,500$$
$$25,000 - x = 13,500$$
$11,500 was invested at 8% and $13,500 was invested at 9%.

32. Let x = the number of prints.
Photo Shop A: $0.11x + 1.60$
Photo Shop B: $0.13x + 1.20$
$0.13x + 1.20 = 0.11x + 1.60$
$0.02x + 1.20 = 1.60$
$\qquad 0.02x = 0.40$
$\qquad\qquad x = 20$
The cost will be the same for 20 prints.
That common price is
$0.11(20) + 1.60 = 0.13(20) + 1.20$
$\qquad\qquad\qquad = \$3.80$

33. Let x = the average weight for an American
woman aged 20 through 29 in 1960.
$x + 0.22x = 157$
$\quad 1.22x = 157$
$\quad \dfrac{1.22x}{1.22} = \dfrac{157}{1.22}$
$\qquad x \approx 129$
The average weight for an American woman
aged 20 through 29 in 1960 was 129 pounds.

34. Let x = the amount invested at 4%.
Let $4000 - x$ = the amount invested that lost 3%.
$0.04x - 0.03(4000 - x) = 55$
$\quad 0.04x - 120 + 0.03x = 55$
$\qquad\qquad 0.07x - 120 = 55$
$\qquad\qquad\quad 0.07x = 175$
$\qquad\qquad\qquad x = \dfrac{175}{0.07}$
$\qquad\qquad\qquad x = 2500$
$\quad 4000 - x = 1500$
\$2500 was invested at 4% and \$1500 lost 3%.

35. Let x = the width of the rectangle
Let $2x + 5$ = the length of the rectangle
$\qquad 2l + 2w = P$
$2(2x + 5) + 2x = 46$
$\quad 4x + 10 + 2x = 46$
$\qquad 6x + 10 = 46$
$\qquad\qquad 6x = 36$
$\qquad\qquad \dfrac{6x}{6} = \dfrac{36}{6}$
$\qquad\qquad x = 6$
$\quad 2x + 5 = 17$
The dimensions of the rectangle are 6 by 17.

36. Let x = the width of the rectangle
Let $2x - 1$ = the length of the rectangle
$\qquad lw = A$
$\quad (2x - 1)x = 28$
$\qquad 2x^2 - x = 28$
$2x^2 - x - 28 = 0$
$(2x + 7)(x - 4) = 0$
$2x + 7 = 0 \quad$ or $\quad x - 4 = 0$
$2x = -7 \qquad\qquad\quad x = 4$
$x = -\dfrac{7}{2}$

$-\dfrac{7}{2}$ must be rejected.

If $x = 4$, then $2x - 1 = 7$
The dimensions of the rectangle are 4 by 7.

37. Let x = the height up the pole at which the wires
are attached.
$x^2 + 5^2 = 13^2$
$x^2 + 25 = 169$
$\quad x^2 = 144$
$\quad x = \pm 12$
-12 must be rejected.
The wires are attached 12 feet up the pole.

38. $N = 62.2x^2 + 7000$
$62.2x^2 + 7000 = N$
$62.2x^2 + 7000 = 46,000$
$\quad 62.2x^2 = 39,000$
$\quad \dfrac{62.2x^2}{62.2} = \dfrac{39,000}{62.2}$
$\qquad x^2 \approx 627$
$\qquad x \approx \pm\sqrt{627}$
$\qquad x \approx \pm 25$
-25 must be rejected.
The equation predicts that there were 46,000
multinational corporations 25 years after 1970,
or 1995. The model describes the actual data
shown in the graph quite well.

39. $P = 0.0049x^2 - 0.359x + 11.78$

$15 = 0.0049x^2 - 0.359x + 11.78$

$0 = 0.0049x^2 - 0.359x - 3.22$

$0 = 0.0049x^2 - 0.359x - 3.22$

$x = \dfrac{-b \pm \sqrt{b^2 - 4ac}}{2a}$

$x = \dfrac{-(-0.359) \pm \sqrt{(-0.359)^2 - 4(0.0049)(-3.22)}}{2(0.0049)}$

$x = \dfrac{0.359 \pm \sqrt{0.191993}}{0.0098}$

$x \approx 81, \quad x \approx -8 \text{ (rejected)}$

The percentage of foreign born Americans will be 15% about 81 years after 1930, or 2011.

40. $(6 - 2i) - (7 - i) = 6 - 2i - 7 + i = -1 - i$

41. $3i(2 + i) = 6i + 3i^2 = -3 + 6i$

42. $(1 + i)(4 - 3i) = 4 - 3i + 4i - 3i^2$

$= 4 + i + 3$

$= 7 + i$

43. $\dfrac{1+i}{1-i} = \dfrac{1+i}{1-i} \cdot \dfrac{1+i}{1+i}$

$= \dfrac{1 + i + i + i^2}{1 - i^2}$

$= \dfrac{1 + 2i - 1}{1 + 1}$

$= \dfrac{2i}{2}$

$= i$

44. $\sqrt{-75} - \sqrt{-12} = 5i\sqrt{3} - 2i\sqrt{3} = 3i\sqrt{3}$

45. $\left(2 - \sqrt{-3}\right)^2 = \left(2 - i\sqrt{3}\right)^2$

$= 4 - 4i\sqrt{3} + 3i^2$

$= 4 - 4i\sqrt{3} - 3$

$= 1 - 4i\sqrt{3}$

Section 1.6

Check Point Exercises

1. $4x^4 = 12x^2$

$4x^4 - 12x^2 = 0$

$4x^2(x^2 - 3) = 0$

$4x^2 = 0 \quad \text{or} \quad x^2 - 3 = 0$

$x^2 = 0 \qquad\qquad x^2 = 3$

$x = \pm\sqrt{0} \qquad\qquad x = \pm\sqrt{3}$

$x = 0 \qquad\qquad x = \pm\sqrt{3}$

The solution set is $\left\{-\sqrt{3}, 0, \sqrt{3}\right\}$.

2. $2x^3 + 3x^2 = 8x + 12$

$x^2(2x + 3) - 4(2x + 3) = 10$

$(2x + 3)(x^2 - 4) = 0$

$2x + 3 = 0 \quad \text{or} \quad x^2 - 4 = 0$

$2x = -3 \qquad\qquad x^2 = 4$

$x = -\dfrac{3}{2} \qquad\qquad x = \pm 2$

The solution set is $\left\{-2, -\dfrac{3}{2}, 2\right\}$.

3. $\sqrt{x+3} + 3 = x$

$\sqrt{x+3} = x - 3$

$\left(\sqrt{x+3}\right)^2 = (x-3)^2$

$x + 3 = x^2 - 6x + 9$

$0 = x^2 - 7x + 6$

$0 = (x-6)(x-1)$

$x - 6 = 0$ or $x - 1 = 0$

$x = 6$ $x = 1$

1 does not check and must be rejected.
The solution set is $\{6\}$.

4. $\sqrt{x+5} - \sqrt{x-3} = 2$

$\sqrt{x+5} = 2 + \sqrt{x-3}$

$\left(\sqrt{x+5}\right)^2 = \left(2 + \sqrt{x-3}\right)^2$

$x + 5 = (2)^2 + 2(2)\left(\sqrt{x-3}\right) + \left(\sqrt{x-3}\right)^2$

$x + 5 = 4 + 4\sqrt{x-3} + x - 3$

$4 = 4\sqrt{x-3}$

$\dfrac{4}{4} = \dfrac{4\sqrt{x-3}}{4}$

$1 = \sqrt{x-3}$

$(1)^2 = \left(\sqrt{x-3}\right)^2$

$1 = x - 3$

$4 = x$

The check indicates that 4 is a solution.
The solution set is $\{4\}$.

5.   **a.** $5x^{3/2} - 25 = 0$

$5x^{3/2} = 25$

$x^{3/2} = 5$

$\left(x^{3/2}\right)^{2/3} = (5)^{2/3}$

$x = 5^{2/3}$ or $\sqrt[3]{25}$

Check:

$5\left(5^{2/3}\right)^{3/2} - 25 = 0$

$5(5) - 25 = 0$

$25 - 25 = 0$

$0 = 0$

The solution set is $\left\{5^{2/3}\right\}$ or $\left\{\sqrt[3]{25}\right\}$.

b. $x^{\frac{2}{3}} - 8 = -4$

$x^{2/3} = 4$

$\left(x^{2/3}\right)^{3/2} = 4^{3/2}$ or

$x = \left(2^2\right)^{3/2}$

$x = 2^3$ $x = (-2)^3$

$x = 8$ $x = -8$

The solution set is $\{-8, 8\}$.

6. $x^4 - 5x^2 + 6 = 0$

$\left(x^2\right)^2 - 5x^2 + 6 = 0$

Let $t = x^2$.

$t^2 - 5t + 6 = 0$

$(t-3)(t-2) = 0$

$t - 3 = 0$ or $t - 2 = 0$

$t = 3$ or $t = 2$

$x^2 = 3$ or $x^2 = 2$

$x = \pm\sqrt{3}$ or $x = \pm\sqrt{2}$

The solution set is $\left\{-\sqrt{3}, \sqrt{3}, -\sqrt{2}, \sqrt{2}\right\}$.

7. $3x^{2/3} - 11x^{1/3} - 4 = 0$

Let $t = x^{1/3}$.

$3t^2 - 11t - 4 = 0$

$(3t+1)(t-4) = 0$

$3t + 1 = 0$ or $t - 4 = 0$

$3t = -1$

$t = -\dfrac{1}{3}$ $t = 4$

$x^{1/3} = -\dfrac{1}{3}$ $x^{1/3} = 4$

$x = \left(-\dfrac{1}{3}\right)^3$ $x = 4^3$

$x = -\dfrac{1}{27}$ $x = 64$

The solution set is $\left\{-\dfrac{1}{27}, 64\right\}$.

8. $|2x-1| = 5$

$2x - 1 = 5$ or $2x - 1 = -5$

$2x = 6$ $2x = -4$

$x = 3$ $x = -2$

The solution set is $\{-2, 3\}$.

9. $4|1-2x|-20=0$

$4|1-2x|=20$

$|1-2x|=5$

$1-2x=5$ or $1-2x=-5$

$-2x=4$ $-2x=-6$

$x=-2$ $x=3$

The solution set is $\{-2, 3\}$.

Exercise Set 1.6

1. $3x^4-48x^2=0$

$3x^2(x^2-16)=0$

$3x^2(x+4)(x-4)=0$

$3x^2=0$ $x+4=0$ $x-4=0$

$x^2=0$ $x=-4$ $x=4$

$x=0$

The solution set is $\{-4, 0, 4\}$.

3. $3x^3+2x^2=12x+8$

$3x^3+2x^2-12x-8=0$

$x^2(3x+2)-4(3x+2)=0$

$(3x+2)(x^2-4)=0$

$3x+2=0$ $x^2-4=0$

$3x=-2$ $x^2=4$

$x=-\dfrac{2}{3}$ $x=\pm 2$

The solution set is $\left\{-2,-\dfrac{2}{3}, 2\right\}$.

5. $2x-3=8x^3-12x^2$

$8x^3-12x^2-2x+3=0$

$4x^2(2x-3)-(2x-3)=0$

$(2x-3)(4x^2-1)=0$

$2x-3=0$ $4x^2-1=0$

$2x=3$ $4x^2=1$

$x^2=\dfrac{1}{4}$

$x=\dfrac{3}{2}$ $x=\pm\dfrac{1}{2}$

The solution set is $\left\{\dfrac{3}{2},\dfrac{1}{2},-\dfrac{1}{2}\right\}$.

7. $4y^3-2=y-8y^2$

$4y^3+8y^2-y-2=0$

$4y^2(y+2)-(y+2)=0$

$(y+2)(4y^2-1)=0$

$y+2=0$ $4y^2-1=0$

$4y^2=1$

$y^2=\dfrac{1}{4}$

$y=-2$ $y=\pm\dfrac{1}{2}$

The solution set is $\left\{-2,\dfrac{1}{2},-\dfrac{1}{2}\right\}$.

9. $2x^4=16x$

$2x^4-16x=0$

$2x\left(x^3-8\right)=0$

$2x=0$ $x^3-8=0$

$x=0$ $(x-2)(x^2+2x+2)=0$

$x-2=0$ $x^2+2x+4=0$

$x=2$ $x=\dfrac{-2\pm\sqrt{2^2-4(1)(4)}}{2(1)}$

$x=\dfrac{-2\pm\sqrt{-12}}{2}$

$x=\dfrac{-2\pm 2i\sqrt{3}}{2}$

$x=-1\pm i\sqrt{3}$

The solution set is $\left\{0,2,-1\pm i\sqrt{3}\right\}$.

11. $\sqrt{3x+18}=x$

$3x+18=x^2$

$x^2-3x-18=0$

$(x+3)(x-6)=0$

$x+3=0$ $x-6=0$

$x=-3$ $x=6$

$\sqrt{3(-3)+18}=-3$ $\sqrt{3(6)+18}=6$

$\sqrt{-9+18}=-3$ $\sqrt{18+18}=6$

$\sqrt{9}=-3$ False $\sqrt{36}=6$

The solution set is $\{6\}$.

13.
$$\sqrt{x+3} = x-3$$
$$x+3 = x^2 - 6x + 9$$
$$x^2 - 7x + 6 = 0$$
$$(x-1)(x-6) = 0$$
$$x - 1 = 0 \quad x - 6 = 0$$
$$x = 1 \qquad x = 6$$
$$\sqrt{1+3} = 1-3 \qquad \sqrt{6+3} = 6-3$$
$$\sqrt{4} = -2 \quad \text{False} \quad \sqrt{9} = 3$$
The solution set is $\{6\}$.

15.
$$\sqrt{2x+13} = x+7$$
$$2x+13 = (x+7)^2$$
$$2x+13 = x^2 + 14x + 49$$
$$x^2 + 12x + 36 = 0$$
$$(x+6)^2 = 0$$
$$x+6 = 0$$
$$x = -6$$
$$\sqrt{2(-6)+13} = -6+7$$
$$\sqrt{-12+13} = 1$$
$$\sqrt{1} = 1$$
The solution set is $\{-6\}$.

17.
$$x - \sqrt{2x+5} = 5$$
$$x - 5 = \sqrt{2x+5}$$
$$(x-5)^2 = 2x+5$$
$$x^2 - 10x + 25 = 2x + 5$$
$$x^2 - 12x + 20 = 0$$
$$(x-2)(x-10) = 0$$
$$x - 2 = 0 \quad x - 10 = 0$$
$$x = 2 \qquad x = 10$$
$$2 - \sqrt{2(2)+5} = 5 \quad 10 - \sqrt{2(10)+5} = 5$$
$$2 - \sqrt{9} = 5 \qquad 10 - \sqrt{25} = 5$$
$$2 - 3 = 5 \quad \text{False} \quad 10 - 5 = 5$$
The solution set is $\{10\}$.

19.
$$\sqrt{2x+19} - 8 = x$$
$$\sqrt{2x+19} = x+8$$
$$\left(\sqrt{2x+19}\right)^2 = (x+8)^2$$
$$2x+19 = x^2 + 16x + 64$$
$$0 = x^2 + 14x + 45$$
$$0 = (x+9)(x+5)$$
$$x + 9 = 0 \quad \text{or} \quad x + 5 = 0$$
$$x = -9 \qquad\qquad x = -5$$
-9 does not check and must be rejected.
The solution set is $\{-5\}$.

21.
$$\sqrt{3x} + 10 = x+4$$
$$\sqrt{3x} = x-6$$
$$3x = (x-6)^2$$
$$3x = x^2 - 12x + 36$$
$$x^2 - 15x + 36 = 0$$
$$(x-12)(x-3) = 0$$
$$x - 12 = 0 \quad x - 3 = 0$$
$$x = 12 \qquad x = 3$$
$$\sqrt{3(12)} + 10 = 12+4 \quad \sqrt{3(3)} + 10 = 3+4$$
$$\sqrt{36} + 10 = 16 \qquad \sqrt{9} + 10 = 7$$
$$6 + 10 = 16 \qquad\qquad 3 + 10 = 7 \text{ False}$$
The solution set is $\{12\}$.

23.
$$\sqrt{x+8} - \sqrt{x-4} = 2$$
$$\sqrt{x+8} = \sqrt{x-4} + 2$$
$$x+8 = (\sqrt{x-4} + 2)^2$$
$$x+8 = x - 4 + 4\sqrt{x-4} + 4$$
$$x+8 = x + 4\sqrt{x-4}$$
$$8 = 4\sqrt{x-4}$$
$$2 = \sqrt{x-4}$$
$$4 = x - 4$$
$$x = 8$$
$$\sqrt{8+8} - \sqrt{8-4} = 2$$
$$\sqrt{16} - \sqrt{4} = 2$$
$$4 - 2 = 2$$
The solution set is $\{8\}$.

25. $\sqrt{x-5} - \sqrt{x-8} = 3$

$\sqrt{x-5} = \sqrt{x-8} + 3$

$x-5 = (\sqrt{x-8} + 3)^2$

$x-5 = x-8 + 6\sqrt{x-8} + 9$

$x-5 = x+1 + 6\sqrt{x-8}$

$-6 = 6\sqrt{x-8}$

$-1 = \sqrt{x-8}$

$1 = x-8$

$x = 9$

$\sqrt{9-5} - \sqrt{9-8} = 3$

$\sqrt{4} - \sqrt{1} = 3$

$2 - 1 = 3$ False

The solution set is the empty set, $\varnothing$.

27. $\sqrt{2x+3} + \sqrt{x-2} = 2$

$\sqrt{2x+3} = 2 - \sqrt{x-2}$

$2x+3 = (2 - \sqrt{x-2})^2$

$2x+3 = 4 - 4\sqrt{x-2} + x - 2$

$x+1 = -4\sqrt{x-2}$

$(x+1)^2 = 16(x-2)$

$x^2 + 2x + 1 = 16x - 32$

$x^2 - 14x + 33 = 0$

$(x-11)(x-3) = 0$

$x - 11 = 0 \quad x - 3 = 0$

$x = 11 \qquad x = 3$

$\sqrt{2(11)+3} + \sqrt{11-2} = 2$

$\sqrt{22+3} + \sqrt{9} = 2$

$5 + 3 = 2$ False

$\sqrt{2(3)+3} + \sqrt{3-2} = 2$

$\sqrt{6+3} + \sqrt{1} = 2$

$3 + 1 = 2$ False

The solution set is the empty set, $\varnothing$.

29. $\sqrt{3\sqrt{x+1}} = \sqrt{3x-5}$

$3\sqrt{x+1} = 3x - 5$

$9(x+1) = 9x^2 - 30x + 25$

$9x^2 - 39x + 16 = 0$

$x = \dfrac{39 \pm \sqrt{945}}{18} = \dfrac{13 \pm \sqrt{105}}{6}$

Check proposed solutions.

The solution set is $\left\{ \dfrac{13 + \sqrt{105}}{6} \right\}$.

31. $x^{3/2} = 8$

$(x^{3/2})^{2/3} = 8^{2/3}$

$x = \sqrt[3]{8}^2$

$x = 2^2$

$x = 4$

$4^{3/2} = 8$

$\sqrt{4}^3 = 8$

$2^3 = 8$

The solution set is {4}.

33. $(x-4)^{3/2} = 27$

$((x-4)^{3/2})^{2/3} = 27^{2/3}$

$x - 4 = \sqrt[3]{27}^2$

$x - 4 = 3^2$

$x - 4 = 9$

$x = 13$

$(13-4)^{3/2} = 27$

$9^{3/2} = 27$

$\sqrt{9}^3 = 27$

$3^3 = 27$

The solution set is {13}.

89

35.
$$6x^{5/2} - 12 = 0$$
$$6x^{5/2} = 12$$
$$x^{5/2} = 2$$
$$(x^{5/2})^{2/5} = 2^{2/5}$$
$$x = \sqrt[5]{2^2}$$
$$x = \sqrt[5]{4}$$
$$6(\sqrt[5]{4})^{5/2} - 12 = 0$$
$$6(4^{1/5})^{5/2} - 12 = 0$$
$$6(4^{1/2}) - 12 = 0$$
$$6(2) - 12 = 0$$

The solution set is $\left\{\sqrt[5]{4}\right\}$.

37.
$$(x-4)^{2/3} = 16$$
$$\left[\cdot 4\right)^{2/3}\right]^{3/2} = (16)^{3/2}$$
$$x - 4 = \left(2^4\right)^{3/2}$$
$$x - 4 = 4^3 \qquad x - 4 = (-4)^3$$
$$x - 4 = 64 \qquad x - 4 = -64$$
$$x = 68 \qquad\qquad x = -60$$

The solution set is $\{-60, 68\}$.

39.
$$(x^2 - x - 4)^{3/4} - 2 = 6$$
$$(x^2 - x - 4)^{3/4} = 8$$
$$((x^2 - x - 4)^{3/4})^{4/3} = 8^{4/3}$$
$$x^2 - x - 4 = \sqrt[3]{8}^{\,4}$$
$$x^2 - x - 4 = 2^4$$
$$x^2 - x - 4 = 16$$
$$x^2 - x - 20 = 0$$
$$(x-5)(x+4) = 0$$
$$x - 5 = 0 \quad x + 4 = 0$$
$$x = 5 \qquad x = -4$$
$$(5^2 - 5 - 4)^{3/4} - 2 = 6$$
$$(25 - 9)^{3/4} - 2 = 6$$
$$16^{3/4} - 2 = 6$$
$$\sqrt[4]{16}^{\,3} - 2 = 6$$
$$2^3 - 2 = 6$$
$$8 - 2 = 6$$
$$((-4)^2 - (-4) - 4)^{3/4} - 2 = 6$$
$$(16 + 4 - 4)^{3/4} - 2 = 6$$
$$16^{3/4} - 2 = 6$$
$$\sqrt[4]{16}^{\,3} - 2 = 6$$
$$2^3 - 2 = 6$$
$$8 - 2 = 6$$

The solution set is $\{5, -4\}$.

41.
$$x^4 - 5x^2 + 4 = 0 \text{ let } t = x^2$$
$$t^2 - 5t + 4 = 0$$
$$(t-1)(t-4) = 0$$
$$t - 1 = 0 \quad t - 4 = 0$$
$$t = 1 \qquad t = 4$$
$$x^2 = 1 \qquad x^2 = 4$$
$$x = \pm 1 \qquad x = \pm 2$$

The solution set is $\{1, -1, 2, -2\}$

43. $9x^4 = 25x^2 - 16$

$9x^4 - 25x^2 + 16 = 0$ let $t = x^2$

$9t^2 - 25t + 16 = 0$

$(9t - 16)(t - 1) = 0$

$9t - 16 = 0 \qquad t - 1 = 0$

$9t = 16 \qquad t = 1$

$t = \dfrac{16}{9} \qquad x^2 = 1$

$\qquad\qquad x = \pm 1$

$x^2 = \dfrac{16}{9}$

$x = \pm\dfrac{4}{3}$

The solution set is $\left\{1, -1, \dfrac{4}{3}, -\dfrac{4}{3}\right\}$.

45. $x - 13\sqrt{x} + 40 = 0$ Let $t = \sqrt{x}$.

$t^2 - 13t + 40 = 0$

$(t - 8)(t - 5) = 0$

$t - 8 = 0 \qquad t - 5 = 0$

$t = 8 \qquad\quad t = 5$

$\sqrt{x} = 8 \qquad \sqrt{x} = 5$

$x = 64 \qquad\quad x = 25$

The solution set is $\{25, 64\}$.

47. $x^{-2} - x^{-1} - 20 = 0$ Let $t = x^{-1}$

$t^2 - t - 20 = 0$

$(t - 5)(t + 4) = 0$

$t - 5 = 0 \quad t + 4 = 0$

$t = 5 \qquad t = -4$

$x^{-1} = 5 \quad x^{-1} = -4$

$\dfrac{1}{x} = 5 \qquad \dfrac{1}{x} = -4$

$1 = 5x \qquad 1 = -4x$

$\dfrac{1}{5} = x \qquad -\dfrac{1}{4} = x$

The solution set is $\left\{-\dfrac{1}{4}, \dfrac{1}{5}\right\}$.

49. $x^{2/3} - x^{1/3} - 6 = 0$ let $t = x^{1/3}$

$t^2 - t - 6 = 0$

$(t - 3)(t + 2) = 0$

$t - 3 = 0 \qquad t + 2 = 0$

$t = 3 \qquad\quad t = -2$

$x^{1/3} = 3 \qquad x^{1/3} = -2$

$x = 3^3 \qquad\quad x = (-2)^3$

$x = 27 \qquad\quad x = -8$

The solution set is $\{27, -8\}$.

51. $x^{3/2} - 2x^{3/4} + 1 = 0$ let $t = x^{3/4}$

$t^2 - 2t + 1 = 0$

$(t - 1)(t - 1) = 0$

$t - 1 = 0$

$t = 1$

$x^{3/4} = 1$

$x = 1^{4/3}$

$x = 1$

The solution set is $\{1\}$.

53. $2x - 3x^{1/2} + 1 = 0$ let $t = x^{1/2}$

$2t^2 - 3t + 1 = 0$

$(2t - 1)(t - 1) = 0$

$2t - 1 = 0 \qquad t - 1 = 0$

$2t = 1$

$t = \dfrac{1}{2} \qquad\qquad t = 1$

$x^{1/2} = \dfrac{1}{2} \qquad x^{1/2} = 1$

$x = \left(\dfrac{1}{2}\right)^2 \qquad x = 1^2$

$x = \dfrac{1}{4} \qquad\qquad x = 1$

The solution set is $\left\{\dfrac{1}{4}, 1\right\}$.

55. $(x - 5)^2 - 4(x - 5) - 21 = 0$ let $t = x - 5$

$t^2 - 4t - 21 = 0$

$(t + 3)(t - 7) = 0$

$t + 3 = 0 \qquad t - 7 = 0$

$t = -3 \qquad\quad t = 7$

$x - 5 = -3 \quad x - 5 = 7$

$x = 2 \qquad\quad x = 12$

The solution set is $\{2, 12\}$.

57. $(x^2-x)^2-14(x^2-x)+24=0$

Let $t=x^2-x$.

$t^2-14t+24=0$

$(t-2)(t-12)=0$

$t=2$ or $t=12$

$x^2-x=2$ or $x^2-x=12$

$x^2-x-2=0$ $x^2-x-12=0$

$(x-2)(x+1)=0$ $(x-4)(x+3)=0$

The solution set is $\{-3,-1,2,4\}$.

59. $\left(y-\dfrac{8}{y}\right)^2+5\left(y-\dfrac{8}{y}\right)-14=0$

Let $t=y-\dfrac{8}{y}$.

$t^2+5t-14=0$

$(t+7)(t-2)=0$

$t=-7$ or $t=2$

$y-\dfrac{8}{y}=-7$ or $y-\dfrac{8}{y}=2$

$y^2+7y-8=0$ $y^2-2y-8=0$

$(y+8)(y-1)=0$ $(y-4)(y+2)=0$

The solution set is $\{-8,-2,1,4\}$.

61. $|x|=8$

$x=8,\ x=-8$

The solution set is $\{8,-8\}$.

63. $|x-2|=7$

$x-2=7$ $x-2=-7$

$x=9$ $x=-5$

The solution set is $\{9,-5\}$.

65. $|2x-1|=5$

$2x-1=5$ $2x-1=-5$

$2x=6$ $2x=-4$

$x=3$ $x=-2$

The solution set is $\{3,-2\}$.

67. $2|3x-2|=14$

$|3x-2|=7$

$3x-2=7$ $3x-2=-7$

$3x=9$ $3x=-5$

$x=3$ $x=-5/3$

The solution set is $\{3,-5/3\}$

69. $7|5x|+2=16$

$7|5x|=14$

$|5x|=2$

$5x=2$ $5x=-2$

$x=2/5$ $x=-2/5$

The solution set is $\left\{\dfrac{2}{5},-\dfrac{2}{5}\right\}$.

71. $2\left|4-\dfrac{5}{2}x\right|+6=18$

$2\left|4-\dfrac{5}{2}x\right|=12$

$\left|4-\dfrac{5}{2}x\right|=6$

$4-\dfrac{5}{2}x=6$ or $4-\dfrac{5}{2}x=-6$

$-\dfrac{5}{2}x=2$ $-\dfrac{5}{2}x=-10$

$-\dfrac{2}{5}\left(-\dfrac{5}{2}\right)x=-\dfrac{2}{5}(2)$ $-\dfrac{2}{5}\left(-\dfrac{5}{2}\right)x=-\dfrac{2}{5}(-10)$

$x=-\dfrac{4}{5}$ $x=4$

The solution set is $\left\{-\dfrac{4}{5},4\right\}$.

73. $|x+1|+5=3$
$\quad\quad |x+1|=-2$
No solution
The solution set is { }.

75. $|2x-1|+3=3$
$\quad\quad |2x-1|=0$
$\quad\quad\quad 2x-1=0$
$\quad\quad\quad\quad 2x=1$
$\quad\quad\quad\quad\quad x=1/2$
The solution set is $\{1/2\}$.

77. $|3x-1|=|x+5|$

$\quad 3x-1=x+5 \quad\quad 3x-1=-x-5$
$\quad\quad 2x-1=5 \quad\quad\quad 4x-1=-5$
$\quad\quad\quad 2x=6 \quad\quad\quad\quad 4x=-4$
$\quad\quad\quad\quad x=3 \quad\quad\quad\quad\quad x=-1$
The solution set is $\{3,-1\}$.

79. Set $y=0$ to find the x–intercept(s).
$$0=\sqrt{x+2}+\sqrt{x-1}-3$$
$$-\sqrt{x+2}=\sqrt{x-1}-3$$
$$\left(-\sqrt{x+2}\right)^2=\left(\sqrt{x-1}-3\right)^2$$
$$x+2=\left(\sqrt{x-1}\right)^2-2\left(\sqrt{x-1}\right)(3)+(3)^2$$
$$x+2=x-1-6\sqrt{x-1}+9$$
$$x+2=x-1-6\sqrt{x-1}+9$$
$$2=8-6\sqrt{x-1}$$
$$-6=-6\sqrt{x-1}$$
$$\frac{-6}{-6}=\frac{-6\sqrt{x-1}}{-6}$$
$$1=\sqrt{x-1}$$
$$(1)^2=\left(\sqrt{x-1}\right)^2$$
$$1=x-1$$
$$2=x$$
The x-intercept is 2.
The corresponding graph is graph (c).

81. Set $y=0$ to find the x–intercept(s).
$$0=x^{\frac{1}{3}}+2x^{\frac{1}{6}}-3$$
Let $t=x^{\frac{1}{6}}$.
$$x^{\frac{1}{3}}+2x^{\frac{1}{6}}-3=0$$
$$\left(x^{\frac{1}{6}}\right)^2+2x^{\frac{1}{6}}-3=0$$
$$t^2+2t-3=0$$
$$(t+3)(t-1)=0$$
$$t+3=0 \quad\text{or}\quad t-1=0$$
$$t=-3 \quad\quad\quad t=1$$
Substitute $x^{\frac{1}{6}}$ for t.
$$x^{\frac{1}{6}}=-3 \quad\text{or}\quad x^{\frac{1}{6}}=1$$
$$\left(x^{\frac{1}{6}}\right)^6=(-3)^6 \quad\quad \left(x^{\frac{1}{6}}\right)^6=(1)^6$$
$$x=729 \quad\quad\quad\quad x=1$$
729 does not check and must be rejected.
The x-intercept is 1.
The corresponding graph is graph (e).

83. Set $y=0$ to find the x–intercept(s).
$$(x+2)^2-9(x+2)+20=0$$
Let $t=x+2$.
$$(x+2)^2-9(x+2)+20=0$$
$$t^2-9t+20=0$$
$$(t-5)(t-4)=0$$
$$t-5=0 \quad\text{or}\quad t-4=0$$
$$t=5 \quad\quad\quad t=4$$
Substitute $x+2$ for t.
$$x+2=5 \quad\text{or}\quad x+2=4$$
$$x=3 \quad\quad\quad x=2$$
The x-intercepts are 2 and 3.
The corresponding graph is graph (f).

85. $|5-4x| = 11$

$5-4x = 11$ $5-4x = -11$
$-4x = 6$ or $-4x = -16$
$x = -\dfrac{3}{2}$ $x = 4$

The solution set is $\left\{ -\dfrac{3}{2}, 4 \right\}$.

87. $x + \sqrt{x+5} = 7$

$\sqrt{x+5} = 7 - x$

$\left(\sqrt{x+5} \right)^2 = (7-x)^2$

$x + 5 = 49 - 14x + x^2$

$0 = x^2 - 15x + 44$

$0 = (x-4)(x-11)$

$x - 4 = 0$ or $x - 11 = 0$
$x = 4$ $x = 11$

11 does not check and must be rejected.
The solution set is $\{4\}$.

89. $2x^3 + x^2 - 8x + 2 = 6$

$2x^3 + x^2 - 8x - 4 = 0$

$x^2(2x+1) - 4(2x+1) = 0$

$(2x+1)(x^2 - 4) = 0$

$(2x+1)(x+2)(x-2) = 0$

$2x+1 = 0$ or $x+2 = 0$ or $x-2 = 0$
$x = -\dfrac{1}{2}$ $x = -2$ $x = 2$

The solution set is $\left\{ -\dfrac{1}{2}, -2, 2 \right\}$.

91. $(x+4)^{\frac{3}{2}} = 8$

$\left((x+4)^{\frac{3}{2}} \right)^{\frac{2}{3}} = (8)^{\frac{2}{3}}$

$x + 4 = \left(\sqrt[3]{8} \right)^2$

$x + 4 = (2)^2$

$x + 4 = 4$

$x = 0$

The solution set is $\{0\}$.

93.

$y_1 = y_2 + 3$

$\left(x^2 - 1 \right)^2 = 2\left(x^2 - 1 \right) + 3$

$\left(x^2 - 1 \right)^2 - 2\left(x^2 - 1 \right) - 3 = 0$

Let $t = x^2 - 1$ and substitute.

$t^2 - 2t - 3 = 0$

$(t+1)(t-3) = 0$

$t + 1 = 0$ or $t - 3 = 0$
$t = -1$ $t = 3$

Substitute $x^2 - 1$ for t.

$x^2 - 1 = -1$ or $x^2 - 1 = 3$
$x^2 = 0$ $x^2 = 4$
$x = 0$ $x = \pm 2$

The solution set is $\{-2, 0, 2\}$.

95. $\left| x^2 + 2x - 36 \right| = 12$

$x^2 + 2x - 36 = 12$ $x^2 + 2x - 36 = -12$
$x^2 + 2x - 48 = 0$ or $x^2 + 2x - 24 = 0$
$(x+8)(x-6) = 0$ $(x+6)(x-4) = 0$

Setting each of the factors above equal to zero
gives $x = -8$, $x = 6$, $x = -6$,   and $x = 4$.
The solution set is $\{-8, -6, 4, 6\}$.

97. $x(x+1)^3 - 42(x+1)^2 = 0$

$(x+1)^2 \left(x(x+1) - 42 \right) = 0$

$(x+1)^2 \left(x^2 + x - 42 \right) = 0$

$(x+1)^2 (x+7)(x-6) = 0$

Setting each of the factors above equal to zero
gives $x = -7$, $x = -1$,   and $x = 6$.
The solution set is $\{-7, -1, 6\}$.

99. Let $x =$ the number.

$$\sqrt{5x-4} = x-2$$
$$\left(\sqrt{5x-4}\right)^2 = (x-2)^2$$
$$5x-4 = x^2 - 4x + 4$$
$$0 = x^2 - 9x + 8$$
$$0 = (x-8)(x-1)$$
$$x-8 = 0 \quad \text{or} \quad x-1 = 0$$
$$x = 8 \qquad\qquad x = 1$$

Check $x = 8$: $\sqrt{5(8)-4} = 8-2$
$$\sqrt{40-4} = 6$$
$$\sqrt{36} = 6$$
$$6 = 6$$

Check $x = 1$: $\sqrt{5(1)-4} = 1-2$
$$\sqrt{5-4} = -1$$
$$\sqrt{-1} \neq -1$$

Discard $x = 1$. The number is 8.

101.
$$r = \sqrt{\frac{3V}{\pi h}}$$
$$r^2 = \left(\sqrt{\frac{3V}{\pi h}}\right)^2$$
$$r^2 = \frac{3V}{\pi h}$$
$$\pi r^2 h = 3V$$
$$\frac{\pi r^2 h}{3} = V$$
$$V = \frac{\pi r^2 h}{3} \quad \text{or} \quad V = \frac{1}{3}\pi r^2 h$$

103. Exclude any value that causes the denominator to equal zero.
$$|x+2| - 14 = 0$$
$$|x+2| = 14$$
$$x+2 = 14 \qquad x+2 = -14$$
$$\text{or}$$
$$x = 12 \qquad\qquad x = -16$$

−16 and 12 must be excluded from the domain.

105. Let $P = 192$.
$$P = 28\sqrt{t} + 80$$
$$192 = 28\sqrt{t} + 80$$
$$112 = 28\sqrt{t}$$
$$\frac{112}{28} = \frac{28\sqrt{t}}{28}$$
$$4 = \sqrt{t}$$
$$(4)^2 = \left(\sqrt{t}\right)^2$$
$$16 = t$$

192 million computers will be sold 16 years after 1996, or 2012.

107. For the year 2100, we use $x = 98$.
$$H = 0.083(98) + 57.9$$
$$= 66.034$$
$$L = 0.36\sqrt{98} + 57.9$$
$$\approx 61.464$$

In the year 2100, the projected high end temperature is about $66°$ and the projected low end temperature is about $61.5°$.

109. Using H:
$$0.083x + 57.9 = 57.9 + 1$$
$$0.083x = 1$$
$$x = \frac{1}{0.083}$$
$$x \approx 12$$

The projected global temperature will exceed the 2002 average by 1 degree in 2014 (12 years after 2002).

Using L:
$$0.36\sqrt{x} + 57.9 = 1 + 57.9$$
$$0.36\sqrt{x} = 1$$
$$\sqrt{x} = \frac{1}{0.36}$$
$$\left(\sqrt{x}\right)^2 = \left(\frac{1}{0.36}\right)^2$$
$$x \approx 8$$

The projected global temperature will exceed the 2002 average by 1 degree in 2010 (8 years after 2002).

111.
$$y = 5000\sqrt{100-x}$$
$$40000 = 5000\sqrt{100-x}$$
$$\frac{40000}{5000} = \frac{5000\sqrt{100-x}}{5000}$$
$$8 = \sqrt{100-x}$$
$$8^2 = \left(\sqrt{100-x}\right)^2$$
$$64 = 100 - x$$
$$-36 = -x$$
$$36 = x$$

40,000 people in the group will survive to age 36. This is shown on the graph as the point $(36, \ 40000)$.

113.
$$365 = 0.2x^{3/2}$$
$$\frac{365}{0.2} = \frac{0.2x^{3/2}}{0.2}$$
$$1825 = x^{3/2}$$
$$1825^2 = \left(x^{3/2}\right)^2$$
$$3,330,625 = x^3$$
$$\sqrt[3]{3,330,625} = \sqrt[3]{x^3}$$
$$149.34 \approx x$$

The average distance of the Earth from the sun is approximately 149 million kilometers.

115. $\sqrt{6^2 + x^2} + \sqrt{8^2 + (10-x)^2} = 18$

$$\sqrt{36 + x^2} = 18 - \sqrt{64 + 100 - 20x + x^2}$$
$$36 + x^2 = 324 - 36\sqrt{x^2 - 20x + 164} + x^2 - 20x + 164$$
$$36\sqrt{x^2 - 20x + 164} = -20x + 452$$
$$9\sqrt{x^2 - 20x + 164} = -5x + 113$$
$$81(x^2 - 20x + 164) = 25x^2 - 1130x + 12769$$
$$81x^2 - 1620x + 13284 = 25x^2 - 1130x + 12769$$
$$56x^2 - 490x + 515 = 0$$
$$x = \frac{490 \pm \sqrt{(-490)^2 - 4(56)(515)}}{2(56)}$$
$$x = \frac{490 \pm 353.19}{112}$$
$$x \approx 1.2 \qquad x \approx 7.5$$

The point should be located approximately either 1.2 feet or 7.5 feet from the base of the 6-foot pole.

125. $x^3 + 3x^2 - x - 3 = 0$
The solution set is $\{-3, -1, 1\}$.
$$(-3)^3 + 3(-3)^2 - (-3) - 3 = 0$$
$$-27 + 27 + 3 - 3 = 0$$
$$(-1)^3 + 3(-1)^2 - (-1) - 3 = 0$$
$$-1 + 3 + 1 - 3 = 0$$
$$1^3 + 3(1)^2 - (1) - 3 = 0$$
$$1 + 3 - 1 - 3 = 0$$

127. $\sqrt{2x+13} - x - 5 = 0$
The solution set is $\{-2\}$.
$$\sqrt{2(-2)+13} - (-2) - 5 = 0$$
$$\sqrt{-4+13} + 2 - 5 = 0$$
$$\sqrt{9} - 3 = 0$$
$$3 - 3 = 0$$

129. a. False; $\left(\sqrt{y+4}+\sqrt{y-1}\right)^2 \neq y+4+y-1$

b. False; if $t=(x^2-2x)^3$, the original equation can be written as $t^3-5t+6=0$, not a quadratic form.

c. False; the other value may be a solution.

d. True

(d) is true

131. $5-\dfrac{2}{x}=\sqrt{5-\dfrac{2}{x}}$

or

$5-\dfrac{2}{x}=0 \qquad 5-\dfrac{2}{x}=1$

$5=\dfrac{2}{x} \qquad -\dfrac{2}{x}=-4$

$5x=2 \qquad -4x=-2$

$x=\dfrac{2}{5} \qquad x=\dfrac{1}{2}$

The solution set is $\left\{\dfrac{2}{5},\dfrac{1}{2}\right\}$.

133. $x^{5/6}+x^{2/3}-2x^{1/2}=0$

$x^{1/2}(x^{2/6}+x^{1/6}-2)=0$ let $t=x^{1/6}$

$x^{1/2}(t^2+t-2)=0$

$x^{1/2}=0 \quad t^2+t-2=0$

$(t-1)(t+2)=0$

$t-1=0 \qquad t+2=0$

$t=1 \qquad t=-2$

$x^{1/6}=1 \qquad x^{1/6}=-2$

$x=1^6 \qquad x=(-2)^6$

$x=0 \quad x=1 \qquad x=64$

64 does not check and must be rejected.
The solution set is {0, 1}.

Section 1.7

Check Point Exercises

1. a. $[-2,\ 5)=\{x|-2 \le x < 5\}$

b. $[1,\ 3.5]=\{x|1 \le x \le 3.5\}$

c. $[-\infty,\ -1)=\{x|x < -1\}$

2. a. Graph $[1,3]$:

Graph $(2,6)$:

To find the intersection, take the portion of the number line that the two graphs have in common.

Numbers in both $[1,3]$ and $(2,6)$:

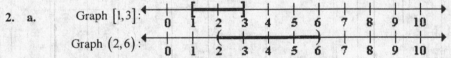

Thus, $[1,3] \cap (2,6) = (2,3]$.

b. Graph $[1,3]$:

Graph $(2,6)$:

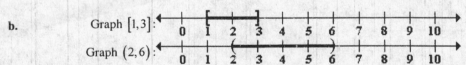

To find the union, take the portion of the number line representing the total collection of numbers in the two graphs.

Numbers in either $[1,3]$ or $(2,6)$ or both:

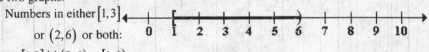

Thus, $[1,3] \cup (2,6) = [1,6)$.

97

3. $2 - 3x \le 5$

$-3x \le 3$

$x \ge -1$

The solution set is $\{x \mid x \ge -1\}$ or $[-1, \infty)$.

4. $3x + 1 > 7x - 15$

$-4x > -16$

$\dfrac{-4x}{-4} < \dfrac{-16}{-4}$

$x < 4$

The solution set is $\{x \mid x < 4\}$ or $(-\infty, 4]$.

5. a. $3(x + 1) > 3x + 2$

$3x + 3 > 3x + 2$

$3 > 2$

$3 > 2$ is true for all values of x.

The solution set is $\{x \mid x \text{ is a real number}\}$.

b. $x + 1 \le x - 1$

$1 \le -1$

$1 \le -1$ is false for all values of x.

The solution set is $\varnothing$.

6. $1 \le 2x + 3 < 11$

$-2 \le 2x < 8$

$-1 \le x < 4$

The solution set is $\{x \mid -1 \le x < 4\}$ or $[-1, 4)$.

7. $|x - 2| < 5$

$-5 < x - 2 < 5$

$-3 < x < 7$

The solution set is $\{x \mid -3 < x < 7\}$ or $(-3, 7)$.

8. $-3|5x - 2| + 20 \ge -19$

$-3|5x - 2| \ge -39$

$\dfrac{-3|5x - 2|}{-3} \le \dfrac{-39}{-3}$

$|5x - 2| \le 13$

$-13 \le 5x - 2 \le 13$

$-11 \le 5x \le 15$

$\dfrac{-11}{5} \le \dfrac{5x}{5} \le \dfrac{15}{5}$

$-\dfrac{11}{5} \le x \le 3$

The solution set is

$\left\{ x \,\middle|\, -\dfrac{11}{5} \le x \le 3 \right\}$ or $\left[-\dfrac{11}{5}, 3 \right]$.

9. $18 < |6 - 3x|$

$6 - 3x < -18 \quad$ or $\quad 6 - 3x > 18$

$-3x < -24 \qquad\qquad -3x > 12$

$\dfrac{-3x}{-3} > \dfrac{-24}{-3} \qquad \dfrac{-3x}{-3} < \dfrac{12}{-3}$

$x > 8 \qquad\qquad\quad x < -4$

The solution set is $\{x \mid x < -4 \text{ or } x > 8\}$

or $(-\infty, -4) \cup (8, \infty)$.

10.   Let x = the number of miles driven in a week.

$260 < 80 + 0.25x$

$180 < 0.25x$

$720 < x$

Driving more than 720 miles in a week makes Basic the better deal.

Exercise Set 1.7

1. $1 < x \le 6$

3. $-5 \le x < 2$

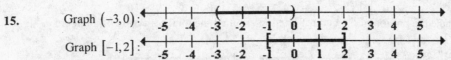

5. $-3 \le x \le 1$

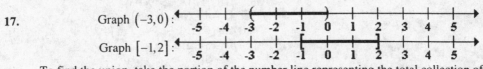

7. $x > 2$

9. $x \ge -3$

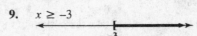

11. $x < 3$

13. $x < 5.5$

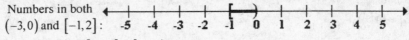

15.   Graph $(-3, 0)$:

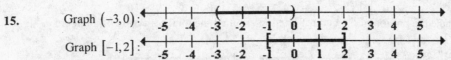

Graph $[-1, 2]$:

To find the intersection, take the portion of the number line that the two graphs have in common.

Numbers in both
$(-3, 0)$ and $[-1, 2]$:

Thus, $(-3, 0) \cap [-1, 2] = [-1, 0)$.

17.   Graph $(-3, 0)$:

Graph $[-1, 2]$:

To find the union, take the portion of the number line representing the total collection of numbers in the two graphs.

Numbers in either $(-3, 0)$
or $[-1, 2]$ or both:

Thus, $(-3, 0) \cup [-1, 2] = (-3, 2]$.

19.   Graph $(-\infty, 5)$:

Graph $[1, 8]$:

To find the intersection, take the portion of the number line that the two graphs have in common.

Numbers in both
$(-\infty, 5)$ and $[1, 8]$:

Thus, $(-\infty, 5) \cap [1, 8] = [1, 5)$.

21.   Graph $(-\infty, 5)$:

Graph $[1, 8]$:

To find the union, take the portion of the number line representing the total collection of numbers in the two graphs.

Numbers in either $(-\infty, 5)$
or $[1, 8]$ or both:

Thus, $(-\infty, 5) \cup [1, 8] = (-\infty, 8]$.

23.

Graph $[3,\infty)$: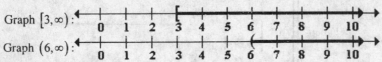

Graph $(6,\infty)$: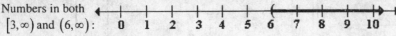

To find the intersection, take the portion of the number line that the two graphs have in common.

Numbers in both $[3,\infty)$ and $(6,\infty)$:

Thus, $[3,\infty) \cap (6,\infty) = (6,\infty)$.

25.

Graph $[3,\infty)$: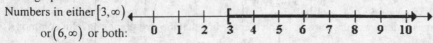

Graph $(6,\infty)$:

To find the union, take the portion of the number line representing the total collection of numbers in the two graphs.

Numbers in either $[3,\infty)$ or $(6,\infty)$ or both: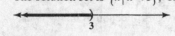

Thus, $[3,\infty) \cup (6,\infty) = [3,\infty)$.

27. $5x + 11 < 26$
$5x < 15$
$x < 3$
The solution set is $\{x \mid x < 3\}$, or $(-\infty, 3)$.

29. $3x - 7 \geq 13$
$3x \geq 20$
$x \geq \dfrac{20}{3}$
The solution set is $\left\{x \mid x > \dfrac{20}{3}\right\}$, or $\left[\dfrac{20}{3}, \infty\right)$.

31. $-9x \geq 36$
$x \leq -4$
The solution set is $\{x \mid x \leq -4\}$, or $(-\infty, -4]$.

33. $8x - 11 \leq 3x - 13$
$8x - 3x \leq -13 + 11$
$5x \leq -2$
$x \leq -\dfrac{2}{5}$
The solution set is $\left\{x \mid x \leq -\dfrac{2}{5}\right\}$, or $\left(-\infty, -\dfrac{2}{5}\right]$.

35. $4(x + 1) + 2 \geq 3x + 6$
$4x + 4 + 2 \geq 3x + 6$
$4x + 6 \geq 3x + 6$
$4x - 3x \geq 6 - 6$
$x \geq 0$
The solution set is $\{x \mid x > 0\}$, or $[0, \infty)$.

37. $2x - 11 < -3(x + 2)$
$2x - 11 < -3x - 6$
$5x < 5$
$x < 1$
The solution set is $\{x \mid x < 1\}$, or $(-\infty, 1)$.

39. $1 - (x + 3) \geq 4 - 2x$
$1 - x - 3 \geq 4 - 2x$
$-x - 2 \geq 4 - 2x$
$x \geq 6$
The solution set is $\{x \mid x \geq 6\}$, or $[6, \infty)$.

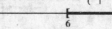

100

41.
$$\frac{x}{4} - \frac{3}{2} \le \frac{x}{2} + 1$$

$$\frac{4x}{4} - \frac{4 \cdot 3}{2} \le \frac{4 \cdot x}{2} + 4 \cdot 1$$

$$x - 6 \le 2x + 4$$

$$-x \le 10$$

$$x \ge -10$$

The solution set is $\{x \mid x \ge -10\}$, or $[-10, \infty)$.

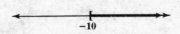

43. $1 - \dfrac{x}{2} > 4$

$$-\frac{x}{2} > 3$$

$$x < -6$$

The solution set is $\{x \mid x, -6\}$, or $(-\infty, -6)$.

45. $\dfrac{x-4}{6} \ge \dfrac{x-2}{9} + \dfrac{5}{18}$

$$3(x-4) \ge 2(x-2) + 5$$

$$3x - 12 \ge 2x - 4 + 5$$

$$x \ge 13$$

The solution set is $\{x \mid x \ge 13\}$, or $[13, \infty)$.

47. $4(3x - 2) - 3x < 3(1 + 3x) - 7$

$$12x - 8 - 3x < 3 + 9x - 7$$

$$9x - 8 < -4 + 9x$$

$$-8 < -4$$

True for all x

The solution set is $\{x \mid x \text{ is any real number}\}$, or

$$(-\infty, \infty).$$

49. $5(x - 2) - 3(x + 4) \ge 2x - 20$

$$5x - 10 - 3x - 12 \ge 2x - 20$$

$$2x - 22 \ge 2x - 20$$

$$-22 \ge -20$$

Not true for any x.

The solution set is the empty set, $\varnothing$.

51. $6 < x + 3 < 8$

$$6 - 3 < x + 3 - 3 < 8 - 3$$

$$3 < x < 5$$

The solution set is $\{x \mid 3 < x < 5\}$, or $(3, 5)$.

53. $-3 \le x - 2 < 1$

$$-1 \le x < 3$$

The solution set is $\{x \mid -1 \le x < 3\}$, or $[-1, 3)$.

55. $-11 < 2x - 1 \le -5$

$$-10 < 2x \le -4$$

$$-5 < x \le -2$$

The solution set is $\{x \mid -5 < x \le -2\}$, or

$$(-5, -2].$$

57. $-3 \le \dfrac{2}{3}x - 5 < -1$

$$2 \le \frac{2}{3}x < 4$$

$$3 \le x < 6$$

The solution set is $\{x \mid 3 \le x < 6\}$, or $[3, 6)$.

59. $|x| < 3$

$$-3 < x < 3$$

The solution set is $\{x \mid -3 < x < 3\}$, or $(-3, 3)$.

61. $|x - 1| \le 2$

$$-2 \le x - 1 \le 2$$

$$-1 \le x \le 3$$

The solution set is $\{x \mid -1 \le x \le 3\}$, or $[-1, 3]$.

62. $|x + 3| \le 4$

$$-4 \le x + 3 \le 4$$

$$-7 \le x \le 1$$

The solution set is $\{x \mid -7 \le x \le 1\}$ or $[-7, 1]$.

63. $|2x - 6| < 8$

$$-8 < 2x - 6 < 8$$

$$-2 < 2x < 14$$

$$-1 < x < 7$$

The solution set is $\{x \mid -1 < x < 7\}$, or $(-1, 7)$.

65. $|2(x - 1) + 4| \le 8$

$$-8 \le 2(x - 1) + 4 \le 8$$

$$-8 \le 2x - 2 + 4 \le 8$$

$$-8 \le 2x + 2 \le 8$$

$$-10 \le 2x \le 6$$

$$-5 \le x \le 3$$

The solution set is $\{x \mid -5 \le x \le 3\}$, or

$$[-5, 3].$$

67. $\left|\dfrac{2y+6}{3}\right| < 2$

$-2 < \dfrac{2y+6}{3} < 2$

$-6 < 2y + 6 < 6$

$-12 < 2y < 0$

$-6 < y < 0$

The solution set is $\{x \mid -6 < y < 0\}$, or $(-6, 0)$.

69. $|x| > 3$

$x > 3$ or $x < -3$

The solution set is $\{x \mid x > 3 \text{ or } x < -3\}$, that is,

$(-\infty, -3)$ or $(3, \infty)$.

71. $|x - 1| \geq 2$

$x - 1 \geq 2$ or $x - 1 \leq -2$

$x \geq 3$ $x \leq -1$

The solution set is $\{x \mid x \leq -1 \text{ or } x \geq 3\}$, that is,

$(-\infty, -1]$ or $[3, \infty)$.

73. $|3x - 8| > 7$

$3x - 8 > 7$ or $3x - 8 < -7$

$3x > 15$ $3x < 1$

$x > 5$ $x < \dfrac{1}{3}$

The solution set is $\left\{x \mid x < \dfrac{1}{3} \text{ or } x > 5\right\}$, that is,

$\left(-\infty, \dfrac{1}{3}\right)$ or $(5, \infty)$.

75. $\left|\dfrac{2x+2}{4}\right| \geq 2$

$\dfrac{2x+2}{4} \geq 2$ or $\dfrac{2x+2}{4} \leq -2$

$2x + 2 \geq 8$ $2x + 2 \leq -8$

$2x \geq 6$ $2x \leq -10$

$x \geq 3$ $x \leq -5$

The solution set is $\{x \mid x \leq -5 \text{ or } x \geq 3\}$, that is,

$(-\infty, -5]$ or $[3, \infty)$.

77. $\left|3 - \dfrac{2}{3}x\right| > 5$

$3 - \dfrac{2}{3}x > 5$ or $3 - \dfrac{2}{3}x < -5$

$-\dfrac{2}{3}x > 2$ $-\dfrac{2}{3}x < -8$

$x < -3$ $x > 12$

The solution set is $\{x \mid x < -3 \text{ or } x > 12\}$, that is,

$(-\infty, -3)$ or $(12, \infty)$.

79. $3|x - 1| + 2 \geq 8$

$3|x - 1| \geq 6$

$|x - 1| \geq 2$

$x - 1 \geq 2$ or $x - 1 \leq -2$

$x \geq 3$ $x \leq -1$

The solution set is $\{x \mid x \leq 1 \text{ or } x \geq 3\}$, that is,

$(-\infty, -1]$ or $[3, \infty)$.

81. $-2|x - 4| \geq -4$

$\dfrac{-2|x-4|}{-2} \leq \dfrac{-4}{-2}$

$|x - 4| \leq 2$

$-2 \leq x - 4 \leq 2$

$2 \leq x \leq 6$

The solution set is $\{x \mid 2 \leq x \leq 6\}$.

83. $-4|1 - x| < -16$

$\dfrac{-4|1-x|}{-4} > \dfrac{-16}{-4}$

$|1 - x| > 4$

$1 - x > 4$ $1 - x < -4$

$-x > 3$ or $-x < -5$

$x < -3$ $x > 5$

The solution set is $\{x \mid x < -3 \text{ or } x > 5\}$.

85. $3 \leq |2x - 1|$

$2x - 1 \geq 3$ $2x - 1 \leq -3$

$2x \geq 4$ or $2x \leq -2$

$x \geq 2$ $x \leq -1$

The solution set is $\{x \mid x \leq -1 \text{ or } x \geq 2\}$.

87. $5 > |4 - x|$ is equivalent to $|4 - x| < 5$.

$$-5 < 4 - x < 5$$
$$-9 < -x < 1$$
$$\frac{-9}{-1} > \frac{-x}{-1} > \frac{1}{-1}$$
$$9 > x > -1$$
$$-1 < x < 9$$

The solution set is $\{x | -1 < x < 9\}$.

89. $1 < |2 - 3x|$ is equivalent to $|2 - 3x| > 1$.

$$2 - 3x > 1$$
$$-3x > -1$$
$$\frac{-3x}{-3} < \frac{-1}{-3} \quad \text{or}$$
$$x < \frac{1}{3}$$

$$2 - 3x < -1$$
$$-3x < -3$$
$$\frac{-3x}{-3} > \frac{-3}{-3}$$
$$x > 1$$

The solution set is $\left\{ x \,\middle|\, x < \frac{1}{3} \text{ or } x > 1 \right\}$.

91. $12 < \left|-2x + \frac{6}{7}\right| + \frac{3}{7}$

$$\frac{81}{7} < \left|-2x + \frac{6}{7}\right|$$

$$-2x + \frac{6}{7} > \frac{81}{7} \quad \text{or} \quad -2x + \frac{6}{7} < -\frac{81}{7}$$

$$-2x > \frac{75}{7} \qquad\qquad -2x < -\frac{87}{7}$$

$$x < -\frac{75}{14} \qquad\qquad x > \frac{87}{14}$$

The solution set is $\left\{ x \,\middle|\, x < -\frac{75}{14} \text{ or } x > \frac{87}{14} \right\}$,

that is, $\left(-\infty, -\frac{75}{14}\right)$ or $\left(\frac{87}{14}, \infty\right)$.

93. $4 + \left|3 - \frac{x}{3}\right| \geq 9$

$$\left|3 - \frac{x}{3}\right| \geq 5$$

$$3 - \frac{x}{3} \geq 5 \quad \text{or} \quad 3 - \frac{x}{3} \leq -5$$

$$-\frac{x}{3} \geq 2 \qquad\qquad -\frac{x}{3} \leq -8$$

$$x \leq -6 \qquad\qquad x \geq 24$$

The solution set is $\{x | x \leq -6 \text{ or } x \geq 24\}$, that is,

$(-\infty, -6]$ or $[24, \infty)$.

95.
$$y_1 \leq y_2$$
$$\frac{x}{2} + 3 \leq \frac{x}{3} + \frac{5}{2}$$
$$6\left(\frac{x}{2} + 3\right) \leq 6\left(\frac{x}{3} + \frac{5}{2}\right)$$
$$\frac{6x}{2} + 6(3) \leq \frac{6x}{3} + \frac{6(5)}{2}$$
$$3x + 18 \leq 2x + 15$$
$$x \leq -3$$

The solution set is $(-\infty, -3]$.

97.
$$y \geq 4$$
$$1 - (x + 3) + 2x \geq 4$$
$$1 - x - 3 + 2x \geq 4$$
$$x - 2 \geq 4$$
$$x \geq 6$$

The solution set is $[6, \infty)$.

99.
$$y < 8$$
$$|3x - 4| + 2 < 8$$
$$|3x - 4| < 6$$
$$-6 < 3x - 4 < 6$$
$$-2 < 3x < 10$$
$$\frac{-2}{3} < \frac{3x}{3} < \frac{10}{3}$$
$$\frac{-2}{3} < x < \frac{10}{3}$$

The solution set is $\left(\frac{-2}{3}, \frac{10}{3}\right)$.

101.
$$y \leq 4$$
$$7 - \left|\frac{x}{2} + 2\right| \leq 4$$
$$-\left|\frac{x}{2} + 2\right| \leq -3$$
$$\left|\frac{x}{2} + 2\right| \geq 3$$

$$\frac{x}{2} + 2 \geq 3 \quad \text{or} \quad \frac{x}{2} + 2 \leq -3$$
$$x + 4 \geq 6 \qquad\qquad x + 4 \leq -6$$
$$x \geq 2 \qquad\qquad\quad x \leq -10$$

The solution set is $(-\infty, -10] \cup [2, \infty)$.

103. The graph's height is below 5 on the interval $(-1,9)$.

105. The solution set is $\{x \mid -1 \le x < 2\}$ or $[-1,2)$.

107. Let x be the number.
$$|4-3x| \ge 5 \quad \text{or} \quad |3x-4| \ge 5$$

$$3x-4 \ge 5 \qquad 3x-4 \le -5$$
$$3x \ge 9 \quad \text{or} \quad 3x \le -1$$
$$x \ge 3 \qquad\qquad x \le -\frac{1}{3}$$

The solution set is $\left\{x \mid x \le -\frac{1}{3} \text{ or } x \ge 3\right\}$ or $\left(-\infty, -\frac{1}{3}\right] \cup [3, \infty)$.

109. $(0,4)$

111. passion $\le$ intimacy or intimacy $\ge$ passion

113. passion<commitment or commitment > passion

115. 9, after 3 years

117. $3.1x + 25.8 > 63$
$$3.1x > 37.2$$
$$x > 12$$
Since x is the number of years after 1994, we calculate 1994+12=2006. 63% of voters will use electronic systems after 2006.

119. $28 \le 20 + 0.40(x-60) \le 40$
$$28 \le 20 + 0.40x - 24 \le 40$$
$$28 \le 0.40x - 4 \le 40$$
$$32 \le 0.40x \le 44$$
$$80 \le x \le 110$$
Between 80 and 110 ten minutes, inclusive.

121. $\left|\dfrac{h-50}{5}\right| \ge 1.645$

$$\frac{h-50}{5} \ge 1.645 \quad \text{or} \quad \frac{h-50}{5} \le -1.645$$
$$h-50 \ge 8.225 \qquad h-50 \le -8.225$$
$$h \ge 58.225 \qquad\quad h \le 41.775$$
The number of outcomes would be 59 or more, or 41 or less.

123. $15 + 0.08x < 3 + .12x$
$$12 < 0.04x$$
$$300 < x$$
Plan A is a better deal when driving more than 300 miles a month.

125. $2 + 0.08x < 8 + 0.05x$
$$0.03x < 6$$
$$x < 200$$
The credit union is a better deal when writing less than 200 checks.

127. $3000 + 3x < 5.5x$
$$3000 < 2.5x$$
$$1200 < x$$
More then 1200 packets of stationary need to be sold each week to make a profit.

129. $245 + 95x \le 3000$
$$95x \le 2755$$
$$x \le 29$$
29 bags or less can be lifted safely.

131. a. $\dfrac{86 + 88 + x}{3} \ge 90$

$$\frac{174 + x}{3} \ge 90$$
$$174 + x \ge 270$$
$$x \ge 96$$
You must get at least a 96.

b. $\dfrac{86 + 88 + x}{3} < 80$

$$\frac{174 + x}{3} < 80$$
$$174 + x < 240$$
$$x < 66$$
This will happen if you get a grade less than 66.

133. Let x = the number of times the bridge is crossed per three month period
The cost with the 3-month pass is
$C_3 = 7.50 + 0.50x$.
The cost with the 6-month pass is $C_6 = 30$.

Because we need to buy two 3-month passes per 6-month pass, we multiply the cost with the 3-month pass by 2.
$$2(7.50 + 0.50x) < 30$$
$$15 + x < 30$$
$$x < 15$$
We also must consider the cost without purchasing a pass. We need this cost to be less than the cost with a 3-month pass.
$$3x > 7.50 + 0.50x$$
$$2.50x > 7.50$$
$$x > 3$$
The 3-month pass is the best deal when making more than 3 but less than 15 crossings per 3-month period.

143.

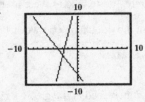

$x < -3$

145 a. The cost of Plan A is $4 + 0.10x$;
The cost of Plan B is $2 + 0.15x$.

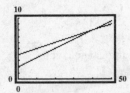

c. 41 or more checks make Plan A better.

d.
$$4 + 0.10x < 2 + 0.15x$$
$$2 < 0.05x$$
$$x > 40$$
The solution set is $\{x \mid x > 40\}$ or $(40, \infty)$.

147. Because $x > y$, $y - x$ represents a negative number. When both sides are multiplied by $(y - x)$ the inequality must be reversed.

149. Model 1:
$$|T - 57| < 7$$
$$-7 < T - 57 < 7$$
$$50 < T < 64$$
Model 2:
$$|T - 50| < 22$$
$$-22 < T - 50 < 22$$
$$28 < T < 72$$

Model 1 describes a city with monthly temperature averages ranging from 50 degrees to 64 degrees Fahrenheit. Model 2 describes a city with monthly temperature averages ranging from 28 degrees to 72 degrees Fahrenheit.

Model 1 describes San Francisco and model 2 describes Albany.

Chapter 1 Review Exercises

1.

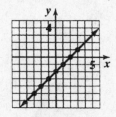

$$y = 2x - 2$$

$x = -3, y = -8$
$x = -2, y = -6$
$x = -1, y = -4$
$x = 0, y = -2$
$x = 1, y = 0$
$x = 2, y = 2$
$x = 3, y = 4$

2.

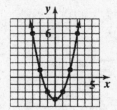

$$y = x^2 - 3$$

$x = -3, y = 6$
$x = -2, y = 1$
$x = -1, y = -2$
$x = 0, y = -3$
$x = 1, y = -2$
$x = 2, y = 1$
$x = 3, y = 6$

3.

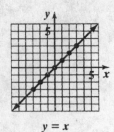

$$y = x$$

$x = -3, y = -3$
$x = -2, y = -2$
$x = -1, y = -1$
$x = 0, y = 0$
$x = 1, y = 1$
$x = 2, y = 2$
$x = 3, y = 3$

4.

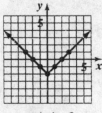

$$y = |x| - 2$$

$x = -3, y = 1$
$x = -2, y = 0$
$x = -1, y = -1$
$x = 0, y = -2$
$x = 1, y = -1$
$x = 2, y = 0$
$x = 3, y = 1$

5. A portion of Cartesian coordinate plane with minimum x-value equal to -20, maximum x-value equal to 40, x-scale equal to 10 and with minimum y-value equal to -5, maximum y-value equal to 5, and y-scale equal to 1.

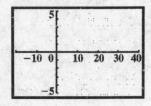

6. x-intercept: -2; The graph intersects the x-axis at $(-2, 0)$.
y-intercept: 2; The graph intersects the y-axis at $(0, 2)$.

7. x-intercepts: 2, -2; The graph intersects the x-axis at $(-2, 0)$ and $(2, 0)$.
y-intercept: -4; The graph intercepts the y-axis at $(0, -4)$.

8. x-intercept: 5; The graph intersects the x-axis at $(5, 0)$.
y-intercept: None; The graph does not intersect the y-axis.

9. Point A is $(91, 125)$. This means that in 1991, 125,000 acres were used for cultivation

10. Opium cultivation was 150,000 acres in 1997.

11. Opium cultivation was at a minimum in 2001 when approximately 25,000 acres were used.

12. Opium cultivation was at a maximum in 2004 when approximately 300,000 acres were used.

13. Opium cultivation did not change between 1991 and 1992.

14. Opium cultivation increased at the greatest rate between 2001 and 2002. The increase in acres used for opium cultivation in this time period was approximately $180,000 - 25,000 = 155,000$ acres.

15. $2x - 5 = 7$
$\quad 2x = 12$
$\quad\; x = 6$
The solution set is $\{6\}$.
This is a conditional equation.

16. $5x + 20 = 3x$
$\quad\; 2x = -20$
$\quad\;\; x = -10$
The solution set is $\{-10\}$.
This is a conditional equation.

17. $7(x - 4) = x + 2$
$7x - 28 = x + 2$
$\quad\;\; 6x = 30$
$\quad\;\;\; x = 5$
The solution set is $\{5\}$.
This is a conditional equation.

18. $1 - 2(6 - x) = 3x + 2$
     $1 - 12 + 2x = 3x + 2$
     $-11 - x = 2$
     $-x = 13$
     $x = -13$
     The solution set is $\{-13\}$.
     This is a conditional equation.

19. $2(x - 4) + 3(x + 5) = 2x - 2$
     $2x - 8 + 3x + 15 = 2x - 2$
     $5x + 7 = 2x - 2$
     $3x = -9$
     $x = -3$
     The solution set is $\{-3\}$.
     This is a conditional equation.

20. $2x - 4(5x + 1) = 3x + 17$
     $2x - 20x - 4 = 3x + 17$
     $-18x - 4 = 3x + 17$
     $-21x = 21$
     $x = -1$
     The solution set is $\{-1\}$.
     This is a conditional equation.

21. $7x + 5 = 5(x + 3) + 2x$
     $7x + 5 = 5x + 15 + 2x$
     $7x + 5 = 7x + 15$
     $5 = 15$
     The solution set is $\varnothing$.
     This is an inconsistent equation.

22. $7x + 13 = 2(2x - 5) + 3x + 23$
     $7x + 13 = 2(2x - 5) + 3x + 23$
     $7x + 13 = 4x - 10 + 3x + 23$
     $7x + 13 = 7x + 13$
     $13 = 13$
     The solution set is all real numbers.
     This is an identity.

23. $\dfrac{2x}{3} = \dfrac{x}{6} + 1$
     $2(2x) = x + 6$
     $4x = x + 6$
     $3x = 6$
     $x = 2$
     The solution set is $\{2\}$.
     This is a conditional equation.

24. $\dfrac{x}{2} - \dfrac{1}{10} = \dfrac{x}{5} + \dfrac{1}{2}$
     $5x - 1 = 2x + 5$
     $3x = 6$
     $x = 2$
     The solution set is $\{2\}$.
     This is a conditional equation.

25. $\dfrac{2x}{3} = 6 - \dfrac{x}{4}$
     $4(2x) = 12(6) - 3x$
     $8x = 72 - 3x$
     $11x = 72$
     $x = \dfrac{72}{11}$
     The solution set is $\left\{\dfrac{72}{11}\right\}$.
     This is a conditional equation.

26. $\dfrac{x}{4} = 2 - \dfrac{x - 3}{3}$
     $\dfrac{12 \cdot x}{4} = 12(2) - \dfrac{12(x - 3)}{3}$
     $3x = 24 - 4x + 12$
     $7x = 36$
     $x = \dfrac{36}{7}$
     The solution set is $\left\{\dfrac{36}{7}\right\}$.
     This is a conditional equation.

27. $\dfrac{3x + 1}{3} - \dfrac{13}{2} = \dfrac{1 - x}{4}$
     $4(3x + 1) - 6(13) = 3(1 - x)$
     $12x + 4 - 78 = 3 - 3x$
     $12x - 74 = 3 - 3x$
     $15x = 77$
     $x = \dfrac{77}{15}$
     The solution set is $\left\{\dfrac{77}{15}\right\}$.
     This is a conditional equation.

28.
$$\frac{9}{4} - \frac{1}{2x} = \frac{4}{x}$$
$$9x - 2 = 16$$
$$9x = 18$$
$$x = 2$$
The solution set is $\{2\}$.
This is a conditional equation.

29.
$$\frac{7}{x-5} + 2 = \frac{x+2}{x-5}$$
$$7 + 2(x-5) = x+2$$
$$7 + 2x - 10 = x+2$$
$$2x - 3 = x+2$$
$$x = 5$$
5 does not check and must be rejected.
The solution set is the empty set, $\varnothing$.
This is an inconsistent equation.

30.
$$\frac{1}{x-1} - \frac{1}{x+1} = \frac{2}{x^2-1}$$
$$\frac{1}{x-1} - \frac{1}{x+1} = \frac{2}{(x+1)(x-1)}$$
$$x + 1 - (x-1) = 2$$
$$x + 1 - x + 1 = 2$$
$$2 = 2$$
The solution set is all real numbers except -1
and 1. This is a conditional equation.

31.
$$\frac{5}{x+3} + \frac{1}{x-2} = \frac{8}{x^2+x-6}$$
$$\frac{5}{x+3} + \frac{1}{x-2} = \frac{8}{(x+3)(x-2)}$$
$$\frac{5(x+3)(x-2)}{x+3} + \frac{(x+3)(x-2)}{x-2} = \frac{8(x+3)(x-2)}{(x+3)(x-2)}$$
$$5(x-2) + 1(x+3) = 8$$
$$5x - 10 + x + 3 = 8$$
$$6x - 7 = 8$$
$$6x = 15$$
$$x = \frac{15}{6}$$
$$x = \frac{5}{2}$$
The solution set is $\left\{\frac{5}{2}\right\}$.
This is a conditional equation.

32.
$$\frac{1}{x+5} = 0$$
$$(x+5)\frac{1}{x+5} = (x+5)(0)$$
$$1 = 0$$
The solution set is the empty set, $\varnothing$.
This is an inconsistent equation.

33.
$$\frac{4}{x+2} + \frac{3}{x} = \frac{10}{x^2+2x}$$
$$\frac{4}{x+2} + \frac{3}{x} = \frac{10}{x(x+2)}$$
$$\frac{4 \cdot x(x+2)}{x+2} + \frac{3 \cdot x(x+2)}{x} = \frac{10 \cdot x(x+2)}{x(x+2)}$$
$$4x + 3(x+2) = 10$$
$$4x + 3x + 6 = 10$$
$$7x + 6 = 10$$
$$7x = 4$$
$$x = \frac{4}{7}$$
The solution set is $\left\{\frac{4}{7}\right\}$.
This is a conditional equation.

34.
$$3 - 5(2x+1) - 2(x-4) = 0$$
$$3 - 5(2x+1) - 2(x-4) = 0$$
$$3 - 10x - 5 - 2x + 8 = 0$$
$$-12x + 6 = 0$$
$$-12x = -6$$
$$x = \frac{-6}{-12}$$
$$x = \frac{1}{2}$$
The solution set is $\left\{\frac{1}{2}\right\}$.
This is a conditional equation.

35.
$$\frac{x+2}{x+3}+\frac{1}{x^2+2x-3}-1=0$$
$$\frac{x+2}{x+3}+\frac{1}{(x+3)(x-1)}-1=0$$
$$\frac{x+2}{x+3}+\frac{1}{(x+3)(x-1)}=1$$
$$\frac{(x+2)(x+3)(x-1)}{x+3}+1=(x+3)(x-1)$$
$$(x+2)(x-1)+1=(x+3)(x-1)$$
$$x^2+x-2+1=x^2+2x-3$$
$$x-1=2x-3$$
$$-x=-2$$
$$x=2$$

The solution set is $\{2\}$.

This is a conditional equation.

36. Let x = the number of calories in Burger King's Chicken Caesar.
$x+125$ = the number of calories in Taco Bell's Express Taco Salad.
$x+95$ = the number of calories in Wendy's Mandarin Chicken Salad.
$$x+(x+125)+(x+95)=1705$$
$$3x+220=1705$$
$$3x=1485$$
$$x=495$$
$$x+125=495+125=620$$
$$x+95=495+95=590$$

There are 495 calories in the Chicken Caesar, 620 calories in the Express Taco Salad, and 590 calories in the Mandarin Chicken Salad.

37. Let x = the number of years after 1970.
$$P=-0.5x+37.4$$
$$18.4=-0.5x+37.4$$
$$-19=-0.5x$$
$$\frac{-19}{-0.5}=\frac{-0.5x}{-0.5}$$
$$38=x$$

If the trend continues only 18.4% of U.S. adults will smoke cigarettes 38 years after 1970, or 2008.

38.
$$15+.05x=5+.07x$$
$$10=.02x$$
$$500=x$$

Both plans cost the same at 500 minutes.

39. Let x = the original price of the phone
$$48=x-0.20x$$
$$48=0.80x$$
$$60=x$$

The original price is $60.

40. Let x = the amount sold to earn $800 in one week
$$800=300+0.05x$$
$$500=0.05x$$
$$10,000=x$$

Sales must be $10,000 in one week to earn $800.

41. Let x = the amount invested at 4%
Let y = the amount invested at 7%
$$x+\quad y=9000$$
$$0.04x+0.07y=555$$

Multiply the first equation by –0.04 and add.
$$-0.04x-0.04y=-360$$
$$\underline{0.04x+0.07y=555}$$
$$0.03y=195$$
$$y=6500$$

Back-substitute 6500 for y in one of the original equations to find x.
$$x+y=9000$$
$$x+6500=9000$$
$$x=2500$$

There was $2500 invested at 4% and $6500 invested at 7%.

42. Let x = the amount invested at 2%
Let $8000-x$ = the amount invested at 5%.
$$0.05(8000-x)=0.02x+85$$
$$400-0.05x=0.02x+85$$
$$-0.05x-0.02x=85-400$$
$$-0.07x=-315$$
$$\frac{-0.07x}{-0.07}=\frac{-315}{-0.07}$$
$$x=4500$$
$$8000-x=3500$$

$4500 was invested at 2% and $3500 was invested at 5%.

43. Let w = the width of the playing field,
Let $3w - 6$ = the length of the playing field

$$P = 2(\text{length}) + 2(\text{width})$$
$$340 = 2(3w - 6) + 2w$$
$$340 = 6w - 12 + 2w$$
$$340 = 8w - 12$$
$$352 = 8w$$
$$44 = w$$

The dimensions are 44 yards by 126 yards.

44. a. Let x = the number of years (after 2007).
College A's enrollment: $14,100 + 1500x$
College B's enrollment: $41,700 - 800x$
$$14,100 + 1500x = 41,700 - 800x$$

b. Check some points to determine that
$y_1 = 14,100 + 1500x$ and
$y_2 = 41,700 - 800x$. Since
$y_1 = y_2 = 32,100$ when $x = 12$, the two
colleges will have the same enrollment in the
year $2007 + 12 = 2019$. That year the
enrollments will be 32,100 students.

45. $vt + gt^2 = s$
$$gt^2 = s - vt$$
$$\frac{gt^2}{t^2} = \frac{s - vt}{t^2}$$
$$g = \frac{s - vt}{t^2}$$

46. $T = gr + gvt$
$$T = g(r + vt)$$
$$\frac{T}{r + vt} = \frac{g(r + vt)}{r + vt}$$
$$\frac{T}{r + vt} = g$$
$$g = \frac{T}{r + vt}$$

47.
$$T = \frac{A - P}{\Pr}$$
$$\Pr(T) = \Pr\frac{A - P}{\Pr}$$
$$\Pr T = A - P$$
$$\Pr T + P = A$$
$$P(rT + 1) = A$$
$$P = \frac{A}{1 + rT}$$

48. $(8 - 3i) - (17 - 7i) = 8 - 3i - 17 + 7i$
$$= -9 + 4i$$

49. $4i(3i - 2) = (4i)(3i) + (4i)(-2)$
$$= 12i^2 - 8i$$
$$= -12 - 8i$$

50. $(7 - i)(2 + 3i)$
$$= 7 \cdot 2 + 7(3i) + (-i)(2) + (-i)(3i)$$
$$= 14 + 21i - 2i + 3$$
$$= 17 + 19i$$

51. $(3 - 4i)^2 = 3^2 + 2 \cdot 3(-4i) + (-4i)^2$
$$= 9 - 24i - 16$$
$$= -7 - 24i$$

52. $(7 + 8i)(7 - 8i) = 7^2 + 8^2 = 49 + 64 = 113$

53.
$$\frac{6}{5 + i} = \frac{6}{5 + i} \cdot \frac{5 - i}{5 - i}$$
$$= \frac{30 - 6i}{25 + 1}$$
$$= \frac{30 - 6i}{26}$$
$$= \frac{15 - 3i}{13}$$
$$= \frac{15}{13} - \frac{3}{13}i$$

54.
$$\frac{3 + 4i}{4 - 2i} = \frac{3 + 4i}{4 - 2i} \cdot \frac{4 + 2i}{4 + 2i}$$
$$= \frac{12 + 6i + 16i + 8i^2}{16 - 4i^2}$$
$$= \frac{12 + 22i - 8}{16 + 4}$$
$$= \frac{4 + 22i}{20}$$
$$= \frac{1}{5} + \frac{11}{10}i$$

55. $\sqrt{-32} - \sqrt{-18} = i\sqrt{32} - i\sqrt{18}$
$$= i\sqrt{16 \cdot 2} - i\sqrt{9 \cdot 2}$$
$$= 4i\sqrt{2} - 3i\sqrt{2}$$
$$= (4i - 3i)\sqrt{2}$$
$$= i\sqrt{2}$$

56. $(-2 + \sqrt{-100})^2 = (-2 + i\sqrt{100})^2$
$$= (-2 + 10i)^2$$
$$= 4 - 40i + (10i)^2$$
$$= 4 - 40i - 100$$
$$= -96 - 40i$$

57. $\dfrac{4 + \sqrt{-8}}{2} = \dfrac{4 + i\sqrt{8}}{2} = \dfrac{4 + 2i\sqrt{2}}{2} = 2 + i\sqrt{2}$

58. $2x^2 + 15x = 8$
$$2x^2 + 15x - 8 = 0$$
$$(2x - 1)(x + 8) = 0$$
$$2x - 1 = 0 \quad x + 8 = 0$$
$$x = \frac{1}{2} \text{ or } x = -8$$

The solution set is $\left\{ \dfrac{1}{2}, -8 \right\}$.

59. $5x^2 + 20x = 0$
$$5x(x + 4) = 0$$
$$5x = 0 \quad x + 4 = 0$$
$$x = 0 \text{ or } x = -4$$
The solution set is $\{0, -4\}$.

60. $2x^2 - 3 = 125$
$$2x^2 = 128$$
$$x^2 = 64$$
$$x = \pm 8$$
The solution set is $\{8, -8\}$.

61. $\dfrac{x^2}{2} + 5 = -3$
$$\frac{x^2}{2} = -8$$
$$x^2 = -16$$
$$\sqrt{x^2} = \pm\sqrt{-16}$$
$$x = \pm 4i$$

62. $(x + 3)^2 = -10$
$$\sqrt{(x + 3)^2} = \pm\sqrt{-10}$$
$$x + 3 = \pm i\sqrt{10}$$
$$x = -3 \pm i\sqrt{10}$$

63. $(3x - 4)^2 = 18$
$$\sqrt{(3x - 4)^2} = \pm\sqrt{18}$$
$$3x - 4 = \pm 3\sqrt{2}$$
$$3x = 4 \pm 3\sqrt{2}$$
$$\frac{3x}{3} = \frac{4 \pm 3\sqrt{2}}{3}$$
$$x = \frac{4 \pm 3\sqrt{2}}{3}$$

64. $x^2 + 20x$
$$\left(\frac{20}{2} \right)^2 = 10^2 = 100$$
$$x^2 + 20x + 100 = (x + 10)^2$$

65. $x^2 - 3x$
$$\left(\frac{3}{2} \right)^2 = \frac{9}{4}$$
$$x^2 - 3x + \frac{9}{4} = \left(x - \frac{3}{2} \right)^2$$

66. $x^2 - 12x = -27$
$$x^2 - 12x + 36 = -27 + 36$$
$$(x - 6)^2 = 9$$
$$x - 6 = \pm 3$$
$$x = 6 \pm 3$$
$$x = 9, 3$$
The solution set is $\{9, 3\}$.

67. $3x^2 - 12x + 11 = 0$
$$x^2 - 4x = -\frac{11}{3}$$
$$x^2 - 4x + 4 = -\frac{11}{3} + 4$$
$$(x - 2)^2 = \frac{1}{3}$$
$$x - 2 = \pm\sqrt{\frac{1}{3}}$$
$$x = 2 \pm \frac{\sqrt{3}}{3}$$

The solution set is $\left\{ 2 + \dfrac{\sqrt{3}}{3}, 2 - \dfrac{\sqrt{3}}{3} \right\}$.

68.
$$x^2 = 2x + 4$$
$$x^2 - 2x - 4 = 0$$
$$x = \frac{2 \pm \sqrt{(-2)^2 - 4(1)(-4)}}{2(1)}$$
$$x = \frac{2 \pm \sqrt{4 + 16}}{2}$$
$$x = \frac{2 \pm \sqrt{20}}{2}$$
$$x = \frac{2 \pm 2\sqrt{5}}{2}$$
$$x = 1 \pm \sqrt{5}$$

The solution set is $\left\{1 + \sqrt{5}, 1 - \sqrt{5}\right\}$.

69. $x^2 - 2x + 19 = 0$
$$x = \frac{2 \pm \sqrt{(-2)^2 - 4(1)(19)}}{2(1)}$$
$$x = \frac{2 \pm \sqrt{4 - 76}}{2}$$
$$x = \frac{2 \pm \sqrt{-72}}{2}$$
$$x = \frac{2 \pm 6i\sqrt{2}}{2}$$
$$x = 1 \pm 3i\sqrt{2}$$

The solution set is $\left\{1 + 3i\sqrt{2}, 1 - 3i\sqrt{2}\right\}$.

70.
$$2x^2 = 3 - 4x$$
$$2x^2 + 4x - 3 = 0$$
$$x = \frac{-4 \pm \sqrt{4^2 - 4(2)(-3)}}{2(2)}$$
$$x = \frac{-4 \pm \sqrt{16 + 24}}{4}$$
$$x = \frac{-4 \pm \sqrt{40}}{4}$$
$$x = \frac{-4 \pm 2\sqrt{10}}{4}$$
$$x = \frac{-2 \pm \sqrt{10}}{2}$$

The solution set is $\left\{\frac{-2 + \sqrt{10}}{2}, \frac{-2 - \sqrt{10}}{2}\right\}$.

71. $x^2 - 4x + 13 = 0$
$$(-4)^2 - 4(1)(13)$$
$$= 16 - 52$$
$$= -36; \text{ 2 complex imaginary solutions}$$

72. $9x^2 = 2 - 3x$
$$9x^2 + 3x - 2 = 0$$
$$3^2 - 4(9)(-2)$$
$$= 9 + 72$$
$$= 81; \text{ 2 unequal real solutions}$$

73. $2x^2 - 11x + 5 = 0$
$$(2x - 1)(x - 5) = 0$$
$$2x - 1 = 0 \quad x - 5 = 0$$
$$x = \frac{1}{2} \text{ or } x = 5$$

The solution set is $\left\{5, \frac{1}{2}\right\}$.

74.
$$(3x + 5)(x - 3) = 5$$
$$3x^2 + 5x - 9x - 15 = 5$$
$$3x^2 - 4x - 20 = 0$$
$$x = \frac{4 \pm \sqrt{(-4)^2 - 4(3)(-20)}}{2(3)}$$
$$x = \frac{4 \pm \sqrt{16 + 240}}{6}$$
$$x = \frac{4 \pm \sqrt{256}}{6}$$
$$x = \frac{4 \pm 16}{6}$$
$$x = \frac{20}{6}, \frac{-12}{6}$$
$$x = \frac{10}{3}, -2$$

The solution set is $\left\{-2, \frac{10}{3}\right\}$.

75. $3x^2 - 7x + 1 = 0$
$$x = \frac{7 \pm \sqrt{(-7)^2 - 4(3)(1)}}{2(3)}$$
$$x = \frac{7 \pm \sqrt{49 - 12}}{6}$$
$$x = \frac{7 \pm \sqrt{37}}{6}$$

The solution set is $\left\{\frac{7 + \sqrt{37}}{6}, \frac{7 - \sqrt{37}}{6}\right\}$.

76. $x^2 - 9 = 0$

$\qquad x^2 = 9$

$\qquad x = \pm 3$

The solution set is $\{-3, 3\}$.

77. $(x-3)^2 - 25 = 0$

$\qquad (x-3)^2 = 25$

$\qquad x - 3 = \pm 5$

$\qquad x = 3 \pm 5$

$\qquad x = 8, -2$

The solution set is $\{8, -2\}$.

78. $3x^2 - x + 2 = 0$

$\qquad x = \dfrac{1 \pm \sqrt{(-1)^2 - 4(3)(2)}}{2(3)}$

$\qquad x = \dfrac{1 \pm \sqrt{1 - 24}}{6}$

$\qquad x = \dfrac{1 \pm \sqrt{-23}}{6}$

$\qquad x = \dfrac{1 \pm i\sqrt{23}}{6}$

The solution set is $\left\{ \dfrac{1 + i\sqrt{23}}{6}, \dfrac{1 - i\sqrt{23}}{6} \right\}$.

79. $\qquad 3x^2 - 10x = 8$

$\qquad 3x^2 - 10x - 8 = 0$

$\qquad (3x + 2)(x - 4) = 0$

$3x + 2 = 0 \qquad x - 4 = 0$

$\qquad\qquad\quad$ or

$3x = -2 \qquad\quad x = 4$

$x = -\dfrac{2}{3}$

The solution set is $\left\{ -\dfrac{2}{3}, 4 \right\}$.

80. $(x+2)^2 + 4 = 0$

$\qquad (x+2)^2 = -4$

$\qquad \sqrt{(x+2)^2} = \pm\sqrt{-4}$

$\qquad x + 2 = \pm 2i$

$\qquad x = -2 \pm 2i$

The solution set is $\{-2 + 2i, -2 - 2i\}$.

81.
$$\frac{5}{x+1} + \frac{x-1}{4} = 2$$

$$\frac{5 \cdot 4(x+1)}{x+1} + \frac{(x-1) \cdot 4(x+1)}{4} = 2 \cdot 4(x+1)$$

$$20 + (x-1)(x+1) = 8(x+1)$$

$$20 + x^2 - 1 = 8x + 8$$

$$x^2 - 8x - 11 = 0$$

$$x = \frac{-b \pm \sqrt{b^2 - 4ac}}{2a}$$

$$x = \frac{-(-8) \pm \sqrt{(-8)^2 - 4(1)(11)}}{2(1)}$$

$$x = \frac{8 \pm \sqrt{20}}{2}$$

$$x = \frac{8 \pm 2\sqrt{5}}{2}$$

$$x = 4 \pm \sqrt{5}$$

The solution set is $\left\{ 4 + \sqrt{5}, 4 - \sqrt{5} \right\}$.

82. $W(t) = 3t^2$

$\qquad 588 = 3t^2$

$\qquad 196 = t^2$

Apply the square root property.

$t^2 = 196$

$t = \pm\sqrt{196}$

$t = \pm 14$

The solutions are -14 and 14. We disregard -14, because we cannot have a negative time measurement. The fetus will weigh 588 grams after 14 weeks.

83. $P = -0.035x^2 + 0.65x + 7.6$

$\quad 0 = -0.035x^2 + 0.65x + 7.6$

$\quad x = \dfrac{-b \pm \sqrt{b^2 - 4ac}}{2a}$

$\quad x = \dfrac{-(0.65) \pm \sqrt{(0.65)^2 - 4(-0.035)(7.6)}}{2(-0.035)}$

$\quad x \approx 27 \quad x \approx -8 \text{ (rejected)}$

If this trend continues, corporations will pay no taxes 27 years after 1985, or 2012.

84.
$$A = lw$$
$$15 = l(2l - 7)$$
$$15 = 2l^2 - 7l$$
$$0 = 2l^2 - 7l - 15$$
$$0 = (2l + 3)(l - 5)$$
$$l = 5$$
$$2l - 7 = 3$$
The length is 5 yards, the width is 3 yards.

85. Let x = height of building
$2x$ = shadow height
$$x^2 + (2x)^2 = 300^2$$
$$x^2 + 4x^2 = 90,000$$
$$5x^2 = 90,000$$
$$x^2 = 18,000$$
$$x \approx \pm 134.164$$
Discard negative height.
The building is approximately 134 meters high.

86.
$$2x^4 = 50x^2$$
$$2x^4 - 50x^2 = 0$$
$$2x^2(x^2 - 25) = 0$$
$$x = 0$$
$$x = \pm 5$$
The solution set is $\{-5, 0, 5\}$.

87.
$$2x^3 - x^2 - 18x + 9 = 0$$
$$x^2(2x - 1) - 9(2x - 1) = 0$$
$$(x^2 - 9)(2x - 1) = 0$$
$$x = \pm 3, \ x = \frac{1}{2}$$
The solution set is $\left\{-3, \frac{1}{2}, 3\right\}$.

88.
$$\sqrt{2x - 3} + x = 3$$
$$\sqrt{2x - 3} = 3 - x$$
$$2x - 3 = 9 - 6x + x^2$$
$$x^2 - 8x + 12 = 0$$
$$x^2 - 8x = -12$$
$$x^2 - 8x + 16 = -12 + 16$$
$$(x - 4)^2 = 4$$
$$x - 4 = \pm 2$$
$$x = 4 + 2$$
$$x = 6, 2$$
The solution set is $\{2\}$.

89.
$$\sqrt{x - 4} + \sqrt{x + 1} = 5$$
$$\sqrt{x - 4} = 5 - \sqrt{x + 1}$$
$$x - 4 = 25 - 10\sqrt{x + 1} + (x + 1)$$
$$x - 4 = 26 + x - 10\sqrt{x + 1}$$
$$-30 = -10\sqrt{x + 1}$$
$$3 = \sqrt{x + 1}$$
$$9 = x + 1$$
$$x = 8$$
The solution set is $\{8\}$.

90.
$$3x^{\frac{3}{4}} - 24 = 0$$
$$3x^{\frac{3}{4}} = 24$$
$$x^{\frac{3}{4}} = 8$$
$$\left(x^{\frac{3}{4}}\right)^{\frac{4}{3}} = (8)^{\frac{4}{3}}$$
$$x = 16$$
The solution set is $\{16\}$.

91.
$$(x - 7)^{\frac{2}{3}} = 25$$
$$\left[(x - 7)^{\frac{2}{3}}\right]^{\frac{3}{2}} = 25^{\frac{3}{2}}$$
$$x - 7 = \left(5^2\right)^{\frac{3}{2}}$$
$$x - 7 = 5^3$$
$$x - 7 = 125$$
$$x = 132$$
The solution set is $\{132\}$.

92. $x^4 - 5x^2 + 4 = 0$

Let $t = x^2$
$$t^2 - 5t + 4 = 0$$
$t = 4$ or $t = 1$
$x^2 = 4$ $x^2 = 1$
$x = \pm 2$ $x = \pm 1$
The solution set is $\{-2, -1, 1, 2\}$.

93. $x^{1/2} + 3x^{1/4} - 10 = 0$

Let $t = x^{1/4}$
$$t^2 + 3t - 10 = 0$$
$$(t + 5)(t - 2) = 0$$
$t = -5$ or $t = 2$
$x^{\frac{1}{4}} = -5$ $x^{\frac{1}{4}} = 2$
$\left(x^{\frac{1}{4}}\right)^4 = (-5)^4$ $\left(x^{\frac{1}{4}}\right)^4 = (2)^4$
$x = 625$ $x = 16$

625 does not check and must be rejected.
The solution set is $\{16\}$.

94. $|2x + 1| = 7$

$2x + 1 = 7$ or $2x + 1 = -7$
$2x = 6$ $2x = -8$
$x = 3$ $x = -8$
The solution set is $\{-4, 3\}$.

95. $2|x - 3| - 6 = 10$

$2|x - 3| = 16$
$|x - 3| = 8$
$x - 3 = 8$ or $x - 3 = -8$
$x = 11$ $x = -5$
The solution set is $\{-5, 11\}$.

96. $3x^{4/3} - 5x^{2/3} + 2 = 0$

Let $t = x^{\frac{2}{3}}$.
$$3t^2 - 5t + 2 = 0$$
$$(3t - 2)(t - 1) = 0$$
$3t - 2 = 0$ or $t - 1 = 0$
$3t = 2$ $t = 1$
$t = \dfrac{2}{3}$ $x^{\frac{2}{3}} = 1$
$x^{\frac{2}{3}} = \dfrac{2}{3}$ $\left(x^{\frac{2}{3}}\right)^{\frac{3}{2}} = \pm(1)^{\frac{3}{2}}$
$\left(x^{\frac{2}{3}}\right)^{\frac{3}{2}} = \pm\left(\dfrac{2}{3}\right)^{\frac{3}{2}}$ $x = \pm 1$

$x = \pm\sqrt[2]{\left(\dfrac{2}{3}\right)^3}$

$x = \pm\dfrac{2}{3}\sqrt{\dfrac{2}{3}}$

$x = \pm\dfrac{2}{3} \cdot \dfrac{\sqrt{2}}{\sqrt{3}} \cdot \dfrac{\sqrt{3}}{\sqrt{3}}$

$x = \pm\dfrac{2\sqrt{6}}{9}$

The solution set is $\left\{-\dfrac{2\sqrt{6}}{9}, \dfrac{2\sqrt{6}}{9}, -1, 1\right\}$.

97. $2\sqrt{x - 1} = x$
$$4(x - 1) = x^2$$
$$4x - 4 = x^2$$
$$x^2 - 4x + 4 = 0$$
$$(x - 2)^2 = 0$$
$$x = 2$$
The solution set is $\{2\}$.

98. $|2x - 5| - 3 = 0$

$2x - 5 = 3$ or $2x - 5 = -3$
$2x = 8$ $2x = 2$
$x = 4$ $x = 1$
The solution set is $\{4, 1\}$.

99. $x^3 + 2x^2 - 9x - 18 = 0$
$$x^2(x + 2) - 9(x + 2) = 0$$
$$(x + 2)(x^2 - 9) = 0$$
$$(x + 2)(x + 3)(x - 3) = 0$$
The solution set is $\{-3, -2, 3\}$.

100. $\sqrt{8-2x} - x = 0$

$\sqrt{8-2x} = x$

$\left(\sqrt{8-2x}\right)^2 = (x)^2$

$8 - 2x = x^2$

$0 = x^2 + 2x - 8$

$0 = (x+4)(x-2)$

$x + 4 = 0$ or $x - 2 = 0$

$x = -4$ $x = 2$

-4 does not check.

The solution set is $\{2\}$.

101. $x^3 + 3x^2 - 2x - 6 = 0$

$x^2(x+3) - 2(x+3) = 0$

$(x+3)(x^2-2) = 0$

$x + 3 = 0$ or $x^2 - 2 = 0$

$x = -3$ $x^2 = 2$

$x = \pm\sqrt{2}$

The solution set is $\left\{-3, -\sqrt{2}, \sqrt{2}\right\}$.

102. $-4|x+1| + 12 = 0$

$-4|x+1| = -12$

$|x+1| = 3$

$x + 1 = 3$ or $x + 1 = -3$

$x = 2$ $x = -4$

The solution set is $\{-4, 2\}$.

103. We need to solve $4.3 = 0.3\sqrt{x} + 3.4$ for x.

$4.3 = 0.3\sqrt{x} + 3.4$

$0.9 = 0.3\sqrt{x}$

$3 = \sqrt{x}$

$3^2 = \left(\sqrt{x}\right)^2$

$9 = x$

The model indicates that the number of HIV infections in India will reach 4.3 million in 2007 ($x = 9$ years after 1998).

104. $\{x | -3 \le x < 5\}$

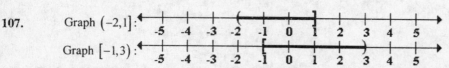

105. $\{x | x > -2\}$

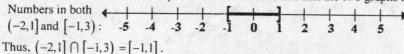

106. $\{x | x \le 0\}$

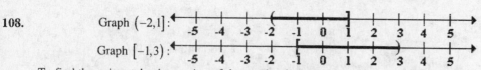

107.   Graph $(-2,1]$:

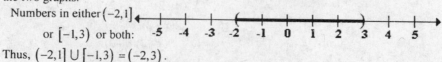

   Graph $[-1,3)$:

To find the intersection, take the portion of the number line that the two graphs have in common.

   Numbers in both

   $(-2,1]$ and $[-1,3)$:

Thus, $(-2,1] \cap [-1,3) = [-1,1]$.

108.   Graph $(-2,1]$:

   Graph $[-1,3)$:

To find the union, take the portion of the number line representing the total collection of numbers in the two graphs.

   Numbers in either $(-2,1]$

      or $[-1,3)$ or both:

Thus, $(-2,1] \cup [-1,3) = (-2,3)$.

109.   Graph $[1,3)$: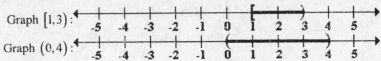

Graph $(0,4)$:

To find the intersection, take the portion of the number line that the two graphs have in common.

Numbers in both
$[1,3)$ and $(0,4)$: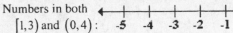

Thus, $[1,3) \cap (0,4) = [1,3)$.

110.   Graph $[1,3)$: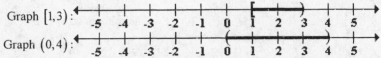

Graph $(0,4)$:

To find the union, take the portion of the number line representing the total collection of numbers in the two graphs.

Numbers in either $[1,3)$
or $(0,4)$ or both: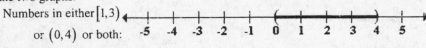

Thus, $[1,3) \cup (0,4) = (0,4)$.

111. $-6x + 3 \le 15$
$\quad\quad -6x \le 12$
$\quad\quad\quad x \ge 2$

The solution set is $[-2, \infty)$.

112. $6x - 9 \ge -4x - 3$
$\quad\quad 10x \ge 6$
$\quad\quad\quad x \ge \dfrac{3}{5}$

The solution set is $\left[\dfrac{3}{5}, \infty\right)$.

113. $\dfrac{x}{3} - \dfrac{3}{4} - 1 > \dfrac{x}{2}$
$12\left(\dfrac{x}{3} - \dfrac{3}{4} - 1\right) > 12\left(\dfrac{x}{2}\right)$
$4x - 9 - 12 > 6x$
$-21 > 2x$
$-\dfrac{21}{2} > x$

The solution set is $\left(-\infty, -\dfrac{21}{2}\right)$.

114. $6x + 5 > -2(x - 3) - 25$
$\quad 6x + 5 > -2x + 6 - 25$
$\quad 8x + 5 > -19$
$\quad\quad 8x > -24$
$\quad\quad\quad x > -3$

The solution set is $(-3, \infty)$.

115. $3(2x - 1) - 2(x - 4) \ge 7 + 2(3 + 4x)$
$\quad 6x - 3 - 2x + 8 \ge 7 + 6 + 8x$
$\quad\quad 4x + 5 \ge 8x + 13$
$\quad\quad\quad -4x \ge 8$
$\quad\quad\quad\quad x \le -2$

The solution set is $[-\infty, -2)$.

116. $5(x - 2) - 3(x + 4) \ge 2x - 20$
$\quad 5x - 10 - 3x - 12 \ge 2x - 20$
$\quad\quad 2x - 22 \ge 2x - 20$
$\quad\quad\quad -22 \ge -20$
The solution set is $\varnothing$.

117. $7 < 2x + 3 \le 9$
$\quad 4 < 2x \le 6$
$\quad 2 < x \le 3$
$(2, 3]$

The solution set is $[2,3)$.

118. $|2x+3| \le 15$

$-15 \le 2x+3 \le 15$

$-18 \le 2x \le 12$

$-9 \le x \le 6$

The solution set is $[-9,6]$.

119. $\left|\dfrac{2x+6}{3}\right| > 2$

$\dfrac{2x+6}{3} > 2 \qquad \dfrac{2x+6}{3} < -2$

$2x+6 > 6 \qquad 2x+6 < -6$

$2x > 0 \qquad\quad 2x < -12$

$x > 0 \qquad\quad x < -6$

The solution set is $(-\infty,-6)$ or $(0,\infty)$.

120. $|2x+5| - 7 \ge -6$

$|2x+5| \ge 1$

$2x+5 \ge 1 \text{ or } 2x+5 \le -1$

$2x \ge -4 \qquad\quad 2x \le -6$

$x \ge -2 \quad\text{ or }\quad x \le -3$

The solution set is $(-\infty,-3]$ or $[-2,\infty)$.

121. $-4|x+2| + 5 \le -7$

$-4|x+2| \le -12$

$|x+2| \ge 3$

$x+2 \ge 3 \qquad x+2 \le -3$

$\qquad\quad$ or

$x \ge 1 \qquad\qquad x \le -5$

The solution set is $(-\infty,-5] \cup [1,\infty)$.

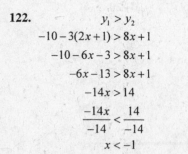

122. $\qquad\qquad y_1 > y_2$

$-10 - 3(2x+1) > 8x+1$

$-10 - 6x - 3 > 8x+1$

$-6x - 13 > 8x+1$

$-14x > 14$

$\dfrac{-14x}{-14} < \dfrac{14}{-14}$

$x < -1$

The solution set is $(-\infty,-1)$.

123. $3 - |2x-5| \ge -6$

$-|2x-5| \ge -9$

$\dfrac{-|2x-5|}{-1} \le \dfrac{-9}{-1}$

$|2x-5| \le 9$

$-9 \le 2x-5 \le 9$

$-4 \le 2x \le 14$

$-2 \le x \le 7$

The solution set is $[-2,7]$.

124. $0.20x + 24 \le 40$

$0.20x \le 16$

$\dfrac{0.20x}{0.20} \le \dfrac{16}{0.20}$

$x \le 80$

A customer can drive no more than 80 miles.

125. $80 \le \dfrac{95+79+91+86+x}{5} < 90$

$400 \le 95+79+91+86+x < 450$

$400 \le 351+x < 450$

$49 \le x < 99$

A grade of at least 49% but less than 99% will result in a B.

126. $0.075x \ge 9000$

$\dfrac{0.075x}{0.075} \ge \dfrac{9000}{0.075}$

$x \ge 120,000$

The investment must be at least \$120,000.

Chapter 1 Test

1. $\qquad 7(x-2) = 4(x+1) - 21$

$7x - 14 = 4x + 4 - 21$

$7x - 14 = 4x - 17$

$3x = -3$

$x = -1$

The solution set is $\{-1\}$.

2. $\qquad -10 - 3(2x+1) - 8x - 1 = 0$

$-10 - 6x - 3 - 8x - 1 = 0$

$-14x - 14 = 0$

$-14x = 14$

$x = -1$

The solution set is $\{-1\}$.

3.
$$\frac{2x-3}{4} = \frac{x-4}{2} - \frac{x+1}{4}$$
$$2x-3 = 2(x-4)-(x+1)$$
$$2x-3 = 2x-8-x-1$$
$$2x-3 = x-9$$
$$x = -6$$
The solution set is $\{-6\}$.

4.
$$\frac{2}{x-3} - \frac{4}{x+3} = \frac{8}{(x-3)(x+3)}$$
$$2(x+3)-4(x-3) = 8$$
$$2x+6-4x+12 = 8$$
$$-2x+18 = 8$$
$$-2x = -10$$
$$x = 5$$
The solution set is $\{5\}$.

5.
$$2x^2 - 3x - 2 = 0$$
$$(2x+1)(x-2) = 0$$
$$2x+1 = 0 \quad \text{or} \quad x-2 = 0$$
$$x = -\frac{1}{2} \quad \text{or} \quad x = 2$$
The solution set is $\left\{-\frac{1}{2}, 2\right\}$.

6.
$$(3x-1)^2 = 75$$
$$3x-1 = \pm\sqrt{75}$$
$$3x = 1 \pm 5\sqrt{3}$$
$$x = \frac{1 \pm 5\sqrt{3}}{3}$$
The solution set is $\left\{\frac{1-5\sqrt{3}}{3}, \frac{1+5\sqrt{3}}{3}\right\}$.

7.
$$(x+3)^2 + 25 = 0$$
$$(x+3)^2 = -25$$
$$x+3 = \pm\sqrt{-25}$$
$$x = -3 \pm 5i$$
The solution set is $\{-3+5i, -3-5i\}$.

8.
$$x(x-2) = 4$$
$$x^2 - 2x - 4 = 0$$
$$x = \frac{-b \pm \sqrt{b^2 - 4ac}}{2a}$$
$$x = \frac{2 \pm \sqrt{(-2)^2 - 4(1)(-4)}}{2}$$
$$x = \frac{2 \pm 2\sqrt{5}}{2}$$
$$x = 1 \pm \sqrt{5}$$
The solution set is $\left\{1-\sqrt{5}, 1+\sqrt{5}\right\}$.

9.
$$4x^2 = 8x - 5$$
$$4x^2 - 8x + 5 = 0$$
$$x = \frac{-b \pm \sqrt{b^2 - 4ac}}{2a}$$
$$x = \frac{8 \pm \sqrt{(-8)^2 - 4(4)(5)}}{2(4)}$$
$$x = \frac{8 \pm \sqrt{-16}}{8}$$
$$x = \frac{8 \pm 4i}{8}$$
$$x = 1 \pm \frac{1}{2}i$$
The solution set is $\left\{1+\frac{1}{2}i, 1-\frac{1}{2}i\right\}$.

10.
$$x^3 - 4x^2 - x + 4 = 0$$
$$x^2(x-4) - 1(x-4) = 0$$
$$(x^2-1)(x-4) = 0$$
$$(x-1)(x+1)(x-4) = 0$$
$$x = 1 \text{ or } x = -1 \text{ or } x = 4$$
The solution set is $\{-1, 1, 4\}$.

11. $\sqrt{x-3}+5=x$

$\qquad \sqrt{x-3}=x-5$

$\qquad\quad x-3=x^2-10x+25$

$x^2-11x+28=0$

$x=\dfrac{11\pm\sqrt{11^2-4(1)(28)}}{2(1)}$

$x=\dfrac{11\pm\sqrt{121-112}}{2}$

$x=\dfrac{11\pm\sqrt{9}}{2}$

$x=\dfrac{11\pm3}{2}$

$x=7$ or $x=4$

4 does not check and must be rejected.
The solution set is $\{7\}$.

12. $\sqrt{8-2x}-x=0$

$\qquad \sqrt{8-2x}=x$

$\qquad \left(\sqrt{8-2x}\right)^2=(x)^2$

$\qquad\quad 8-2x=x^2$

$\qquad\qquad 0=x^2+2x-8$

$\qquad\qquad 0=(x+4)(x-2)$

$x+4=0$ or $x-2=0$

$\quad x=-4\qquad\qquad x=2$

-4 does not check and must be rejected.
The solution set is $\{2\}$.

13. $\sqrt{x+4}+\sqrt{x-1}=5$

$\qquad \sqrt{x+4}=5-\sqrt{x-1}$

$\qquad\quad x+4=25-10\sqrt{x-1}+(x-1)$

$\qquad\quad x+4=25-10\sqrt{x-1}+x-1$

$\qquad\quad -20=-10\sqrt{x-1}$

$\qquad\qquad 2=\sqrt{x-1}$

$\qquad\qquad 4=x-1$

$\qquad\qquad x=5$

The solution set is $\{5\}$.

14. $5x^{3/2}-10=0$

$5x^{3/2}=10$

$x^{3/2}=2$

$x=2^{2/3}$

$x=\sqrt[3]{4}$

The solution set is $\left\{\sqrt[3]{4}\right\}$.

15. $x^{2/3}-9x^{1/3}+8=0$ let $t=x^{1/3}$

$t^2-9t+8=0$

$(t-1)(t-8)=0$

$t=1\qquad t=8$

$x^{1/3}=1\quad x^{1/3}=8$

$\quad x=1\qquad x=512$

The solution set is $\{1,512\}$.

16. $\left|\dfrac{2}{3}x-6\right|=2$

$\dfrac{2}{3}x-6=2\qquad \dfrac{2}{3}x-6=-2$

$\dfrac{2}{3}x=8\qquad\quad \dfrac{2}{3}x=4$

$\quad x=12\qquad\qquad x=6$

The solution set is $\{6,12\}$.

17. $-3|4x-7|+15=0$

$-3|4x-7|=-15$

$|4x-7|=5$

$4x-7=5\qquad\qquad 4x-7=-5$

$\qquad\qquad\quad$ or

$4x=12\qquad\qquad 4x=2$

$x=3\qquad\qquad\quad x=\dfrac{1}{2}$

The solution set is $\left\{\dfrac{1}{2},3\right\}$

18. $\dfrac{1}{x^2}-\dfrac{4}{x}+1=0$

$\dfrac{x^2}{x^2}-\dfrac{4x^2}{x}+x^2=0$

$1-4x+x^2=0$

$x^2-4x+1=0$

$x=\dfrac{-b\pm\sqrt{b^2-4ac}}{2a}$

$x=\dfrac{-(-4)\pm\sqrt{(-4)^2-4(1)(1)}}{2(1)}$

$x=\dfrac{4\pm\sqrt{12}}{2}$

$x=\dfrac{4\pm2\sqrt{3}}{2}$

$x=2\pm\sqrt{3}$

The solution set is $\left\{2+\sqrt{3},2-\sqrt{3}\right\}$.

19. $\dfrac{2x}{x^2+6x+8}+\dfrac{2}{x+2}=\dfrac{x}{x+4}$

$$\dfrac{2x}{(x+4)(x+2)}+\dfrac{2}{x+2}=\dfrac{x}{x+4}$$

$$\dfrac{2x(x+4)(x+2)}{(x+4)(x+2)}+\dfrac{2(x+4)(x+2)}{x+2}=\dfrac{x(x+4)(x+2)}{x+4}$$

$$2x+2(x+4)=x(x+2)$$

$$2x+2x+8=x^2+2x$$

$$2x+8=x^2$$

$$0=x^2-2x-8$$

$$0=(x-4)(x+2)$$

$x-4=0$ or $x+2=0$

$x=4$ $\qquad$ $x=-2$ (rejected)

The solution set is $\{4\}$.

20. $3(x+4)\geq 5x-12$

$3x+12\geq 5x-12$

$-2x\geq -24$

$x\leq 12$

The solution set is $(-\infty,12]$.

21. $\dfrac{x}{6}+\dfrac{1}{8}\leq\dfrac{x}{2}-\dfrac{3}{4}$

$4x+3\leq 12x-18$

$-8x\leq -21$

$x\geq\dfrac{21}{8}$

The solution set is $\left[\dfrac{21}{8},\infty\right)$.

22. $-3\leq\dfrac{2x+5}{3}<6$

$-9\leq 2x+5<18$

$-14\leq 2x<13$

$-7\leq x<\dfrac{13}{2}$

The solution set is $\left[-7,\dfrac{13}{2}\right)$.

23. $|3x+2|\geq 3$

$3x+2\geq 3$ or $3x+2\leq -3$

$3x\geq 1$ $\qquad$ $3x\leq -5$

$x\geq\dfrac{1}{3}$ $\qquad$ $x\leq-\dfrac{5}{3}$

The solution set is $\left(-\infty,-\dfrac{5}{3}\right]\cup\left[\dfrac{1}{3},\infty\right)$.

24. $-3\leq y\leq 7$

$-3\leq 2x-5\leq 7$

$2\leq 2x\leq 12$

$1\leq x\leq 6$

The solution set is $[1,6]$.

25. $y\geq 1$

$\left|\dfrac{2-x}{4}\right|\geq 1$

$\dfrac{2-x}{4}\geq 1$ or $\dfrac{2-x}{4}\leq -1$

$2-x\geq 4$ $\qquad$ $2-x\leq -4$

$-x\geq 2$ $\qquad$ $-x\leq -6$

$x\leq -2$ $\qquad$ $x\geq 6$

The solution set is $(-\infty,-2]\cup[6,\infty)$.

26.   Graph $[-1,2)$: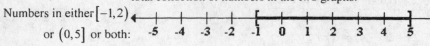

Graph $(0,5]$: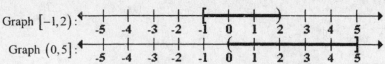

To find the union, take the portion of the number line representing the total collection of numbers in the two graphs.

Numbers in either $[-1,2)$ or $(0,5]$ or both: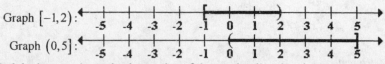

Thus,
$$[-1,2) \cup (0,5] = [-1,5].$$

27.   Graph $[-1,2)$:

Graph $(0,5]$:

To find the intersection, take the portion of the number line that the two graphs have in common.

Numbers in both $[-1,2)$ and $(0,5]$:

Thus, $[-1,2) \cap (0,5] = (0,2)$.

28. $V = \dfrac{1}{3}lwh$

$3V = lwh$

$\dfrac{3V}{lw} = \dfrac{lwh}{lw}$

$\dfrac{3V}{lw} = h$

$h = \dfrac{3V}{lw}$

29. $y - y_1 = m(x - x_1)$

$y - y_1 = mx - mx_1$

$-mx = y_1 - mx_1 - y$

$\dfrac{-mx}{-m} = \dfrac{y_1 - mx_1 - y}{-m}$

$x = \dfrac{y - y_1}{m} + x_1$

30.

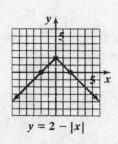

$y = 2 - |x|$

31.

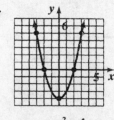

$y = x^2 - 4$

32. $(6 - 7i)(2 + 5i) = 12 + 30i - 14i - 35i^2$
$$= 12 + 16i + 35$$
$$= 47 + 16i$$

33. $\dfrac{5}{2-i} = \dfrac{5}{2-i} \cdot \dfrac{2+i}{2+i}$

$\qquad = \dfrac{5(2+i)}{4+1}$

$\qquad = \dfrac{5(2+i)}{5}$

$\qquad = 2 + i$

34. $2\sqrt{-49} + 3\sqrt{-64} = 2(7i) + 3(8i)$
$$= 14i + 24i$$
$$= 38i$$

35. $43x + 575 = 1177$
$$43x = 602$$
$$x = 14$$

The system's income will be $1177 billion 14 years after 2004, or 2018.

36.
$$B = 0.07x^2 + 47.4x + 500$$
$$1177 = 0.07x^2 + 47.4x + 500$$
$$0 = 0.07x^2 + 47.4x - 677$$
$$0 = 0.07x^2 + 47.4x - 677$$
$$x = \frac{-b \pm \sqrt{b^2 - 4ac}}{2a}$$
$$x = \frac{-(47.4) \pm \sqrt{(47.4)^2 - 4(0.07)(-677)}}{2(0.07)}$$
$$x \approx 14, \quad x \approx -691 \text{ (rejected)}$$
The system's income will be $1177 billion 14 years after 2004, or 2018.

37. The formulas model the data quite well.

38. Let $x =$ the number of books in 2002.
Let $x + 62 =$ the number of books in 2003.
Let $x + 190 =$ the number of books in 2004.
$$(x) + (x + 62) + (x + 190) = 2598$$
$$x + x + 62 + x + 190 = 2598$$
$$3x + 252 = 2598$$
$$3x = 2346$$
$$x = 782$$
$$x + 62 = 844$$
$$x + 190 = 972$$
The number of books in 2002, 2003, and 2004 were 782, 844, and 972 respectively.

39.
$$29700 + 150x = 5000 + 1100x$$
$$24700 = 950x$$
$$26 = x$$
In 26 years, the cost will be $33,600.

40. Let $x =$ amount invested at 8%
$10000 - x =$ amount invested at 10%
$$.08x + .1(10000 - x) = 940$$
$$.08x + 1000 - .1x = 940$$
$$-.02x = -60$$
$$x = 3000$$
$$10000 - x = 7000$$
$3000 at 8%, $7000 at 10%

41.
$$l = 2w + 4$$
$$A = lw$$
$$48 = (2w + 4)w$$
$$48 = 2w^2 + 4w$$
$$0 = 2w^2 + 4w - 48$$
$$0 = w^2 + 2w - 24$$
$$0 = (w + 6)(w - 4)$$

$$w + 6 = 0 \qquad w - 4 = 0$$
$$w = -6 \qquad\quad w = 4$$
$$2w + 4 = 2(4) + 4 = 12$$
width is 4 feet, length is 12 feet

42.
$$24^2 + x^2 = 26^2$$
$$576 + x^2 = 676$$
$$x^2 = 100$$
$$x = \pm 10$$
The wire should be attached 10 feet up the pole.

43. Let $x =$ the original selling price
$$20 = x - 0.60x$$
$$20 = 0.40x$$
$$50 = x$$
The original price is $50.

44. Let $x =$ the number of local calls
The monthly cost using Plan A is $C_A = 25$.
The monthly cost using Plan B is $C_B = 13 + 0.06x$.
For Plan A to be better deal, it must cost less than Plan B.
$$C_A < C_B$$
$$25 < 13 + 0.06x$$
$$12 < 0.06x$$
$$200 < x$$
$$x > 200$$
Plan A is a better deal when more than 200 local calls are made per month.

Chapter 2

Check Point Exercises

1. The domain is the set of all first components: {5, 10, 15, 20, 25}. The range is the set of all second components: {12.8, 16.2, 18.9, 20.7, 21.8}.

2. **a.** The relation is not a function since the two ordered pairs (5, 6) and (5, 8) have the same first component but different second components.

    b. The relation is a function since no two ordered pairs have the same first component and different second components.

3. **a.** $2x + y = 6$

    $y = -2x + 6$

    For each value of x, there is one and only one value for y, so the equation defines y as a function of x.

    b. $x^2 + y^2 = 1$

    $y^2 = 1 - x^2$

    $y = \pm\sqrt{1 - x^2}$

    Since there are values of x (all values between -1 and 1 exclusive) that give more than one value for y (for example, if $x = 0$, then $y = \pm\sqrt{1 - 0^2} = \pm 1$), the equation does not define y as a function of x.

4. **a.** $f(-5) = (-5)^2 - 2(-5) + 7$

    $= 25 - (-10) + 7$

    $= 42$

    b. $f(x + 4) = (x + 4)^2 - 2(x + 4) + 7$

    $= x^2 + 8x + 16 - 2x - 8 + 7$

    $= x^2 + 6x + 15$

    c. $f(-x) = (-x)^2 - 2(-x) + 7$

    $= x^2 - (-2x) + 7$

    $= x^2 + 2x + 7$

5.

x	$f(x) = 2x$	(x, y)
-2	-4	$(-2, -4)$
-1	-2	$(-1, -2)$
0	0	$(0, 0)$
1	2	$(1, 2)$
2	4	$(2, 4)$

124

x	$g(x) = 2x - 3$	(x, y)
-2	$g(-2) = 2(-2) - 3 = -7$	$(-2, -7)$
-1	$g(-1) = 2(-1) - 3 = -5$	$(-1, -5)$
0	$g(0) = 2(0) - 3 = -3$	$(0, -3)$
1	$g(1) = 2(1) - 3 = -1$	$(1, -1)$
2	$g(2) = 2(2) - 3 = 1$	$(2, 1)$

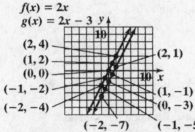

The graph of g is the graph of f shifted down 3 units.

6. The graph (c) fails the vertical line test and is therefore not a function.
    y is a function of x for the graphs in (a) and (b).

7. **a.** $f(10) \approx 16$ **b.** $x \approx 8$

8. **a.**   Domain $= \{x \mid -2 \leq x \leq 1\}$ or $[-2, 1]$.
        Range $= \{y \mid 0 \leq y \leq 3\}$ or $[0, 3]$.

    b.   Domain $= \{x \mid -2 < x \leq 1\}$ or $(-2, 1]$.
        Range $= \{y \mid -1 \leq y < 2\}$ or $[-1, 2)$.

    c.   Domain $= \{x \mid -3 \leq x < 0\}$ or $[-3, 0)$.
        Range $= \{y \mid y = -3, -2, -1\}$.

Exercise Set 2.1

1. The relation is a function since no two ordered pairs have the same first component and different second components. The domain is {1, 3, 5} and the range is {2, 4, 5}.

3. The relation is not a function since the two ordered pairs (3, 4) and (3, 5) have the same first component but different second components (the same could be said for the ordered pairs (4, 4) and (4, 5)). The domain is {3, 4} and the range is {4, 5}.

5. The relation is a function because no two ordered pairs have the same first component and different second components The domain is
    {3, 4, 5, 7} and the range is {-2, 1, 9}.

7. The relation is a function since there are no same first components with different second components. The domain is {-3, -2, -1, 0} and the range is {-3, -2, -1, 0}.

9. The relation is not a function since there are ordered pairs with the same first component and different second components. The domain is $\{1\}$ and the range is $\{4, 5, 6\}$.

11. $x + y = 16$
    $$y = 16 - x$$
    Since only one value of y can be obtained for each value of x, y is a function of x.

13. $x^2 + y = 16$
    $$y = 16 - x^2$$
    Since only one value of y can be obtained for each value of x, y is a function of x.

15. $x^2 + y^2 = 16$
    $$y^2 = 16 - x^2$$
    $$y = \pm\sqrt{16 - x^2}$$
    If $x = 0$, $y = \pm 4$.
    Since two values, $y = 4$ and $y = -4$, can be obtained for one value of x, y is not a function of x.

17. $x = y^2$
    $$y = \pm\sqrt{x}$$
    If $x = 1$, $y = \pm 1$.
    Since two values, $y = 1$ and $y = -1$, can be obtained for $x = 1$, y is not a function of x.

19. $y = \sqrt{x + 4}$
    Since only one value of y can be obtained for each value of x, y is a function of x.

21. $x + y^3 = 8$
    $$y^3 = 8 - x$$
    $$y = \sqrt[3]{8 - x}$$
    Since only one value of y can be obtained for each value of x, y is a function of x.

23. $xy + 2y = 1$
    $$y(x + 2) = 1$$
    $$y = \frac{1}{x + 2}$$
    Since only one value of y can be obtained for each value of x, y is a function of x.

25. $|x| - y = 2$
    $$-y = -|x| + 2$$
    $$y = |x| - 2$$
    Since only one value of y can be obtained for each value of x, y is a function of x.

27. **a.** $f(6) = 4(6) + 5 = 29$

    b. $f(x + 1) = 4(x + 1) + 5 = 4x + 9$

    c. $f(-x) = 4(-x) + 5 = -4x + 5$

29. a. $g(-1) = (-1)^2 + 2(-1) + 3$
$$= 1 - 2 + 3$$
$$= 2$$

b. $g(x+5) = (x+5)^2 + 2(x+5) + 3$
$$= x^2 + 10x + 25 + 2x + 10 + 3$$
$$= x^2 + 12x + 38$$

c. $g(-x) = (-x)^2 + 2(-x) + 3$
$$= x^2 - 2x + 3$$

31. a. $h(2) = 2^4 - 2^2 + 1$
$$= 16 - 4 + 1$$
$$= 13$$

b. $h(-1) = (-1)^4 - (-1)^2 + 1$
$$= 1 - 1 + 1$$
$$= 1$$

c. $h(-x) = (-x)^4 - (-x)^2 + 1 = x^4 - x^2 + 1$

d. $h(3a) = (3a)^4 - (3a)^2 + 1$
$$= 81a^4 - 9a^2 + 1$$

33. a. $f(-6) = \sqrt{-6+6} + 3 = \sqrt{0} + 3 = 3$

b. $f(10) = \sqrt{10+6} + 3$
$$= \sqrt{16} + 3$$
$$= 4 + 3$$
$$= 7$$

c. $f(x-6) = \sqrt{x-6+6} + 3 = \sqrt{x} + 3$

35. a. $f(2) = \dfrac{4(2)^2 - 1}{2^2} = \dfrac{15}{4}$

b. $f(-2) = \dfrac{4(-2)^2 - 1}{(-2)^2} = \dfrac{15}{4}$

c. $f(-x) = \dfrac{4(-x)^2 - 1}{(-x)^2} = \dfrac{4x^2 - 1}{x^2}$

37. **a.** $f(6) = \dfrac{6}{|6|} = 1$

    b. $f(-6) = \dfrac{-6}{|-6|} = \dfrac{-6}{6} = -1$

    c. $f(r^2) = \dfrac{r^2}{|r^2|} = \dfrac{r^2}{r^2} = 1$

39.

x	$f(x) = x$	(x, y)
-2	$f(-2) = -2$	$(-2, -2)$
-1	$f(-1) = -1$	$(-1, -1)$
0	$f(0) = 0$	$(0, 0)$
1	$f(1) = 1$	$(1, 1)$
2	$f(2) = 2$	$(2, 2)$

x	$g(x) = x + 3$	(x, y)
-2	$g(-2) = -2 + 3 = 1$	$(-2, 1)$
-1	$g(-1) = -1 + 3 = 2$	$(-1, 2)$
0	$g(0) = 0 + 3 = 3$	$(0, 3)$
1	$g(1) = 1 + 3 = 4$	$(1, 4)$
2	$g(2) = 2 + 3 = 5$	$(2, 5)$

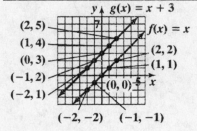

The graph of g is the graph of f shifted up 3 units.

41.

x	$f(x) = -2x$	(x, y)
-2	$f(-2) = -2(-2) = 4$	$(-2, 4)$
-1	$f(-1) = -2(-1) = 2$	$(-1, 2)$
0	$f(0) = -2(0) = 0$	$(0, 0)$
1	$f(1) = -2(1) = -2$	$(1, -2)$
2	$f(2) = -2(2) = -4$	$(2, -4)$

x	$g(x) = -2x - 1$	(x, y)
-2	$g(-2) = -2(-2) - 1 = 3$	$(-2, 3)$
-1	$g(-1) = -2(-1) - 1 = 1$	$(-1, 1)$
0	$g(0) = -2(0) - 1 = -1$	$(0, -1)$
1	$g(1) = -2(1) - 1 = -3$	$(1, -3)$
2	$g(2) = -2(2) - 1 = -5$	$(2, -5)$

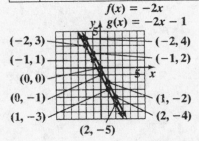

The graph of g is the graph of f shifted down 1 unit.

43.

x	$f(x) = x^2$	(x, y)
-2	$f(-2) = (-2)^2 = 4$	$(-2, 4)$
-1	$f(-1) = (-1)^2 = 1$	$(-1, 1)$
0	$f(0) = (0)^2 = 0$	$(0, 0)$
1	$f(1) = (1)^2 = 1$	$(1, 1)$
2	$f(2) = (2)^2 = 4$	$(2, 4)$

x	$g(x) = x^2 + 1$	(x, y)
-2	$g(-2) = (-2)^2 + 1 = 5$	$(-2, 5)$
-1	$g(-1) = (-1)^2 + 1 = 2$	$(-1, 2)$
0	$g(0) = (0)^2 + 1 = 1$	$(0, 1)$
1	$g(1) = (1)^2 + 1 = 2$	$(1, 2)$
2	$g(2) = (2)^2 + 1 = 5$	$(2, 5)$

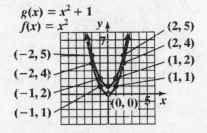

The graph of g is the graph of f shifted up 1 unit.

129

45.

x	$f(x) = |x|$	(x, y)
−2	$f(-2) = |-2| = 2$	$(-2, 2)$
−1	$f(-1) = |-1| = 1$	$(-1, 1)$
0	$f(0) = |0| = 0$	$(0, 0)$
1	$f(1) = |1| = 1$	$(1, 1)$
2	$f(2) = |2| = 2$	$(2, 2)$

x	$g(x) = |x| - 2$	(x, y)
−2	$g(-2) = |-2| - 2 = 0$	$(-2, 0)$
−1	$g(-1) = |-1| - 2 = -1$	$(-1, -1)$
0	$g(0) = |0| - 2 = -2$	$(0, -2)$
1	$g(1) = |1| - 2 = -1$	$(1, -1)$
2	$g(2) = |2| - 2 = 0$	$(2, 0)$

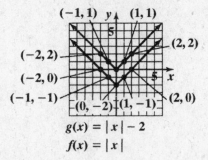

$$g(x) = |x| - 2$$
$$f(x) = |x|$$

The graph of g is the graph of f shifted down 2 units.

47.

x	$f(x) = x^3$	(x, y)
−2	$f(-2) = (-2)^3 = -8$	$(-2, -8)$
−1	$f(-1) = (-1)^3 = -1$	$(-1, -1)$
0	$f(0) = (0)^3 = 0$	$(0, 0)$
1	$f(1) = (1)^3 = 1$	$(1, 1)$
2	$f(2) = (2)^3 = 8$	$(2, 8)$

x	$g(x) = x^3 + 2$	(x, y)
−2	$g(-2) = (-2)^3 + 2 = -6$	$(-2, -6)$
−1	$g(-1) = (-1)^3 + 2 = 1$	$(-1, 1)$
0	$g(0) = (0)^3 + 2 = 2$	$(0, 2)$
1	$g(1) = (1)^3 + 2 = 3$	$(1, 3)$
2	$g(2) = (2)^3 + 2 = 10$	$(2, 10)$

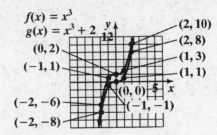

The graph of g is the graph of f shifted up 2 units.

49.

x	$f(x) = 3$	(x, y)
-2	$f(-2) = 3$	$(-2, 3)$
-1	$f(-1) = 3$	$(-1, 3)$
0	$f(0) = 3$	$(0, 3)$
1	$f(1) = 3$	$(1, 3)$
2	$f(2) = 3$	$(2, 3)$

x	$g(x) = 5$	(x, y)
-2	$g(-2) = 5$	$(-2, 5)$
-1	$g(-1) = 5$	$(-1, 5)$
0	$g(0) = 5$	$(0, 5)$
1	$g(1) = 5$	$(1, 5)$
2	$g(2) = 5$	$(2, 5)$

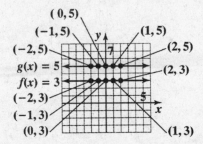

The graph of g is the graph of f shifted up 2 units.

51.

x	$f(x) = \sqrt{x}$	(x,y)
0	$f(0) = \sqrt{0} = 0$	$(0,0)$
1	$f(1) = \sqrt{1} = 1$	$(1,1)$
4	$f(4) = \sqrt{4} = 2$	$(4,2)$
9	$f(9) = \sqrt{9} = 3$	$(9,3)$

x	$g(x) = \sqrt{x} - 1$	(x,y)
0	$g(0) = \sqrt{0} - 1 = -1$	$(0,-1)$
1	$g(1) = \sqrt{1} - 1 = 0$	$(1,0)$
4	$g(4) = \sqrt{4} - 1 = 1$	$(4,1)$
9	$g(9) = \sqrt{9} - 1 = 2$	$(9,2)$

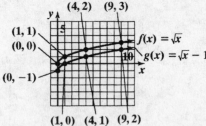

The graph of g is the graph of f shifted down 1 unit.

53.

x	$f(x) = \sqrt{x}$	(x,y)
0	$f(0) = \sqrt{0} = 0$	$(0,0)$
1	$f(1) = \sqrt{1} = 1$	$(1,1)$
4	$f(4) = \sqrt{4} = 2$	$(4,2)$
9	$f(9) = \sqrt{9} = 3$	$(9,3)$

x	$g(x) = \sqrt{x-1}$	(x,y)
1	$g(1) = \sqrt{1-1} = 0$	$(1,0)$
2	$g(2) = \sqrt{2-1} = 1$	$(2,1)$
5	$g(5) = \sqrt{5-1} = 2$	$(5,2)$
10	$g(10) = \sqrt{10-1} = 3$	$(10,3)$

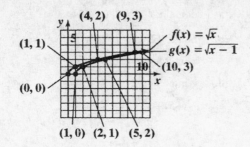

The graph of g is the graph of f shifted right 1 unit.

55. function

57. function

59. not a function

61. function

63. function

65. $f(-2) = -4$

67. $f(4) = 4$

69. $f(-3) = 0$

71. $g(-4) = 2$

73. $g(-10) = 2$

75. When $x = -2$, $g(x) = 1$.

77. **a.** domain: $(-\infty, \infty)$

   b. range: $[-4, \infty)$

   c. x-intercepts: -3 and 1

   d. y-intercept: -3

   e. $f(-2) = -3$ and $f(2) = 5$

79. **a.** domain: $(-\infty, \infty)$

   b. range: $[1, \infty)$

   c. x-intercept: none

   d. y-intercept: 1

   e. $f(-1) = 2$ and $f(3) = 4$

81. **a.** domain: $[0, 5)$

   b. range: $[-1, 5)$

   c. x-intercept: 2

   d. y-intercept: -1

   e. $f(3) = 1$

83. **a.** domain: $[0, \infty)$

   b. range: $[1, \infty)$

   c. x-intercept: none

   d. y-intercept: 1

   e. $f(4) = 3$

85. **a.** domain: $[-2, 6]$

   b. range: $[-2, 6]$

   c. x-intercept: 4

   d. y-intercept: 4

   e. $f(-1) = 5$

87. **a.** domain: $(-\infty, \infty)$

   b. range: $(-\infty, -2]$

   c. x-intercept: none

   d. y-intercept: -2

   e. $f(-4) = -5$ and $f(4) = -2$

89. a. domain: $(-\infty, \infty)$

   b. range: $(0, \infty)$

   c. x-intercept: none

   d. y-intercept: 1.5

   e. $f(4) = 6$

91. a. domain: $\{-5, -2, 0, 1, 3\}$

   b. range: $\{2\}$

   c. x-intercept: none

   d. y-intercept: 2

   e. $f(-5) + f(3) = 2 + 2 = 4$

93.
$$g(1) = 3(1) - 5 = 3 - 5 = -2$$
$$f(g(1)) = f(-2) = (-2)^2 - (-2) + 4$$
$$= 4 + 2 + 4 = 10$$

95.
$$\sqrt{3 - (-1)} - (-6)^2 + 6 \div (-6) \cdot 4$$
$$= \sqrt{3 + 1} - 36 + 6 \div (-6) \cdot 4$$
$$= \sqrt{4} - 36 + -1 \cdot 4$$
$$= 2 - 36 + -4$$
$$= -34 + -4$$
$$= -38$$

97.
$$f(-x) - f(x)$$
$$= (-x)^3 + (-x) - 5 - (x^3 + x - 5)$$
$$= -x^3 - x - 5 - x^3 - x + 5 = -2x^3 - 2x$$

99. a. $\{(\text{U.S., } 80\%), (\text{Japan, } 64\%),$
$(\text{France, } 64\%), (\text{Germany, } 61\%),$
$(\text{England, } 59\%), (\text{China}, 47\%)\}$

   b. Yes, the relation is a function. Each element in the domain corresponds to only one element in the range.

   c. $\{(80\%, \text{U.S.}), (64\%, \text{Japan}),$
$(64\%, \text{France}), (61\%, \text{Germany}),$
$(59\%, \text{England}), (47\%, \text{China})\}$

   d. No, the relation is not a function. 64% in the domain corresponds to both Japan and France in the range.

101. $W(16) = 0.07(16) + 4.1$
$$= 1.12 + 4.1 = 5.22$$
In 2000 there were 5.22 million women enrolled in U.S. colleges.
$(2000, 5.22)$

103. $W(20) = 0.07(20) + 4.1$

$= 1.4 + 4.1 = 5.5$

$M(20) = 0.01(20) + 3.9$

$= 0.2 + 3.9 = 4.1$

$W(20) - M(20) = 5.5 - 4.1 = 1.4$

In 2004, there will be 1.4 million more women than men enrolled in U.S. colleges.

105. a. According to the graph, women's earnings were about 73% of men's in 2000.

b. $P(x) = 0.012x^2 - 0.16x + 60$

$P(40) = 0.012(40)^2 - 0.16(40) + 60 = 72.8$

According to the function, women's earnings were about 72.8% of men's in 2000.

c. $\dfrac{27,355}{37,339} \approx 0.733 = 73.3\%$

The answers in parts (a) and (b) model the actual data quite well.

107. $C(x) = 100,000 + 100x$

$C(90) = 100,000 + 100(90) = \$109,000$

It will cost \$109,000 to produce 90 bicycles.

109.
$$T(x) = \frac{40}{x} + \frac{40}{x+30}$$
$$T(30) = \frac{40}{30} + \frac{40}{30+30}$$
$$= \frac{80}{60} + \frac{40}{60}$$
$$= \frac{120}{60}$$
$$= 2$$

If you travel 30 mph going and 60 mph returning, your total trip will take 2 hours.

121. a. false; the domain of f is $[-4, 4]$

b. false; the range of f is $[-2, 2)$

c. true; $f(-1) - f(4) = 1 - (-1) = 2$

d. false; $f(0) < 1$ x

(c) is true.

123. Answers may vary.

An example is $\{(1,1),(2,1)\}$

Section 2.2

Check Point Exercises

1. a. $f(x) = -2x^2 + x + 5$

$f(x+h) = -2(x+h)^2 + (x+h) + 5$

$= -2(x^2 + 2xh + h^2) + x + h + 5$

$= -2x^2 - 4xh - 2h^2 + x + h + 5$

b. $\dfrac{f(x+h) - f(x)}{h}$

$= \dfrac{-2x^2 - 4xh - 2h^2 + x + h + 5 - \left(-2x^2 + x + 5\right)}{h}$

$= \dfrac{-2x^2 - 4xh - 2h^2 + x + h + 5 + 2x^2 - x - 5}{h}$

$= \dfrac{-4xh - 2h^2 + h}{h}$

$= \dfrac{h(-4x - 2h + 1)}{h}$

$= -4x - 2h + 1$

2. $C(t) = \begin{cases} 20 & \text{if } 0 \le t \le 60 \\ 20 + 0.40(t - 60) & \text{if } t > 60 \end{cases}$

b. Since $0 \le 40 \le 60$, $C(40) = 20$
With 40 calling minutes, the cost is \$20.
This is represented by $(40, 20)$.

c. Since $80 > 60$, $C(80) = 20 + 0.40(80 - 60) = 28$
With 80 calling minutes, the cost is \$28.
This is represented by $(80, 28)$.

3. The function is increasing on the interval $(-\infty, -1)$, decreasing on the interval $(-1, 1)$, and increasing on the interval $(1, \infty)$.

4. a. $f(-x) = (-x)^2 + 6 = x^2 + 6 = f(x)$
The function is even.

b. $g(-x) = 7(-x)^3 - (-x) = -7x^3 + x = -f(x)$
The function is odd.

c. $h(-x) = (-x)^5 + 1 = -x^5 + 1$
The function is neither even nor odd.

Exercise Set 2.2

1. $\dfrac{f(x+h)-f(x)}{h}$

$=\dfrac{4(x+h)-4x}{h}$

$=\dfrac{4x+4h-4x}{h}$

$=\dfrac{4h}{h}$

$=4$

3. $\dfrac{f(x+h)-f(x)}{h}$

$=\dfrac{3(x+h)+7-(3x+7)}{h}$

$=\dfrac{3x+3h+7-3x-7}{h}$

$=\dfrac{3h}{h}$

$=3$

5. $\dfrac{f(x+h)-f(x)}{h}$

$=\dfrac{(x+h)^2-x^2}{h}$

$=\dfrac{x^2+2xh+h^2-x^2}{h}$

$=\dfrac{2xh+h^2}{h}$

$=\dfrac{h(2x+h)}{h}$

$=2x+h$

7. $\dfrac{f(x+h)-f(x)}{h}$

$=\dfrac{(x+h)^2-4(x+h)+3-(x^2-4x+3)}{h}$

$=\dfrac{x^2+2xh+h^2-4x-4h+3-x^2+4x-3}{h}$

$=\dfrac{2xh+h^2-4h}{h}$

$=\dfrac{h(2x+h-4)}{h}$

$=2x+h-4$

9. $\dfrac{f(x+h)-f(x)}{h}$

$=\dfrac{2(x+h)^2+(x+h)-1-(2x^2+x-1)}{h}$

$=\dfrac{2x^2+4xh+2h^2+x+h-1-2x^2-x+1}{h}$

$=\dfrac{4xh+2h^2+h}{h}$

$=\dfrac{h(4x+2h+1)}{h}$

$=4x+2h+1$

11. $\dfrac{f(x+h)-f(x)}{h}$

$=\dfrac{-(x+h)^2+2(x+h)+4-(-x^2+2x+4)}{h}$

$=\dfrac{-x^2-2xh-h^2+2x+2h+4+x^2-2x-4}{h}$

$=\dfrac{-2xh-h^2+2h}{h}$

$=\dfrac{h(-2x-h+2)}{h}$

$=-2x-h+2$

13. $\dfrac{f(x+h)-f(x)}{h}$

$=\dfrac{-2(x+h)^2+5(x+h)+7-(-2x^2+5x+7)}{h}$

$=\dfrac{-2x^2-4xh-2h^2+5x+5h+7+2x^2-5x-7}{h}$

$=\dfrac{-4xh-2h^2+5h}{h}$

$=\dfrac{h(-4x-2h+5)}{h}$

$=-4x-2h+5$

15.
$$\frac{f(x+h)-f(x)}{h}$$
$$=\frac{-2(x+h)^2-(x+h)+3-(-2x^2-x+3)}{h}$$
$$=\frac{-2x^2-4xh-2h^2-x-h+3+2x^2+x-3}{h}$$
$$=\frac{-4xh-2h^2-h}{h}$$
$$=\frac{h(-4x-2h-1)}{h}$$
$$=-4x-2h-1$$

17. $\frac{f(x+h)-f(x)}{h}=\frac{6-6}{h}=\frac{0}{h}=0$ $f(x)=6$

19.
$$\frac{f(x+h)-f(x)}{h} \quad f(x)=\frac{1}{x}$$
$$=\frac{\frac{1}{x+h}-\frac{1}{x}}{h}$$
$$=\frac{\frac{x}{x(x+h)}+\frac{-(x+h)}{x(x+h)}}{h}$$
$$=\frac{\frac{x-x-h}{x(x+h)}}{h}$$
$$=\frac{\frac{-h}{x(x+h)}}{h}$$
$$=\frac{-h}{x(x+h)}\cdot\frac{1}{h}$$
$$=\frac{-1}{x(x+h)}$$

21.
$$\frac{f(x+h)-f(x)}{h}$$
$$=\frac{\sqrt{x+h}-\sqrt{x}}{h}$$
$$=\frac{\sqrt{x+h}-\sqrt{x}}{h}\cdot\frac{\sqrt{x+h}+\sqrt{x}}{\sqrt{x+h}+\sqrt{x}}$$
$$=\frac{x+h-x}{h\left(\sqrt{x+h}+\sqrt{x}\right)}$$
$$=\frac{h}{h\left(\sqrt{x+h}+\sqrt{x}\right)}$$
$$=\frac{1}{\sqrt{x+h}+\sqrt{x}}$$

23.   **a.** $f(-2)=3(-2)+5=-1$

      b. $f(0)=4(0)+7=7$

      c. $f(3)=4(3)+7=19$

25.   **a.** $g(0)=0+3=3$

      b. $g(-6)=-(-6+3)=-(-3)=3$

      c. $g(-3)=-3+3=0$

27.   **a.** $h(5)=\frac{5^2-9}{5-3}=\frac{25-9}{2}=\frac{16}{2}=8$

      b. $h(0)=\frac{0^2-9}{0-3}=\frac{-9}{-3}=3$

      c. $h(3)=6$

29.   **a.**   increasing: $(-1,\infty)$

      b.   decreasing: $(-\infty,-1)$

      c.   constant: none

31.   **a.**   increasing: $(0,\infty)$

      b.   decreasing: none

      c.   constant: none

33.   **a.**   increasing: none

      b.   decreasing: $(-2,6)$

      c.   constant: none

35. a. increasing: $(-\infty, -1)$

b. decreasing: none

c. constant: $(-1, \infty)$

37. a. increasing: $(-\infty, 0)$ or $(1.5, 3)$

b. decreasing: $(0, 1.5)$ or $(3, \infty)$

c. constant: none

39. a. increasing: $(-2, 4)$

b. decreasing: none

c. constant: $(-\infty, -2)$ or $(4, \infty)$

41. a. $x = 0$, relative maximum = 4

b. $x = -3, 3$, relative minimum = 0

43. a. $x = -2$, relative maximum = 21

b. $x = 1$, relative minimum = -6

45. $f(x) = x^3 + x$

$f(-x) = (-x)^3 + (-x)$

$f(-x) = -x^3 - x = -(x^3 + x)$

$f(-x) = -f(x)$, odd function

47. $g(x) = x^2 + x$

$g(-x) = (-x)^2 + (-x)$

$g(-x) = x^2 - x$, neither

49. $h(x) = x^2 - x^4$

$h(-x) = (-x)^2 - (-x)^4$

$h(-x) = x^2 - x^4$

$h(-x) = h(x)$, even function

51. $f(x) = x^2 - x^4 + 1$

$f(-x) = (-x)^2 - (-x)^4 + 1$

$f(-x) = x^2 - x^4 + 1$

$f(-x) = f(x)$, even function

53. $f(x) = \dfrac{1}{5}x^6 - 3x^2$

$f(-x) = \dfrac{1}{5}(-x)^6 - 3(-x)^2$

$f(-x) = \dfrac{1}{5}x^6 - 3x^2$

$f(-x) = f(x)$, even function

55. $f(x) = x\sqrt{1 - x^2}$

$f(-x) = -x\sqrt{1 - (-x)^2}$

$f(-x) = -x\sqrt{1 - x^2}$

$\quad\quad = -\left(x\sqrt{1 - x^2}\right)$

$f(-x) = -f(x)$, odd function

57. The graph is symmetric with respect to the *y*-axis. The function is even.

59. The graph is symmetric with respect to the origin. The function is odd.

61. a. Domain: $(-\infty, \infty)$

b. Range: $[-4, \infty)$

c. *x*-intercepts: 1, 7

d. *y*-intercept: 4

e. $(4, \infty)$

f. $(0, 4)$

g. $(-\infty, 0)$

    h. $x = 4$

    i. $y = -4$

    j. $f(-3) = 4$

    k. $f(2) = -2$ and $f(6) = -2$

    l.   neither ; $f(-x) \neq x$, $f(-x) \neq -x$

63. **a.**   Domain: $(-\infty, 3]$

    b.   Range: $(-\infty, 4]$

    c. x-intercepts: $-3, 3$

    d. $f(0) = 3$

    e. $(-\infty, 1)$

    f. $(1, 3)$

    g. $(-\infty, -3]$

    h. $f(1) = 4$

    i. $x = 1$

    j.   positive; $f(-1) = +2$

65. $f(1.06) = 1$

67. $f\left(\dfrac{1}{3}\right) = 0$

69. $f(-2.3) = -3$

71. $\sqrt{f(-1.5) + f(-0.9)} - \left[f(\pi)\right]^2 + f(-3) \div f(1) \cdot f(-\pi)$

      $= \sqrt{1+0} - \left[-4\right]^2 + 2 \div (-2) \cdot 3$

      $= \sqrt{1} - 16 + (-1) \cdot 3$

      $= 1 - 16 - 3$

      $= -18$

73. $30 + 0.30(t - 120) = 30 + 0.3t - 36 = 0.3t - 6$

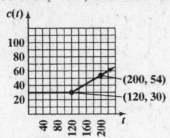

75. $C(t) = \begin{cases} 50 & \text{if } 0 \le t \le 400 \\ 50 + 0.30(t - 400) & \text{if } t > 400 \end{cases}$

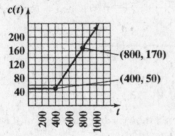

77. $f(60) \approx 3.1$

In 1960, about 3.1% of the population were Jewish-Americans.

79. $x \approx 19$ and $x \approx 64$

In 1919 and 1964, about 3% of the population were Jewish-Americans.

81. In 1940, the maximum of 3.7% of the population were Jewish-American.

83. Each year corresponds to only 1 percentage.

85. Increasing: (45, 74)

Decreasing: (16, 45)

The number of accidents occurring per 50 million miles driven increases with age starting at age 45, while it decreases with age starting at age 16.

87. Answers may vary. An example is 16 and 74 year olds will have 526.4 accidents per 50 million miles.

89. $f(30) = 61.9(30) + 132 = 1989$ cigarettes per adult

This describes the actual data quite well.

91. The maximum occurred in 1960. Graph estimates will vary near 4100.

$f(50) = -2.2(50)^2 + 256(50) - 3503 = 3797$ cigarettes per adult

The function does not describe the actual data reasonably well.

141

93.

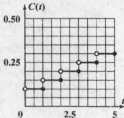

103.

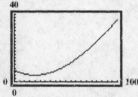

The number of doctor visits decreases during childhood and then increases as you get older. The minimum is (20.29, 3.99), which means that the minimum number of doctor visits, about 4, occurs at around age 20.

105.

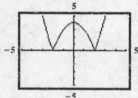

Increasing: $(-2, 0)$ or $(2, \infty)$
Decreasing: $(-\infty, -2)$ or $(0, 2)$

107.

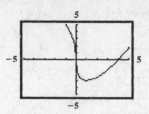

Increasing: $(1, \infty)$
Decreasing: $(-\infty, 1)$

109.

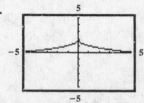

Increasing: $(-\infty, 0)$
Decreasing: $(0, \infty)$

113. a. h is even if both f and g are even or if both f and g are odd.

f and g are both even:

$$h(-x) = \frac{f(-x)}{g(-x)} = \frac{f(x)}{g(x)} = h(x)$$

f and g are both odd:

$$h(-x) = \frac{f(-x)}{g(-x)} = \frac{-f(x)}{-g(x)} = \frac{f(x)}{g(x)} = h(x)$$

b. h is odd if f is odd and g is even or if f is even and g is odd.

f is odd and g is even:

$$h(-x) = \frac{f(-x)}{g(-x)} = \frac{-f(x)}{g(x)} = -\frac{f(x)}{g(x)} = -h(x)$$

f is even and g is odd:

$$h(-x) = \frac{f(-x)}{g(-x)} = \frac{f(x)}{-g(x)} = -\frac{f(x)}{g(x)} = -h(x)$$

Section 2.3

Check Point Exercises

1. a. $m = \dfrac{-2 - 4}{-4 - (-3)} = \dfrac{-6}{-1} = 6$

b. $m = \dfrac{5 - (-2)}{-1 - 4} = \dfrac{7}{-5} = -\dfrac{7}{5}$

2. $y - y_1 = m(x - x_1)$

$y - (-5) = 6(x - 2)$

$y + 5 = 6x - 12$

$y = 6x - 17$

3. $m = \dfrac{-6 - (-1)}{-1 - (-2)} = \dfrac{-5}{1} = -5$,

so the slope is –5. Using the point (–2, –1), we get the point slope equation:

$y - y_1 = m(x - x_1)$

$y - (-1) = -5[x - (-2)]$

$y + 1 = -5(x + 2)$. Solve the equation for y:

$y + 1 = -5x - 10$

$y = -5x - 11$.

4.   The slope m is $\frac{3}{5}$ and the y-intercept is 1, so one point on the line is (1, 0). We can find a second point on the line by using the slope $m = \frac{3}{5} = \frac{\text{Rise}}{\text{Run}}$: starting at the point (0, 1), move 3 units up and 5 units to the right, to obtain the point (5, 4).

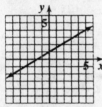

$f(x) = \dfrac{3}{5}x + 1$

5.   All ordered pairs that are solutions of $x = -3$ have a value of x that is always –3. Any value can be used for y.

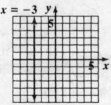

143

6. $3x + 6y - 12 = 0$

$$6y = -3x + 12$$

$$y = \frac{-3}{6}x + \frac{12}{6}$$

$$y = -\frac{1}{2}x + 2$$

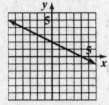

$3x + 6y - 12 = 0$

The slope is $-\frac{1}{2}$ and the y-intercept is 2.

7. Find the x-intercept:

$$3x - 2y - 6 = 0$$
$$3x - 2(0) - 6 = 0$$
$$3x - 6 = 0$$
$$3x = 6$$
$$x = 2$$

Find the y-intercept:

$$3x - 2y - 6 = 0$$
$$3(0) - 2y - 6 = 0$$
$$-2y - 6 = 0$$
$$-2y = 6$$
$$y = -3$$

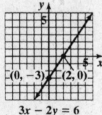

$(0, -3)$ $(2, 0)$

$3x - 2y = 6$

8. $m = \dfrac{\text{Change in } y}{\text{Change in } x} = \dfrac{32.8 - 30.0}{20 - 10} = \dfrac{2.8}{10} = 0.28$

$$y - y_1 = m(x - x_1)$$
$$y - 30.0 = 0.28(x - 10)$$
$$y - 30.0 = 0.28x - 2.8$$
$$y = 0.28x + 27.2$$

2020 is 50 years after 1970.

$$y = 0.28x + 27.2$$
$$y = 0.28(50) + 27.2$$
$$y = 41.2$$

In 2020 the median age is expected to be 41.2.

Exercise Set 2.3

1. $m = \dfrac{10 - 7}{8 - 4} = \dfrac{3}{4}$; rises

3. $m = \dfrac{2 - 1}{2 - (-2)} = \dfrac{1}{4}$; rises

5. $m = \dfrac{2 - (-2)}{3 - 4} = \dfrac{0}{-1} = 0$; horizontal

7. $m = \dfrac{-1 - 4}{-1 - (-2)} = \dfrac{-5}{1} = -5$; falls

9. $m = \dfrac{-2 - 3}{5 - 5} = \dfrac{-5}{0}$ undefined; vertical

11. $m = 2$, $x_1 = 3$, $y_1 = 5$;
point-slope form: $y - 5 = 2(x - 3)$;
slope-intercept form: $y - 5 = 2x - 6$
$$y = 2x - 1$$

13. $m = 6$, $x_1 = -2$, $y_1 = 5$;
point-slope form: $y - 5 = 6(x + 2)$;
slope-intercept form: $y - 5 = 6x + 12$
$$y = 6x + 17$$

15. $m = -3$, $x_1 = -2$, $y_1 = -3$;
point-slope form: $y + 3 = -3(x + 2)$;
slope-intercept form: $y + 3 = -3x - 6$
$$y = -3x - 9$$

17. $m = -4$, $x_1 = -4$, $y_1 = 0$;
point-slope form: $y - 0 = -4(x + 4)$;
slope-intercept form: $y = -4(x + 4)$
$$y = -4x - 16$$

19. $m = -1$, $x_1 = \dfrac{-1}{2}$, $y_1 = -2$;

point-slope form: $y + 2 = -1\left(x + \dfrac{1}{2}\right)$;

slope-intercept form: $y + 2 = -x - \dfrac{1}{2}$

$$y = -x - \dfrac{5}{2}$$

21. $m = \dfrac{1}{2}$, $x_1 = 0$, $y_1 = 0$;

point-slope form: $y - 0 = \dfrac{1}{2}(x - 0)$;

slope-intercept form: $y = \dfrac{1}{2}x$

23. $m = -\dfrac{2}{3}$, $x_1 = 6$, $y_1 = -2$;

point-slope form: $y + 2 = -\dfrac{2}{3}(x - 6)$;

slope-intercept form: $y + 2 = -\dfrac{2}{3}x + 4$

$$y = -\dfrac{2}{3}x + 2$$

25. $m = \dfrac{10 - 2}{5 - 1} = \dfrac{8}{4} = 2$;

point-slope form: $y - 2 = 2(x - 1)$ using $(x_1,\, y_1) = (1,\, 2)$, or $y - 10 = 2(x - 5)$ using $(x_1,\, y_1) = (5,\, 10)$;

slope-intercept form: $y - 2 = 2x - 2$ or

$$y - 10 = 2x - 10,$$
$$y = 2x$$

27. $m = \dfrac{3 - 0}{0 - (-3)} = \dfrac{3}{3} = 1$;

point-slope form: $y - 0 = 1(x + 3)$ using $(x_1,\, y_1) = (-3,\, 0)$, or $y - 3 = 1(x - 0)$ using $(x_1,\, y_1) = (0,\, 3)$; slope-intercept form: $y = x + 3$

29. $m = \dfrac{4 - (-1)}{2 - (-3)} = \dfrac{5}{5} = 1$;

point-slope form: $y + 1 = 1(x + 3)$ using $(x_1,\, y_1) = (-3,\, -1)$, or $y - 4 = 1(x - 2)$ using $(x_1,\, y_1) = (2,\, 4)$; slope-intercept form: $y + 1 = x + 3$ or

$$y - 4 = x - 2$$
$$y = x + 2$$

31. $m = \dfrac{6 - (-2)}{3 - (-3)} = \dfrac{8}{6} = \dfrac{4}{3}$;

point-slope form: $y + 2 = \dfrac{4}{3}(x + 3)$ using $(x_1,\, y_1) = (-3,\, -2)$, or $y - 6 = \dfrac{4}{3}(x - 3)$ using $(x_1,\, y_1) = (3,\, 6)$;

slope-intercept form: $y + 2 = \dfrac{4}{3x} + 4$ or

$$y - 6 = \dfrac{4}{3}x - 4,$$
$$y = \dfrac{4}{3}x + 2$$

33. $m = \dfrac{-1 - (-1)}{4 - (-3)} = \dfrac{0}{7} = 0$;

point-slope form: $y + 1 = 0(x + 3)$ using $(x_1,\, y_1) = (-3,\, -1)$, or $y + 1 = 0(x - 4)$ using $(x_1,\, y_1) = (4,\, -1)$;

slope-intercept form: $y + 1 = 0$, so

$$y = -1$$

35. $m = \dfrac{0-4}{-2-2} = \dfrac{-4}{-4} = 1$;

point-slope form: $y - 4 = 1(x - 2)$ using $(x_1, y_1) = (2, 4)$, or $y - 0 = 1(x + 2)$ using $(x_1, y_1) = (-2, 0)$;

slope-intercept form: $y - 9 = x - 2$, or
$$y = x + 2$$

37. $m = \dfrac{4-0}{0-\left(-\frac{1}{2}\right)} = \dfrac{4}{\frac{1}{2}} = 8$;

point-slope form: $y - 4 = 8(x - 0)$ using $(x_1, y_1) = (0, 4)$, or $y - 0 = 8\left(x + \frac{1}{2}\right)$ using $(x_1, y_1) = \left(-\frac{1}{2}, 0\right)$; or

$y - 0 = 8\left(x + \frac{1}{2}\right)$

slope-intercept form: $y = 8x + 4$

39. $m = 2; b = 1$

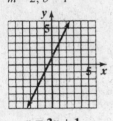

$y = 2x + 1$

41. $m = -2; b = 1$

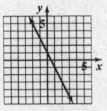

$f(x) = -2x + 1$

43. $m = \dfrac{3}{4}; b = -2$

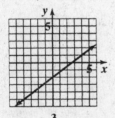

$f(x) = \dfrac{3}{4}x - 2$

45. $m = -\dfrac{3}{5}; b = 7$

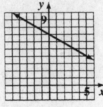

$y = -\dfrac{3}{5}x + 7$

47. $m = -\dfrac{1}{2}; b = 0$

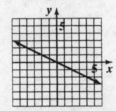

$g(x) = -\dfrac{1}{2}x$

49. $y = -2$

51. $y = -3$
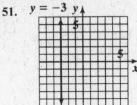

53. $y = 0$
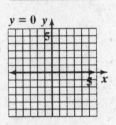

55. $f(x) = 1$
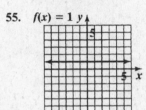

57. $3x - 18 = 0$
$$3x = 18$$
$$x = 6$$
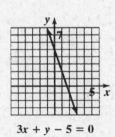

59. a. $3x + y - 5 = 0$
$$y - 5 = -3x$$
$$y = -3x + 5$$

b. $m = -3;\ b = 5$

c.
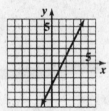
$$3x + y - 5 = 0$$

61. a. $2x + 3y - 18 = 0$
$$2x - 18 = -3y$$
$$-3y = 2x - 18$$
$$y = \frac{2}{-3}x - \frac{18}{-3}$$
$$y = -\frac{2}{3}x + 6$$

b. $m = -\dfrac{2}{3};\ b = 6$

c.
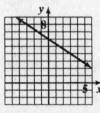
$$2x + 3y - 18 = 0$$

63. a. $8x - 4y - 12 = 0$
$$8x - 12 = 4y$$
$$4y = 8x - 12$$
$$y = \frac{8}{4}x - \frac{12}{4}$$
$$y = 2x - 3$$

b. $m = 2;\ b = -3$

c.
$$8x - 4y - 12 = 0$$

65. a. $3y - 9 = 0$
$$3y = 9$$
$$y = 3$$

b. $m = 0;\ b = 3$

c.
$$3y - 9 = 0$$

147

67. Find the x-intercept:
$$6x - 2y - 12 = 0$$
$$6x - 2(0) - 12 = 0$$
$$6x - 12 = 0$$
$$6x = 12$$
$$x = 2$$
Find the y-intercept:
$$6x - 2y - 12 = 0$$
$$6(0) - 2y - 12 = 0$$
$$-2y - 12 = 0$$
$$-2y = 12$$
$$y = -6$$

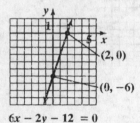

$$6x - 2y - 12 = 0$$

69. Find the x-intercept:
$$2x + 3y + 6 = 0$$
$$2x + 3(0) + 6 = 0$$
$$2x + 6 = 0$$
$$2x = -6$$
$$x = -3$$
Find the y-intercept:
$$2x + 3y + 6 = 0$$
$$2(0) + 3y + 6 = 0$$
$$3y + 6 = 0$$
$$3y = -6$$
$$y = -2$$

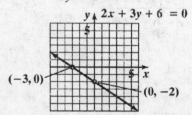

71. Find the x-intercept:
$$8x - 2y + 12 = 0$$
$$8x - 2(0) + 12 = 0$$
$$8x + 12 = 0$$
$$8x = -12$$
$$\frac{8x}{8} = \frac{-12}{8}$$
$$x = \frac{-3}{2}$$
Find the y-intercept:
$$8x - 2y + 12 = 0$$
$$8(0) - 2y + 12 = 0$$
$$-2y + 12 = 0$$
$$-2y = -12$$
$$y = -6$$

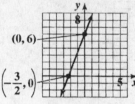

$$8x - 2y + 12 = 0$$

73.
$$m = \frac{0 - a}{b - 0} = \frac{-a}{b} = -\frac{a}{b}$$

Since a and b are both positive, $-\dfrac{a}{b}$ is negative. Therefore, the line falls.

75.
$$m = \frac{(b + c) - b}{a - a} = \frac{c}{0}$$
The slope is undefined.
The line is vertical.

77.
$$Ax + By = C$$
$$By = -Ax + C$$
$$y = -\frac{A}{B}x + \frac{C}{B}$$

The slope is $-\dfrac{A}{B}$ and the y-intercept is $\dfrac{C}{B}$.

79.
$$-3 = \frac{4-y}{1-3}$$
$$-3 = \frac{4-y}{-2}$$
$$6 = 4-y$$
$$2 = -y$$
$$-2 = y$$

81. $3x - 4f(x) = 6$
$$-4f(x) = -3x + 6$$
$$f(x) = \frac{3}{4}x - \frac{3}{2}$$

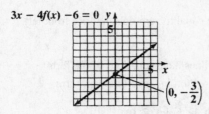

83. Using the slope-intercept form for the equation of a line:
$$-1 = -2(3) + b$$
$$-1 = -6 + b$$
$$5 = b$$

85. m_1, m_3, m_2, m_4

87. **a.** First we must find the slope using $(10,16)$ and $(16,12.7)$.
$$m = \frac{12.7 - 16}{16 - 10} = -\frac{3.3}{6} = -0.55$$
Then use the slope and one of the points to write the equation in point-slope form.
$$y - y_1 = m(x - x_1)$$
$$y - 16 = -0.55(x - 10)$$
or
$$y - 12.7 = -0.55(x - 16)$$

b. $y - 16 = -0.55(x - 10)$
$$y - 16 = -0.55x + 5.5$$
$$y = -0.55x + 21.5$$
$$f(x) = -0.55x + 21.5$$

c. $f(20) = -0.55(20) + 21.5 = 10.5$
The linear function predicts 10.5% of adult women will be on weight-loss diets in 2007.

89. **a.** points: $(0,73.7), (5,74.7), (10,75.4)$
$(15,75.8), (19,76.7), (20,77.0), (21,77.2)$

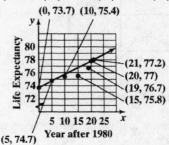

b. $m = \dfrac{\text{Change in } y}{\text{Change in } x} = \dfrac{77.0 - 74.7}{20 - 5} \approx 0.15$
$$y - y_1 = m(x - x_1)$$
$$y - 74.7 = 0.15(x - 5) \quad \text{[point-slope]}$$
$$y - 74.7 = 0.15x - 0.75$$
$$y = 0.15x + 73.95 \quad \text{[slope-intercept]}$$

c. $E(x) = 0.15x + 73.95$
$$E(40) = 0.15(40) + 73.95$$
$$= 79.95$$
In 2020 the life expectancy is expected to be 79.95.

91. $(10, 230)$ $(60, 110)$ Points may vary.
$$m = \frac{110 - 230}{60 - 10} = -\frac{120}{50} = -2.4$$
$$y - 230 = -2.4(x - 10)$$
$$y - 230 = -2.4x + 24$$
$$y = -2.4x + 254$$
Answers may vary for predictions.

101. Two points are $(0, 6)$ and $(10, -24)$.
$$m = \frac{-24 - 6}{10 - 0} = \frac{-30}{10} = -3.$$
Check: $y = mx + b: y = -3x + 6$.

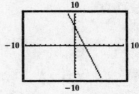

103. Two points are $(0, -2)$ and $(10, 5.5)$.

$$m = \frac{5.5 - (-2)}{10 - 0} = \frac{7.5}{10} = 0.75 \text{ or } \frac{3}{4}.$$

Check: $y = mx + b : y = \frac{3}{4}x - 2$.

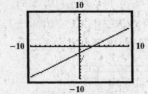

105. Statement **c.** is true.

Statement **a.** is false. One nonnegative slope is 0. A line with slope equal to zero does not rise from left to right.

Statement **b.** is false. Slope-intercept form is $y = mx + b$. Vertical lines have equations of the form $x = a$. Equations of this form have undefined slope and cannot be written in slope-intercept form.

Statement **d.** is false. The graph of $x = 7$ is a vertical line through the point $(7, 0)$.

107.

We are given that the y-intercept is -6 and the slope is $\frac{1}{2}$.

So the equation of the line is $y = \frac{1}{2}x - 6$.

We can put this equation in the form $ax + by = c$ to find the missing coefficients.

$$y = \frac{1}{2}x - 6$$

$$y - \frac{1}{2}x = -6$$

$$2\left(y - \frac{1}{2}x\right) = 2(-6)$$

$$2y - x = -12$$

$$x - 2y = 12$$

Therefore, the coefficient of x is 1 and the coefficient of y is -2.

109. Let $(25, 40)$ and $(125, 280)$ be ordered pairs (M, E) where M is degrees Madonna and E is degrees Elvis. Then

$$m = \frac{280 - 40}{125 - 25} = \frac{240}{100} = 2.4. \text{ Using } (x_1, y_1) = (25, 40),$$

point-slope form tells us that
$E - 40 = 2.4 (M - 25)$ or
$E = 2.4 M - 20$.

Section 2.4

Check Point Exercises

1. The slope of the line $y = 3x + 1$ is 3.
$$y - y_1 = m(x - x_1)$$
$$y - 5 = 3(x - (-2))$$
$$y - 5 = 3(x + 2) \text{ point-slope}$$
$$y - 5 = 3x + 6$$
$$y = 3x + 11 \text{ slope-intercept}$$

2. a. Write the equation in slope-intercept form:
$$x + 3y - 12 = 0$$
$$3y = -x + 12$$
$$y = -\frac{1}{3}x + 4$$

   The slope of this line is $-\frac{1}{3}$ thus the slope of any line perpendicular to this line is 3.

   b. Use $m = 3$ and the point $(-2, -6)$ to write the equation.
$$y - y_1 = m(x - x_1)$$
$$y - (-6) = 3(x - (-2))$$
$$y + 6 = 3(x + 2)$$
$$y + 6 = 3x + 6$$
$$-3x + y = 0$$
$$3x - y = 0 \text{ general form}$$

3. $m = \dfrac{\text{Change in } y}{\text{Change in } x} = \dfrac{12 - 10}{2010 - 1995} = \dfrac{2}{15} \approx 0.13$

   The slope indicates that the number of U.S. men living alone is projected to increase by 0.13 million each year.

4. a. $\dfrac{f(x_2) - f(x_1)}{x_2 - x_1} = \dfrac{1^3 - 0^3}{1 - 0} = 1$

   b. $\dfrac{f(x_2) - f(x_1)}{x_2 - x_1} = \dfrac{2^3 - 1^3}{2 - 1} = \dfrac{8 - 1}{1} = 7$

   c. $\dfrac{f(x_2) - f(x_1)}{x_2 - x_1} = \dfrac{0^3 - (-2)^3}{0 - (-2)} = \dfrac{8}{2} = 4$

5. $\dfrac{f(x_2) - f(x_1)}{x_2 - x_1} = \dfrac{f(3) - f(1)}{3 - 1} = \dfrac{0.05 - 0.03}{3 - 1} = 0.01$

Exercise Set 2.4

1. Since L is parallel to $y = 2x$, we know it will have slope $m = 2$. We are given that it passes through (4, 2). We use the slope and point to write the equation in point-slope form.

$$y - y_1 = m(x - x_1)$$
$$y - 2 = 2(x - 4)$$

Solve for y to obtain slope-intercept form.

$$y - 2 = 2(x - 4)$$
$$y - 2 = 2x - 8$$
$$y = 2x - 6$$

In function notation, the equation of the line is $f(x) = 2x - 6$.

3. Since L is perpendicular to $y = 2x$, we know it will have slope $m = -\frac{1}{2}$. We are given that it passes through (2, 4). We use the slope and point to write the equation in point-slope form.

$$y - y_1 = m(x - x_1)$$
$$y - 4 = -\frac{1}{2}(x - 2)$$

Solve for y to obtain slope-intercept form.

$$y - 4 = -\frac{1}{2}(x - 2)$$
$$y - 4 = -\frac{1}{2}x + 1$$
$$y = -\frac{1}{2}x + 5$$

In function notation, the equation of the line is $f(x) = -\frac{1}{2}x + 5$.

5. $m = -4$ since the line is parallel to $y = -4x + 3$; $x_1 = -8$, $y_1 = -10$;

   point-slope form: $y + 10 = -4(x + 8)$
   slope-intercept form: $y + 10 = -4x - 32$
   $$y = -4x - 42$$

7. $m = -5$ since the line is perpendicular to $y = \frac{1}{5}x + 6$; $x_1 = 2$, $y_1 = -3$;

   point-slope form: $y + 3 = -5(x - 2)$
   slope-intercept form: $y + 3 = -5x + 10$
   $$y = -5x + 7$$

9. $2x - 3y - 7 = 0$
   $$-3y = -2x + 7$$
   $$y = \frac{2}{3}x - \frac{7}{3}$$

   The slope of the given line is $\frac{2}{3}$, so $m = \frac{2}{3}$ since the lines are parallel.

   point-slope form: $y - 2 = \frac{2}{3}(x + 2)$

   general form: $2x - 3y + 10 = 0$

11. $x - 2y - 3 = 0$

$$-2y = -x + 3$$

$$y = \frac{1}{2}x - \frac{3}{2}$$

The slope of the given line is $\frac{1}{2}$, so $m = -2$ since the lines are perpendicular.

point-slope form: $y + 7 = -2(x - 4)$

general form: $2x + y - 1 = 0$

13. $\dfrac{15 - 0}{5 - 0} = \dfrac{15}{5} = 3$

15. $\dfrac{5^2 + 2 \cdot 5 - (3^2 + 2 \cdot 3)}{5 - 3}$

$$= \frac{25 + 10 - (9 + 6)}{2}$$

$$= \frac{20}{2}$$

$$= 10$$

17. $\dfrac{\sqrt{9} - \sqrt{4}}{9 - 4} = \dfrac{3 - 2}{5} = \dfrac{1}{5}$

19. Since the line is perpendicular to $x = 6$ which is a vertical line, we know the graph of f is a horizontal line with 0 slope. The graph of f passes through $(-1, 5)$, so the equation of f is $f(x) = 5$.

21. First we need to find the equation of the line with x – intercept of 2 and y – intercept of –4. This line will pass through $(2, 0)$ and $(0, -4)$. We use these points to find the slope.

$$m = \frac{-4 - 0}{0 - 2} = \frac{-4}{-2} = 2$$

Since the graph of f is perpendicular to this line, it will have slope $m = -\dfrac{1}{2}$.

Use the point $(-6, 4)$ and the slope $-\dfrac{1}{2}$ to find the equation of the line.

$$y - y_1 = m(x - x_1)$$

$$y - 4 = -\frac{1}{2}(x - (-6))$$

$$y - 4 = -\frac{1}{2}(x + 6)$$

$$y - 4 = -\frac{1}{2}x - 3$$

$$y = -\frac{1}{2}x + 1$$

$$f(x) = -\frac{1}{2}x + 1$$

23. First put the equation $3x - 2y - 4 = 0$ in slope-intercept form.

$$3x - 2y - 4 = 0$$
$$-2y = -3x + 4$$
$$y = \frac{3}{2}x - 2$$

The equation of f will have slope $-\frac{2}{3}$ since it is perpendicular to the line above and the same

$y-$ intercept -2.

So the equation of f is $f(x) = -\frac{2}{3}x - 2$.

25. The slope indicates that the global average temperature is projected to increase by 0.01 degrees Fahrenheit each year.

27. The slope indicates that the percentage of U.S. adults who smoked cigarettes decreased by 0.52% each year.

29. $f(x) = 13x + 222$

31. $f(x) = -2.40x + 52.40$

33. $\dfrac{f(x_2) - f(x_1)}{x_2 - x_1} = \dfrac{f(2003) - f(1997)}{2003 - 1997} = \dfrac{25.2 - 32.5}{2003 - 1997} \approx -1.22$

41.
$$y = \frac{1}{3}x + 1$$
$$y = -3x - 2$$

a. The lines are perpendicular because their slopes are negative reciprocals of each other. This is verified because product of their slopes is -1.

b.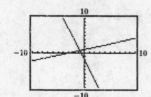

The lines do not appear to be perpendicular.

c.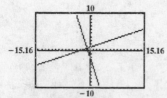

The lines appear to be perpendicular. The calculator screen is rectangular and does not have the same width and height. This causes the scale of the x–axis to differ from the scale on the y–axis despite using the same scale in the window settings. In part (b), this causes the lines not to appear perpendicular when indeed they are. The zoom square feature compensates for this and in part (c), the lines appear to be perpendicular.

154

43.

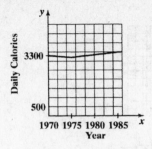

45.   The slope of the line containing $(1,-3)$ and $(-2,4)$ has slope

$$m = \frac{4-(-3)}{-2-1} = \frac{4+3}{-3} = \frac{7}{-3} = -\frac{7}{3}.$$

Solve $Ax+y-2=0$ for y to obtain slope-intercept form.

$Ax+y-2=0$

$y=-Ax+2$

So the slope of this line is $-A$.

This line is perpendicular to the line above so its slope is $\frac{3}{7}$. Therefore, $-A=\frac{3}{7}$ so $A=-\frac{3}{7}$.

Mid-Chapter 2 Check Point

1.   The relation is not a function.
The domain is $\{1,2\}$.
The range is $\{-6,4,6\}$.

2.   The relation is a function.
The domain is $\{0,2,3\}$.
The range is $\{1,4\}$.

3.   The relation is a function.
The domain is $\{x \mid -2 \le x < 2\}$.
The range is $\{y \mid 0 \le y \le 3\}$.

4.   The relation is not a function.
The domain is $\{x \mid -3 < x \le 4\}$.
The range is $\{y \mid -1 \le y \le 2\}$.

5.   The relation is not a function.
The domain is $\{-2,-1,0,1,2\}$.
The range is $\{-2,-1,1,3\}$.

6.   The relation is a function.
The domain is $\{x \mid x \le 1\}$.
The range is $\{y \mid y \ge -1\}$.

7. $x^2+y=5$
$y=-x^2+5$
For each value of x, there is one and only one value for y, so the equation defines y as a function of x.

8. $x+y^2=5$
$y^2=5-x$
$y=\pm\sqrt{5-x}$
Since there are values of x that give more than one value for y (for example, if $x=4$, then $y=\pm\sqrt{5-4}=\pm1$), the equation does not define y as a function of x.

9.   Each value of x corresponds to exactly one value of y.

10. Domain: $(-\infty,\infty)$

11. Range: $(-\infty,4]$

12. x-intercepts: -6 and 2

13. y-intercept: 3

14. increasing: $(-\infty,-2)$

15. decreasing: $(-2,\infty)$

155

16. $x = -2$

17. $f(-2) = 4$

18. $f(-4) = 3$

19. $f(-7) = -2$ and $f(3) = -2$

20. $f(-6) = 0$ and $f(2) = 0$

21. $(-6, 2)$

22. $f(100)$ is negative.

23. neither; $f(-x) \neq x$ and $f(-x) \neq -x$

24. $\dfrac{f(x_2) - f(x_1)}{x_2 - x_1} = \dfrac{f(4) - f(-4)}{4 - (-4)} = \dfrac{-5 - 3}{4 + 4} = -1$

25. $y = -2x$

26. $y = -2$

27. $x + y = -2$

28. $y = \dfrac{1}{3}x - 2$

29. $x = 3.5$

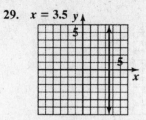

30.

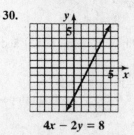

$4x - 2y = 8$

31.

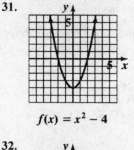

$f(x) = x^2 - 4$

32.

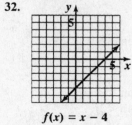

$f(x) = x - 4$

33.

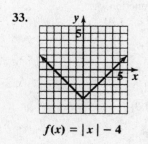

$f(x) = |x| - 4$

34. $5y = -3x$

$$y = -\frac{3}{5}x$$

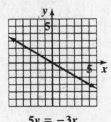

$5y = -3x$

35. $5y = 20$

$$y = 4$$

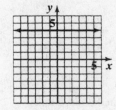

$5y = 20$

36.

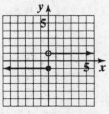

$$f(x) = \begin{cases} -1 \text{ if } x \le 0 \\ 1 \text{ if } x > 0 \end{cases}$$

37. a. $f(-x) = -2(-x)^2 - x - 5 = -2x^2 - x - 5$

neither; $f(-x) \ne x$ and $f(-x) \ne -x$

b. $\dfrac{f(x+h) - f(x)}{h}$

$$= \frac{-2(x+h)^2 + (x+h) - 5 - (-2x^2 + x - 5)}{h}$$

$$= \frac{-2x^2 - 4xh - 2h^2 + x + h - 5 + 2x^2 - x + 5}{h}$$

$$= \frac{-4xh - 2h^2 + h}{h}$$

$$= \frac{h(-4x - 2h + 1)}{h}$$

$$= -4x - 2h + 1$$

38. $C(x) = \begin{cases} 30 & \text{if } 0 \le t \le 200 \\ 30 + 0.40(t - 200) & \text{if } t > 200 \end{cases}$

a. $C(150) = 30$

b. $C(250) = 30 + 0.40(250 - 200) = 50$

39. $y - y_1 = m(x - x_1)$

$$y - 3 = -2(x - (-4))$$

$$y - 3 = -2(x + 4)$$

$$y - 3 = -2x - 8$$

$$y = -2x - 5$$

$$f(x) = -2x - 5$$

40. $m = \dfrac{\text{Change in } y}{\text{Change in } x} = \dfrac{1 - (-5)}{2 - (-1)} = \dfrac{6}{3} = 2$

$$y - y_1 = m(x - x_1)$$

$$y - 1 = 2(x - 2)$$

$$y - 1 = 2x - 4$$

$$y = 2x - 3$$

$$f(x) = 2x - 3$$

41. $3x - y - 5 = 0$

$$-y = -3x + 5$$

$$y = 3x - 5$$

The slope of the given line is 3, and the lines are parallel, so $m = 3$.

$$y - y_1 = m(x - x_1)$$

$$y - (-4) = 3(x - 3)$$

$$y + 4 = 3x - 9$$

$$y = 3x - 13$$

$$f(x) = 3x - 13$$

42. $2x - 5y - 10 = 0$

$-5y = -2x + 10$

$\dfrac{-5y}{-5} = \dfrac{-2x}{-5} + \dfrac{10}{-5}$

$y = \dfrac{2}{5}x - 2$

The slope of the given line is $\dfrac{2}{5}$, and the lines

are perpendicular, so $m = -\dfrac{5}{2}$.

$y - y_1 = m(x - x_1)$

$y - (-3) = -\dfrac{5}{2}\big(x - (-4)\big)$

$y + 3 = -\dfrac{5}{2}x - 10$

$y = -\dfrac{5}{2}x - 13$

$f(x) = -\dfrac{5}{2}x - 13$

43. $m_1 = \dfrac{\text{Change in } y}{\text{Change in } x} = \dfrac{0 - (-4)}{7 - 2} = \dfrac{4}{5}$

$m_2 = \dfrac{\text{Change in } y}{\text{Change in } x} = \dfrac{6 - 2}{1 - (-4)} = \dfrac{4}{5}$

The slope of the lines are equal thus the lines are parallel.

44. The slope indicates that the percentage of U.S. colleges offering distance learning is increasing by 7.8% each year.

45. $\dfrac{f(x_2) - f(x_1)}{x_2 - x_1} = \dfrac{f(2) - f(-1)}{2 - (-1)}$

$\qquad = \dfrac{\big(3(2)^2 - 2\big) - \big(3(-1)^2 - (-1)\big)}{2 + 1}$

$\qquad = 2$

Section 2.5

Check Point Exercises

1. Shift up vertically 3 units.

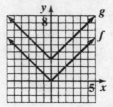

2. Shift to the right 4 units.

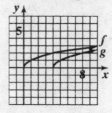

3. Shift to the right 1 unit and down 2 units.

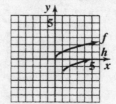

4. Reflect about the x-axis.

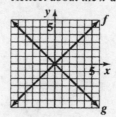

5. Reflect about the y-axis.

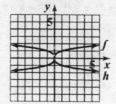

6.   Vertically stretch the graph of $f(x) = |x|$.

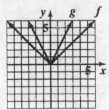

7.   **a.**   Horizontally shrink the graph of $y = f(x)$.

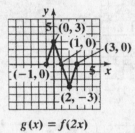

$$g(x) = f(2x)$$

b.   Horizontally stretch the graph of $y = f(x)$.

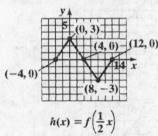

$$h(x) = f\left(\frac{1}{2}x\right)$$

8.   The graph of $y = f(x)$ is shifted 1 unit left, shrunk by a factor of $\frac{1}{3}$, reflected about the x-axis, then shifted down 2 units.

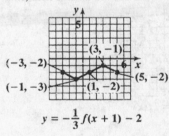

$$y = -\frac{1}{3}f(x + 1) - 2$$

9.   The graph of $f(x) = x^2$ is shifted 1 unit right, stretched by a factor of 2, then shifted up 3 units.

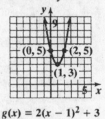

$$g(x) = 2(x - 1)^2 + 3$$

Exercise Set 2.5

1.

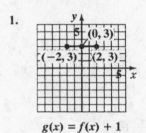

$$g(x) = f(x) + 1$$

3.

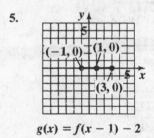

$$g(x) = f(x + 1)$$

5.

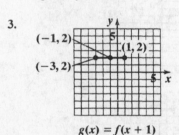

$$g(x) = f(x - 1) - 2$$

7.

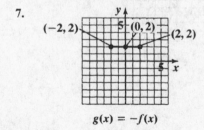

$$g(x) = -f(x)$$

9.

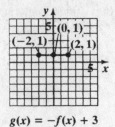

$$g(x) = -f(x) + 3$$

11.

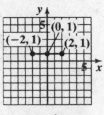

$$g(x) = \frac{1}{2}f(x)$$

13. $g(x) = f\left(\frac{1}{2}x\right)$

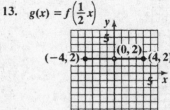

15.

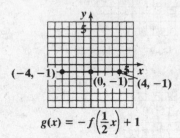

$$g(x) = -f\left(\frac{1}{2}x\right) + 1$$

17.

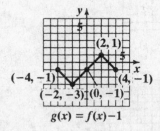

$$g(x) = f(x) - 1$$

19.

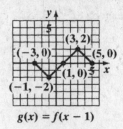

$$g(x) = f(x - 1)$$

21.

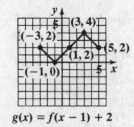

$$g(x) = f(x - 1) + 2$$

23.

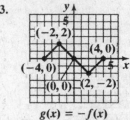

$$g(x) = -f(x)$$

25.

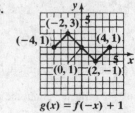

$$g(x) = f(-x) + 1$$

27.

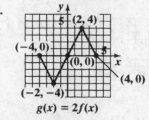

$$g(x) = 2f(x)$$

29.

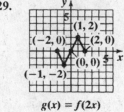

$$g(x) = f(2x)$$

160

31.

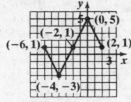

$$g(x) = 2f(x+2) + 1$$

33.

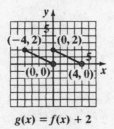

$$g(x) = f(x) + 2$$

35.

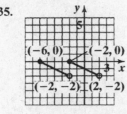

$$g(x) = f(x+2)$$

37.

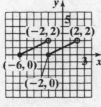

$$g(x) = -f(x+2)$$

39.

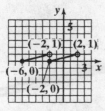

$$g(x) = -\frac{1}{2}f(x+2)$$

41.

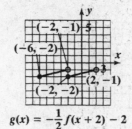

$$g(x) = -\frac{1}{2}f(x+2) - 2$$

43.

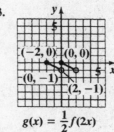

$$g(x) = \frac{1}{2}f(2x)$$

45.

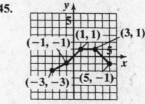

$$g(x) = f(x-1) - 1$$

47.

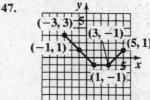

$$g(x) = -f(x-1) + 1$$

49.

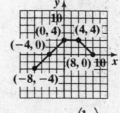

$$g(x) = 2f\left(\frac{1}{2}x\right)$$

51.

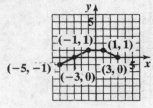

$$g(x) = \frac{1}{2}f(x + 1)$$

53.

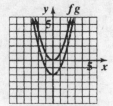

55.

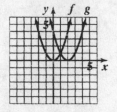

57.

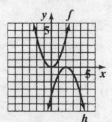

59.

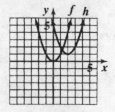

61.

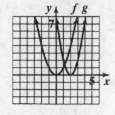

63.

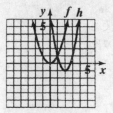

65.

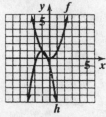

67.

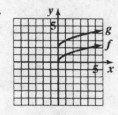

69.

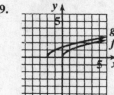

71.

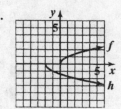

73.

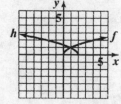

75.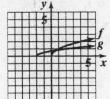

77.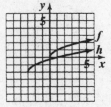

79.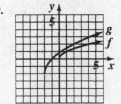

81.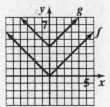

83.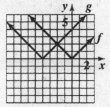

85.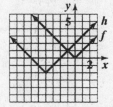

87.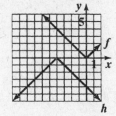

89.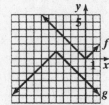

91.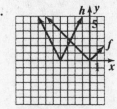

93.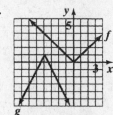

95.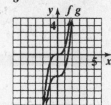

97.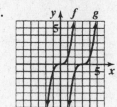

99.
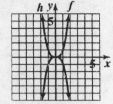

111.

101.
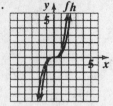

113.
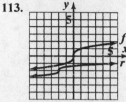

103.
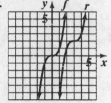

115.
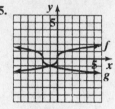

105.
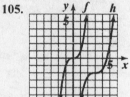

117.
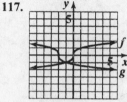

107.
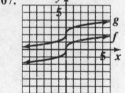

119.
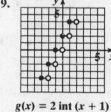

$g(x) = 2 \text{ int } (x + 1)$

109.
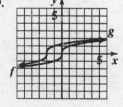

121.
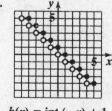

$h(x) = \text{int } (-x) + 1$

123. $y = \sqrt{x - 2}$

125. $y = (x + 1)^2 - 4$

127. a.   First, vertically stretch the graph of $f(x) = \sqrt{x}$ by the factor 2.9; then shift the result up 20.1 units.

   b. $f(x) = 2.9\sqrt{x} + 20.1$

   $f(48) = 2.9\sqrt{48} + 20.1 \approx 40.2$

   The model describes the actual data very well.

   c. $\dfrac{f(x_2) - f(x_1)}{x_2 - x_1}$

   $= \dfrac{f(10) - f(0)}{10 - 0}$

   $= \dfrac{\left(2.9\sqrt{10} + 20.1\right) - \left(2.9\sqrt{0} + 20.1\right)}{10 - 0}$

   $= \dfrac{29.27 - 20.1}{10}$

   ≈ 0.9

   0.9 inches per month

   d. $\dfrac{f(x_2) - f(x_1)}{x_2 - x_1}$

   $= \dfrac{f(60) - f(50)}{60 - 50}$

   $= \dfrac{\left(2.9\sqrt{60} + 20.1\right) - \left(2.9\sqrt{50} + 20.1\right)}{60 - 50}$

   $= \dfrac{42.5633 - 40.6061}{10}$

   ≈ 0.2

   This rate of change is lower than the rate of change in part (c). The relative leveling off of the curve shows this difference.

135. a.

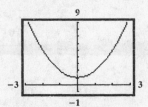

   b.

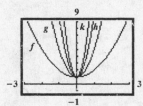

136. a.

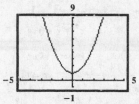

   b.

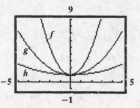

137. a.   False; the graph of g is a translation of three units upward and three units to the left of the graph of f.

   b.   False; the graph of f is a reflection of the graph of $y = \sqrt{x}$ in the x-axis, while the graph of g is a reflection of the graph of $y = \sqrt{x}$ in the y-axis.

c. False; $g(x) = 5x^2 - 10$, so the graph of g can be obtained by stretching f five units followed by a downward shift of ten units.

d. True

(d) is true.

139. $g(x) = -|x - 5| + 1$

141. $g(x) = -\dfrac{1}{4}\sqrt{16 - x^2} - 1$

143. $(a,\ 2b)$

145. $(a,\ b - 3)$

Section 2.6

Check Point Exercises

1.
a. The function $f(x) = x^2 + 3x - 17$ contains neither division nor an even root. The domain of f is the set of all real numbers or $(-\infty, \infty)$.

b. The denominator equals zero when $x = 7$ or $x = -7$. These values must be excluded from the domain. Domain of $g = (-\infty, -7) \cup (-7, 7) \cup (7, \infty)$.

c. Since $h(x) = \sqrt{9x - 27}$ contains an even root; the quantity under the radical must be greater than or equal to 0.
$$9x - 27 \geq 0$$
$$9x \geq 27$$
$$x \geq 3$$
Thus, the domain of h is $\{x \mid x \geq 3\}$, or the interval $[3, \infty)$.

2.
a. $(f + g)(x) = f(x) + g(x)$
$$= x - 5 + (x^2 - 1)$$
$$= x - 5 + x^2 - 1$$
$$= -x^2 + x - 6$$

b. $(f - g)(x) = f(x) - g(x)$
$$= x - 5 - (x^2 - 1)$$
$$= x - 5 - x^2 + 1$$
$$= -x^2 + x - 4$$

c. $(fg)(x) = (x - 5)(x^2 - 1)$
$$= x(x^2 - 1) - 5(x^2 - 1)$$
$$= x^3 - x - 5x^2 + 5$$
$$= x^3 - 5x^2 - x + 5$$

d. $\left(\dfrac{f}{g}\right)(x) = \dfrac{f(x)}{g(x)}$
$$= \dfrac{x - 5}{x^2 - 1},\ x \neq \pm 1$$

166

3. **a.** $(f+g)(x) = f(x) + g(x)$

$$= \sqrt{x-3} + \sqrt{x+1}$$

b. Domain of f:　$x - 3 \geq 0$

$$x \geq 3$$

$$[3, \infty)$$

Domain of g:　$x + 1 \geq 0$

$$x \geq -1$$

$$[-1, \infty)$$

The domain of $f + g$ is the set of all real numbers that are common to the domain of f and the domain of g. Thus, the domain of $f + g$ is $[3, \infty)$.

4. **a.** $(f \circ g)(x) = f(g(x))$

$$= 5(2x^2 - x - 1) + 6$$

$$= 10x^2 - 5x - 5 + 6$$

$$= 10x^2 - 5x + 1$$

b. $(g \circ f)(x) = g(f(x))$

$$= 2(5x+6)^2 - (5x+6) - 1$$

$$= 2(25x^2 + 60x + 36) - 5x - 6 - 1$$

$$= 50x^2 + 120x + 72 - 5x - 6 - 1$$

$$= 50x^2 + 115x + 65$$

5. **a.** $f \circ g(x) = \dfrac{4}{\dfrac{1}{x} + 2} = \dfrac{4x}{1 + 2x}$

b. $\left\{ x \mid x \neq 0, \ x \neq -\dfrac{1}{2} \right\}$

6. $h(x) = f \circ g$ where $f(x) = \sqrt{x}; \quad g(x) = x^2 + 5$

Exercise Set 2.6

1. The function contains neither division nor an even root. The domain $= (-\infty, \infty)$

3. The denominator equals zero when $x = 4$. This value must be excluded from the domain.

Domain: $(-\infty, 4) \cup (4, \infty)$.

5. The function contains neither division nor an even root. The domain $= (-\infty, \infty)$

7. The values that make the denominator equal zero must be excluded from the domain.

Domain: $(-\infty, -3) \cup (-3, 5) \cup (5, \infty)$

9. The values that make the denominators equal zero must be excluded from the domain.

Domain: $(-\infty, -7) \cup (-7, 9) \cup (9, \infty)$

11. The first denominator cannot equal zero. The values that make the second denominator equal zero must be excluded from the domain.
Domain: $(-\infty,-1)\cup(-1,1)\cup(1,\infty)$

13. Exclude x for $x=0$.

Exclude x for $\dfrac{3}{x}-1=0$.

$$\dfrac{3}{x}-1=0$$
$$x\left(\dfrac{3}{x}-1\right)=x(0)$$
$$3-x=0$$
$$-x=-3$$
$$x=3$$
Domain: $(-\infty,0)\cup(0,3)\cup(3,\infty)$

15. Exclude x for $x-1=0$.
$$x-1=0$$
$$x=1$$
Exclude x for $\dfrac{4}{x-1}-2=0$.

$$\dfrac{4}{x-1}-2=0$$
$$(x-1)\left(\dfrac{4}{x-1}-2\right)=(x-1)(0)$$
$$4-2(x-1)=0$$
$$4-2x+2=0$$
$$-2x+6=0$$
$$-2x=-6$$
$$x=3$$
Domain: $(-\infty,1)\cup(1,3)\cup(3,\infty)$

17. The expression under the radical must not be negative.
$$x-3\ge0$$
$$x\ge3$$
Domain: $[3,\infty)$

19. The expression under the radical must be positive.
$$x-3>0$$
$$x>3$$
Domain: $(3,\infty)$

21. The expression under the radical must not be negative.
$$5x+35\ge0$$
$$5x\ge-35$$
$$x\ge-7$$
Domain: $[-7,\infty)$

23. The expression under the radical must not be negative.
$$24 - 2x \geq 0$$
$$-2x \geq -24$$
$$\frac{-2x}{-2} \leq \frac{-24}{-2}$$
$$x \leq 12$$
Domain: $(-\infty, 12]$

25. The expressions under the radicals must not be negative.
$$\begin{array}{ccc} x - 2 \geq 0 & & x + 3 \geq 0 \\ & \text{and} & \\ x \geq 2 & & x \geq -3 \end{array}$$
To make both inequalities true, $x \geq 2$.
Domain: $[2, \infty)$

27. The expression under the radical must not be negative.
$$x - 2 \geq 0$$
$$x \geq 2$$
The denominator equals zero when $x = 5$.
Domain: $[2,5) \cup (5, \infty)$.

29. Find the values that make the denominator equal zero and must be excluded from the domain.
$$x^3 - 5x^2 - 4x + 20$$
$$= x^2(x - 5) - 4(x - 5)$$
$$= (x - 5)(x^2 - 4)$$
$$= (x - 5)(x + 2)(x - 2)$$
−2, 2, and 5 must be excluded.
Domain: $(-\infty, -2) \cup (-2, 2) \cup (2, 5) \cup (5, \infty)$

31. $(f + g)(x) = 3x + 2$
Domain: $(-\infty, \infty)$
$(f - g)(x) = f(x) - g(x)$
$\qquad = (2x + 3) - (x - 1)$
$\qquad = x + 4$
Domain: $(-\infty, \infty)$
$(fg)(x) = f(x) \cdot g(x)$
$\qquad = (2x + 3) \cdot (x - 1)$
$\qquad = 2x^2 + x - 3$
Domain: $(-\infty, \infty)$
$\left(\dfrac{f}{g}\right)(x) = \dfrac{f(x)}{g(x)} = \dfrac{2x + 3}{x - 1}$
Domain: $(-\infty, 1) \cup (1, \infty)$

33. $(f + g)(x) = 3x^2 + x - 5$
Domain: $(-\infty, \infty)$
$(f - g)(x) = -3x^2 + x - 5$
Domain: $(-\infty, \infty)$
$(fg)(x) = (x - 5)(3x^2) = 3x^3 - 15x^2$
Domain: $(-\infty, \infty)$
$\left(\dfrac{f}{g}\right)(x) = \dfrac{x - 5}{3x^2}$
Domain: $(-\infty, 0) \cup (0, \infty)$

35. $(f+g)(x) = 2x^2 - 2$

Domain: $(-\infty, \infty)$

$(f-g)(x) = 2x^2 - 2x - 4$

Domain: $(-\infty, \infty)$

$(fg)(x) = (2x^2 - x - 3)(x+1)$

$\qquad = 2x^3 + x^2 - 4x - 3$

Domain: $(-\infty, \infty)$

$\left(\dfrac{f}{g}\right)(x) = \dfrac{2x^2 - x - 3}{x+1}$

$\qquad = \dfrac{(2x-3)(x+1)}{(x+1)} = 2x - 3$

Domain: $(-\infty, -1) \cup (-1, \infty)$

37. $(f+g)(x) = (3 - x^2) + (x^2 + 2x - 15)$

$\qquad = 2x - 12$

Domain: $(-\infty, \infty)$

$(f-g)(x) = (3 - x^2) - (x^2 + 2x - 15)$

$\qquad = -2x^2 - 2x + 18$

Domain: $(-\infty, \infty)$

$(fg)(x) = (3 - x^2)(x^2 + 2x - 15)$

$\qquad = -x^4 - 2x^3 + 18x^2 + 6x - 45$

Domain: $(-\infty, \infty)$

$\left(\dfrac{f}{g}\right)(x) = \dfrac{3 - x^2}{x^2 + 2x - 15}$

Domain: $(-\infty, -5) \cup (-5, 3) \cup (3, \infty)$

39. $(f+g)(x) = \sqrt{x} + x - 4$

Domain: $[0, \infty)$

$(f-g)(x) = \sqrt{x} - x + 4$

Domain: $[0, \infty)$

$(fg)(x) = \sqrt{x}(x-4)$

Domain: $[0, \infty)$

$\left(\dfrac{f}{g}\right)(x) = \dfrac{\sqrt{x}}{x-4}$

Domain: $[0, 4) \cup (4, \infty)$

41. $(f+g)(x) = 2 + \dfrac{1}{x} + \dfrac{1}{x} = 2 + \dfrac{2}{x} = \dfrac{2x+2}{x}$

Domain: $(-\infty, 0) \cup (0, \infty)$

$(f-g)(x) = 2 + \dfrac{1}{x} - \dfrac{1}{x} = 2$

Domain: $(-\infty, 0) \cup (0, \infty)$

$(fg)(x) = \left(2 + \dfrac{1}{x}\right) \cdot \dfrac{1}{x} = \dfrac{2}{x} + \dfrac{1}{x^2} = \dfrac{2x+1}{x^2}$

Domain: $(-\infty, 0) \cup (0, \infty)$

$\left(\dfrac{f}{g}\right)(x) = \dfrac{2 + \frac{1}{x}}{\frac{1}{x}} = \left(2 + \dfrac{1}{x}\right) \cdot x = 2x + 1$

Domain: $(-\infty, 0) \cup (0, \infty)$

43. $(f+g)(x) = f(x) + g(x)$

$\qquad = \dfrac{5x+1}{x^2 - 9} + \dfrac{4x-2}{x^2 - 9}$

$\qquad = \dfrac{9x-1}{x^2 - 9}$

Domain: $(-\infty, -3) \cup (-3, 3) \cup (3, \infty)$

$(f-g)(x) = f(x) - g(x)$

$\qquad = \dfrac{5x+1}{x^2 - 9} - \dfrac{4x-2}{x^2 - 9}$

$\qquad = \dfrac{x+3}{x^2 - 9}$

$\qquad = \dfrac{1}{x-3}$

Domain: $(-\infty, -3) \cup (-3, 3) \cup (3, \infty)$

$(fg)(x) = f(x) \cdot g(x)$

$\qquad = \dfrac{5x+1}{x^2 - 9} \cdot \dfrac{4x-2}{x^2 - 9}$

$\qquad = \dfrac{(5x+1)(4x-2)}{\left(x^2 - 9\right)^2}$

Domain: $(-\infty, -3) \cup (-3, 3) \cup (3, \infty)$

$\left(\dfrac{f}{g}\right)(x) = \dfrac{\frac{5x+1}{x^2 - 9}}{\frac{4x-2}{x^2 - 9}}$

$\qquad = \dfrac{5x+1}{x^2 - 9} \cdot \dfrac{x^2 - 9}{4x-2}$

$\qquad = \dfrac{5x+1}{4x-2}$

The domain must exclude -3, 3, and any values that make $4x - 2 = 0$.

$4x - 2 = 0$

$\quad 4x = 2$

$\quad x = \dfrac{1}{2}$

Domain: $(-\infty, -3) \cup \left(-3, \frac{1}{2}\right) \cup \left(\frac{1}{2}, 3\right) \cup (3, \infty)$

45. $(f+g)(x) = \sqrt{x+4} + \sqrt{x-1}$

Domain: $[1, \infty)$

$(f-g)(x) = \sqrt{x+4} - \sqrt{x-1}$

Domain: $[1, \infty)$

$(fg)(x) = \sqrt{x+4} \cdot \sqrt{x-1} = \sqrt{x^2+3x-4}$

Domain: $[1, \infty)$

$\left(\dfrac{f}{g}\right)(x) = \dfrac{\sqrt{x+4}}{\sqrt{x-1}}$

Domain: $(1, \infty)$

47. $(f+g)(x) = \sqrt{x-2} + \sqrt{2-x}$

Domain: $\{2\}$

$(f-g)(x) = \sqrt{x-2} - \sqrt{2-x}$

Domain: $\{2\}$

$(fg)(x) = \sqrt{x-2} \cdot \sqrt{2-x} = \sqrt{-x^2+4x-4}$

Domain: $\{2\}$

$\left(\dfrac{f}{g}\right)(x) = \dfrac{\sqrt{x-2}}{\sqrt{2-x}}$

Domain: $\varnothing$

49. $f(x) = 2x;\ g(x) = x + 7$

  a. $(f \circ g)(x) = 2(x+7) = 2x+14$

  b. $(g \circ f)(x) = 2x+7$

  c. $(f \circ g)(2) = 2(2)+14 = 18$

51. $f(x) = x + 4;\ g(x) = 2x + 1$

  a. $(f \circ g)(x) = (2x+1)+4 = 2x+5$

  b. $(g \circ f)(x) = 2(x+4)+1 = 2x+9$

  c. $(f \circ g)(2) = 2(2)+5 = 9$

53. $f(x) = 4x - 3;\ g(x) = 5x^2 - 2$

  a. $(f \circ g)(x) = 4(5x^2-2)-3$

                $= 20x^2 - 11$

  b. $(g \circ f)(x) = 5(4x-3)^2 - 2$

                $= 5(16x^2 - 24x + 9) - 2$

                $= 80x^2 - 120x + 43$

  c. $(f \circ g)(2) = 20(2)^2 - 11 = 69$

55. $f(x) = x^2 + 2;\ g(x) = x^2 - 2$

  a. $(f \circ g)(x) = (x^2-2)^2 + 2$

                $= x^4 - 4x^2 + 4 + 2$

                $= x^4 - 4x^2 + 6$

  b. $(g \circ f)(x) = (x^2+2)^2 - 2$

                $= x^4 + 4x^2 + 4 - 2$

                $= x^4 + 4x^2 + 2$

  c. $(f \circ g)(2) = 2^4 - 4(2)^2 + 6 = 6$

57. $f(x) = 4 - x;\ g(x) = 2x^2 + x + 5$

  a. $(f \circ g)(x) = 4 - \left(2x^2 + x + 5\right)$

                $= 4 - 2x^2 - x - 5$

                $= -2x^2 - x - 1$

  b. $(g \circ f)(x) = 2(4-x)^2 + (4-x) + 5$

                $= 2(16 - 8x + x^2) + 4 - x + 5$

                $= 32 - 16x + 2x^2 + 4 - x + 5$

                $= 2x^2 - 17x + 41$

  c. $(f \circ g)(2) = -2(2)^2 - 2 - 1 = -11$

59. $f(x) = \sqrt{x};\ g(x) = x - 1$

  a. $(f \circ g)(x) = \sqrt{x-1}$

  b. $(g \circ f)(x) = \sqrt{x} - 1$

  c. $(f \circ g)(2) = \sqrt{2-1} = \sqrt{1} = 1$

61. $f(x) = 2x - 3;\ g(x) = \dfrac{x+3}{2}$

  a. $(f \circ g)(x) = 2\left(\dfrac{x+3}{2}\right) - 3$

                $= x + 3 - 3$

                $= x$

  b. $(g \circ f)(x) = \dfrac{(2x-3)+3}{2} = \dfrac{2x}{2} = x$

  c. $(f \circ g)(2) = 2$

63. $f(x) = \dfrac{1}{x}; \quad g(x) = \dfrac{1}{x}$

    a. $(f \circ g)(x) = \dfrac{1}{\frac{1}{x}} = x$

    b. $(g \circ f)(x) = \dfrac{1}{\frac{1}{x}} = x$

    c. $(f \circ g)(2) = 2$

65. **a.** $(f \circ g)(x) = f\left(\dfrac{1}{x}\right) = \dfrac{2}{\frac{1}{x}+3}, x \neq 0$

$$= \dfrac{2(x)}{\left(\dfrac{1}{x}+3\right)(x)}$$

$$= \dfrac{2x}{1+3x}$$

    b. We must exclude 0 because it is excluded from g.

        We must exclude $-\dfrac{1}{3}$ because it causes the denominator of $f \circ g$ to be 0.

        Domain: $\left(-\infty, -\dfrac{1}{3}\right) \cup \left(-\dfrac{1}{3}, 0\right) \cup (0, \infty)$.

67. **a.** $(f \circ g)(x) = f\left(\dfrac{4}{x}\right) = \dfrac{\frac{4}{x}}{\frac{4}{x}+1}$

$$= \dfrac{\left(\dfrac{4}{x}\right)(x)}{\left(\dfrac{4}{x}+1\right)(x)}$$

$$= \dfrac{4}{4+x}, x \neq -4$

    b. We must exclude 0 because it is excluded from g.
        We must exclude -4 because it causes the denominator of $f \circ g$ to be 0.
        Domain: $(-\infty, -4) \cup (-4, 0) \cup (0, \infty)$.

69. **a.** $f \circ g(x) = f(x-2) = \sqrt{x-2}$

    b. The expression under the radical in $f \circ g$ must not be negative.
        $x - 2 \geq 0$
          $x \geq 2$
        Domain: $[2, \infty)$.

71. a. $(f \circ g)(x) = f(\sqrt{1-x})$

$$= \left(\sqrt{1-x}\right)^2 + 4$$

$$= 1 - x + 4$$

$$= 5 - x$$

b.   The domain of $f \circ g$ must exclude any values that are excluded from g.

$$1 - x \geq 0$$

$$-x \geq -1$$

$$x \leq 1$$

Domain: $(-\infty, 1]$.

73. $f(x) = x^4 \quad g(x) = 3x - 1$

75. $f(x) = \sqrt[3]{x} \quad g(x) = x^2 - 9$

77. $f(x) = |x| \quad g(x) = 2x - 5$

79. $f(x) = \dfrac{1}{x} \quad g(x) = 2x - 3$

81. $(f + g)(-3) = f(-3) + g(-3) = 4 + 1 = 5$

83. $(fg)(2) = f(2)g(2) = (-1)(1) = -1$

85.   The domain of $f + g$ is $[-4, 3]$.

87.   The graph of $f + g$

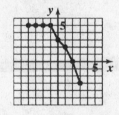

89. $(f \circ g)(-1) = f(g(-1)) = f(-3) = 1$

91. $(g \circ f)(0) = g(f(0)) = g(2) = -6$

93. $(f \circ g)(x) = 7$

$$2(x^2 - 3x + 8) - 5 = 7$$

$$2x^2 - 6x + 16 - 5 = 7$$

$$2x^2 - 6x + 11 = 7$$

$$2x^2 - 6x + 4 = 0$$

$$x^2 - 3x + 2 = 0$$

$$(x-1)(x-2) = 0$$

$$x - 1 = 0 \quad \text{or} \quad x - 2 = 0$$

$$x = 1 \qquad\qquad x = 2$$

95.   Domain: $\{0, 1, 2, 3, 4, 5, 6, 7, 8\}$

97. a. $(B - D)(x) = (26,208x + 3,869,910) - (17,964x + 2,300,198)$

$$= 26,208x + 3,869,910 - 17,964x - 2,300,198$$

$$= 8244x + 1,569,712$$

This function represents the net change in population from births and deaths.

b. $(B - D)(x) = 8244x + 1,569,712$

$(B - D)(8) = 8244(8) + 1,569,712 = 1,635,664$

The U.S. population increased by 1,635,664 in 2003.

c. $4,093,000 - 2,423,000 = 1,670,000$

The difference of the functions modeled this value reasonably well.

99. $f + g$ represents the total world population in year x.

101. $(f + g)(2000) \approx 6$ billion people.

103. $(R-C)(20,000)$

$= 65(20,000) - (600,000 + 45(20,000))$

$= -200,000$

The company lost $200,000 since costs exceeded revenues.

$(R-C)(30,000)$

$= 65(30,000) - (600,000 + 45(30,000))$

$= 0$

The company broke even.

105. a. f gives the price of the computer after a $400 discount. g gives the price of the computer after a 25% discount.

b. $(f \circ g)(x) = 0.75x - 400$

This models the price of a computer after first a 25% discount and then a $400 discount.

c. $(g \circ f)(x) = 0.75(x - 400)$

This models the price of a computer after first a $400 discount and then a 25% discount.

d. The function $f \circ g$ models the greater discount, since the 25% discount is taken on the regular price first.

113.

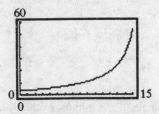

The per capita cost of Medicare is rising.

115.

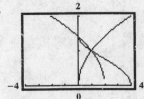

$(f \circ g)(x) = \sqrt{2 - \sqrt{x}}$

The domain of g is $[0, \infty)$.

The expression under the radical in $f \circ g$ must not be negative.

$2 - \sqrt{x} \ge 0$

$-\sqrt{x} \ge -2$

$\sqrt{x} \le 2$

$x \le 4$

Domain: $[0, 4]$

117. $(f \circ g)(x) = (f \circ g)(-x)$

$f(g(x)) = f(g(-x))$ since g is even

$f(g(x)) = f(g(x))$ so $f \circ g$ is even

119.

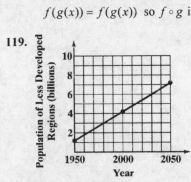

174

Section 2.7

Check Point Exercises

1. $f(g(x)) = 4\left(\dfrac{x+7}{4}\right) - 7 = x$

$g(f(x)) = \dfrac{(4x-7)+7}{4} = x$

$f(g(x)) = g(f(x)) = x$

2. $f(x) = 2x + 7$

Replace $f(x)$ with y:

$y = 2x + 7$

Interchange x and y:

$x = 2y + 7$

Solve for y:

$x = 2y + 7$

$x - 7 = 2y$

$\dfrac{x-7}{2} = y$

Replace y with $f^{-1}(x)$:

$f^{-1}(x) = \dfrac{x-7}{2}$

3. $f(x) = 4x^3 - 1$

Replace $f(x)$ with y:

$y = 4x^3 - 1$

Interchange x and y:

$x = 4y^3 - 1$

Solve for y:

$x = 4y^3 - 1$

$x + 1 = 4y^3$

$\dfrac{x+1}{4} = y^3$

$\sqrt[3]{\dfrac{x+1}{4}} = y$

Replace y with $f^{-1}(x)$:

$f^{-1}(x) = \sqrt[3]{\dfrac{x+1}{4}}$

Alternative form for answer:

$f(x)^{-1} = \sqrt[3]{\dfrac{x+1}{4}} = \dfrac{\sqrt[3]{x+1}}{\sqrt[3]{4}}$

$= \dfrac{\sqrt[3]{x+1}}{\sqrt[3]{4}} \cdot \dfrac{\sqrt[3]{2}}{\sqrt[3]{2}} = \dfrac{\sqrt[3]{2x+2}}{\sqrt[3]{8}}$

$= \dfrac{\sqrt[3]{2x+2}}{2}$

4. $f(x) = \dfrac{3}{x} - 1$

Replace $f(x)$ with y:

$y = \dfrac{3}{x} - 1$

Interchange x and y:

$x = \dfrac{3}{y} - 1$

Solve for y:

$x = \dfrac{3}{y} - 1$

$xy = 3 - y$

$xy + y = 3$

$y(x+1) = 3$

$y = \dfrac{3}{x+1}$

Replace y with $f^{-1}(x)$:

$f^{-1}(x) = \dfrac{3}{x+1}$

5. The graphs of (b) and (c) pass the horizontal line test and thus have an inverse.

6. Find points of f^{-1}.

$f(x)$	$f^{-1}(x)$
$(-2,-2)$	$(-2,-2)$
$(-1,0)$	$(0,-1)$
$(1,2)$	$(2,1)$

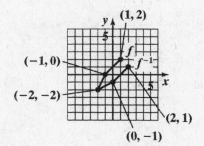

175

7. $f(x) = x^2 + 1$

Replace $f(x)$ with y:

$y = x^2 + 1$

Interchange x and y:

$x = y^2 + 1$

Solve for y:

$x = y^2 + 1$

$x - 1 = y^2$

$\sqrt{x-1} = y$

Replace y with $f^{-1}(x)$:

$f^{-1}(x) = \sqrt{x-1}$

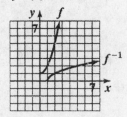

Exercise Set 2.7

1. $f(x) = 4x; g(x) = \dfrac{x}{4}$

$f(g(x)) = 4\left(\dfrac{x}{4}\right) = x$

$g(f(x)) = \dfrac{4x}{4} = x$

f and g are inverses.

3. $f(x) = 3x + 8; \ g(x) = \dfrac{x-8}{3}$

$f(g(x)) = 3\left(\dfrac{x-8}{3}\right) + 8 = x - 8 + 8 = x$

$g(f(x)) = \dfrac{(3x+8)-8}{3} = \dfrac{3x}{3} = x$

f and g are inverses.

5. $f(x) = 5x - 9; \ g(x) = \dfrac{x+5}{9}$

$f(g(x)) = 5\left(\dfrac{x+5}{9}\right) - 9$

$= \dfrac{5x+25}{9} - 9$

$= \dfrac{5x-56}{9}$

$g(f(x)) = \dfrac{5x-9+5}{9} = \dfrac{5x-4}{9}$

f and g are not inverses.

7. $f(x) = \dfrac{3}{x-4}; g(x) = \dfrac{3}{x} + 4$

$f(g(x)) = \dfrac{3}{\frac{3}{x} + 4 - 4} = \dfrac{3}{\frac{3}{x}} = x$

$g(f(x)) = \dfrac{3}{\frac{3}{x-4}} + 4$

$= 3 \cdot \left(\dfrac{x-4}{3}\right) + 4$

$= x - 4 + 4$

$= x$

f and g are inverses.

9. $f(x) = -x; g(x) = -x$

$f(g(x)) = -(-x) = x$

$g(f(x)) = -(-x) = x$

f and g are inverses.

11. a. $f(x) = x + 3$

$y = x + 3$

$x = y + 3$

$y = x - 3$

$f^{-1}(x) = x - 3$

b. $f(f^{-1}(x)) = x - 3 + 3 = x$

$f^{-1}(f(x)) = x + 3 - 3 = x$

13. a.
$$f(x) = 2x$$
$$y = 2x$$
$$x = 2y$$
$$y = \frac{x}{2}$$
$$f^{-1}(x) = \frac{x}{2}$$

b.
$$f(f^{-1}(x)) = 2\left(\frac{x}{2}\right) = x$$
$$f^{-1}(f(x)) = \frac{2x}{2} = x$$

15. a.
$$f(x) = 2x + 3$$
$$y = 2x + 3$$
$$x = 2y + 3$$
$$x - 3 = 2y$$
$$y = \frac{x-3}{2}$$
$$f^{-1}(x) = \frac{x-3}{2}$$

b.
$$f(f^{-1}(x)) = 2\left(\frac{x-3}{2}\right) + 3$$
$$= x - 3 + 3$$
$$= x$$
$$f^{-1}(f(x)) = \frac{2x+3-3}{2} = \frac{2x}{2} = x$$

17. a.
$$f(x) = x^3 + 2$$
$$y = x^3 + 2$$
$$x = y^3 + 2$$
$$x - 2 = y^3$$
$$y = \sqrt[3]{x-2}$$
$$f^{-1}(x) = \sqrt[3]{x-2}$$

b.
$$f(f^{-1}(x)) = \left(\sqrt[3]{x-2}\right)^3 + 2$$
$$= x - 2 + 2$$
$$= x$$
$$f^{-1}(f(x)) = \sqrt[3]{x^3 + 2 - 2} = \sqrt[3]{x^3} = x$$

19. a.
$$f(x) = (x+2)^3$$
$$y = (x+2)^3$$
$$x = (y+2)^3$$
$$\sqrt[3]{x} = y + 2$$
$$y = \sqrt[3]{x} - 2$$
$$f^{-1}(x) = \sqrt[3]{x} - 2$$

b.
$$f(f^{-1}(x)) = \left(\sqrt[3]{x} - 2 + 2\right)^3 = \left(\sqrt[3]{x}\right)^3 = x$$
$$f^{-1}(f(x)) = \sqrt[3]{(x+2)^3} - 2$$
$$= x + 2 - 2$$
$$= x$$

21. a.
$$f(x) = \frac{1}{x}$$
$$y = \frac{1}{x}$$
$$x = \frac{1}{y}$$
$$xy = 1$$
$$y = \frac{1}{x}$$
$$f^{-1}(x) = \frac{1}{x}$$

b.
$$f(f^{-1}(x)) = \frac{1}{\frac{1}{x}} = x$$
$$f^{-1}(f(x)) = \frac{1}{\frac{1}{x}} = x$$

23. a.
$$f(x) = \sqrt{x}$$
$$y = \sqrt{x}$$
$$x = \sqrt{y}$$
$$y = x^2$$
$$f^{-1}(x) = x^2, x \geq 0$$

b.
$$f(f^{-1}(x)) = \sqrt{x^2} = |x| = x \text{ for } x \geq 0.$$
$$f^{-1}(f(x)) = (\sqrt{x})^2 = x$$

177

25. a.

$$f(x) = \frac{7}{x} - 3$$

$$y = \frac{7}{x} - 3$$

$$x = \frac{7}{y} - 3$$

$$xy = 7 - 3y$$

$$xy + 3y = 7$$

$$y(x + 3) = 7$$

$$y = \frac{7}{x + 3}$$

$$f^{-1}(x) = \frac{7}{x + 3}$$

b.

$$f\left(f^{-1}(x)\right) = \frac{7}{\dfrac{7}{x + 3}} - 3 = x$$

$$f^{-1}\left(f(x)\right) = \frac{7}{\dfrac{7}{x} - 3 + 3} = x$$

27. a.

$$f(x) = \frac{2x + 1}{x - 3}$$

$$y = \frac{2x + 1}{x - 3}$$

$$x = \frac{2y + 1}{y - 3}$$

$$x(y - 3) = 2y + 1$$

$$xy - 3x = 2y + 1$$

$$xy - 2y = 3x + 1$$

$$y(x - 2) = 3x + 1$$

$$y = \frac{3x + 1}{x - 2}$$

$$f^{-1}(x) = \frac{3x + 1}{x - 2}$$

b.

$$f(f^{-1}(x)) = \frac{2\left(\dfrac{3x+1}{x-2}\right) + 1}{\dfrac{3x+1}{x-2} - 3}$$

$$= \frac{2(3x+1) + x - 2}{3x + 1 - 3(x - 2)} = \frac{6x + 2 + x - 2}{3x + 1 - 3x + 6}$$

$$= \frac{7x}{7} = x$$

$$f^{-1}(f(x)) = \frac{3\left(\dfrac{2x+1}{x-3}\right) + 1}{\dfrac{2x+1}{x-3} - 2}$$

$$= \frac{3(2x+1) + x - 3}{2x + 1 - 2(x - 3)}$$

$$= \frac{6x + 3 + x - 3}{2x + 1 - 2x + 6} = \frac{7x}{7} = x$$

29. The function fails the horizontal line test, so it does not have an inverse function.

31. The function fails the horizontal line test, so it does not have an inverse function.

33. The function passes the horizontal line test, so it does have an inverse function.

35.

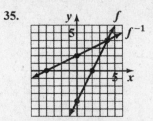

37.

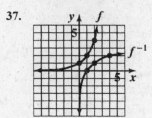

39. a.

$$f(x) = 2x - 1$$

$$y = 2x - 1$$

$$x = 2y - 1$$

$$x + 1 = 2y$$

$$\frac{x + 1}{2} = y$$

$$f^{-1}(x) = \frac{x + 1}{2}$$

b.

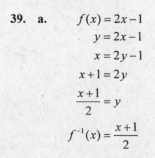

c. Domain of f: $(-\infty, \infty)$

Range of f: $(-\infty, \infty)$

Domain of f^{-1}: $(-\infty, \infty)$

Range of f^{-1}: $(-\infty, \infty)$

41. a.
$$f(x) = x^2 - 4$$
$$y = x^2 - 4$$
$$x = y^2 - 4$$
$$x + 4 = y^2$$
$$\sqrt{x+4} = y$$
$$f^{-1}(x) = \sqrt{x+4}$$

b.
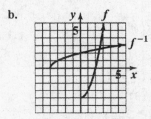

c. Domain of f: $[0, \infty)$

Range of f: $[-4, \infty)$

Domain of f^{-1}: $[-4, \infty)$

Range of f^{-1}: $[0, \infty)$

43. a.
$$f(x) = (x-1)^2$$
$$y = (x-1)^2$$
$$x = (y-1)^2$$
$$-\sqrt{x} = y - 1$$
$$-\sqrt{x} + 1 = y$$
$$f^{-1}(x) = 1 - \sqrt{x}$$

b.
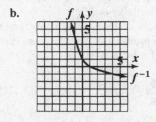

c. Domain of f: $(-\infty, 1]$

Range of f: $[0, \infty)$

45. a.
$$f(x) = x^3 - 1$$
$$y = x^3 - 1$$
$$x = y^3 - 1$$
$$x + 1 = y^3$$
$$\sqrt[3]{x+1} = y$$
$$f^{-1}(x) = \sqrt[3]{x+1}$$

b.
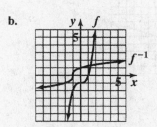

c. Domain of f: $(-\infty, \infty)$

Range of f: $(-\infty, \infty)$

Domain of f^{-1}: $(-\infty, \infty)$

Range of f^{-1}: $(-\infty, \infty)$

47. a.
$$f(x) = (x+2)^3$$
$$y = (x+2)^3$$
$$x = (y+2)^3$$
$$\sqrt[3]{x} = y + 2$$
$$\sqrt[3]{x} - 2 = y$$
$$f^{-1}(x) = \sqrt[3]{x} - 2$$

b.

c. Domain of f: $(-\infty, \infty)$

Range of f: $(-\infty, \infty)$

Domain of f^{-1}: $(-\infty, \infty)$

Range of f^{-1}: $(-\infty, \infty)$

179

49. a.
$$f(x) = \sqrt{x-1}$$
$$y = \sqrt{x-1}$$
$$x = \sqrt{y-1}$$
$$x^2 = y-1$$
$$x^2 + 1 = y$$
$$f^{-1}(x) = x^2 + 1$$

b.

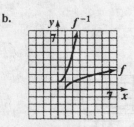

c. Domain of f: $[1, \infty)$
Range of f: $[0, \infty)$
Domain of f^{-1}: $[0, \infty)$
Range of f^{-1}: $[1, \infty)$

51. a.
$$f(x) = \sqrt[3]{x} + 1$$
$$y = \sqrt[3]{x} + 1$$
$$x = \sqrt[3]{y} + 1$$
$$x - 1 = \sqrt[3]{y}$$
$$(x-1)^3 = y$$
$$f^{-1}(x) = (x-1)^3$$

b.

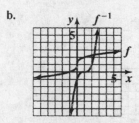

c. Domain of f: $(-\infty, \infty)$
Range of f: $(-\infty, \infty)$
Domain of f^{-1}: $(-\infty, \infty)$
Range of f^{-1}: $(-\infty, \infty)$

53. $f(g(1)) = f(1) = 5$

55. $(g \circ f)(-1) = g(f(-1)) = g(1) = 1$

57. $f^{-1}(g(10)) = f^{-1}(-1) = 2$, since $f(2) = -1$.

59.
$$(f \circ g)(0) = f(g(0))$$
$$= f(4 \cdot 0 - 1)$$
$$= f(-1) = 2(-1) - 5 = -7$$

61. Let $f^{-1}(1) = x$. Then
$$f(x) = 1$$
$$2x - 5 = 1$$
$$2x = 6$$
$$x = 3$$
Thus, $f^{-1}(1) = 3$

63.
$$g(f[h(1)]) = g\left(f\left[1^2 + 1 + 2\right]\right)$$
$$= g(f(4))$$
$$= g(2 \cdot 4 - 5)$$
$$= g(3)$$
$$= 4 \cdot 3 - 1 = 11$$

65. a. {(Zambia, −7.3), (Colombia, −4.5), (Poland, −2.8), (Italy, −2.8), (United States, −1.9)}

b. {(−7.3, Zambia), (−4.5, Colombia), (−2.8, Poland), (−2.8, Italy), (−1.9, United States)} This relation is not a function because −2.8 corresponds to two elements in the range.

67. a. It passes the horizontal line test and is one-to-one.

b. $f^{-1}(0.25) = 15$ If there are 15 people in the room, the probability that 2 of them have the same birthday is 0.25.
$f^{-1}(0.5) = 21$ If there are 21 people in the room, the probability that 2 of them have the same birthday is 0.5.
$f^{-1}(0.7) = 30$ If there are 30 people in the room, the probability that 2 of them have the same birthday is 0.7.

69.
$$f(g(x)) = \frac{9}{5}\left[\frac{5}{9}(x - 32)\right] + 32$$
$$= x - 32 + 32$$
$$= x$$

f and *g* are inverses.

77.

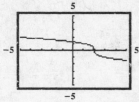

one-to-one

79.

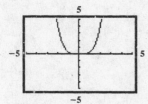

not one-to-one

81.

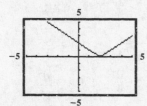

not one-to-one

83.

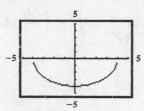

not one-to-one

85.

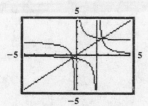

f and *g* are inverses

87. a. False. The inverse is $\{(4,1), (7,2)\}$.

b. False. $f(x) = 5$ is a horizontal line, so it does not pass the horizontal line test.

c. False. $f^{-1}(x) = \dfrac{x}{3}$.

d. True. The domain of *f* is the range of f^{-1} and the range of *f* is the domain of f^{-1}.

(d) is true.

89.

$$f(x) = \frac{3x-2}{5x-3}$$

$$y = \frac{3x-2}{5x-3}$$

$$x = \frac{3y-2}{5y-3}$$

$$x(5y-3) = 3y-2$$

$$5xy - 3x = 3y - 2$$

$$5xy - 3y = 3x - 2$$

$$y(5x-3) = 3x - 2$$

$$y = \frac{3x-2}{5x-3}$$

$$f^{-1}(x) = \frac{3x-2}{5x-3}$$

Note: An alternative approach is to show that $(f \circ f)(x) = x$.

91.
$$8 + f^{-1}(x-1) = 10$$
$$f^{-1}(x-1) = 2$$
$$f(2) = x-1$$
$$6 = x-1$$
$$7 = x$$
$$x = 7$$

Section 2.8

Check Point Exercises

1.
$$d = \sqrt{(x_2 - x_1)^2 + (y_2 - y_1)^2}$$
$$d = \sqrt{(1-(-4))^2 + (-3-9)^2}$$
$$= \sqrt{(5)^2 + (-12)^2}$$
$$= \sqrt{25 + 144}$$
$$= \sqrt{169}$$
$$= 13$$

2. $\left(\dfrac{1+7}{2}, \dfrac{2+(-3)}{2} \right) = \left(\dfrac{8}{2}, \dfrac{-1}{2} \right) = \left(4, -\dfrac{1}{2} \right)$

3. $h = 0$, $k = 0$, $r = 4$;
$$(x-0)^2 + (y-0)^2 = 4^2$$
$$x^2 + y^2 = 16$$

181

4. $h = 5,\ k = -6,\ r = 10;$

$$(x-5)^2 + [y-(-6)]^2 = 10^2$$
$$(x-5)^2 + (y+6)^2 = 100$$

5. **a.** $(x+3)^2 + (y-1)^2 = 4$

$[x-(-3)]^2 + (y-1)^2 = 2^2$

So in the standard form of the circle's
equation $(x-h)^2 + (y-k)^2 = r^2$,

we have $h = -3,\ k = 1,\ r = 2.$

center: $(h,\ k) = (-3,\ 1)$

radius: $r = 2$

b.

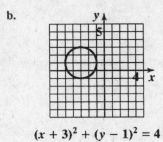

$(x + 3)^2 + (y - 1)^2 = 4$

c. Domain: $[-5, -1]$

Range: $[-1, 3]$

6.

$$x^2 + y^2 + 4x - 4y - 1 = 0$$
$$x^2 + y^2 + 4x - 4y - 1 = 0$$
$$\left(x^2 + 4x \quad\right) + \left(y^2 - 4y \quad\right) = 0$$
$$\left(x^2 + 4x + 4\right) + \left(y^2 + 4y + 4\right) = 1 + 4 + 4$$
$$(x+2)^2 + (y-2)^2 = 9$$
$$[x-(-x)]^2 + (y-2)^2 = 3^2$$

So in the standard form of the circle's equation
$(x-h)^2 + (y-k)^2 = r^2$, we have
$h = -2,\ k = 2,\ r = 3$.

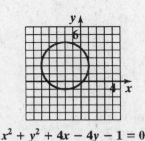

$x^2 + y^2 + 4x - 4y - 1 = 0$

Exercise Set 2.8

1. $d = \sqrt{(14-2)^2 + (8-3)^2}$

$= \sqrt{12^2 + 5^2}$

$= \sqrt{144 + 25}$

$= \sqrt{169}$

$= 13$

3. $d = \sqrt{(-6-4)^2 + (3-(-1))^2}$

$= \sqrt{(-10)^2 + (4)^2}$

$= \sqrt{100 + 16}$

$= \sqrt{116}$

$= 2\sqrt{29}$

≈ 10.77

5. $d = \sqrt{(-3-0)^2 + (4-0)^2}$

$= \sqrt{3^2 + 4^2}$

$= \sqrt{9 + 16}$

$= \sqrt{25}$

$= 5$

7. $d = \sqrt{[3-(-2)]^2 + [-4-(-6)]^2}$

$= \sqrt{5^2 + 2^2}$

$= \sqrt{25 + 4}$

$= \sqrt{29}$

≈ 5.39

9. $d = \sqrt{(4-0)^2 + [1-(-3)]^2}$

$= \sqrt{4^2 + 4^2}$

$= \sqrt{16 + 16}$

$= \sqrt{32}$

$= 4\sqrt{2}$

≈ 5.66

11. $d = \sqrt{(-.5-3.5)^2 + (6.2-8.2)^2}$

$= \sqrt{(-4)^2 + (-2)^2}$

$= \sqrt{16 + 4}$

$= \sqrt{20}$

$= 2\sqrt{5}$

≈ 4.47

13. $d = \sqrt{(\sqrt{5}-0)^2 + [0-(-\sqrt{3})]^2}$

$= \sqrt{(\sqrt{5})^2 + (\sqrt{3})^2}$

$= \sqrt{5+3}$

$= \sqrt{8}$

$= 2\sqrt{2}$

≈ 2.83

15. $d = \sqrt{(-\sqrt{3}-3\sqrt{3})^2 + (4\sqrt{5}-\sqrt{5})^2}$

$= \sqrt{(-4\sqrt{3})^2 + (3\sqrt{5})^2}$

$= \sqrt{16(3)+9(5)}$

$= \sqrt{48+45}$

$= \sqrt{93}$

≈ 9.64

17. $d = \sqrt{\left(\dfrac{1}{3}-\dfrac{7}{3}\right)^2 + \left(\dfrac{6}{5}-\dfrac{1}{5}\right)^2}$

$= \sqrt{(-2)^2 + 1^2}$

$= \sqrt{4+1}$

$= \sqrt{5}$

≈ 2.24

19. $\left(\dfrac{6+2}{2}, \dfrac{8+4}{2}\right) = \left(\dfrac{8}{2}, \dfrac{12}{2}\right) = (4,6)$

21. $\left(\dfrac{-2+(-6)}{2}, \dfrac{-8+(-2)}{2}\right)$

$= \left(\dfrac{-8}{2}, \dfrac{-10}{2}\right) = (-4,-5)$

23. $\left(\dfrac{-3+6}{2}, \dfrac{-4+(-8)}{2}\right)$

$= \left(\dfrac{3}{2}, \dfrac{-12}{2}\right) = \left(\dfrac{3}{2}, -6\right)$

25. $\left(\dfrac{\dfrac{-7}{2}+\left(-\dfrac{5}{2}\right)}{2}, \dfrac{\dfrac{3}{2}+\left(-\dfrac{11}{2}\right)}{2}\right)$

$= \left(\dfrac{\dfrac{-12}{2}}{2}, \dfrac{\dfrac{-8}{2}}{2}\right) = \left(-\dfrac{6}{2}, \dfrac{-4}{2}\right) = (-3,-2)$

27. $\left(\dfrac{8+(-6)}{2}, \dfrac{3\sqrt{5}+7\sqrt{5}}{2}\right)$

$= \left(\dfrac{2}{2}, \dfrac{10\sqrt{5}}{2}\right) = (1, 5\sqrt{5})$

29. $\left(\dfrac{\sqrt{18}+\sqrt{2}}{2}, \dfrac{-4+4}{2}\right)$

$= \left(\dfrac{3\sqrt{2}+\sqrt{2}}{2}, \dfrac{0}{2}\right) = \left(\dfrac{4\sqrt{2}}{2}, 0\right) = (2\sqrt{2},0)$

31. $(x-0)^2 + (y-0)^2 = 7^2$

$x^2 + y^2 = 49$

33. $(x-3)^2 + (y-2)^2 = 5^2$

$(x-3)^2 + (y-2)^2 = 25$

35. $[x-(-1)]^2 + (y-4)^2 = 2^2$

$(x+1)^2 + (y-4)^2 = 4$

37. $[x-(-3)]^2 + [y-(-1)]^2 = \left(\sqrt{3}\right)^2$

$(x+3)^2 + (y+1)^2 = 3$

39. $[x-(-4)]^2 + (y-0)^2 = 10^2$

$(x+4)^2 + (y-0)^2 = 100$

41. $x^2 + y^2 = 16$

$(x-0)^2 + (y-0)^2 = y^2$

$h = 0,\ k = 0,\ r = 4;$

center $= (0, 0);$ radius $= 4$

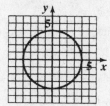

$x^2 + y^2 = 16$

Domain: $[-4,4]$

Range: $[-4,4]$

43. $(x-3)^2 + (y-1)^2 = 36$

$(x-3)^2 + (y-1)^2 = 6^2$

$h = 3, k = 1, r = 6;$

center $= (3, 1);$ radius $= 6$

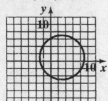

$(x - 3)^2 + (y - 1)^2 = 36$

Domain: $[-3, 9]$

Range: $[-5, 7]$

45. $(x+3)^2 + (y-2)^2 = 4$

$[x-(-3)]^2 + (y-2)^2 = 2^2$

$h = -3, k = 2, r = 2$

center $= (-3, 2);$ radius $= 2$

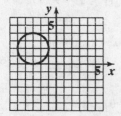

$(x + 3)^2 + (y - 2)^2 = 4$

Domain: $[-5, -1]$

Range: $[0, 4]$

47. $(x+2)^2 + (y+2)^2 = 4$

$[x-(-2)]^2 + [y-(-2)]^2 = 2^2$

$h = -2, k = -2, r = 2$

center $= (-2, -2);$ radius $= 2$

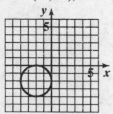

$(x + 2)^2 + (y + 2)^2 = 4$

Domain: $[-4, 0]$

Range: $[-4, 0]$

49. $x^2 + y^2 + 6x + 2y + 6 = 0$

$(x^2 + 6x) + (y^2 + 2y) = -6$

$(x^2 + 6x + 9) + (y^2 + 2y + 1) = 9 + 1 - 6$

$(x+3)^2 + (y+1)^2 = 4$

$[x-(-3)]^2 + [9-(-1)]^2 = 2^2$

center $= (-3, -1);$ radius $= 2$

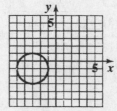

$x^2 + y^2 + 6x + 2y + 6 = 0$

51. $x^2 + y^2 - 10x - 6y - 30 = 0$

$(x^2 - 10x) + (y^2 - 6y) = 30$

$(x^2 - 10x + 25) + (y^2 - 6y + 9) = 25 + 9 + 30$

$(x-5)^2 + (y-3)^2 = 64$

$(x-5)^2 + (y-3)^2 = 8^2$

center $= (5, 3);$ radius $= 8$

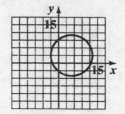

$x^2 + y^2 - 10x - 6y - 30 = 0$

53.
$$x^2 + y^2 + 8x - 2y - 8 = 0$$
$$\left(x^2 + 8x\right) + \left(y^2 - 2y\right) = 8$$
$$\left(x^2 + 8x + 16\right) + \left(y^2 - 2y + 1\right) = 16 + 1 + 8$$
$$(x+4)^2 + (y-1)^2 = 25$$
$$[x - (-4)]^2 + (y-1)^2 = 5^2$$
center = (–4, 1); radius = 5

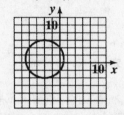

$$x^2 + y^2 + 8x - 2y - 8 = 0$$

55.
$$x^2 - 2x + y^2 - 15 = 0$$
$$\left(x^2 - 2x\right) + y^2 = 15$$
$$\left(x^2 - 2x + 1\right) + (y-0)^2 = 1 + 0 + 15$$
$$(x-1)^2 + (y-0)^2 = 16$$
$$(x-1)^2 + (y-0)^2 = 4^2$$
center = (1, 0); radius = 4

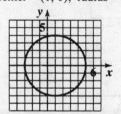

$$x^2 - 2x + y^2 - 15 = 0$$

57.
$$x^2 + y^2 - x + 2y + 1 = 0$$
$$x^2 - x + y^2 + 2y = -1$$
$$x^2 - x + \frac{1}{4} + y^2 + 2y + 1 = -1 + \frac{1}{4} + 1$$
$$\left(x - \frac{1}{2}\right)^2 + (y+1)^2 = \frac{1}{4}$$

center = $\left(\dfrac{1}{2}, -1\right)$; radius = $\dfrac{1}{2}$

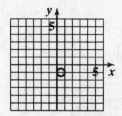

$$x^2 + y^2 - x + 2y + 1 = 0$$

59.
$$x^2 + y^2 + 3x - 2y - 1 = 0$$
$$x^2 + 3x + y^2 - 2y = 1$$
$$x^2 + 3x + \frac{9}{4} + y^2 - 2y + 1 = 1 + \frac{9}{4} + 1$$
$$\left(x + \frac{3}{2}\right)^2 + (y-1)^2 = \frac{17}{4}$$

center = $\left(-\dfrac{3}{2}, 1\right)$; radius = $\dfrac{\sqrt{17}}{2}$

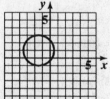

$$x^2 + y^2 + 3x - 2y - 1 = 0$$

61. a. Since the line segment passes through the center, the center is the midpoint of the segment.
$$M = \left(\frac{x_1 + x_2}{2}, \frac{y_1 + y_2}{2}\right)$$
$$= \left(\frac{3+7}{2}, \frac{9+11}{2}\right) = \left(\frac{10}{2}, \frac{20}{2}\right)$$
$$= (5, 10)$$
The center is $(5, 10)$.

b. The radius is the distance from the center to one of the points on the circle. Using the point $(3, 9)$, we get:
$$d = \sqrt{(5-3)^2 + (10-9)^2}$$
$$= \sqrt{2^2 + 1^2} = \sqrt{4+1}$$
$$= \sqrt{5}$$
The radius is $\sqrt{5}$ units.

185

c.
$$(x-5)^2+(y-10)^2=\left(\sqrt{5}\right)^2$$
$$(x-5)^2+(y-10)^2=5$$

63. $x^2+y^2=16$
$x-y=4$

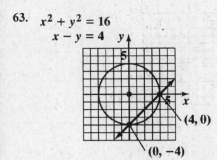

Intersection points: $(0,-4)$ and $(4,0)$

Check $(0,-4)$:

$0^2+(-4)^2=16 \qquad 0-(-4)=4$

$\qquad 16=16$ true $\qquad 4=4$ true

Check $(4,0)$:

$4^2+0^2=16 \qquad 4-0=4$

$\qquad 16=16$ true $\qquad 4=4$ true

The solution set is $\{(0,-4),(4,0)\}$.

65. $(x-2)^2+(y+3)^2=4$
$y=x-3$

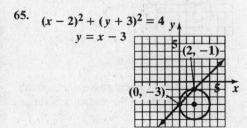

Intersection points: $(0,-3)$ and $(2,-1)$

Check $(0,-3)$:

$(0-2)^2+(-3+3)^2=9 \qquad -3=0-3$

$\qquad (-2)^2+0^2=4 \qquad -3=-3$ true

$\qquad\qquad 4=4$

$\qquad\qquad\qquad$ true

Check $(2,-1)$:

$(2-2)^2+(-1+3)^2=4 \qquad -1=2-3$

$\qquad 0^2+2^2=4 \qquad -1=-1$ true

$\qquad\qquad 4=4$

$\qquad\qquad\qquad$ true

The solution set is $\{(0,-3),(2,-1)\}$.

67.
$$d=\sqrt{[65-(-115)]^2+(70-170)^2}$$
$$d=\sqrt{(65+115)^2+(-100)^2}$$
$$d=\sqrt{180^2+10000}$$
$$d=\sqrt{32400+10000}$$
$$d=\sqrt{42400}$$
$$d=205.9 \text{ miles}$$
$$\frac{205.9 \text{ miles}}{400}=0.5 \text{ hours or 30 minutes}$$

69. If we place L.A. at the origin, then we want the equation of a circle with center at $(-2.4,-2.7)$ and radius 30.
$$(x-(-2.4))^2+(y-(-2.7))^2=30^2$$
$$(x+2.4)^2+(y+2.7)^2=900$$

77.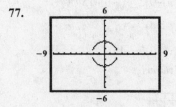

79.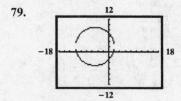

81. The distance for A to B:

$$\overline{AB} = \sqrt{(3-1)^2 + [3+d-(1+d)]^2}$$
$$= \sqrt{2^2 + 2^2}$$
$$= \sqrt{4+4}$$
$$= \sqrt{8}$$
$$= 2\sqrt{2}$$

The distance from B to C:

$$\overline{BC} = \sqrt{(6-3)^2 + [3+d-(6+d)]^2}$$
$$= \sqrt{3^2 + (-3)^2}$$
$$= \sqrt{9+9}$$
$$= \sqrt{18}$$
$$= 3\sqrt{2}$$

The distance for A to C:

$$\overline{AC} = \sqrt{(6-1)^2 + [6+d-(1+d)]^2}$$
$$= \sqrt{5^2 + 5^2}$$
$$= \sqrt{25+25}$$
$$= \sqrt{50}$$
$$= 5\sqrt{2}$$
$$\overline{AB} + \overline{BC} = \overline{AC}$$
$$2\sqrt{2} + 3\sqrt{2} = 5\sqrt{2}$$
$$5\sqrt{2} = 5\sqrt{2}$$

83. Both circles have center (2, –3). The smaller circle has radius 5 and the larger circle has radius 6. The smaller circle is inside of the larger circle. The area between them is given by

$$\pi(6)^2 - \pi(5)^2 = 36\pi - 25\pi$$
$$= 11\pi$$
$$\approx 34.56 \text{ square units.}$$

Chapter 2 Review Exercises

1. function
domain: {2, 3, 5}
range: {7}

2. function
domain: {1, 2, 13}
range: {10, 500, π}

3. not a function
domain: {12, 14}
range: {13, 15, 19}

4. $2x + y = 8$
$y = -2x + 8$
Since only one value of y can be obtained for each value of x, y is a function of x.

5. $3x^2 + y = 14$
$y = -3x^2 + 14$
Since only one value of y can be obtained for each value of x, y is a function of x.

6. $2x + y^2 = 6$

$\quad\quad y^2 = -2x + 6$

$\quad\quad y = \pm\sqrt{-2x + 6}$

Since more than one value of y can be obtained
from some values of x, y is not a function of x.

7. $f(x) = 5 - 7x$

   a. $f(4) = 5 - 7(4) = -23$

   b. $f(x+3) = 5 - 7(x+3)$
       $\quad\quad\quad = 5 - 7x - 21$
       $\quad\quad\quad = -7x - 16$

   c. $f(-x) = 5 - 7(-x) = 5 + 7x$

8. $g(x) = 3x^2 - 5x + 2$

   a. $g(0) = 3(0)^2 - 5(0) + 2 = 2$

   b. $g(-2) = 3(-2)^2 - 5(-2) + 2$
       $\quad\quad\quad = 12 + 10 + 2$
       $\quad\quad\quad = 24$

   c. $g(x-1) = 3(x-1)^2 - 5(x-1) + 2$
       $\quad\quad\quad = 3(x^2 - 2x + 1) - 5x + 5 + 2$
       $\quad\quad\quad = 3x^2 - 11x + 10$

   d. $g(-x) = 3(-x)^2 - 5(-x) + 2$
       $\quad\quad\quad = 3x^2 + 5x + 2$

9.   a. $g(13) = \sqrt{13 - 4} = \sqrt{9} = 3$

   b. $g(0) = 4 - 0 = 4$

   c. $g(-3) = 4 - (-3) = 7$

10.   a. $f(-2) = \dfrac{(-2)^2 - 1}{-2 - 1} = \dfrac{3}{-3} = -1$

   b. $f(1) = 12$

   c. $f(2) = \dfrac{2^2 - 1}{2 - 1} = \dfrac{3}{1} = 3$

11.   The vertical line test shows that this is not the
graph of a function.

12.   The vertical line test shows that this is the
graph of a function.

13.   The vertical line test shows that this is the
graph of a function.

14.   The vertical line test shows that this is not the
graph of a function.

15.   The vertical line test shows that this is not the
graph of a function.

16.   The vertical line test shows that this is the
graph of a function.

17. $\dfrac{8(x+h) - 11 - (8x - 11)}{h}$

$= \dfrac{8x + 8h - 11 - 8x + 11}{h}$

$= \dfrac{8h}{8}$

$= 8$

18. $\dfrac{-2(x+h)^2 + (x+h) + 10 - \left(-2x^2 + x + 10\right)}{h}$

$= \dfrac{-2\left(x^2 + 2xh + h^2\right) + x + h + 10 + 2x^2 - x - 10}{h}$

$= \dfrac{-2x^2 - 4xh - 2h^2 + x + h + 10 + 2x^2 - x - 10}{h}$

$= \dfrac{-4xh - 2h^2 + h}{h}$

$= \dfrac{h\left(-4x - 2h + 1\right)}{h}$

$-4x - 2h + 1$

19.   a.   domain: $[-3, 5)$

   b.   range: $[-5, 0]$

   c. x-intercept: -3

   d. y-intercept: -2

   e.   increasing: $(-2, 0)$ or $(3, 5)$
       decreasing: $(-3, -2)$ or $(0, 3)$

   f. $f(-2) = -3$ and $f(3) = -5$

20. a. domain: $(-\infty, \infty)$

     b. range: $(-\infty, \infty)$

     c. x-intercepts: -2 and 3

     d. y-intercept: 3

     e. increasing: $(-5, 0)$
         decreasing: $(-\infty, -5)$ or $(0, \infty)$

     f. $f(-2) = 0$ and $f(6) = -3$

21. a. domain: $(-\infty, \infty)$

     b. range: $[-2, 2]$

     c. x-intercept: 0

     d. y-intercept: 0

     e. increasing: $(-2, 2)$
         constant: $(-\infty, -2)$ or $(2, \infty)$

     f. $f(-9) = -2$ and $f(14) = 2$

22. a. 0, relative maximum -2

     b. $-2, 3$, relative minimum $-3, -5$

23. a. 0, relative maximum 3

     b. -5, relative minimum -6

24. $f(x) = x^3 - 5x$

$$f(-x) = (-x)^3 - 5(-x)$$
$$= -x^3 + 5x$$
$$= -f(x)$$

The function is odd. The function is symmetric with respect to the origin.

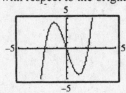

25. $f(x) = x^4 - 2x^2 + 1$

$$f(-x) = (-x)^4 - 2(-x)^2 + 1$$
$$= x^4 - 2x^2 + 1$$
$$= f(x)$$

The function is even. The function is symmetric with respect to the y-axis.

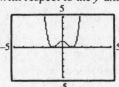

26. $f(x) = 2x\sqrt{1 - x^2}$

$$f(-x) = 2(-x)\sqrt{1 - (-x)^2}$$
$$= -2x\sqrt{1 - x^2}$$
$$= -f(x)$$

The function is odd. The function is symmetric with respect to the origin.

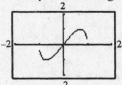

27. a. Yes, the eagle's height is a function of time since the graph passes the vertical line test.

     b. Decreasing: $(3, 12)$
         The eagle descended.

     c. Constant: $(0, 3)$ or $(12, 17)$
         The eagle's height held steady during the first 3 seconds and the eagle was on the ground for 5 seconds.

     d. Increasing: $(17, 30)$
         The eagle was ascending.

28.

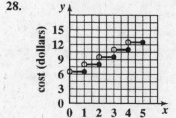

29. $m = \dfrac{1-2}{5-3} = \dfrac{-1}{2} = -\dfrac{1}{2}$; falls

30. $m = \dfrac{-4-(-2)}{-3-(-1)} = \dfrac{-2}{-2} = 1$; rises

31. $m = \dfrac{\frac{1}{4}-\frac{1}{4}}{6-(-3)} = \dfrac{0}{9} = 0$; horizontal

32. $m = \dfrac{10-5}{-2-(-2)} = \dfrac{5}{0}$ undefined; vertical

33. point-slope form: $y - 2 = -6(x + 3)$
slope-intercept form: $y = -6x - 16$

34. $m = \dfrac{2-6}{-1-1} = \dfrac{-4}{-2} = 2$
point-slope form: $y - 6 = 2(x - 1)$
or $y - 2 = 2(x + 1)$
slope-intercept form: $y = 2x + 4$

35. $3x + y - 9 = 0$
$y = -3x + 9$
$m = -3$
point-slope form:
$y + 7 = -3(x - 4)$
slope-intercept form:
$y = -3x + 12 - 7$
$y = -3x + 5$

36. perpendicular to $y = \dfrac{1}{3}x + 4$

$m = -3$
point-slope form:
$y - 6 = -3(x + 3)$
slope-intercept form:
$y = -3x - 9 + 6$
$y = -3x - 3$

37. Write $6x - y - 4 = 0$ in slope intercept form.
$6x - y - 4 = 0$
$\quad -y = -6x + 4$
$\quad\quad y = 6x - 4$
The slope of the perpendicular line is 6, thus the

slope of the desired line is $m = -\dfrac{1}{6}$.

$$y - y_1 = m(x - x_1)$$
$$y - (-1) = -\tfrac{1}{6}\left(x - (-12)\right)$$
$$y + 1 = -\tfrac{1}{6}(x + 12)$$
$$y + 1 = -\tfrac{1}{6}x - 2$$
$$6y + 6 = -x - 12$$
$$x + 6y + 18 = 0$$

38. slope: $\dfrac{2}{5}$; y-intercept: -1

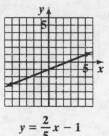

$$y = \dfrac{2}{5}x - 1$$

39. slope: -4; y-intercept: 5

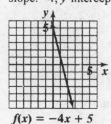

$$f(x) = -4x + 5$$

40. $2x + 3y + 6 = 0$
$$3y = -2x - 6$$
$$y = -\dfrac{2}{3}x - 2$$

slope: $-\dfrac{2}{3}$; y-intercept: -2

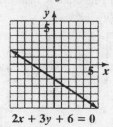

$$2x + 3y + 6 = 0$$

190

41. $2y - 8 = 0$

$\qquad 2y = 8$

$\qquad y = 4$

slope: 0; y-intercept: 4

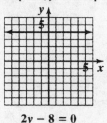

$2y - 8 = 0$

42. $2x - 5y - 10 = 0$

Find x-intercept:

$2x - 5(0) - 10 = 0$

$\qquad 2x - 10 = 0$

$\qquad 2x = 10$

$\qquad x = 5$

Find y-intercept:

$2(0) - 5y - 10 = 0$

$\qquad -5y - 10 = 0$

$\qquad -5y = 10$

$\qquad y = -2$

$2x - 5y - 10 = 0$

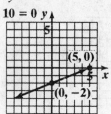

43. $2x - 10 = 0$

$\qquad 2x = 10$

$\qquad x = 5$

$2x - 10 = 0$

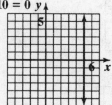

44. a. First, find the slope. $(1, 1.5)$

and $(3, 3.4)$.

$$m = \frac{3.4 - 1.5}{3 - 1} = \frac{1.9}{2} = 0.95$$

Next, use the slope and one of the points to write the point-slope equation of the line.

$y - 1.5 = 0.95(x - 1)$ or $y - 3.4 = 0.95(x - 3)$

b. $y - 1.5 = 0.95(x - 1)$

$\quad y - 1.5 = 0.95x - 0.95$

$\qquad\quad y = 0.95x - 0.55$

c. Since 2009 is 2009-1999 = 10, let $x = 10$.

$y = 0.95(10) + 0.55$

$\quad = 9.5 + 0.55 = 10.05$

$10.05 billion in revenue was earned from online gambling in 2009.

45. a. $(1999, 41315)$ and $(2001, 41227)$

$$m = \frac{41227 - 41315}{2001 - 1999} = \frac{-88}{2} = -44$$

The number of new AIDS diagnoses decreased at a rate of 44 each year from 1999 to 2001.

b. $(2001, 41227)$ and $(2003, 43045)$

$$m = \frac{43045 - 41227}{2003 - 2001} = \frac{1818}{2} = 909$$

The number of new AIDS diagnoses increased at a rate of 909 each year from 2001 to 2003.

c. $(1999, 41315)$ and $(2003, 43045)$

$$m = \frac{43045 - 41315}{2003 - 1999} = \frac{1730}{4} = 432.5$$

$$\frac{-44 + 909}{2} = \frac{865}{2} = 432.5$$

Yes, the slope equals the average of the two values.

46. $\dfrac{9^2 - 4(9) - [4^2 - 4 \cdot 5]}{9 - 5} = \dfrac{40}{4} = 10$

47. $y = g(x)$

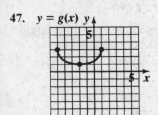

48. $y = g(x)$

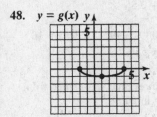

49.

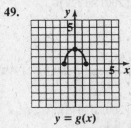

$y = g(x)$

50.

$y = g(x)$

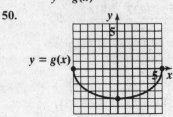

51.

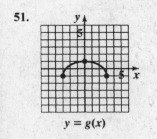

$y = g(x)$

52.

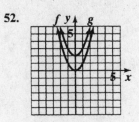

53.

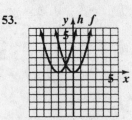

54.

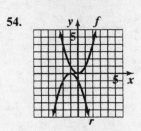

55.

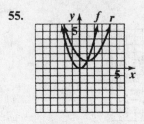

56.

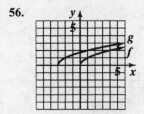

57.

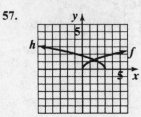

192

58.
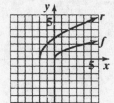

59.
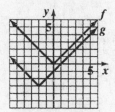

60.
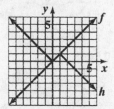

61.
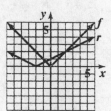

62.
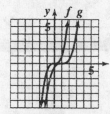

63.
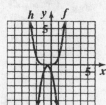

64.
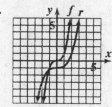

65.
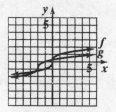

66.
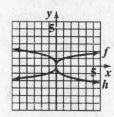

67.
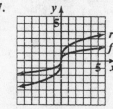

68. domain: $(-\infty, \infty)$

69. The denominator is zero when $x = 7$. The domain is $(-\infty, 7) \cup (7, \infty)$.

70. The expressions under each radical must not be negative.
$8 - 2x \geq 0$
$-2x \geq -8$
$x \leq 4$
Domain: $(-\infty, 4]$.

71. The denominator is zero when $x = -7$ or $x = 3$.
Domain: $(-\infty, -7) \cup (-7, 3) \cup (3, \infty)$

72. The expressions under each radical must not be negative. The denominator is zero when $x = 5$.
$x - 2 \geq 0$
$x \geq 2$
Domain: $[2, 5) \cup (5, \infty)$

73. The expressions under each radical must not be negative.
$x - 1 \geq 0$ and $x + 5 \geq 0$
$x \geq 1$ $x \geq -5$
Domain: $[1, \infty)$

193

74. $f(x) = 3x - 1; g(x) = x - 5$

$(f + g)(x) = 4x - 6$

Domain: $(-\infty, \infty)$

$(f - g)(x) = (3x - 1) - (x - 5) = 2x + 4$

Domain: $(-\infty, \infty)$

$(fg)(x) = (3x - 1)(x - 5) = 3x^2 - 16x + 5$

Domain: $(-\infty, \infty)$

$\left(\dfrac{f}{g}\right)(x) = \dfrac{3x - 1}{x - 5}$

Domain: $(-\infty, 5) \cup (5, \infty)$

75. $f(x) = x^2 + x + 1; g(x) = x^2 - 1$

$(f + g)(x) = 2x^2 + x$

Domain: $(-\infty, \infty)$

$(f - g)(x) = (x^2 + x + 1) - (x^2 - 1) = x + 2$

Domain: $(-\infty, \infty)$

$(fg)(x) = (x^2 + x + 1)(x^2 - 1)$

$\qquad = x^4 + x^3 - x - 1$

$\left(\dfrac{f}{g}\right)(x) = \dfrac{x^2 + x + 1}{x^2 - 1}$

Domain: $(-\infty, -1) \cup (-1, 1) \cup (1, \infty)$

76. $\qquad f(x) = \sqrt{x + 7}; g(x) = \sqrt{x - 2}$

$(f + g)(x) = \sqrt{x + 7} + \sqrt{x - 2}$

Domain: $[2, \infty)$

$(f - g)(x) = \sqrt{x + 7} - \sqrt{x - 2}$

Domain: $[2, \infty)$

$(fg)(x) = \sqrt{x + 7} \cdot \sqrt{x - 2}$

$\qquad = \sqrt{x^2 + 5x - 14}$

Domain: $[2, \infty)$

$\left(\dfrac{f}{g}\right)(x) = \dfrac{\sqrt{x + 7}}{\sqrt{x - 2}}$

Domain: $(2, \infty)$

77. $f(x) = x^2 + 3; g(x) = 4x - 1$

a. $(f \circ g)(x) = (4x - 1)^2 + 3$

$\qquad = 16x^2 - 8x + 4$

b. $(g \circ f)(x) = 4(x^2 + 3) - 1$

$\qquad = 4x^2 + 11$

c. $(f \circ g)(3) = 16(3)^2 - 8(3) + 4 = 124$

78. $f(x) = \sqrt{x}; \;\; g(x) = x + 1$

a. $(f \circ g)(x) = \sqrt{x + 1}$

b. $(g \circ f)(x) = \sqrt{x} + 1$

c. $(f \circ g)(3) = \sqrt{3 + 1} = \sqrt{4} = 2$

79. a.

$(f \circ g)(x) = f\left(\dfrac{1}{x}\right)$

$= \dfrac{\dfrac{1}{x} + 1}{\dfrac{1}{x} - 2} = \dfrac{\left(\dfrac{1}{x} + 1\right)x}{\left(\dfrac{1}{x} - 2\right)x} = \dfrac{1 + x}{1 - 2x}$

b. $\quad x \neq 0 \qquad\qquad 1 - 2x \neq 0$

$\qquad\qquad\qquad\qquad\qquad x \neq \dfrac{1}{2}$

$\qquad (-\infty, 0) \cup \left(0, \dfrac{1}{2}\right) \cup \left(\dfrac{1}{2}, \infty\right)$

80. a. $(f \circ g)(x) = f(x + 3) = \sqrt{x + 3 - 1} = \sqrt{x + 2}$

b. $\quad x + 2 \geq 0$

$\qquad x \geq -2 \qquad [-2, \infty)$

81. $f(x) = x^4 \qquad g(x) = x^2 + 2x - 1$

82. $f(x) = \sqrt[3]{x} \qquad g(x) = 7x + 4$

83. $f(x) = \frac{3}{5}x + \frac{1}{2}; g(x) = \frac{5}{3}x - 2$

$f(g(x)) = \frac{3}{5}\left(\frac{5}{3}x - 2\right) + \frac{1}{2}$

$\qquad = x - \frac{6}{5} + \frac{1}{2}$

$\qquad = x - \frac{7}{10}$

$g(f(x)) = \frac{5}{3}\left(\frac{3}{5}x + \frac{1}{2}\right) - 2$

$\qquad = x + \frac{5}{6} - 2$

$\qquad = x - \frac{7}{6}$

f and *g* are not inverses of each other.

84. $f(x) = 2 - 5x; g(x) = \frac{2 - x}{5}$

$f(g(x)) = 2 - 5\left(\frac{2 - x}{5}\right)$

$\qquad = 2 - (2 - x)$

$\qquad = x$

$g(f(x)) = \frac{2 - (2 - 5x)}{5} = \frac{5x}{5} = x$

f and *g* are inverses of each other.

85. a. $f(x) = 4x - 3$

$\qquad y = 4x - 3$

$\qquad x = 4y - 3$

$\qquad y = \frac{x + 3}{4}$

$\qquad f^{-1}(x) = \frac{x + 3}{4}$

b. $f(f^{-1}(x)) = 4\left(\frac{x + 3}{4}\right) - 3$

$\qquad\qquad = x + 3 - 3$

$\qquad\qquad = x$

$f^{-1}(f(x)) = \frac{(4x - 3) + 3}{4} = \frac{4x}{4} = x$

86. a. $f(x) = 8x^3 + 1$

$\qquad y = 8x^3 + 1$

$\qquad x = 8y^3 + 1$

$\qquad x - 1 = 8y^3$

$\qquad \frac{x - 1}{8} = y^3$

$\qquad \sqrt[3]{\frac{x - 1}{8}} = y$

$\qquad \frac{\sqrt[3]{x - 1}}{2} = y$

$\qquad f^{-1}(x) = \frac{\sqrt[3]{x - 1}}{2}$

b. $f\left(f^{-1}(x)\right) = 8\left(\frac{\sqrt[3]{x - 1}}{2}\right)^3 + 1$

$\qquad\qquad = 8\left(\frac{x - 1}{8}\right) + 1$

$\qquad\qquad = x - 1 + 1$

$\qquad\qquad = x$

$f^{-1}\left(f(x)\right) = \frac{\sqrt[3]{(8x^3 + 1) - 1}}{2}$

$\qquad\qquad = \frac{\sqrt[3]{8x^3}}{2}$

$\qquad\qquad = \frac{2x}{2}$

$\qquad\qquad = x$

87. a. $f(x) = \frac{2}{x} + 5$

$\qquad y = \frac{2}{x} + 5$

$\qquad x = \frac{2}{y} + 5$

$\qquad xy = 2 + 5y$

$\qquad xy - 5y = 2$

$\qquad y(x - 5) = 2$

$\qquad y = \frac{2}{x - 5}$

$\qquad f^{-1}(x) = \frac{2}{x - 5}$

b. $f\left(f^{-1}(x)\right) = \dfrac{2}{\dfrac{2}{x-5}} + 5$

$\qquad = \dfrac{2(x-5)}{2} + 5$

$\qquad = x - 5 + 5$

$\qquad = x$

$f^{-1}\left(f(x)\right) = \dfrac{2}{\dfrac{2}{x} + 5 - 5}$

$\qquad = \dfrac{2}{\dfrac{2}{x}}$

$\qquad = \dfrac{2x}{2}$

$\qquad = x$

88. The inverse function exists.

89. The inverse function does not exist since it does not pass the horizontal line test.

90. The inverse function exists.

91. The inverse function does not exist since it does not pass the horizontal line test.

92.

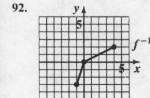

93. $f(x) = 1 - x^2$

$\quad y = 1 - x^2$

$\quad x = 1 - y^2$

$\quad y^2 = 1 - x$

$\quad y = \sqrt{1-x}$

$\quad f^{-1}(x) = \sqrt{1-x}$

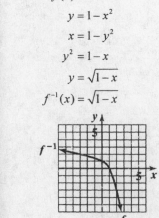

94. $f(x) = \sqrt{x} + 1$

$\qquad y = \sqrt{x} + 1$

$\qquad x = \sqrt{y} + 1$

$\qquad x - 1 = \sqrt{y}$

$\qquad (x-1)^2 = y$

$\qquad f^{-1}(x) = (x-1)^2, \quad x \ge 1$

$f(x) = \sqrt{x} + 1$

$g(x) = (x-1)^2, x \ge 1$

95. $d = \sqrt{[3-(-2)]^2 + [9-(-3)]^2}$

$\quad = \sqrt{5^2 + 12^2}$

$\quad = \sqrt{25 + 144}$

$\quad = \sqrt{169}$

$\quad = 13$

96. $d = \sqrt{[-2-(-4)]^2 + (5-3)^2}$

$\quad = \sqrt{2^2 + 2^2}$

$\quad = \sqrt{4+4}$

$\quad = \sqrt{8}$

$\quad = 2\sqrt{2}$

$\quad \approx 2.83$

97. $\left(\dfrac{2+(-12)}{2}, \dfrac{6+4}{2}\right) = \left(\dfrac{-10}{2}, \dfrac{10}{2}\right) = (-5, 5)$

98. $\left(\dfrac{4+(-15)}{2}, \dfrac{-6+2}{2}\right) = \left(\dfrac{-11}{2}, \dfrac{-4}{2}\right) = \left(\dfrac{-11}{2}, -2\right)$

99. $x^2 + y^2 = 3^2$

$\quad x^2 + y^2 = 9$

100. $(x-(-2))^2 + (y-4)^2 = 6^2$

$\qquad (x+2)^2 + (y-4)^2 = 36$

101. center: (0, 0); radius: 1

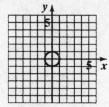

$$x^2 + y^2 = 1$$
Domain: $[-1, 1]$
Range: $[-1, 1]$

102. center: (–2, 3); radius: 3

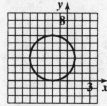

$$(x + 2)^2 + (y - 3)^2 = 9$$
Domain: $[-5, 1]$
Range: $[0, 6]$

103.
$$x^2 + y^2 - 4x + 2y - 4 = 0$$
$$x^2 - 4x \quad + y^2 + 2y \quad = 4$$
$$x^2 - 4x + 4 + y^2 + 2y + 1 = 4 + 4 + 1$$
$$(x - 2)^2 + (y + 1)^2 = 9$$
center: (2, –1); radius: 3

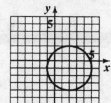

$$x^2 + y^2 - 4x + 2y - 4 = 0$$
Domain: $[-1, 5]$
Range: $[-4, 2]$

Chapter 2 Test

1. (b), (c), and (d) are not functions.

2. **a.** $f(4) - f(-3) = 3 - (-2) = 5$

    b. domain: $(-5, 6]$

    c. range: $[-4, 5]$

    d. increasing: $(-1, 2)$

    e. decreasing: $(-5, -1)$ or $(2, 6)$

    f. $2, f(2) = 5$

    g. $(-1, -4)$

    h. x-intercepts: –4, 1, and 5.

    i. y-intercept: –3

3. **a.** –2, 2

    b. –1, 1

    c. 0

    d. even; $f(-x) = f(x)$

    e. no; f fails the horizontal line test

    f. $f(0)$ is a relative minimum.

    g.

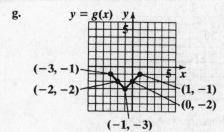

    h.

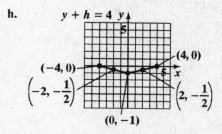

i.

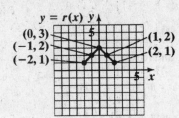

j. $\dfrac{f(x_2)-f(x_1)}{x_2-x_1} = \dfrac{-1-0}{1-(-2)} = -\dfrac{1}{3}$

4. $y + y = 4$

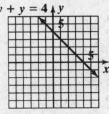

Domain: $(-\infty,\infty)$

Range: $(-\infty,\infty)$

5. $x^2 + y^2 = 4$

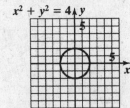

Domain: $[-2,2]$

Range: $[-2,2]$

6. $f(x) = 4$

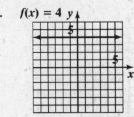

Domain: $(-\infty,\infty)$

Range: $\{4\}$

7.

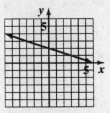

$f(x) = -\dfrac{1}{3}x + 2$

Domain: $(-\infty,\infty)$

Range: $(-\infty,\infty)$

8.

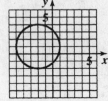

$(x + 2)^2 + (y - 1)^2 = 9$

Domain: $[-5,1]$

Range: $[-2,4]$

9.

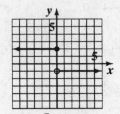

$f(x) = \begin{cases} 2 \text{ if } x \le 0 \\ -1 \text{ if } x > 0 \end{cases}$

Domain: $(-\infty,\infty)$

Range: $\{-1,2\}$

10.

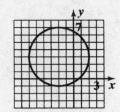

$x^2 + y^2 + 4x + 6y - 3 = 0$

Domain: $[-6,2]$

Range: $[-1,7]$

11.

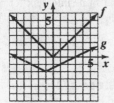

Domain of f: $(-\infty, \infty)$

Range of f: $[0, \infty)$

Domain of g: $(-\infty, \infty)$

Range of g: $[-2, \infty)$

12.

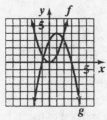

Domain of f: $(-\infty, \infty)$

Range of f: $[0, \infty)$

Domain of g: $(-\infty, \infty)$

Range of g: $(-\infty, 4]$

13.

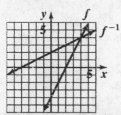

Domain of f: $(-\infty, \infty)$

Range of f: $(-\infty, \infty)$

Domain of f^{-1}: $(-\infty, \infty)$

Range of f^{-1}: $(-\infty, \infty)$

14.

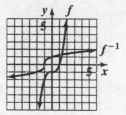

Domain of f: $(-\infty, \infty)$

Range of f: $(-\infty, \infty)$

Domain of f^{-1}: $(-\infty, \infty)$

Range of f^{-1}: $(-\infty, \infty)$

15.

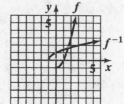

Domain of f: $[0, \infty)$

Range of f: $[-1, \infty)$

Domain of f^{-1}: $[-1, \infty)$

Range of f^{-1}: $[0, \infty)$

16.
$$f(x) = x^2 - x - 4$$
$$f(x-1) = (x-1)^2 - (x-1) - 4$$
$$= x^2 - 2x + 1 - x + 1 - 4$$
$$= x^2 - 3x - 2$$

17.
$$\frac{f(x+h) - f(x)}{h}$$
$$= \frac{(x+h)^2 - (x+h) - 4 - \left(x^2 - x - 4\right)}{h}$$
$$= \frac{x^2 + 2xh + h^2 - x - h - 4 - x^2 + x + 4}{h}$$
$$= \frac{2xh + h^2 - h}{h}$$
$$= \frac{h(2x + h - 1)}{h}$$
$$= 2x + h - 1$$

18.
$$(g - f)(x) = 2x - 6 - \left(x^2 - x - 4\right)$$
$$= 2x - 6 - x^2 + x + 4$$
$$= -x^2 + 3x - 2$$

199

19. $\left(\dfrac{f}{g}\right)(x) = \dfrac{x^2 - x - 4}{2x - 6}$

Domain: $(-\infty, 3) \cup (3, \infty)$

20. $(f \circ g)(x) = f\big(g(x)\big)$

$\quad = (2x - 6)^2 - (2x - 6) - 4$

$\quad = 4x^2 - 24x + 36 - 2x + 6 - 4$

$\quad = 4x^2 - 26x + 38$

21. $(g \circ f)(x) = g\big(f(x)\big)$

$\quad = 2(x^2 - x - 4) - 6$

$\quad = 2x^2 - 2x - 8 - 6$

$\quad = 2x^2 - 2x - 14$

22. $g\big(f(-1)\big) = 2\big((-1)^2 - (-1) - 4\big) - 6$

$\quad = 2(1 + 1 - 4) - 6$

$\quad = 2(-2) - 6$

$\quad = -4 - 6$

$\quad = -10$

23. $f(x) = x^2 - x - 4$

$f(-x) = (-x)^2 - (-x) - 4$

$\quad = x^2 + x - 4$

f is neither even nor odd.

24. $m = \dfrac{-8 - 1}{-1 - 2} = \dfrac{-9}{-3} = 3$

point-slope form: $y - 1 = 3(x - 2)$
or $y + 8 = 3(x + 1)$
slope-intercept form: $y = 3x - 5$

25. $y = -\dfrac{1}{4}x + 5$ so $m = 4$

point-slope form: $y - 6 = 4(x + 4)$
slope-intercept form: $y = 4x + 22$

26. Write $4x + 2y - 5 = 0$ in slope intercept form.

$4x + 2y - 5 = 0$

$\quad 2y = -4x + 5$

$\quad y = -2x + \dfrac{5}{2}$

The slope of the parallel line is –2, thus the slope of the desired line is $m = -2$.

$\quad y - y_1 = m(x - x_1)$

$\quad y - (-10) = -2\big(x - (-7)\big)$

$\quad y + 10 = -2(x + 7)$

$\quad y + 10 = -2x - 14$

$\quad 2x + y + 24 = 0$

27. a. $(2, 4.85)$ and $(5, 4.49)$

First, find the slope using the points $(2, 4.85)$ and $(5, 4.49)$

$$m = \frac{4.49 - 4.85}{5 - 2} = \frac{-0.36}{3} = -0.12$$

Then use the slope and one of the points to write the equation in point-slope form.

$\quad y - y_1 = m(x - x_1)$

$\quad y - 4.85 = -0.12(x - 2)$

or

$\quad y - 4.49 = -0.12(x - 5)$

b. Solve for y to obtain slope-intercept form.

$\quad y - 4.85 = -0.12(x - 2)$

$\quad y - 4.85 = -0.12x + 0.24$

$\quad y = -0.12x + 5.09$

$\quad f(x) = -0.12x + 5.09$

c. To predict the minimum hourly inflation-adjusted wages in 2007, let $x = 2007 - 1997 = 10$.

$\quad f(10) = -0.12(10) + 5.09 = 3.89$

The linear function predicts the minimum hourly inflation-adjusted wage in 2007 to $3.89.

28. $\dfrac{3(10)^2 - 5 - [3(6)^2 - 5]}{10 - 6}$

$= \dfrac{205 - 103}{4}$

$= \dfrac{192}{4}$

$= 48$

29.　$g(-1) = 3 - (-1) = 4$

　　　$g(7) = \sqrt{7-3} = \sqrt{4} = 2$

30.　The denominator is zero when $x = 1$ or $x = -5$.

　　Domain: $(-\infty, -5) \cup (-5, 1) \cup (1, \infty)$

31.　The expressions under each radical must not be negative.

　　$x + 5 \geq 0$　　and　$x - 1 \geq 0$

　　　$x \geq -5$　　　　　$x \geq 1$

　　Domain: $[1, \infty)$

32.　$(f \circ g)(x) = \dfrac{7}{\dfrac{2}{x} - 4} = \dfrac{7x}{2 - 4x}$

　　　$x \neq 0,\quad 2 - 4x \neq 0$

　　　　　$x \neq \dfrac{1}{2}$

　　Domain: $(-\infty, 0) \cup \left(0, \dfrac{1}{2}\right) \cup \left(\dfrac{1}{2}, \infty\right)$

33.　$f(x) = x^7$　　　$g(x) = 2x + 3$

34.　$d = \sqrt{(x_2 - x_1)^2 + (y_2 - y_1)^2}$

　　$d = \sqrt{(x_2 - x_1)^2 + (y_2 - y_1)^2}$

　　　$= \sqrt{(5-2)^2 + (2-(-2))^2}$

　　　$= \sqrt{3^2 + 4^2}$

　　　$= \sqrt{9 + 16}$

　　　$= \sqrt{25}$

　　　$= 5$

　　$\left(\dfrac{x_1 + x_2}{2}, \dfrac{y_1 + y_2}{2}\right) = \left(\dfrac{2+5}{2}, \dfrac{-2+2}{2}\right)$

　　　　　　　　　$= \left(\dfrac{7}{2}, 0\right)$

　　The length is 5 and the midpoint is $\left(\dfrac{7}{2}, 0\right)$.

Cumulative Review Exercises (Chapters 1–2)

1.　Domain: $[0, 2]$
　　Range: $[0, 2]$

2.　$f(x) = 1$ at $\dfrac{1}{2}$ and $\dfrac{3}{2}$.

3.　relative maximum: 2

4.　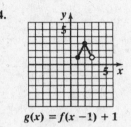
　　$g(x) = f(x - 1) + 1$

5.　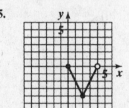

6.　$(x+3)(x-4) = 8$
　　　$x^2 - x - 12 = 8$
　　　$x^2 - x - 20 = 0$
　　　$(x+4)(x-5) = 0$
　　$x + 4 = 0$　or　$x - 5 = 0$
　　　$x = -4$　or　　$x = 5$

7.　$3(4x-1) = 4 - 6(x-3)$
　　　$12x - 3 = 4 - 6x + 18$
　　　　$18x = 25$
　　　　　$x = \dfrac{25}{18}$

8.　$\sqrt{x} + 2 = x$
　　　$\sqrt{x} = x - 2$
　　　$(\sqrt{x})^2 = (x-2)^2$
　　　$x = x^2 - 4x + 4$
　　　$0 = x^2 - 5x + 4$
　　　$0 = (x-1)(x-4)$
　　$x - 1 = 0$　or　$x - 4 = 0$
　　　$x = 1$　or　　　$x = 4$

　　A check of the solutions shows that $x = 1$ is an extraneous solution. The only solution is $x = 4$.

9. $x^{2/3} - x^{1/3} - 6 = 0$

Let $u = x^{1/3}$. Then $u^2 = x^{2/3}$.

$$u^2 - u - 6 = 0$$
$$(u + 2)(u - 3) = 0$$
$$u = -2 \quad \text{or} \quad u = 3$$
$$x^{1/3} = -2 \quad \text{or} \quad x^{1/3} = 3$$
$$x = (-2)^3 \quad \text{or} \quad x = 3^3$$
$$x = -8 \quad \text{or} \quad x = 27$$

10. $\dfrac{x}{2} - 3 \le \dfrac{x}{4} + 2$

$$4\left(\frac{x}{2} - 3\right) \le 4\left(\frac{x}{4} + 2\right)$$
$$2x - 12 \le x + 8$$
$$x \le 20$$

The solution set is $(-\infty, 20]$.

11.

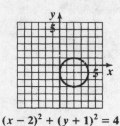

$3(x) - 6y - 12 = 0$

Domain: $(-\infty, \infty)$

Range: $(-\infty, \infty)$

12.

$(x - 2)^2 + (y + 1)^2 = 4$

Domain: $[0, 4]$

Range: $[-3, 1]$

13.

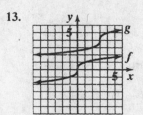

Domain of f: $(-\infty, \infty)$

Range of f: $(-\infty, \infty)$

Domain of g: $(-\infty, \infty)$

Range of g: $(-\infty, \infty)$

14.

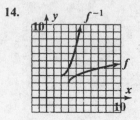

Domain of f: $[3, \infty)$

Range of f: $[2, \infty)$

Domain of f^{-1}: $[2, \infty)$

Range of f^{-1}: $[3, \infty)$

15. $\dfrac{f(x + h) - f(x)}{h}$

$$= \frac{\left(4 - (x + h)^2\right) - \left(4 - x^2\right)}{h}$$
$$= \frac{4 - (x^2 + 2xh + h^2) - \left(4 - x^2\right)}{h}$$
$$= \frac{4 - x^2 - 2xh - h^2 - 4 + x^2}{h}$$
$$= \frac{-2xh - h^2}{h}$$
$$= \frac{h(-2x - h)}{h}$$
$$= -2x - h$$

16. $(f \circ g)(x) = f\big(g(x)\big)$

$(f \circ g)(x) = f(x+5)$

$$0 = 4 - (x+5)^2$$
$$0 = 4 - (x^2 + 10x + 25)$$
$$0 = 4 - x^2 - 10x - 25$$
$$0 = -x^2 - 10x - 21$$
$$0 = x^2 + 10x + 21$$
$$0 = (x+7)(x+3)$$

The value of $(f \circ g)(x)$ will be 0 when $x = -3$ or $x = -7$.

17. $y = -\dfrac{1}{4}x + \dfrac{1}{3}$, so $m = 4$.

point-slope form: $y - 5 = 4(x + 2)$
slope-intercept form: $y = 4x + 13$
general form: $4x - y + 13 = 0$

18. $0.07x + 0.09(6000 - x) = 510$

$$0.07x + 540 - 0.09x = 510$$
$$-0.02x = -30$$
$$x = 1500$$
$$6000 - x = 4500$$

$1500 was invested at 7% and $4500 was invested at 9%.

19. $200 + 0.05x = .15x$

$$200 = 0.10x$$
$$2000 = x$$

For $2000 in sales, the earnings will be the same.

20. width $= w$
length $= 2w + 2$
$2(2w + 2) + 2w = 22$
$4w + 4 + 2w = 22$
$6w = 18$
$w = 3$
$2w + 2 = 8$
The garden is 3 feet by 8 feet.

Chapter 3

Section 3.1

Check Point Exercises

1. $f(x) = -(x-1)^2 + 4$

$$f(x) = \overset{a=-1}{-}\left(x - \overset{h=1}{1}\right)^2 + \overset{k=4}{4}$$

Step 1: The parabola opens down because $a < 0$.

Step 2: find the vertex: $(1, 4)$

Step 3: find the x-intercepts:

$$0 = -(x-1)^2 + 4$$

$$(x-1)^2 = 4$$

$$x - 1 = \pm 2$$

$$x = 1 \pm 2$$

$$x = 3 \text{ or } x = -1$$

Step 4: find the y-intercept:

$$f(0) = -(0-1)^2 + 4 = 3$$

Step 5: The axis of symmetry is $x = 1$.

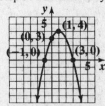

$$f(x) = -(x-1)^2 + 4$$

2. $f(x) = (x-2)^2 + 1$

Step 1: The parabola opens up because $a > 0$.

Step 2: find the vertex: $(2, 1)$

Step 3: find the x-intercepts:

$$0 = (x-2)^2 + 1$$

$$(x-2)^2 = -1$$

$$x - 2 = \sqrt{-1}$$

$$x = 2 \pm i$$

The equation has no real roots, thus the parabola has no x-intercepts.

Step 4: find the y-intercept:

$$f(0) = (0-2)^2 + 1 = 5$$

Step 5: The axis of symmetry is $x = 2$.

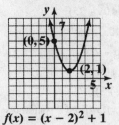

$$f(x) = (x - 2)^2 + 1$$

3. $f(x) = -x^2 + 4x + 1$

Step 1: The parabola opens down because $a < 0$.

Step 2: find the vertex:

$$x = -\frac{b}{2a} = -\frac{4}{2(-1)} = 2$$

$$f(2) = -2^2 + 4(2) + 1 = 5$$

The vertex is $(2, 5)$.

Step 3: find the x-intercepts:

$$0 = -x^2 + 4x + 1$$

$$x = \frac{-b \pm \sqrt{b^2 - 4ac}}{2a}$$

$$x = \frac{-4 \pm \sqrt{4^2 - 4(-1)(1)}}{2(-1)}$$

$$x = \frac{-4 \pm \sqrt{20}}{-2}$$

$$x = 2 \pm \sqrt{5}$$

The x-intercepts are $x \approx -0.2$ and $x \approx -4.2$.

Step 4: find the y-intercept:

$$f(0) = -0^2 + 4(0) + 1 = 1$$

Step 5: The axis of symmetry is $x = 2$.

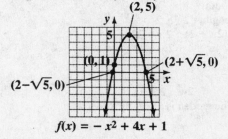

$$f(x) = -x^2 + 4x + 1$$

4. $f(x) = 4x^2 - 16x + 1000$

    a. $a = 4$. The parabola opens upward and has a minimum value.

    b. $x = \dfrac{-b}{2a} = \dfrac{16}{8} = 2$

    $f(2) = 4(2)^2 - 16(2) + 1000 = 984$

    The minimum point is 984 at $x = 2$.

    c. Domain: $(-\infty, \infty)$ Range: $[984, \infty)$

5. $f(x) = 0.4x^2 - 36x + 1000$

    Because $a > 0$, the function has a minimum value.

    $x = -\dfrac{b}{2a} = -\dfrac{-36}{2(0.4)} = 45$

    $f(45) = 0.4(45)^2 - 36(45) + 1000 = 190$

    The age of a driver having the least number of car accidents is 45. The minimum number of accidents per 50 million miles driven is 190.

6. Let x = one of the numbers;
    $x - 8$ = the other number.

    The product is $f(x) = x(x - 8) = x^2 - 8x$

    The x-coordinate of the minimum is

    $x = -\dfrac{b}{2a} = -\dfrac{-8}{2(1)} = -\dfrac{-8}{2} = 4$.

    $f(4) = (4)^2 - 8(4)$
    $= 16 - 32 = -16$

    The vertex is $(4, -16)$.

    The minimum product is -16. This occurs when the two number are 4 and $4 - 8 = -4$.

7. Maximize the area of a rectangle constructed with 120 feet of fencing.
    Let x = the length of the rectangle. Let y = the width of the rectangle.
    Since we need an equation in one variable, use the perimeter to express y in terms of x.
    $2x + 2y = 120$

    $2y = 120 - 2x$

    $y = \dfrac{120 - 2x}{2} = 60 - x$

    We need to maximize $A = xy = x(60 - x)$.

    Rewrite A as a function of x.

    $A(x) = x(60 - x) = -x^2 + 60x$

    Since $a = -1$ is negative, we know the function opens downward and has a maximum at

$x = -\dfrac{b}{2a} = -\dfrac{60}{2(-1)} = -\dfrac{60}{-2} = 30.$

When the length x is 30, the width y is
$y = 60 - x = 60 - 30 = 30$.

The dimensions of the rectangular region with maximum area are 30 feet by 30 feet. This gives an area of $30 \cdot 30 = 900$ square feet.

Exercise Set 3.1

1. vertex: (1, 1)
    $h(x) = (x - 1)^2 + 1$

3. vertex: (1, -1)
    $j(x) = (x - 1)^2 - 1$

5. The graph is $f(x) = x^2$ translated down one.
    $h(x) = x^2 - 1$

7. The point (1, 0) is on the graph and
    $g(1) = 0$. $g(x) = x^2 - 2x + 1$

9. $f(x) = 2(x - 3)^2 + 1$
    $h = 3, k = 1$
    The vertex is at (3, 1).

11. $f(x) = -2(x + 1)^2 + 5$
    $h = -1, k = 5$
    The vertex is at (-1, 5).

13. $f(x) = 2x^2 - 8x + 3$

    $x = \dfrac{-b}{2a} = \dfrac{8}{4} = 2$

    $f(2) = 2(2)^2 - 8(2) + 3$
    $= 8 - 16 + 3 = -5$
    The vertex is at (2, -5).

15. $f(x) = -x^2 - 2x + 8$

    $x = \dfrac{-b}{2a} = \dfrac{2}{-2} = -1$

    $f(-1) = -(-1)^2 - 2(-1) + 8$
    $= -1 + 2 + 8 = 9$
    The vertex is at (-1, 9).

17. $f(x) = (x-4)^2 - 1$

vertex: $(4, -1)$

x-intercepts:

$0 = (x-4)^2 - 1$

$1 = (x-4)^2$

$\pm 1 = x - 4$

$x = 3$ or $x = 5$

y-intercept:

$f(0) = (0-4)^2 - 1 = 15$

The axis of symmetry is $x = 4$.

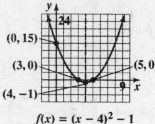

$f(x) = (x-4)^2 - 1$

Domain: $(-\infty, \infty)$

Range: $[-1, \infty)$

19. $f(x) = (x-1)^2 + 2$

vertex: $(1, 2)$

x-intercepts:

$0 = (x-1)^2 + 2$

$(x-1)^2 = -2$

$x - 1 = \pm\sqrt{-2}$

$x = 1 \pm i\sqrt{2}$

No x-intercepts.

y-intercept:

$f(0) = (0-1)^2 + 2 = 3$

The axis of symmetry is $x = 1$.

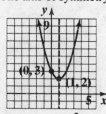

$f(x) = (x-1)^2 + 2$

Domain: $(-\infty, \infty)$

Range: $[2, \infty)$

21. $y - 1 = (x-3)^2$

$y = (x-3)^2 + 1$

vertex: $(3, 1)$

x-intercepts:

$0 = (x-3)^2 + 1$

$(x-3)^2 = -1$

$x - 3 = \pm i$

$x = 3 \pm i$

No x-intercepts.

y-intercept: 10

$y = (0-3)^2 + 1 = 10$

The axis of symmetry is $x = 3$.

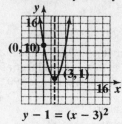

$y - 1 = (x-3)^2$

Domain: $(-\infty, \infty)$

Range: $[1, \infty)$

23. $f(x) = 2(x+2)^2 - 1$

vertex: $(-2, -1)$

x-intercepts:

$0 = 2(x+2)^2 - 1$

$2(x+2)^2 = 1$

$(x+2)^2 = \dfrac{1}{2}$

$x + 2 = \pm\dfrac{1}{\sqrt{2}}$

$x = -2 \pm \dfrac{1}{\sqrt{2}} = -2 \pm \dfrac{\sqrt{2}}{2}$

y-intercept:

$f(0) = 2(0+2)^2 - 1 = 7$

The axis of symmetry is $x = -2$.

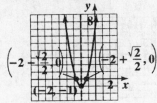

$$f(x) = 2(x+2)^2 - 1$$

Domain: $(-\infty, \infty)$

Range: $[-1, \infty)$

25. $f(x) = 4 - (x-1)^2$

$f(x) = -(x-1)^2 + 4$

vertex: (1, 4)

x-intercepts:

$0 = -(x-1)^2 + 4$

$(x-1)^2 = 4$

$x - 1 = \pm 2$

$x = -1$ or $x = 3$

y-intercept:

$f(x) = -(0-1)^2 + 4 = 3$

The axis of symmetry is $x = 1$.

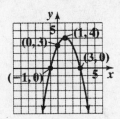

$$f(x) = 4 - (x-1)^2$$

Domain: $(-\infty, \infty)$

Range: $(-\infty, 4]$

27. $f(x) = x^2 - 2x - 3$

$f(x) = (x^2 - 2x + 1) - 3 - 1$

$f(x) = (x-1)^2 - 4$

vertex: (1, -4)

x-intercepts:

$0 = (x-1)^2 - 4$

$(x-1)^2 = 4$

$x - 1 = \pm 2$

$x = -1$ or $x = 3$

y-intercept: -3

$f(0) = 0^2 - 2(0) - 3 = -3$

The axis of symmetry is $x = 1$.

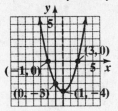

$$f(x) = x^2 + 3x - 10$$

Domain: $(-\infty, \infty)$

Range: $[-4, \infty)$

29. $f(x) = x^2 + 3x - 10$

$f(x) = \left(x^2 + 3x + \dfrac{9}{4}\right) - 10 - \dfrac{9}{4}$

$f(x) = \left(x + \dfrac{3}{2}\right)^2 - \dfrac{49}{4}$

vertex: $\left(-\dfrac{3}{2}, -\dfrac{49}{4}\right)$

x-intercepts:

$0 = \left(x + \dfrac{3}{2}\right)^2 - \dfrac{49}{4}$

$\left(x + \dfrac{3}{2}\right)^2 = \dfrac{49}{4}$

$x + \dfrac{3}{2} = \pm\dfrac{7}{2}$

$x = -\dfrac{3}{2} \pm \dfrac{7}{2}$

$x = 2$ or $x = -5$

y-intercept:

$f(x) = 0^2 + 3(0) - 10 = -10$

The axis of symmetry is $x = -\dfrac{3}{2}$.

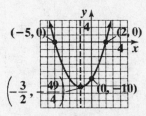

$$f(x) = x^2 + 3x - 10$$

Domain: $(-\infty, \infty)$

Range: $\left[-\dfrac{49}{4}, \infty\right)$

31. $f(x) = 2x - x^2 + 3$

   $f(x) = -x^2 + 2x + 3$

   $f(x) = -(x^2 - 2x + 1) + 3 + 1$

   $f(x) = -(x-1)^2 + 4$

   vertex: $(1, 4)$

   x-intercepts:

   $0 = -(x-1)^2 + 4$

   $(x-1)^2 = 4$

   $x - 1 = \pm 2$

   $x = -1$ or $x = 3$

   y-intercept:

   $f(0) = 2(0) - (0)^2 + 3 = 3$

   The axis of symmetry is $x = 1$.

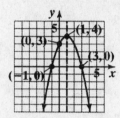

   $f(x) = 2x - x^2 + 3$

   Domain: $(-\infty, \infty)$

   Range: $(-\infty, 4]$

33. $f(x) = x^2 + 6x + 3$

   $f(x) = (x^2 + 6x + 9) + 3 - 9$

   $f(x) = (x+3)^2 - 6$

   vertex: $(-3, -6)$

   x-intercepts:

   $0 = (x+3)^2 - 6$

   $(x+3)^2 = 6$

   $x + 3 = \pm\sqrt{6}$

   $x = -3 \pm \sqrt{6}$

   y-intercept:

   $f(0) = (0)^2 + 6(0) + 3$

   $f(0) = 3$

The axis of symmetry is $x = -3$.

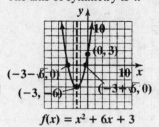

   $f(x) = x^2 + 6x + 3$

Domain: $(-\infty, \infty)$

Range: $[-6, \infty)$

35. $f(x) = 2x^2 + 4x - 3$

   $f(x) = 2(x^2 + 2x \quad) - 3$

   $f(x) = 2(x^2 + 2x + 1) - 3 - 2$

   $f(x) = 2(x+1)^2 - 5$

   vertex: $(-1, -5)$

   x-intercepts:

   $0 = 2(x+1)^2 - 5$

   $2(x+1)^2 = 5$

   $(x+1)^2 = \dfrac{5}{2}$

   $x + 1 = \pm\sqrt{\dfrac{5}{2}}$

   $x = -1 \pm \dfrac{\sqrt{10}}{2}$

   y-intercept:

   $f(0) = 2(0)^2 + 4(0) - 3$

   $f(0) = -3$

   The axis of symmetry is $x = -1$.

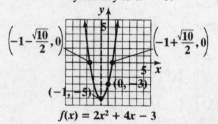

   $f(x) = 2x^2 + 4x - 3$

Domain: $(-\infty, \infty)$

Range: $[-5, \infty)$

37. $f(x) = 2x - x^2 - 2$

$f(x) = -x^2 + 2x - 2$

$f(x) = -\left(x^2 - 2x + 1\right) - 2 + 1$

$f(x) = -\left(x - 1\right)^2 - 1$

vertex: $(1, -1)$

x-intercepts:

$0 = -\left(x - 1\right)^2 - 1$

$\left(x - 1\right)^2 = -1$

$x - 1 = \pm i$

$x = 1 \pm i$

No x-intercepts.

y-intercept:

$f(0) = 2(0) - (0)^2 - 2 = -2$

The axis of symmetry is $x = 1$.

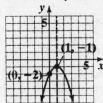

$f(x) = 2x - x^2 - 2$

Domain: $(-\infty, \infty)$

Range: $(-\infty, -1]$

39. $f(x) = 3x^2 - 12x - 1$

a. $a = 3$. The parabola opens upward and has a minimum value.

b. $x = \dfrac{-b}{2a} = \dfrac{12}{6} = 2$

$f(2) = 3(2)^2 - 12(2) - 1$

$= 12 - 24 - 1 = -13$

The minimum is -13 at $x = 2$.

c. Domain: $(-\infty, \infty)$ Range: $[-13, \infty)$

41. $f(x) = -4x^2 + 8x - 3$

a. $a = -4$. The parabola opens downward and has a maximum value.

b. $x = \dfrac{-b}{2a} = \dfrac{-8}{-8} = 1$

$f(1) = -4(1)^2 + 8(1) - 3$

$= -4 + 8 - 3 = 1$

The maximum is 1 at $x = 1$.

c. Domain: $(-\infty, \infty)$ Range: $(-\infty, 1]$

43. $f(x) = 5x^2 - 5x$

a. $a = 5$. The parabola opens upward and has a minimum value.

b. $x = \dfrac{-b}{2a} = \dfrac{5}{10} = \dfrac{1}{2}$

$f\left(\dfrac{1}{2}\right) = 5\left(\dfrac{1}{2}\right)^2 - 5\left(\dfrac{1}{2}\right)$

$= \dfrac{5}{4} - \dfrac{5}{2} = \dfrac{5}{4} - \dfrac{10}{4} = \dfrac{-5}{4}$

The minimum is $\dfrac{-5}{4}$ at $x = \dfrac{1}{2}$.

c. Domain: $(-\infty, \infty)$ Range: $\left[\dfrac{-5}{4}, \infty\right)$

45. Since the parabola opens up, the vertex $(-1, -2)$ is a minimum point.

Domain: $(-\infty, \infty)$. Range: $[-2, \infty)$

47. Since the parabola has a maximum, it opens down from the vertex $(10, -6)$.

Domain: $(-\infty, \infty)$. Range: $(-\infty, -6]$

49. $(h, k) = (5, 3)$

$f(x) = 2(x - h)^2 + k = 2(x - 5)^2 + 3$

51. $(h, k) = (-10, -5)$

$f(x) = 2(x - h)^2 + k$

$= 2[x - (-10)]^2 + (-5)$

$= 2(x + 10)^2 - 5$

53. Since the vertex is a maximum, the parabola opens down and $a = -3$.

$(h, k) = (-2, 4)$

$f(x) = -3(x - h)^2 + k$

$= -3[x - (-2)]^2 + 4$

$= -3(x + 2)^2 + 4$

55. Since the vertex is a minimum, the parabola opens up and $a = 3$.

$$(h, k) = (11, 0)$$

$$f(x) = 3(x - h)^2 + k$$

$$= 3(x - 11)^2 + 0$$

$$= 3(x - 11)^2$$

57. $x = -\dfrac{b}{2a} = -\dfrac{-0.104}{2(0.005)} = 10.4$

Wine consumption was at a minimum 10.4 years after 1980, or about 1990.

$$f(10) = 0.005(10)^2 - 0.104(10) + 2.626$$

$$= 0.005(100) - 1.04 + 2.626$$

$$= 0.5 - 1.04 + 2.626$$

$$= 2.086$$

$$\approx 2.1$$

In 1990 the function suggests that per capita wine consumption was about 2.1 gallons. This models the graph's data quite well.

59. a. $t = -\dfrac{b}{2a} = -\dfrac{64}{2(-16)} = -\dfrac{64}{-32} = 2$

$$s(2) = -16(2)^2 + 64(2) + 200$$

$$= -16(4) + 128 + 200$$

$$= -64 + 128 + 200 = 264$$

The ball reaches a maximum height of 264 feet 2 seconds after it is thrown.

b.
$$0 = -16t^2 + 64t + 200$$

$$0 = t^2 - 4t - 12.5$$

$$a = 1 \quad b = -4 \quad c = -12.5$$

$$t = \dfrac{-(-4) \pm \sqrt{(-4)^2 - 4(1)(-12.5)}}{2(1)}$$

$$= \dfrac{4 \pm \sqrt{16 + 50}}{2} = \dfrac{4 \pm \sqrt{66}}{2}$$

$$\approx \dfrac{4 \pm 8.1}{2}$$

$$= \dfrac{4 + 8.1}{2} \quad \text{or} \quad \dfrac{4 - 8.1}{2}$$

$$= \dfrac{12.1}{2} \qquad\qquad \dfrac{-4.1}{2}$$

$$\approx 6.1 \qquad\qquad\quad \approx -2.1$$

We disregard –2.1 because we can't have a negative time measurement. The solution is 6.1 and we conclude that the ball will hit the ground in approximately 6.1 seconds.

c. $s(0) = -16(0)^2 + 64(0) + 200$

$$= -16(0) + 0 + 200 = 200$$

At $t = 0$, the ball has not yet been thrown and is at a height of 200 feet. This is the height of the building.

d.

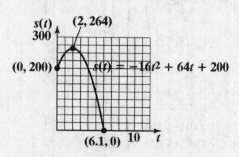

61. Let $x =$ one of the numbers;
$16 - x =$ the other number.

The product is $f(x) = x(16 - x)$
$$= 16x - x^2 = -x^2 + 16x$$

The x-coordinate of the maximum is

$$x = -\dfrac{b}{2a} = -\dfrac{16}{2(-1)} = -\dfrac{16}{-2} = 8.$$

$$f(8) = -8^2 + 16(8) = -64 + 128 = 64$$

The vertex is (8, 64). The maximum product is 64. This occurs when the two number are 8 and $16 - 8 = 8$.

63. Let $x =$ one of the numbers;
$x - 16 =$ the other number.

The product is $f(x) = x(x - 16) = x^2 - 16x$

The x-coordinate of the minimum is

$$x = -\dfrac{b}{2a} = -\dfrac{-16}{2(1)} = -\dfrac{-16}{2} = 8.$$

$$f(8) = (8)^2 - 16(8)$$

$$= 64 - 128 = -64$$

The vertex is $(8, -64)$. The minimum product is -64. This occurs when the two number are 8 and $8 - 16 = -8$.

65. Maximize the area of a rectangle constructed along a river with 600 feet of fencing.
Let x = the width of the rectangle;
$600 - 2x$ = the length of the rectangle
We need to maximize.

$A(x) = x(600 - 2x)$

$= 600x - 2x^2 = -2x^2 + 600x$

Since $a = -2$ is negative, we know the function opens downward and has a maximum at

$x = -\dfrac{b}{2a} = -\dfrac{600}{2(-2)} = -\dfrac{600}{-4} = 150.$

When the width is $x = 150$ feet, the length is $600 - 2(150) = 600 - 300 = 300$ feet.

The dimensions of the rectangular plot with maximum area are 150 feet by 300 feet. This gives an area of $150 \cdot 300 = 45,000$ square feet.

67. Maximize the area of a rectangle constructed with 50 yards of fencing.
Let x = the length of the rectangle. Let y = the width of the rectangle.
Since we need an equation in one variable, use the perimeter to express y in terms of x.
$2x + 2y = 50$

$2y = 50 - 2x$

$y = \dfrac{50 - 2x}{2} = 25 - x$

We need to maximize $A = xy = x(25 - x)$. Rewrite A as a function of x.

$A(x) = x(25 - x) = -x^2 + 25x$

Since $a = -1$ is negative, we know the function opens downward and has a maximum at

$x = -\dfrac{b}{2a} = -\dfrac{25}{2(-1)} = -\dfrac{25}{-2} = 12.5.$

When the length x is 12.5, the width y is
$y = 25 - x = 25 - 12.5 = 12.5.$

The dimensions of the rectangular region with maximum area are 12.5 yards by 12.5 yards. This gives an area of $12.5 \cdot 12.5 = 156.25$ square yards.

69. Maximize the area of the playground with 600 feet of fencing.
Let x = the length of the rectangle. Let y = the width of the rectangle.
Since we need an equation in one variable, use the perimeter to express y in terms of x.
$2x + 3y = 600$

$3y = 600 - 2x$

$y = \dfrac{600 - 2x}{3}$

$y = 200 - \dfrac{2}{3}x$

We need to maximize $A = xy = x\left(200 - \dfrac{2}{3}x\right)$.

Rewrite A as a function of x.

$A(x) = x\left(200 - \dfrac{2}{3}x\right) = -\dfrac{2}{3}x^2 + 200x$

Since $a = -\dfrac{2}{3}$ is negative, we know the function opens downward and has a maximum at

$x = -\dfrac{b}{2a} = -\dfrac{200}{2\left(-\dfrac{2}{3}\right)} = -\dfrac{200}{-\dfrac{4}{3}} = 150.$

When the length x is 150, the width y is

$y = 200 - \dfrac{2}{3}x = 200 - \dfrac{2}{3}(150) = 100.$

The dimensions of the rectangular playground with maximum area are 150 feet by 100 feet. This gives an area of $150 \cdot 100 = 15,000$ square feet.

71. Maximize the cross-sectional area of the gutter:
$A(x) = x(20 - 2x)$

$= 20x - 2x^2 = -2x^2 + 20x.$

Since $a = -2$ is negative, we know the function opens downward and has a maximum at

$x = -\dfrac{b}{2a} = -\dfrac{20}{2(-2)} = -\dfrac{20}{-4} = 5.$

When the height x is 5, the width is
$20 - 2x = 20 - 2(5) = 20 - 10 = 10.$

$A(5) = -2(5)^2 + 20(5)$

$= -2(25) + 100 = -50 + 100 = 50$

The maximum cross-sectional area is 50 square inches. This occurs when the gutter is 5 inches deep and 10 inches wide.

73. a. $C(x) = 0.55x + 525$

b. $P(x) = R - C$

$P(x) = -0.001x^2 + 3x - 0.55x - 525$

$P(x) = -0.001x^2 + 2.45x - 525$

c. $x = \dfrac{-2.45}{2(-0.001)} = 1225$

$P(x) = -0.001(1225)^2 + 2.45(1225) - 525$

$= 975.63$

The maximum profit will be \$975.63 per week obtained by selling 1225 sandwiches.

81. $y = 2x^2 - 82x + 720$

a.
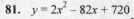
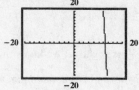

You can only see a little of the parabola.

b. $a = 2;\ b = -82$

$x = -\dfrac{b}{2a} = -\dfrac{-82}{4} = 20.5$

$y = 2(20.5)^2 - 82(20.5) + 720$

$= 840.5 - 1681 + 720$

$= -120.5$

vertex: $(20.5, -120.5)$

c. Ymax = 750

d. You can choose Xmin and Xmax so the x-value of the vertex is in the center of the graph. Choose Ymin to include the y-value of the vertex.

83. $y = -4x^2 + 20x + 160$

$x = \dfrac{-b}{2a} = \dfrac{-20}{-8} = 2.5$

$y = -4(2.5)^2 + 20(2.5) + 160$

$= -2.5 + 50 + 160 = 185$

The vertex is at $(2.5, 185)$.

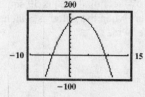

85. $y = 0.01x^2 + 0.6x + 100$

$x = \dfrac{-b}{2a} = \dfrac{-0.6}{0.02} = -30$

$y = 0.01(-30)^2 + 0.6(-30) + 100$

$= 9 - 18 + 100 = 91$

The vertex is at $(-30, 91)$.

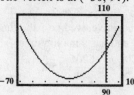

87. Statement **a** is true. Since quadratic functions represent parabolas, we know that the function has a maximum or a minimum. This means that the range cannot be $(-\infty, \infty)$.

Statement **b** is false. The vertex is $(5, -1)$.

Statement **c** is false. The graph has no x-intercepts. To find x-intercepts, set $y = 0$ and solve for x.

$0 = -2(x+4)^2 - 8$

$2(x+4)^2 = -8$

$(x+4)^2 = -4$

Because the solutions to the equation are imaginary, we know that there are no x-intercepts.

Statement **d** is false. The x-coordinate of the maximum is $-\dfrac{b}{2a} = -\dfrac{1}{2(-1)} = -\dfrac{1}{-2} = \dfrac{1}{2}$ and the y-coordinate of the vertex of the parabola is

$f\left(-\dfrac{b}{2a}\right) = f\left(\dfrac{1}{2}\right)$

$= -\left(\dfrac{1}{2}\right)^2 + \dfrac{1}{2} + 1$

$= -\dfrac{1}{4} + \dfrac{1}{2} + 1$

$= -\dfrac{1}{4} + \dfrac{2}{4} + \dfrac{4}{4} = \dfrac{5}{4}.$

The maximum y-value is $\dfrac{5}{4}$.

89. Vertex $(3, 2)$ Axis: $x = 3$
second point $(0, 11)$

91. We know $(h,k) = (-3,-4)$, so the equation is of the form $f(x) = a(x-h)^2 + k$

$$= a[x-(-3)]^2 + (-1)$$
$$= a(x+3)^2 - 1$$

We use the point $(-2,-3)$ on the graph to determine the value of a: $f(x) = a(x+3)^2 - 1$

$$-3 = a(-2+3)^2 - 1$$
$$-3 = a(1)^2 - 1$$
$$-3 = a - 1$$
$$-2 = a$$

Thus, the equation of the parabola is
$$f(x) = -2(x+3)^2 - 1.$$

93. Let x = the number of trees over 50 that will be planted.
The function describing the annual yield per lemon tree when $x+50$ trees are planted per acre is
$$f(x) = (x+50)(320-4x)$$
$$= 320x - 4x^2 + 16000 - 200x$$
$$= -4x^2 + 120x + 16000.$$
This represents the number of lemon trees planted per acre multiplied by yield per tree.

The x-coordinate of the maximum is
$$-\frac{b}{2a} = -\frac{120}{2(-4)} = -\frac{120}{-8} = 15$$ and the y-coordinate
of the vertex of the parabola is
$$f\left(-\frac{b}{2a}\right) = f(15)$$
$$= -4(15)^2 + 120(15) + 16000$$
$$= -4(225) + 1800 + 16000$$
$$= -900 + 1800 + 16000$$
$$= 16900$$
The maximum lemon yield is 16,900 pounds when $50 + 15 = 65$ lemon trees are planted per acre.

Section 3.2

Check Point Exercises

1. Since n is even and $a_n > 0$, the graph rises to the left and to the right.

2. Since n is odd and the leading coefficient is negative, the function falls to the right. Since the ratio cannot be negative, the model won't be appropriate.

3. The graph does not show the function's end behavior. Since $a_n > 0$ and n is odd, the graph should fall to the left.

4. $f(x) = x^3 + 2x^2 - 4x - 8$
$$0 = x^2(x+2) - 4(x+2)$$
$$0 = (x+2)(x^2 - 4)$$
$$0 = (x+2)^2(x-2)$$
$$x = 2 \text{ or } x = -2$$
The zeros are 2 and –2.

5. $f(x) = x^4 - 4x^2$
$$x^4 - 4x^2 = 0$$
$$x^2(x^2 - 4) = 0$$
$$x^2(x+2)(x-2) = 0$$
$$x = 0 \text{ or } x = -2 \text{ or } x = 2$$
The zeros are 0, –2, and 2.

6. $f(x) = -4\left(x + \frac{1}{2}\right)^2 (x-5)^3$
$$-4\left(x + \frac{1}{2}\right)^2 (x-5)^3 = 0$$
$$x = -\frac{1}{2} \text{ or } x = 5$$

The zeros are $-\frac{1}{2}$, with multiplicity 2, and 5, with multiplicity 3.

Because the multiplicity of $-\frac{1}{2}$ is even, the graph touches the x-axis and turns around at this zero.
Because the multiplicity of 5 is odd, the graph crosses the x-axis at this zero.

7. $f(-3) = 3(-3)^3 - 10(-3) + 9 = -42$
$f(-2) = 3(-2)^3 - 10(-2) + 9 = 5$
The sign change shows there is a zero between –3 and –2.

8. $f(x) = x^3 - 3x^2$

Since $a_n > 0$ and n is odd, the graph falls to the left and rises to the right.

$x^3 - 3x^2 = 0$

$x^2(x-3) = 0$

$x = 0$ or $x = 3$

The x-intercepts are 0 and 3.

$f(0) = 0^3 - 3(0)^2 = 0$

The y-intercept is 0.

$f(-x) = (-x)^3 - 3(-x)^2 = -x^3 - 3x^2$

No symmetry.

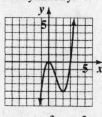

$f(x) = x^3 - 3x^2$

Exercise Set 3.2

1. polynomial function;
degree: 3

3. polynomial function;
degree: 5

5. not a polynomial function

7. not a polynomial function

9. not a polynomial function

11. polynomial function

13. Not a polynomial function because graph is not continuous.

15. (b)

17. (a)

19. $f(x) = 5x^3 + 7x^2 - x + 9$

Since $a_n > 0$ and n is odd, the graph of $f(x)$ falls to the left and rises to the right.

21. $f(x) = 5x^4 + 7x^2 - x + 9$

Since $a_n > 0$ and n is even, the graph of $f(x)$ rises to the left and to the right.

23. $f(x) = -5x^4 + 7x^2 - x + 9$

Since $a_n < 0$ and n is even, the graph of $f(x)$ falls to the left and to the right.

25. $f(x) = 2(x-5)(x+4)^2$

$x = 5$ has multiplicity 1;
The graph crosses the x-axis.
$x = -4$ has multiplicity 2;
The graph touches the x-axis and turns around.

27. $f(x) = 4(x-3)(x+6)^3$

$x = 3$ has multiplicity 1;
The graph crosses the x-axis.
$x = -6$ has multiplicity 3;
The graph crosses the x-axis.

29. $f(x) = x^3 - 2x^2 + x$

$\qquad = x\left(x^2 - 2x + 1\right)$

$\qquad = x(x-1)^2$

$x = 0$ has multiplicity 1;
The graph crosses the x-axis.
$x = 1$ has multiplicity 2;
The graph touches the x-axis and turns around.

31. $f(x) = x^3 + 7x^2 - 4x - 28$

$\qquad = x^2(x+7) - 4(x+7)$

$\qquad = \left(x^2 - 4\right)(x+7)$

$\qquad = (x-2)(x+2)(x+7)$

$x = 2$, $x = -2$ and $x = -7$ have multiplicity 1;
The graph crosses the x-axis.

33. $f(x) = x^3 - x - 1$

$f(1) = -1$

$f(2) = 5$

The sign change shows there is a zero between the given values.

35. $f(x) = 2x^4 - 4x^2 + 1$

$f(-1) = -1$

$f(0) = 1$

The sign change shows there is a zero between the given values.

37. $f(x) = x^3 + x^2 - 2x + 1$

$f(-3) = -11$

$f(-2) = 1$

The sign change shows there is a zero between the given values.

39. $f(x) = 3x^3 - 10x + 9$

$f(-3) = -42$

$f(-2) = 5$

The sign change shows there is a zero between the given values.

41. $f(x) = x^3 + 2x^2 - x - 2$

a. Since $a_n > 0$ and n is odd, $f(x)$ rises to the right and falls to the left.

b.
$$x^3 + 2x^2 - x - 2 = 0$$
$$x^2(x+2) - (x+2) = 0$$
$$(x+2)(x^2 - 1) = 0$$
$$(x+2)(x-1)(x+1) = 0$$
$$x = -2, x = 1, x = -1$$

The zeros at -2, -1, and 1 have odd multiplicity so $f(x)$ crosses the x-axis at these points.

c.
$$f(0) = (0)^3 + 2(0)^2 - 0 - 2$$
$$= -2$$
The y-intercept is -2.

d.
$$f(-x) = (-x) + 2(-x)^2 - (-x) - 2$$
$$= -x^3 + 2x^2 + x - 2$$
$$-f(x) = -x^3 - 2x^2 + x + 2$$
The graph has neither origin symmetry or y-axis symmetry.

e. The graph has 2 turning points and $2 \le 3 - 1$.

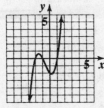

$y = x^3 + 2x^2 - x - 2$

43. $f(x) = x^4 - 9x^2$

a. Since $a_n > 0$ and n is even, $f(x)$ rises to the left and the right.

b.
$$x^4 - 9x^2 = 0$$
$$x^2(x^2 - 9) = 0$$
$$x^2(x-3)(x+3) = 0$$
$$x = 0, x = 3, x = -3$$

The zeros at -3 and 3 have odd multiplicity, so $f(x)$ crosses the x-axis at these points. The root at 0 has even multiplicity, so $f(x)$ touches the x-axis at 0.

c. $f(0) = (0)^4 - 9(0)^2 = 0$
The y-intercept is 0.

d.
$$f(-x) = x^4 - 9x^2$$
$$f(-x) = f(x)$$
The graph has y-axis symmetry.

e. The graph has 3 turning points and $3 \le 4 - 1$.

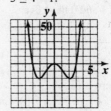

$f(x) = x^4 - 9x^2$

45. $f(x) = -x^4 + 16x^2$

a. Since $a_n < 0$ and n is even, $f(x)$ falls to the left and the right.

b.
$$-x^4 + 16x^2 = 0$$
$$x^2(-x^2 + 16) = 0$$
$$x^2(4-x)(4+x) = 0$$
$$x = 0, x = 4, x = -4$$
The zeros at -4 and 4 have odd multiplicity, so $f(x)$ crosses the x-axis at these points. The root at 0 has even multiplicity, so $f(x)$ touches the x-axis at 0.

c. $f(0) = (0)^4 - 9(0)^2 = 0$
The y-intercept is 0.

d. $f(-x) = -x^4 + 16x^2$

$f(-x) = f(x)$

The graph has y-axis symmetry.

e. The graph has 3 turning points and

$3 \leq 4 - 1$.

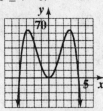

$f(x) = -x^4 + 16x^2$

47. $f(x) = x^4 - 2x^3 + x^2$

a. Since $a_n > 0$ and n is even, $f(x)$ rises to the left and the right.

b. $x^4 - 2x^3 + x^2 = 0$

$x^2(x^2 - 2x + 1) = 0$

$x^2(x-1)(x-1) = 0$

$x = 0, x = 1$

The zeros at 1 and 0 have even multiplicity, so $f(x)$ touches the x-axis at 0 and 1.

c. $f(0) = (0)^4 - 2(0)^3 + (0)^2 = 0$

The y-intercept is 0.

d. $f(-x) = x^4 + 2x^3 + x^2$

The graph has neither y-axis nor origin symmetry.

e. The graph has 3 turning points and

$3 \leq 4 - 1$.

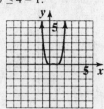

$f(x) = x^4 - 2x^3 + x^2$

49. $f(x) = -2x^4 + 4x^3$

a. Since $a_n < 0$ and n is even, $f(x)$ falls to the left and the right.

b. $-2x^4 + 4x^3 = 0$

$x^3(-2x + 4) = 0$

$x = 0, x = 2$

The zeros at 0 and 2 have odd multiplicity, so $f(x)$ crosses the x-axis at these points.

c. $f(0) = -2(0)^4 + 4(0)^3 = 0$

The y-intercept is 0.

d. $f(-x) = -2x^4 - 4x^3$

The graph has neither y-axis nor origin symmetry.

e. The graph has 1 turning point and

$1 \leq 4 - 1$.

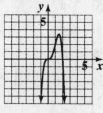

$f(x) = -2x^4 + 4x^3$

51. $f(x) = 6x^3 - 9x - x^5$

a. Since $a_n < 0$ and n is odd, $f(x)$ rises to the left and falls to the right.

b. $-x^5 + 6x^3 - 9x = 0$

$-x(x^4 - 6x^2 + 9) = 0$

$-x(x^2 - 3)(x^2 - 3) = 0$

$x = 0, x = \pm\sqrt{3}$

The root at 0 has odd multiplicity so $f(x)$ crosses the x-axis at $(0, 0)$. The zeros at $-\sqrt{3}$ and $\sqrt{3}$ have even multiplicity so $f(x)$ touches the x-axis at $\sqrt{3}$ and $-\sqrt{3}$.

c. $f(0) = -(0)^5 + 6(0)^3 - 9(0) = 0$

The y-intercept is 0.

d. $f(-x) = x^5 - 6x^3 + 9x$

$f(-x) = -f(x)$

The graph has origin symmetry.

216

e.   The graph has 4 turning point and
     $4 \le 5 - 1$.

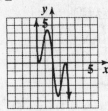

$$f(x) = 6x^3 - 9x - x^5$$

53. $f(x) = 3x^2 - x^3$

a.   Since $a_n < 0$ and n is odd, $f(x)$ rises to the left and falls to the right.

b. $-x^3 + 3x^2 = 0$
     $-x^2(x-3) = 0$
     $x = 0, x = 3$
     The zero at 3 has odd multiplicity so $f(x)$ crosses the x-axis at that point. The root at 0 has even multiplicity so $f(x)$ touches the axis at $(0, 0)$.

c. $f(0) = -(0)^3 + 3(0)^2 = 0$
     The y-intercept is 0.

d. $f(-x) = x^3 + 3x^2$
     The graph has neither y-axis nor origin symmetry.

e.   The graph has 2 turning point and $2 \le 3 - 1$.

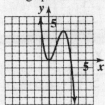

$$f(x) = 3x^2 - x^3$$

55. $f(x) = -3(x-1)^2(x^2-4)$

a.   Since $a_n < 0$ and n is even, $f(x)$ falls to the left and the right.

b. $-3(x-1)^2(x^2-4) = 0$
     $x = 1, x = -2, x = 2$
     The zeros at -2 and 2 have odd multiplicity, so $f(x)$ crosses the x-axis at these points. The root at 1 has even multiplicity, so $f(x)$ touches the x-axis at $(1, 0)$.

c. $f(0) = -3(0-1)^2(0^2-4)^3$
     $= -3(1)(-4) = 12$
     The y-intercept is 12.

d. $f(-x) = -3(-x-1)^2(x^2-4)$
     The graph has neither y-axis nor origin symmetry.

e.   The graph has 1 turning point and $1 \le 4 - 1$.

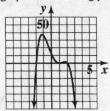

$$f(x) = -3(x - 1)^2 (x^2 - 4)$$

57. $f(x) = x^2(x-1)^3(x+2)$

a.   Since $a_n > 0$ and n is even, $f(x)$ rises to the left and the right.

b. $x = 0, x = 1, x = -2$
     The zeros at 1 and -2 have odd multiplicity so $f(x)$ crosses the x-axis at those points. The root at 0 has even multiplicity so $f(x)$ touches the axis at $(0, 0)$.

c. $f(0) = 0^2(0-1)^3(0+2) = 0$
     The y-intercept is 0.

d. $f(-x) = x^2(-x-1)^3(-x+2)$
     The graph has neither y-axis nor origin symmetry.

e.   The graph has 2 turning points and $2 \le 6 - 1$.

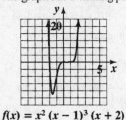

$$f(x) = x^2 (x - 1)^3 (x + 2)$$

59. $f(x) = -x^2(x-1)(x+3)$

   a. Since $a_n < 0$ and n is even, $f(x)$ falls to the left and the right.

   b. $x = 0, x = 1, x = -3$
   The zeros at 1 and –3 have odd multiplicity so $f(x)$ crosses the x-axis at those points. The root at 0 has even multiplicity so $f(x)$ touches the axis at $(0, 0)$.

   c. $f(0) = -0^2(0-1)(0+3) = 0$
   The y-intercept is 0.

   d. $f(-x) = -x^2(-x-1)(-x+3)$
   The graph has neither y-axis nor origin symmetry.

   e. The graph has 3 turning points and $3 \le 4 - 1$.

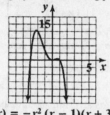

$f(x) = -x^2(x-1)(x+3)$

61. $f(x) = -2x^3(x-1)^2(x+5)$

   a. Since $a_n < 0$ and n is even, $f(x)$ falls to the left and the right.

   b. $x = 0, x = 1, x = -5$
   The roots at 0 and –5 have odd multiplicity so $f(x)$ crosses the x-axis at those points. The root at 1 has even multiplicity so $f(x)$ touches the axis at $(1, 0)$.

   c. $f(0) = -2(0)^3(0-1)^2(0+5) = 0$
   The y-intercept is 0.

   d. $f(-x) = 2x^3(-x-1)^2(-x+5)$
   The graph has neither y-axis nor origin symmetry.

   e. The graph has 2 turning points and $2 \le 6 - 1$.

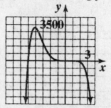

$f(x) = -2x^3(x-1)^2(x+5)$

63. $f(x) = (x-2)^2(x+4)(x-1)$

   a. Since $a_n > 0$ and n is even, $f(x)$ rises to the left and rises the right.

   b. $x = 2, x = -4, x = 1$
   The zeros at –4 and 1 have odd multiplicity so $f(x)$ crosses the x-axis at those points. The root at 2 has even multiplicity so $f(x)$ touches the axis at $(2, 0)$.

   c. $f(0) = (0-2)^2(0+4)(0-1) = -16$
   The y-intercept is –16.

   d. $f(-x) = (-x-2)^2(-x+4)(-x-1)$
   The graph has neither y-axis nor origin symmetry.

   e. The graph has 3 turning points and $3 \le 4 - 1$.

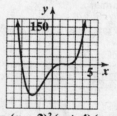

$f(x) = (x-2)^2(x+4)(x-1)$

65. a. The x-intercepts of the graph are -2, 1, and 4, so they are the zeros. Since the graph actually crosses the x-axis at all three places, all three have odd multiplicity.

   b. Since the graph has two turning points, the function must be at least of degree 3. Since -2, 1, and 4 are the zeros, $x+2$, $x-1$, and $x-4$ are factors of the function. The lowest odd multiplicity is 1. From the end behavior, we can tell that the leading coefficient must be positive. Thus, the function is $f(x) = (x+2)(x-1)(x-4)$.

   c. $f(0) = (0+2)(0-1)(0-4) = 8$

67. a. The *x*-intercepts of the graph are −1 and 3, so they are the zeros. Since the graph crosses the *x*-axis at −1, it has odd multiplicity. Since the graph touches the *x*-axis and turns around at 3, it has even multiplicity.

b. Since the graph has two turning points, the function must be at least of degree 3. Since −1 and 3 are the zeros, $x+1$ and $x-3$ are factors of the function. The lowest odd multiplicity is 1, and the lowest even multiplicity is 2. From the end behavior, we can tell that the leading coefficient must be positive. Thus, the function is $f(x)=(x+1)(x-3)^2$.

c. $f(0)=(0+1)(0-3)^2=9$

69. a. The *x*-intercepts of the graph are −3 and 2, so they are the zeros. Since the graph touches the *x*-axis and turns around at both −3 and 2, both have even multiplicity.

b. Since the graph has three turning points, the function must be at least of degree 4. Since −3 and 2 are the zeros, $x+3$ and $x-2$ are factors of the function. The lowest even multiplicity is 2. From the end

behavior, we can tell that the leading coefficient must be negative. Thus, the function is $f(x)=-(x+3)^2(x-2)^2$.

c. $f(0)=-(0+3)^2(0-2)^2=-36$

71. a. The *x*-intercepts of the graph are −2, −1, and 1, so they are the zeros. Since the graph crosses the *x*-axis at −1 and 1, they both have odd multiplicity. Since the graph touches the *x*-axis and turns around at −2, it has even multiplicity.

b. Since the graph has five turning points, the function must be at least of degree 6. Since −2, −1, and 1 are the zeros, $x+2$, $x+1$, and $x-1$ are factors of the function. The lowest even multiplicity is 2, and the lowest odd multiplicity is 1. However, to reach degree 6, one of the odd multiplicities must be 3. From the end behavior, we can tell that the leading coefficient must be positive. The function is $f(x)=(x+2)^2(x+1)(x-1)^3$.

c. $f(0)=(0+2)^2(0+1)(0-1)^3=-4$

73. $f(x)=-2212x^2+57,575x+107,896$

$f(10)=-2212(10)^2+57,575(10)+107,896=462,446$

$g(x)=-84x^3-702x^2+50,609x+113,435$

$g(10)=-84(10)^3-702(10)^2+50,609(10)+113,435=465,325$

The graph indicates that *f* provides a better description because $f(10)$ is closer to the actual amount of 458,551.

75. The leading coefficient is negative and the degree is even. This means that the graph will fall to the right. This function will not be useful in modeling the number of cumulative AIDS deaths over an extended period of time because the cumulative number of deaths cannot decrease.

77. a. The percentage of white classmates was increasing from 1970 through 1980 and from 1985 through 1990.

b. The percentage of white classmates was decreasing from 1980 through 1985 and from 1990 through 2002.

c. Three turning points are shown in the graph.

d. Since there are three turning points, the degree of the polynomial function of best fit would be 4.

e. The leading coefficient would be negative because the graph falls to the left and falls to the right.

97.

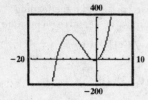

99.

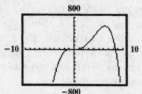

101.

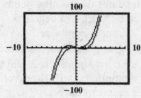

103. a. False; $f(x)$ falls to the left and rises to the right.

b. False

c. True; There are many 3rd degree polynomials with the same three x-intercepts.

d. False; a function with origin symmetry either falls to the left and rises to the right, or rises to the left and falls to the right.

     (c) is true.

105. $f(x) = x^3 - 2x^2$

Section 3.3

Check Point Exercises

1.
$$\begin{array}{r} x+5 \\ x+9\overline{)x^2+14x+45} \\ \underline{x^2+9x} \\ 5x+45 \\ \underline{5x+45} \\ 0 \end{array}$$

The answer is $x + 5$.

2.
$$\begin{array}{r} 2x^2+3x-2 \\ x-3\overline{)2x^3-3x^2-11x+7} \\ \underline{2x^3-6x^2} \\ 3x^2-11x \\ \underline{3x^2-9x} \\ -2x+7 \\ \underline{-2x+6} \\ 1 \end{array}$$

The answer is $2x^2+3x-2+\dfrac{1}{x-3}$.

3.
$$\begin{array}{r} 2x^2+7x+14 \\ x^2-2x\overline{)2x^4+3x^3+0x^2-7x-10} \\ \underline{2x^4-4x^3} \\ 7x^3+0x^2 \\ \underline{7x^3-14x^2} \\ 14x^2-7x \\ \underline{14x^2-28x} \\ 21x-10 \end{array}$$

The answer is $2x^2+7x+14+\dfrac{21x-10}{x^2-2x}$.

4.

-2	1	0	-7	-6
		-2	4	6
	1	-2	-3	0

The answer is x^2-2x-3.

5.

-4	3	4	-5	3
		-12	32	-108
	3	-8	27	-105

$f(-4) = -105$

6.

-1	15	14	-3	-2
		-15	1	2
	15	-1	-2	0

$15x^2 - x - 2 = 0$

$(3x+1)(5x-2) = 0$

$x = -\dfrac{1}{3}$ or $x = \dfrac{2}{5}$

The solution set is $\left\{-1, -\dfrac{1}{3}, \dfrac{2}{5}\right\}$.

Exercise Set 3.3

1.
$$x+5\overline{)x^2+8x+15}$$ quotient $x+3$
$$\underline{x^2+5x}$$
$$3x+15$$
$$\underline{3x+15}$$
$$0$$

The answer is $x+3$.

3.
$$x+2\overline{)x^3+5x^2+7x+2}$$ quotient x^2+3x+1
$$\underline{x^3+2x^2}$$
$$3x^2+7x$$
$$\underline{3x^2+6x}$$
$$x+2$$
$$\underline{x+2}$$
$$0$$

The answer is x^2+3x+1.

5.
$$3x-1\overline{)6x^3+7x^2+12x-5}$$ quotient $2x^2+3x+5$
$$\underline{6x^3-2x^2}$$
$$9x^2+12x$$
$$\underline{9x^2-3x}$$
$$15x-5$$
$$\underline{15x-5}$$
$$0$$

The answer is $2x^2+3x+5$.

7.
$$3x-2\overline{)12x^2+x-4}$$ quotient $4x+3+\dfrac{2}{3x-2}$
$$\underline{12x^2-8x}$$
$$9x-4$$
$$\underline{9x-6}$$
$$2$$

The answer is $4x+3+\dfrac{2}{3x-2}$.

9.
$$x+3\overline{)2x^3+7x^2+9x-20}$$ quotient $2x^2+x+6-\dfrac{38}{x+3}$
$$\underline{2x^3+6x^2}$$
$$x^2+9x$$
$$\underline{x^2+3x}$$
$$6x-20$$
$$\underline{6x+18}$$
$$-38$$

The answer is $2x^2+x+6-\dfrac{38}{x+3}$.

11.
$$x-4\overline{)4x^4-4x^2+6x}$$ quotient $4x^3+16x^2+60x+246+\dfrac{984}{x-4}$
$$\underline{4x^4-16x^3}$$
$$16x^3-4x^2$$
$$\underline{16x^3-64x^2}$$
$$60x^2+6x$$
$$\underline{60x^2-240x}$$
$$246x$$
$$\underline{246x-984}$$
$$984$$

The answer is
$$4x^3+16x^2+60x+246+\dfrac{984}{x-4}.$$

13.
$$3x^2-x-3\overline{)6x^3+13x^2-11x-15}$$ quotient $2x+5$
$$\underline{6x^3-2x^2-6x}$$
$$15x^2-5x-15$$
$$\underline{15x^2-5x-15}$$
$$0$$

The answer is $2x+5$.

221

15.

$$\begin{array}{r} 6x^2 + 3x - 1 \\ 3x^2+1{\overline{\smash{\big)}\,18x^4 + 9x^3 + 3x^2}} \\ \underline{18x^4 + 6x^2} \\ 9x^3 - 3x^2 \\ \underline{9x^3 + 3x} \\ -3x^2 - 3x \\ \underline{-3x^2 - 1} \\ -3x + 1 \end{array}$$

The answer is $6x^2 + 3x - 1 - \dfrac{3x-1}{3x^2+1}$.

17. $(2x^2 + x - 10) \div (x-2)$

$$\begin{array}{r|rrr} 2 & 2 & 1 & -10 \\ & & 4 & 10 \\ \hline & 2 & 5 & 0 \end{array}$$

The answer is $2x + 5$.

19. $(3x^2 + 7x - 20) \div (x+5)$

$$\begin{array}{r|rrr} -5 & 3 & 7 & -20 \\ & & -15 & 40 \\ \hline & 3 & -8 & 20 \end{array}$$

The answer is $3x - 8 + \dfrac{20}{x+5}$.

21. $(4x^3 - 3x^2 + 3x - 1) \div (x-1)$

$$\begin{array}{r|rrrr} 1 & 4 & -3 & 3 & -1 \\ & & 4 & 1 & 4 \\ \hline & 4 & 1 & 4 & 3 \end{array}$$

The answer is $4x^2 + x + 4 + \dfrac{3}{x-1}$.

23. $(6x^5 - 2x^3 + 4x^2 - 3x + 1) \div (x-2)$

$$\begin{array}{r|rrrrrr} 2 & 6 & 0 & -2 & 4 & -3 & 1 \\ & & 12 & 24 & 44 & 96 & 186 \\ \hline & 6 & 12 & 22 & 48 & 93 & 187 \end{array}$$

The answer is

$6x^4 + 12x^3 + 22x^2 + 48x + 93 + \dfrac{187}{x-2}$.

25. $(x^2 - 5x - 5x^3 + x^4) \div (5+x) \Rightarrow$

$(x^4 - 5x^3 + x^2 - 5x) \div (x+5)$

$$\begin{array}{r|rrrrr} -5 & 1 & -5 & 1 & -5 & 0 \\ & & -5 & 50 & -255 & 1300 \\ \hline & 1 & -10 & 51 & -260 & 1300 \end{array}$$

The answer is

$x^3 - 10x^2 + 51x - 260 + \dfrac{1300}{x+5}$.

27. $\dfrac{x^5 + x^3 - 2}{x-1}$

$$\begin{array}{r|rrrrrr} 1 & 1 & 0 & 1 & 0 & 0 & -2 \\ & & 1 & 1 & 2 & 2 & 2 \\ \hline & 1 & 1 & 2 & 2 & 2 & 0 \end{array}$$

The answer is $x^4 + x^3 + 2x^2 + 2x + 2$.

29. $\dfrac{x^4 - 256}{x-4}$

$$\begin{array}{r|rrrrr} 4 & 1 & 0 & 0 & 0 & -256 \\ & & 4 & 16 & 64 & 256 \\ \hline & 1 & 4 & 16 & 64 & 0 \end{array}$$

The answer is $x^3 + 4x^2 + 16x + 64$.

31. $\dfrac{2x^5 - 3x^4 + x^3 - x^2 + 2x - 1}{x+2}$

$$\begin{array}{r|rrrrrr} -2 & 2 & -3 & 1 & -1 & 2 & -1 \\ & & -4 & 14 & -30 & 62 & -128 \\ \hline & 2 & -7 & 15 & -31 & 64 & -129 \end{array}$$

The answer is

$2x^4 - 7x^3 + 15x^2 - 31x + 64 - \dfrac{129}{x+2}$.

33. $f(x) = 2x^3 - 11x^2 + 7x - 5$

$$\begin{array}{r|rrrr} 4 & 2 & -11 & 7 & -5 \\ & & 8 & -12 & -20 \\ \hline & 2 & -3 & -5 & -25 \end{array}$$

$f(4) = -25$

35. $f(x) = 3x^3 - 7x^2 - 2x + 5$

$$\begin{array}{r|rrrr} -3 & 3 & -7 & -2 & 5 \\ & & -9 & 48 & -138 \\ \hline & 3 & -16 & 46 & -133 \end{array}$$

$f(-3) = -133$

37. $f(x) = x^4 + 5x^3 + 5x^2 - 5x - 6$

$$\begin{array}{r|rrrrr} 3 & 1 & 5 & 5 & -5 & -6 \\ & & 3 & 24 & 87 & 246 \\ \hline & 1 & 8 & 29 & 82 & 240 \end{array}$$

$f(3) = 240$

39. $f(x) = 2x^4 - 5x^3 - x^2 + 3x + 2$

$$\begin{array}{r|rrrrr} -\frac{1}{2} & 2 & -5 & -1 & 3 & 2 \\ & & -1 & 3 & -1 & -1 \\ \hline & 2 & -6 & 2 & 2 & 1 \end{array}$$

$f\left(-\dfrac{1}{2}\right) = 1$

41. Dividend: $x^3 - 4x^2 + x + 6$
Divisor: $x + 1$

$$\begin{array}{r|rrrr} -1 & 1 & -4 & 1 & 6 \\ & & -1 & 5 & -6 \\ \hline & 1 & -5 & 6 & 0 \end{array}$$

The quotient is $x^2 - 5x + 6$.
$(x+1)(x^2 - 5x + 6) = 0$
$(x+1)(x-2)(x-3) = 0$
$x = -1, x = 2, x = 3$
The solution set is $\{-1, 2, 3\}$.

43. $2x^3 - 5x^2 + x + 2 = 0$

$$\begin{array}{r|rrrr} 2 & 2 & -5 & 1 & 2 \\ & & 4 & -2 & -2 \\ \hline & 2 & -1 & -1 & 0 \end{array}$$

$(x-2)(2x^2 - x - 1) = 0$
$(x-2)(2x+1)(x-1) = 0$
$x = 2, \ x = -\dfrac{1}{2}, \ x = 1$

The solution set is $\left\{-\dfrac{1}{2}, 1, 2\right\}$.

45. $12x^3 + 16x^2 - 5x - 3 = 0$

$$\begin{array}{r|rrrr} -\frac{3}{2} & 12 & 16 & -5 & -3 \\ & & -18 & 3 & 3 \\ \hline & 12 & -2 & -2 & 0 \end{array}$$

$\left(x + \dfrac{3}{2}\right)(12x^2 - 2x - 2) = 0$

$\left(x + \dfrac{3}{2}\right)2(6x^2 - x - 1) = 0$

$\left(x + \dfrac{3}{2}\right)2(3x+1)(2x-1) = 0$

$x = -\dfrac{3}{2}, \ x = -\dfrac{1}{3}, \ x = \dfrac{1}{2}$

The solution set is $\left\{-\dfrac{3}{2}, -\dfrac{1}{3}, \dfrac{1}{2}\right\}$.

47. The graph indicates that 2 is a solution to the equation.

$$\begin{array}{r|rrrr} 2 & 1 & 2 & -5 & -6 \\ & & 2 & 8 & 6 \\ \hline & 1 & 4 & 3 & 0 \end{array}$$

The remainder is 0, so 2 is a solution.
$x^3 + 2x^2 - 5x - 6 = 0$
$(x-2)(x^2 + 4x + 3) = 0$
$(x-2)(x+3)(x+1) = 0$
The solutions are 2, -3, and -1, or $\{-3, -1, 2\}$.

49. The table indicates that 1 is a solution to the equation.

$$\begin{array}{r|rrrr} 1 & 6 & -11 & 6 & -1 \\ & & 6 & -5 & 1 \\ \hline & 6 & -5 & 1 & 0 \end{array}$$

The remainder is 0, so 1 is a solution.
$6x^3 - 11x^2 + 6x - 1 = 0$
$(x-1)(6x^2 - 5x + 1) = 0$
$(x-1)(3x-1)(2x-1) = 0$

The solutions are 1, $\dfrac{1}{3}$, and $\dfrac{1}{2}$, or $\left\{\dfrac{1}{3}, \dfrac{1}{2}, 1\right\}$.

51. a. $14x^3 - 17x^2 - 16x - 177 = 0$

$$\underline{3|}\quad 14 \quad -17 \quad -16 \quad -177$$
$$\qquad\qquad 42 \quad\; 75 \quad\; 177$$
$$\overline{\qquad 14 \quad\; 25 \quad\; 59 \quad\quad 0}$$

The remainder is 0 so 3 is a solution.

$14x^3 - 17x^2 - 16x - 177$
$= (x - 3)(14x^2 + 25x + 59)$

b. $f(x) = 14x^3 - 17x^2 - 16x + 34$

We need to find x when $f(x) = 211$.

$f(x) = 14x^3 - 17x^2 - 16x + 34$

$211 = 14x^3 - 17x^2 - 16x + 34$

$0 = 14x^3 - 17x^2 - 16x - 177$

This is the equation obtained in part **a.** One solution is 3. It can be used to find other solutions (if they exist).

$14x^3 - 17x^2 - 16x - 177 = 0$

$(x - 3)(14x^2 + 25x + 59) = 0$

The polynomial $14x^2 + 25x + 59$ cannot be factored, so the only solution is $x = 3$. The female moth's abdominal width is 3 millimeters.

53. $A = l \cdot w$ so

$$l = \frac{A}{w} = \frac{0.5x^3 - 0.3x^2 + 0.22x + 0.06}{x + 0.2}$$

$$\underline{-0.2|}\quad 0.5 \quad -0.3 \quad 0.22 \quad 0.06$$
$$\qquad\qquad\quad -0.1 \quad 0.08 \quad -0.06$$
$$\overline{\qquad\;\; 0.5 \quad -0.4 \quad 0.3 \quad\quad 0}$$

Therefore, the length of the rectangle is $0.5x^2 - 0.4x + 0.3$ units.

55. a.

$$f(30) = \frac{80(30) - 8000}{30 - 110} = 70$$

(30, 70) At a 30% tax rate, the government tax revenue will be $70 ten billion.

b. $\underline{110\;|}\quad 80 \quad\; -8000$
$$\qquad\qquad\qquad\quad 8800$$
$$\overline{\qquad\qquad 80 \quad\;\; 800}$$

$$f(x) = 80 + \frac{800}{x - 110}$$

$$f(30) = 80 + \frac{800}{80 - 110} = 70$$

(30, 70) same answer as in **a.**

c. $f(x)$ is not a polynomial function. It is a rational function because it is the quotient of two linear polynomials.

65.   Exercise 43:

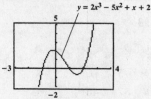
$y = 2x^3 - 5x^2 + x + 2$

Exercise 44:

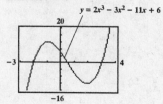
$y = 2x^3 - 3x^2 - 11x + 6$

Exercise 45

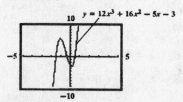
$y = 12x^3 + 16x^2 - 5x - 3$

Exercise 46:

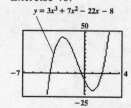
$y = 3x^3 + 7x^2 - 22x - 8$

67.

$$\begin{array}{r}
5x^2 + 2x - 4 \\
4x + 3\overline{)20x^3 + 23x^2 - 10x + k} \\
\underline{20x^3 + 15x^2}\quad\qquad\qquad \\
8x^2 - 10\qquad\quad \\
\underline{8x^2 + 6x}\qquad\quad \\
-16x + k \\
\underline{-16x - 12} \\
\end{array}$$

To get a remainder of zero, k must equal -12.
$k = -12$

69.

$$x^n + 1 \overline{\smash{)}\,x^{3n} \qquad\qquad\qquad +1}$$

$$\begin{array}{r} x^{2n} - x^n + 1 \\ \underline{x^{3n} + x^{2n}} \\ -x^{2n} \\ \underline{-x^{2n} - x^n} \\ x^n + 1 \\ \underline{x^n + 1} \\ 0 \end{array}$$

71. $x^4 - 4x^3 - 9x^2 + 16x + 20 = 0$

$$\begin{array}{r|rrrrr} 5| & 1 & -4 & -9 & 16 & 20 \\ & & 5 & 5 & -20 & -20 \\ \hline & 1 & 1 & -4 & -4 & 0 \end{array}$$

The remainder is zero and 5 is a solution to the equation.

$x^4 - 4x^3 - 9x^2 + 16x + 20$

$= (x - 5)(x^3 + x^2 - 4x - 4)$

To solve the equation, we set it equal to zero and factor.

$(x - 5)(x^3 + x^2 - 4x - 4) = 0$

$(x - 5)(x^2(x + 1) - 4(x + 1)) = 0$

$(x - 5)(x + 1)(x^2 - 4) = 0$

$(x - 5)(x + 1)(x + 2)(x - 2) = 0$

Apply the zero product principle.

$x - 5 = 0 \qquad x + 1 = 0$

$\quad x = 5 \qquad\qquad x = -1$

$x + 2 = 0 \qquad x - 2 = 0$

$\quad x = -2 \qquad\qquad x = 2$

The solutions are $-2, \ -1, \ 2$ and 5 and the solution set is $\{-2, -1, 2, 5\}$.

Section 3.4

Check Point Exercises

1. $p: \pm 1, \ \pm 2, \ \pm 3, \ \pm 6$

     $q: \pm 1$

     $\dfrac{p}{q}: \pm 1, \ \pm 2, \ \pm 3, \ \pm 6$

     are the possible rational zeros.

2. $p: \pm 1, \ \pm 3$

     $q: \pm 1, \ \pm 2, \ \pm 4$

     $\dfrac{p}{q}: \pm 1, \ \pm 3, \ \pm \dfrac{1}{2}, \ \pm \dfrac{1}{4}, \ \pm \dfrac{3}{2}, \ \pm \dfrac{3}{4}$

     are the possible rational zeros.

3. $\pm 1, \ \pm 2, \ \pm 4, \ \pm 5, \ \pm 10, \ \pm 20$ are possible rational zeros

$$\begin{array}{r|rrrr} 1 & 1 & 8 & 11 & -20 \\ & & 1 & 9 & 20 \\ \hline & 1 & 9 & 20 & 0 \end{array}$$

     1 is a zero.

     $x^2 + 9x + 20 = 0$

     $(x + 4)(x + 5) = 0$

     $x = -4 \ \text{ or } \ x = -5$

     The solution set is $\{1, -4, -5\}$.

4. $\pm 1, \ \pm 2$ are possible rational zeros

$$\begin{array}{r|rrrr} 2 & 1 & 1 & -5 & -2 \\ & & 2 & 6 & 2 \\ \hline & 1 & 3 & 1 & 0 \end{array}$$

     2 is a zero.

     $x^2 + 3x + 1 = 0$

     $x = \dfrac{-b \pm \sqrt{b^2 - 4ac}}{2a}$

     $x = \dfrac{-3 \pm \sqrt{3^2 - 4(1)(1)}}{2(1)}$

     $= \dfrac{-3 \pm \sqrt{5}}{2}$

     The solution set is $\left\{ 2, \dfrac{-3 + \sqrt{5}}{2}, \dfrac{-3 - \sqrt{5}}{2} \right\}$.

5. $\pm 1, \pm 13$ are possible rational zeros.

$$
\begin{array}{r|rrrrr}
1 & 1 & -6 & 22 & -30 & 13 \\
  &   & 1 & -5 & 17 & -13 \\
\hline
  & 1 & -5 & 17 & -13 & 0
\end{array}
$$

1 is a zero.

$$
\begin{array}{r|rrrr}
1 & 1 & 5 & 17 & -13 \\
  &   & 1 & -4 & 13 \\
\hline
  & 1 & -4 & 13 & 0
\end{array}
$$

1 is a double root.

$x^2 - 4x + 13 = 0$

$x = \dfrac{4 \pm \sqrt{16-52}}{2} = \dfrac{4 \pm \sqrt{-36}}{2} = 2 + 3i$

The solution set is $\{1,\ 2+3i,\ 2-3i\}$.

6. $(x+3)(x-i)(x+i) = (x+3)(x^2+1)$

$f(x) = a_n(x+3)(x^2+1)$

$f(1) = a_n(1+3)(1^2+1) = 8a_n = 8$

$a_n = 1$

$f(x) = (x+3)(x^2+1)$ or $x^3 + 3x^2 + x + 3$

7. $f(x) = x^4 - 14x^3 + 71x^2 - 154x + 120$

$f(-x) = x^4 + 14x^3 + 71x^2 + 154x + 120$

Since $f(x)$ has 4 changes of sign, there are 4, 2, or 0 positive real zeros.
Since $f(-x)$ has no changes of sign, there are no negative real zeros.

Exercise Set 3.4

1. $f(x) = x^3 + x^2 - 4x - 4$

$p: \pm 1, \pm 2, \pm 4$

$q: \pm 1$

$\dfrac{p}{q}: \pm 1, \pm 2, \pm 4$

3. $f(x) = 3x^4 - 11x^3 - x^2 + 19x + 6$

$p: \pm 1, \pm 2, \pm 3, \pm 6$

$q: \pm 1, \pm 3$

$\dfrac{p}{q}: \pm 1, \pm 2, \pm 3, \pm 6, \pm \dfrac{1}{3}, \pm \dfrac{2}{3}$

5. $f(x) = 4x^4 - x^3 + 5x^2 - 2x - 6$

$p: \pm 1, \pm 2, \pm 3, \pm 6$

$q: \pm 1, \pm 2, \pm 4$

$\dfrac{p}{q}: \pm 1, \pm 2, \pm 3, \pm 6, \pm \dfrac{1}{2}, \pm \dfrac{1}{4}, \pm \dfrac{3}{2}, \pm \dfrac{3}{4}$

7. $f(x) = x^5 - x^4 - 7x^3 + 7x^2 - 12x - 12$

$p: \pm 1, \pm 2, \pm 3 \pm 4 \pm 6 \pm 12$

$q: \pm 1$

$\dfrac{p}{q}: \pm 1, \pm 2, \pm 3 \pm 4 \pm 6 \pm 12$

9. $f(x) = x^3 + x^2 - 4x - 4$

a. $p: \pm 1, \pm 2, \pm 4$

$q: \pm 1$

$\dfrac{p}{q}: \pm 1, \pm 2, \pm 4$

b.
$$
\begin{array}{r|rrrr}
2 & 1 & 1 & -4 & -4 \\
  &   & 2 & 6 & 4 \\
\hline
  & 1 & 3 & 2 & 0
\end{array}
$$

2 is a zero.

c. $x^3 + x^2 - 4x - 4 = 0$

$(x-2)(x^2 + 3x + 2) = 0$

$(x-2)(x+2)(x+1) = 0$

$x - 2 = 0 \quad x + 2 = 0 \quad x + 1 = 0$

$x = 2, \ x = -2, \ x = -1$

The solution set is $\{2, -2, -1\}$.

11. $f(x) = 2x^3 - 3x^2 - 11x + 6$

a. $p: \pm 1, \pm 2, \pm 3, \pm 6$

$q: \pm 1, \pm 2$

$\dfrac{p}{q}: \pm 1, \pm 2, \pm 3, \pm 6, \pm \dfrac{1}{2}, \pm \dfrac{3}{2}$

b.
$$
\begin{array}{r|rrrr}
3 & 2 & -3 & -11 & 6 \\
  &   & 6 & 9   & -6 \\
\hline
  & 2 & 3 & -2 & 0
\end{array}
$$

3 is a zero.

c. $2x^3 - 3x^2 - 11x + 6 = 0$

$(x-3)(2x^2 + 3x - 2) = 0$

$(x-3)(2x-1)(x+2) = 0$

$x = 3, \ x = \dfrac{1}{2}, \ x = -2$

The solution set is $\left\{ 3, \dfrac{1}{2}, -2 \right\}$.

13. a. $f(x) = x^3 + 4x^2 - 3x - 6$

$p: \pm 1, \pm 2, \pm 3, \pm 6$

$q: \pm 1$

$\dfrac{p}{q}: \pm 1, \pm 2, \pm 3, \pm 6$

b.

-1	1	4	-3	-6
		-1	-3	6
	1	3	-6	0

-1 is a zero.

c. $x^2 + 3x - 6 = 0$

$x = \dfrac{-b \pm \sqrt{b^2 - 4ac}}{2a}$

$x = \dfrac{-3 \pm \sqrt{3^2 - 4(1)(-6)}}{2(1)}$

$= \dfrac{-3 \pm \sqrt{33}}{2}$

The solution set is

$\left\{ -1, \dfrac{-3 + \sqrt{33}}{2}, \dfrac{-3 - \sqrt{33}}{2} \right\}$.

15. a. $f(x) = 2x^3 + 6x^2 + 5x + 2$

$p: \pm 1, \pm 2$

$q: \pm 1, \pm 2$

$\dfrac{p}{q}: \pm 1, \pm 2, \pm \dfrac{1}{2}$

b.

-2	2	6	5	2
		-4	-4	-2
	2	2	1	0

-2 is a zero.

c. $2x^2 + 2x + 1 = 0$

$x = \dfrac{-b \pm \sqrt{b^2 - 4ac}}{2a}$

$x = \dfrac{-2 \pm \sqrt{2^2 - 4(2)(1)}}{2(2)}$

$= \dfrac{-2 \pm \sqrt{-4}}{4}$

$= \dfrac{-2 \pm 2i}{4}$

$= \dfrac{-1 \pm i}{2}$

The solution set is $\left\{ -2, \dfrac{-1 + i}{2}, \dfrac{-1 - i}{2} \right\}$.

17. $x^3 - 2x^2 - 11x + 12 = 0$

a. $p: \pm 1, \pm 2, \pm 3, \pm 4, \pm 6, \pm 12$

$q: \pm 1$

$\dfrac{p}{q}: \pm 1, \pm 2, \pm 3, \pm 4, \pm 6, \pm 12$

b.

4	1	-2	-11	12
		4	8	-12
	1	2	-3	0

4 is a root.

c. $x^3 - 2x^2 - 11x + 12$

$(x-4)(x^2 + 2x - 3) = 0$

$(x-4)(x+3)(x-1) = 0$

$x - 4 = 0 \quad x + 3 = 0 \quad x - 1 = 0$

$x = 4 \qquad x = -3 \qquad x = 1$

The solution set is $\{-3, 1, 4\}$.

19. $x^3 - 10x - 12 = 0$

a. $p: \pm 1, \pm 2, \pm 3, \pm 4, \pm 6, \pm 12$

$q: \pm 1$

$\dfrac{p}{q}: \pm 1, \pm 2, \pm 3, \pm 4, \pm 6, \pm 12$

b.

-2	1	0	-10	-12
		-2	4	12
	1	-2	-6	0

-2 is a root.

227

c. $x^3 - 10x - 12 = 0$

$(x+2)(x^2 - 2x - 6) = 0$

$x = \dfrac{2 \pm \sqrt{4+24}}{2} = \dfrac{2 \pm \sqrt{28}}{2}$

$= \dfrac{2 \pm 2\sqrt{7}}{2} = 1 \pm \sqrt{7}$

The solution set is $\left\{-2, 1+\sqrt{7}, 1-\sqrt{7}\right\}$.

21. $6x^3 + 25x^2 - 24x + 5 = 0$

a. $p: \pm 1, \pm 5$

$q: \pm 1, \pm 2, \pm 3, \pm 6$

$\dfrac{p}{q}: \pm 1, \pm 5, \pm\dfrac{1}{2}, \pm\dfrac{5}{2}, \pm\dfrac{1}{3}, \pm\dfrac{5}{3}, \pm\dfrac{1}{6}, \pm\dfrac{5}{6}$

b.

-5	6	25	-24	5
		-30	25	-5
	6	-5	1	0

-5 is a root.

c. $6x^3 + 25x^2 - 24x + 5 = 0$

$(x+5)(6x^2 - 5x + 1) = 0$

$(x+5)(2x-1)(3x-1) = 0$

$x+5 = 0 \quad 2x-1 = 0 \quad 3x-1 = 0$

$x = -5, \quad x = \dfrac{1}{2}, \quad x = \dfrac{1}{3}$

The solution set is $\left\{-5, \dfrac{1}{2}, \dfrac{1}{3}\right\}$.

23. $x^4 - 2x^3 - 5x^2 + 8x + 4 = 0$

a. $p: \pm 1, \pm 2, \pm 4$

$q: \pm 1$

$\dfrac{p}{q}: \pm 1, \pm 2, \pm 4$

b.

2	1	-2	-5	8	4
		2	0	-10	-4
	1	0	-5	-2	0

2 is a root.

c. $x^4 - 2x^3 - 5x^2 + 8x + 4 = 0$

$(x-2)(x^3 - 5x - 2) = 0$

-2	1	0	-5	-2
		-2	4	2
	1	-2	-1	0

-2 is a zero of $x^3 - 5x - 2 = 0$.

$(x-2)(x+2)(x^2 - 2x - 1) = 0$

$x = \dfrac{2 \pm \sqrt{4+4}}{2} = \dfrac{2 \pm \sqrt{8}}{2} = \dfrac{2 \pm 2\sqrt{2}}{2}$

$= 1 \pm \sqrt{2}$

The solution set is

$\left\{-2, 2, 1+\sqrt{2}, 1-\sqrt{2}\right\}$.

25. $(x-1)(x+5i)(x-5i)$

$= (x-1)(x^2 + 25)$

$= x^3 + 25x - x^2 - 25$

$= x^3 - x^2 + 25x - 25$

$f(x) = a_n(x^3 - x^2 + 25x - 25)$

$f(-1) = a_n(-1-1-25-25)$

$-104 = a_n(-52)$

$a_n = 2$

$f(x) = 2(x^3 - x^2 + 25x - 25)$

$f(x) = 2x^3 - 2x^2 + 50x - 50$

27. $(x+5)(x-4-3i)(x-4+3i)$

$\quad = (x+5)(x^2 - 4x + 3ix - 4x + 16 - 12i$

$\quad\quad -3ix + 12i - 9i^2)$

$\quad = (x+5)(x^2 - 8x + 25)$

$\quad = (x^3 - 8x^2 + 25x + 5x^2 - 40x + 125)$

$\quad = x^3 - 3x^2 - 15x + 125$

$\quad f(x) = a_n(x^3 - 3x^2 - 15x + 125)$

$\quad f(2) = a_n\left(2^3 - 3(2)^2 - 15(2) + 125\right)$

$\quad 91 = a_n(91)$

$\quad a_n = 1$

$\quad f(x) = 1(x^3 - 3x^2 - 15x + 125)$

$\quad f(x) = x^3 - 3x^2 - 15x + 125$

29. $(x-i)(x+i)(x-3i)(x+3i)$

$\quad = (x^2 - i^2)(x^2 - 9i^2)$

$\quad = (x^2 + 1)(x^2 + 9)$

$\quad = x^4 + 10x^2 + 9$

$\quad f(x) = a_n(x^4 + 10x^2 + 9)$

$\quad f(-1) = a_n((-1)^4 + 10(-1)^2 + 9)$

$\quad 20 = a_n(20)$

$\quad a_n = 1$

$\quad f(x) = x^4 + 10x^2 + 9$

31. $(x+2)(x-5)(x-3+2i)(x-3-2i)$

$\quad = (x^2 - 3x - 10)(x^2 - 3x - 2ix - 3x + 9 + 6i + 2ix - 6i - 4i^2)$

$\quad = (x^2 - 3x - 10)(x^2 - 6x + 13)$

$\quad = x^4 - 6x + 13x^2 - 3x^3 + 18x^2 - 39x - 10x^2 + 60x - 130$

$\quad = x^4 - 9x^3 + 21x^2 + 21x - 130$

$\quad f(x) = a_n\left(x^4 - 9x^3 + 21x^2 + 21x - 130\right)$

$\quad f(1) = a_n(1 - 9 + 21 + 21 - 130)$

$\quad -96 = a_n(-96)$

$\quad a_n = 1$

$\quad f(x) = x^4 - 9x^3 + 21x^2 + 21x - 130$

33. $f(x) = x^3 + 2x^2 + 5x + 4$

Since $f(x)$ has no sign variations,
no positive real roots exist.

$f(-x) = -x^3 + 2x^2 - 5x + 4$

Since $f(-x)$ has 3 sign variations,
3 or 1 negative real roots exist.

35. $f(x) = 5x^3 - 3x^2 + 3x - 1$

Since $f(x)$ has 3 sign variations, 3 or 1 positive
real roots exist.

$f(-x) = -5x^3 - 3x^2 - 3x - 1$

Since $f(-x)$ has no sign variations, no negative
real roots exist.

37. $f(x) = 2x^4 - 5x^3 - x^2 - 6x + 4$

Since $f(x)$ has 2 sign variations, 2 or 0 positive
real roots exist.

$f(-x) = 2x^4 + 5x^3 - x^2 + 6x + 4$

Since $f(-x)$ has 2 sign variations, 2 or 0 negative
real roots exist.

39. $f(x) = x^3 - 4x^2 - 7x + 10$

$p : \pm 1, \pm 2, \pm 5, \pm 10$

$q : \pm 1$

$\dfrac{p}{q} : \pm 1, \pm 2, \pm 5, \pm 10$

Since $f(x)$ has 2 sign variations, 0 or 2 positive
real zeros exist.

$f(-x) = -x^3 - 4x^2 + 7x + 10$

Since $f(-x)$ has 1 sign variation, exactly one
negative real zeros exists.

$$
\begin{array}{r|rrrr}
-2 & 1 & -4 & -7 & 10 \\
   &   & -2 & 12 & -10 \\
\hline
   & 1 & -6 & 5 & 0
\end{array}
$$

-2 is a zero.

$$f(x) = (x+2)(x^2 - 6x + 5)$$
$$= (x+2)(x-5)(x-1)$$

$x = -2, x = 5, x = 1$
The solution set is $\{-2, 5, 1\}$.

41. $2x^3 - x^2 - 9x - 4 = 0$

$p : \pm 1, \pm 2, \pm 4$

$q : \pm 1, \pm 2$

$\dfrac{p}{q} : \pm 1, \pm 2, \pm 4 \pm \dfrac{1}{2}$

1 positive real root exists.

$f(-x) = -2x^3 - x^2 + 9x - 4$ 2 or no negative real
roots exist.

$$
\begin{array}{r|rrrr}
-\dfrac{1}{2} & 2 & -1 & -9 & -4 \\
              &   & -1 & 1 & 4 \\
\hline
              & 2 & -2 & -8 & 0
\end{array}
$$

$-\dfrac{1}{2}$ is a root.

$$\left(x + \dfrac{1}{2}\right)(2x^2 - 2x - 8) = 0$$

$$2\left(x + \dfrac{1}{2}\right)(x^2 - x - 4) = 0$$

$$x = \dfrac{1 \pm \sqrt{1 + 16}}{2} = \dfrac{1 \pm \sqrt{17}}{2}$$

The solution set is
$$\left\{ -\dfrac{1}{2}, \dfrac{1 + \sqrt{17}}{2}, \dfrac{1 - \sqrt{17}}{2} \right\}.$$

43. $f(x) = x^4 - 2x^3 + x^2 + 12x + 8$

$p : \pm 1, \pm 2, \pm 4, \pm 8$

$q : \pm 1$

$\dfrac{p}{q} : \pm 1, \pm 2, \pm 4, \pm 8$

Since $f(x)$ has 2 sign changes, 0 or 2 positive
roots exist.

$f(-x) = (-x)^4 - 2(-x)^3 + (-x)^2 - 12x + 8$
$\quad = x^4 + 2x^3 + x^2 - 12x + 8$

Since $f(-x)$ has 2 sign changes, 0 or 2 negative
roots exist.

$$
\begin{array}{r|rrrrr}
-1 & 1 & -2 & 1 & 12 & 8 \\
   &   & -1 & 4 & -4 & -8 \\
\hline
   & 1 & -3 & 4 & 8 & 0
\end{array}
$$

$$
\begin{array}{r|rrrr}
-1 & 1 & -3 & 4 & 8 \\
   &   & -1 & 4 & -8 \\
\hline
   & 1 & -4 & 8 & 0
\end{array}
$$

$0 = x^2 - 4x + 8$

$x = \dfrac{-(-4) \pm \sqrt{(-4)^2 - 4(1)(8)}}{2(1)}$

$x = \dfrac{4 \pm \sqrt{16 - 32}}{2}$

$x = \dfrac{4 \pm \sqrt{-16}}{2}$

$x = \dfrac{4 \pm 4i}{2}$

$x = 2 \pm 2i$

The solution set is $\{-1, -1, 2 + 2i, 2 - 2i\}$.

45. $x^4 - 3x^3 - 20x^2 - 24x - 8 = 0$

$p: \pm 1, \pm 2, \pm 4, \pm 8$

$q: \pm 1$

$\dfrac{p}{q}: \pm 1, \pm 2, \pm 4 \pm 8$

1 positive real root exists.
3 or 1 negative real roots exist.

$$
\begin{array}{r|rrrrr}
-1 & 1 & -3 & -20 & -24 & -8 \\
   &   & -1 & 4 & 16 & 8 \\
\hline
   & 1 & -4 & -16 & -8 & 0
\end{array}
$$

$(x + 1)\left(x^3 - 4x^2 - 16x - 8\right) = 0$

$$
\begin{array}{r|rrrr}
-2 & 1 & -4 & -16 & -8 \\
   &   & -2 & 12 & 8 \\
\hline
   & 1 & -6 & -4 & 0
\end{array}
$$

$(x + 1)(x + 2)\left(x^2 - 6x - 4\right) = 0$

$x = \dfrac{6 \pm \sqrt{36 + 16}}{2} = \dfrac{6 \pm \sqrt{52}}{2}$

$= \dfrac{6 \pm 2\sqrt{13}}{2} = \dfrac{3 \pm \sqrt{13}}{2}$

The solution set is
$\left\{-1, -2, 3 \pm \sqrt{13}, 3 - \sqrt{13}\right\}$.

47. $f(x) = 3x^4 - 11x^3 - x^2 + 19x + 6$

$p: \pm 1, \pm 2, \pm 3, \pm 6$

$q: \pm 1, \pm 3$

$\dfrac{p}{q}: \pm 1, \pm 2, \pm 3, \pm 6, \pm \dfrac{1}{3}, \pm \dfrac{2}{3}$

2 or no positive real zeros exists.

$f(-x) = 3x^4 + 11x^3 - x^2 - 19x + 6$

2 or no negative real zeros exist.

$$
\begin{array}{r|rrrrr}
-1 & 3 & -11 & -1 & 19 & 6 \\
   &   & -3 & 14 & -13 & -6 \\
\hline
   & 3 & -14 & 13 & 6 & 0
\end{array}
$$

$f(x) = (x + 1)\left(3x^3 - 14x^2 + 13x + 6\right)$

$$
\begin{array}{r|rrrr}
2 & 3 & -14 & 13 & 6 \\
  &   & 6 & -16 & -6 \\
\hline
  & 3 & -8 & -3 & 0
\end{array}
$$

$f(x) = (x + 1)(x - 2)\left(3x^2 - 8x - 3\right)$

$= (x + 1)(x - 2)(3x + 1)(x - 3)$

$x = -1, \; x = 2 \; x = -\dfrac{1}{3}, \; x = 3$

The solution set is $\left\{-1, 2, -\dfrac{1}{3}, 3\right\}$.

49. $4x^4 - x^3 + 5x^2 - 2x - 6 = 0$

$p: \pm 1, \pm 2, \pm 3, \pm 6$

$q: \pm 1, \pm 2, \pm 4$

$\dfrac{p}{q}: \pm 1, \pm 2, \pm 3, \pm 6, \pm \dfrac{1}{2}, \pm \dfrac{3}{2}, \pm \dfrac{1}{4}, \pm \dfrac{3}{4}$

3 or 1 positive real roots exists.
1 negative real root exists.

$$
\begin{array}{r|rrrrr}
1 & 4 & -1 & 5 & -2 & -6 \\
  &   & 4 & 3 & 8 & 6 \\
\hline
  & 4 & 3 & 8 & 6 & 0
\end{array}
$$

$(x - 1)(4x^3 + 3x^2 + 8x + 6) = 0$

$4x^3 + 3x^2 + 8x + 6 = 0$ has no positive real roots.

$$
\begin{array}{r|rrrr}
-\frac{3}{4} & 4 & 3 & 8 & 6 \\
             &   & -3 & 0 & -6 \\
\hline
             & 4 & 0 & 8 & 0
\end{array}
$$

$(x - 1)\left(x + \dfrac{3}{4}\right)\left(4x^2 + 8\right) = 0$

$4(x - 1)\left(x + \dfrac{3}{4}\right)\left(x^2 + 2\right) = 0$

$x^2 + 2 = 0$

$x^2 = -2$

$x = \pm i\sqrt{2}$

The solution set is $\left\{1, -\dfrac{3}{4}, i\sqrt{2}, -i\sqrt{2}\right\}$.

231

51. $2x^5 + 7x^4 - 18x^2 - 8x + 8 = 0$

$p: \pm 1, \pm 2, \pm 4, \pm 8$

$q: \pm 1, \pm 2$

$\dfrac{p}{q}: \pm 1, \pm 2, \pm 4, \pm 8, \pm \dfrac{1}{2}$

2 or no positive real roots exists.

3 or 1 negative real root exist.

$$\begin{array}{r|rrrrrr} -2 & 2 & 7 & 0 & -18 & -8 & 8 \\ & & -4 & -6 & 12 & 12 & -8 \\ \hline & 2 & 3 & -6 & -6 & 4 & 0 \end{array}$$

$(x+2)(2x^4 + 3x^3 - 6x^2 - 6x + 4) = 0$

$4x^3 + 3x^2 + 8x + 6 = 0$ has no positive real roots.

$$\begin{array}{r|rrrrr} -2 & 2 & 3 & -6 & -6 & 4 \\ & & -4 & 2 & 8 & -4 \\ \hline & 2 & -1 & -4 & 2 & 0 \end{array}$$

$(x+2)^2 (2x^3 - x^2 - 4x + 2)$

$$\begin{array}{r|rrrr} \frac{1}{2} & 2 & -1 & -4 & 2 \\ & & 1 & 0 & 2 \\ \hline & 2 & 0 & -4 & 0 \end{array}$$

$(x+2)^2 \left(x - \dfrac{1}{2}\right)(2x^2 - 4) = 0$

$2(x+2)^2 \left(x - \dfrac{1}{2}\right)(x^2 - 2) = 0$

$x^2 - 2 = 0$

$x^2 = 2$

$x = \pm \sqrt{2}$

The solution set is $\left\{-2, \dfrac{1}{2}, \sqrt{2}, -\sqrt{2}\right\}$.

53. $f(x) = -x^3 + x^2 + 16x - 16$

a. From the graph provided, we can see that -4 is an x-intercept and is thus a zero of the function. We verify this below:

$$\begin{array}{r|rrrr} -4 & -1 & 1 & 16 & -16 \\ & & 4 & -20 & 16 \\ \hline & -1 & 5 & -4 & 0 \end{array}$$

Thus, $-x^3 + x^2 + 16x - 16 = 0$

$(x+4)(-x^2 + 5x - 4) = 0$

$-(x+4)(x^2 - 5x + 4) = 0$

$-(x+4)(x-1)(x-4) = 0$

$x + 4 = 0$ or $x - 1 = 0$ or $x - 4 = 0$

$x = -4$ $x = 1$ $x = 4$

The zeros are -4, 1, and 4.

b.

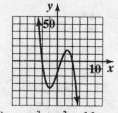

$$f(x) = -x^3 + x^2 + 16x - 16$$

55. $f(x) = 4x^3 - 8x^2 - 3x + 9$

a. From the graph provided, we can see that -1 is an x-intercept and is thus a zero of the function. We verify this below:

$$\begin{array}{r|rrrr} -1 & 4 & -8 & -3 & 9 \\ & & -4 & 12 & -9 \\ \hline & 4 & -12 & 9 & 0 \end{array}$$

Thus, $4x^3 - 8x^2 - 3x + 9 = 0$

$(x+1)(4x^2 - 12x + 9) = 0$

$(x+1)(2x-3)^2 = 0$

$x + 1 = 0$ or $(2x-3)^2 = 0$

$x = -1$ $2x - 3 = 0$

$2x = 3$

$x = \dfrac{3}{2}$

The zeros are -1 and $\dfrac{3}{2}$.

b.

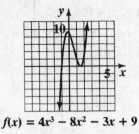

$f(x) = 4x^3 - 8x^2 - 3x + 9$

57. $f(x) = 2x^4 - 3x^3 - 7x^2 - 8x + 6$

a. From the graph provided, we can see that $\frac{1}{2}$
is an x-intercept and is thus a zero of the
function. We verify this below:

$$
\begin{array}{r|rrrrr}
\frac{1}{2} & 2 & -3 & -7 & -8 & 6 \\
  &   & 1 & -1 & -4 & -6 \\
\hline
  & 2 & -2 & -8 & -12 & 0 \\
\end{array}
$$

Thus, $2x^4 - 3x^3 - 7x^2 - 8x + 6 = 0$

$$\left(x - \frac{1}{2}\right)\left(2x^3 - 2x^2 - 8x - 12\right) = 0$$

$$2\left(x - \frac{1}{2}\right)\left(x^3 - x^2 - 4x - 6\right) = 0$$

To factor $x^3 - x^2 - 4x - 6$, we use the
Rational Zero Theorem to determine possible
rational zeros.

Factors of the constant term -6:
$\pm 1, \pm 2, \pm 3, \pm 6$

Factors of the leading coefficient 1: ± 1

The possible rational zeros are:

$$\frac{\text{Factors of } -6}{\text{Factors of } 1} = \frac{\pm 1, \pm 2, \pm 3, \pm 6}{\pm 1}$$

$$= \pm 1, \pm 2, \pm 3, \pm 6$$

We test values from above until we find a
zero. One possibility is shown next:

Test 3:

$$
\begin{array}{r|rrrr}
3 & 1 & -1 & -4 & -6 \\
  &   & 3 & 6 & 6 \\
\hline
  & 1 & 2 & 2 & 0 \\
\end{array}
$$

The remainder is 0, so 3 is a zero of f.

$$2x^4 - 3x^3 - 7x^2 - 8x + 6 = 0$$

$$\left(x - \frac{1}{2}\right)\left(2x^3 - 2x^2 - 8x - 12\right) = 0$$

$$2\left(x - \frac{1}{2}\right)\left(x^3 - x^2 - 4x - 6\right) = 0$$

$$2\left(x - \frac{1}{2}\right)(x - 3)\left(x^2 + 2x + 2\right) = 0$$

Note that $x^2 + x + 1$ will not factor, so we use
the quadratic formula:
$a = 1 \quad b = 2 \quad c = 2$

$$x = \frac{-2 \pm \sqrt{2^2 - 4(1)(2)}}{2(1)}$$

$$= \frac{-2 \pm \sqrt{-4}}{2} = \frac{-2 \pm 2i}{2} = -1 \pm i$$

The zeros are $\frac{1}{2}$, 3, and $-1 \pm i$.

b.

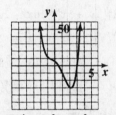

$f(x) = 2x^4 - 3x^3 - 7x^2 - 8x + 6$

59. $f(x) = 3x^5 + 2x^4 - 15x^3 - 10x^2 + 12x + 8$

a. From the graph provided, we can see that 1
and 2 are x-intercepts and are thus zeros of
the function. We verify this below:

$$
\begin{array}{r|rrrrrr}
1 & 3 & 2 & -15 & -10 & 12 & 8 \\
  &   & 3 & 5 & -10 & -20 & -8 \\
\hline
  & 3 & 5 & -10 & -20 & -8 & 0 \\
\end{array}
$$

Thus, $3x^5 + 2x^4 - 15x^3 - 10x^2 + 12x + 8$

$$= (x - 1)\left(3x^4 + 5x^3 - 10x^2 - 20x - 8\right)$$

$$
\begin{array}{r|rrrrr}
2 & 3 & 5 & -10 & -20 & -8 \\
  &   & 6 & 22 & 24 & 8 \\
\hline
  & 3 & 11 & 12 & 4 & 0 \\
\end{array}
$$

Thus, $3x^5 + 2x^4 - 15x^3 - 10x^2 + 12x + 8$

$$= (x - 1)\left(3x^4 + 5x^3 - 10x^2 - 20x - 8\right)$$

$$= (x - 1)(x - 2)\left(3x^3 + 11x^2 + 12x + 4\right)$$

To factor $3x^3 + 11x^2 + 12x + 4$, we use the
Rational Zero Theorem to determine possible
rational zeros.

233

Factors of the constant term 4:
$\pm 1, \ \pm 2, \ \pm 4$

Factors of the leading coefficient 3: $\pm 1, \ \pm 3$

The possible rational zeros are:

$$\frac{\text{Factors of } 4}{\text{Factors of } 3} = \frac{\pm 1, \ \pm 2, \ \pm 4}{\pm 1, \ \pm 3}$$

$$= \pm 1, \ \pm 2, \ \pm 4, \ \pm \frac{1}{3}, \ \pm \frac{2}{3}, \ \pm \frac{4}{3}$$

We test values from above until we find a zero. One possibility is shown next:

Test -1:

$$\begin{array}{r|rrrr} -1 & 3 & 11 & 12 & 4 \\ & & -3 & -8 & -4 \\ \hline & 3 & 8 & 4 & 0 \end{array}$$

The remainder is 0, so -1 is a zero of f. We can now finish the factoring:

$$3x^5 + 2x^4 - 15x^3 - 10x^2 + 12x + 8 = 0$$

$$(x-1)\left(3x^4 + 5x^3 - 10x^2 - 20x - 8\right) = 0$$

$$(x-1)(x-2)\left(3x^3 + 11x^2 + 12x + 4\right) = 0$$

$$(x-1)(x-2)(x+1)\left(3x^2 + 8x + 4\right) = 0$$

$$(x-1)(x-2)(x+1)(3x+2)(x+2) = 0$$

$$x = 1, \ x = 2, \ x = -1, \ x = -\frac{2}{3}, x = -2$$

The zeros are -2, -1, $-\dfrac{2}{3}$, 1 and 2.

b.

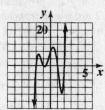

$$f(x) = 3x^5 + 2x^4 - 15x^3 - 10x^2 + 12x + 8$$

61. a. $f(x) = 27$, $x = 40$ People in the arts complete 27% of their work in their 40's.

   b.   The polynomial will have a degree 2 with a negative leading coefficient.

63. If you are 25, the equivalent age for dogs is 3 years.

65. Answers may vary.

---

67. $x(10 - 2x)(8 - 2x) = 48$

$$x(80 - 36x + 4x^2) = 48$$

$$4x^3 - 36x^2 + 80x - 48 = 0$$

$$x^3 - 9x^2 + 20x - 12 = 0$$

$$\begin{array}{r|rrrr} 2 & 1 & -9 & 20 & -12 \\ & & 2 & -14 & 12 \\ \hline & 1 & -7 & 6 & 0 \end{array}$$

$$(x-2)\left(x^2 - 7x + 6\right) = 0$$

$$(x-2)(x-6)(x-1) = 0$$

$$x = 2 \ \ x = 6 \ \ x = 1$$

If $x = 6$, $10 - 2x < 0$

$x = 1$ in. or $x = 2$ in.

77. $6x^3 - 19x^2 + 16x - 4 = 0$

$p: \pm 1, \pm 2, \pm 4$

$q: \pm 1, \pm 2, \pm 3, \pm 6$

$$\frac{p}{q}: \pm 1, \pm 2, \pm 4, \pm \frac{1}{2}, \pm \frac{1}{3}, \pm \frac{2}{3}, \pm \frac{4}{3}, \pm \frac{1}{6}$$

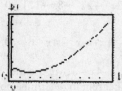

From the graph, we see that the solutions are $\dfrac{1}{2}, \dfrac{2}{3}$ and 2.

79. $4x^4 + 4x^3 + 7x^2 - x - 2 = 0$

$p: \pm 1, \pm 2$

$q: \pm 1, \pm 2, \pm 4$

$$\frac{p}{q}: \pm 1, \pm 2, \pm \frac{1}{2}, \pm \frac{1}{4}$$

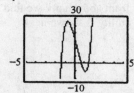

From the graph, we see that the solutions are $-\dfrac{1}{2}$ and $\dfrac{1}{2}$.

81. $f(x) = x^5 - x^4 + x^3 - x^2 + x - 8$

$f(x)$ has 5 sign variations, so either 5, 3, or 1 positive real roots exist.

$f(-x) = -x^5 - x^4 - x^3 - x^2 - x - 8$

$f(-x)$ has no sign variations, so no negative real roots exist.

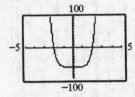

83. $f(x) = x^3 - 6x - 9$

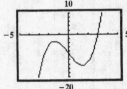

1 real zero
2 nonreal complex zeros

85. $f(x) = 3x^4 + 4x^3 - 7x^2 - 2x - 3$

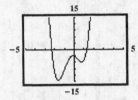

87. a. False; the equation has 0 sign variations, so no positive roots exist.

b. False; Descartes' Rule gives the maximum possible number of real roots.

c. False; every polynomial equation of degree 3 has at least one <u>real</u> root.

d. True

(d) is true.

89. $(2x+1)(x+5)(x+2) - 3x(x+5) = 208$

$(2x^2 + 11x + 5)(x+2) - 3x^2 - 15x = 208$

$2x^3 + 4x^2 + 11x^2 + 22x + 5x$

$+ 10 - 3x^2 - 15x = 208$

$2x^3 + 15x^2 + 27x - 3x^2 - 15x - 198 = 0$

$2x^3 + 12x^2 + 12x - 198 = 0$

$2(x^3 + 6x^2 + 6x - 99) = 0$

$$
\begin{array}{r|rrrr}
3 & 1 & 6 & 6 & -99 \\
  &   & 3 & 27 & 99 \\
\hline
  & 1 & 9 & 33 & 0 \\
\end{array}
$$

$x^2 + 9x + 33 = 0$

$b^2 - 4ac = -51$

$x = 3$ in.

91. Because the polynomial has two obvious changes of direction; the smallest degree is 3.

93. Because the polynomial has two obvious changes of direction and two roots have multiplicity 2, the smallest degree is 5.

95. Answers may vary.

Mid-Chapter 3 Check Point

1. $f(x) = (x-3)^2 - 4$

The parabola opens up because $a > 0$.
The vertex is $(3, -4)$.
x-intercepts:

$0 = (x-3)^2 - 4$

$(x-3)^2 = 4$

$x - 3 = \pm\sqrt{4}$

$x = 3 \pm 2$

The equation has x-intercepts at $x = 1$ and $x = 5$.
y-intercept:

$f(0) = (0-3)^2 - 4 = 5$

Domain: $(-\infty, \infty)$ Range: $[-4, \infty)$

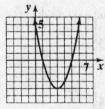

$f(x) = (x-3)^2 - 4$

2. $f(x) = 5 - (x+2)^2$

The parabola opens down because $a < 0$.

The vertex is $(-2, 5)$.

x-intercepts:

$$0 = 5 - (x+2)^2$$

$$(x+2)^2 = 5$$

$$x + 2 = \pm\sqrt{5}$$

$$x = -2 \pm \sqrt{5}$$

y-intercept:

$$f(0) = 5 - (0+2)^2 = 1$$

Domain: $(-\infty, \infty)$ Range: $(-\infty, 5]$

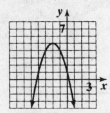

$f(x) = 5 - (x + 2)^2$

3. $f(x) = -x^2 - 4x + 5$

The parabola opens down because $a < 0$.

vertex: $x = -\dfrac{b}{2a} = -\dfrac{-4}{2(-1)} = -2$

$$f(-2) = -(-2)^2 - 4(-2) + 5 = 9$$

The vertex is $(-2, 9)$.

x-intercepts:

$$0 = -x^2 - 4x + 5$$

$$x = \frac{-b \pm \sqrt{b^2 - 4ac}}{2a}$$

$$x = \frac{-(-4) \pm \sqrt{(-4)^2 - 4(-1)(5)}}{2(-1)}$$

$$x = \frac{4 \pm \sqrt{36}}{-2}$$

$$x = -2 \pm 3$$

The x-intercepts are $x = 1$ and $x = -5$.

y-intercept:

$$f(0) = -0^2 - 4(0) + 5 = 5$$

Domain: $(-\infty, \infty)$ Range: $(-\infty, 9]$

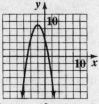

$f(x) = -x^2 - 4x + 5$

4. $f(x) = 3x^2 - 6x + 1$

The parabola opens up because $a > 0$.

vertex: $x = -\dfrac{b}{2a} = -\dfrac{-6}{2(3)} = 1$

$$f(1) = 3(1)^2 - 6(1) + 1 = -2$$

The vertex is $(1, -2)$.

x-intercepts:

$$0 = 3x^2 - 6x + 1$$

$$x = \frac{-b \pm \sqrt{b^2 - 4ac}}{2a}$$

$$x = \frac{-(-6) \pm \sqrt{(-6)^2 - 4(3)(1)}}{2(3)}$$

$$x = \frac{6 \pm \sqrt{24}}{6}$$

$$x = \frac{3 \pm \sqrt{6}}{3}$$

y-intercept:

$$f(0) = 3(0)^2 - 6(0) + 1 = 1$$

Domain: $(-\infty, \infty)$ Range: $[-2, \infty)$

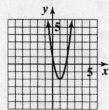

$f(x) = 3x^2 - 6x + 1$

5. $f(x) = (x-2)^2 (x+1)^3$

$$(x-2)^2 (x+1)^3 = 0$$

Apply the zero-product principle:

$(x-2)^2 = 0$ or $(x+1)^3 = 0$

$x - 2 = 0$ $x + 1 = 0$

$x = 2$ $x = -1$

The zeros are -1 and 2.

The graph of f crosses the x-axis at -1, since the zero has multiplicity 3. The graph touches the x-

axis and turns around at 2 since the zero has multiplicity 2.

Since f is an odd-degree polynomial, degree 5, and since the leading coefficient, 1, is positive, the graph falls to the left and rises to the right.

Plot additional points as necessary and construct the graph.

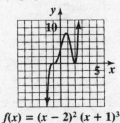

$f(x) = (x - 2)^2 (x + 1)^3$

6. $f(x) = -(x-2)^2 (x+1)^2$

$-(x-2)^2 (x+1)^2 = 0$

Apply the zero-product principle:

$(x-2)^2 = 0$ or $(x+1)^2 = 0$

$x-2 = 0$ $x+1 = 0$

$x = 2$ $x = -1$

The zeros are -1 and 2.

The graph touches the x-axis and turns around both at -1 and 2 since both zeros have multiplicity 2.

Since f is an even-degree polynomial, degree 4, and since the leading coefficient, -1, is negative, the graph falls to the left and falls to the right.

Plot additional points as necessary and construct the graph.

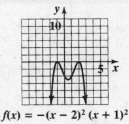

$f(x) = -(x - 2)^2 (x + 1)^2$

7. $f(x) = x^3 - x^2 - 4x + 4$

$x^3 - x^2 - 4x + 4 = 0$

$x^2 (x-1) - 4(x-1) = 0$

$(x^2 - 4)(x-1) = 0$

$(x+2)(x-2)(x-1) = 0$

Apply the zero-product principle:

$x+2 = 0$ or $x-2 = 0$ or $x-1 = 0$

$x = -2$ $x = 2$ $x = 1$

The zeros are -2, 1, and 2.

The graph of f crosses the x-axis at all three zeros, -2, 1, and 2, since all have multiplicity 1.

Since f is an odd-degree polynomial, degree 3, and since the leading coefficient, 1, is positive, the graph falls to the left and rises to the right.

Plot additional points as necessary and construct the graph.

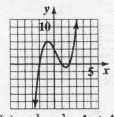

$f(x) = x^3 - x^2 - 4x + 4$

8. $f(x) = x^4 - 5x^2 + 4$

$x^4 - 5x^2 + 4 = 0$

$(x^2 - 4)(x^2 - 1) = 0$

$(x+2)(x-2)(x+1)(x-1) = 0$

Apply the zero-product principle,

$x = -2$, $x = 2$, $x = -1$, $x = 1$

The zeros are -2, -1, 1, and 2.

The graph crosses the x-axis at all four zeros, -2, -1, 1, and 2., since all have multiplicity 1.

Since f is an even-degree polynomial, degree 4, and since the leading coefficient, 1, is positive, the graph rises to the left and rises to the right.

Plot additional points as necessary and construct the graph.

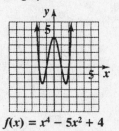

$f(x) = x^4 - 5x^2 + 4$

9. $f(x) = -(x+1)^6$

$-(x+1)^6 = 0$

$(x+1)^6 = 0$

$x+1 = 0$

$x = -1$

The zero is are -1.

The graph touches the x-axis and turns around at -1 since the zero has multiplicity 6.

Since f is an even-degree polynomial, degree 6, and since the leading coefficient, -1, is negative, the graph falls to the left and falls to the right.

Plot additional points as necessary and construct the graph.

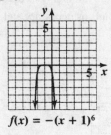

$f(x) = -(x+1)^6$

10. $f(x) = -6x^3 + 7x^2 - 1$

To find the zeros, we use the Rational Zero Theorem:

List all factors of the constant term -1: ± 1

List all factors of the leading coefficient -6: $\pm 1, \pm 2, \pm 3, \pm 6$

The possible rational zeros are:

$$\frac{\text{Factors of } -1}{\text{Factors of } -6} = \frac{\pm 1}{\pm 1, \pm 2, \pm 3, \pm 6}$$

$$= \pm 1, \pm \frac{1}{2}, \pm \frac{1}{3}, \pm \frac{1}{6}$$

We test values from the above list until we find a zero. One is shown next:

Test 1:

$$\begin{array}{r|rrrr} 1 & -6 & 7 & 0 & -1 \\ & & -6 & 1 & 1 \\ \hline & -6 & 1 & 1 & 0 \end{array}$$

The remainder is 0, so 1 is a zero. Thus,

$$-6x^3 + 7x^2 - 1 = 0$$

$$(x-1)(-6x^2 + x + 1) = 0$$

$$-(x-1)(6x^2 - x - 1) = 0$$

$$-(x-1)(3x+1)(2x-1) = 0$$

Apply the zero-product property:

$$x = 1, \quad x = -\frac{1}{3}, \quad x = \frac{1}{2}$$

The zeros are $-\frac{1}{3}$, $\frac{1}{2}$, and 1.

The graph of f crosses the x-axis at all three zeros, $-\frac{1}{3}$, $\frac{1}{2}$, and 1, since all have multiplicity 1.

Since f is an odd-degree polynomial, degree 3, and since the leading coefficient, -6, is negative, the graph rises to the left and falls to the right.

Plot additional points as necessary and construct the graph.

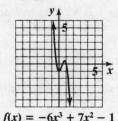

$f(x) = -6x^3 + 7x^2 - 1$

11. $f(x) = 2x^3 - 2x$

$$2x^3 - 2x = 0$$

$$2x(x^2 - 1) = 0$$

$$2x(x+1)(x-1) = 0$$

Apply the zero-product principle:

$$x = 0, \qquad x = -1, \qquad x = 1$$

The zeros are -1, 0, and 1.

The graph of f crosses the x-axis at all three zeros, -1, 0, and 1, since all have multiplicity 1.

Since f is an odd-degree polynomial, degree 3, and since the leading coefficient, 2, is positive, the graph falls to the left and rises to the right.

Plot additional points as necessary and construct the graph.

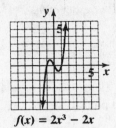

$f(x) = 2x^3 - 2x$

12. $f(x) = x^3 - 2x^2 + 26x$

$x^3 - 2x^2 + 26x = 0$

$x(x^2 - 2x + 26) = 0$

Note that $x^2 - 2x + 26$ does not factor, so we use the quadratic formula:

$x = 0$ or $x^2 - 2x + 26 = 0$

$a = 1, \ b = -2, \ c = 26$

$x = \dfrac{-(-2) \pm \sqrt{(-2)^2 - 4(1)(26)}}{2(1)}$

$= \dfrac{2 \pm \sqrt{-100}}{2} = \dfrac{2 \pm 10i}{2} = 1 \pm 5i$

The zeros are 0 and $1 \pm 5i$.

The graph of f crosses the x-axis at 0 (the only real zero), since it has multiplicity 1.

Since f is an odd-degree polynomial, degree 3, and since the leading coefficient, 1, is positive, the graph falls to the left and rises to the right.

Plot additional points as necessary and construct the graph.

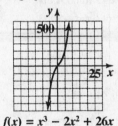

$f(x) = x^3 - 2x^2 + 26x$

13. $f(x) = -x^3 + 5x^2 - 5x - 3$

To find the zeros, we use the Rational Zero Theorem:
List all factors of the constant term -3:
$\pm 1, \ \pm 3$

List all factors of the leading coefficient -1:
± 1

The possible rational zeros are:

$\dfrac{\text{Factors of } -3}{\text{Factors of } -1} = \dfrac{\pm 1, \ \pm 3}{\pm 1} = \pm 1, \ \pm 3$

We test values from the previous list until we find a zero. One is shown next:

Test 3:

$$\begin{array}{r|rrrr} 3 & -1 & 5 & -5 & -3 \\ & & -3 & 6 & 3 \\ \hline & -1 & 2 & 1 & 0 \end{array}$$

The remainder is 0, so 3 is a zero. Thus,

$-x^3 + 5x^2 - 5x - 3 = 0$

$(x - 3)(-x^2 + 2x + 1) = 0$

$-(x - 3)(x^2 - 2x - 1) = 0$

Note that $x^2 - 2x - 1$ does not factor, so we use the quadratic formula:

$x - 3 = 0$ or $x^2 - 2x - 1 = 0$

$x = 3$ $a = 1, \ b = -2, \ c = -1$

$x = \dfrac{-(-2) \pm \sqrt{(-2)^2 - 4(1)(-1)}}{2(1)}$

$= \dfrac{2 \pm \sqrt{8}}{2} = \dfrac{2 \pm 2\sqrt{2}}{2} = 1 \pm \sqrt{2}$

The zeros are 3 and $1 \pm \sqrt{2}$.

The graph of f crosses the x-axis at all three zeros, 3 and $1 \pm \sqrt{2}$, since all have multiplicity 1.

Since f is an odd-degree polynomial, degree 3, and since the leading coefficient, -1, is negative, the graph rises to the left and falls to the right.

Plot additional points as necessary and construct the graph.

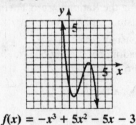

$f(x) = -x^3 + 5x^2 - 5x - 3$

239

14. $x^3 - 3x + 2 = 0$

We begin by using the Rational Zero Theorem to determine possible rational roots.

Factors of the constant term 2: $\pm 1, \pm 2$

Factors of the leading coefficient 1: ± 1

The possible rational zeros are:

$$\frac{\text{Factors of } 2}{\text{Factors of } 1} = \frac{\pm 1, \pm 2}{\pm 1} = \pm 1, \pm 2$$

We test values from above until we find a root. One is shown next:

Test 1:

$$\underline{1|}\ \ \begin{array}{rrrr} 1 & 0 & -3 & 2 \\ & 1 & 1 & -2 \\ \hline 1 & 1 & -2 & 0 \end{array}$$

The remainder is 0, so 1 is a root of the equation. Thus,

$$x^3 - 3x + 2 = 0$$
$$(x-1)(x^2 + x - 2) = 0$$
$$(x-1)(x+2)(x-1) = 0$$
$$(x-1)^2(x+2) = 0$$

Apply the zero-product property:

$(x-1)^2 = 0$ or $x + 2 = 0$

$x - 1 = 0$ $\qquad\qquad x = -2$

$x = 1$

The solutions are -2 and 1, and the solution set is $\{-2, 1\}$.

15. $6x^3 - 11x^2 + 6x - 1 = 0$

We begin by using the Rational Zero Theorem to determine possible rational roots.

Factors of the constant term -1: ± 1

Factors of the leading coefficient 6: $\pm 1, \pm 2, \pm 3, \pm 6$

The possible rational zeros are:

$$\frac{\text{Factors of } -1}{\text{Factors of } 6} = \frac{\pm 1}{\pm 1, \pm 2, \pm 3, \pm 6}$$
$$= \pm 1, \pm \frac{1}{2}, \pm \frac{1}{3}, \pm \frac{1}{6}$$

We test values from above until we find a root. One is shown next:

Test 1:

$$\underline{1|}\ \ \begin{array}{rrrr} 6 & -11 & 6 & -1 \\ & 6 & -5 & 1 \\ \hline 6 & -5 & 1 & 0 \end{array}$$

The remainder is 0, so 1 is a root of the equation. Thus,

$$6x^3 - 11x^2 + 6x - 1 = 0$$
$$(x-1)(6x^2 - 5x + 1) = 0$$
$$(x-1)(3x-1)(2x-1) = 0$$

Apply the zero-product property:

$x - 1 = 0$ or $3x - 1 = 0$ or $2x - 1 = 0$

$x = 1$ $\qquad x = \dfrac{1}{3}$ $\qquad x = \dfrac{1}{2}$

The solutions are $\dfrac{1}{3}, \dfrac{1}{2}$ and 1, and the solution set is $\left\{\dfrac{1}{3}, \dfrac{1}{2}, 1\right\}$.

16. $(2x+1)(3x-2)^3(2x-7) = 0$

Apply the zero-product property:

$2x + 1 = 0$ or $(3x-2)^3 = 0$ or $2x - 7 = 0$

$x = -\dfrac{1}{2}$ $\qquad 3x - 2 = 0$ $\qquad\qquad x = \dfrac{7}{2}$

$\qquad\qquad\qquad x = \dfrac{2}{3}$

The solutions are $-\dfrac{1}{2}, \dfrac{2}{3}$ and $\dfrac{7}{2}$, and the

solution set is $\left\{-\dfrac{1}{2}, \dfrac{2}{3}, \dfrac{7}{2}\right\}$.

17. $2x^3 + 5x^2 - 200x - 500 = 0$

We begin by using the Rational Zero Theorem to determine possible rational roots.

Factors of the constant term -500:

$\pm 1, \pm 2, \pm 4, \pm 5, \pm 10, \pm 20, \pm 25,$

$\pm 50, \pm 100, \pm 125, \pm 250, \pm 500$

Factors of the leading coefficient 2: $\pm 1, \pm 2$

The possible rational zeros are:

$$\frac{\text{Factors of } 500}{\text{Factors of } 2} = \pm 1, \pm 2, \pm 4, \pm 5,$$

$\pm 10, \pm 20, \pm 25, \pm 50, \pm 100, \pm 125,$

$\pm 250, \pm 500, \pm \dfrac{1}{2}, \pm \dfrac{5}{2}, \pm \dfrac{25}{2}, \pm \dfrac{125}{2}$

We test values from above until we find a root. One is shown next:

Test 10:

$$\underline{10|}\ \ \begin{array}{rrrr} 2 & 5 & -200 & -500 \\ & 20 & 250 & 500 \\ \hline 2 & 25 & 50 & 0 \end{array}$$

The remainder is 0, so 10 is a root of the equation. Thus,

$$2x^3 + 5x^2 - 200x - 500 = 0$$

$$(x-10)(2x^2 + 25x + 50) = 0$$

$$(x-10)(2x+5)(x+10) = 0$$

Apply the zero-product property:

$x - 10 = 0$ or $2x + 5 = 0$ or $x + 10 = 0$

$x = 10$ $x = -\dfrac{5}{2}$ $x = -10$

The solutions are -10, $-\dfrac{5}{2}$, and 10, and the

solution set is $\left\{-10,\ -\dfrac{5}{2},\ 10\right\}$.

18. $x^4 - x^3 - 11x^2 = x + 12$

$x^4 - x^3 - 11x^2 - x - 12 = 0$

We begin by using the Rational Zero Theorem to determine possible rational roots.

Factors of the constant term -12:
$\pm 1,\ \pm 2,\ \pm 3,\ \pm 4,\ \pm 6,\ \pm 12$

Factors of the leading coefficient 1: ± 1

The possible rational zeros are:

$$\dfrac{\text{Factors of } -12}{\text{Factors of } 1}$$

$$= \dfrac{\pm 1,\ \pm 2,\ \pm 3,\ \pm 4,\ \pm 6,\ \pm 12}{\pm 1}$$

$$= \pm 1,\ \pm 2,\ \pm 3,\ \pm 4,\ \pm 6,\ \pm 12$$

We test values from this list we find a root. One possibility is shown next:

Test -3:

$$\begin{array}{r|rrrrr}
-3 & 1 & -1 & -11 & -1 & -12 \\
   &   & -3 & 12 & -3 & 12 \\
\hline
   & 1 & -4 & 1 & -4 & 0
\end{array}$$

The remainder is 0, so -3 is a root of the equation. Using the Factor Theorem, we know that $x - 1$ is a factor. Thus,

$$x^4 - x^3 - 11x^2 - x - 12 = 0$$

$$(x+3)(x^3 - 4x^2 + x - 4) = 0$$

$$(x+3)\left[x^2(x-4) + 1(x-4)\right] = 0$$

$$(x+3)(x-4)(x^2+1) = 0$$

As this point we know that -3 and 4 are roots of the equation. Note that $x^2 + 1$ does not

factor, so we use the square-root principle:

$$x^2 + 1 = 0$$

$$x^2 = -1$$

$$x = \pm\sqrt{-1} = \pm i$$

The roots are -3, 4, and $\pm i$, and the solution set is $\{-3,\ 4,\ \pm i\}$.

19. $2x^4 + x^3 - 17x^2 - 4x + 6 = 0$

We begin by using the Rational Zero Theorem to determine possible rational roots.

Factors of the constant term 6:
$\pm 1,\ \pm 2,\ \pm 3,\ \pm 6$

Factors of the leading coefficient 4: $\pm 1,\ \pm 2$

The possible rational roots are:

$$\dfrac{\text{Factors of } 6}{\text{Factors of } 2} = \dfrac{\pm 1,\ \pm 2,\ \pm 3,\ \pm 6}{\pm 1,\ \pm 2}$$

$$= \pm 1,\ \pm 2,\ \pm 3,\ \pm 6,\ \pm\dfrac{1}{2},\ \pm\dfrac{3}{2}$$

We test values from above until we find a root. One possibility is shown next:

Test -3:

$$\begin{array}{r|rrrrr}
-3 & 2 & 1 & -17 & -4 & 6 \\
   &   & -6 & 15 & 6 & -6 \\
\hline
   & 2 & -5 & -2 & 2 & 0
\end{array}$$

The remainder is 0, so -3 is a root. Using the Factor Theorem, we know that $x + 3$ is a factor of the polynomial. Thus,

$$2x^4 + x^3 - 17x^2 - 4x + 6 = 0$$

$$(x+3)(2x^3 - 5x^2 - 2x + 2) = 0$$

To solve the equation above, we need to factor $2x^3 - 5x^2 - 2x + 2$. We continue testing potential roots:

Test $\dfrac{1}{2}$:

$$\begin{array}{r|rrrr}
\frac{1}{2} & 2 & -5 & -2 & 2 \\
            &   & 1 & -2 & -2 \\
\hline
            & 2 & -4 & -4 & 0
\end{array}$$

The remainder is 0, so $\dfrac{1}{2}$ is a zero and $x - \dfrac{1}{2}$ is a factor.

Summarizing our findings so far, we have

$$2x^4 + x^3 - 17x^2 - 4x + 6 = 0$$

$$(x+3)(2x^3 - 5x^2 - 2x + 2) = 0$$

$$(x+3)\left(x - \frac{1}{2}\right)(2x^2 - 4x - 4) = 0$$

$$2(x+3)\left(x - \frac{1}{2}\right)(x^2 - 2x - 2) = 0$$

At this point, we know that -3 and $\frac{1}{2}$ are roots of the equation. Note that $x^2 - 2x - 2$ does not factor, so we use the quadratic formula:

$$x^2 - 2x - 2 = 0$$

$$a = 1, \quad b = -2, \quad c = -2$$

$$x = \frac{-(-2) \pm \sqrt{(-2)^2 - 4(1)(-2)}}{2(1)}$$

$$= \frac{2 \pm \sqrt{4+8}}{2} = \frac{2 \pm \sqrt{12}}{2} = \frac{2 \pm 2\sqrt{3}}{2} = 1 \pm \sqrt{3}$$

The solutions are -3, $\frac{1}{2}$, and $1 \pm \sqrt{3}$, and the

solution set is $\left\{-3, \; \frac{1}{2}, \; 1 \pm \sqrt{3}\right\}$.

20. $P(x) = -x^2 + 150x - 4425$

Since $a = -1$ is negative, we know the function opens down and has a maximum at

$$x = -\frac{b}{2a} = -\frac{150}{2(-1)} = -\frac{150}{-2} = 75.$$

$$P(75) = -75^2 + 150(75) - 4425$$

$$= -5625 + 11,250 - 4425 = 1200$$

The company will maximize its profit by manufacturing and selling 75 cabinets per day. The maximum daily profit is $1200.

21. Let x = one of the numbers;
$-18 - x$ = the other number
The product is $f(x) = x(-18 - x) = -x^2 - 18x$
The x-coordinate of the maximum is

$$x = -\frac{b}{2a} = -\frac{-18}{2(-1)} = -\frac{-18}{-2} = -9.$$

$$f(-9) = -9\left[-18 - (-9)\right]$$

$$= -9(-18 + 9) = -9(-9) = 81$$

The vertex is $(-9, 81)$. The maximum product is 81. This occurs when the two number are -9 and $-18 - (-9) = -9$.

22. Let x = height of triangle;
$40 - 2x$ = base of triangle

$$A = \frac{1}{2}bh = \frac{1}{2}x(40 - 2x)$$

$$A(x) = 20x - x^2$$

The height at which the triangle will have

maximum area is $x = -\frac{b}{2a} = -\frac{20}{2(-1)} = 10.$

$$A(10) = 20(10) - (10)^2 = 100$$

The maximum area is 100 squares inches.

23.
$$\begin{array}{r} 2x^2 - x - 3 \\ 3x^2 - 1 \overline{)6x^4 - 3x^3 - 11x^2 + 2x + 4} \end{array}$$

$$\begin{array}{r} 6x^4 \quad\quad -2x^2 \\ \hline -3x^3 - 9x^2 + 2x \\ -3x^3 \quad\quad + x \\ \hline -9x^2 + x + 4 \\ -9x^2 \quad\quad + 3 \\ \hline x + 1 \end{array}$$

$$2x^2 - x - 3 + \frac{x+1}{3x^2 - 1}$$

24. $\left(2x^4 - 13x^3 + 17x^2 + 18x - 24\right) \div (x - 4)$

$$\begin{array}{c|ccccc} 4 & 2 & -13 & 17 & 18 & -24 \\ & & 8 & -20 & -12 & 24 \\ \hline & 2 & -5 & -3 & 6 & 0 \end{array}$$

The quotient is $2x^3 - 5x^2 - 3x + 6$.

25. $(x-1)(x-i)(x+i) = (x-1)(x^2+1)$

$$f(x) = a_n(x-1)(x^2+1)$$

$$f(-1) = a_n(-1-1)\left((-1)^2 + 1\right) = -4a_n = 8$$

$$a_n = -2$$

$$f(x) = -2(x-1)(x^2+1) \text{ or } -2x^3 + 2x^2 - 2x + 2$$

26. $(x-2)(x-2)(x-3i)(x+3i)$

$$= (x-2)(x-2)(x^2+9)$$

$$f(x) = a_n(x-2)(x-2)(x^2+9)$$

$$f(0) = a_n(0-2)(0-2)(0^2+9)$$

$$36 = 36a_n$$

$$a_n = 1$$

$$f(x) = 1(x-2)(x-2)(x^2+9)$$

$$f(x) = x^4 - 4x^3 + 13x^2 - 36x + 36$$

27. $f(x) = x^3 - x - 5$

$f(1) = 1^3 - 1 - 5 = -5$

$f(2) = 2^3 - 2 - 5 = 1$

Yes, the function must have a real zero between 1 and 2 because $f(1)$ and $f(2)$ have opposite signs.

Section 3.5

Check Point Exercises

1. **a.** $x - 5 = 0$

$x = 5$

$\{x \mid x \neq 5\}$

b. $x^2 - 25 = 0$

$x^2 = 25$

$x = \pm 5$

$\{x \mid x \neq 5, x \neq -5\}$

c. The denominator cannot equal zero. All real numbers.

2. **a.** $x^2 - 1 = 0$

$x^2 = 1$

$x = 1, x = -1$

b. $g(x) = \dfrac{x-1}{x^2-1} = \dfrac{x-1}{(x-1)(x+1)} = \dfrac{1}{x+1}$

$x = -1$

c. The denominator cannot equal zero. No vertical asymptotes.

3. **a.** Since $n = m$, $y = \dfrac{9}{3} = 3$

$y = 3$ is a horizontal asymptote.

b. Since $n < m$, $y = 0$ is a horizontal asymptote.

c. Since $n > m$, there is no horizontal asymptote.

4. Begin with the graph of $f(x) = \dfrac{1}{x}$.

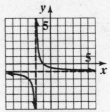

$$g(x) = \frac{1}{x+2} - 1$$

Shift the graph 2 units to the left by subtracting 2 from each x-coordinate. Shift the graph 1 unit down by subtracting 1 from each y-coordinate.

5. $f(x) = \dfrac{3x}{x-2}$

$f(-x) = \dfrac{3(-x)}{-x-2} = \dfrac{3x}{x+2}$

no symmetry

$f(0) = \dfrac{3(0)}{0-2} = 0$

The y-intercept is 0.

$3x = 0$

$x = 0$

The x-intercept is 0.

Vertical asymptote:

$x - 2 = 0$

$x = 2$

Horizontal asymptote:

$y = \dfrac{3}{1} = 3$

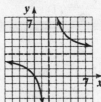

$$f(x) = \frac{3x}{x-2}$$

6. $f(x) = \dfrac{2x^2}{x^2 - 9}$

$f(-x) = \dfrac{2(-x)^2}{(-x)^2 - 9} = \dfrac{2x^2}{x^2 - 9} = f(x)$

The y-axis symmetry.

$f(0) = \dfrac{2(0)^2}{0^2 - 9} = 0$

The y-intercept is 0.

$2x^2 = 0$

$x = 0$

The x-intercept is 0.

vertical asymptotes:

$x^2 - 9 = 0$

$x = 3, x = -3$

horizontal asymptote:

$y = \dfrac{2}{1} = 2$

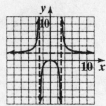

$f(x) = \dfrac{2x^2}{x^2 - 9}$

7. $f(x) = \dfrac{x^4}{x^2 + 2}$

$f(-x) = \dfrac{(-x)^4}{(-x)^2 + 2} = \dfrac{x^4}{x^2 + 2} = f(x)$

y-axis symmetry

$f(0) = \dfrac{0^4}{0^2 + 2} = 0$

The y-intercept is 0.

$x^4 = 0$

$x = 0$

The x-intercept is 0.

vertical asymptotes:

$x^2 + 2 = 0$

$x^2 = -2$

no vertical asymptotes

horizontal asymptote:

Since $n > m$, there is no horizontal asymptote.

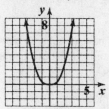

$f(x) = \dfrac{x^4}{x^2 + 2}$

8.

$$
\begin{array}{r|rrr}
2 & 2 & -5 & 7 \\
  &   & 4 & -2 \\
\hline
  & 2 & -1 & 5
\end{array}
$$

the equation of the slant asymptote is
$y = 2x - 1$.

9.   **a.** $C(x) = 500x + 600,000$

   b. $\overline{C}(x) = \dfrac{500x + 600,000}{x}$

   c. $\overline{C}(1000) = \dfrac{500(1000) + 600,000}{1000} = 1100$

The cost per computer to replace 1000 computers would be \$1100.

$\overline{C}(10000) = \dfrac{500(10000) + 600,000}{10000} = 560$

The cost per computer to replace 10,000 computers would be \$560.

$\overline{C}(100,000) = \dfrac{500(100,000) + 600,000}{100,000}$
$= 506$

The cost per computer to replace 100,000 computers would be \$506.

   d. $y = 500$
The more computers the company replaces, the closer the average cost comes to \$500.

244

Exercise Set 3.5

1. $f(x) = \dfrac{5x}{x-4}$

$\{x \mid x \neq 4\}$

3. $g(x) = \dfrac{3x^2}{(x-5)(x+4)}$

$\{x \mid x \neq 5, x \neq -4\}$

5. $h(x) = \dfrac{x+7}{x^2-49}$

$x^2 - 49 = (x-7)(x+7)$

$\{x \mid x \neq 7, x \neq -7\}$

7. $f(x) = \dfrac{x+7}{x^2+49}$

all real numbers

9. $-\infty$

11. $-\infty$

13. 0

15. $+\infty$

17. $-\infty$

19. 1

21. $f(x) = \dfrac{x}{x+4}$

$x + 4 = 0$

$x = -4$

vertical asymptote: $x = -4$

23. $g(x) = \dfrac{x+3}{x(x+4)}$

$x(x+4) = 0$

$x = 0, x = -4$

vertical asymptotes: $x = 0$, $x = -4$

25. $h(x) = \dfrac{x}{x(x+4)} = \dfrac{1}{x+4}$

$x + 4 = 0$

$x = -4$

vertical asymptote: $x = -4$

27. $r(x) = \dfrac{x}{x^2+4}$

$x^2 + 4$ has no real zeros

There are no vertical asymptotes.

29. $f(x) = \dfrac{12x}{3x^2+1}$

$n < m$

horizontal asymptote: $y = 0$

31. $g(x) = \dfrac{12x^2}{3x^2+1}$

$n = m,$

horizontal asymptote: $y = \dfrac{12}{3} = 4$

33. $h(x) = \dfrac{12x^3}{3x^2+1}$

$n > m$

no horizontal asymptote

35. $f(x) = \dfrac{-2x+1}{3x+5}$

$n = m$

horizontal asymptote: $y = -\dfrac{2}{3}$

37. $g(x) = \dfrac{1}{x-1}$

Shift the graph of $f(x) = \dfrac{1}{x}$ 1 unit to the right.

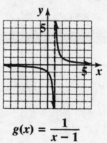

$g(x) = \dfrac{1}{x-1}$

39. $h(x) = \dfrac{1}{x} + 2$

Shift the graph of $f(x) = \dfrac{1}{x}$ 2 units up.

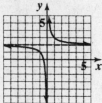

$$h(x) = \frac{1}{x} + 2$$

41. $g(x) = \dfrac{1}{x+1} - 2$

Shift the graph of $f(x) = \dfrac{1}{x}$ 1 unit left and 2 units down.

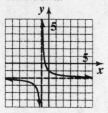

$$g(x) = \frac{1}{x+1} - 2$$

43. $g(x) = \dfrac{1}{(x+2)^2}$

Shift the graph of $f(x) = \dfrac{1}{x^2}$ 2 units left.

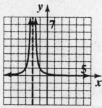

$$g(x) = \frac{1}{(x+2)^2}$$

45. $h(x) = \dfrac{1}{x^2} - 4$

Shift the graph of $f(x) = \dfrac{1}{x^2}$ 4 units down.

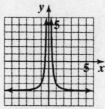

$$h(x) = \frac{1}{x^2} - 4$$

47. $h(x) = \dfrac{1}{(x-3)^2} + 1$

Shift the graph of $f(x) = \dfrac{1}{x^2}$ 3 units right and 1 unit up.

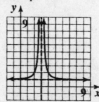

$$h(x) = \frac{1}{(x-3)^2} + 1$$

49. $f(x) = \dfrac{4x}{x-2}$

$$f(-x) = \frac{4(-x)}{(-x)-2} = \frac{4x}{x+2}$$

$$f(-x) \neq f(x), f(-x) \neq -f(x)$$

no symmetry

y-intercept: $y = \dfrac{4(0)}{0-2} = 0$

x-intercept: $4x = 0$

$x = 0$

vertical asymptote:

$x - 2 = 0$

$\quad x = 2$

horizontal asymptote:

$n = m$, so $y = \dfrac{4}{1} = 4$

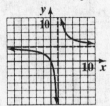

$$f(x) = \dfrac{4x}{x-2}$$

51. $f(x) = \dfrac{2x}{x^2 - 4}$

$f(-x) = \dfrac{2(-x)}{(-x)^2 - 4} = -\dfrac{2x}{x^2 - 4} = -f(x)$

Origin symmetry

y-intercept: $\dfrac{2(0)}{0^2 - 4} = \dfrac{0}{-4} = 0$

x-intercept:
$2x = 0$
$x = 0$

vertical asymptotes:
$x^2 - 4 = 0$
$x = \pm 2$

horizontal asymptote:
$n < m$ so $y = 0$

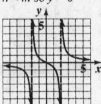

$$f(x) = \dfrac{2x}{x^2 - 4}$$

53. $f(x) = \dfrac{2x^2}{x^2 - 1}$

$f(-x) = \dfrac{2(-x)^2}{(-x)^2 - 1} = \dfrac{2x^2}{x^2 - 1} = f(x)$

y-axis symmetry

y-intercept: $y = \dfrac{2(0)^2}{0^2 - 1} = \dfrac{0}{1} = 0$

x-intercept:
$2x^2 = 0$
$x = 0$

vertical asymptote:
$x^2 - 1 = 0$
$x^2 = 1$
$x = \pm 1$

horizontal asymptote:

$n = m$, so $y = \dfrac{2}{1} = 2$

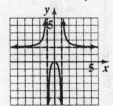

$$f(x) = \dfrac{2x^2}{x^2 - 1}$$

55. $f(x) = \dfrac{-x}{x + 1}$

$f(-x) = \dfrac{-(-x)}{(-x) + 1} = \dfrac{x}{-x + 1}$

$f(-x) \neq f(x), f(-x) \neq -f(x)$
no symmetry

y-intercept: $y = \dfrac{-(0)}{0 + 1} = \dfrac{0}{1} = 0$

x-intercept:
$-x = 0$
$x = 0$

vertical asymptote:
$x + 1 = 0$
$x = -1$

horizontal asymptote:

$n = m$, so $y = \dfrac{-1}{1} = -1$

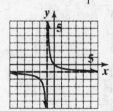

$$f(x) = \dfrac{-x}{x + 1}$$

247

57. $f(x) = -\dfrac{1}{x^2 - 4}$

$f(-x) = -\dfrac{1}{(-x)^2 - 4} = -\dfrac{1}{x^2 - 4} = f(x)$

y-axis symmetry

y-intercept: $y = -\dfrac{1}{0^2 - 4} = \dfrac{1}{4}$

x-intercept: $-1 \neq 0$
no x-intercept
vertical asymptotes:

$x^2 - 4 = 0$
$\quad x^2 = 4$
$\quad\quad x = \pm 2$

horizontal asymptote:
$n < m$ or $y = 0$

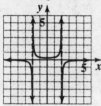

$f(x) = -\dfrac{1}{x^2 - 4}$

59. $f(x) = \dfrac{2}{x^2 + x - 2}$

$f(-x) = -\dfrac{2}{(-x)^2 - x - 2} = \dfrac{2}{x^2 - x - 2}$

$f(-x) \neq f(x), f(-x) \neq -f(x)$
no symmetry

y-intercept: $y = \dfrac{2}{0^2 + 0 - 2} = \dfrac{2}{-2} = -1$

x-intercept: none
vertical asymptotes:

$\quad x^2 + x - 2 = 0$
$(x + 2)(x - 1) = 0$
$x = -2, x = 1$

horizontal asymptote:
$n < m$ so $y = 0$

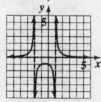

$f(x) = \dfrac{2}{x^2 + x - 2}$

61. $f(x) = \dfrac{2x^2}{x^2 + 4}$

$f(-x) = \dfrac{2(-x)^2}{(-x)^2 + 4} = \dfrac{2x^2}{x^2 + 4} = f(x)$

y axis symmetry

y-intercept: $y = \dfrac{2(0)^2}{0^2 + 4} = 0$

x-intercept: $2x^2 = 0$
$x = 0$
vertical asymptote: none
horizontal asymptote:

$n = m$, so $y = \dfrac{2}{1} = 2$

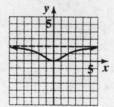

$f(x) = \dfrac{2x^2}{x^2 + 4}$

63. $f(x) = \dfrac{x + 2}{x^2 + x - 6}$

$f(-x) = \dfrac{-x + 2}{(-x)^2 - (-x) - 6} = \dfrac{-x + 2}{x^2 + x - 6}$

$f(-x) \neq f(x), f(-x) \neq -f(x)$
no symmetry

y-intercept: $y = \dfrac{0 + 2}{0^2 + 0 - 6} = -\dfrac{2}{6} = -\dfrac{1}{3}$

x-intercept:
$x + 2 = 0$
$x = -2$
vertical asymptotes:
$x^2 + x - 6 = 0$
$(x + 3)(x - 2)$
$x = -3, x = 2$

horizontal asymptote:
$n < m$, so $y = 0$

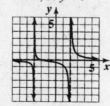

$f(x) = \dfrac{x + 2}{x^2 + x - 6}$

248

65. $f(x) = \dfrac{x^4}{x^2 + 2}$

$f(-x) = \dfrac{(-x)^4}{(-x)^2 + 2} = \dfrac{x^4}{x^2 + 2} = f(x)$

y-axis symmetry

y-intercept: $y = \dfrac{0^4}{0^2 + 2} = 0$

x-intercept: $x^4 = 0$
$x = 0$

vertical asymptote: none
horizontal asymptote:
$n > m$, so none

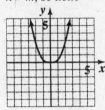

$$f(x) = \dfrac{x^4}{x^2 + 2}$$

67. $f(x) = \dfrac{x^2 + x - 12}{x^2 - 4}$

$f(-x) = \dfrac{(-x)^2 - x - 12}{(-x)^2 - 4} = \dfrac{x^2 - x - 12}{x^2 - 4}$

$f(-x) \neq f(x), f(-x) \neq -f(x)$

no symmetry

y-intercept: $y = \dfrac{0^2 + 0 - 12}{0^2 - 4} = 3$

x-intercept: $x^2 + x - 12 = 0$
$\qquad\qquad (x - 3)(x + 4) = 0$
$\qquad\qquad\qquad x = 3, x = -4$

vertical asymptotes:
$\qquad x^2 - 4 = 0$
$(x - 2)(x + 2) = 0$
$\qquad\qquad x = 2, x = -2$

horizontal asymptote:
$n = m$, so $y = \dfrac{1}{1} = 1$

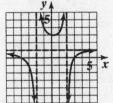

$$f(x) = \dfrac{x^2 + x - 12}{x^2 - 4}$$

69. $f(x) = \dfrac{3x^2 + x - 4}{2x^2 - 5x}$

$f(-x) = \dfrac{3(-x)^2 - x - 4}{2(-x)^2 + 5x} = \dfrac{3x^2 - x - 4}{2x^2 + 5x}$

$f(-x) \neq f(x), f(-x) \neq -f(x)$

no symmetry

y-intercept: $y = \dfrac{3(0)^2 + 0 - 4}{2(0)^2 - 5(0)} = \dfrac{-4}{0}$

no y-intercept
x-intercepts:
$\qquad\qquad 3x^2 + x - 4 = 0$
$\qquad\quad (3x + 4)(x - 1) = 0$
$\qquad 3x + 4 = 0 \ \ x - 1 = 0$
$\qquad\qquad 3x = -4$
$\qquad\qquad\qquad x = -\dfrac{4}{3}, x = 1$

vertical asymptotes:
$2x^2 - 5x = 0$
$x(2x - 5) = 0$
$x = 0, 2x = 5$
$\qquad\quad x = \dfrac{5}{2}$

horizontal asymptote:
$n = m$, so $y = \dfrac{3}{2}$

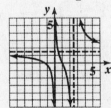

$$f(x) = \dfrac{3x^2 + x - 4}{2x^2 - 5x}$$

71. a. Slant asymptote:

$$f(x) = x - \frac{1}{x}$$

$$y = x$$

b. $f(x) = \dfrac{x^2 - 1}{x}$

$$f(-x) = \frac{(-x)^2 - 1}{(-x)} = \frac{x^2 - 1}{-x} = -f(x)$$

Origin symmetry

y-intercept: $y = \dfrac{0^2 - 1}{0} = \dfrac{-1}{0}$

no y-intercept

x-intercepts: $x^2 - 1 = 0$

$x = \pm 1$

vertical asymptote: $x = 0$

horizontal asymptote:

$n < m$, so none exist.

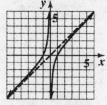

$$f(x) = \frac{x^2 - 1}{x}$$

73. a. Slant asymptote:

$$f(x) = x + \frac{1}{x}$$

$$y = x$$

b. $f(x) = \dfrac{x^2 + 1}{x}$

$$f(-x) = \frac{(-x)^2 + 1}{-x} = \frac{x^2 + 1}{-x} = -f(x)$$

Origin symmetry

y-intercept: $y = \dfrac{0^2 + 1}{0} = \dfrac{1}{0}$

no y-intercept

x-intercept:

$x^2 + 1 = 0$

$x^2 = -1$

no x-intercept

vertical asymptote: $x = 0$

horizontal asymptote:

$n > m$, so none exist.

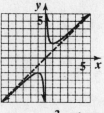

$$f(x) = \frac{x^2 + 1}{x}$$

75. a. Slant asymptote:

$$f(x) = x + 4 + \frac{6}{x - 3}$$

$$y = x + 4$$

b. $f(x) = \dfrac{x^2 + x - 6}{x - 3}$

$$f(-x) = \frac{(-x)^2 + (-x) - 6}{-x - 3} = \frac{x^2 - x - 6}{-x - 3}$$

$f(-x) \neq g(x)$, $g(-x) \neq -g(x)$

No symmetry

y-intercept: $y = \dfrac{0^2 + 0 - 6}{0 - 3} = \dfrac{-6}{-3} = 2$

x-intercept:

$x^2 + x - 6 = 0$

$(x + 3)(x - 2) = 0$

$x = -3$ and $x = 2$

vertical asymptote:

$x - 3 = 0$

$x = 3$

horizontal asymptote:

$n > m$, so none exist.

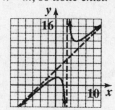

$$f(x) = \frac{x^2 + x - 6}{x - 3}$$

250

77. $f(x) = \dfrac{x^3 + 1}{x^2 + 2x}$

  a. slant asymptote:

$$\begin{array}{r} x-2 \\ x^2+2x\overline{\big)x^3\quad\quad+1} \\ \underline{x^3+2x^2} \\ -2x^2 \\ \underline{-2x^2+4x} \\ -4x+1 \end{array}$$

$$y = x - 2$$

  b. $f(-x) = \dfrac{(-x)^3 + 1}{(-x)^2 + 2(-x)} = \dfrac{-x^3 + 1}{x^2 - 2x}$

$$f(-x) \neq f(x), \; f(-x) \neq -f(x)$$

no symmetry

y-intercept: $y = \dfrac{0^3 + 1}{0^2 + 2(0)} = \dfrac{1}{0}$

no y-intercept

x-intercept: $x^3 + 1 = 0$

$$x^3 = -1$$

$$x = -1$$

vertical asymptotes:

$$x^2 + 2x = 0$$

$$x(x + 2) = 0$$

$$x = 0, \; x = -2$$

horizontal asymptote:

$n > m$, so none

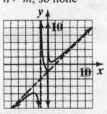

$$f(x) = \dfrac{x^3 + 1}{x^2 + 2x}$$

79. $\dfrac{5x^2}{x^2 - 4} \cdot \dfrac{x^2 + 4x + 4}{10x^3}$

$$= \dfrac{\cancel{5}\, \cancel{x^2}}{(x+2)(x-2)} \cdot \dfrac{(x+2)^{\cancel{2}}}{\cancel{10}\, x^{\cancel{3}1}}_{2}$$

$$= \dfrac{x + 2}{2x(x - 2)}$$

So, $f(x) = \dfrac{x + 2}{2x(x - 2)}$

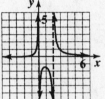

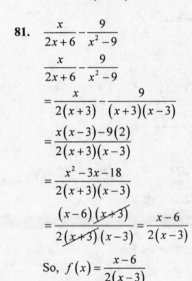

$$f(x) = \dfrac{x + 2}{2x(x - 2)}$$

81. $\dfrac{x}{2x + 6} - \dfrac{9}{x^2 - 9}$

$$\dfrac{x}{2x + 6} - \dfrac{9}{x^2 - 9}$$

$$= \dfrac{x}{2(x+3)} - \dfrac{9}{(x+3)(x-3)}$$

$$= \dfrac{x(x-3) - 9(2)}{2(x+3)(x-3)}$$

$$= \dfrac{x^2 - 3x - 18}{2(x+3)(x-3)}$$

$$= \dfrac{(x-6)\cancel{(x+3)}}{2\cancel{(x+3)}(x-3)} = \dfrac{x-6}{2(x-3)}$$

So, $f(x) = \dfrac{x - 6}{2(x - 3)}$

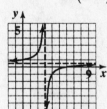

$$f(x) = \dfrac{x - 6}{2(x - 3)}$$

83.

$$\frac{1-\dfrac{3}{x+2}}{1+\dfrac{1}{x-2}} = \frac{1-\dfrac{3}{x+2}}{1+\dfrac{1}{x-2}} \cdot \frac{(x+2)(x-2)}{(x+2)(x-2)}$$

$$= \frac{(x+2)(x-2)-3(x-2)}{(x+2)(x-2)+(x+2)}$$

$$= \frac{x^2-4-3x+6}{x^2-4+x+2}$$

$$= \frac{x^2-3x+2}{x^2+x-2}$$

$$= \frac{(x-2)(x-1)}{(x+2)(x-1)} = \frac{x-2}{x+2}$$

So, $f(x) = \dfrac{x-2}{x+2}$

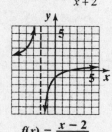

$$f(x) = \frac{x-2}{x+2}$$

85. $g(x) = \dfrac{2x+7}{x+3} = \dfrac{1}{x+3} + 2$

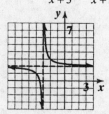

$$f(x) = \frac{1}{x+3} + 2$$

87. $g(x) = \dfrac{3x-7}{x-2} = \dfrac{-1}{x-2} + 3$

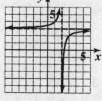

$$f(x) = \frac{-1}{x-2} + 3$$

89. a. $C(x) = 100x + 100,000$

b. $\overline{C}(x) = \dfrac{100x + 100,000}{x}$

c. $\overline{C}(500) = \dfrac{100(500) + 100,000}{500} = \$300$

When 500 bicycles are manufactured, it costs \$300 to manufacture each.

$\overline{C}(1000) = \dfrac{100(1000) + 100,000}{1000} = \$200$

When 1000 bicycles are manufactured, it costs \$200 to manufacture each.

$\overline{C}(2000) = \dfrac{100(2000) + 100,000}{2000} = \$150$

When 2000 bicycles are manufactured, it costs \$150 to manufacture each.

$\overline{C}(4000) = \dfrac{100(4000) + 100,000}{4000} = \$125$

When 4000 bicycles are manufactured, it costs \$125 to manufacture each.
The average cost decreases as the number of bicycles manufactured increases.

d. $n = m$, so $y = \dfrac{100}{1} = 100$.

As greater numbers of bicycles are manufactured, the average cost approaches \$100.

91. a. From the graph the pH level of the human mouth 42 minutes after a person eats food containing sugar will be about 6.0.

b. From the graph, the pH level is lowest after about 6 minutes.

$$f(6) = \frac{6.5(6)^2 - 20.4(6) + 234}{6^2 + 36}$$
$$= 4.8$$

The pH level after 6 minutes (i.e. the lowest pH level) is 4.8.

c. From the graph, the pH level appears to approach 6.5 as time goes by. Therefore, the normal pH level must be 6.5.

d. $y = 6.5$

Over time, the pH level rises back to the normal level.

e. During the first hour, the pH level drops quickly below normal, and then slowly begins to approach the normal level.

93. $P(10) = \dfrac{100(10-1)}{10} = 90$ $(10, 90)$

For a disease that smokers are 10 times more likely to contact than non-smokers, 90% of the deaths are smoking related.

95. $y = 100$ As incidence of the diseases increases, the percent of death approaches, but never gets to be, 100%.

97.   **a.** $\dfrac{128.3}{134.5} \approx 0.954$

In 1995, there were 954 males per 1000 females.

b. $\dfrac{141.7}{146.7} \approx 0.966$

In 2002, there were 966 males per 1000 females.

c. $f(x) = \dfrac{1.256x + 74.2}{1.324x + 76.71}$

d.   1995 is 45 years after 1950, so we find

$f(45) = \dfrac{1.256(45) + 74.2}{1.324(45) + 76.71} \approx 0.959$

The model predicts 959 males per 1000 females in 1995. The result from the function modeled the actual number fairly well.

e.   2002 is 52 years after 1950, so we find

$f(52) = \dfrac{1.256(52) + 74.2}{1.324(52) + 76.71} \approx 0.958$

The model predicts 958 males per 1000 females in 2002. The result from the function modeled the actual number fairly well.

f. $y = \dfrac{1.256}{1.324}$ or $y = 0.949$

This means that over time, the number of males per 1000 females will approach 949.

109.

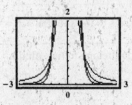

The graph approaches the horizontal asymptote faster and the vertical asymptote slower as n increases.

111.   **a.** $f(x) = \dfrac{27725(x-14)}{x^2 + 9} - 5x$

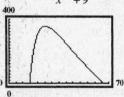

b.   The graph increases from late teens until about the age of 25, and then the number of arrests decreases.

c.   At age 25 the highest number arrests occurs. There are about 356 arrests for every 100,000 drivers.

113.   **a.**   False, $\sqrt[4]{x-3} = (x-3)^{1/2}$ is not a polynomial function.

b.   False, $n = m$ so the horizontal asymptote is $y = \dfrac{4}{1} = 4$

c.   False, $n = m$ so the horizontal asymptote is $y = \dfrac{3000}{1} = 3000$, not 30,000.

d.   True

(d) is true.

114.–116. Answers may vary.

Section 3.6

Check Point Exercises

1.
$$x^2 - x > 20$$
$$x^2 - x - 20 > 0$$
$$(x+4)(x-5) > 0$$

Solve the related quadratic equation.
$$(x+4)(x-5) = 0$$

Apply the zero product principle.
$$x+4 = 0 \quad \text{or} \quad x-5 = 0$$
$$x = -4 \qquad\qquad x = 5$$

The boundary points are –2 and 4.

Test Interval	Test Number	Test	Conclusion
$(-\infty, -4)$	–5	$(-5)^2 - (-5) > 20$ $30 > 20$, true	$(-\infty, -4)$ belongs to the solution set.
$(-4, 5)$	0	$(0)^2 - (0) > 20$ $0 > 20$, false	$(-4, 5)$ does not belong to the solution set.
$(5, \infty)$	10	$(10)^2 - (10) > 20$ $90 > 20$, true	$(5, \infty)$ belongs to the solution set.

The solution set is $(-\infty, -4) \cup (5, \infty)$ or $\{x \mid x < -4 \text{ or } x > 5\}$.

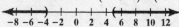

2.
$$x^3 + 3x^2 \le x + 3$$
$$x^3 + 3x^2 - x - 3 \le 0$$
$$(x+1)(x-1)(x+3) \le 0$$
$$(x+1)(x-1)(x+3) = 0$$
$$x+1 = 0 \quad \text{or} \quad x-1 = 0 \quad \text{or} \quad x+3 = 0$$
$$x = -1 \qquad\qquad x = 1 \qquad\qquad x = -3$$

Test Interval	Test Number	Test	Conclusion
$(-\infty, -3)$	-4	$(-4)^3 + 3(-4)^2 \le (-4) + 3$ $-16 \le -1$ true	$(-\infty, -3)$ belongs to the solution set.
$(-3, -1]$	-2	$(-2)^3 + 3(-2)^2 \le (-2) + 3$ $4 \le 1$ false	$(-3, -1]$ does not belong to the solution set.
$[-1, 1]$	0	$(0)^3 + 3(0)^2 \le (0) + 3$ $0 \le 3$ true	$[-1, 1]$ belongs to the solution set.
$[1, \infty)$	2	$(6+3)(6-5) > 0$ true	$[1, \infty)$ does not belong to the solution set.

The solution set is $(-\infty, -3] \cup [-1, 1]$ or $\{x \mid x \le -3 \text{ or } -1 \le x \le 1\}$.

254

3.

$$\frac{2x}{x+1} \geq 1$$

$$\frac{2x}{x+1} - 1 \geq 0$$

$$\frac{x-1}{x+1} \geq 0$$

$$x - 1 = 0 \quad \text{or} \quad x + 1 = 0$$

$$x = 1 \qquad\qquad x = -1$$

Test Interval	Test Number	Test	Conclusion
$(-\infty, -1)$	-2	$\dfrac{2(-2)}{-2+1} \geq 1$ $4 \geq 1$, true	$(-\infty, -1)$ belongs to the solution set.
$(-1, 1]$	0	$\dfrac{2(0)}{0+1} \geq 1$ $0 \geq 1$, false	$(-1, 1]$ does not belong to the solution set.
$[1, \infty)$	2	$\dfrac{2(2)}{2+1} \geq 1$ $\dfrac{4}{3} \geq 1$, true	$[1, \infty)$ belongs to the solution set.

The solution set is $(-\infty, -1) \cup [1, \infty)$ or $\{x \mid x < -1 \text{ or } x \geq 1\}$.

4.

$$-16t^2 + 80t > 64$$

$$-16t^2 + 80t - 64 > 0$$

$$-16(t-1)(t-4) > 0$$

$$t - 1 = 0 \quad \text{or} \quad t - 4 = 0$$

$$t = 1 \qquad\qquad t = 4$$

Test Interval	Test Number	Test	Conclusion
$(-\infty, 1)$	0	$-16(0)^2 + 80(0) > 64$ $0 > 64$, false	$(-\infty, 1)$ does not belong to the solution set.
$(1, 4)$	2	$-16(2)^2 + 80(2) > 64$ $96 > 64$, true	$(1, 4)$ belongs to the solution set.
$(4, \infty)$	5	$-16(5)^2 + 80(5) > 64$ $0 > 64$, false	$(4, \infty)$ does not belong to the solution set.

The object will be more than 64 feet above the ground between 1 and 4 seconds.

Exercise Set 3.6

1. $(x-4)(x+2) > 0$
   $x = 4$ or $x = -2$

T	F	T
	-2	4

   Test -3: $(-3-4)(-3+2) > 0$
   $\qquad\qquad 7 > 0$ True
   Test 0: $(0-4)(0+2) > 0$
   $\qquad\qquad -8 > 0$ False
   Test 5: $(5-4)(5+2) > 0$
   $\qquad\qquad 7 > 0$ True
   $(-\infty, -2)$ or $(4, \infty)$

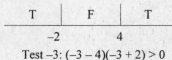

3. $(x-7)(x+3) \le 0$
   $x = 7$ or $x = -3$

F	T	F
	-3	7

   Test -4: $(-4-7)(-4+3) \le 0$
   $\qquad\quad 11 \le 0$ False
   Test 0: $(0-7)(0+3) \le 0$
   $\qquad\quad -21 \le 0$ True
   Test 8: $(8-7)(8+3) \le 0$
   $\qquad\quad 11 \le 0$ False
   The solution set is $[-3, 7]$.

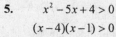

5. $x^2 - 5x + 4 > 0$
   $(x-4)(x-1) > 0$
   $x = 4$ or $x = 1$

T	F	T
	1	4

   Test 0: $0^2 - 5(0) + 4 > 0$
   $\qquad\qquad 4 > 0$ True
   Test 2: $2^2 - 5(2) + 4 > 0$
   $\qquad\qquad -2 > 0$ False
   Test 5: $5^2 - 5(5) + 4 > 0$
   $\qquad\qquad 4 > 0$ True
   The solution set is $(-\infty, 1)$ or $(4, \infty)$.

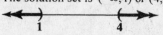

7. $x^2 + 5x + 4 > 0$
   $(x+1)(x+4) > 0$
   $x = -1$ or $x = -4$

T	F	T
	-4	-1

   Test -5: $(-5)^2 + 5(-5) + 4 > 0$
   $\qquad\qquad 4 > 0$ True
   Test -3: $(-3)^2 + 5(-3) + 4 > 0$
   $\qquad\qquad -2 > 0$ False
   Test 0: $0^2 + 5(0) + 4 > 0$
   $\qquad\qquad 4 > 0$ True
   The solution set is $(-\infty, -4)$ or $(-1, \infty)$.

9. $x^2 - 6x + 9 < 0$
   $(x-3)(x-3) < 0$
   $\qquad\qquad x = 3$

F	F
3	

   Test 0: $0^2 - 6(0) + 9 < 0$
   $\qquad\qquad\qquad 9 < 0$ False
   Test 4: $4^2 - 6(4) + 9 < 0$
   $\qquad\qquad\qquad 1 < 0$ False
   The solution set is the empty set, $\varnothing$.

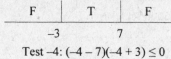

11.
$$3x^2 + 10x - 8 \le 0$$
$$(3x - 2)(x + 4) \le 0$$
$$x = \frac{2}{3} \text{ or } x = -4$$

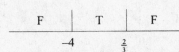

Test -5: $3(-5)^2 + 10(-5) - 8 \le 0$
$$17 \le 0 \text{ False}$$

Test 0: $3(0)^2 + 10(0) - 8 \le 0$
$$8 \le 0 \text{ True}$$

Test 1: $3(1)^2 + 10(1) - 8 \le 0$
$$5 \le 0 \text{ False}$$

The solution set is $\left[-4, \frac{2}{3} \right]$.

13.
$$2x^2 + x < 15$$
$$2x^2 + x - 15 < 0$$
$$(2x - 5)(x + 3) < 0$$
$$2x - 5 = 0 \quad \text{or} \quad x + 3 = 0$$
$$2x = 5$$
$$x = \frac{5}{2} \quad \text{or} \quad x = -3$$

F	T	F
	-3	$\frac{5}{2}$

Test -4: $2(-4)^2 + (-4) < 15$
$$28 < 15 \text{ False}$$

Test 0: $2(0)^2 + 0 < 15$
$$0 < 15 \text{ True}$$

Test 3: $2(3)^2 + 3 < 15$
$$21 < 15 \text{ False}$$

The solution set is $\left(-3, \frac{5}{2} \right)$.

15.
$$4x^2 + 7x < -3$$
$$4x^2 + 7x + 3 < 0$$
$$(4x + 3)(x + 1) < 0$$
$$4x + 3 = 0 \quad \text{or} \quad x + 1 = 0$$
$$4x - 3 = 0$$
$$x = -\frac{3}{4} \quad \text{or} \quad x = -1$$

F	T	F
	-1	$-\frac{3}{4}$

Test -2: $4(-2)^2 + 7(-2) < -3$
$$2 < -3 \text{ False}$$

Test $-\frac{7}{8}$: $4\left(-\frac{7}{8} \right)^2 + 7\left(-\frac{7}{8} \right) < -3$
$$\frac{49}{16} - \frac{49}{8} < -3$$
$$-\frac{49}{16} < -3 \text{ True}$$

Test 0: $4(0)^2 + 7(0) < -3$
$$0 < -3 \text{ False}$$

The solution set is $\left(-1, -\frac{3}{4} \right)$.

17.
$$5x \le 2 - 3x^2$$
$$3x^2 + 5x - 2 \le 0$$
$$(3x - 1)(x + 2) \le 0$$
$$3x - 1 = 0 \text{ or } x + 2 = 0$$
$$3x = 1$$
$$3x - 1 = 0 \quad \text{or} \quad x + 2 = 0$$
$$3x = 1$$
$$x = \frac{1}{3} \quad \text{or} \quad x = -2$$

F	T	F
	-2	$\frac{1}{3}$

Test -3: $5(-3) \le 2 - 3(-3)^2$
$$-15 \le -25 \text{ False}$$

Test 0: $5(0) \le 2 - 3(0)^2$
$$0 \le 2 \text{ True}$$

Test 1: $5(1) \le 2 - 3(1)^2$
$$5 \le -1 \text{ False}$$

257

The solution set is $\left[-2,\dfrac{1}{3}\right]$.

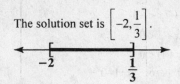

19. $x^2 - 4x \geq 0$

$x(x-4) \geq 0$

$x = 0$ or $x - 4 = 0$

$\qquad\qquad x = 4$

T		F		T
	0		4	

Test -1: $(-1)^2 - 4(-1) \geq 0$

$\qquad\qquad 5 \geq 0$ True

Test 1: $(1)^2 - 4(1) \geq 0$

$\qquad\qquad -3 \geq 0$ False

$\qquad\quad 0 \leq 2$ True

Test 5: $5^2 - 4(5) \geq 0$

$\qquad\qquad 5 \geq 0$ True

The solution set is $(-\infty, 0]$ or $[4, \infty)$.

21. $2x^2 + 3x > 0$

$x(2x+3) > 0$

$x = 0$ or $x = -\dfrac{3}{2}$

T		F		T
	$-\frac{3}{2}$		0	

Test -2: $2(-2)^2 + 3(-2) > 0$

$\qquad\quad 2 > 0$ True

Test -1: $2(-1)^2 + 3(-1) > 0$

$\qquad\quad -1 > 0$ False

Test 1: $2(1)^2 + 3(1) > 0$

$\qquad\quad 5 > 0$ True

The solution set is $\left(-\infty, -\dfrac{3}{2}\right)$ or $(0, \infty)$.

23. $-x^2 + x \geq 0$

$\quad x^2 - x \leq 0$

$\quad x(x-1) \leq 0$

$\quad x = 0$ or $x = 1$

F		T		F
	0		1	

Test -1: $-(-1)^2 + (-1) \geq 0$

$\qquad\qquad -2 \geq 0$ False

Test $\dfrac{1}{2}$: $-\left(\dfrac{1}{2}\right)^2 + \left(\dfrac{1}{2}\right) \geq 0$

$\qquad\qquad \dfrac{1}{4} \geq 0$ True

Test 2: $-(2)^2 + 2 \geq 0$

$\qquad\qquad -2 \geq 0$ False

The solution set is $[0, 1]$.

25. $\qquad x^2 \leq 4x - 2$

$x^2 - 4x + 2 \leq 0$

Solve $x^2 - 4x + 2 = 0$

$x = \dfrac{-b \pm \sqrt{b^2 - 4ac}}{2a}$

$x = \dfrac{-(-4) \pm \sqrt{(-4)^2 - 4(1)(2)}}{2(1)}$

$\quad = \dfrac{4 \pm \sqrt{8}}{2}$

$\quad = 2 \pm \sqrt{2}$

$x \approx 0.59$ or $x \approx 3.41$

F		T		F
	0.59		3.41	

The solution set is

$\left[2 - \sqrt{2}, 2 + \sqrt{2}\right]$ or $[0.59, 3.41]$.

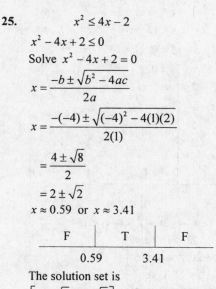

27. $x^2 - 6x + 9 < 0$

Solve $x^2 - 6x + 9 = 0$

$(x-3)(x-3) = 0$

$(x-3)^2 = 0$

$x = 3$

F		F
	3	

The solution set is the empty set, $\varnothing$.

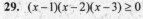

29. $(x-1)(x-2)(x-3) \geq 0$

Boundary points: 1, 2, and 3
Test one value in each interval.

F	T	F	T
1	2	3	

The solution set is $[1, 2] \cup [3, \infty)$.

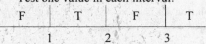

31. $x^3 + 2x^2 - x - 2 \geq 0$

$x^2(x+2) - 1(x+2) \geq 0$

$(x+2)(x^2 - 1) \geq 0$

$(x+2)(x-1)(x+1) \geq 0$

Boundary points: -2, -1, and 2
Test one value in each interval.

F	T	F	T
-2	-1	2	

The solution set is $[-2, -1] \cup [1, \infty)$.

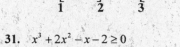

33. $x^3 + 2x^2 - x - 2 \geq 0$

$x^2(x-3) - 9(x-3) \geq 0$

$(x-3)(x^2 - 9) \geq 0$

$(x-3)(x+3)(x-3) \geq 0$

Boundary points: -3 and 3
Test one value in each interval.

T	F	F
-3	3	

The solution set is $(-\infty, -3]$.

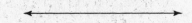

35. $x^3 + x^2 + 4x + 4 > 0$

$x^2(x+1) + 4(x+1) \geq 0$

$(x+1)(x^2 + 4) \geq 0$

Boundary point: -1
Test one value in each interval.

F	T
-1	

The solution set is $(-1, \infty)$.

37. $x^3 - 9x^2 \geq 0$

$x^2(x-9) \geq 0$

Boundary points: 0 and 9
Test one value in each interval.

F	F	T
0	9	

The solution set is $[0,0] \cup [9, \infty)$.

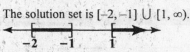

39. $\dfrac{x-4}{x+3} > 0$

$x - 4 = 0 \quad x + 3 = 0$

$x = 4 \qquad x = -3$

T	F	T
-3	4	

The solution set is $(-\infty, -3) \cup (4, \infty)$.

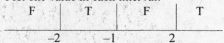

41. $\dfrac{x+3}{x+4} < 0$

$x = -3 \quad$ or $\quad x = -4$

F	T	F
-4	-3	

The solution set is $(-4, -3)$.

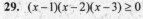

43. $\dfrac{-x+2}{x-4} \geq 0$

$x = 2$ or $x = 4$

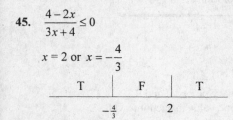

The solution set is $[2, 4)$.

45. $\dfrac{4-2x}{3x+4} \leq 0$

$x = 2$ or $x = -\dfrac{4}{3}$

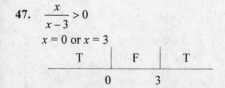

The solution set is $\left(-\infty, \dfrac{-4}{3}\right) \cup [2, \infty)$.

47. $\dfrac{x}{x-3} > 0$

$x = 0$ or $x = 3$

T		F		T
	0		3	

The solution set is $(-\infty, 0) \cup (3, \infty)$.

49. $\dfrac{(x+4)(x-1)}{x+2} \leq 0$

$x = -4$ or $x = -2$ or $x = 1$.

T		F		T		F
	-4		-2		1	

Values of $x = -4$ or $x = 1$ result in $f(x) = 0$ and, therefore must be included in the solution set.

The solution set is $(-\infty, -4] \cup (-2, 1]$

51. $\dfrac{x+1}{x+3} < 2$

$\dfrac{x+1}{x+3} - 2 < 0$

$\dfrac{x+1-2(x+3)}{x+3} < 0$

$\dfrac{x+1-2x-6}{x+3} < 0$

$\dfrac{-x-5}{x+3} < 0$

$x =$ or $x = -3$

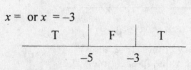

The solution set is $(-\infty, -5) \cup (-3, \infty)$.

53. $\dfrac{x+4}{2x-1} \leq 3$

$\dfrac{x+4}{2x-1} - 3 \leq 0$

$\dfrac{x+4-3(2x-1)}{2x-1} \leq 0$

$\dfrac{x+4-6x+3}{2x-1} \leq 0$

$\dfrac{-5x+7}{2x-1} \leq 0$

$x = \dfrac{7}{5}$ or $x = \dfrac{1}{2}$

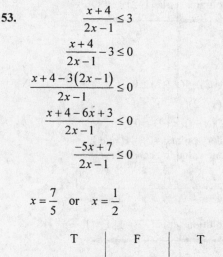

55.
$$\frac{x-2}{x+2} \le 2$$
$$\frac{x-2}{x+2} - 2 \le 0$$
$$\frac{x-2-2(x+2)}{x+2} \le 0$$
$$\frac{x-2-2x-4}{x+2} \le 0$$
$$\frac{-x-6}{x+2} \le 0$$

$x = -6$ or $x = -2$

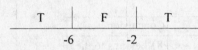

T	F	T
-6	-2	

The solution set is $(-\infty, -6] \cup (-2, \infty)$.

57. $f(x) = \sqrt{2x^2 - 5x + 2}$

The domain of this function requires that
$2x^2 - 5x + 2 \ge 0$
Solve $2x^2 - 5x + 2 = 0$
$(x-2)(2x-1) = 0$
$x = \frac{1}{2}$ or $x = 2$

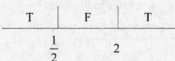

T	F	T
$\frac{1}{2}$	2	

The domain is $\left(-\infty, \frac{1}{2} \right] \cup [2, \infty)$.

59. $f(x) = \sqrt{\frac{2x}{x+1} - 1}$

The domain of this function requires that
$\frac{2x}{x+1} - 1 \ge 0$ or $\frac{x-1}{x+1} \ge 0$
$x = -1$ or $x = 1$

T	F	T
-1	1	

The value $x = 1$ results in 0 and, thus, it must be included in the domain.
The domain is $(-\infty, -1) \cup [1, \infty)$.

261

61. $\left| x^2 + 2x - 36 \right| > 12$

Express the inequality without the absolute value symbol:

$x^2 + 2x - 36 < -12$ or $x^2 + 2x - 36 > 12$

$x^2 + 2x - 24 < 0$ $x^2 + 2x - 48 > 0$

Solve the related quadratic equations.

$x^2 + 2x - 24 = 0$ or $x^2 + 2x - 48 = 0$

$(x + 6)(x - 4) = 0$ $(x + 8)(x - 6) = 0$

Apply the zero product principle.

$x + 6 = 0$ or $x - 4 = 0$ or $x + 8 = 0$ or $x - 6 = 0$

    $x = -6$ $x = 4$ $x = -8$ $x = 6$

The boundary points are -8, -6, 4 and 6.

Test Interval	Test Number	Test	Conclusion
$(-\infty, -8)$	-9	$\left\| (-9)^2 + 2(-9) - 36 \right\| > 12$ $27 > 12$, True	$(-\infty, -8)$ belongs to the solution set.
$(-8, -6)$	-7	$\left\| (-7)^2 + 2(-7) - 36 \right\| > 12$ $1 > 12$, False	$(-8, -6)$ does not belong to the solution set.
$(-6, 4)$	0	$\left\| 0^2 + 2(0) - 36 \right\| > 12$ $36 > 12$, True	$(-6, 4)$ belongs to the solution set.
$(4, 6)$	5	$\left\| 5^2 + 2(5) - 36 \right\| > 12$ $1 > 12$, False	$(4, 6)$ does not belong to the solution set.
$(6, \infty)$	7	$\left\| 7^2 + 2(7) - 36 \right\| > 12$ $27 > 12$, True	$(6, \infty)$ belongs to the solution set.

The solution set is $(-\infty, -8) \cup (-6, 4) \cup (6, \infty)$ or $\{x \mid x < -8 \text{ or } -6 < x < 4 \text{ or } x > 6\}$.

262

63. $\dfrac{3}{x+3} > \dfrac{3}{x-2}$

Express the inequality so that one side is zero.

$$\frac{3}{x+3} - \frac{3}{x-2} > 0$$

$$\frac{3(x-2)}{(x+3)(x-2)} - \frac{3(x+3)}{(x+3)(x-2)} > 0$$

$$\frac{3x-6-3x-9}{(x+3)(x-2)} < 0$$

$$\frac{-15}{(x+3)(x-2)} < 0$$

Find the values of x that make the denominator zero.

$$x+3 = 0 \qquad x-2 = 0$$
$$x = -3 \qquad x = 2$$

The boundary points are -3 and 2.

Test Interval	Test Number	Test	Conclusion
$(-\infty, -3)$	-4	$\dfrac{3}{-4+3} > \dfrac{3}{-4-2}$ $-3 > \dfrac{1}{2}$, False	$(-\infty, -3)$ does not belong to the solution set.
$(-3, 2)$	0	$\dfrac{3}{0+3} > \dfrac{3}{0-2}$ $1 > -\dfrac{3}{2}$, True	$(-3, 2)$ belongs to the solution set.
$(2, \infty)$	3	$\dfrac{3}{3+3} > \dfrac{3}{3-2}$ $\dfrac{1}{2} > 3$, False	$(2, \infty)$ does not belong to the solution set.

The solution set is $(-3, 2)$ or $\{x \mid -3 < x < 2\}$.

263

65. $\dfrac{x^2 - x - 2}{x^2 - 4x + 3} > 0$

Find the values of x that make the numerator and denominator zero.

$x^2 - x - 2 = 0$ $\qquad$ $x^2 - 4x + 3 = 0$

$(x-2)(x+1) = 0$ $\qquad$ $(x-3)(x-1) = 0$

Apply the zero product principle.

$x - 2 = 0$ or $x + 1 = 0$ $\qquad$ $x - 3 = 0$ or $x - 1 = 0$

$\quad x = 2$ $\qquad\quad x = -1$ $\qquad\quad x = 3$ $\qquad\qquad x = 1$

The boundary points are -1, 1, 2 and 3.

Test Interval	Test Number	Test	Conclusion
$(-\infty, -1)$	-2	$\dfrac{(-2)^2 - (-2) - 2}{(-2)^2 - 4(-2) + 3} > 0$ $\dfrac{4}{15} > 0$, True	$(-\infty, -1)$ belongs to the solution set.
$(-1, 1)$	0	$\dfrac{0^2 - 0 - 2}{0^2 - 4(0) + 3} > 0$ $-\dfrac{2}{3} > 0$, False	$(-1, 1)$ does not belong to the solution set.
$(1, 2)$	1.5	$\dfrac{1.5^2 - 1.5 - 2}{1.5^2 - 4(1.5) + 3} > 0$ $\dfrac{5}{3} > 0$, True	$(1, 2)$ belongs to the solution set.
$(2, 3)$	2.5	$\dfrac{2.5^2 - 2.5 - 2}{2.5^2 - 4(2.5) + 3} > 0$ $-\dfrac{7}{3} > 0$, False	$(2, 3)$ does not belong to the solution set.
$(3, \infty)$	4	$\dfrac{4^2 - 4 - 2}{4^2 - 4(4) + 3} > 0$ $\dfrac{10}{3} > 0$, True	$(3, \infty)$ belongs to the solution set.

The solution set is $(-\infty, -1) \cup (1, 2) \cup (3, \infty)$ or $\left\{ x \mid x < -1 \text{ or } 1 < x < 2 \text{ or } x > 3 \right\}$.

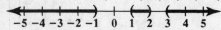

67.
$$2x^3 + 11x^2 \geq 7x + 6$$
$$2x^3 + 11x^2 - 7x - 6 \geq 0$$

The graph of $f(x) = 2x^3 + 11x^2 - 7x - 6$ appears to cross the x-axis at -6, $-\dfrac{1}{2}$, and 1. We verify this numerically by substituting these values into the function:

$$f(-6) = 2(-6)^3 + 11(-6)^2 - 7(-6) - 6 = 2(-216) + 11(36) - (-42) - 6 = -432 + 396 + 42 - 6 = 0$$

$$f\left(-\frac{1}{2}\right) = 2\left(-\frac{1}{2}\right)^3 + 11\left(-\frac{1}{2}\right)^2 - 7\left(-\frac{1}{2}\right) - 6 = 2\left(-\frac{1}{8}\right) + 11\left(\frac{1}{4}\right) - \left(-\frac{7}{2}\right) - 6 = -\frac{1}{4} + \frac{11}{4} + \frac{7}{2} - 6 = 0$$

$$f(1) = 2(1)^3 + 11(1)^2 - 7(1) - 6 = 2(1) + 11(1) - 7 - 6 = 2 + 11 - 7 - 6 = 0$$

Thus, the boundaries are -6, $-\dfrac{1}{2}$, and 1. We need to find the intervals on which $f(x) \geq 0$. These intervals are indicated on the graph where the curve is above the x-axis. Now, the curve is above the x-axis when $-6 < x < -\dfrac{1}{2}$ and when $x > 1$. Thus, the solution set is $\left\{ x \;\middle|\; -6 \leq x \leq -\dfrac{1}{2} \text{ or } x \geq 1 \right\}$ or $\left[-6, -\dfrac{1}{2}\right] \cup [1, \infty)$.

69.
$$\frac{1}{4(x+2)} \leq -\frac{3}{4(x-2)}$$

$$\frac{1}{4(x+2)} + \frac{3}{4(x-2)} \leq 0$$

Simplify the left side of the inequality:

$$\frac{x-2}{4(x+2)} + \frac{3(x+2)}{4(x-2)} = \frac{x-2+3x+6}{4(x+2)(x-2)} = \frac{4x+4}{4(x+2)(x-2)} = \frac{4(x+1)}{4(x+2)(x-2)} = \frac{x+1}{x^2-4}.$$

The graph of $f(x) = \dfrac{x+1}{x^2-4}$ crosses the x-axis at -1, and has vertical asymptotes at $x = -2$ and $x = 2$. Thus, the boundaries are -2, -1, and 1. We need to find the intervals on which $f(x) \leq 0$. These intervals are indicated on the graph where the curve is below the x-axis. Now, the curve is below the x-axis when $x < -2$ and when $-1 < x < 2$. Thus, the solution set is $\{x \mid x < -2 \text{ or } -1 \leq x < 2\}$ or $(-\infty, -2) \cup [-1, 2)$.

71. $s(t) = -16t^2 + 8t + 87$

The diver's height will exceed that of the cliff when $s(t) > 87$

$$-16t^2 + 8t + 87 > 87$$
$$-16t^2 + 8t > 0$$
$$-8t(2t - 1) > 0$$

The boundaries are 0 and $\dfrac{1}{2}$. Testing each interval shows that the diver will be higher than the cliff for the first half second after beginning the jump. The interval is $\left(0, \dfrac{1}{2}\right)$.

73. $f(8) = 27(8) + 163 = 216 + 163 = 379$

$g(8) = 1.2(8)^2 + 15.2(8) + 181.4 = 1.2(64) + 121.6 + 181.4$

$= 76.8 + 121.6 + 181.4 = 379.8$

Since the graph indicates that Medicare spending will reach \$379 billion, we conclude that both functions model the data quite well.

75. $g(x) = 1.2x^2 + 15.2x + 181.4$

To find when spending exceeds \$536.6 billion, solve the inequality $1.2x^2 + 15.2x + 181.4 > 536.6$.
Solve the related quadratic equation using the quadratic formula.

$1.2x^2 + 15.2x + 181.4 = 536.6$

$1.2x^2 + 15.2x - 355.2 = 0$

$a = 1.2 \quad b = 15.2 \quad c = -355.2$

$x = \dfrac{-15.2 \pm \sqrt{15.2^2 - 4(1.2)(-355.2)}}{2(1.2)} = \dfrac{-15.2 \pm \sqrt{231.04 + 1704.96}}{2.4}$

$= \dfrac{-15.2 \pm \sqrt{1936}}{2.4} = \dfrac{-15.2 \pm 44}{2.4}$

$= \dfrac{-15.2 - 44}{2.4} \quad \text{or} \quad \dfrac{-15.2 + 44}{2.4} = -24\dfrac{2}{3} \quad \text{or} \quad 12$

We disregard $-24\dfrac{2}{3}$ since x represents the number of years after 1995 and cannot be negative. The boundary point is 12.

Test Interval	Test Number	Test	Conclusion
$(0, 12)$	1	$1.2(1)^2 + 15.2(1) + 181.4 > 536.6$ $197.8 > 536.6$, false	$(0, 12)$ does not belong to the solution set.
$(12, \infty)$	13	$1.2(13)^2 + 15.2(13) + 181.4 > 536.6$ $581.8 > 536.6$, true	$(12, \infty)$ belongs to the solution set.

The solution set is $(12, \infty)$. This means that spending will exceed \$536.6 billion after $1995 + 12 = 2007$.

77. $f(x) = \dfrac{15}{x}$

If the time must be limited to 3 hours, then $\dfrac{15}{x} < 3$.

$\dfrac{15}{x} < 3$

$\dfrac{15}{x} - 3 < 0$

$\dfrac{-3(x - 5)}{x} < 0$

The boundaries are 0 and 5. Testing each interval shows that $\dfrac{15}{x} < 3$ on the intervals of $(-\infty, 0)$ and $(5, \infty)$.

However, a rate below 0 does not fit the constraints of this problem. Thus the solution is $(5, \infty)$.

The graph agrees with this solution.

For rates above 5 mph, the height of the graph is always at or below 3 hours.

79. As $x \to \infty$, the graph approaches 0. This shows that the higher the running rate, the less time it will take to complete the 95 miles.

81. To obtain the function that is displayed on the graph, let x represent the hiking rate and, thus, 9x will represent the driving rate.

$$\overbrace{f(x)}^{\text{total time}} = \frac{\overbrace{\text{driving distance}}^{\text{driving time}}}{\text{driving rate}} + \frac{\overbrace{\text{hiking distance}}^{\text{hiking time}}}{\text{hiking rate}}$$

$$f(x) = \frac{90}{9x} + \frac{5}{x}$$

$$= \frac{10}{x} + \frac{5}{x}$$

$$= \frac{15}{x}$$

83.
$$2l + 2w = P$$
$$2l + 2w = 180$$
$$2l = 180 - 2w$$
$$l = 90 - w$$

We want to restrict the area to 800 square feet. That is,

$$A \le 800$$
$$l \cdot w \le 800$$
$$(90 - w)w \le 800$$
$$90w - w^2 \le 800$$
$$-w^2 + 90w - 800 \le 0$$
$$w^2 - 90w + 800 \ge 0$$
$$w^2 - 90w + 800 = 0$$
$$(w - 80)(w - 10) = 0$$
$$w - 80 = 0 \quad \text{or} \quad w - 10 = 0$$
$$w = 80 \qquad\qquad w = 10$$

Assuming the width is the shorter side, we ignore the larger solution.

Test Interval	Test Number	Test	Conclusion
$(0,10)$	5	$90(5) - (5)^2 \le 800$ true	$(0,10)$ is part of the solution set
$(10,45)$	20	$90(20) - (20)^2 \le 800$ false	$(10,45)$ is not part of the solution set

The solution set is $\{w \mid 0 < w \le 10\}$ or $(0,10]$.

The length of the shorter side cannot exceed 10 feet.

87. Answers will vary.

89.

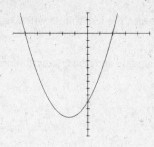

The solution set is $(-\infty, -5) \cup (2, \infty)$.

91.

The solution set is $(-2, -1)$ or $(2, \infty)$.

93. Graph $y_1 = \dfrac{x+2}{x-3}$ and $y_2 = 2$

y_1 less than or equal to y_2 for $x < 3$ or $x \geq 8$.

The solution set is $(-\infty, 3) \cup [8, \infty)$

95. **a.** False

$x^2 > 25$

Solution: $(-\infty, -5) \cup (5, \infty)$

b. False

Subtract 2 from both sides and solve.

$\dfrac{x - 2 - 2(x+3)}{x+3} < 0$

Note that when multiplying by $x + 3$, $x + 3$ may be negative.

c. False

The solution set of the first inequality is $(-\infty, -3) \cup (1, \infty)$. The solution set of the second inequality is $(-\infty, -3) \cup (1, \infty)$.

d. True

(d) is true.

97. One possible solution: $\dfrac{x-3}{x+4} \geq 0$

99. Because any number squared other than zero is positive, the solution includes only 2.

101. Because any number squared other than zero is positive, and the reciprocal of zero is undefined, the solution is all real numbers except 2.

103.

$$\sqrt{27 - 3x^2} \geq 0$$

$$27 - 3x^2 \geq 0$$

$$9 - x^2 \geq 0$$

$$(3 - x)(3 + x) \geq 0$$

$$3 - x = 0 \qquad 3 + x = 0$$

$$x = 3 \text{ or} \qquad x = -3$$

Test -4: $\sqrt{27 - 3(-4)^2} \geq 0$

$$\sqrt{27 - 48} \geq 0$$

$$\sqrt{-21} \geq 0$$

no graph- imaginary

Test 0: $\sqrt{27 - 3(0)^2} \geq 0$

$$\sqrt{27} \geq 0 \text{ True}$$

Test 4: $\sqrt{27 - 3(4)^2} \geq 0$

$$\sqrt{27 - 48} \geq 0$$

$$\sqrt{-21} \geq 0$$

no graph -imaginary

The solution set is $[-3, 3]$.

Section 3.7

Check Point Exercises

1. y varies directly as x is expressed as $y = kx$.

The volume of water, W, varies directly as the time, t can be expressed as $W = kt$.

Use the given values to find k.

$W = kt$

$30 = k(5)$

$6 = k$

Substitute the value of k into the equation.

$W = kt$

$W = 6t$

Use the equation to find W when $t = 11$.

$W = 6t$

$\quad = 6(11)$

$\quad = 66$

A shower lasting 11 minutes will use 66 gallons of water.

2. y varies directly as the square of x is expressed as $y = kx$.

The distance, s, varies directly as the square of the speed, v can be expressed as $s = kv^2$.

Use the given values to find k.

$$s = kv^2$$
$$200 = k(60)^2$$
$$0.0556 = k$$

Substitute the value of k into the equation.

$$s = kv^2$$
$$s = 0.0556v^2$$

Use the equation to find s when $v = 100$.

$$s = 0.0556v^2$$
$$= 0.0556(100)^2$$
$$= 556$$

A car traveling 100 mph will require 556 feet to stop.

3. y varies inversely as x is expressed as $y = \dfrac{k}{x}$.

The length, L, varies inversely as the frequency, f can be expressed as $L = \dfrac{k}{f}$.

Use the given values to find k.

$$L = \frac{k}{f}$$
$$8 = \frac{k}{640}$$
$$5120 = k$$

Substitute the value of k into the equation.

$$L = \frac{k}{f}$$
$$L = \frac{5120}{f}$$

Use the equation to find f when $L = 10$.

$$L = \frac{5120}{f}$$
$$10 = \frac{5120}{f}$$
$$10f = 5120$$
$$f = 512$$

A 10 inch violin string will have a frequency of 512 cycles per second.

4. let M represent the number of minutes
let Q represent the number of problems
let P represent the number of people
M varies directly as Q and inversely as P is expressed as $M = \dfrac{kQ}{P}$.

Use the given values to find k.

$$M = \frac{kQ}{P}$$
$$32 = \frac{k(16)}{4}$$
$$8 = k$$

Substitute the value of k into the equation.

$$M = \frac{kQ}{P}$$
$$M = \frac{8Q}{P}$$

Use the equation to find M when $P = 8$ and $Q = 24$.

$$M = \frac{8Q}{P}$$
$$M = \frac{8(24)}{8}$$
$$M = 24$$

It will take 24 minutes for 8 people to solve 24 problems.

5. V varies jointly with h and r^2 and can be modeled as $V = khr^2$.

Use the given values to find k.

$$V = khr^2$$
$$120\pi = k(10)(6)^2$$
$$\frac{\pi}{3} = k$$

Therefore, the volume equation is $V = \dfrac{1}{3}hr^2$.

$$V = \frac{\pi}{3}(2)(12)^2 = 96\pi \text{ cubic feet}$$

Exercise Set 3.7

1. Use the given values to find k.

$$y = kx$$
$$65 = k \cdot 5$$
$$\frac{65}{5} = \frac{k \cdot 5}{5}$$
$$13 = k$$

The equation becomes $y = 13x$.

When $x = 12$, $y = 13x = 13 \cdot 12 = 156$.

3. Since y varies inversely with x, we have $y = \dfrac{k}{x}$.

Use the given values to find k.

$$y = \frac{k}{x}$$
$$12 = \frac{k}{5}$$
$$5 \cdot 12 = 5 \cdot \frac{k}{5}$$
$$60 = k$$

The equation becomes $y = \dfrac{60}{x}$.

When $x = 2$, $y = \dfrac{60}{2} = 30$.

5. Since y varies inversely as x and inversely as the square of z, we have $y = \dfrac{kx}{z^2}$.

Use the given values to find k.

$$y = \frac{kx}{z^2}$$
$$20 = \frac{k(50)}{5^2}$$
$$20 = \frac{k(50)}{25}$$
$$20 = 2k$$
$$10 = k$$

The equation becomes $y = \dfrac{10x}{z^2}$.

When $x = 3$ and $z = 6$,

$$y = \frac{10x}{z^2} = \frac{10(3)}{6^2} = \frac{10(3)}{36} = \frac{30}{36} = \frac{5}{6}.$$

7. Since y varies jointly as x and z, we have $y = kxz$.

Use the given values to find k.

$$y = kxz$$
$$25 = k(2)(5)$$
$$25 = k(10)$$
$$\frac{25}{10} = \frac{k(10)}{10}$$
$$\frac{5}{2} = k$$

The equation becomes $y = \dfrac{5}{2}xz$.

When $x = 8$ and $z = 12$, $y = \dfrac{5}{2}(8)(12) = 240$.

9. Since y varies jointly as a and b and inversely as the square root of c, we have $y = \dfrac{kab}{\sqrt{c}}$.

Use the given values to find k.

$$y = \frac{kab}{\sqrt{c}}$$
$$12 = \frac{k(3)(2)}{\sqrt{25}}$$
$$12 = \frac{k(6)}{5}$$
$$12(5) = \frac{k(6)}{5}(5)$$
$$60 = 6k$$
$$\frac{60}{6} = \frac{6k}{6}$$
$$10 = k$$

The equation becomes $y = \dfrac{10ab}{\sqrt{c}}$.

When $a = 5$, $b = 3$, $c = 9$,

$$y = \frac{10ab}{\sqrt{c}} = \frac{10(5)(3)}{\sqrt{9}} = \frac{150}{3} = 50.$$

11. $x = kyz$;

Solving for y:

$$x = kyz$$
$$\frac{x}{kz} = \frac{kyz}{yz}.$$
$$y = \frac{x}{kz}$$

13.
$$x = \frac{kz^3}{y};$$

Solving for y

$$x = \frac{kz^3}{y}$$

$$xy = y \cdot \frac{kz^3}{y}$$

$$xy = kz^3$$

$$\frac{xy}{x} = \frac{kz^3}{x}$$

$$y = \frac{kz^3}{x}$$

15.
$$x = \frac{kyz}{\sqrt{w}};$$

Solving for y:

$$x = \frac{kyz}{\sqrt{w}}$$

$$x\left(\sqrt{w}\right) = \left(\sqrt{w}\right)\frac{kyz}{\sqrt{w}}$$

$$x\sqrt{w} = kyz$$

$$\frac{x\sqrt{w}}{kz} = \frac{kyz}{kz}$$

$$y = \frac{x\sqrt{w}}{kz}$$

17. $x = kz(y + w)$;
Solving for y:

$$x = kz(y + w)$$

$$x = kzy + kzw$$

$$x - kzw = kzy$$

$$\frac{x - kzw}{kz} = \frac{kzy}{kz}$$

$$y = \frac{x - kzw}{kz}$$

19.
$$x = \frac{kz}{y - w};$$

Solving for y:

$$x = \frac{kz}{y - w}$$

$$(y - w)x = (y - w)\frac{kz}{y - w}$$

$$xy - wx = kz$$

$$xy = kz + wx$$

$$\frac{xy}{x} = \frac{kz + wx}{x}$$

$$y = \frac{xw + kz}{x}$$

21. Since T varies directly as B, we have $T = kB$.
Use the given values to find k.

$$T = kB$$

$$3.6 = k(4)$$

$$\frac{3.6}{4} = \frac{k(4)}{4}$$

$$0.9 = k$$

The equation becomes $T = 0.9B$.
When $B = 6$, $T = 0.9(6) = 5.4$.
The tail length is 5.4 feet.

23. Since B varies directly as D, we have $B = kD$.
Use the given values to find k.

$$B = kD$$

$$8.4 = k(12)$$

$$\frac{8.4}{12} = \frac{k(12)}{12}$$

$$k = \frac{8.4}{12} = 0.7$$

The equation becomes $B = 0.7D$.
When $B = 56$,

$$56 = 0.7D$$

$$\frac{56}{0.7} = \frac{0.7D}{0.7}$$

$$D = \frac{56}{0.7} = 80$$

It was dropped from 80 inches.

25. Since a man's weight varies directly as the cube of his height, we have $w = kh^3$.
Use the given values to find k.

$$w = kh^3$$

$$170 = k(70)^3$$

$$170 = k(343,000)$$

$$\frac{170}{343,000} = \frac{k(343,000)}{343,000}$$

$$0.000496 = k$$

The equation becomes $w = 0.000496h^3$.
When $h = 107$,

$$w = 0.000496(107)^3$$

$$= 0.000496(1,225,043) \approx 607.$$

Robert Wadlow's weight was approximately 607 pounds.

27. Since the banking angle varies inversely as the turning radius, we have $B = \dfrac{k}{r}$.
Use the given values to find k.

$$B = \frac{k}{r}$$

$$28 = \frac{k}{4}$$

$$28(4) = 28\left(\frac{k}{4}\right)$$

$$112 = k$$

The equation becomes $B = \dfrac{112}{r}$.

When $r = 3.5$, $B = \dfrac{112}{r} = \dfrac{112}{3.5} = 32$.

The banking angle is 32 when the turning radius is 3.5 feet.

29. Since intensity varies inversely as the square of the distance, we have pressure, we have

$$I = \frac{k}{d}.$$

Use the given values to find k.

$$I = \frac{k}{d^2}.$$

$$62.5 = \frac{k}{3^2}$$

$$62.5 = \frac{k}{9}$$

$$9(62.5) = 9\left(\frac{k}{9}\right)$$

$$562.5 = k$$

The equation becomes $I = \dfrac{562.5}{d^2}$.

When $d = 2.5$, $I = \dfrac{562.5}{2.5^2} = \dfrac{562.5}{6.25} = 90$

The intensity is 90 milliroentgens per hour.

31. Since index varies directly as weight and inversely as the square of one's height, we have $I = \dfrac{kw}{h^2}$.
Use the given values to find k.

$$I = \frac{kw}{h^2}$$

$$35.15 = \frac{k(180)}{60^2}$$

$$35.15 = \frac{k(180)}{3600}$$

$$(3600)35.15 = \frac{k(180)}{3600}$$

$$126540 = k(180)$$

$$k = \frac{126540}{180} = 703$$

The equation becomes $I = \dfrac{703w}{h^2}$.

When $w = 170$ and $h = 70$,

$$I = \frac{703(170)}{(70)^2} \approx 24.4.$$

This person has a BMI of 24.4 and is not overweight.

33. Since heat loss varies jointly as the area and temperature difference, we have $L = kAD$. Use the given values to find k.

    $L = kAD$

    $1200 = k(3 \cdot 6)(20)$

    $1200 = 360k$

    $\dfrac{1200}{360} = \dfrac{360k}{360}$

    $k = \dfrac{10}{3}$

    The equation becomes $L = \dfrac{10}{3}AD$

    When $A = 6 \cdot 9 = 54$, $D = 10$,

    $L = \dfrac{10}{3}(9 \cdot 6)(10) = 1800$.

    The heat loss is 1800 Btu.

35. Since intensity varies inversely as the square of the distance from the sound source, we

    have $I = \dfrac{k}{d^2}$. If you move to a seat twice as

    far, then $d = 2d$. So we have

    $I = \dfrac{k}{(2d)^2} = \dfrac{k}{4d^2} = \dfrac{1}{4} \cdot \dfrac{k}{d^2}$. The intensity will

    be multiplied by a factor of $\dfrac{1}{4}$. So the sound

    intensity is $\dfrac{1}{4}$ of what it was originally.

37. **a.** Since the average number of phone calls varies jointly as the product of the populations and inversely as the square of

    the distance, we have $C = \dfrac{kP_1 P_2}{d^2}$.

    b. Use the given values to find k.

    $C = \dfrac{kP_1 P_2}{d^2}$

    $326,000 = \dfrac{k(777,000)(3,695,000)}{(420)^2}$

    $326,000 = \dfrac{k(2.87 \times 10^{12})}{176,400}$

    $326,000 = 16269841.27k$

    $0.02 \approx k$

    The equation becomes $C = \dfrac{0.02 P_1 P_2}{d^2}$.

c. $C = \dfrac{0.02(650,000)(490,000)}{(400)^2}$

≈ 39813

The average number of calls is approximately 39,813 daily phone calls.

39. **a.**
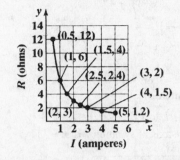

b. Current varies inversely as resistance. Answers will vary.

c. Since the current varies inversely as

resistance we have $R = \dfrac{k}{I}$. Using one of

the given ordered pairs to find k.

$12 = \dfrac{k}{0.5}$

$12(0.5) = \dfrac{k}{0.5}(0.5)$

$k = 6$

The equation becomes $R = \dfrac{6}{I}$.

45. z varies directly as the square root of x and inversely as the square of y.

49. Pressure, P, varies directly as the square of wind velocity, v, can be modeled as $P = kv^2$.

    If $v = x$ then $P = k(x)^2 = kx^2$

    If $v = 2x$ then $P = k(2x)^2 = 4kx^2$

    If the wind speed doubles the pressure is 4 times more destructive.

51. The Heat, H, varies directly as the square of the voltage, v, and inversely as the resistance, r.

    $H = \dfrac{kv^2}{r}$

    If the voltage remains constant, to triple the heat the resistant must be reduced by a multiple of 3.

Chapter 3 Review Exercises

1. $f(x) = -(x+1)^2 + 4$

vertex: $(-1, 4)$

x-intercepts:

$0 = -(x+1)^2 + 4$

$(x+1)^2 = 4$

$x + 1 = \pm 2$

$x = -1 \pm 2$

$x = -3$ or $x = 1$

y-intercept:

$f(0) = -(0+1)^2 + 4 = 3$

The axis of symmetry is $x = -1$.

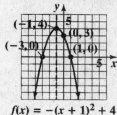

$f(x) = -(x + 1)^2 + 4$

Domain: $(-\infty, \infty)$ Range: $(-\infty, 4]$

2. $f(x) = (x+4)^2 - 2$

vertex: $(-4, -2)$

x-intercepts:

$0 = (x+4)^2 - 2$

$(x+4)^2 = 2$

$x + 4 = \pm\sqrt{2}$

$x = -4 \pm \sqrt{2}$

y-intercept:

$f(0) = (0+4)^2 - 2 = 14 = -1$

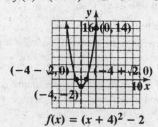

$f(x) = (x + 4)^2 - 2$

The axis of symmetry is $x = -4$.

Domain: $(-\infty, \infty)$ Range: $[-2, \infty)$

3. $f(x) = -x^2 + 2x + 3$

$= -(x^2 - 2x + 1) + 3 + 1$

$f(x) = -(x-1)^2 + 4$

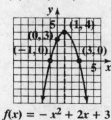

$f(x) = -x^2 + 2x + 3$

Domain: $(-\infty, \infty)$ Range: $(-\infty, 4]$

4. $f(x) = 2x^2 - 4x - 6$

$f(x) = 2(x^2 - 2x + 1) - 6 - 2$

$2(x-1)^2 - 8$

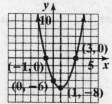

$f(x) = 2x^2 - 4x - 6$

axis of symmetry: $x = 1$

Domain: $(-\infty, \infty)$ Range: $[-8, \infty)$

5. $f(x) = -x^2 + 14x - 106$

a. Since $a < 0$ the parabola opens down with the maximum value occurring at

$x = -\dfrac{b}{2a} = -\dfrac{14}{2(-1)} = 7$.

The maximum value is $f(7)$.

$f(7) = -(7)^2 + 14(7) - 106 = -57$

b. Domain: $(-\infty, \infty)$ Range: $(-\infty, -57]$

6. $f(x) = 2x^2 + 12x + 703$

a. Since $a > 0$ the parabola opens up with the minimum value occurring at

$x = -\dfrac{b}{2a} = -\dfrac{12}{2(2)} = -3$.

The minimum value is $f(-3)$.

$f(-3) = 2(-3)^2 + 12(-3) + 703 = 685$

b. Domain: $(-\infty, \infty)$ Range: $[685, \infty)$

7. $f(x) = -0.02x^2 + x + 1$

Since $a = -0.02$ is negative, we know the function opens downward and has a maximum

at $x = -\dfrac{b}{2a} = -\dfrac{1}{2(-0.02)} = -\dfrac{1}{-0.04} = 25.$ When

25 inches of rain falls, the maximum growth will occur. The maximum growth is

$f(25) = -0.02(25)^2 + 25 + 1$
$= -0.02(625) + 25 + 1$
$= -12.5 + 25 + 1 = 13.5.$

A maximum yearly growth of 13.5 inches occurs when 25 inches of rain falls per year.

8. According to the graph, the vertex (maximum point) is (25, 5). This means that the maximum divorce rate of 5 divorces per 1000 people occurred in the year 1960 + 25 = 1985.

9. Maximize the area using $A = lw.$

$A(x) = x(1000 - 2x)$

$A(x) = -2x^2 + 1000x$

Since $a = -2$ is negative, we know the function opens downward and has a maximum at

$x = -\dfrac{b}{2a} = -\dfrac{1000}{2(-2)} = -\dfrac{1000}{-4} = 250.$

The maximum area is achieved when the width is 250 yards. The maximum area is

$A(250) = 250(1000 - 2(250))$
$= 250(1000 - 500)$
$= 250(500) = 125,000.$

The area is maximized at 125,000 square yards when the width is 250 yards and the length is $1000 - 2 \cdot 250 = 500$ yards.

10. Let x = one of the numbers
Let $14 + x$ = the other number

We need to minimize the function
$P(x) = x(14 + x)$
$= 14x + x^2$
$= x^2 + 14x.$
The minimum is at
$x = -\dfrac{b}{2a} = -\dfrac{14}{2(1)} = -\dfrac{14}{2} = -7.$

The other number is $14 + x = 14 + (-7) = 7.$

The numbers which minimize the product are 7 and -7. The minimum product is $-7 \cdot 7 = -49.$

11. $f(x) = -x^3 + 12x^2 - x$

The graph rises to the left and falls to the right and goes through the origin, so graph (c) is the best match.

12. $g(x) = x^6 - 6x^4 + 9x^2$

The graph rises to the left and rises to the right, so graph (b) is the best match.

13. $h(x) = x^5 - 5x^3 + 4x$

The graph falls to the left and rises to the right and crosses the y-axis at zero, so graph (a) is the best match.

14. $f(x) = -x^4 + 1$

$f(x)$ falls to the left and to the right so graph (d) is the best match.

15. The leading coefficient is -0.87 and the degree is 3. This means that the graph will fall to the right. This function is not useful in modeling the number of thefts over an extended period of time. The model predicts that eventually, the number of thefts would be negative. This is impossible.

16. In the polynomial, $f(x) = -x^4 + 21x^2 + 100,$ the leading coefficient is -1 and the degree is 4. Applying the Leading Coefficient Test, we know that even-degree polynomials with negative leading coefficient will fall to the left and to the right. Since the graph falls to the right, we know that the elk population will die out over time.

17. $f(x) = -2(x - 1)(x + 2)^2(x + 5)^3$
$x = 1$, multiplicity 1, the graph crosses the x-axis
$x = -2$, multiplicity 2, the graph touches the x-axis
$x = -5$, multiplicity 5, the graph crosses the x-axis

18. $f(x) = x^3 - 5x^2 - 25x + 125$
$\qquad = x^2(x - 5) - 25(x - 5)$
$\qquad = (x^2 - 25)(x - 5)$
$\qquad = (x + 5)(x - 5)^2$
$x = -5$, multiplicity 1, the graph crosses the x-axis
$x = 5$, multiplicity 2, the graph touches the x-axis

19. $f(x) = x^3 - 2x - 1$

$f(1) = (1)^3 - 2(1) - 1 = -2$

$f(2) = (2)^3 - 2(2) - 1 = 3$

The sign change shows there is a zero between the given values.

20. $f(x) = x^3 - x^2 - 9x + 9$

a. Since n is odd and $a_n > 0$, the graph falls to the left and rises to the right.

b. $f(-x) = (-x)^3 - (-x)^2 - 9(-x) + 9$

$= -x^3 - x^2 + 9x + 9$

$f(-x) \neq f(x), f(-x) \neq -f(x)$

no symmetry

c. $f(x) = (x-3)(x+3)(x-1)$

zeros: $3, -3, 1$

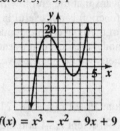

$f(x) = x^3 - x^2 - 9x + 9$

21. $f(x) = 4x - x^3$

a. Since n is odd and $a_n < 0$, the graph rises to the left and falls to the right.

b. $f(-x) = -4x + x^3$

$f(-x) = -f(x)$

origin symmetry

c. $f(x) = x(x^2 - 4) = x(x-2)(x+2)$

zeros: $x = 0, 2, -2$

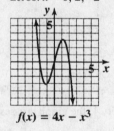

$f(x) = 4x - x^3$

22. $f(x) = 2x^3 + 3x^2 - 8x - 12$

a. Since h is odd and $a_n > 0$, the graph falls to the left and rises to the right.

b. $f(-x) = -2x^3 + 3x^2 + 8x - 12$

$f(-x) \neq f(x), f(-x) = -f(x)$

no symmetry

c. $f(x) = (x-2)(x+2)(2x+3)$

zeros: $x = 2, -2, -\dfrac{3}{2}$

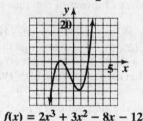

$f(x) = 2x^3 + 3x^2 - 8x - 12$

23. $g(x) = -x^4 + 25x^2$

a. The graph falls to the left and to the right.

b. $f(-x) = -(-x)^4 + 25(-x)^2$

$= -x^4 + 25x^2 = f(x)$

y-axis symmetry

c. $-x^4 + 25x^2 = 0$

$-x^2(x^2 - 25) = 0$

$-x^2(x-5)(x+5) = 0$

zeros: $x = -5, 0, 5$

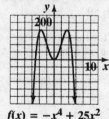

$f(x) = -x^4 + 25x^2$

24. $f(x) = -x^4 + 6x^3 - 9x^2$

   a. The graph falls to the left and to the right.

   b. $f(-x) = -(-x)^4 + 6(-x)^3 - 9(-x)$

          $= -x^4 - 6x^3 - 9x^2 \, f(-x) \neq f(x)$

       $f(-x) \neq -f(x)$

   no symmetry

   c. $= -x^2(x^2 - 6x + 9) = 0$

       $-x^2(x-3)(x-3) = 0$

       zeros: $x = 0, 3$

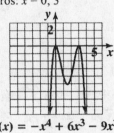

$$f(x) = -x^4 + 6x^3 - 9x^2$$

25. $f(x) = 3x^4 - 15x^3$

   a. The graph rises to the left and to the right.

   b. $f(-x) = 3(-x)^4 - 15(-x)^3 = 3x^4 + 15x^3$

       $f(-x) \neq f(x), \; f(-x) \neq -f(x)$

       no symmetry

   c $3x^4 - 15x^3 = 0$

       $3x^3(x-5) = 0$

       zeros: $x = 0, 5$

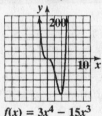

$$f(x) = 3x^4 - 15x^3$$

26. $f(x) = 2x^2(x-1)^3(x+2)$

Since $a_n > 0$ and n is even, $f(x)$ rises to the left and the right.

$x = 0, x = 1, x = -2$

The zeros at 1 and -2 have odd multiplicity so $f(x)$ crosses the x-axis at those points. The root at 0 has even multiplicity so $f(x)$ touches the axis at $(0, 0)$

$$f(0) = 2(0)^2(0-1)^3(0+2) = 0$$

The y-intercept is 0.

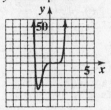

$$f(x) = 2x^2 (x - 1)^3 (x + 2)$$

27. $f(x) = -x^3(x+4)^2(x-1)$

Since $a_n < 0$ and n is even, $f(x)$ falls to the left and the right.

$x = 0, x = -4, x = 1$

The roots at 0 and 1 have odd multiplicity so $f(x)$ crosses the x-axis at those points. The root at -4 has even multiplicity so $f(x)$ touches the axis at $(-4, 0)$

$$f(0) = -(0)^3(0+4)^2(0-1) = 0$$

The y-intercept is 0.

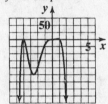

$$f(x) = -x^3 (x + 4)^2 (x - 1)$$

28.

$$\begin{array}{r} 4x^2 - 7x + 5 \\ x+1\overline{)4x^3 - 3x^2 - 2x + 1} \\ \underline{4x^3 + 4x^2} \\ -7x^2 - 2x \\ \underline{-7x^2 - 7x} \\ 5x + 1 \\ \underline{5x + 5} \\ -4 \end{array}$$

Quotient: $4x^2 - 7x + 5 - \dfrac{4}{x+1}$

29.

$$\begin{array}{r} 2x^2 - 4x + 1 \\ 5x-3\overline{\smash{\big)}\,10x^3 - 26x^2 + 17x - 13} \\ \underline{10x^3 + 6x^2} \\ -20x^2 + 17x \\ \underline{-20x^2 + 12x} \\ 5x - 13 \\ \underline{5x - 3} \\ -10 \end{array}$$

Quotient: $2x^2 - 4x + 1 - \dfrac{10}{5x-3}$

30.

$$\begin{array}{r} 2x^2 + 3x - 1 \\ 2x^2+1\overline{\smash{\big)}\,4x^4 + 6x^3 + 3x - 1} \\ \underline{4x^2 + 2x^2} \\ 6x^3 - 2x^2 + 3x \\ \underline{6x^2 + 3x} \\ -2x^2 - 1 \\ \underline{-2x^2 - 1} \\ 0 \end{array}$$

31. $(3x^4 + 11x^3 - 20x^3 + 7x + 35) \div (x+5)$

$$\begin{array}{r|rrrrr} -5 & 3 & 11 & -20 & 7 & 35 \\ & & -15 & 20 & 0 & -35 \\ \hline & 3 & -4 & 0 & 7 & 0 \end{array}$$

Quotient: $3x^3 - 4x^2 + 7$

32. $(3x^4 - 2x^2 - 10x) \div (x-2)$

$$\begin{array}{r|rrrrr} 2 & 3 & 0 & -2 & -10 & 0 \\ & & 6 & 12 & 20 & 20 \\ \hline & 3 & 6 & 10 & 10 & 20 \end{array}$$

Quotient: $3x^3 + 6x^2 + 10x + 10 + \dfrac{20}{x-2}$

33. $f(x) = 2x^3 - 7x^2 + 9x - 3$

$$\begin{array}{r|rrrr} -13 & 2 & -7 & 9 & -3 \\ & & -26 & 429 & -5694 \\ \hline & 2 & -33 & 438 & -5697 \end{array}$$

Quotient: $f(-13) = -5697$

34. $f(x) = 2x^3 + x^2 - 13x + 6$

$$\begin{array}{r|rrrr} 2 & 2 & 1 & -13 & 6 \\ & & 4 & 10 & -6 \\ \hline & 2 & 5 & -3 & 0 \end{array}$$

$f(x) = (x-2)(2x^2 + 5x - 3)$
$ = (x-2)(2x-1)(x+3)$

Zeros: $x = 2, \dfrac{1}{2}, -3$

35. $x^3 - 17x + 4 = 0$

$$\begin{array}{r|rrrr} 4 & 1 & 0 & -17 & 4 \\ & & 4 & 16 & -4 \\ \hline & 1 & 4 & -1 & 0 \end{array}$$

$(x-4)(x^2 + 4x - 1) = 0$

$x = \dfrac{-4 \pm \sqrt{16+4}}{2} = \dfrac{-4 \pm 2\sqrt{5}}{2} = -2 \pm \sqrt{5}$

The solution set is $\left\{4, -2 + \sqrt{5}, -2 - \sqrt{5}\right\}$.

36. $f(x) = x^4 - 6x^3 + 14x^2 - 14x + 5$

$p : \pm 1, \pm 5$

$q : \pm 1$

$\dfrac{p}{q} : \pm 1, \pm 5$

37. $f(x) = 3x^5 - 2x^4 - 15x^3 + 10x^2 + 12x - 8$

$p : \pm 1, \pm 2, \pm 4, \pm 8$

$q : \pm 1, \pm 3$

$\dfrac{p}{q} : \pm 1, \pm 2, \pm 4, \pm 8, \pm \dfrac{8}{3}, \pm \dfrac{4}{3}, \pm \dfrac{2}{3}, \pm \dfrac{1}{3}$

38. $f(x) = 3x^4 - 2x^3 - 8x + 5$

$f(x)$ has 2 sign variations, so $f(x) = 0$ has 2 or 0 positive solutions.

$f(-x) = 3x^4 + 2x^3 + x + 5$

$f(-x)$ has no sign variations, so $f(x) = 0$ has no negative solutions.

39. $f(x) = 2x^5 - 3x^3 - 5x^2 + 3x - 1$

$f(x)$ has 3 sign variations, so $f(x) = 0$ has 3 or 1 positive real roots.

$f(-x) = -2x^5 + 3x^3 - 5x^2 - 3x - 1$

$f(-x)$ has 2 sign variations, so $f(x) = 0$ has 2 or 0 negative solutions.

40. $f(x) = f(-x) = 2x^4 + 6x^2 + 8$

No sign variations exist for either $f(x)$ or $f(-x)$, so no real roots exist.

41. $f(x) = x^3 + 3x^2 - 4$

a. $p: \pm 1, \pm 2, \pm 4$
$q: \pm 1$

$\dfrac{p}{q}: \pm 1, \pm 2, \pm 4$

b. 1 sign variation $\Rightarrow$ 1 positive real zero
$f(-x) = -x^3 + 3x^2 - 4$
2 sign variations $\Rightarrow$ 2 or no negative real zeros

c.

$$\begin{array}{r|rrrr} 1 & 1 & 3 & 0 & -4 \\ & & 1 & 4 & -4 \\ \hline & 1 & 4 & 4 & 0 \end{array}$$

1 is a zero.

d. $(x-1)(x^2 + 4x + 4) = 0$
$(x-1)(x+2)^2 = 0$
$x = 1$ or $x = -2$
The solution set is $\{1, -2\}$.

42. $f(x) = 6x^3 + x^2 - 4x + 1$

a. $p: \pm 1$
$q: \pm 1, \pm 2, \pm 3, \pm 6$
$\dfrac{p}{q}: \pm 1, \pm\dfrac{1}{2}, \pm\dfrac{1}{3}, \pm\dfrac{1}{6}$

b. $f(x) = 6x^3 + x^2 - 4x + 1$
2 sign variations; 2 or 0 positive real zeros.
$f(-x) = -6x^3 + x^2 + 4x + 1$
1 sign variation; 1 negative real zero.

c.

$$\begin{array}{r|rrrr} -1 & 6 & 1 & -4 & 1 \\ & & -6 & 5 & -1 \\ \hline & 6 & -5 & 1 & 0 \end{array}$$

-1 is a zero.

d. $6x^3 + x^2 - 4x + 1 = 0$
$(x+1)(6x^2 - 5x + 1) = 0$
$(x+1)(3x-1)(2x-1) = 0$
$x = -1$ or $x = \dfrac{1}{3}$ or $x = \dfrac{1}{2}$
The solution set is $\left\{-1, \dfrac{1}{3}, \dfrac{1}{2}\right\}$.

43. $f(x) = 8x^3 - 36x^2 + 46x - 15$

a. $p: \pm 1, \pm 3, \pm 5, \pm 15$
$q: \pm 1, \pm 2, \pm 4, \pm 8$

$\dfrac{p}{q}: \pm 1, \pm 3, \pm 5, \pm 15, \pm\dfrac{1}{2}, \pm\dfrac{1}{4}, \pm\dfrac{1}{8},$

$\pm\dfrac{3}{2}, \pm\dfrac{3}{4}, \pm\dfrac{3}{8}, \pm\dfrac{5}{2}, \pm\dfrac{5}{4},$

$\pm\dfrac{5}{8}, \pm\dfrac{15}{2}, \pm\dfrac{15}{4}, \pm\dfrac{15}{8}$

b. $f(x) = 8x^3 - 36x^2 + 46x - 15$
3 sign variations; 3 or 1 positive real solutions.
$f(-x) = -8x^3 - 36x^2 - 46x - 15$
0 sign variations; no negative real solutions.

c.

$$\begin{array}{r|rrrr} \frac{1}{2} & 8 & -36 & 46 & -15 \\ & & 4 & -16 & 15 \\ \hline & 8 & -32 & 30 & 0 \end{array}$$

$\dfrac{1}{2}$ is a zero.

d.

$$8x^3 - 36x^2 + 46x - 15 = 0$$

$$\left(x - \dfrac{1}{2}\right)(8x^2 - 32x + 30) = 0$$

$$2\left(x - \dfrac{1}{2}\right)(4x^2 - 16x + 15) = 0$$

$$2\left(x - \dfrac{1}{2}\right)(2x - 5)(2x - 3) = 0$$

$$x = \dfrac{1}{2} \text{ or } x = \dfrac{5}{2} \text{ or } x = \dfrac{3}{2}$$

The solution set is $\left\{\dfrac{1}{2}, \dfrac{3}{2}, \dfrac{5}{2}\right\}$.

44. $2x^3 + 9x^2 - 7x + 1 = 0$

   a. $p: \pm 1$
      $q: \pm 1, \pm 2$

      $\dfrac{p}{q}: \pm 1, \pm \dfrac{1}{2}$

   b. $f(x) = 2x^3 + 9x^2 - 7x + 1$
      2 sign variations; 2 or 0 positive real zeros.
      $f(-x) = -2x^3 + 9x^2 + 7x + 1$
      1 sign variation; 1 negative real zero.

   c.

$\dfrac{1}{2}$	2	9	-7	1
		1	5	-1
	2	10	-2	0

      $-\dfrac{1}{2}$ is a zero.

   d.
$$2x^3 + 9x^2 - 7x + 1 = 0$$
$$\left(x - \dfrac{1}{2}\right)(2x^2 + 10x - 2) = 0$$
$$2\left(x - \dfrac{1}{2}\right)(x^2 + 5x - 1) = 0$$

      Solving $x^2 + 5x - 1 = 0$ using the quadratic

      formula gives $x = \dfrac{-5 \pm \sqrt{29}}{2}$

      The solution set is

$$\left\{ \dfrac{1}{2}, \dfrac{-5 + \sqrt{29}}{2}, \dfrac{-5 - \sqrt{29}}{2} \right\}.$$

45. $x^4 - x^3 - 7x^2 + x + 6 = 0$

   a. $p = \dfrac{p}{q}: \pm 1, \pm 2, \pm 3, \pm 6$

   b. $f(x) = x^4 - x^3 - 7x^2 + x + 6$
      2 sign variations; 2 or 0 positive real zeros.
      $f(-x) = x^4 + x^3 - 7x^2 - x + 6$
      2 sign variations; 2 or 0 negative real zeros.

   c.

1	1	-1	-7	1	6
		1	0	-7	-6
	1	0	-7	-6	0

-1	1	0	-7	-6
		-1	1	6
	1	-1	-6	0

   d.
$$x^4 - x^3 - 7x^2 + x + 6 = 0$$
$$(x-1)(x+1)(x^2 - x + 6) = 0$$
$$(x-1)(x+1)(x-3)(x+2) = 0$$
      The solution set is $\{-2, -1, 1, 3\}$.

46. $4x^4 + 7x^2 - 2 = 0$

   a. $p: \pm 1, \pm 2$
      $q: \pm 1, \pm 2, \pm 4$

      $\dfrac{p}{q}: \pm 1, \pm 2, \pm \dfrac{1}{2}, \pm \dfrac{1}{4}$

   b. $f(x) = 4x^4 + 7x^2 - 2$
      1 sign variation; 1 positive real zero.
      $f(-x) = 4x^4 + 7x^2 - 2$
      1 sign variation; 1 negative real zero.

   c.

$\dfrac{1}{2}$	4	0	7	0	-2
		2	1	4	2
	4	2	8	4	0

$-\dfrac{1}{2}$	4	2	8	4
		-2	0	-4
	4	0	8	0

d.
$$4x^4 + 7x^2 - 2 = 0$$

$$\left(x - \frac{1}{2}\right)\left(x + \frac{1}{2}\right)(4x^2 + 8) = 0$$

$$4\left(x - \frac{1}{2}\right)\left(x + \frac{1}{2}\right)(x^2 + 2) = 0$$

Solving $x^2 + 2 = 0$ using the quadratic formula gives $x = \pm 2i$

The solution set is $\left\{ -\frac{1}{2}, \frac{1}{2}, 2i, -2i \right\}$.

47. $f(x) = 2x^4 + x^3 - 9x^2 - 4x + 4$

a. $p: \pm 1, \pm 2, \pm 4$
$q: \pm 1, \pm 2$

$\dfrac{p}{q}: \pm 1, \pm 2, \pm 4, \pm \dfrac{1}{2}$

b. $f(x) = 2x^4 + x^3 - 9x^2 - 4x + 4$
2 sign variations; 2 or 0 positive real zeros.
$f(-x) = 2x^4 - x^3 - 9x^2 + 4x + 4$
2 sign variations; 2 or 0 negative real zeros.

c.

2	2	1	−9	−4	4
		4	10	2	−4
	2	5	1	−2	0

−1	2	5	1	−2
		−2	−3	2
	2	3	−2	0

d. $2x^2 + 3x - 2 = 0$
$(2x - 1)(x + 2) = 0$

$x = -2$ or $x = \dfrac{1}{2}$

The solution set is $\left\{ -2, -1, \dfrac{1}{2}, 2 \right\}$.

48. $f(x) = a_n(x - 2)(x - 2 + 3i)(x - 2 - 3i)$
$f(x) = a_n(x - 2)(x^2 - 4x + 13)$
$f(1) = a_n(1 - 2)\left[1^2 - 4(1) + 13\right]$
$-10 = -10 a_n$
$a_n = 1$
$f(x) = 1(x - 2)(x^2 - 4x + 13)$
$f(x) = x^3 - 4x^2 + 13x - 2x^2 + 8x - 26$
$f(x) = x^3 - 6x^2 + 21x - 26$

49.
$$f(x) = a_n(x - i)(x + i)(x + 3)^2$$
$$f(x) = a_n(x^2 + 1)(x^2 + 6x + 9)$$
$$f(-1) = a_n\left[(-1)^2 + 1\right]\left[(-1)^2 + 6(-1) + 9\right]$$
$$16 = 8a_n$$
$$a_n = 2$$
$$f(x) = 2(x^2 + 1)(x^2 + 6x + 9)$$
$$f(x) = 2(x^4 + 6x^3 + 9x^2 + x^2 + 6x + 9)$$
$$f(x) = 2x^4 + 12x^3 + 20x^2 + 12x + 18$$

50. $f(x) = 2x^4 + 3x^3 + 3x - 2$
$p: \pm 1, \pm 2$
$q: \pm 1, \pm 2$

$\dfrac{p}{q}: \pm 1, \pm 2, \pm \dfrac{1}{2}$

−2	2	3	0	3	−2
		−4	2	−4	2
	2	−1	2	−1	0

$$2x^4 + 3x^3 + 3x - 2 = 0$$
$$(x + 2)(2x^3 - x^2 + 2x - 1) = 0$$
$$(x + 2)[x^2(2x - 1) + (2x - 1)] = 0$$
$$(x + 2)(2x - 1)(x^2 + 1) = 0$$
$$x = -2, \ x = \frac{1}{2} \text{ or } x = \pm i$$

The zeros are -2, $\dfrac{1}{2}$, $\pm i$.

$$f(x) = (x - i)(x + i)(x + 2)(2x - 1)$$

51. $g(x) = x^4 - 6x^3 + x^2 + 24x + 16$
$p: \pm 1, \pm 2, \pm 4, \pm 8, \pm 16$
$q: \pm 1$

$\dfrac{p}{q}: \pm 1, \pm 2, \pm 4, \pm 8, \pm 16$

−1	1	−6	1	24	16
		−1	7	−8	−16
	1	−7	8	16	0

$$x^4 - 6x^3 + x^2 + 24x + 16 = 0$$
$$(x + 1)(x^3 - 7x^2 + 8x + 16) = 0$$

$$\begin{array}{r|rrrr} -1 & 1 & -7 & 8 & 16 \\ & & -1 & 8 & -16 \\ \hline & 1 & -8 & 16 & 0 \end{array}$$

$(x+1)^2(x^2-8x+16)=0$

$(x+1)^2(x-4)^2=0$

$x=-1$ or $x=4$

$g(x)=(x+1)^2(x-4)^2$

52. 4 real zeros, one with multiplicity two

53. 3 real zeros; 2 nonreal complex zeros

54. 2 real zeros, one with multiplicity two; 2 nonreal complex zeros

55. 1 real zero; 4 nonreal complex zeros

56. $g(x)=\dfrac{1}{(x+2)^2}-1$

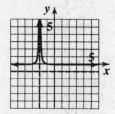

$$g(x) = \frac{1}{(x+2)^2} - 1$$

57. $h(x)=\dfrac{1}{x-1}+3$

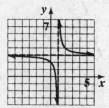

$$h(x) = \frac{1}{x-1} + 3$$

58. $f(x)=\dfrac{2x}{x^2-9}$

Symmetry: $f(-x)=-\dfrac{2x}{x^2-9}=-f(x)$

origin symmetry

x-intercept:

$0=\dfrac{2x}{x^2-9}$

$2x=0$

$x=0$

y-intercept: $y=\dfrac{2(0)}{0^2-9}=0$

Vertical asymptote:

$x^2-9=0$

$(x-3)(x+3)=0$

$x=3$ and $x=-3$

Horizontal asymptote:

$n<m$, so $y=0$

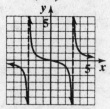

$$f(x) = \frac{2x}{x^2-9}$$

59. $g(x)=\dfrac{2x-4}{x+3}$

Symmetry: $g(-x)=\dfrac{-2x-4}{x+3}$

$g(-x)\neq g(x)$, $g(-x)\neq -g(x)$

No symmetry

x-intercept:

$2x-4=0$

$x=2$

y-intercept: $y=\dfrac{2(0)-4}{(0)+3}=-\dfrac{4}{3}$

Vertical asymptote:

$x+3=0$

$x=-3$

Horizontal asymptote:

$n=m$, so $y=\dfrac{2}{1}=2$

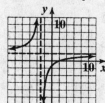

$$f(x) = \frac{2x-4}{x+3}$$

60. $h(x) = \dfrac{x^2 - 3x - 4}{x^2 - x - 6}$

Symmetry: $h(-x) = \dfrac{x^2 + 3x - 4}{x^2 + x - 6}$

$h(-x) \neq h(x), h(-x) \neq -h(x)$
No symmetry
x-intercepts:
$x^2 - 3x - 4 = 0$
$(x - 4)(x + 1)$
$x = 4 \quad x = -1$

y-intercept: $y = \dfrac{0^2 - 3(0) - 4}{0^2 - 0 - 6} = \dfrac{2}{3}$

Vertical asymptotes:
$x^2 - x - 6 = 0$
$(x - 3)(x + 2) = 0$
$x = 3, -2$

Horizontal asymptote:
$n = m$, so $y = \dfrac{1}{1} = 1$

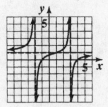

$h(x) = \dfrac{x^2 - 3x - 4}{x^2 - x - 6}$

61. $r(x) = \dfrac{x^2 + 4x + 3}{(x + 2)^2}$

Symmetry: $r(-x) = \dfrac{x^2 - 4x + 3}{(-x + 2)^2}$

$r(-x) \neq r(x), r(-x) \neq -r(x)$
No symmetry
x-intercepts:
$x^2 + 4x + 3 = 0$
$(x + 3)(x + 1) = 0$
$x = -3, -1$

y-intercept: $y = \dfrac{0^2 + 4(0) + 3}{(0 + 2)^2} = \dfrac{3}{4}$

Vertical asymptote:
$x + 2 = 0$
$x = -2$

Horizontal asymptote:
$n = m$, so $y = \dfrac{1}{1} = 1$

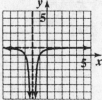

$r(x) = \dfrac{x^2 + 4x + 3}{(x + 4)^2}$

62. $y = \dfrac{x^2}{x + 1}$

Symmetry: $f(-x) = \dfrac{x^2}{-x + 1}$

$f(-x) \neq f(x), f(-x) \neq -f(x)$
No symmetry
x-intercept:
$x^2 = 0$
$x = 0$

y-intercept: $y = \dfrac{0^2}{0 + 1} = 0$

Vertical asymptote:
$x + 1 = 0$
$x = -1$

$n > m$, no horizontal asymptote.
Slant asymptote:

$y = x - 1 + \dfrac{1}{x + 1}$

$y = x - 1$

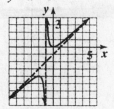

$y = \dfrac{x^2}{x + 1}$

63. $y = \dfrac{x^2 + 2x - 3}{x - 3}$

Symmetry: $f(-x) = \dfrac{x^2 - 2x - 3}{-x - 3}$

$f(-x) \neq f(x), f(-x) \neq -f(x)$

No symmetry

x-intercepts:

$x^2 + 2x - 3 = 0$

$(x + 3)(x - 1) = 0$

$x = -3, 1$

y-intercept: $y = \dfrac{0^2 + 2(0) - 3}{0 - 3} = \dfrac{-3}{-3} = 1$

Vertical asymptote:

$x - 3 = 0$

$x = 3$

Horizontal asymptote:

$n > m$, so no horizontal asymptote.

Slant asymptote:

$y = x + 5 + \dfrac{12}{x - 3}$

$y = x + 5$

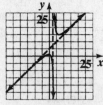

$$f(x) = \dfrac{x^2 + 2x - 3}{x - 3}$$

64. $f(x) = \dfrac{-2x^3}{x^2 + 1}$

Symmetry: $f(-x) = \dfrac{2}{x^2 + 1} = -f(x)$

Origin symmetry

x-intercept:

$-2x^3 = 0$

$x = 0$

y-intercept: $y = \dfrac{-2(0)^3}{0^2 + 1} = \dfrac{0}{1} = 0$

Vertical asymptote:

$x^2 + 1 = 0$

$x^2 = -1$

No vertical asymptote.

Horizontal asymptote:

$n > m$, so no horizontal asymptote.

Slant asymptote:

$f(x) = -2x + \dfrac{2x}{x^2 + 1}$

$y = -2x$

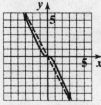

$$f(x) = \dfrac{-2x^3}{x^2 + 1}$$

65. $g(x) = \dfrac{4x^2 - 16x + 16}{2x - 3}$

Symmetry: $g(-x) = \dfrac{4x^2 + 16x + 16}{-2x - 3}$

$g(-x) \neq g(x), g(-x) \neq -g(x)$

No symmetry

x-intercept:

$4x^2 - 16x + 16 = 0$

$4(x - 2)^2 = 0$

$x = 2$

y-intercept:

$y = \dfrac{4(0)^2 - 16(0) + 16}{2(0) - 3} = -\dfrac{16}{3}$

Vertical asymptote:

$2x - 3 = 0$

$x = \dfrac{3}{2}$

Horizontal asymptote:

$n > m$, so no horizontal asymptote.

Slant asymptote:

$g(x) = 2x - 5 + \dfrac{1}{2x - 3}$

$y = 2x - 5$

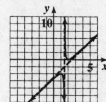

$$g(x) = \dfrac{4x^2 - 16x + 16}{2x - 3}$$

66. a. $C(x) = 50,000 + 25x$

b. $\overline{C}(x) = \dfrac{25x + 50,000}{x}$

c. $\overline{C}(50) = \dfrac{25(50) + 50,000}{50} = 1025$

When 50 calculators are manufactured, it costs $1025 to manufacture each.

$\overline{C}(100) = \dfrac{25(100) + 50,000}{100} = 525$

When 100 calculators are manufactured, it costs $525 to manufacture each.

$\overline{C}(1000) = \dfrac{25(1000) + 50,000}{1000} = 75$

When 1,000 calculators are manufactured, it costs $75 to manufacture each.

$\overline{C}(100,000) = \dfrac{25(100,000) + 50,000}{100,000} = 25.5$

When 100,000 calculators are manufactured, it costs $25.50 to manufacture each.

d. $n = m$, so $y = \dfrac{25}{1} = 25$ is the horizontal asymptote. Minimum costs will approach $25.

70. a. $f(x) = \dfrac{1.96x + 3.14}{3.04x + 21.79}$

b. $y = \dfrac{1.96}{3.04} = 0.645$

The percentage of inmates that are in for violent crimes will approach 64.5%.

c.   Answers may vary.

71. $2x^2 + 5x - 3 < 0$
Solve the related quadratic equation.
$2x^2 + 5x - 3 = 0$
$(2x - 1)(x + 3) = 0$

The boundary points are -3 and $\dfrac{1}{2}$.

Testing each interval gives a solution set of $\left(-3, \dfrac{1}{2}\right)$.

67. a. $C(90) - C(50) = \dfrac{200(90)}{100 - 90} - \dfrac{200(50)}{100 - 50}$
$C(90) - C(50) = 1800 - 200$
$C(90) - C(50) = 1600$
The difference in cost of removing 90% versus 50% of the contaminants is 16 million dollars.

b. $x = 100$; No amount of money can remove 100% of the contaminants, since $C(x)$ increases without bound as x approaches 100.

68. $f(x) = \dfrac{150x + 120}{0.05x + 1}$

$n = m$, so $y = \dfrac{150}{0.05} = 3000$

The number of fish available in the pond approaches 3000.

69. $P(x) = \dfrac{72,900}{100x^2 + 729}$

$n < m$ so $y = 0$

As the number of years of education increases the percentage rate of unemployment approaches zero.

72. $2x^2 + 9x + 4 \geq 0$

Solve the related quadratic equation.

$$2x^2 + 9x + 4 = 0$$
$$(2x+1)(x+4) = 0$$

The boundary points are -4 and $-\frac{1}{2}$.

Testing each interval gives a solution set of $\left(-\infty, -4\right] \cup \left[-\frac{1}{2}, \infty\right)$

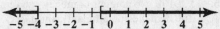

73. $x^3 + 2x^2 > 3x$

Solve the related quadratic equation.

$$x^3 + 2x^2 = 3x$$
$$x^3 + 2x^2 - 3x = 0$$
$$x(x^2 + 2x - 3) = 0$$
$$x(x+3)(x-1) = 0$$

The boundary points are -3, 0, and 1.

Testing each interval gives a solution set of $\left(-3, 0\right) \cup \left(1, \infty\right)$

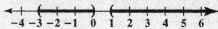

74. $\dfrac{x-6}{x+2} > 0$

Find the values of x that make the numerator and denominator zero.
The boundary points are -2 and 6.

Testing each interval gives a solution set of $\left(-\infty, -2\right) \cup \left(6, \infty\right)$.

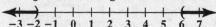

75. $\dfrac{(x+1)(x-2)}{x-1} \geq 0$

Find the values of x that make the numerator and denominator zero.
The boundary points are -1, 1 and 2. We exclude 1 from the solution set, since this would make the denominator zero.

Testing each interval gives a solution set of $\left[-1, 1\right) \cup \left[2, \infty\right)$.

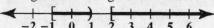

76. $\dfrac{x+3}{x-4} \le 5$

Express the inequality so that one side is zero.

$$\dfrac{x+3}{x-4} - 5 \le 0$$

$$\dfrac{x+3}{x-4} - \dfrac{5(x-4)}{x-4} \le 0$$

$$\dfrac{-4x+23}{x-4} \le 0$$

Find the values of x that make the numerator and denominator zero.

The boundary points are 4 and $\dfrac{23}{4}$. We exclude 4 from the solution set, since this would make the denominator zero.

Testing each interval gives a solution set of $(-\infty, 4) \cup \left[\dfrac{23}{4}, \infty\right)$.

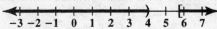

77. $s = -16t^2 + v_0 t + s_0$

$32 < -16t^2 + 48t + 0$

$0 < -16t^2 + 48t - 32$

$0 < -16(t^2 - 3t + 2)$

$0 < -16(t-2)(t-1)$

	F		T		F
		1		2	

The projectile's height exceeds 32 feet during the time period from 1 to 2 seconds.

78. $b = ke$

$98 = k \cdot 1400$

$k = 0.07$

$b = 0.07e$

$b = 0.07(2200) = \$154$

79. $d = kt^2$

$144 = k(3)^2$

$k = 16$

$d = 16t^2$

$d = 16(10)^2 = 1,600$ ft

80. $t = \dfrac{k}{r}$

$4 = \dfrac{k}{50}$

$k = 200$

$t = \dfrac{200}{r}$

$t = \dfrac{200}{40} = 5$ hours

81. $l = \dfrac{k}{d^2}$

$28 = \dfrac{k}{8^2}$

$k = 1792$

$l = \dfrac{1792}{d^2}$

$l = \dfrac{1792}{4^2} = 112$ decibels

82. $t = \dfrac{kc}{w}$

$10 = \dfrac{k \cdot 30}{6}$

$10 = 5h$

$h = 2$

$t = \dfrac{2c}{w}$

$t = \dfrac{2(40)}{5} = 16$ hours

83. $V = khB$

$175 = k \cdot 15 \cdot 35$

$k = \dfrac{1}{3}$

$V = \dfrac{1}{3} hB$

$V = \dfrac{1}{3} \cdot 20 \cdot 120 = 800 \text{ ft}^3$

Chapter 3 Test

1. $f(x) = (x+1)^2 + 4$

vertex: $(-1, 4)$

axis of symmetry: $x = -1$

x-intercepts:

$(x+1)^2 + 4 = 0$

$x^2 + 2x + 5 = 0$

$x = \dfrac{-2 \pm \sqrt{4-20}}{2} = -1 \pm 2i$

no x-intercepts

y-intercept:

$f(0) = (0+1)^2 + 4 = 5$

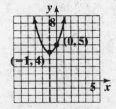

$f(x) = (x + 1)^2 + 4$

Domain: $(-\infty, \infty)$; Range: $[4, \infty)$

2. $f(x) = x^2 - 2x - 3$

$x = \dfrac{-b}{2a} = \dfrac{2}{2} = 1$

$f(1) = 1^2 - 2(1) - 3 = -4$

vertex: $(1, -4)$

axis of symmetry $x = 1$

x-intercepts:

$x^2 - 2x - 3 = 0$

$(x-3)(x+1) = 0$

$x = 3$ or $x = -1$

y-intercept:

$f(0) = 0^2 - 2(0) - 3 = -3$

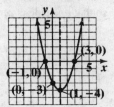

$f(x) = x^2 - 2x - 3$

Domain: $(-\infty, \infty)$; Range: $[-4, \infty)$

3. $f(x) = -2x^2 + 12x - 16$

Since the coefficient of x^2 is negative, the graph of $f(x)$ opens down and $f(x)$ has a maximum point.

$x = \dfrac{-12}{2(-2)} = 3$

$f(3) = -2(3)^2 + 12(3) - 16$

$= -18 + 36 - 16$

$= 2$

Maximum point: $(3, 2)$

Domain: $(-\infty, \infty)$; Range: $(-\infty, 2]$

4. $f(x) = -x^2 + 46x - 360$

$x = -\dfrac{b}{2a} = \dfrac{-46}{-2} = 23$

23 computers will maximize profit.

$f(23) = -(23)^2 + 46(23) - 360 = 169$

Maximum daily profit = $16,900.

5. Let x = one of the numbers;

$14 - x$ = the other number.

The product is $f(x) = x(14 - x)$

$f(x) = x(14 - x) = -x^2 + 14x$

The x-coordinate of the maximum is

$x = -\dfrac{b}{2a} = -\dfrac{14}{2(-1)} = -\dfrac{14}{-2} = 7$.

$f(7) = -7^2 + 14(7) = 49$

The vertex is $(7, 49)$. The maximum product is 49. This occurs when the two number are 7 and $14 - 7 = 7$.

6. a. $f(x) = x^3 - 5x^2 - 4x + 20$
   $$x^3 - 5x^2 - 4x + 20 = 0$$
   $$x^2(x - 5) - 4(x - 5) = 0$$
   $$(x - 5)(x - 2)(x + 2) = 0$$
   $$x = 5, 2, -2$$
   The solution set is $\{5, 2, -2\}$.

   b. The degree of the polynomial is odd and the leading coefficient is positive. Thus the graph falls to the left and rises to the right.

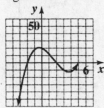

7. $f(x) = x^5 - x$
   Since the degree of the polynomial is odd and the leading coefficient is positive, the graph of f should fall to the left and rise to the right. The x-intercepts should be -1 and 1.

8. a. The integral root is 2.

   b.
   $$\begin{array}{r|rrrr} 2 & 6 & -19 & 16 & -4 \\ & & 12 & -14 & 4 \\ \hline & 6 & -7 & 2 & 0 \end{array}$$
   $$6x^2 - 7x + 2 = 0$$
   $$(3x - 2)(2x - 1) = 0$$
   $$x = \frac{2}{3} \text{ or } x = \frac{1}{2}$$

   The other two roots are $\frac{1}{2}$ and $\frac{2}{3}$.

9. $2x^3 + 11x^2 - 7x - 6 = 0$
   $p: \pm 1, \pm 2, \pm 3, \pm 6$
   $q: \pm 1, \pm 2$
   $$\frac{p}{q}: \pm 1, \pm 2, \pm 3, \pm 6, \pm \frac{1}{2}, \pm \frac{3}{2}$$

10. $f(x) = 3x^5 - 2x^4 - 2x^2 + x - 1$
    $f(x)$ has 3 sign variations.
    $f(-x) = -3x^5 - 2x^4 - 2x^2 - x - 1$
    $f(-x)$ has no sign variations.
    There are 3 or 1 positive real solutions and no negative real solutions.

11. $x^3 + 9x^2 + 16x - 6 = 0$
    Since the leading coefficient is 1, the possible rational zeros are the factors of 6
    $$p = \frac{p}{q}: \pm 1, \pm 2, \pm 3, \pm 6$$
    $$\begin{array}{r|rrrr} -3 & 1 & 9 & 16 & -6 \\ & & -3 & -18 & 6 \\ \hline & 1 & 6 & -2 & 0 \end{array}$$
    Thus $x = 3$ is a root.
    Solve the quotient $x^2 + 6x - 2 = 0$ using the quadratic formula to find the remaining roots.
    $$x = \frac{-b \pm \sqrt{b^2 - 4ac}}{2a}$$
    $$x = \frac{-(6) \pm \sqrt{(6)^2 - 4(1)(-2)}}{2(1)}$$
    $$= \frac{-6 \pm \sqrt{44}}{2}$$
    $$= -3 \pm \sqrt{11}$$
    The zeros are -3, $-3 + \sqrt{11}$, and $-3 - \sqrt{11}$.

12. $f(x) = 2x^4 - x^3 - 13x^2 + 5x + 15$

    a. Possible rational zeros are:
    $p: \pm 1, \pm 3, \pm 5, \pm 15$
    $q: \pm 1, \pm 2$
    $$\frac{p}{q}: \pm 1, \pm 3, \pm 5, \pm 15, \pm \frac{1}{2}, \pm \frac{3}{2}, \pm \frac{5}{2}, \pm \frac{15}{2}$$

    b. Verify that -1 and $\frac{3}{2}$ are zeros as it appears in the graph:
    $$\begin{array}{r|rrrrr} -1 & 2 & -1 & -13 & 5 & 15 \\ & & -2 & 3 & 10 & -15 \\ \hline & 2 & -3 & -10 & 15 & 0 \end{array}$$
    $$\begin{array}{r|rrrr} \frac{3}{2} & 2 & -3 & -10 & 15 \\ & & 3 & 0 & -15 \\ \hline & 2 & 0 & -10 & 0 \end{array}$$
    Thus, -1 and $\frac{3}{2}$ are zeros, and the polynomial factors as follows:
    $$2x^4 - x^3 - 13x^2 + 5x + 15 = 0$$
    $$(x + 1)(2x^3 - 3x^2 - 10x + 15) = 0$$
    $$(x + 1)\left(x - \frac{3}{2}\right)(2x^2 - 10) = 0$$

289

Find the remaining zeros by solving:

$$2x^2 - 10 = 0$$
$$2x^2 = 10$$
$$x^2 = 5$$
$$x = \pm\sqrt{5}$$

The zeros are -1, $\dfrac{3}{2}$, and $\pm\sqrt{5}$.

13. $f(x)$ has zeros at -2 and 1. The zero at -2 has multiplicity of 2.

$$x^3 + 3x^2 - 4 = (x - 1)(x + 2)^2$$

14. $f(x) = a_0(x + 1)(x - 1)(x + i)(x - i)$

$$= a_0(x^2 - 1)(x^2 + 1)$$
$$= a_0(x^4 - 1)$$

Since $f(3) = 160$, then

$$a_0(3^4 - 1) = 160$$
$$a_0(80) = 160$$
$$a_0 = \dfrac{160}{80}$$
$$a_0 = 2$$
$$f(x) = 2(x^4 - 1) = 2x^4 - 2$$

15. $f(x) = -3x^3 - 4x^2 + x + 2$

The graph shows a root at $x = -1$.
Use synthetic division to verify this root.

$$
\begin{array}{r|rrrr}
-1 & -3 & -4 & 1 & 2 \\
   &   & 3 & 1 & 4 \\
\hline
   & -3 & -1 & 2 & 0 \\
\end{array}
$$

Factor the quotient to find the remaining zeros.

$$-3x^2 - x + 2 = 0$$
$$-(3x - 2)(x + 1) = 0$$

The zeros (x-intercepts) are -1 and $\dfrac{2}{3}$.

The y-intercept is $f(0) = 2$

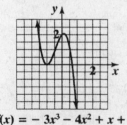

$$f(x) = -3x^3 - 4x^2 + x + 2$$

16. $f(x) = \dfrac{1}{(x + 3)^2}$

Domain: $\{x \mid x \neq -3\}$ or $(-\infty, -3) \cup (-3, \infty)$

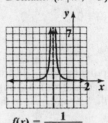

$$f(x) = \dfrac{1}{(x + 3)^2}$$

17. $f(x) = \dfrac{1}{x - 1} + 2$

Domain: $\{x \mid x \neq 1\}$ or $(-\infty, 1) \cup (1, \infty)$

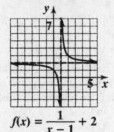

$$f(x) = \dfrac{1}{x - 1} + 2$$

18. $f(x) = \dfrac{x}{x^2 - 16}$

Domain: $\{x \mid x \neq 4, x \neq -4\}$

Symmetry: $f(-x) = \dfrac{-x}{x^2 - 16} = -f(x)$

y-axis symmetry
x-intercept: $x = 0$

y-intercept: $y = \dfrac{0}{0^2 - 16} = 0$

Vertical asymptotes:

$$x^2 - 16 = 0$$
$$(x - 4)(x + 4) = 0$$
$$x = 4, -4$$

Horizontal asymptote:
$n < m$, so $y = 0$ is the horizontal asymptote.

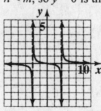

$$f(x) = \dfrac{x}{x^2 - 16}$$

19. $f(x) = \dfrac{x^2 - 9}{x - 2}$

Domain: $\{x \mid x \neq 2\}$

Symmetry: $f(-x) = \dfrac{x^2 - 9}{-x - 2}$

$f(-x) \neq f(x), f(-x) \neq -f(x)$
No symmetry

x-intercepts:
$x^2 - 9 = 0$
$(x - 3)(x + 3) = 0$
$x = 3, -3$

y-intercept: $y = \dfrac{0^2 - 9}{0 - 2} = \dfrac{9}{2}$

Vertical asymptote:
$x - 2 = 0$
$x = 2$
Horizontal asymptote:
$n > m$, so no horizontal asymptote exists.

Slant asymptote: $f(x) = x + 2 - \dfrac{5}{x - 2}$

$y = x + 2$

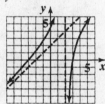

$f(x) = \dfrac{x^2 - 9}{x - 2}$

20. $f(x) = \dfrac{x + 1}{x^2 + 2x - 3}$

$x^2 + 2x - 3 = (x + 3)(x - 1)$

Domain: $\{x \mid x \neq -3, x \neq 1\}$

Symmetry: $f(-x) = \dfrac{-x + 1}{x^2 - 2x - 3}$

$f(-x) \neq f(x), f(-x) \neq -f(x)$
No symmetry
x-intercept:
$x + 1 = 0$
$x = -1$

y-intercept: $y = \dfrac{0 + 1}{0^2 + 2(0) - 3} = -\dfrac{1}{3}$

Vertical asymptotes:
$x^2 + 2x - 3 = 0$
$(x + 3)(x - 1) = 0$
$x -3, 1$

Horizontal asymptote:
$n < m$, so $y = 0$ is the horizontal asymptote.

$f(x) = \dfrac{x + 1}{x^2 + 2x - 3}$

21. $f(x) = \dfrac{4x^2}{x^2 + 3}$

Domain: all real numbers

Symmetry: $f(-x) = \dfrac{4x^2}{x^2 + 3} = f(x)$

y-axis symmetry
x-intercept:
$4x^2 = 0$
$x = 0$

y-intercept: $y = \dfrac{4(0)^2}{0^2 + 3} = 0$

Vertical asymptote:
$x^2 + 3 = 0$
$x^2 = -3$
No vertical asymptote.
Horizontal asymptote:

$n = m$, so $y = \dfrac{4}{1} = 4$ is the horizontal asymptote.

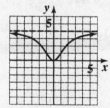

$f(x) = \dfrac{4x^2}{x^2 + 3}$

22. a. $\overline{C}(x) = \dfrac{300{,}000 + 10x}{x}$

b. Since the degree of the numerator equals the degree of the denominator, the

horizontal asymptote is $x = \dfrac{10}{1} = 10$.

This represents the fact that as the number of televisions produced increases, the average approaches \$10 per unit.

291

23. **a.** When $x = 5, y = 0.89$
After 5 learning tries, 89% of the responses were correct.

b. When $x = 11, y = 0.95$
After 11 learning tries, 95% of the responses were correct.

c. $y = .9/.9 = 1$
As the number of learning tries increases, the correct responses approaches 100%.

24. $$x^2 < x + 12$$
$$x^2 - x - 12 < 0$$
$$(x + 3)(x - 4) < 0$$
Boundary values: –3 and 4
Solution set: $(-3, 4)$

25. $$\frac{2x + 1}{x - 3} \le 3$$
$$\frac{2x + 1}{x - 3} - 3 \le 0$$
$$\frac{10 - x}{x - 3} \le 0$$
Boundary values: 3 and 10
Solution set: $(-\infty, 3) \cup [10, \infty)$

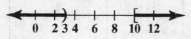

26. $$i = \frac{k}{d^2}$$
$$20 = \frac{k}{15^2}$$
$$4500 = k$$

$$i = \frac{4500}{d^2} = \frac{4500}{10^2} = 45 \text{ foot-candles}$$

Cumulative Review Exercises (Chapters P–3)

1. Domain: $(-2, 2)$ Range: $[0, \infty)$

2. The zero at –1 touches the x-axis at turns around so it must have a minimum multiplicity of 2. The zero at 1 touches the x-axis at turns around so it must have a minimum multiplicity of 2.

3. There is a relative maximum at the point (0, 3).

4. $(f \circ f)(-1) = f\big(f(-1)\big) = f(0) = 3$

5. $f(x) \to \infty$ as $\underline{x \to -2^+}$ or as $\underline{x \to 2^-}$

6.

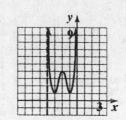

7. $|2x - 1| = 3$
$2x - 1 = 3$
$2x = 4$
$x = 2$
$2x - 1 = -3$
$2x = -2$
$x = -1$
The solution set is $\{2, -1\}$.

8. $3x^2 - 5x + 1 = 0$
$$x = \frac{5 \pm \sqrt{25 - 12}}{6} = \frac{5 \pm \sqrt{13}}{6}$$
The solution set is $\left\{ \dfrac{5 + \sqrt{13}}{6}, \dfrac{5 - \sqrt{13}}{6} \right\}$.

9. $9 + \dfrac{3}{x} = \dfrac{2}{x^2}$
$9x^2 + 3x = 2$
$9x^2 + 3x - 2 = 0$
$(3x - 1)(3x + 2) = 0$
$3x - 1 = 0 \qquad 3x + 2 = 0$
$x = \dfrac{1}{3} \quad$ or $\quad x = -\dfrac{2}{3}$
The solution set is $\left\{ \dfrac{1}{3}, -\dfrac{2}{3} \right\}$.

10. $x^3 + 2x^2 - 5x - 6 = 0$

$p: \pm 1, \pm 2, \pm 3, \pm 6$

$q: \pm 1$

$\dfrac{p}{q}: \pm 1, \pm 2, \pm 3, \pm 6$

$$
\begin{array}{r|rrrr}
-3 & 1 & 2 & -5 & -6 \\
   &   & -3 & 3 & 6 \\
\hline
   & 1 & -1 & -2 & 0
\end{array}
$$

$x^3 + 2x^2 - 5x - 6 = 0$

$(x+3)(x^2 - x - 2) = 0$

$(x+3)(x+1)(x-2) = 0$

$x = -3$ or $x = -1$ or $x = 2$

The solution set is $\{-3, -1, 2\}$.

11. $|2x - 5| > 3$

$2x - 5 > 3$

$2x > 8$

$x > 4$

$2x - 5 < -3$

$2x < 2$

$x < 1$

$(-\infty, 1)$ or $(4, \infty)$

12. $\qquad 3x^2 > 2x + 5$

$3x^2 - 2x - 5 > 0$

$3x^2 - 2x - 5 = 0$

$(3x - 5)(x + 1) = 0$

$x = \dfrac{5}{3}$ or $x = -1$

Test intervals are $(-\infty, -1)$, $\left(-1, \dfrac{5}{3}\right)$, $\left(\dfrac{5}{3}, \infty\right)$.

Testing points, the solution is

$(-\infty, -1)$ or $\left(\dfrac{5}{3}, \infty\right)$.

13. $f(x) = x^3 - 4x^2 - x + 4$

x-intercepts:

$x^3 - 4x^2 - x + 4 = 0$

$x^2(x - 4) - 1(x - 4) = 0$

$(x - 4)(x^2 - 1) = 0$

$(x - 4)(x + 1)(x - 1) = 0$

$x = -1, 1, 4$

x-intercepts:

$f(0) = 0^3 - 4(0)^2 - 0 + 4 = 4$

The degree of the polynomial is odd and the leading coefficient is positive. Thus the graph falls to the left and rises to the right.

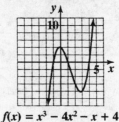

$f(x) = x^3 - 4x^2 - x + 4$

14. $f(x) = x^2 + 2x - 8$

$x = \dfrac{-b}{2a} = \dfrac{-2}{2} = -1$

$f(-1) = (-1)^2 + 2(-1) - 8$

$\qquad = 1 - 2 - 8 = -9$

vertex: $(-1, -9)$

x-intercepts:

$x^2 + 2x - 8 = 0$

$(x + 4)(x - 2) = 0$

$x = -4$ or $x = 2$

y-intercept: $f(0) = -8$

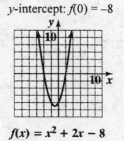

$f(x) = x^2 + 2x - 8$

15. $f(x) = x^2(x - 3)$

zeros: $x = 0$ (multiplicity 2) and $x = 3$

y-intercept: $y = 0$

$f(x) = x^3 - 3x^2$

$n = 3$, $a_n = 0$ so the graph falls to the left and rises to the right.

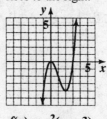

$f(x) = x^2(x - 3)$

16. $f(x) = \dfrac{x-1}{x-2}$

vertical asymptote: $x = 2$

horizontal asymptote: $y = 1$

x-intercept: $x = 1$

y-intercept: $y = \dfrac{1}{2}$

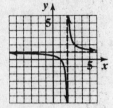

17.

18.

$x^2 + y^2 - 2x + 4y - 4 = 0$

19. $(f \circ g)(x) = f(g(x))$

$\qquad = 2(4x-1)^2 - (4x-1) - 1$

$\qquad = 32x^2 - 20x + 2$

20. $\dfrac{f(x+h) - f(x)}{h} = \dfrac{\left[2(x+h)^2 - (x+h) - 1\right] - \left[2x^2 - x - 1\right]}{h}$

$\qquad = \dfrac{2x^2 + 4hx - x + 2h^2 - h - 1 - 2x^2 + x + 1}{h}$

$\qquad = \dfrac{4hx + 2h^2 - h}{h}$

$\qquad = 4x + 2h - 1$

Chapter 4

Section 4.1

Check Point Exercises

1. Substitute 60 for x and evaluate the function at 60. $f(60) = 13.49(0.967)^{-60} - 1 \approx 1$
   Thus, one O-ring is expected to fail at a temperature of 60°F.

2. Begin by setting up a table of coordinates.

x	$f(x) = 3^x$
-3	$f(-3) = 3^{-3} = \frac{1}{27}$
-2	$f(-2) = 3^{-2} = \frac{1}{9}$
-1	$f(-1) = 3^{-1} = \frac{1}{3}$
0	$f(0) = 3^0 = 1$
1	$f(1) = 3^1 = 3$
2	$f(2) = 3^2 = 9$
3	$f(3) = 3^3 = 27$

   Plot these points, connecting them with a continuous curve.

   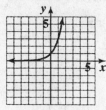

   $f(x) = 3^x$

3. Begin by setting up a table of coordinates.

x	$f(x) = \left(\frac{1}{3}\right)^x$
-2	$\left(\frac{1}{3}\right)^{-2} = 9$
-1	$\left(\frac{1}{3}\right)^{-1} = 3$
0	$\left(\frac{1}{3}\right)^0 = 1$
1	$\left(\frac{1}{3}\right)^1 = \frac{1}{3}$
2	$\left(\frac{1}{3}\right)^2 = \frac{1}{9}$

   Plot these points, connecting them with a continuous curve.

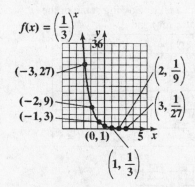

4. Note that the function $g(x) = 3^{x-1}$ has the general form $g(x) = b^{x+c}$ where $c = -1$. Because $c < 0$, we graph $g(x) = 3^{x-1}$ by shifting the graph of $f(x) = 3^x$ one unit to the right. Construct a table showing some of the coordinates for f and g.

x	$f(x) = 3^x$	$g(x) = 3^{x-1}$
-2	$3^{-2} = \frac{1}{9}$	$3^{-2-1} = 3^{-3} = \frac{1}{27}$
-1	$3^{-1} = \frac{1}{3}$	$3^{-1-1} = 3^{-2} = \frac{1}{9}$
0	$3^0 = 1$	$3^{0-1} = 3^{-1} = \frac{1}{3}$
1	$3^1 = 3$	$3^{1-1} = 3^0 = 1$
2	$3^2 = 9$	$3^{2-1} = 3^1 = 3$

   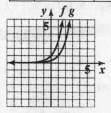

   $f(x) = 3^x$
   $g(x) = 3^x - 1$

295

5. Note that the function $g(x) = 2^x + 1$ has the general form $g(x) = b^x + c$ where $c = 1$. Because $c > 0$, we graph $g(x) = 2^x + 1$ by shifting the graph of $f(x) = 2^x$ up one unit. Construct a table showing some of the coordinates for f and g.

x	$f(x) - 2^x$	$g(x) = 2^x + 1$
-2	$2^{-2} = \frac{1}{4}$	$2^{-2} + 1 = \frac{1}{4} + 1 = \frac{5}{4}$
-1	$2^{-1} = \frac{1}{2}$	$2^{-1} + 1 = \frac{1}{2} + 1 = \frac{3}{2}$
0	$2^0 = 1$	$2^0 + 1 = 1 + 1 = 2$
1	$2^1 = 2$	$2^1 + 1 = 2 + 1 = 3$
2	$2^2 = 4$	$2^2 + 1 = 4 + 1 = 5$

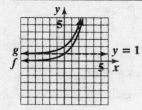

$$f(x) = 2^x$$
$$g(x) = 2^x + 1$$

6. $f(x) = 6.4e^{0.0123x}$

The year 2050 is 46 years after 2004. Find $f(46)$.

$$f(x) = 6.4e^{0.0123x}$$
$$f(46) = 6.4e^{0.0123(46)}$$
$$\approx 11.27$$

The world population is predicted to be 11.27 billion in 2050.

7.   a. $A = P\left(1 + \frac{r}{n}\right)^{nt}$

$$A = 10,000\left(1 + \frac{0.08}{4}\right)^{4(5)}$$
$$= \$14,859.47$$

b. $A = Pe^{rt}$
$$A = 10,000e^{0.08(5)}$$
$$= \$14,918.25$$

5. $4^{-1.5} = 0.125$

7. $e^{2.3} \approx 9.974$

9. $e^{-0.95} \approx 0.387$

11.

x	$f(x) = 4^x$
-2	$4^{-2} = \frac{1}{16}$
-1	$4^{-1} = \frac{1}{4}$
0	$4^0 = 1$
1	$4^1 = 4$
2	$4^2 = 16$

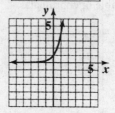

$$f(x) = 4^x$$

13.

x	$g(x) = \left(\frac{3}{2}\right)^x$
-2	$\left(\frac{3}{2}\right)^{-2} = \frac{4}{9}$
-1	$\left(\frac{3}{2}\right)^{-1} = \frac{2}{3}$
0	$\left(\frac{3}{2}\right)^0 = 1$
1	$\left(\frac{3}{2}\right)^1 = \frac{3}{2}$
2	$\left(\frac{3}{2}\right)^2 = \frac{9}{4}$

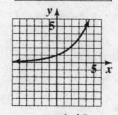

$$g(x) = \left(\frac{3}{2}\right)^x$$

Exercise Set 4.1

1. $2^{3.4} \approx 10.556$

3. $3^{\sqrt{5}} \approx 11.665$

15.

x	$h(x) = \left(\frac{1}{2}\right)^x$
-2	$\left(\frac{1}{2}\right)^{-2} = 4$
-1	$\left(\frac{1}{2}\right)^{-1} = 2$
0	$\left(\frac{1}{2}\right)^{0} = 1$
1	$\left(\frac{1}{2}\right)^{1} = \frac{1}{2}$
2	$\left(\frac{1}{2}\right)^{2} = \frac{1}{4}$

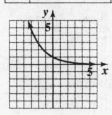

$$h(x) = \left(\frac{1}{2}\right)^x$$

17.

x	$f(x) = (0.6)^x$
-2	$(0.6)^{-2} = 2.\overline{7}$
-1	$(0.6)^{-1} = 1.\overline{6}$
0	$(0.6)^{0} = 1$
1	$(0.6)^{1} = 0.6$
2	$(0.6)^{2} = 0.36$

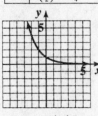

$$f(x) = (0.6)^x$$

19. This is the graph of $f(x) = 3^x$ reflected about the x-axis and about the y-axis, so the function is $H(x) = -3^{-x}$.

21. This is the graph of $f(x) = 3^x$ reflected about the x-axis, so the function is $F(x) = -3^x$.

23. This is the graph of $f(x) = 3^x$ shifted one unit downward, so the function is $h(x) = 3^x - 1$.

25. The graph of $g(x) = 2^{x+1}$ can be obtained by shifting the graph of $f(x) = 2^x$ one unit to the left.

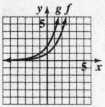

$$f(x) = 2^x$$
$$g(x) = 2^x + 1$$

Asymptote: $y = 0$

Domain: $(-\infty, \infty)$; Range: $(0, \infty)$

27. The graph of $g(x) = 2^x - 1$ can be obtained by shifting the graph of $f(x) = 2^x$ downward one unit.

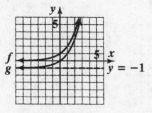

$$f(x) = 2^x$$
$$g(x) = 2^x - 1$$

Asymptote: $y = -1$

Domain: $(-\infty, \infty)$; Range: $(-1, \infty)$

29. The graph of $h(x) = 2^{x+1} - 1$ can be obtained by shifting the graph of $f(x) = 2^x$ one unit to the left and one unit downward.

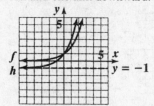

$$f(x) = 2^x$$
$$h(x) = 2^{x+1} - 1$$

Asymptote: $y = -1$

Domain: $(-\infty, \infty)$; Range: $(-1, \infty)$

31. The graph of $g(x) = -2^x$ can be obtained by reflecting the graph of $f(x) = 2^x$ about the x-axis.

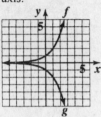

$$f(x) = 2^x$$
$$g(x) = -2^x$$

Asymptote: $y = 0$

Domain: $(-\infty, \infty)$; Range: $(-\infty, 0)$

33. The graph of $g(x) = 2 \cdot 2^x$ can be obtained by vertically stretching the graph of $f(x) = 2^x$ by a factor of two.

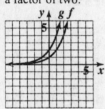

$$f(x) = 2^x$$
$$g(x) = 2 \cdot 2^x$$

Asymptote: $y = 0$

Domain: $(-\infty, \infty)$; Range: $(0, \infty)$

35. The graph of $g(x) = e^{x-1}$ can be obtained by moving $f(x) = e^x$ 1 unit right.

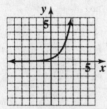

$$g(x) = e^{x-1}$$

Asymptote: $y = 0$

Domain: $(-\infty, \infty)$; Range: $(0, \infty)$

37. The graph of $g(x) = e^x + 2$ can be obtained by moving $f(x) = e^x$ 2 units up.

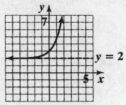

$$g(x) = e^x + 2$$

Asymptote: $y = 2$

Domain: $(-\infty, \infty)$; Range: $(2, \infty)$

39. The graph of $h(x) = e^{x-1} + 2$ can be obtained by moving $f(x) = e^x$ 1 unit right and 2 units up.

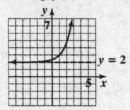

$$h(x) = e^{x-1} + 2$$

Asymptote: $y = 2$

Domain: $(-\infty, \infty)$; Range: $(2, \infty)$

41. The graph of $h(x) = e^{-x}$ can be obtained by reflecting $f(x) = e^x$ about the y-axis.

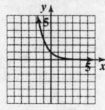

$$h(x) = e^{-x}$$

Asymptote: $y = 0$

Domain: $(-\infty, \infty)$; Range: $(0, \infty)$

43. The graph of $g(x) = 2e^x$ can be obtained by stretching $f(x) = e^x$ vertically by a factor of 2.

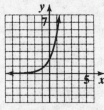

$$g(x) = 2e^x$$

Asymptote: $y = 0$

Domain: $(-\infty, \infty)$; Range: $(0, \infty)$

45. The graph of $h(x) = e^{2x} + 1$ can be obtained by stretching $f(x) = e^x$ horizontally by a factor of 2 and then moving the graph up 1 unit.

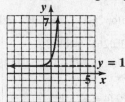

$$h(x) = e^{2x} + 1$$

Asymptote: $y = 1$

Domain: $(-\infty, \infty)$; Range: $(1, \infty)$

47. The graph of $g(x)$ can be obtained by reflecting $f(x)$ about the y-axis.

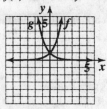

$$f(x) = 3^x$$
$$g(x) = 3^{-x}$$

Asymptote of $f(x)$: $y = 0$

Asymptote of $g(x)$: $y = 0$

49. The graph of $g(x)$ can be obtained by vertically shrinking $f(x)$ by a factor of $\frac{1}{3}$.

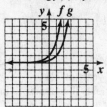

$$f(x) = 3^x$$
$$g(x) = \frac{1}{3} \cdot 3^x$$

Asymptote of $f(x)$: $y = 0$

Asymptote of $g(x)$: $y = 0$

51. The graph of $g(x)$ can be obtained by moving the graph of $f(x)$ one space to the right and one space up.

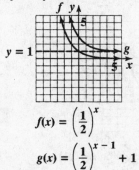

$$f(x) = \left(\frac{1}{2}\right)^x$$
$$g(x) = \left(\frac{1}{2}\right)^{x-1} + 1$$

Asymptote of $f(x)$: $y = 0$

Asymptote of $g(x)$: $y = 1$

53. **a.** $A = 10,000\left(1 + \dfrac{0.055}{2}\right)^{2(5)}$

$\approx \$13,116.51$

b. $A = 10,000\left(1 + \dfrac{0.055}{4}\right)^{4(5)}$

$\approx \$13,140.67$

c. $A = 10,000\left(1 + \dfrac{0.055}{12}\right)^{12(5)}$

$\approx \$13,157.04$

d. $A = 10,000e^{0.055(5)}$

$\approx \$13,165.31$

55. $A = 12,000\left(1+\dfrac{0.07}{12}\right)^{12(3)}$

   $\approx 14,795.11$ (7% yield)

   $A = 12,000e^{0.0685(3)}$

   $\approx 14,737.67$ (6.85% yield)

   Investing \$12,000 for 3 years at 7% compounded monthly yields the greater return.

57.

x	$f(x) = 2^x$	$g(x) = 2^{-x}$
-2	$\dfrac{1}{4}$	4
-1	$\dfrac{1}{2}$	2
0	1	1
1	2	$\dfrac{1}{2}$
2	4	$\dfrac{1}{4}$

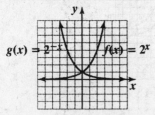

The point of intersection is $(0,1)$.

59

x	$y = 2^x$
-2	$\dfrac{1}{4}$
-1	$\dfrac{1}{2}$
0	1
1	2
2	4

y	$x = 2^y$
-2	$\dfrac{1}{4}$
-1	$\dfrac{1}{2}$
0	1
1	2
2	4

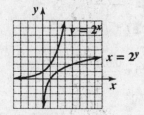

61. The graph is of the form $y = b^x$.

   Substitute values from the point $(1, 4)$ to find b.

   $y = b^x$

   $4 = b^1$

   $4 = b$

   The equation of the graph is $y = 4^x$

63. The graph is of the form $y = -b^x$.

   Substitute values from the point $(1, -e)$ to find b.

   $y = -b^x$

   $-e = -b^1$

   $e = b$

   The equation of the graph is $y = -e^x$

65. a. $f(0) = 574(1.026)^0$

   $= 574(1) = 574$

   India's population in 1974 was 574 million.

   b. $f(27) = 574(1.026)^{27} \approx 1148$

   India's population in 2001 will be 1148 million.

   c. Since $2028 - 1974 = 54$, find

   $f(54) = 574(1.026)^{54} \approx 2295$.

   India's population in 2028 will be 2295 million.

   d. $2055 - 1974 = 81$, find

   $f(54) = 574(1.026)^{81} \approx 4590$.

   India's population in 2055 will be 4590 million.

   e. India's population appears to be doubling every 27 years.

67. $S = 465,000(1 + 0.06)^{10}$

   $= 465,000(1.06)^{10} \approx \$832,744$

69. $2^{1.7} \approx 3.249009585$

   $2^{1.73} \approx 3.317278183$

   $2^{1.732} \approx 3.321880096$

   $2^{1.73205} \approx 3.321995226$

   $2^{1.7320508} \approx 3.321997068$

   $2^{\sqrt{3}} \approx 3.321997085$

   The closer the exponent is to $\sqrt{3}$, the closer the value is to $2^{\sqrt{3}}$.

300

71. $f(45) = 0.16(45) + 1.43 = 8.63$

$g(45) = 1.8e^{0.04(45)} \approx 10.9$

The linear function is a better model for the graph's value of 8.9.

73. a. $f(0) = 80e^{-0.5(0)} + 20$

$= 80e^0 + 20$

$= 80(1) + 20$

$= 100$

100% of the material is remembered at the moment it is first learned.

b. $f(1) = 80e^{-0.5(1)} + 20 \approx 68.5$

68.5% of the material is remembered 1 week after it is first learned.

c. $f(4) = 80e^{-0.5(4)} + 20 \approx 30.8$

30.8% of the material is remembered 4 week after it is first learned.

d. $f(52) = 80e^{-0.5(52)} + 20 \approx 20$

20% of the material is remembered 1 year after it is first learned.

75. $f(4) = \dfrac{258,051}{1 + 6.78e^{-1.21(4)}} \approx 244,921$

$g(4) = 55,979.5(4) + 36,217.8 \approx 260,136$

$f(x)$ is a better model for the graph's value of 246,570.

83.

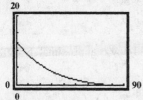

When $x = 31$, $y \approx 3.77$. NASA would not have launched the *Challenger*, since nearly 4 O-rings are expected to fail.

85. a.

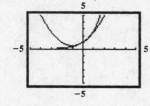

b.

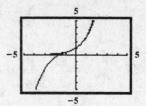

c.

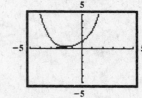

d. Answers may vary.

87. $y = 3^x$ is (d). y increases as x increases, but not as quickly as $y = 5^x$. $y = 5^x$ is (c). $y = \left(\dfrac{1}{3}\right)^x$ is (a).

$y = \left(\dfrac{1}{3}\right)^x$ is the same as $y = 3^{-x}$, so it is (d) reflected about the y-axis. $y = \left(\dfrac{1}{5}\right)^x$ is (b).

$y = \left(\dfrac{1}{5}\right)^x$ is the same as $y = 5^{-x}$, so it is (c) reflected about the y-axis.

89. a. $\cosh(-x) = \dfrac{e^{-x} + e^{-(-x)}}{2}$

$= \dfrac{e^{-x} + e^x}{2}$

$= \dfrac{e^x + e^{-x}}{2}$

$= \cosh x$

b. $\sinh(-x) = \dfrac{e^{-x} - e^{-(-x)}}{2}$

$= \dfrac{e^{-x} - e^x}{2}$

$= \dfrac{-\left(-e^{-x} + e^x\right)}{2}$

$= -\dfrac{e^x - e^{-x}}{2}$

$= -\sinh x$

c.
$$(\cosh x)^2 - (\sinh x)^2 \overset{?}{=} 1$$

$$\left(\frac{e^x + e^{-x}}{2}\right)^2 - \left(\frac{e^x - e^{-x}}{2}\right)^2 \overset{?}{=} 1$$

$$\frac{e^{2x} + 2 + e^{-2x}}{4} - \frac{e^{2x} - 2 + e^{-2x}}{4} \overset{?}{=} 1$$

$$\frac{e^{2x} + 2 + e^{-2x} - e^{2x} + 2 - e^{-2x}}{4} \overset{?}{=} 1$$

$$\frac{4}{4} \overset{?}{=} 1$$

$$1 = 1$$

Section 4.2

Check Point Exercises

1.   a. $3 = \log_7 x$ means $7^3 = x$.

   b. $2 = \log_b 25$ means $b^2 = 25$.

   c. $\log_4 26 = y$ means $4^y = 26$.

2.   a. $2^5 = x$ means $5 = \log_2 x$.

   b. $b^3 = 27$ means $3 = \log_b 27$.

   c. $e^y = 33$ means $y = \log_e 33$.

3.   a.   Question: 10 to what power gives 100?
   $\log_{10} 100 = 2$ because $10^2 = 100$.

   b.   Question: 3 to what power gives 3?
   $\log_3 3 = 1$ because $3^1 = 3$.

   c.   Question: 36 to what power gives 6?
   $\log_{36} 6 = \dfrac{1}{2}$ because $36^{\frac{1}{2}} = \sqrt{36} = 6$

4.   a.   Because $\log_b b = 1$, we conclude
   $\log_9 9 = 1$.

   b.   Because $\log_b 1 = 0$, we conclude
   $\log_8 1 = 0$.

5.   a.   Because $\log_b b^x = x$, we conclude
   $\log_7 7^8 = 8$.

   b.   Because $b^{\log_b x} = x$, we conclude
   $3^{\log_3 17} = 17$.

6.   First, set up a table of coordinates for $f(x) = 3^x$.

x	-2	-1	0	1	2	3
$f(x) = 3^x$	$\frac{1}{9}$	$\frac{1}{3}$	1	3	9	27

Reversing these coordinates gives the coordinates for the inverse function
   $g(x) = \log_3 x$.

x	$\frac{1}{9}$	$\frac{1}{3}$	1	3	9	27
$g(x) = \log_3 x$	-2	-1	0	1	2	3

The graph of the inverse can also be drawn by reflecting the graph of $f(x) = 3^x$ about the line $y = x$.

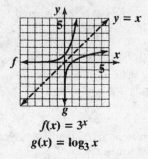

$$f(x) = 3^x$$
$$g(x) = \log_3 x$$

7.   The domain of h consists of all x for which $x - 5 > 0$. Solving this inequality for x, we obtain $x > 5$. Thus, the domain of h is $(5, \infty)$.

8.   Substitute the boy's age, 10, for x and evaluate the function at 10.
$$f(10) = 29 + 48.8 \log(10 + 1)$$
$$= 29 + 48.8 \log(11)$$
$$\approx 80$$
Thus, a 10-year-old boy is approximately 80% of his adult height.

9.   Because $I = 10{,}000\, I_0$,
$$R = \log \frac{10{,}000 I_0}{I_0}$$
$$= \log 10{,}000$$
$$= 4$$
The earthquake registered 4.0 on the Richter scale.

10. a. The domain of f consists of all x for which $4 - x > 0$. Solving this inequality for x, we obtain $x < 4$. Thus, the domain of f is $(-\infty, 4)$.

b. The domain of g consists of all x for which $x^2 > 0$. Solving this inequality for x, we obtain $x < 0$ or $x > 0$. Thus the domain of g is $(-\infty, 0) \cup (0, \infty)$.

11. Find the temperature increase after 30 minutes by substituting 30 for x and evaluating the function at 30.

$$f(x) = 13.4 \ln x - 11.6$$
$$f(30) = 13.4 \ln 30 - 11.6$$
$$\approx 34$$

The function models the actual increase shown in the graph quite well.

Exercise Set 4.2

1. $2^4 = 16$

3. $3^2 = x$

5. $b^5 = 32$

7. $6^y = 216$

9. $\log_2 8 = 3$

11. $\log_2 \dfrac{1}{16} = -4$

13. $\log_8 2 = \dfrac{1}{3}$

15. $\log_{13} x = 2$

17. $\log_b 1000 = 3$

19. $\log_7 200 = y$

21. $\log_4 16 = 2$ because $4^2 = 16$.

23. $\log_2 64 = 6$ because $2^6 = 64$.

25. $\log_5 \dfrac{1}{5} = -1$ because $5^{-1} = \dfrac{1}{5}$.

27. $\log_2 \dfrac{1}{8} = -3$ because $2^{-3} = \dfrac{1}{8}$.

29. $\log_7 \sqrt{7} = \dfrac{1}{2}$ because $7^{\frac{1}{2}} = \sqrt{7}$.

31. $\log_2 \dfrac{1}{\sqrt{2}} = -\dfrac{1}{2}$ because $2^{-\frac{1}{2}} = \dfrac{1}{\sqrt{2}}$.

33. $\log_{64} 8 = \dfrac{1}{2}$ because $64^{\frac{1}{2}} = \sqrt{64} = 8$.

35. Because $\log_b b = 1$, we conclude $\log_5 5 = 1$.

37. Because $\log_b 1 = 0$, we conclude $\log_4 1 = 0$.

39. Because $\log_b b^x = x$, we conclude $\log_5 5^7 = 7$.

41. Because $b^{\log_b x} = x$, we conclude $8^{\log_8 19} = 19$.

43. First, set up a table of coordinates for $f(x) = 4^x$.

x	-2	-1	0	1	2	3
$f(x) = 4x$	$\frac{1}{16}$	$\frac{1}{4}$	1	4	16	64

Reversing these coordinates gives the coordinates for the inverse function $g(x) = \log_4 x$.

x	$\frac{1}{16}$	$\frac{1}{4}$	1	4	16	64
$g(x) = \log_{4x}$	-2	-1	0	1	2	3

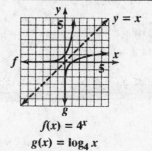

$$f(x) = 4^x$$
$$g(x) = \log_4 x$$

45. First, set up a table of coordinates for
$f(x) = \left(\dfrac{1}{2}\right)^x$.

x	-2	-1	0	1	2	3
$f(x) = \left(\frac{1}{2}\right)^x$	4	2	1	$\frac{1}{2}$	$\frac{1}{4}$	$\frac{1}{8}$

Reversing these coordinates gives the coordinates for the inverse function $g(x) = \log_{1/2} x$.

x	4	2	1	$\frac{1}{2}$	$\frac{1}{4}$	$\frac{1}{8}$
$g(x) = \log_{1/2} x$	-2	-1	0	1	2	3

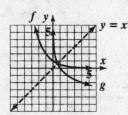

$$f(x) = \left(\frac{1}{2}\right)^x$$
$$g(x) = \log_{1/2} x$$

47. This is the graph of $f(x) = \log_3 x$ reflected about the x-axis and shifted up one unit, so the function is $H(x) = 1 - \log_3 x$.

49. This is the graph of $f(x) = \log_3 x$ shifted down one unit, so the function is $h(x) = \log_3 x - 1$.

51. This is the graph of $f(x) = \log_3 x$ shifted right one unit, so the function is $g(x) = \log_3 (x-1)$.

53.

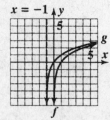

$$f(x) = \log_2 x$$
$$g(x) = \log_2 (x+1)$$

vertical asymptote: $x = -1$
Domain: $(-1, \infty)$; Range: $(-\infty, \infty)$

55.

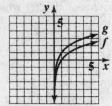

$$f(x) = \log_2 x$$
$$g(x) = 1 + \log_2 x$$

vertical asymptote: $x = 0$
Domain: $(0, \infty)$; Range: $(-\infty, \infty)$

57.

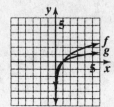

$$f(x) = \log_2 x$$
$$g(x) = \frac{1}{2} \log_2 x$$

vertical asymptote: $x = 0$
Domain: $(0, \infty)$; Range: $(-\infty, \infty)$

59.

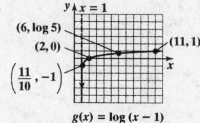

$$g(x) = \log (x - 1)$$

vertical asymptote: $x = 1$
Domain: $(1, \infty)$; Range: $(-\infty, \infty)$

61.

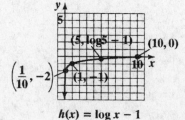

$$h(x) = \log x - 1$$

vertical asymptote: $x = 0$
Domain: $(0, \infty)$; Range: $(-\infty, \infty)$

63.

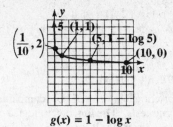

$$g(x) = 1 - \log x$$

vertical asymptote: $x = 0$
Domain: $(0, \infty)$; Range: $(-\infty, \infty)$

65.

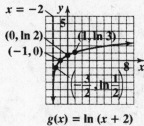

$$g(x) = \ln (x + 2)$$

vertical asymptote: $x = -2$
Domain: $(-2, \infty)$; Range: $(-\infty, \infty)$

67.

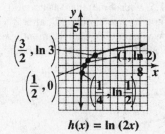

$$h(x) = \ln (2x)$$

vertical asymptote: $x = 0$
Domain: $(0, \infty)$; Range: $(-\infty, \infty)$

69.

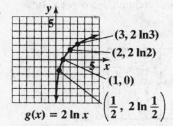

$$g(x) = 2 \ln x$$

vertical asymptote: $x = 0$
Domain: $(0, \infty)$; Range: $(-\infty, \infty)$

71.

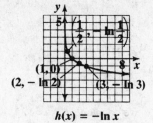

$$h(x) = -\ln x$$

vertical asymptote: $x = 0$
Domain: $(0, \infty)$; Range: $(-\infty, \infty)$

73.

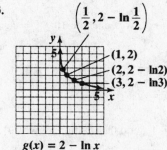

$$g(x) = 2 - \ln x$$

vertical asymptote: $x = 0$
Domain: $(0, \infty)$; Range: $(-\infty, \infty)$

75. The domain of f consists of all x for which $x + 4 > 0$. Solving this inequality for x, we obtain $x > -4$. Thus, the domain of f is $(-4, \infty)$.

77. The domain of f consists of all x for which $2 - x > 0$. Solving this inequality for x, we obtain $x < 2$. Thus, the domain of f is $(-\infty, 2)$.

79. The domain of f consists of all x for which $(x - 2)^2 > 0$. Solving this inequality for x, we obtain $x < 2$ or $x > 2$. Thus, the domain of f is $(-\infty, 2)$ or $(2, \infty)$.

81. $\log 100 = \log_{10} 100 = 2$ because $10^2 = 100$.

83. Because $\log 10^x = x$, we conclude $\log 10^7 = 7$.

85. Because $10^{\log x} = x$, we conclude $10^{\log 33} = 33$.

87. $\ln 1 = 0$ because $e^0 = 1$.

89. Because $\ln e^x = x$, we conclude $\ln e^6 = 6$.

305

91. $\ln\dfrac{1}{e^6} = \ln e^{-6}$

Because $\ln e^x = x$ we conclude

$\ln e^{-6} = -6$, so $\ln\dfrac{1}{e^6} = -6$.

93. Because $e^{\ln x} = x$, we conclude $e^{\ln 125} = 125$.

95. Because $\ln e^x = x$, we conclude $\ln e^{9x} = 9x$.

97. Because $e^{\ln x} = x$, we conclude $e^{\ln 5x^2} = 5x^2$.

99. Because $10^{\log x} = x$, we conclude $10^{\log\sqrt{x}} = \sqrt{x}$.

101. $\log_3(x-1) = 2$

$\qquad 3^2 = x-1$

$\qquad 9 = x-1$

$\qquad 10 = x$

The solution is 10, and the solution set is $\{10\}$.

103. $\log_4 x = -3$

$\qquad 4^{-3} = x$

$\qquad x = \dfrac{1}{4^3} = \dfrac{1}{64}$

The solution is $\dfrac{1}{64}$, and the solution set is $\left\{\dfrac{1}{64}\right\}$.

105. $\log_3\left(\log_7 7\right) = \log_3 1 = 0$

107. $\log_2\left(\log_3 81\right) = \log_2\left(\log_3 3^4\right)$

$\qquad\qquad = \log_2 4 = \log_2 2^2 = 2$

109. For $f(x) = \ln(x^2 - x - 2)$ to be real,

$x^2 - x - 2 > 0$.

Solve the related equation to find the boundary points:

$\qquad x^2 - x - 2 = 0$

$\qquad (x+1)(x-2) = 0$

The boundary points are –1 and 2. Testing each interval gives a domain of $(-\infty, -1)\cup(2,\infty)$.

111. For $f(x) = \ln\left(\dfrac{x+1}{x-5}\right)$ to be real, $\dfrac{x+1}{x-5} > 0$.

The boundary points are –1 and 5. Testing each interval gives a domain of $(-\infty, -1)\cup(5,\infty)$.

113. $f(13) = 62 + 35\log(13{-}4) \approx 95.4$

She is approximately 95.4% of her adult height.

115. Since $2003 - 1997 = 6$, we find $f(6)$:

$\qquad f(6) = -4.9\ln 6 + 73.8 \approx 65$

In 2003, approximately 65% of U.S. companies performed drug tests. The function modeled the actual number very well. It gives the actual percent.

117. $D = 10\log\left[10^{12}(6.3\times10^6)\right] \approx 188$

Yes, the sound can rupture the human eardrum.

119. a. $f(0) = 88 - 15\ln(0+1) = 88$

The average score on the original exam was 88.

b. $f(2) = 88 - 15\ln(2+1) = 71.5$
$f(4) = 88 - 15\ln(4+1) = 63.9$
$f(6) = 88 - 15\ln(6+1) = 58.8$
$f(8) = 88 - 15\ln(8+1) = 55$
$f(10) = 88 - 15\ln(10+1) = 52$
$f(12) = 88 - 15\ln(12+1) = 49.5$

The average score after 2 months was about 71.5, after 4 months was about 63.9, after 6 months was about 58.8, after 8 months was about 55, after 10 months was about 52, and after one year was about 49.5.

c.

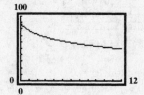

Material retention decreases as time passes.

129.

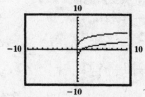

$g(x)$ is $f(x)$ shifted 3 units upward.

131.

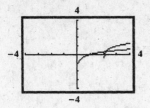

$g(x)$ is $f(x)$ shifted right 2 units and upward 1 unit.

133. a.

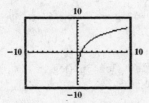

b.

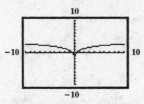

c.

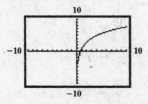

d They are the same.
$\log_b MN = \log_b M + \log_b N$

e. The sum of the logarithms of its factors.

135. a. False; $\dfrac{\log_2 8}{\log_2 4} = \dfrac{3}{2}$

b. False; $\log x$ is not defined for $x < 0$.

c. False; the domain is $(0, \infty)$.

d. True

(d) is true.

137. $\log_4\left[\log_3\left(\log_2 8\right)\right]$

$= \log_4\left[\log_3\left(\log_2 2^3\right)\right]$

$= \log_4\left[\log_3 3\right] = \log_4 1 = 0$

Section 4.3

Check Point Exercises

1. a. $\log_6(7 \cdot 11) = \log_6 7 + \log_6 11$

b. $\log(100x) = \log 100 + \log x$
$\quad\quad\quad\quad = 2 + \log x$

2. a. $\log_8\left(\dfrac{23}{x}\right) = \log_8 23 - \log_8 x$

b. $\ln\left(\dfrac{e^5}{11}\right) = \ln e^5 - \ln 11$
$\quad\quad\quad\quad = 5 - \ln 11$

3. a. $\log_6 3^9 = 9\log_6 3$

b. $\ln \sqrt[3]{x} = \ln x^{1/3} = \dfrac{1}{3}\ln x$

c. $\log(x+4)^2 = 2\log(x+4)$

4. a. $\log_b x^4 \sqrt[3]{y}$

$= \log_b x^4 y^{1/3}$

$= \log_b x^4 + \log_b y^{1/3}$

$= 4\log_b x + \dfrac{1}{3}\log_b y$

b. $\log_5 \dfrac{\sqrt{x}}{25y^3}$

$= \log_5 \dfrac{x^{1/2}}{25y^3}$

$= \log_5 x^{1/2} - \log_5 25y^3$

$= \log_5 x^{1/2} - \left(\log_5 5^2 + \log_5 y^3\right)$

$= \tfrac{1}{2}\log_5 x - \log_5 5^2 - \log_5 y^3$

$= \tfrac{1}{2}\log_5 x - 2\log_5 5 - 3\log_5 y$

$= \tfrac{1}{2}\log_5 x - 2 - 3\log_5 y$

5. a. $\log 25 + \log 4 = \log(25 \cdot 4) = \log 100 = 2$

b. $\log(7x+6) - \log x = \log\dfrac{7x+6}{x}$

307

6. a. $\ln x^2 + \dfrac{1}{3}\ln(x+5)$

$= \ln x^2 + \ln(x+5)^{1/3}$

$= \ln x^2 (x+5)^{1/3}$

$= \ln x^2 \sqrt[3]{x+5}$

b. $2\log(x-3) - \log x$

$= \log(x-3)^2 - \log x$

$= \log \dfrac{(x-3)^2}{x}$

c. $\dfrac{1}{4}\log_b x - 2\log_b 5 - 10\log_b y$

$= \log_b x^{1/4} - \log_b 5^2 - \log_b y^{10}$

$= \log_b x^{1/4} - \left(\log_b 25 - \log_b y^{10}\right)$

$= \log_b x^{1/4} - \log_b 25 y^{10}$

$= \log_b \dfrac{x^{1/4}}{25 y^{10}}$ or $\log_b \dfrac{\sqrt[4]{x}}{25 y^{10}}$

7. $\log_7 2506 = \dfrac{\log 2506}{\log 7} \approx 4.02$

8. $\log_7 2506 = \dfrac{\ln 2506}{\ln 7} \approx 4.02$

Exercise Set 4.3

1. $\log_5(7\cdot 3) = \log_5 7 + \log_5 3$

3. $\log_7(7x) = \log_7 7 + \log_7 x = 1 + \log_7 x$

5. $\log(1000x) = \log 1000 + \log x = 3 + \log x$

7. $\log_7\left(\dfrac{7}{x}\right) = \log_7 7 - \log_7 x = 1 - \log_7 x$

9. $\log\left(\dfrac{x}{100}\right) = \log x - \log 100 = \log_x - 2$

11. $\log_4\left(\dfrac{64}{y}\right) = \log_4 64 - \log_4 y$

$= 3 - \log_4 y$

13. $\ln\left(\dfrac{e^2}{5}\right) = \ln e^2 - \ln 5 = 2\ln e - \ln 5 = 2 - \ln 5$

15. $\log_b x^3 = 3\log_b x$

17. $\log N^{-6} = -6\log N$

19. $\ln \sqrt[5]{x} = \ln x^{(1/5)} = \dfrac{1}{5}\ln x$

21. $\log_b x^2 y = \log_b x^2 + \log_b y = 2\log_b x + \log_b y$

23. $\log_4\left(\dfrac{\sqrt{x}}{64}\right) = \log_4 x^{1/2} - \log_4 64 = \dfrac{1}{2}\log_4 x - 3$

25. $\log_6\left(\dfrac{36}{\sqrt{x+1}}\right) = \log_6 36 - \log_6(x+1)^{1/2}$

$= 2 - \dfrac{1}{2}\log_6(x+1)$

27. $\log_b\left(\dfrac{x^2 y}{z^2}\right) = \log_b\left(x^2 y\right) - \log_b z^2$

$= \log_b x^2 + \log_b y - \log_b z^2$

$= 2\log_b x + \log_b y - 2\log_b z$

29. $\log \sqrt{100x} = \log(100x)^{1/2}$

$= \dfrac{1}{2}\log(100x)$

$= \dfrac{1}{2}(\log 100 + \log x)$

$= \dfrac{1}{2}(2 + \log x)$

$= 1 + \dfrac{1}{2}\log x$

31. $\log \sqrt[3]{\dfrac{x}{y}} = \log\left(\dfrac{x}{y}\right)^{1/3}$

$= \dfrac{1}{3}\left[\log\left(\dfrac{x}{y}\right)\right]$

$= \dfrac{1}{3}(\log x - \log y)$

$= \dfrac{1}{3}\log x - \dfrac{1}{3}\log y$

33. $\log_b \dfrac{\sqrt{x}\,y^3}{z^3}$

$= \log_b x^{1/2} + \log_b y^3 - \log_b z^3$

$= \dfrac{1}{2}\log_b x + 3\log_b y - 3\log_b z$

35.
$$\log_5 \sqrt[3]{\frac{x^2 y}{25}}$$
$$= \log_5 x^{2/3} + \log_5 y^{1/3} - \log_5 25^{1/3}$$
$$= \frac{2}{3}\log_5 x + \frac{1}{3}\log_5 y - \log_5 5^{2/3}$$
$$= \frac{2}{3}\log_5 x + \frac{1}{3}\log_5 y - \frac{2}{3}$$

37.
$$\ln\left[\frac{x^3 \sqrt{x^2+1}}{(x+1)^4}\right]$$
$$= \ln x^3 + \ln\sqrt{x^2+1} - \ln(x+1)^4$$
$$= 3\ln x + \frac{1}{2}\ln(x^2+1) - 4\ln(x+1)$$

39.
$$\log\left[\frac{10x^2 \sqrt[3]{1-x}}{7(x+1)^2}\right]$$
$$= \log 10 + \log x^2 + \log\sqrt[3]{1-x} - \log 7 - \log(x+1)^2$$
$$= 1 + 2\log x + \frac{1}{3}\log(1-x) - \log 7 - 2\log(x+1)$$

41. $\log 5 + \log 2 = \log(5\cdot 2) = \log 10 = 1$

43. $\ln x + \ln 7 = \ln(7x)$

45. $\log_2 96 - \log_2 3 = \log_2\left(\dfrac{96}{3}\right) = \log_2 32 = 5$

47. $\log(2x+5) - \log x = \log\left(\dfrac{2x+5}{x}\right)$

49. $\log x + 3\log y = \log x + \log y^3 = \log(xy^3)$

51.
$$\frac{1}{2}\ln x + \ln y = \ln x^{1/2} + \ln y$$
$$= \ln\left(x^{\frac{1}{2}} y\right) \text{ or } \ln\left(y\sqrt{x}\right)$$

53.
$$2\log_b x + 3\log_b y = \log_b x^2 + \log_b y^3$$
$$= \log_b(x^2 y^3)$$

55. $5\ln x - 2\ln y = \ln x^5 - \ln y^2 = \ln\left(\dfrac{x^5}{y^2}\right)$

57.
$$3\ln x - \frac{1}{3}\ln y = \ln x^3 - \ln y^{1/3}$$
$$= \ln\left(\frac{x^3}{y^{1/3}}\right) \text{ or } \ln\left(\frac{x^3}{\sqrt[3]{y}}\right)$$

59.
$$4\ln(x+6) - 3\ln x = \ln(x+6)^4 - \ln x^3$$
$$= \ln\frac{(x+6)^4}{x^3}$$

61.
$$3\ln x + 5\ln y - 6\ln z$$
$$= \ln x^3 + \ln y^5 - \ln z^6$$
$$= \ln\frac{x^3 y^5}{z^6}$$

63.
$$\frac{1}{2}\left(\log x + \log y\right)$$
$$= \frac{1}{2}(\log xy)$$
$$= \log(xy)^{1/2}$$
$$= \log\sqrt{xy}$$

65.
$$\frac{1}{2}(\log_5 x + \log_5 y) - 2\log_5(x+1)$$
$$= \frac{1}{2}\log_5 xy - \log_5(x+1)^2$$
$$= \log_5(xy)^{1/2} - \log_5(x+1)^2$$
$$= \log_5\frac{(xy)^{1/2}}{(x+1)^2}$$
$$= \log_5\frac{\sqrt{xy}}{(x+1)^2}$$

67.
$$\frac{1}{3}[2\ln(x+5) - \ln x - \ln(x^2-4)]$$
$$= \frac{1}{3}[\ln(x+5)^2 - \ln x - \ln(x^2-4)]$$
$$= \frac{1}{3}\left[\ln\frac{(x+5)^2}{x(x^2-4)}\right]$$
$$= \ln\left[\frac{(x+5)^2}{x(x^2-4)}\right]^{1/3}$$
$$= \ln\sqrt[3]{\frac{(x+5)^2}{x(x^2-4)}}$$

69. $\log x + \log\left(x^2 - 1\right) - \log 7 - \log(x+1)$

$= \log x + \log\left(x^2 - 1\right) - \left(\log 7 + \log(x+1)\right)$

$= \log\left(x\left(x^2 - 1\right)\right) - \log\left(7(x+1)\right)$

$= \log \dfrac{x\left(x^2 - 1\right)}{7(x+1)}$

$= \log \dfrac{x(x+1)(x-1)}{7(x+1)}$

$= \log \dfrac{x(x-1)}{7}$

71. $\log_5 13 = \dfrac{\log 13}{\log 5} \approx 1.5937$

73. $\log_{14} 87.5 = \dfrac{\ln 87.5}{\ln 14} \approx 1.6944$

75. $\log_{0.1} 17 = \dfrac{\log 17}{\log 0.1} \approx -1.2304$

77. $\log_\pi 63 = \dfrac{\ln 63}{\ln \pi} \approx 3.6193$

79.

$y = \log_3 x = \dfrac{\log x}{\log 3}$

81.

$y = \log_2(x+2) = \dfrac{\log(x+2)}{\log 2}$

83. $\log_b \dfrac{3}{2} = \log_b 3 - \log_b 2 = C - A$

85. $\log_b 8 = \log_b 2^3 = 3\log_b 2 = 3A$

87.

$\log_b \sqrt{\dfrac{2}{27}} = \log_b \left(\dfrac{2}{27}\right)^{\frac{1}{2}}$

$= \dfrac{1}{2} \log_b \left(\dfrac{2}{3^3}\right)$

$= \dfrac{1}{2}\left(\log_b 2 - \log_b 3^3\right)$

$= \dfrac{1}{2}\left(\log_b 2 - 3\log_b 3\right)$

$= \dfrac{1}{2}\log_b 2 - \dfrac{3}{2}\log_b 3$

$= \dfrac{1}{2}A - \dfrac{3}{2}C$

89. false; $\ln e = 1$

91. false; $\log_4\left(2x\right)^3 = 3\log_4\left(2x\right)$

93. true; $x\log 10^x = x \cdot x = x^2$

95. true; $\ln(5x) + \ln 1 = \ln 5x + 0 = \ln 5x$

97. false; $\log(x+3) - \log(2x) = \log \dfrac{x+3}{2x}$

99. true; quotient rule

101. true; $\log_3 7 = \dfrac{\log 7}{\log 3} = \dfrac{1}{\frac{\log 3}{\log 7}} = \dfrac{1}{\log_7 3}$

103. a. $D = 10\log\left(\dfrac{I}{I_0}\right)$

b. $D_1 = 10\log\left(\dfrac{100I}{I_0}\right)$

$= 10\log\left(100I - I_0\right)$

$= 10\log 100 + 10\log I - 10\log I_0$

$= 10(2) + 10\log I - 10\log I_0$

$= 20 + 10\log\left(\dfrac{I}{I_0}\right)$

This is 20 more than the loudness level of the softer sound. This means that the 100 times louder sound will be 20 decibels louder.

113. a. $y = \log_3 x = \dfrac{\ln x}{\ln 3}$

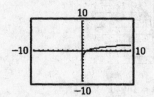

b.

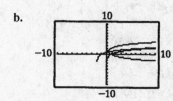

To obtain the graph of $y = 2 + \log_3 x$, shift the graph of $y = \log_3 x$ two units upward. To obtain the graph of $y = \log_3(x + 2)$, shift the graph of $y = \log_3 x$ two units left. To obtain the graph of $y = -\log_3 x$, reflect the graph of $y = \log_3 x$ about the x-axis.

115. $\log_3 x = \dfrac{\log x}{\log 3}$;

$\log_{25} x = \dfrac{\log x}{\log 25}$;

$\log_{100} x = \dfrac{\log x}{\log 100}$

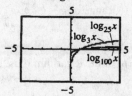

a.   top graph: $y = \log_{100} x$
bottom graph: $y = \log_3 x$

b.   top graph: $y = \log_3 x$
bottom graph: $y = \log_{100} x$

c.   Comparing graphs of $\log_b x$ for $b > 1$, the graph of the equation with the largest b will be on the top in the interval $(0, 1)$ and on the bottom in the interval $(1, \infty)$.

121. a.   False;

$\log_7 49 - \log_7 7 = \log_7 \dfrac{49}{7} = \log_7 7 = 1$

$\dfrac{\log_7 49}{\log_7 7} = \dfrac{2}{1} = 2$

b.   False;
$3\log_b x + 3\log_b y = \log_b (xy)^3$
$\neq \log_b \left(x^3 + y^3 \right)$

c.   False;
$\log_b (xy)^5 = 5\log_b (xy)$
$= 5(\log_b x + \log_b y)$
$\neq (\log_b x + \log_b y)^5$

d.   True;
$\ln \sqrt{2} = \ln 2^{1/2}$
$= \dfrac{1}{2}\ln 2 = \dfrac{\ln 2}{2}$

(d) is true.

123. $\log_7 9 = \dfrac{\log 9}{\log 7} = \dfrac{\log 3^2}{\log 7} = \dfrac{2\log 3}{\log 7}$

$= \dfrac{2A}{B}$

125. $\dfrac{\log_b (x + h) - \log_b x}{h}$

$= \dfrac{\log_b \dfrac{x + h}{x}}{h}$

$= \dfrac{\log_b \left(1 + \dfrac{h}{x} \right)}{h}$

$= \dfrac{1}{h}\log_b \left(1 + \dfrac{h}{x} \right)$

$= \log_b \left(1 + \dfrac{x}{h} \right)^{1/h}$

Mid-Chapter 4 Check Point

1.

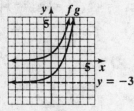

$$f(x) = 2^x$$
$$g(x) = 2^x - 3$$

Asymptote of f: $y = 0$
Asymptote of g: $y = -3$
Domain of f = Domain of $g = (-\infty, \infty)$
Range of f = $(0, \infty)$
Range of $g = (-3, \infty)$

2.

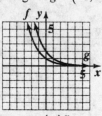

$$f(x) = \left(\frac{1}{2}\right)^x$$

$$g(x) = \left(\frac{1}{2}\right)^{x-1}$$

Asymptote of f: $y = 0$
Asymptote of g: $y = 0$
Domain of f = Domain of $g = (-\infty, \infty)$
Range of f = Range of $g = (0, \infty)$

3.

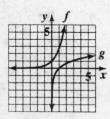

$$f(x) = e^x$$
$$g(x) = \ln x$$

Asymptote of f: $y = 0$
Asymptote of g: $x = 0$
Domain of f = Range of $g = (-\infty, \infty)$
Range of f = Domain of $g = (0, \infty)$

4.

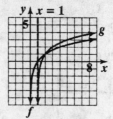

$$f(x) = \log_2 x$$
$$g(x) = \log_2 (x - 1) + 1$$

Asymptote of f: $x = 0$
Asymptote of g: $x = 1$
Domain of $f = (0, \infty)$
Domain of $g = (1, \infty)$
Range of f = Range of $g = (-\infty, \infty)$

5.

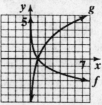

$$f(x) = \log_{1/2} x$$
$$g(x) = -2 \log_{1/2} x$$

Asymptote of f: $x = 0$
Asymptote of g: $x = 0$
Domain of f = Domain of $g = (0, \infty)$
Range of f = Range of $g = (-\infty, \infty)$

6. $f(x) = \log_3 (x + 6)$
The argument of the logarithm must be positive:
$x + 6 > 0$
$$x > -6$$
Domain: $\{x \mid x > -6\}$ or $(-6, \infty)$.

7. $f(x) = \log_3 x + 6$
The argument of the logarithm must be positive:
$x > 0$
Domain: $\{x \mid x > 0\}$ or $(0, \infty)$.

312

8. $\log_3(x+6)^2$

The argument of the logarithm must be positive.

Now $(x+6)^2$ is always positive, except when $x=-6$

Domain: $\{x \mid x \neq 0\}$ or $(-\infty, -6) \cup (-6, \infty)$.

9. $f(x) = 3^{x+6}$

Domain: $\{x \mid x \text{ is a real number}\}$ or $(-\infty, \infty)$.

10. $\log_2 8 + \log_5 25 = \log_2 2^3 + \log_5 5^2$
$$= 3 + 2 = 5$$

11. $\log_3 \dfrac{1}{9} = \log_3 \dfrac{1}{3^2} = \log_3 3^{-2} = -2$

12. Let $\log_{100} 10 = y$
$$100^y = 10$$
$$\left(10^2\right)^y = 10^1$$
$$10^{2y} = 10^1$$
$$2y = 1$$
$$y = \frac{1}{2}$$

13. $\log \sqrt[3]{10} = \log 10^{\frac{1}{3}} = \dfrac{1}{3}$

14. $\log_2(\log_3 81) = \log_2\left(\log_3 3^4\right)$
$$= \log_2 4 = \log_2 2^2 = 2$$

15. $\log_3\left(\log_2 \dfrac{1}{8}\right) = \log_3\left(\log_2 \dfrac{1}{2^3}\right)$
$$= \log_3\left(\log_2 2^{-3}\right)$$
$$= \log_3(-3)$$
$$= \text{not possible}$$

This expression is impossible to evaluate.

16. $6^{\log_6 5} = 5$

17. $\ln e^{\sqrt{7}} = \sqrt{7}$

18. $10^{\log 13} = 13$

19. $\log_{100} 0.1 = y$
$$100^y = 0.1$$
$$\left(10^2\right)^y = \frac{1}{10}$$
$$10^{2y} = 10^{-1}$$
$$2y = -1$$
$$y = -\frac{1}{2}$$

20. $\log_\pi \pi^{\sqrt{\pi}} = \sqrt{\pi}$

21. $\log\left(\dfrac{\sqrt{xy}}{1000}\right) = \log\left(\sqrt{xy}\right) - \log 1000$
$$= \log(xy)^{\frac{1}{2}} - \log 10^3$$
$$= \frac{1}{2}\log(xy) - 3$$
$$= \frac{1}{2}(\log x + \log y) - 3$$
$$= \frac{1}{2}\log x + \frac{1}{2}\log y - 3$$

22. $\ln\left(e^{19} x^{20}\right) = \ln e^{19} + \ln x^{20}$
$$= 19 + 20\ln x$$

23. $8\log_7 x - \dfrac{1}{3}\log_7 y = \log_7 x^8 - \log_7 y^{\frac{1}{3}}$
$$= \log_7\left(\frac{x^8}{y^{\frac{1}{3}}}\right)$$
$$= \log_7\left(\frac{x^8}{\sqrt[3]{y}}\right)$$

24. $7\log_5 x + 2\log_5 x = \log_5 x^7 + \log_5 x^2$
$$= \log_5\left(x^7 \cdot x^2\right)$$
$$= \log_5 x^9$$

25. $\dfrac{1}{2}\ln x - 3\ln y - \ln(z-2)$
$$= \ln x^{\frac{1}{2}} - \ln y^3 - \ln(z-2)$$
$$= \ln \sqrt{x} - \left[\ln y^3 + \ln(z-2)\right]$$
$$= \ln \sqrt{x} - \ln\left[y^3(z-2)\right]$$
$$= \ln\left[\frac{\sqrt{x}}{y^3(z-2)}\right]$$

26. Continuously: $A = 8000e^{0.08(3)}$

$$\approx 10,170$$

Monthly: $A = 8000\left(1 + \dfrac{0.08}{12}\right)^{12 \cdot 3}$

$$\approx 10,162$$

$10,170 - 10,162 = 8$

Interest returned will be $8 more if compounded continuously.

Section 4.4

Check Point Exercises

1. **a.** $5^{3x-6} = 125$

$5^{3x-6} = 5^3$

$3x - 6 = 3$

$3x = 9$

$x = 3$

b. $8^{x+2} = 4^{x-3}$

$\left(2^3\right)^{x+2} = \left(2^2\right)^{x-3}$

$2^{3x+6} = 2^{2x-6}$

$3x + 6 = 2x - 6$

$x = -12$

2. $5^x = 134$

$\ln 5^x = \ln 134$

$x \ln 5 = \ln 134$

$x = \dfrac{\ln 134}{\ln 5} \approx 3.04$

The solution set is $\left\{\dfrac{\ln 134}{\ln 5}\right\}$, approximately 3.04.

3.

$7e^{2x} = 63$

$e^{2x} = 9$

$\ln e^{2x} = \ln 9$

$2x = \ln 9$

$x = \dfrac{\ln 9}{2} \approx 1.10$

The solution set is $\left\{\dfrac{\ln 9}{2}\right\}$, approximately 1.10.

4.
$$3^{2x-1} = 7^{x+1}$$

$$\ln 3^{2x-1} = \ln 7^{x+1}$$

$$(2x - 1)\ln 3 = (x + 1)\ln 7$$

$$2x \ln 3 - \ln 3 = x \ln 7 + \ln 7$$

$$2x \ln 3 - x \ln 7 = \ln 3 + \ln 7$$

$$x(2\ln 3 - \ln 7) = \ln 3 + \ln 7$$

$$x = \dfrac{\ln 3 + \ln 7}{2\ln 3 - \ln 7}$$

$$x \approx 12.11$$

5. $e^{2x} - 8e^x + 7 = 0$

$\left(e^x - 7\right)\left(e^x - 1\right) = 0$

$e^x - 7 = 0 \quad$ or $\quad e^x - 1 = 0$

$\quad e^x = 7 \qquad\qquad e^x = 1$

$\ln e^x = \ln 7 \qquad \ln e^x = \ln 1$

$\quad x = \ln 7 \qquad\qquad x = 0$

The solution set is $\{0, \ln 7\}$. The solutions are 0 and (approximately) 1.95.

6. **a.** $\log_2 (x - 4) = 3$

$2^3 = x - 4$

$8 = x - 4$

$12 = x$

Check:

$\log_2 (x - 4) = 3$

$\log_2 (12 - 4) = 3$

$\log_2 8 = 3$

$3 = 3$

The solution set is $\{12\}$.

b. $4 \ln 3x = 8$

$\ln 3x = 2$

$e^{\ln 3x} = e^2$

$3x = e^2$

$x = \dfrac{e^2}{3} \approx 2.46$

314

Check
$$4\ln 3x = 8$$
$$4\ln 3\left(\frac{e^2}{3}\right) = 8$$
$$4\ln e^2 = 8$$
$$4(2) = 8$$
$$8 = 8$$

The solution set is $\left\{\dfrac{e^2}{3}\right\}$,

approximately 2.46.

7.
$$\log x + \log(x-3) = 1$$
$$\log x(x-3) = 1$$
$$10^1 = x(x-3)$$
$$10 = x^2 - 3x$$
$$0 = x^2 - 3x - 10$$
$$0 = (x-5)(x+2)$$
$$x - 5 = 0 \quad \text{or} \quad x + 2 = 0$$
$$x = 5 \quad \text{or} \qquad x = -2$$

Check
Checking 5:
$$\log 5 + \log(5-3) = 1$$
$$\log 5 + \log 2 = 1$$
$$\log(5 \cdot 2) = 1$$
$$\log 10 = 1$$
$$1 = 1$$

Checking –2:
$$\log x + \log(x-3) = 1$$
$$\log(-2) + \log(-2-3) \; 0 \; 1$$

Negative numbers do not have logarithms so –2 does not check.
The solution set is {5}.

8.
$$\ln(x-3) = \ln(7x-23) - \ln(x+1)$$
$$\ln(x-3) = \ln\frac{7x-23}{x+1}$$
$$x - 3 = \frac{7x-23}{x+1}$$
$$(x-3)(x+1) = 7x - 23$$
$$x^2 - 2x - 3 = 7x - 23$$
$$x^2 - 9x + 20 = 0$$
$$(x-4)(x-5) = 0$$
$$x = 4 \quad \text{or} \quad x = 5$$

Both values produce true statements.
The solution set is {4, 5}

9. For a risk of 7%, let $R = 7$ in
$$R = 6e^{12.77x}$$
$$6e^{12.77x} = 7$$
$$e^{12.77x} = \frac{7}{6}$$
$$\ln e^{12.77x} = \ln\left(\frac{7}{6}\right)$$
$$12.77x = \ln\left(\frac{7}{6}\right)$$
$$x = \frac{\ln\left(\frac{7}{6}\right)}{12.77} \approx 0.01$$

For a blood alcohol concentration of 0.01, the risk of a car accident is 7%.

10.
$$A = P\left(1+\frac{r}{n}\right)^{nt}$$
$$3600 = 1000\left(1+\frac{0.08}{4}\right)^{4t}$$
$$1000\left(1-\frac{0.08}{4}\right)^{4t} = 3600$$
$$1000(1+0.02)^{4t} = 3600$$
$$1000(1.02)^{4t} = 3600$$
$$(1.02)^{4t} = \ln 3.6$$
$$4t\ln(1.02) = \ln 3.6$$
$$t = \frac{\ln 3.6}{4\ln 1.02}$$
$$\approx 16.2$$

After approximately 16.2 years, the $1000 will grow to an accumulated value of $3600.

11. $f(x) = 34.1\ln x + 117.7$
Solve equation when $f(x) = 210$.
$$34.1\ln x + 117.7 = 210$$
$$34.1\ln x = 92.3$$
$$\ln x = \frac{92.3}{34.1}$$
$$\log_e x = \frac{92.3}{34.1}$$
$$e^{\frac{92.3}{34.1}} = x$$
$$15 \approx x$$

Approximately 15 years after 1999, in the year 2014, there will be 210 million Internet users in the United States.

Exercise Set 4.4

1.
$$2^x = 64$$
$$2^x = 2^6$$
$$x = 6$$
The solution is 6, and the solution set is $\{6\}$.

3.
$$5^x = 125$$
$$5^x = 5^3$$
$$x = 3$$
The solution is 3, and the solution set is $\{3\}$.

5.
$$2^{2x-1} = 32$$
$$2^{2x-1} = 2^5$$
$$2x - 1 = 5$$
$$2x = 6$$
$$x = 3$$
The solution is 3, and the solution set is $\{3\}$.

7.
$$4^{2x-1} = 64$$
$$4^{2x-1} = 4^3$$
$$2x - 1 = 3$$
$$2x = 4$$
$$x = 2$$
The solution is 2, and the solution set is $\{2\}$.

9.
$$32^x = 8$$
$$\left(2^5\right)^x = 2^3$$
$$2^{5x} = 2^3$$
$$5x = 3$$
$$x = \frac{3}{5}$$
The solution is $\frac{3}{5}$, and the solution set is $\left\{\frac{3}{5}\right\}$.

11.
$$9^x = 27$$
$$\left(3^2\right)^x = 3^3$$
$$3^{2x} = 3^3$$
$$2x = 3$$
$$x = \frac{3}{2}$$
The solution is $\frac{3}{2}$, and the solution set is $\left\{\frac{3}{2}\right\}$.

13.
$$3^{1-x} = \frac{1}{27}$$
$$3^{1-x} = \frac{1}{3^3}$$
$$3^{1-x} = 3^{-3}$$
$$1 - x = -3$$
$$-x = -4$$
$$x = 4$$
The solution set is $\{4\}$.

15.
$$6^{\frac{x-3}{4}} = \sqrt{6}$$
$$6^{\frac{x-3}{4}} = 6^{\frac{1}{2}}$$
$$\frac{x-3}{4} = \frac{1}{2}$$
$$2(x-3) = 4(1)$$
$$2x - 6 = 4$$
$$2x = 10$$
$$x = 5$$
The solution is 5, and the solution set is $\{5\}$.

17.
$$4^x = \frac{1}{\sqrt{2}}$$
$$\left(2^2\right)^x = \frac{1}{2^{\frac{1}{2}}}$$
$$2^{2x} = 2^{-\frac{1}{2}}$$
$$2x = -\frac{1}{2}$$
$$x = \frac{1}{2}\left(-\frac{1}{2}\right) = -\frac{1}{4}$$
The solution is $-\frac{1}{4}$, and the solution set is $\left\{-\frac{1}{4}\right\}$.

19.
$$8^{x+3} = 16^{x-1}$$
$$\left(2^3\right)^{x+3} = \left(2^4\right)^{x-1}$$
$$2^{3x+9} = 2^{4x-4}$$
$$3x + 9 = 4x - 4$$
$$13 = x$$
The solution set is $\{13\}$.

21.
$$e^{x+1} = \frac{1}{e}$$
$$e^{x+1} = e^{-1}$$
$$x + 1 = -1$$
$$x = -2$$
The solution set is $\{-2\}$.

23. $10^x = 3.91$

$\ln 10^x = \ln 3.91$

$x \ln 10 = \ln 3.91$

$x = \dfrac{\ln 3.91}{\ln 10} \approx 0.59$

25. $e^x = 5.7$

$\ln e^x = 5.7$

$x = \ln 5.7 \approx 1.74$

27. $5^x = 17$

$\ln 5^x = \ln 17$

$x \ln 5 = \ln 17$

$x = \dfrac{\ln 17}{\ln 5} \approx 1.76$

29. $5e^x = 23$

$e^x = \dfrac{23}{5}$

$\ln e^x = \ln \dfrac{23}{5}$

$x = \ln \dfrac{23}{5} \approx 1.53$

31. $3e^{5x} = 1977$

$e^{5x} = 659$

$\ln e^{5x} = \ln 659$

$x = \dfrac{\ln 659}{5} \approx 1.30$

33. $e^{1-5x} = 793$

$\ln e^{1-5x} = \ln 793$

$(1-5x)(\ln e) = \ln 793$

$1-5x = \ln 793$

$5x = 1 - \ln 793$

$x = \dfrac{1-\ln 793}{5} \approx -1.14$

35. $e^{5x-3} - 2 = 10,476$

$e^{5x-3} = 10,478$

$\ln e^{5x-3} = \ln 10,478$

$(5x-3)\ln e = \ln 10,478$

$5x - 3 = \ln 10,478$

$5x = \ln 10,478 + 3$

$x = \dfrac{\ln 10,478 + 3}{5} \approx 2.45$

37. $7^{x+2} = 410$

$\ln 7^{x+2} = \ln 410$

$(x+2)\ln 7 = \ln 410$

$x+2 = \dfrac{\ln 410}{\ln 7}$

$x = \dfrac{\ln 410}{\ln 7} - 2 \approx 1.09$

39. $7^{0.3x} = 813$

$\ln 7^{0.3x} = \ln 813$

$0.3x \ln 7 = \ln 813$

$x = \dfrac{\ln 813}{0.3 \ln 7} \approx 11.48$

41. $5^{2x+3} = 3^{x-1}$

$\ln 5^{2x+3} = \ln 3^{x-1}$

$(2x+3)\ln 5 = (x-1)\ln 3$

$2x \ln 5 + 3 \ln 5 = x \ln 3 - \ln 3$

$3 \ln 5 + \ln 3 = x \ln 3 - 2x \ln 5$

$3 \ln 5 + \ln 3 = x(\ln 3 - 2 \ln 5)$

$\dfrac{3 \ln 5 + \ln 3}{\ln 3 - 2 \ln 5} = x$

$-2.80 \approx x$

43. $e^{2x} - 3e^x + 2 = 0$

$(e^x - 2)(e^x - 1) = 0$

$e^x - 2 = 0 \quad$ or $\quad e^x - 1 = 0$

$e^x = 2 \qquad\qquad e^x = 1$

$\ln e^x = \ln 2 \qquad \ln e^x = \ln 1$

$x = \ln 2 \qquad\qquad x = 0$

The solution set is $\{0, \ln 2\}$. The solutions are 0 and (approximately) 0.69.

45. $e^{4x} + 5e^{2x} - 24 = 0$

$(e^{2x} + 8)(e^{2x} - 3) = 0$

$e^{2x} + 8 = 0 \quad$ or $\quad e^{2x} - 3 = 0$

$e^{2x} = -8 \qquad\qquad e^{2x} = 3$

$\ln e^{2x} = \ln(-8) \qquad \ln e^{2x} = \ln 3$

$2x = \ln(-8) \qquad\qquad 2x = \ln 3$

$\ln(-8)$ does not exist $\qquad x = \dfrac{\ln 3}{2}$

$x = \dfrac{\ln 3}{2} \approx 0.55$

47.
$$3^{2x} + 3^x - 2 = 0$$
$$(3^x + 2)(3^x - 1) = 0$$

$3^x + 2 = 0$	$3^x - 1 = 0$
$3^x = -2$	$3^x = 1$
$\log 3^x = \log(-2)$	$\log 3^x = \log 1$
can't do	$x \log 3 = 0$

$$x = \frac{0}{\log 3}$$
$$x = 0$$

The solution set is $\{0\}$.

49.
$$\log_3 x = 4$$
$$3^4 = x$$
$$81 = x$$

51.
$$\ln x = 2$$
$$e^2 = x$$
$$7.39 \approx x$$

53.
$$\log_4(x + 5) = 3$$
$$4^3 = x + 5$$
$$59 = x$$

55.
$$\log_3(x - 4) = -3$$
$$3^{-3} = x - 4$$
$$\frac{1}{27} = x - 4$$
$$4\frac{1}{27} = x$$
$$4.04 \approx x$$

57.
$$\log_4(3x + 2) = 3$$
$$4^3 = 3x + 2$$
$$64 = 3x + 2$$
$$62 = 3x$$
$$\frac{62}{3} = x$$
$$20.67 \approx x$$

59.
$$5 \ln 2x = 20$$
$$\ln 2x = 4$$
$$e^{\ln 2x} = e^4$$
$$2x = e^4$$
$$x = \frac{e^4}{2} \approx 27.30$$

61.
$$6 + 2 \ln x = 5$$
$$2 \ln x = -1$$
$$\ln x = -\frac{1}{2}$$
$$e^{\ln x} = e^{-1/2}$$
$$x = e^{-1/2} \approx 0.61$$

63.
$$\ln \sqrt{x + 3} = 1$$
$$e^{\ln \sqrt{x+3}} = e^1$$
$$\sqrt{x + 3} = e$$
$$x + 3 = e^2$$
$$x = e^2 - 3 \approx 4.39$$

65.
$$\log_5 x + \log_5(4x - 1) = 1$$
$$\log_5(4x^2 - x) = 1$$
$$4x^2 - x = 5$$
$$4x^2 - x - 5 = 0$$
$$(4x - 5)(x + 1) = 0$$
$$x = \frac{5}{4} \text{ or } x = -1$$

$x = -1$ does not check because $\log_5(-1)$ does not exist.

The solution set is $\left\{\frac{5}{4}\right\}$.

67.
$$\log_3(x - 5) + \log_3(x + 3) = 2$$
$$\log_3[(x - 5)(x + 3)] = 2$$
$$(x - 5)(x + 3) = 3^2$$
$$x^2 - 2x - 15 = 9$$
$$x^2 - 2x - 24 = 0$$
$$(x - 6)(x + 4) = 0$$
$$x = 6 \text{ or } x = -4$$

$x = -4$ does not check because $\log_3(-4 - 5)$ does not exist. The solution set is $\{6\}$.

69. $\log_2(x+2) - \log_2(x-5) = 3$

$$\log_2\left(\frac{x+2}{x-5}\right) = 3$$

$$\frac{x+2}{x-5} = 2^3$$

$$\frac{x+2}{x-5} = 8$$

$$x+2 = 8(x-5)$$

$$x+2 = 8x-40$$

$$7x = 42$$

$$x = 6$$

71. $2\log_3(x+4) = \log_3 9 + 2$

$$2\log_3(x+4) = 2+2$$

$$2\log_3(x+4) = 4$$

$$\log_3(x+4) = 2$$

$$3^2 = x+4$$

$$9 = x+4$$

$$5 = x$$

73. $\log_2(x-6) + \log_2(x-4) - \log_2 x = 2$

$$\log_2\frac{(x-6)(x-4)}{x} = 2$$

$$\frac{(x-6)(x-4)}{x} = 2^2$$

$$x^2 - 10x + 24 = 4x$$

$$x^2 - 14x + 24 = 0$$

$$(x-12)(x-2) = 0$$

$$x-12 = 0 \qquad x-2 = 0$$

$$x = 12 \qquad x = 2$$

The solution set is {12} since $\log_2(2-6) = \log_2(-4)$ is not possible.

75. $\log(x+4) = \log x + \log 4$

$$\log(x+4) = \log 4x$$

$$x+4 = 4x$$

$$4 = 3x$$

$$x = \frac{4}{3}$$

This value is rejected. The solution set is $\left\{\frac{4}{3}\right\}$.

77. $\log(3x-3) = \log(x+1) + \log 4$

$$\log(3x-3) = \log(4x+4)$$

$$3x-3 = 4x+4$$

$$-7 = x$$

This value is rejected. The solution set is $\{\ \}$.

79. $2\log x = \log 25$

$$\log x^2 = \log 25$$

$$x^2 = 25$$

$$x = \pm 5$$

-5 is rejected. The solution set is {5}.

81. $\log(x+4) - \log 2 = \log(5x+1)$

$$\log\frac{x+4}{2} = \log(5x+1)$$

$$\frac{x+4}{2} = 5x+1$$

$$x+4 = 10x+2$$

$$-9x = -2$$

$$x = \frac{2}{9}$$

$$x \approx 0.22$$

83. $2\log x - \log 7 = \log 112$

$$\log x^2 - \log 7 = \log 112$$

$$\log\frac{x^2}{7} = \log 112$$

$$\frac{x^2}{7} = 112$$

$$x^2 = 784$$

$$x = \pm 28$$

-28 is rejected. The solution set is {28}.

85. $\log x + \log(x+3) = \log 10$

$$\log(x^2+3x) = \log 10$$

$$x^2+3x = 10$$

$$x^2+3x-10 = 0$$

$$(x+5)(x-2) = 0$$

$$x = -5 \ \text{or} \ x = 2$$

-5 is rejected. The solution set is {2}.

87. $\ln(x-4) + \ln(x+1) = \ln(x-8)$

$\ln(x^2 - 3x - 4) = \ln(x-8)$

$x^2 - 3x - 4 = x - 8$

$x^2 - 4x + 4 = 0$

$(x-2)(x-2) = 0$

$x = 2$

2 is rejected. The solution set is { }.

89. $\ln(x-2) - \ln(x+3) = \ln(x-1) - \ln(x+7)$

$\ln\dfrac{x-2}{x+3} = \ln\dfrac{x-1}{x+7}$

$\dfrac{x-2}{x+3} = \dfrac{x-1}{x+7}$

$(x-2)(x+7) = (x+3)(x-1)$

$x^2 + 5x - 14 = x^2 + 2x - 3$

$3x = 11$

$x = \dfrac{11}{3}$

$x \approx 3.67$

91. $5^{2x} \cdot 5^{4x} = 125$

$5^{2x+4x} = 5^3$

$5^{6x} = 5^3$

$6x = 3$

$x = \dfrac{1}{2}$

93. $2|\ln x| - 6 = 0$

$2|\ln x| = 6$

$|\ln x| = 3$

$\ln x = 3$ or $\ln x = -3$

$x = e^3$ $\qquad x = e^{-3}$

$x \approx 20.09$ $\qquad x \approx 0.05$

95. $3^{x^2} = 45$

$\ln 3^{x^2} = \ln 45$

$x^2 \ln 3 = \ln 45$

$x^2 = \dfrac{\ln 45}{\ln 3}$

$x = \pm\sqrt{\dfrac{\ln 45}{\ln 3}} \approx \pm 1.86$

97. $\ln(2x+1) + \ln(x-3) - 2\ln x = 0$

$\ln(2x+1) + \ln(x-3) - \ln x^2 = 0$

$\ln\dfrac{(2x+1)(x-3)}{x^2} = 0$

$\dfrac{(2x+1)(x-3)}{x^2} = e^0$

$\dfrac{2x^2 - 5x - 3}{x^2} = 1$

$2x^2 - 5x - 3 = x^2$

$x^2 - 5x - 3 = 0$

$x = \dfrac{-b \pm \sqrt{b^2 - 4ac}}{2a}$

$x = \dfrac{-(-5) \pm \sqrt{(-5)^2 - 4(1)(-3)}}{2(1)}$

$x = \dfrac{5 \pm \sqrt{37}}{2}$

$x = \dfrac{5 + \sqrt{37}}{2} \approx 5.54$

$x = \dfrac{5 - \sqrt{37}}{2} \approx -0.54$ (rejected)

The solution set is $\left\{\dfrac{5+\sqrt{37}}{2}\right\}$.

99.
$5^{x^2-12} = 25^{2x}$

$5^{x^2-12} = \left(5^2\right)^{2x}$

$5^{x^2-12} = 5^{4x}$

$x^2 - 12 = 4x$

$x^2 - 4x - 12 = 0$

$(x-6)(x+2) = 0$

Apply the zero product property:

$x - 6 = 0$ or $x + 2 = 0$

$x = 6$ $\qquad\qquad x = -2$

The solutions are -2 and 6, and the solution set is $\{-2, 6\}$.

101. $25 = 6e^{12.77x}$

$$\frac{25}{6} = e^{12.77x}$$

$$\ln\frac{25}{6} = \ln e^{12.77x}$$

$$\ln\frac{25}{6} = 12.77x$$

$$\frac{\ln\frac{25}{6}}{12.77} = x$$

$$0.112 \approx x$$

A blood alcohol level of about 0.11 corresponds to a 25% risk of a car accident.

103. a. $A = 18.9e^{0.005(0)}$

$A = 18.9$ million

b. $19.6 = 18.9e^{0.0055t}$

$$\frac{19.6}{18.9} = e^{0.0055t}$$

$$\ln\frac{19.6}{18.9} = \ln e^{0.0055t}$$

$$\ln\frac{19.6}{18.9} = 0.0055t$$

$$\frac{\ln\frac{19.6}{18.9}}{0.0055} = t$$

$$6.6 \approx t$$

In 2007 the population of New York will reach 19.6 million.

105.

$$20,000 = 12,500\left(1 + \frac{0.0575}{4}\right)^{4t}$$

$$12,500(1.014375)^{4t} = 20,000$$

$$(1.014375)^{4t} = 1.6$$

$$\ln(1.014375)^{4t} = \ln 1.6$$

$$4t\ln(1.014375) = \ln 1.6$$

$$t = \frac{\ln 1.6}{4\ln 1.014375} \approx 8.2$$

8.2 years

107.

$$1400 = 1000\left(1 + \frac{r}{360}\right)^{360\cdot 2}$$

$$\left(1 + \frac{r}{360}\right)^{720} = 1.4$$

$$\ln\left(1 + \frac{r}{360}\right)^{720} = \ln 1.4$$

$$720\ln\left(1 + \frac{r}{360}\right) = \ln 1.4$$

$$\ln\left(1 + \frac{r}{360}\right) = \frac{\ln 1.4}{720}$$

$$e^{\ln(1 + r/360)} = e^{(\ln 1.4)/720}$$

$$1 + \frac{r}{360} = e^{(\ln 1.4)/720} - 1$$

$$r = 360(e^{(\ln 1.4)/720}) - 1$$

$$\approx 0.168$$

16.8%

109. accumulated amount $= 2(8000) = 16,000$

$$16,000 = 8000e^{0.08t}$$

$$e^{0.08t} = 2$$

$$\ln e^{0.08t} = \ln 2$$

$$0.08t = \ln 2$$

$$t = \frac{\ln 2}{0.08}$$

$$t \approx 8.7$$

The amount would double in 8.7 years.

111. accumulated amount $= 3(2350) = 7050$

$$7050 = 2350e^{r\cdot 7}$$

$$e^{7r} = 3$$

$$\ln e^{7r} = \ln 3$$

$$7r = \ln 3$$

$$r = \frac{\ln 3}{7} \approx 0.157$$

15.7%

113. a. $f(x) = 13.4 + 46.3 \ln x$

$f(3) = 13.4 + 46.3 \ln 3 \approx 64.3$

The function result of 64.3% models the actual value of 63% very well.

b. $f(x) = 13.4 + 46.3 \ln x$

$96 = 13.4 + 46.3 \ln x$

$82.6 = 46.3 \ln x$

$\dfrac{82.6}{46.3} = \ln x$

$x = e^{\frac{82.6}{46.3}}$

$x \approx 6$

The function predicts that 96% of email will be spam 6 years after 2000, or 2006.

115. $30 \log_2 x = 45$

$\log_2 x = 1.5$

$x = 2^{1.5} \approx 2.8$

Only half the students recall the important features of the lecture after 2.8 days. (2.8, 50)

117. $2.4 = -\log x$

$\log x = -2.4$

$x = 10^{-2.4} \approx 0.004$

The hydrogen ion concentration was $10^{-2.4}$, approximately 0.004 moles per liter.

123.

The intersection point is (2, 8).
Verify: $x = 2$

$2^{x+1} = 8$

$2^{2+1} = 2$

$2^3 = 8$

$8 = 8$

The solution set is {2}.

125.

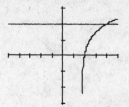

The intersection point is (4, 2).
Verify: $x = 4$

$\log_3(4 \cdot 4 - 7) = 2$

$\log_3 9 = 2$

$2 = 2$

The solution set is {4}.

127.

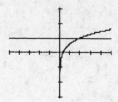

The intersection point is (2, 1).
Verify: $x = 2$

$\log(2+3) + \log 2 = 1$

$\log 5 + \log 2 = 1$

$\log(5 \cdot 2) = 1$

$\log 10 = 1$

$1 = 1$

The solution set is {2}.

129.

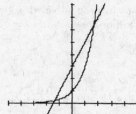

There are 2 points of intersection, approximately $(-1.391606, 0.21678798)$ and $(1.6855579, 6.3711158)$.
Verify $x \approx -1.391606$
$3^x = 2x + 3$
$3^{-1.391606} \approx 2(-1.391606) + 3$
$0.2167879803 \approx 0.216788$
Verify $x \approx 1.6855579$
$3^x = 2x + 3$
$3^{1.6855579} \approx 2(1.6855579) + 3$
$6.37111582 \approx 6.371158$
The solution set is $\{-1.391606, 1.6855579\}$.

131.

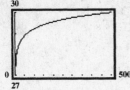

As the distance from the eye increases, barometric air pressure increases, leveling off at about 30 inches of mercury.

133.

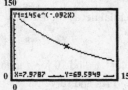

When $P = 70$, $t \approx 7.9$, so it will take about 7.9 minutes.
Verify:

$$70 = 45e^{-0.092(7.9)}$$

$$70 \approx 70.10076749$$

The runner's pulse will be 70 beats per minute after about 7.9 minutes.

135. a.   False; $\log(x+3) = 2$ means $x + 3 = 10^2$

   b.   False; $\log(7x+3) - \log(2x+5) = 4$ means

$$\log\frac{7x+3}{2x+5} = 4 \text{ which means } \frac{7x+3}{2x+5} = 10^4$$

   c.   True; $x = \dfrac{1}{k}\ln y$

$$kx = \ln y$$
$$e^{kx} = e^{\ln y}$$
$$e^{kx} = y$$

   d.   False; The equation $x^{10} = 5.71$ has no variable in an exponent so is not an exponential equation.

       (c) is true

137.
$$(\ln x)^2 = \ln x^2$$
$$(\ln x)^2 = 2\ln x$$
$$(\ln x)^2 - 2\ln x = 0$$
$$\ln x(\ln x - 2) = 0$$
$$\ln x = 2$$
$$e^{\ln x} = e^2 \text{ or } \begin{array}{l} \ln x = 0 \\ x = 1 \end{array}$$
$$x = e^2$$

The solution set is $\{1, e^2\}$.

Check with graphing utility:

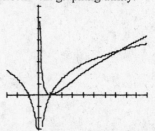

There are two points of intersection: $(1, 0)$ and approximately $(7.3890561, 4)$. Since $e^2 \approx 7.3890566099$, the graph verifies $x = 1$ and $x = e^2$, so the solution set is $\{1, e^2\}$ as determined algebraically.

139. $\ln(\ln x) = 0$
$$e^{\ln(\ln x)} = e^0$$
$$\ln x = 1$$
$$e^{\ln x} = e^1$$
$$x = e$$

The solution set is $\{e\}$.

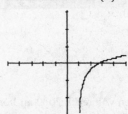

The graph of $\ln(\ln(x))$ crosses the graph $y = 0$ at approximately 2.718.

Section 4.5

Check Point Exercises

1.   a.   Use the exponential growth model
$A = A_0 e^{kt}$ with 1990 corresponding to $t = 0$
when the population was 643 million:
$A = 643 e^{kt}$
Substitute $t = 2000 - 1990 = 10$ when the
population was 813 million, so $A = 813$, to
find k.

$$813 = 643 e^{k10}$$

$$\frac{813}{643} = e^{k10}$$

$$\ln \frac{813}{643} = \ln e^{k10}$$

$$\ln \frac{813}{643} = 10k$$

$$\frac{\ln \frac{813}{643}}{10} = k$$

$$0.023 \approx k$$

So the exponential growth function is
$A = 643 e^{0.023t}$

b.   Substitute 2000 for A in the model from
part (a) and solve for t.

$$2000 = 643 e^{0.023t}$$

$$\frac{2000}{643} = e^{0.023t}$$

$$\ln \frac{2000}{643} = \ln e^{0.023t}$$

$$\ln \frac{2000}{643} = 0.023t$$

$$\frac{\ln \frac{2000}{643}}{0.023} = t$$

$$49 \approx t$$

The population will reach 2000 million, or
two billion, about 49 years after 1990, in
2039.

2.   a.   In the exponential decay model $A = A_0 e^{kt}$,
substitute $\frac{A_0}{2}$ for A since the amount
present after 28 years is half the original
amount.

$$\frac{A_0}{2} = A_0 e^{k \cdot 28}$$

$$e^{28k} = \frac{1}{2}$$

$$\ln e^{28k} = \ln \frac{1}{2}$$

$$28k = \ln \frac{1}{2}$$

$$k = \frac{\ln^{1/2}}{28} \approx -0.0248$$

So the exponential decay model is
$A = A_0 e^{-0.0248t}$

b.   Substitute 60 for A_0 and 10 for A in the
model from part (a) and solve for t.

$$10 = 60 e^{-0.0248t}$$

$$e^{-0.0248t} = \frac{1}{6}$$

$$\ln e^{-0.0248t} = \ln \frac{1}{6}$$

$$-0.0248t = \ln \frac{1}{6}$$

$$t = \frac{\ln \frac{1}{6}}{-0.0248} \approx 72$$

The strontium-90 will decay to a level of
10 grams about 72 years after the accident.

3.   a.   The time prior to learning trials
corresponds to $t = 0$.

$$f(0) = \frac{0.8}{1 + e^{-0.2(0)}} = 0.4$$

The proportion of correct responses prior
to learning trials was 0.4.

b.   Substitute 10 for t in the model:

$$f(10) = \frac{0.8}{1 + e^{-0.2(10)}} \approx 0.7$$

The proportion of correct responses after
10 learning trials was 0.7.

c.   In the logistic growth model,
$f(t) = \frac{c}{1 + ae^{-bt}}$, the constant c represents
the limiting size that $f(t)$ can attain. The
limiting size of the proportion of correct
responses as continued learning trials take
place is 0.8.

4. Scatter plot:

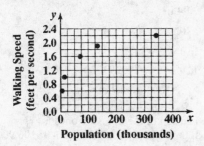

Because the data in the scatter plot increase rapidly at first and then begin to level off, the shape suggests that a logarithmic function is a good choice for modeling the data.

5. Scatter plot:

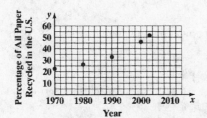

Because the data in the scatter plot appear to increase more and more rapidly, the shape suggests that an exponential function is a good choice for modeling the data.

6. $y = ab^x$ is equivalent to $y = ae^{(\ln b)x}$.

For $y = 4(7.8)^x$, $a = 4$, $b = 7.8$.

Thus, $y = 4(7.8)^x$ is equivalent to $y = 4e^{(\ln 7.8)x}$ in terms of a natural logarithm. Rounded to three decimal places, the model is approximately equivalent to $y = 4e^{2.054x}$.

Exercise Set 4.5

1. Since 2003 is 0 years after 2003, find A when $t = 0$:

$A = 127.2e^{0.001t}$

$A = 127.2e^{0.001(0)}$

$A = 127.2e^{0}$

$A = 127.2(1)$

$A = 127.2$

In 2003, the population was 127.2 million.

3. Iraq has the greatest growth rate at 2.8% per year.

5. Substitute $A = 1238$ into the model for India and solve for t:

$$1238 = 1049.7e^{0.015t}$$

$$\frac{1238}{1049.7} = e^{0.015t}$$

$$\ln \frac{1238}{1049.7} = \ln e^{0.015t}$$

$$\ln \frac{1238}{1049.7} = 0.015t$$

$$t = \frac{\ln \dfrac{1238}{1049.7}}{0.015} \approx 11$$

Now, $2003 + 11 = 2014$. The population of India will be 1238 million in approximately the year 2014.

7. a. $A_0 = 6.04$. Since 2050 is 50 years after 2000, when $t = 50$, $A = 10$.

$$A = A_0 e^{kt}$$

$$10 = 6.04e^{k(50)}$$

$$\frac{10}{6.04} = e^{50k}$$

$$\ln\left(\frac{10}{6.04}\right) = \ln e^{50k}$$

$$\ln\left(\frac{10}{6.04}\right) = 50k$$

$$k = \frac{\ln\left(\dfrac{10}{6.04}\right)}{50} \approx 0.01$$

Thus, the growth function is $A = 6.04e^{0.01t}$.

b.
$$9 = 6.04e^{0.01t}$$

$$\frac{9}{6.04} = e^{0.01t}$$

$$\ln\left(\frac{9}{6.04}\right) = \ln e^{0.01t}$$

$$\ln\left(\frac{9}{6.04}\right) = 0.01t$$

$$t = \frac{\ln\left(\dfrac{9}{6.04}\right)}{0.01} \approx 40$$

Now, $2000 + 40 = 2040$, so the population will be 9 million is approximately the year 2040.

9.
$$A = 16e^{-0.000121t}$$
$$A = 16e^{-0.000121(5715)}$$
$$A = 16e^{-0.691515}$$
$$A \approx 8.01$$
Approximately 8 grams of carbon-14 will be present in 5715 years.

11. After 10 seconds, there will be $16 \cdot \frac{1}{2} = 8$ grams

present. After 20 seconds, there will be $8 \cdot \frac{1}{2} = 4$

grams present. After 30 seconds, there will be

$4 \cdot \frac{1}{2} = 2$ grams present. After 40 seconds, there will

be $2 \cdot \frac{1}{2} = 1$ grams present. After 50 seconds, there

will be $1 \cdot \frac{1}{2} = \frac{1}{2}$ gram present.

13.
$$A = A_0 e^{-0.000121t}$$
$$15 = 100e^{-0.000121t}$$
$$\frac{15}{100} = e^{-0.000121t}$$
$$\ln 0.15 = \ln e^{-0.000121t}$$
$$\ln 0.15 = -0.000121t$$
$$t = \frac{\ln 0.15}{-0.000121} \approx 15{,}679$$
The paintings are approximately 15,679 years old.

15. a.
$$\frac{1}{2} = 1e^{k1.31}$$
$$\ln \frac{1}{2} = \ln e^{1.31k}$$
$$\ln \frac{1}{2} = 1.31k$$
$$k = \frac{\ln \frac{1}{2}}{1.31} \approx -0.52912$$
The exponential model is given by
$A = A_0 e^{-0.52912t}$.

b.
$$A = A_0 e^{-0.52912t}$$
$$0.945 A_0 = A_0 e^{-0.52912t}$$
$$0.945 = e^{-0.52912t}$$
$$\ln 0.945 = \ln e^{-0.52912t}$$
$$\ln 0.945 = -0.52912t$$
$$t = \frac{\ln 0.945}{-0.52912} \approx 0.1069$$
The age of the dinosaur ones is approximately 0.1069 billion or 106,900,000 years old.

17.
$$2A_0 = A_0 e^{kt}$$
$$2 = e^{kt}$$
$$\ln 2 = \ln e^{kt}$$
$$\ln 2 = kt$$
$$t = \frac{\ln 2}{k}$$
The population will double in $t = \frac{\ln 2}{k}$ years.

19. $A = e^{0.007t}$

a. $k = 0.007$, so New Zealand's growth rate is 0.7%.

b.
$$t = \frac{\ln 2}{k}$$
$$t = \frac{\ln 2}{0.007} \approx 99$$
New Zealand's population will double in approximately 99 years.

21. a. When the epidemic began, $t = 0$.
$$f(0) = \frac{100{,}000}{1 + 5000e^0} \approx 20$$
Twenty people became ill when the epidemic began.

b. $f(4) = \frac{100{,}000}{1 + 5{,}000e^{-4}} \approx 1080$

About 1080 people were ill at the end of the fourth week.

c. In the logistic growth model,
$$f(t) = \frac{c}{1 + ae^{-bt}},$$
the constant c represents the limiting size that $f(t)$ can attain. The limiting size of the population that becomes ill is 100,000 people.

23. $f(x) = \dfrac{12.85}{1 + 4.21e^{-0.026(x)}}$

$f(54) = \dfrac{12.85}{1 + 4.21e^{-0.026(54)}} \approx 6.3$

The function models the data very well.

25.

$f(x) = \dfrac{12.85}{1 + 4.21e^{-0.026(x)}}$

$8 = \dfrac{12.85}{1 + 4.21e^{-0.026(x)}}$

$8\left(1 + 4.21e^{-0.026(x)}\right) = 12.85$

$8 + 33.68e^{-0.026(x)} = 12.85$

$33.68e^{-0.026(x)} = 4.85$

$e^{-0.026(x)} = \dfrac{4.85}{33.68}$

$\ln e^{-0.026(x)} = \ln \dfrac{4.85}{33.68}$

$-0.026x = \ln \dfrac{4.85}{33.68}$

$x = \dfrac{\ln \frac{4.85}{33.68}}{-0.026}$

$x \approx 75$

The world population will reach 8 billion 75 years after 1949, or 2024.

27. $P(20) = \dfrac{90}{1 + 271e^{-0.122(20)}} \approx 3.7$

The probability that a 20-year-old has some coronary heart disease is about 3.7%.

29.

$0.5 = \dfrac{1.9}{1 + 271e^{-0.122t}}$

$0.5\left(1 + 271e^{-0.122t}\right) = 0.9$

$1 + 271e^{-0.122t} = 1.8$

$271e^{-0.122t} = 0.8$

$e^{-0.122t} = \dfrac{0.8}{271}$

$\ln e^{-0.122t} = \ln \dfrac{0.8}{271}$

$-0.122t = \ln \dfrac{0.8}{271}$

$t = \dfrac{\ln \frac{0.8}{271}}{-0.122} \approx 48$

The probability of some coronary heart disease is 0.5 at about age 48.

31. a.

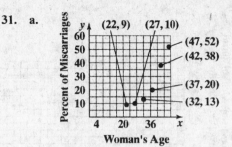

b. An exponential function appears to be the best choice for modeling the data.

33. a.

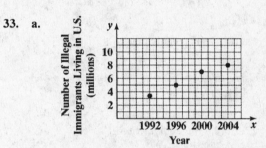

b. A linear function appear to be the best choice for modeling the data.

35. a.

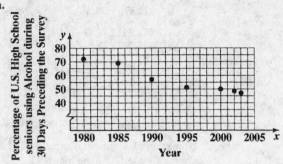

b. An exponential function appears to be the best choice for modeling the data.

37. $y = 100(4.6)^x$ is equivalent to
$y = 100e^{(\ln 4.6)x}$;
Using $\ln 4.6 \approx 1.526$,
$y = 100e^{1.526x}$.

39. $y = 2.5(0.7)^x$ is equivalent to
$y = 2.5e^{(\ln 0.7)x}$;
Using $\ln 0.7 \approx -0.357$,
$y = 2.5e^{-0.357x}$.

For Exercises 51 – 53, enter the data in L1 and L2:

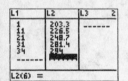

51.

The logarithmic model is
$y = 194.328 + 22.758 \ln x$. Since $r = 0.881$ is
fairly close to 1, the model fits the data okay, but
not great.

53.

```
PwrReg
y=a*x^b
a=196.6191762
b=.0943892895
r²=.8157235653
r=.9031741611
```

The power regression model is
$y = 196.619x^{0.094}$. Since $r = 0.903$, the model
fits the data fairly well.

55.

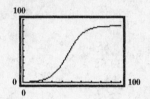

The probability of coronary heart disease starts
increasing at a more rapid rate at about age 20.
At about age 60, the rate of increase starts to
slow down.

59. Use $T_0 = 210$, $C = 70$, $t = 30$, and $T = 140$ to
determine the constant k:
$$T = C + (T_0 - C)e^{-kt}$$
$$140 = 70 + (210 - 70)e^{-k(30)}$$
$$140 = 70 + 140e^{-30k}$$
$$70 = 140e^{-30k}$$
$$\frac{70}{140} = \frac{140e^{-30k}}{140}$$
$$0.5 = e^{-30k}$$
$$\ln 0.5 = \ln e^{-30k}$$
$$\ln 0.5 = -30k$$
$$k = \frac{\ln 0.5}{-30} \approx 0.0231$$

Thus, the model for these conditions is
$T = 70 + 140e^{-0.0231t}$.

Evaluate the model for $t = 40$:
$T = 70 + 140e^{-0.0231(40)} \approx 126$

Thus, the temperature of the cake after 40
minutes will be approximately $126°F$.

Chapter 4 Review Exercises

1. This is the graph of $f(x) = 4^x$ reflected about the y-axis, so the function is $g(x) = 4^{-x}$.

2. This is the graph of $f(x) = 4^x$ reflected about the x-axis and about the y-axis, so the function is $h(x) = -4^{-x}$.

3. This is the graph of $f(x) = 4^x$ reflected about the x-axis and about the y-axis then shifted upward 3 units, so the function is $r(x) = -4^{-x} + 3$.

4. This is the graph of $f(x) = 4^x$.

5. The graph of $g(x)$ shifts the graph of $f(x)$ one unit to the right.

    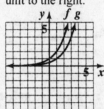

    $f(x) = 2^x$
    $g(x) = 2^{x-1}$

    Asymptote of f: $y = 0$
    Asymptote of g: $y = 0$
    Domain of f = Domain of $g = (-\infty, \infty)$
    Range of f = Range of $g = (0, \infty)$

6. The graph of $g(x)$ shifts the graph of $f(x)$ one unit down.

    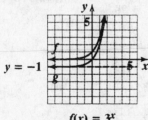

    $f(x) = 3^x$
    $g(x) = 3^x - 1$

    Asymptote of f: $y = 0$
    Asymptote of g: $y = -1$
    Domain of f = Domain of $g = (-\infty, \infty)$
    Range of $f = (0, \infty)$
    Range of $g = (-1, \infty)$

7. The graph of $g(x)$ reflects the graph of $f(x)$ about the y – axis.

    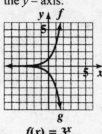

    $f(x) = 3^x$
    $g(x) = -3^x$

    Asymptote of f: $y = 0$
    Asymptote of g: $y = 0$
    Domain of f = Domain of $g = (-\infty, \infty)$
    Range of $f = (0, \infty)$
    Range of $g = (-\infty, 0)$

8. The graph of $g(x)$ reflects the graph of $f(x)$ about the x – axis.

    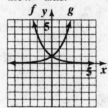

    $f(x) = \left(\dfrac{1}{2}\right)^x$

    $g(x) = \left(\dfrac{1}{2}\right)^{-x}$

    Asymptote of f: $y = 0$
    Asymptote of g: $y = 0$
    Domain of f = Domain of $g = (-\infty, \infty)$
    Range of f = Range of $g = (0, \infty)$

329

9. The graph of $g(x)$ vertically stretches the graph of $f(x)$ by a factor of 2.

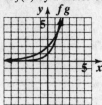

$$f(x) = e^x$$
$$g(x) = 2e^{x/2}$$

Asymptote of f: $y = 0$
Asymptote of g: $y = 0$
Domain of f = Domain of $g = (-\infty, \infty)$
Range of f = Range of $g = (0, \infty)$

10. 5.5% compounded semiannually:

$$A = 5000\left(1 + \frac{0.055}{2}\right)^{2 \cdot 5} \approx 6558.26$$

5.25% compounded monthly:

$$A = 5000\left(1 + \frac{0.0525}{12}\right)^{12 \cdot 5} \approx 6497.16$$

5.5% compounded semiannually yields the greater return.

11. 7% compounded monthly:

$$A = 14,000\left(1 + \frac{0.07}{12}\right)^{12 \cdot 10} \approx 28,135.26$$

6.85% compounded continuously:

$$A = 14,000e^{0.0685(10)} \approx 27,772.81$$

7% compounded monthly yields the greater return.

12. a. When first taken out of the microwave, the temperature of the coffee was 200°.

    b. After 20 minutes, the temperature of the coffee was about 120°.
$$T = 70 + 130e^{-0.04855(20)} \approx 119.23$$
Using a calculator, the temperature is about 119°.

    c. The coffee will cool to about 70°;
The temperature of the room is 70°.

13. $49^{1/2} = 7$

14. $4^3 = x$

15. $3^y = 81$

16. $\log_6 216 = 3$

17. $\log_b 625 = 4$

18. $\log_{13} 874 = y$

19. $\log_4 64 = 3$ because $4^3 = 64$.

20. $\log_5 \frac{1}{25} = -2$ because $5^{-2} = \frac{1}{25}$.

21. $\log_3(-9)$ cannot be evaluated since $\log_b x$ is defined only for $x > 0$.

22. $\log_{16} 4 = \frac{1}{2}$ because $16^{1/2} = \sqrt{16} = 4$.

23. Because $\log_b b = 1$,
we conclude $\log_{17} 17 = 1$.

24. Because $\log_b b^x = x$,
we conclude $\log_3 3^8 = 8$.

25. Because $\ln e^x = x$,
we conclude $\ln e^5 = 5$.

26. $\log_3 \frac{1}{\sqrt{3}} = \log_3 \frac{1}{3^{\frac{1}{2}}} = \log_3 3^{-\frac{1}{2}} = -\frac{1}{2}$

27. $\ln \frac{1}{e^2} = \ln e^{-2} = -2$

28. $\log \frac{1}{1000} = \log \frac{1}{10^3} = \log 10^{-3} = -3$

29. Because $\log_b b = 1$,
we conclude $\log_8 8 = 1$.
So, $\log_3(\log_8 8) = \log_3 1$.
Because $\log_b 1 = 0$
we conclude $\log_3 1 = 0$.
Therefore, $\log_3(\log_8 8) = 0$.

30.

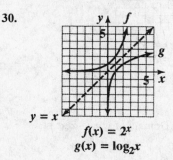

$$f(x) = 2^x$$
$$g(x) = \log_2 x$$

31.

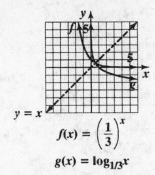

$$f(x) = \left(\frac{1}{3}\right)^x$$

$$g(x) = \log_{1/3} x$$

32. This is the graph of $f(x) = \log x$ reflected about the *y*-axis, so the function is $g(x) = \log(-x)$.

33. This is the graph of $f(x) = \log x$ shifted left 2 units, reflected about the *y*-axis, then shifted upward one unit, so the function is $r(x) = 1 + \log(2-x)$.

34. This is the graph of $f(x) = \log x$ shifted left 2 units then reflected about the *y*-axis, so the function is $h(x) = \log(2-x)$.

35. This is the graph of $f(x) = \log x$.

36.

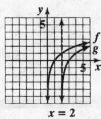

$$x = 2$$

$$f(x) = \log_2 x$$

$$g(x) = \log_2(x-2)$$

x-intercept: (3, 0)
vertical asymptote: $x = 2$
Domain: $(2, \infty)$
Range: $(-\infty, \infty)$

37.

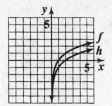

$$f(x) = \log_2 x$$

$$h(x) = -1 + \log_2 x$$

x-intercept: (2, 0)
vertical asymptote: $x = 0$
Domain: $(0, \infty)$
Range: $(-\infty, \infty)$

38.

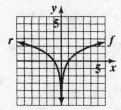

$$f(x) = \log_2 x$$

$$r(x) = \log_2(-x)$$

x-intercept: (−1, 0)
vertical asymptote: $x = 0$
Domain: $(-\infty, 0)$
Range: $(-\infty, \infty)$

39.

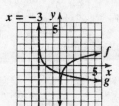

$$f(x) = \log x$$

$$g(x) = -\log(x+3)$$

Asymptote of *f*: $x = 0$
Asymptote of *g*: $x = -3$
Domain of $f = (0, \infty)$
Domain of $g = (-3, \infty)$
Range of *f* = Range of $g = (-\infty, \infty)$

40.

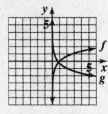

$$f(x) = \ln x$$
$$g(x) = -\ln(2x)$$

Asymptote of f: $x = 0$
Asymptote of g: $x = 0$
Domain of f = Domain of g = $(0, \infty)$
Range of f = Range of g = $(-\infty, \infty)$

41. The domain of f consists of all x for which $x + 5 > 0$.
Solving this inequality for x, we obtain $x > -5$.
Thus the domain of f is $(-5, \infty)$

42. The domain of f consists of all x for which $3 - x > 0$.
Solving this inequality for x, we obtain $x < 3$.
Thus, the domain of f is $(-\infty, 3)$.

43. The domain of f consists of all x for which $(x - 1)^2 > 0$.
Solving this inequality for x, we obtain $x < 1$ or $x > 1$. Thus, the domain of f is $(-\infty, 1) \cup (1, \infty)$.

44. Because $\ln e^x = x$, we conclude $\ln e^{6x} = 6x$.

45. Because $e^{\ln x} = x$, we conclude $e^{\ln \sqrt{x}} = \sqrt{x}$.

46. Because $10^{\log x} = x$, we conclude $10^{\log 4x^2} = 4x^2$.

47. $R = \log \dfrac{1000 I_0}{I_0} = \log 1000 = 3$
The Richter scale magnitude is 3.0.

48. a. $f(0) = 76 - 18\log(0 + 1) = 76$
When first given, the average score was 76.

b. $f(2) = 76 - 18\log(2 + 1) \approx 67$
$f(4) = 76 - 18\log(4 + 1) \approx 63$
$f(6) = 76 - 18\log(6 + 1) \approx 61$
$f(8) = 76 - 18\log(8 + 1) \approx 59$
$f(12) = 76 - 18\log(12 + 1) \approx 56$
After 2, 4, 6, 8, and 12 months, the average scores are about 67, 63, 61, 59, and 56, respectively.

c.

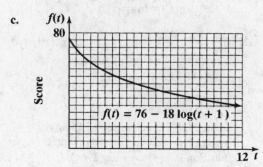

Time (months)

Retention decreases as time passes.

49. $t = \dfrac{1}{0.06} \ln\left(\dfrac{12}{12 - 5}\right) \approx 8.98$
It will take about 9 weeks.

50. $\log_6\left(36x^3\right)$
$= \log_6 36 + \log_6 x^3$
$= \log_6 36 + 3\log_6 x$
$= 2 + 3\log_6 x$

51. $\log_4 \dfrac{\sqrt{x}}{64} = \log_4 x^{1/2} - \log_4 64$
$= \dfrac{1}{2}\log_4 x - 3$

52. $\log_2 \dfrac{xy^2}{64} = \log_2 xy^2 - \log_2 64$
$= \log_2 x + \log_2 y^2 - \log_2 64$
$= \log_2 x + 2\log_2 y - 6$

332

53. $\ln \sqrt[3]{\dfrac{x}{e}}$

$= \ln \left(\dfrac{x}{e}\right)^{1/3}$

$= \dfrac{1}{3}\left[\ln x - \ln e\right]$

$= \dfrac{1}{3}\ln x - \dfrac{1}{3}\ln e$

$= \dfrac{1}{3}\ln x - \dfrac{1}{3}$

54. $\log_b 7 + \log_b 3$

$= \log_b (7 \cdot 3)$

$= \log_b 21$

55. $\log 3 - 3\log x$

$= \log 3 - \log x^3$

$= \log \dfrac{3}{x^3}$

56. $3\ln x + 4\ln y$

$= \ln x^3 + \ln y^4$

$= \ln \left(x^3 y^4\right)$

57. $\dfrac{1}{2}\ln x - \ln y$

$= \ln x^{1/2} - \ln y$

$= \ln \dfrac{\sqrt{x}}{y}$

58. $\log_6 72{,}348 = \dfrac{\log 72{,}348}{\log 6} \approx 6.2448$

59. $\log_4 0.863 = \dfrac{\ln 0.863}{\ln 4} \approx -0.1063$

60. true; $(\ln x)(\ln 1) = (\ln x)(0) = 0$

61. false; $\log(x+9) - \log(x+1) = \log\dfrac{(x+9)}{(x+1)}$

62. false; $\log_2 x^4 = 4\log_2 x$

63. true; $\ln e^x = x \ln e$

64. $2^{4x-2} = 64$

$2^{4x-2} = 2^6$

$4x - 2 = 6$

$4x = 8$

$x = 2$

65. $125^x = 25$

$\left(5^3\right)^x = 5^2$

$5^{3x} = 5^2$

$3x = 2$

$x = \dfrac{2}{3}$

66. $9^{x+2} = 27^{-x}$

$\left(3^2\right)^{x+2} = \left(3^3\right)^{-x}$

$3^{2x+4} = 3^{-3x}$

$2x + 4 = -3x$

$5x = -4$

$x = -\dfrac{4}{5}$

67. $8^x = 12{,}143$

$\ln 8^x = \ln 12{,}143$

$x \ln 8 = \ln 12{,}143$

$x = \dfrac{\ln 12{,}143}{\ln 8} \approx 4.52$

68. $9e^{5x} = 1269$

$e^{5x} = 141$

$\ln e^{5x} = \ln 141$

$5x = \ln 141$

$x = \dfrac{\ln 141}{5} \approx 0.99$

69. $e^{12-5x} - 7 = 123$

$e^{12-5x} = 130$

$\ln e^{12-5x} = \ln 130$

$12 - 5x = \ln 130$

$5x = 12 - \ln 130$

$x = \dfrac{12 - \ln 130}{5} \approx 1.43$

70.
$$5^{4x+2} = 37,500$$
$$\ln 5^{4x+2} = \ln 37,500$$
$$(4x+2)\ln 5 = \ln 37,500$$
$$4x\ln 5 + 2\ln 5 = \ln 37,500$$
$$4x\ln 5 = \ln 37,500 - 2\ln 5$$
$$x = \frac{\ln 37,500 - 2\ln 5}{4\ln 5} \approx 1.14$$

71.
$$3^{x+4} = 7^{2x-1}$$
$$\ln 3^{x+4} = \ln 7^{2x-1}$$
$$(x+4)\ln 3 = (2x-1)\ln 7$$
$$x\ln 3 + 4\ln 3 = 2x\ln 7 - \ln 7$$
$$x\ln 3 - 2x\ln 7 = -4\ln 3 - \ln 7$$
$$x(\ln 3 - 2\ln 7) = -4\ln 3 - \ln 7$$
$$x = \frac{-4\ln 3 - \ln 7}{\ln 3 - 2\ln 7}$$
$$x = \frac{4\ln 3 + \ln 7}{2\ln 7 - \ln 3}$$
$$x \approx 2.27$$

72.
$$e^{2x} - e^x - 6 = 0$$
$$(e^x - 3)(e^x + 2) = 0$$
$$e^x - 3 = 0 \quad \text{or} \quad e^x + 2 = 0$$
$$e^x = 3 \qquad\qquad e^x = -2$$
$$\ln e^x = \ln 3 \quad \ln e^x = \ln(-2)$$
$$x = \ln 3 \qquad\qquad x = \ln(-2)$$
$$x = \ln 3 \approx 1.099 \quad \ln(-2) \text{ does not exist.}$$

The solution set is $\{\ln 3\}$,
approximately 1.10.

73. $\log_4 (3x-5) = 3$
$$3x - 5 = 4^3$$
$$3x - 5 = 64$$
$$3x = 69$$
$$x = 23$$
The solutions set is $\{23\}$.

74. $3 + 4\ln(2x) = 15$
$$4\ln(2x) = 12$$
$$\ln(2x) = 3$$
$$2x = e^3$$
$$x = \frac{e^3}{2}$$
$$x \approx 10.04$$
The solutions set is $\left\{\dfrac{e^3}{2}\right\}$.

75. $\log_2 (x+3) + \log_2 (x-3) = 4$
$$\log_2 (x+3)(x-3) = 4$$
$$\log_2 (x^2 - 9) = 4$$
$$x^2 - 9 = 2^4$$
$$x^2 - 9 = 16$$
$$x^2 = 25$$
$$x = \pm 5$$
$x = -5$ does not check because $\log_2(-5+3)$
does not exist.
The solution set is $\{5\}$.

76. $\log_3 (x-1) - \log_3 (x+2) = 2$
$$\log_3 \frac{x-1}{x+2} = 2$$
$$\frac{x-1}{x-2} = 3^2$$
$$\frac{x-1}{x+2} = 9$$
$$x - 1 = 9(x+2)$$
$$x - 1 = 9x + 18$$
$$8x = -19$$
$$x = -\frac{19}{8}$$
$x = -\dfrac{19}{8}$ does not check because
$\log_3\left(-\dfrac{19}{8} - 1\right)$ does not exist.
The solution set is $\varnothing$.

77. $\ln(x+4) - \ln(x+1) = \ln x$

$$\ln\frac{x+4}{x+1} = \ln x$$

$$\frac{x+4}{x+1} = x$$

$$x(x+1) = x+4$$

$$x^2 + x = x+4$$

$$x^2 = 4$$

$$x = \pm 2$$

$x = -2$ does not check and must be rejected.
The solution set is $\{2\}$.

78. $\log_4(2x+1) = \log_4(x-3) + \log_4(x+5)$

$$\log_4(2x+1) = \log_4(x-3) + \log_4(x+5)$$

$$\log_4(2x+1) = \log_4\left(x^2 + 2x - 15\right)$$

$$2x+1 = x^2 + 2x - 15$$

$$16 = x^2$$

$$x^2 = 16$$

$$x = \pm 4$$

$x = -4$ does not check and must be rejected.
The solution set is $\{4\}$.

79. $P(x) = 14.7 e^{-0.21x}$

$$4.6 = 14.7 e^{-0.21x}$$

$$\frac{4.6}{14.7} = e^{-0.21x}$$

$$\ln\frac{4.6}{14.7} = \ln e^{-0.21x}$$

$$\ln\frac{4.6}{14.7} = -0.21x$$

$$t = \frac{\ln\dfrac{4.6}{14.7}}{-0.21} \approx 5.5$$

The peak of Mt. Everest is about 5.5 miles above sea level.

80. $f(t) = 364(1.005)^t$

$$560 = 364(1.005)^t$$

$$\frac{560}{364} = (1.005)^t$$

$$\ln\frac{560}{364} = \ln(1.005)^t$$

$$\ln\frac{560}{364} = t\ln 1.005$$

$$t = \frac{\ln\dfrac{560}{364}}{\ln 1.005} \approx 86.4$$

The carbon dioxide concentration will be double the pre-industrial level approximately 86 years after the year 2000 in the year 2086.

81. $W(x) = 0.37\ln x + 0.05$

$$3.38 = 0.37\ln x + 0.05$$

$$3.33 = 0.37\ln x$$

$$\frac{3.33}{0.37} = \ln x$$

$$9 = \ln x$$

$$e^9 = e^{\ln x}$$

$$x = e^9 \approx 8103$$

The population of New York City is approximately 8103 thousand, or 8,103,000.

82. $20,000 = 12,500\left(1 + \dfrac{0.065}{4}\right)^{4t}$

$$12,500(1.01625)^{4t} = 20,000$$

$$(1.01625)^{4t} = 1.6$$

$$\ln(1.01625)^{4t} = \ln 1.6$$

$$4t\ln 1.01625 = \ln 1.6$$

$$t = \frac{\ln 1.6}{4\ln 1.01625} \approx 7.3$$

It will take about 7.3 years.

83. $3 \cdot 50,000 = 50,000 e^{0.075t}$

$$50,000 e^{0.075t} = 150,000$$

$$e^{0.075} = 3$$

$$\ln e^{0.075t} = \ln 3$$

$$0.075t = \ln 3$$

$$t = \frac{\ln 3}{0.075} \approx 14.6$$

It will take about 14.6 years.

335

84. When an investment value triples, $A = 3P$.
$$3P = Pe^{5r}$$
$$e^{5r} = 3$$
$$\ln e^{5r} = \ln 3$$
$$5r = \ln 3$$
$$r = \frac{\ln 3}{5} \approx 0.2197$$

The interest rate would need to be about 22%

85. a.
$$35.3 = 22.4e^{k10}$$
$$\frac{35.3}{22.4} = e^{10k}$$
$$\ln \frac{35.3}{22.4} = \ln e^{10k}$$
$$\ln \frac{35.3}{22.4} = 10k$$
$$\frac{\ln \frac{35.3}{22.4}}{10} = k$$
$$0.045 \approx k$$
$$A = 22.4e^{0.045t}$$

b. $A = 22.4e^{0.045(20)} \approx 55.1$
In 2010, the population will be about 55.1 million.

c.
$$60 = 22.4e^{0.045t}$$
$$\frac{60}{22.4} = e^{0.045t}$$
$$\ln \frac{60}{22.4} = \ln e^{0.045t}$$
$$\ln \frac{60}{22.4} = 0.045t$$
$$\frac{\ln \frac{60}{22.4}}{0.045} = t$$
$$22 \approx t$$

The population will reach 60 million about 22 years after 1990, in 2012.

86. Use the half-life of 140 days to find k.
$$A = A_0 e^{kt}$$
$$\frac{1}{2} = e^{k\,140}$$
$$\frac{1}{2} = e^{140k}$$
$$\ln \frac{1}{2} = \ln e^{140k}$$
$$\ln \frac{1}{2} = 140k$$
$$\frac{\ln \frac{1}{2}}{140} = k$$
$$k \approx -0.004951$$

Use $A = A_0 e^{kt}$ to find t.
$$A = A_0 e^{-0.004951t}$$
$$0.2 = e^{-0.004951t}$$
$$\ln 0.2 = \ln e^{-0.004951t}$$
$$\ln 0.2 = -0.004951t$$
$$t = \frac{\ln 0.2}{-0.004951}$$
$$t \approx 325$$

It will take about 325 days for the substance to decay to 20% of its original amount.

87. a. $f(0) = \dfrac{500,000}{1 + 2499e^{-0.92(0)}} = 200$

200 people became ill when the epidemic began.

b. $f(6) = \dfrac{500,000}{1 + 2499e^{-0.92(6)}} = 45,411$

45,410 were ill after 6 weeks.

c. 500,000 people

88. a.

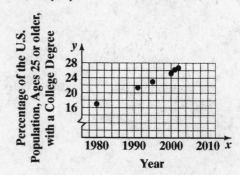

b. An exponential or linear function appears to be the best choice for modeling the data.

336

89. a.

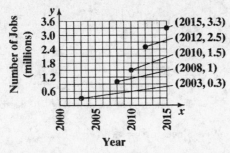

Year

b. An exponential function appears to be the best choice for modeling the data.

90. $y = 73(2.6)^x$

$y = 73e^{(\ln 2.6)x}$

$y = 73e^{0.956x}$

91. $y = 6.5(0.43)^x$

$y = 6.5e^{(\ln 0.43)x}$

$y = 6.5e^{-0.844x}$

Chapter 4 Test

1.

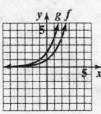

$f(x) = 2^x$

$g(x) = 2^x + 1$

2.

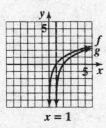

$x = 1$

$f(x) = \log_2 x$

$g(x) = \log_2(x - 1)$

3. $5^3 = 125$

4. $\log_{36} 6 = \dfrac{1}{2}$

5. The domain of f consists of all x for which $3 - x > 0$. Solving this inequality for x, we obtain $x < 3$.

Thus, the domain of f is $(-\infty, 3)$.

6. $\log_4 (64x^5) = \log_4 64 + \log_4 x^5$

$= 3 + 5 \log_4 x$

7. $\log_3 \dfrac{\sqrt[3]{x}}{81} = \log_3 x^{\frac{1}{3}} - \log_3 81$

$= \dfrac{1}{3} \log_3 x - 4$

8. $6 \log x + 2 \log y = \log x^6 + \log y^2$

$= \log (x^6 y^2)$

9. $\ln 7 - 3 \ln x = \ln 7 - \ln x^3$

$= \ln \dfrac{7}{x^3}$

10. $\log_{15} 71 = \dfrac{\log 71}{\log 15} \approx 1.5741$

11. $3^{x-2} = 9^{x+4}$

$3^{x-2} = (3^2)^{x+4}$

$3^{x-2} = 3^{2x+8}$

$x - 2 = 2x + 8$

$-x = 10$

$x = -10$

12. $5^x = 1.4$

$\ln 5^x = \ln 1.4$

$x \ln 5 = \ln 1.4$

$x = \dfrac{\ln 1.4}{\ln 5} \approx 0.2091$

13. $400e^{0.005x} = 1600$

$e^{0.005x} = 4$

$\ln e^{0.005x} = \ln 4$

$0.005x = \ln 4$

$x = \dfrac{\ln 4}{0.005} \approx 277.2589$

14. $e^{2x} - 6e^x + 5 = 0$

$\left(e^x - 5\right)\left(e^x - 1\right) = 0$

$e^x - 5 = 0 \qquad$ or $\quad e^x - 1 = 0$

$\quad e^x = 5 \qquad\qquad\qquad e^x = 1$

$\ln e^x = \ln 5 \qquad\qquad \ln e^x = \ln 1$

$\quad x = \ln 5 \qquad\qquad\qquad x = \ln 1$

$\quad x \approx 1.6094 \qquad\qquad\quad x = 0$

The solution set is $\{0, \ln 5\}$; $\ln \approx 1.6094$.

15. $\log_6 \left(4x - 1\right) = 3$

$\qquad 4x - 1 = 6^3$

$\qquad 4x - 1 = 216$

$\qquad 4x = 217$

$\qquad x = \dfrac{217}{4} = 54.25$

16. $2 \ln 3x = 8$

$\quad \ln 3x = 4$

$\qquad 3x = e^4$

$\qquad x = \dfrac{e^4}{3} \approx 18.1994$

17. $\log x + \log\left(x + 15\right) = 2$

$\qquad \log\left(x^2 + 15x\right) = 2$

$\qquad\qquad x^2 + 15x = 10^2$

$\qquad x^2 + 15x - 100 = 0$

$\qquad \left(x + 20\right)\left(x - 5\right) = 0$

$\qquad\qquad x + 20 = 0$ or $x - 5 = 0$

$x = -20 \qquad x = 5$

$x = -20$ does not check because $\log(-20)$ does not exist.

The solution set is $\{5\}$.

18. $\ln\left(x - 4\right) - \ln\left(x + 1\right) = \ln 6$

$\qquad \ln \dfrac{x - 4}{x + 1} = \ln 6$

$\qquad \dfrac{x - 4}{x + 1} = 6$

$\qquad 6(x + 1) = x - 4$

$\qquad 6x + 6 = x - 4$

$\qquad 5x = -10$

$\qquad x = -2$

$x = -2$ does not check and must be rejected.

The solution set is $\{ \ \}$.

19. $D = 10 \log \dfrac{10^{12} I_0}{I_0}$

$\quad = 10 \log 10^{12}$

$\quad = 10 \cdot 12$

$\quad = 120$

The loudness of the sound is 120 decibels.

20. Since $\ln e^x = x$, $\ln e^{5x} = 5x$.

21. $\log_b b = 1$ because $b^1 = b$.

22. $\log_6 1 = 0$ because $6^0 = 1$.

23. 6.5% compounded semiannually:

$A = 3,000\left(1 + \dfrac{0.065}{2}\right)^{2(10)} \approx \$5,687.51$

6% compounded continuously:

$A = 3,000 e^{0.06(10)} \approx \$5,466.36$

6.5% compounded semiannually yields about $221 more than 6% compounded continuously.

24.

$8000 = 4000\left(1 + \dfrac{0.05}{4}\right)^{4t}$

$\dfrac{8000}{4000} = \left(1 + 0.0125\right)^{4t}$

$2 = \left(1.0125\right)^{4t}$

$\ln 2 = \ln\left(1.0125\right)^{4t}$

$\ln 2 = 4t \ln\left(1.0125\right)$

$\dfrac{\ln 2}{4 \ln\left(1.0125\right)} = \dfrac{4t \ln\left(1.0125\right)}{4 \ln\left(1.0125\right)}$

$t = \dfrac{\ln 2}{4 \ln\left(1.0125\right)} \approx 13.9$

It will take approximately 13.9 years for the money to grow to $8000.

25.

$2 = 1 e^{r \cdot 10}$

$2 = e^{10r}$

$\ln 2 = \ln e^{10r}$

$\ln 2 = 10r$

$r = \dfrac{\ln 2}{10} \approx 0.069$

The money will double in 10 years with an interest rate of approximately 6.9%.

26. a. $P(0) = 82.3e^{-0.002(0)}$

$\qquad = 82.3e^0 = 82.3(1) = 82.3$

In 2003, the population of Germany was 82.3 million.

b. The population of Germany is decreasing. We can tell the model has a negative, $k = -0.002$.

c. $81.5 = 82.3e^{-0.002t}$

$\dfrac{81.5}{82.3} = e^{-0.002t}$

$\ln\dfrac{81.5}{82.3} = \ln e^{-0.002t}$

$\ln\dfrac{81.5}{82.3} = -0.002t$

$t = \dfrac{\ln\dfrac{81.5}{82.3}}{-0.002} \approx 5$

The population of Germany will be 81.5 million approximately 5 years after 2003 in the year 2008.

27. In 1990, $t = 0$ and $A_0 = 509$
In 2000, $t = 2000 - 1990 = 10$ and
$A = 729$.

$729 = 509e^{k10}$

$\dfrac{729}{509} = e^{10k}$

$\ln\dfrac{729}{509} = \ln e^{10k}$

$\ln\dfrac{729}{509} = 10k$

$\dfrac{\ln\dfrac{729}{509}}{10} = k$

$0.036 \approx k$

The exponential growth function is
$A = 509e^{0.036t}$.

28. When the amount remaining is 5%, $A = 0.05A_0$.

$0.05A_0 = A_0e^{-0.000121t}$

$e^{-0.000121t} = 0.05$

$\ln e^{-0.000121t} = \ln 0.05$

$-0.000121t = \ln 0.05$

$t = \dfrac{\ln 0.05}{-0.000121} \approx 24{,}758$

The man died about 24,758 years ago.

29. a. $f(0) = \dfrac{140}{1+9e^{-0.165(0)}} = 14$

Fourteen elk were initially introduced to the habitat.

b. $f(10) = \dfrac{140}{1+9e^{-0.165(10)}} \approx 51$

After 10 years, about 51 elk are expected.

c. In the logistic growth model,

$f(t) = \dfrac{c}{1+ae^{-bt}}$,

the constant c represents the limiting size that $f(t)$ can attain. The limiting size of the elk population is 140 elk.

30. Plot the ordered pairs.

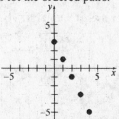

The values appear to belong to a linear function.

31. Plot the ordered pairs.

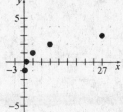

The values appear to belong to a logarithmic function.

32. Plot the ordered pairs.

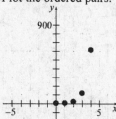

The values appear to belong to an exponential function.

33. Plot the ordered pairs.

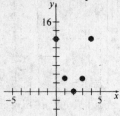

The values appear to belong to a quadratic function.

34.
$$y = 96(0.38)^x$$
$$y = 96e^{(\ln 0.38)x}$$
$$y = 96e^{-0.968x}$$

Cumulative Review Exercises (Chapters 1–4)

1. $|3x - 4| = 2$

$3x - 4 = 2$ or $3x - 4 = -2$

$3x = 6$ $\qquad$ $3x = 2$

$x = 2$ $\qquad$ $x = \dfrac{2}{3}$

The solution set is $\left\{ \dfrac{2}{3}, 2 \right\}$.

2. $\sqrt{2x - 5} - \sqrt{x - 3} = 1$

$\sqrt{2x - 5} = 1 + \sqrt{x - 3}$

$\left(\sqrt{2x - 5} \right)^2 = \left(1 + \sqrt{x - 3} \right)^2$

$2x - 5 = 1 + 2\sqrt{x - 3} + x - 3$

$2x - 5 = x - 2 + 2\sqrt{x - 3}$

$x - 3 = 2\sqrt{x - 3}$

$(x - 3)^2 = \left(2\sqrt{x - 3} \right)^2$

$(x - 3)^2 = 4(x - 3)$

$x^2 - 6x + 9 = 4x - 12$

$x^2 - 10x + 21 = 0$

$(x - 3)(x - 7) = 0$

$x = 3$ or $x = 7$

Both solutions satisfy the original equation when checked.
The solution set is $\{3, 7\}$.

3. $x^4 + x^3 - 3x^2 - x + 2 = 0$

$p: \pm 1, \pm 2$

$q: \pm 1$

$\dfrac{p}{q}: \pm 1, \pm 2$

-2	1	1	-3	-1	2
		-2	2	2	-2
	1	-1	-1	1	0

$(x + 2)(x^3 - x^2 - x + 1) = 0$

$(x + 2)[x^2(x - 1) - (x - 1)] = 0$

$(x + 2)(x^2 - 1)(x - 1) = 0$

$(x + 2)(x + 1)(x - 1)(x - 1) = 0$

$(x + 2)(x + 1)(x - 1)^2 = 0$

$x + 2 = 0$ $\quad$ or $\quad$ $x + 1 = 0$ $\quad$ or $\quad$ $x - 1 = 0$

$x = -2$ $\qquad\qquad$ $x = -1$ $\qquad\qquad$ $x = 1$

The solution set is $\{-2, -1, 1\}$.

4. $e^{5x} - 32 = 96$

$e^{5x} = 128$

$\ln e^{5x} = \ln 128$

$5x = \ln 128$

$x = \dfrac{\ln 128}{5} \approx 0.9704$

The solution set is $\left\{ \dfrac{\ln 128}{5} \right\}$,

approximately 0.9704.

5. $\log_2 (x + 5) + \log_2 (x - 1) = 4$

$\log_2 [(x + 5)(x - 1)] = 4$

$(x + 5)(x - 1) = 2^4$

$x^2 + 4x - 5 = 16$

$x^2 + 4x - 21 = 0$

$(x + 7)(x - 3) = 0$

$x + 7 = 0$ $\quad$ or $\quad$ $x - 3 = 0$

$x = -7$ $\qquad\qquad$ $x = 3$

$x = -7$ does not check because $\log_2 (-7 + 5)$ does not exist.
The solution set is $\{3\}$.

6. $\ln(x+4)+\ln(x+1)=2\ln(x+3)$

$\ln((x+4)(x+1))=\ln(x+3)^2$

$(x+4)(x+1)=(x+3)^2$

$x^2+5x+4=x^2+6x+9$

$5x+4=6x+9$

$-x=5$

$x=-5$

$x=-5$ does not check and must be rejected.
The solution set is { }.

7. $14-5x\ge-6$

$-5x\ge-20$

$x\le4$

The solution set is $(-\infty,4]$.

8. $|2x-4|\le2$

$2x-4\le2$ and $2x-4\ge-2$

$2x\le6$ $\qquad$ $2x\ge2$

$x\le3$ $\qquad$ and $x\ge1$

The solution set is $[1,3]$.

9. Circle with center: $(3,-2)$ and radius of 2

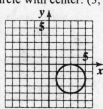

$(x-3)^2+(y+2)^2=4$

10. Parabola with vertex: $(2,-1)$

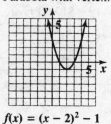

$f(x)=(x-2)^2-1$

11. x-intercepts:

$x^2-1=0$

$x^2=1$

$x=\pm1$

The x-intercepts are $(1,0)$ and $(-1,0)$.

vertical asymptotes:

$x^2-4=0$

$x^2=4$

$x=\pm2$

The vertical asymptotes are $x=2$ and $x=-2$.

Horizontal asymptote: y 5 1

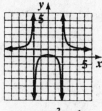

$f(x)=\dfrac{x^2-1}{x^2-4}$

12. x-intercepts:

$x-2=0$ or $x+1=0$

$x=2$ $\qquad$ or $x=-1$

The x-intercepts are $(2,0)$ and $(-1,0)$.

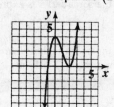

$f(x)=(x-2)^2(x+1)$

13.

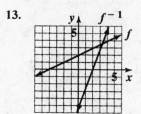

$f(x)=2x-4$

$f^{-1}(x)=\dfrac{x+4}{2}$

14.

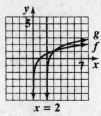

$$x = 2$$
$$f(x) = \ln x$$
$$g(x) = \ln (x - 2) + 1$$

15. $m = \dfrac{3 - (-3)}{1 - 3} = \dfrac{6}{-2} = -3$

Using $(1, 3)$ point-slope form:

$$y - 3 = -3(x - 1)$$

slope-intercept form:

$$y - 3 = -3(x - 1)$$
$$y - 3 = -3x + 3$$
$$y = -3x + 6$$

16. $(f \circ g)(x) = f(x + 2)$

$$= (x + 2)^2$$
$$= x^2 + 4x + 4$$

$(g \circ f)(x) = g(x^2)$

$$= x^2 + 2$$

17. y varies inversely as the square of x is expressed as $y = \dfrac{k}{x^2}$.

The hours, H, vary inversely as the square of the number of cups of coffee, C can be expressed as $H = \dfrac{k}{C^2}$.

Use the given values to find k.

$$H = \dfrac{k}{C^2}$$

$$8 = \dfrac{k}{2^2}$$

$$32 = k$$

Substitute the value of k into the equation.

$$H = \dfrac{k}{C^2}$$

$$H = \dfrac{32}{C^2}$$

Use the equation to find H when $C = 4$.

$$H = \dfrac{32}{C^2}$$

$$H = \dfrac{32}{4^2}$$

$$H = 2$$

If 4 cups of coffee are consumed you should expect to sleep 2 hours.

18. $s(t) = -16t^2 + 64t + 5$

The ball reaches its maximum height at

$$t = \dfrac{-b}{2a} = \dfrac{-(64)}{2(-16)} = 2 \text{ seconds.}$$

The maximum height is $s(2)$.

$$s(2) = -16(2)^2 + 64(2) + 5 = 69 \text{ feet.}$$

19. $s(t) = -16t^2 + 64t + 5$

Let $s(t) = 0$:

$$0 = -16t^2 + 64t + 5$$

Use the quadratic formula to solve.

$$t = \dfrac{-b \pm \sqrt{b^2 - 4ac}}{2a}$$

$$t = \dfrac{-(64) \pm \sqrt{(64)^2 - 4(-16)(5)}}{2(-16)}$$

$$t \approx 4.1, \quad t \approx -0.1$$

The negative value is rejected.
The ball hits the ground after about 4.1 seconds.

20. $40x + 10(1.5x) = 660$

$$40x + 15x = 660$$

$$55x = 660$$

$$x = 12$$

Your normal hourly salary is \$12 per hour.

Chapter 5

Section 5.1

Check Point Exercises

1. **a.**
$$2x = 3y = -4$$
$$2(1) - 3(2) = -4$$
$$2 - 6 = -4$$
$$-4 = -4 \text{ true}$$
$$2x + y = 4$$
$$2(1) + 2 = 4$$
$$2 + 2 = 4$$
$$4 = 4 \text{ true}$$
$(1, 2)$ is a solution of the system.

b.
$$2x = 3y = -4$$
$$2(7) - 3(6) = -4$$
$$14 - 18 = -4$$
$$-4 = -4 \text{ true}$$
$$2x + y = 4$$
$$2(7) + 6 = 4$$
$$14 + 6 = 4$$
$$20 = 4 \text{ false}$$
$(7, 6)$ is not a solution of the system.

2.
$$3x + 2y = 4$$
$$2x + y = 1$$
Solve $2x + y = 1$ for y.
$$2x + y = 1$$
$$y = 1 - 2x$$
Substitute $1 - 2x$ for y in the other equation and solve.
$$3x + 2\overbrace{(1 - 2x)}^{y} = 4$$
$$3x + 2 - 4x = 4$$
$$-x = 2$$
$$x = -2$$
Back-substitute the obtained value:
$$3x + 2y = 4$$
$$3(-2) + 2y = 4$$
$$-6 + 2y = 4$$
$$2y = 10$$
$$y = 5$$
Checking these values in both equations shows that $(-2, 5)$ is the solution of the system.

3. Rewrite one or both equations:
$$4x + 5y = 3 \xrightarrow{\text{No change}} 4x + 5y = 3$$
$$2x - 3y = 7 \xrightarrow{\text{Mult. by } -2} \underline{-4x + 6y = -14}$$
$$11y = -11$$
$$y = -1$$
Back-substitute into either equation:
$$4x + 5y = 3$$
$$4x + 5(-1) = 3$$
$$4x - 5 = 3$$
$$4x = 8$$
$$x = 2$$
Checking confirms the solution set is $\{(2, -1)\}$.

4. Rewrite both equations in the form $Ax + By = C$:
$$2x = 9 + 3y \rightarrow 2x - 3y = 9$$
$$4y = 8 - 3x \rightarrow 3x + 4y = 8$$
Rewrite with opposite coefficients, then add and solve:
$$2x - 3y = 9 \xrightarrow{\text{Mult. by } 4} 8x - 12y = 36$$
$$3x + 4y = 8 \xrightarrow{\text{Mult. by } 3} \underline{9x + 12y = 24}$$
$$17x = 60$$
$$x = \frac{60}{17}$$
Back-substitute into either equation:
$$4y = 8 - 3x$$
$$4y = 8 - 3\left(\frac{60}{17}\right)$$
$$4y = -\frac{44}{17}$$
$$y = -\frac{11}{17}$$
Checking confirms the solution is $\left(\frac{60}{17}, -\frac{11}{17}\right)$.

343

5. Rewrite with a pair of opposite coefficients, then add:

$$5x - 2y = 4 \xrightarrow{\text{Mult. by 2}} 10x - 4y = 8$$

$$-10x + 4y = 7 \xrightarrow{\text{No change}} \underline{-10x + 4y = 7}$$

$$0 = 15$$

The statement $0 = 15$ is false which indicates that the system has no solution. The solution set is the empty set, $\varnothing$.

6. Substitute $4y - 8$ for x in the other equation:

$$5\overbrace{(4y - 8)}^{x} - 20y = -40$$

$$20y - 40 - 20y = -40$$

$$-40 = -40$$

The statement $-40 = -40$ is true which indicates that the system has infinitely many solutions.

The solution set is $\{(x, y) \mid x = 4y - 8\}$ or

$$\{(x, y) \mid 5x - 20y = -40\}.$$

7. a. $C(x) = 300,000 + 30x$

b. $R(x) = 80x$

c. $R(x) = C(x)$

$$80x = 300,000 + 30x$$

$$50x = 300,000$$

$$x = 6000$$

$$C(6000) = 300,000 + 30(6000) = 480,000$$

Break even point (6000, 480000)

The company will need to make 6000 pairs of shoes and earn \$480,000 to break even.

Exercise Set 5.1

1. $x + 3y = 11$

$$2 + 3(3) = 11$$

$$2 + 9 = 11$$

$$11 = 11 \text{ true}$$

$$x - 5y = -13$$

$$2 - 5(3) = -13$$

$$2 - 15 = -13$$

$$-13 = -13 \text{ true}$$

$(2, 3)$ is a solution.

3. $2x + 3y = 17$

$$2(2) + 3(5) = 17$$

$$4 + 15 = 17$$

$$19 = 17 \text{ false}$$

$(2, 5)$ is not a solution.

5. $x + y = 4$

$$y = 3x$$

Substitute the expression $3x$ for y in the first equation and solve for x.

$$x + 3x = 4$$

$$4x = 4$$

$$x = 1$$

Substitute 1 for x in the second equation.

$$y = 3(1) = 3$$

The solution set is $\{(1, 3)\}$.

7. $x + 3y = 8$

$$y = 2x - 9$$

Substitute the expression $2x - 9$ for y in the first equation and solve for x.

$$x + 3(2x - 9) = 8$$

$$x + 6x - 27 = 8$$

$$7x = 35$$

$$x = 5$$

Substitute 5 for x in the second equation.

$$y = 2(5) - 9 = 10 - 9 = 1$$

The solution set is $\{(5, 1)\}$.

9. $x = 4y - 2$

$$x = 6y + 8$$

Substitute the expression $4y - 2$ for x in the second equation and solve for y.

$$4y - 2 = 6y + 8$$

$$-10 = 2y$$

$$-5 = y$$

Substitute -5 for y in the equation $x = 4y - 2$.

$$x = 4(-5) - 2 = -22$$

The solution set is $\{(-22, -5)\}$.

11. $5x + 2y = 0$

$$x - 3y = 0$$

Solve the second equation for x.

$$x = 3y$$

Substitute the expression $3y$ for x in the first equation and solve for y.

$$5(3y) + 2y = 0$$

$$15y + 2y = 0$$

$$17y = 0$$

$$y = 0$$

Substitute 0 for y in the equation $x = 3y$.

$$y = 3(0) = 0$$

The solution set is $\{(0, 0)\}$.

13. $2x + 5y = -4$
$3x - y = 11$
Solve the second equation for y.
$-y = -3x + 11$
$y = 3x - 11$
Substitute the expression $3x - 11$ for y in the first equation and solve for x.
$2x + 5(3x - 11) = -4$
$2x + 15x - 55 = -4$
$17x = 51$
$x = 3$
Substitute 3 for x in the equation $y = 3x - 11$.
$y = 3(3) - 11 = 9 - 11 = -2$
The solution set is $\{(3, -2)\}$.

15. $2x - 3y = 8 - 2x$
$2x + 4y = x + 3y + 14$
Solve the second equation for y.
$y = -2x + 14$
Substitute the expression $-2x + 14$ for y in the first equation and solve for x.
$2x - 3(-2x + 14) = 8 - 2x$
$2x + 6x - 42 = 8 - 2x$
$8x - 42 = 8 - 2x$
$10x = 50$
$x = 5$
Substitute 5 for x in the equation $y = -2x + 14$.
$y = -2(5) + 14 = -10 + 14 = 4$
The solution set is $\{(5, 4)\}$.

17. $y = \dfrac{1}{3}x + \dfrac{2}{3}$

$y = \dfrac{5}{7}x - 2$

Substitute the expression $y = \dfrac{1}{3}x + \dfrac{2}{3}$ for y in

the second equation and solve for x.
$\dfrac{1}{3}x + \dfrac{2}{3} = \dfrac{5}{7}x - 2$
$7x + 14 = 15x - 42$
$56 = 8x$
$7 = x$

Substitute 7 for x in the equation $y = \dfrac{1}{3}x + \dfrac{2}{3}$

and solve for y.
$y = \dfrac{1}{3}(7) + \dfrac{2}{3} = \dfrac{7}{3} + \dfrac{2}{3} = \dfrac{9}{3} = 3$
The solution set is $\{(7, 3)\}$.

19. Eliminate y by adding the equations.
$x + y = 1$
$\underline{x - y = 3}$
$2x = 4$
$x = 2$
Substitute 2 for x in the first equation.
$2 + y = 1$
$y = -1$
The solution set is $\{(2, -1)\}$.

21. Eliminate y by adding the equations.
$2x + 3y = 6$
$\underline{2x - 3y = 6}$
$4x = 12$
$x = 3$
Substitute 3 for x in the first equation.
$2(3) + 3y = 6$
$6 + 3y = 6$
$3y = 0$
$y = 0$
The solution set is $\{(3, 0)\}$.

23. $x + 2y = 2$
$-4x + 3y = 25$
Eliminate x by multiplying the first equation by 4 and adding the resulting equations.
$4x + 8y = 8$
$\underline{-4x + 3y = 25}$
$11y = 33$
$y = 3$
Substitute 3 for y in the first equation.
$x + 2(3) = 2$
$x + 6 = 2$
$x = -4$
The solution set is $\{(-4, 3)\}$.

25. $4x + 3y = 15$
$2x - 5y = 1$
Eliminate x by multiplying the second equation by -2 and adding the resulting equations.
$4x + 3y = 15$
$\underline{-4x + 10y = -2}$
$13y = 13$
$y = 1$
Substitute 1 for y in the second equation.
$2x - 5(1) = 1$
$2x = 6$
$x = 3$
The solution set is $\{(3, 1)\}$.

345

27. $3x - 4y = 11$
$2x + 3y = -4$
Eliminate x by multiplying the first equation by
2 and the second equation by –3. Add the
resulting equations.
$6x - 8y = 22$
$\underline{-6x - 9y = 12}$
$-17y = 34$
$y = -2$
Substitute –2 for y in the second equation.
$2x + 3(-2) = -4$
$2x - 6 = -4$
$2x = 2$
$x = 1$
The solution set is $\{(1, -2)\}$.

29. $3x = 4y + 1$
$3y = 1 - 4x$
Arrange the system so that variable terms appear
on the left and constants appear on the right.
$3x - 4y = 1$
$4x + 3y = 1$
Eliminate y by multiplying the first equation by
3 and the second equation by 4. Add the
resulting equations.
$9x - 12y = 3$
$\underline{16x + 12y = 4}$
$25x = 7$
$x = \dfrac{7}{25}$
Substitute $\dfrac{7}{25}$ for x in the second equation.
$3y = 1 - 4\left(\dfrac{7}{25}\right)$
$3y = \dfrac{-3}{25}$
$y = \dfrac{-1}{25}$
The solution set is $\left\{\left(\dfrac{7}{25}, -\dfrac{1}{25}\right)\right\}$.

31. The substitution method is used here to solve the
system.
$x = 9 - 2y$
$x + 2y = 13$
Substitute the expression $9 - 2y$ for x in the
second equation and solve for y.
$9 - 2y + 2y = 13$
$9 = 13$
The false statement $9 = 13$ indicates that the
system has no solution.
The solution set is the empty set, $\varnothing$.

33. The substitution method is used here to solve the
system.
$y = 3x - 5$
$21x - 35 = 7y$
Substitute the expression $3x - 5$ for y in the
second equation and solve for x.
$21x - 35 = 7(3x - 5)$
$21x - 35 = 21x - 35$
$-35 = -35$
This true statement indicates that the system has
infinitely many solutions.
The solution set is $\left\{(x, y) \mid y = 3x - 5\right\}$

35. The elimination method is used here to solve the
system.
$3x - 2y = -5$
$4x + y = 8$
Eliminate y by multiplying the second equation
by 2 and adding the resulting equations.
$3x - 2y = -5$
$\underline{8x + 2y = 16}$
$11x = 11$
$x = 1$
Substitute 1 for x in the second equation.
$4(1) + y = 8$
$y = 4$
The solution set is $\{(1, 4)\}$.

37. The elimination method is used here to solve the
system.
$x + 3y = 2$
$3x + 9y = 6$
Eliminate x by multiplying the first equation by
–3 and adding the resulting equations.
$-3x - 9y = -6$
$\underline{3x + 9y = 6}$
$0 = 0$
This true statement indicates that the system has
infinitely many solutions.
The solution set is $\left\{(x, y) \mid x + 3y = 2\right\}$.

39. First multiply each term in the first equation by 4 to eliminate the fractions.

$$\frac{x}{4} - \frac{y}{4} = -1$$

$$x - y = -4$$

Multiply the first equation by -1 and add to the second equation and solve for y.

$$-x + y = 4$$
$$x + 4y = -9$$
$$\overline{\;5y = -5}$$
$$y = -1$$

Substitute -1 for y in the equation $x - y = -4$ and solve for x.

$$x - (-1) = -4$$
$$x + 1 = -4$$
$$x = -5$$

The solution set is $\{(-5, -1)\}$.

41. Rearrange the equations to get in the standard form.

$$2x - 3y = 4$$
$$4x + 5y = 3$$

Multiply the first equation by -2 and add to the second equation. Solve for y.

$$-4x + 6y = -8$$
$$4x + 5y = 3$$
$$\overline{\;11y = -5}$$
$$y = -\frac{5}{11}$$

Multiply the first equation by 5 and the second equation by 3 and add the equations. Solve for x.

$$10x - 15y = 20$$
$$12x + 15y = 9$$
$$\overline{\;22x = 29}$$
$$x = \frac{29}{22}$$

The solution set is $\left\{\left(\dfrac{29}{22}, -\dfrac{5}{11}\right)\right\}$.

43. Add the equations to eliminate y.

$$x + y = 7$$
$$x - y = -1$$
$$\overline{\;2x = 6}$$
$$x = 3$$

Substitute 3 for x in the first equation.

$$3 + y = 7$$
$$y = 4$$

The numbers are 3 and 4.

45.
$$3x - y = 1$$
$$x + 2y = 12$$

Eliminate y by multiplying the first equation by 2 and adding the resulting equations.

$$6x - 2y = 2$$
$$x + 2y = 12$$
$$\overline{\;7x = 14}$$
$$x = 2$$

Substitute 2 for x in the first equation.

$$3(2) - y = 1$$
$$6 - y = 1$$
$$-y = -5$$
$$y = 5$$

The numbers are 2 and 5.

47.
$$\frac{x+2}{2} - \frac{y+4}{3} = 3$$
$$\frac{x+y}{5} = \frac{x-y}{2} - \frac{5}{2}$$

Start by multiplying each equation by its LCD and simplifying to clear the fractions.

$$\frac{x+2}{2} - \frac{y+4}{3} = 3$$
$$\frac{x+y}{5} = \frac{x-y}{2} - \frac{5}{2}$$

Start by multiplying each equation by its LCD and simplifying to clear the fractions.

$$6\left(\frac{x+2}{2} - \frac{y+4}{3}\right) = 6(3)$$
$$3(x+2) - 2(y+4) = 18$$
$$3x + 6 - 2y - 8 = 18$$
$$3x - 2y = 20$$

$$10\left(\frac{x+y}{5}\right) = 10\left(\frac{x-y}{2} - \frac{5}{2}\right)$$
$$2(x+y) = 5(x-y) - 5(5)$$
$$2x + 2y = 5x - 5y - 25$$
$$3x - 7y = 25$$

We now need to solve the equivalent system of equations:

$3x - 2y = 20$

$3x - 7y = 25$

Subtract the two equations:

$3x - 2y = 20$

$-(3x - 7y = 25)$

$\overline{\qquad\qquad}$

$5y = -5$

$y = -1$

Back-substitute this value for y and solve for x.

$3x - 2y = 20$

$3x - 2(-1) = 20$

$3x + 2 = 20$

$3x = 18$

$x = 6$

The solution is $(6, -1)$.

49. $5ax + 4y = 17$

$ax + 7y = 22$

Multiply the second equation by -5 and add the equations.

$5ax + 4y = 17$

$-5ax - 35y = -110$

$\overline{\qquad\qquad}$

$-31y = -93$

$y = 3$

Back-substitute into one of the original equations to solve for x.

$ax + 7y = 22$

$ax + 7(3) = 22$

$ax + 21 = 22$

$ax = 1$

$x = \dfrac{1}{a}$

The solution is $\left(\dfrac{1}{a}, 3\right)$.

51. $f(-2) = 11 \quad \rightarrow \quad -2m + b = 11$

$f(3) = -9 \quad \rightarrow \quad 3m + b = -9$

We need to solve the resulting system of equations:

$-2m + b = 11$

$3m + b = -9$

Subtract the two equations:

$-2m + b = 11$

$3m + b = -9$

$\overline{\qquad\qquad}$

$-5m = 20$

$m = -4$

Back-substitute into one of the original equations to solve for b.

$-2m + b = 11$

$-2(-4) + b = 11$

$8 + b = 11$

$b = 3$

Therefore, $m = -4$ and $b = 3$.

53. The solution to a system of linear equations is the point of intersection of the graphs of the equations in the system. If $(6, 2)$ is a solution, then we need to find the lines that intersect at that point. Looking at the graph, we see that the graphs of $x + 3y = 12$ and $x - y = 4$ intersect at the point $(6, 2)$. Therefore, the desired system of equations is

$x + 3y = 12 \quad$ or $\quad y = -\dfrac{1}{3}x + 4$

$x - y = 4 \qquad\qquad y = x - 4$

55. At the break-even point, $R(x) = C(x)$.

$10000 + 30x = 50x$

$10000 = 20x$

$10000 = 20x$

$500 = x$

Five hundred radios must be produced and sold to break-even.

57. $R(x) = 50x$

$R(200) = 50(200) = 10000$

$C(x) = 10000 + 30x$

$C(200) = 10000 + 30(200)$

$= 10000 + 6000 = 16000$

$R(200) - C(200) = 10000 - 16000$

$= -6000$

This means that if 200 radios are produced and sold the company will lose \$6,000.

59. a. $P(x) = R(x) - C(x)$

$\qquad = 50x - (10000 + 30x)$

$\qquad = 50x - 10000 - 30x$

$\qquad = 20x - 10000$

$\quad P(x) = 20x - 10000$

b. $P(10000) = 20(10000) - 10000$

$\qquad = 200000 - 10000 = 190000$

If 10,0000 radios are produced and sold the profit will be $190,000.

61. a.   The cost function is:

$C(x) = 18,000 + 20x$

b.   The revenue function is:

$R(x) = 80x$

c.   At the break-even point, $R(x) = C(x)$.

$80x = 18000 + 20x$

$60x = 18000$

$x = 300$

$R(x) = 80x$

$R(300) = 80(300)$

$\qquad = 24,000$

When approximately 300 canoes are produced the company will break-even with cost and revenue at $24,000.

63. a.   The cost function is:

$C(x) = 30000 + 2500x$

b.   The revenue function is:

$R(x) = 3125x$

c.   At the break-even point, $R(x) = C(x)$.

$3125x = 30000 + 2500x$

$625x = 30000$

$x = 48$

After 48 sold out performances, the investor will break-even. ($150,000)

65. a. $N_d = -5p + 750$

$\qquad = -5(120) + 750$

$\qquad = -600 + 750$

$\qquad = 150$

$N_s = 2.5(120) = 300$

If the price of the televisions is $120, 150 sets can be sold and 300 sets can be supplied.

b.   To find the price at which supply and demand are equal, we set the two equations equal to each other and solve for p.

$-5p + 750 = 2.5p$

$750 = 7.5p$

$\dfrac{750}{7.5} = p$

$100 = p$

$N = 2.5(100) = 250$.

Supply and demand will be equal if the price of the televisions is $100. At that price, 250 sets can be supplied and sold.

67.   Solve $-x + y = 16$ for y

$-x + y = 16$

$y = x + 16$

Substitute for y in the other equation:

$13x + 12\overbrace{(x + 16)}^{y} = 992$

$13x + 12x + 192 = 992$

$25x = 800$

$x = 32$

Substitute $x = 32$ into either equation to find y.

$y = x + 16$

$y = 32 + 16$

$y = 48$

The percentages will both be 48% 32 years after 1988, or 2020.

69. a. $y = 0.04x + 5.48$

b. $y = 0.17x + 1.84$

c.   To find the year when the costs will be the same, we set the two equations equal to each other and solve for x.

$0.04x + 5.48 = 0.17x + 1.84$

$-0.13x = -3.64$

$x = 28$

The costs will be the same 28 years after 2000, or 2028.

$y = 0.17x + 1.84$

$y = 0.17(28) + 1.84$

$y = 6.6$

The cost of each program in 2028 will be 6.6% of the GDP. After that year, Medicare will have the greater cost.

71. a.

$$m = \frac{25.3 - 38}{17 - 0} = \frac{-12.7}{17} \approx -0.75$$

From the point $(0, 38)$ we have that the y-intercept is $b = 38$. Therefore, the equation of the line is $y = -0.75x + 38$.

b.

$$m = \frac{23 - 40}{17 - 0} = \frac{-17}{17} = -1$$

From the point $(0, 40)$ we have that the y-intercept is $b = 40$. Therefore, the equation of the line is $y = -x + 40$.

c. To find the year when cigarette use is the same, we set the two equations equal to each other and solve for x.

$$-0.75x + 38 = -x + 40$$
$$0.25x + 38 = 40$$
$$0.25x = 2$$
$$x = \frac{2}{0.25} = 8$$
$$y = -(8) + 40 = 32$$

Cigarette use was the same for African Americans and Hispanics in 1993 (8 years after 1985). At that time, 32% of each group used cigarettes.

73. $x + 2y = 1980$
$2x + y = 2670$
Multiply the first equation by -2 and add to the second equation. Solve for y.

$$-2x - 4y = -3960$$
$$2x + y = 2670$$
$$-3y = -1290$$
$$y = 430$$

Substitute 430 for y in the second equation and solve for x.
$2x + 430 = 2670$
$2x = 2240$
$x = 1120$
There are 1120 calories in a pan pizza and 430 calories in a beef burrito.

75. $x + y = 300 + 241$ or $x + y = 541$
$2x + 3y = 1257$
Multiply the first equation by -2 and add to the second equation. Solve for y.

$$-2x - 2y = -1082$$
$$2x + 3y = 1257$$
$$y = 175$$

Substitute 175 for y in the first equation and solve for x.
$x + 175 = 541$
$x = 366$
There are 366 mg in scrambled eggs and 175 mg in a Double Beef Whopper.

77. $x + y = 200$
$100x + 80y = 17000$
Multiply the first equation by -100 and add to the second equation. Solve for y.

$$-100x - 100y = -20000$$
$$100x + 80y = 17000$$
$$-20y = -3000$$
$$y = 150$$

Substitute 150 for y in the first equation and solve for x.
$x + 150 = 200$
$x = 50$
There are 50 rooms with kitchenettes and 150 rooms without.

79. $2x + 2y = 360$
$20x + 8(2y) = 3280$
Multiply the first equation by -10 and add to the second equation. Solve for y.

$$-20x - 20y = -3600$$
$$20x + 16y = 3280$$
$$-4y = -320$$
$$y = 80$$

Substitute 80 for y in the first equation and solve for x.
$2x + 2(80) = 360$
$2x + 160 = 360$
$2x = 200$
$x = 100$
The lot is 100 feet long and 80 feet wide.

81. $(x + y)2 = 16$
$(x - y)2 = 8$

Multiply to remove the parentheses and then add the two equations together. Solve for x.

$2x + 2y = 16$
$2x - 2y = 8$
$4x = 24$
$x = 6$

Substitute 6 for x in the first equation and solve for y.

$2(6) + 2y = 16$
$12 + 2y = 16$
$2y = 4$
$y = 2$

The crew rows 6 mph and the current is 2 mph.

83. $x + 2y = 180$
$(2x - 30) + y = 180$

Rewrite the second equation in standard form.

$x + 2y = 180$
$2x + y = 210$

Multiply the first equation by -2 and add the equations.

$-2x - 4y = -360$
$\underline{2x + y = 210}$
$-3y = -150$
$y = 50$

Back-substitute to solve for x.

$x + 2y = 180$
$x + 2(50) = 180$
$x + 100 = 180$
$x = 80$

The three interior angles measure $80°$, $50°$, and $50°$.

97. x = first lucky number
y = second lucky number
$3x + 6y = 12$
$x + 2y = 5$

Eliminate x by multiplying the second equation by -3 and adding the resulting equations.

$3x + 6y = 12$
$\underline{-3x - 6y = -15}$
$0 = -3$

The false statement $0 = -3$ indicates that the system has no solution. Therefore, the twin who always lies is talking.

Section 5.2

Check Point Exercises

1.
$$x - 2y + 3z = 22$$
$$-1 - 2(-4) + 3(5) = 22$$
$$-1 + 8 + 15 = 22$$
$$22 = 22 \text{ true}$$
$$2x - 3y - z = 5$$
$$2(-1) - 3(-4) - 5 = 5$$
$$-2 + 12 - 5 = 5$$
$$5 = 5 \text{ true}$$
$$3x + y - 5z = -32$$
$$3(-1) - 4 - 5(5) = -32$$
$$-3 - 4 - 25 = -32$$
$$-32 = -32 \text{ true}$$

$(-1, -4, 5)$ is a solution of the system.

2.
$$x + 4y - z = 20$$
$$3x + 2y + z = 8$$
$$2x - 3y + 2z = -16$$

Eliminate z from Equations 1 and 2 by adding Equation 1 and Equation 2.

$x + 4y - z = 20$
$\underline{3x + 2y + z = 8}$
$4x + 6y = 28$ Equation 4

Eliminate z from Equations 2 and 3 by multiplying Equation 2 by -2 and adding the resulting equation to Equation 3.

$-6x - 4y - 2z = -16$
$\underline{2x - 3y + 2z = -16}$
$-4x - 7y = -32$ Equation 5

Solve Equations 4 and 5 for x and y by adding Equation 4 and Equation 5.

$4x + 6y = 28$
$\underline{-4x - 7y = -32}$
$-y = -4$
$y = 4$

Substitute 4 for y in Equation 4 and solve for x.

$4x + 6(4) = 28$
$4x + 24 = 28$
$4x = 4$
$x = 1$

Substitute 1 for x and 4 for y in Equation 2 and solve for z.

$$3(1) + 2(4) + z = 8$$
$$3 + 8 + z = 8$$
$$11 + z = 8$$
$$z = -3$$

The solution set is $\{(1, 4, -3)\}$.

3.
$$2y - z = 7$$
$$x + 2y + z = 17$$
$$2x - 3y + 2z = -1$$

Eliminate x and z from Equations 2 and 3 by multiplying Equation 2 by -2 and adding the resulting equation to Equation 3.

$$-2x - 4y - 2z = -34$$
$$\underline{2x - 3y + 2z = -1}$$
$$-7y = -35$$
$$y = 5$$

Substitute 5 for y in Equation 1 and solve for z.

$$2(5) - z = 7$$
$$10 - z = 7$$
$$-z = -3$$
$$z = 3$$

Substitute 5 for y and 3 for z in Equation 2 and solve for x.

$$x + 2(5) + 3 = 17$$
$$x + 10 + 3 = 17$$
$$x + 13 = 17$$
$$x = 4$$

The solution set is $\{(4, 5, 3)\}$.

4. $(1, 4), (2, 1), (3, 4)$

$$y = ax^2 + bx + c$$

Substitute 1 for x and 4 for y in
$y = ax^2 + bx + c$.

$$4 = a(1)^2 + b(1) + c$$
$$4 = a + b + c \quad \text{Equation 1}$$

Substitute 2 for x and 1 for y in
$y = ax^2 + bx + c$.

$$1 = a(2)^2 + b(2) + c$$
$$1 = 4a + 2b + c \quad \text{Equation 2}$$

Substitute 3 for x and 4 for y in
$y = ax^2 + bx + c$.

$$4 = a(3)^2 + b(3) + c$$
$$4 = 9a + 3b + c \quad \text{Equation 3}$$

Eliminate c from Equations 1 and 2 by multiplying Equation 2 by -1 and adding the

resulting equation to Equation 1.

$$4 = a + b + c$$
$$\underline{-1 = -4a - 2b - c}$$
$$3 = -3a - b \quad \text{Equation 4}$$

Eliminate c from Equation 2 and 3 by multiplying Equation 3 by -1 and adding the resulting equation to Equation 2.

$$1 = 4a + 2b + c$$
$$\underline{-4 = -9a - 3b - c}$$
$$-3 = -5a - b \quad \text{Equation 5}$$

Solve Equations 4 and 5 for a and b by multiplying Equation 5 by -1 and adding the resulting equation to Equation 4.

$$3 = -3a - b$$
$$\underline{3 = 5a + b}$$
$$6 = 2a$$
$$a = 3$$

Substitute 3 for a in Equation 4 and solve for b.

$$3 = -3(3) - b$$
$$3 = -9 - b$$
$$12 = -b$$
$$b = -12$$

Substitute 3 for a and -12 for b in Equation 1 and solve for c.

$$4 = 3 - 12 + c$$
$$4 = -9 + c$$
$$c = 13$$

Substituting 3 for a, -12 for b, and 13 for c in the quadratic equation $y = ax^2 + bx + c$ gives

$$y = 3x^2 - 12x + 13 .$$

Exercise Set 5.2

1.
$$x + y + z = 4$$
$$2 - 1 + 3 = 4$$
$$4 = 4 \text{ true}$$
$$x - 2y - z = 1$$
$$2(2) - 2(-1) - 3 = 1$$
$$4 + 2 - 3 = 1$$
$$1 = 1 \text{ true}$$
$$2x - y - 2z = -1$$
$$2(2) - (-1) - 2(3) = -1$$
$$4 + 1 - 6 = -1$$
$$-1 = -1 \text{ false}$$

$(2, -1, 3)$ is a solution.

3. $x - 2y = 2$

$\quad\quad 4 - 2(1) = 2$

$\quad\quad\quad 4 - 2 = 2$

$\quad\quad\quad\quad 2 = 2 \;\; \text{true}$

$\quad\quad 2x + 3y = 11$

$\quad\quad 2(4) + 3(1) = 11$

$\quad\quad\quad 8 + 3 = 11$

$\quad\quad\quad\quad 11 = 11 \; \text{true}$

$\quad\quad y - 4z = -7$

$\quad\quad 1 - 4(2) = -7$

$\quad\quad\quad 1 - 8 = -7$

$\quad\quad\quad\quad -7 = -7 \; \text{true}$

$(4, 1, 2)$ is a solution.

5. $x + y + 2z = 11$

$\quad\quad x + y + 3z = 14$

$\quad\quad x + 2y - z = 5$

Eliminate x and y from Equations 1 and 2 by multiplying Equation 2 by -1 and adding the resulting equation to Equation 1.

$\quad -x - y - 3z = -14$

$\quad \underline{\;\;x + y + 2z = 11\;\;}$

$\quad\quad\quad\quad\quad -z = -3$

$\quad\quad\quad\quad\quad\;\; z = 3$

Substitute 3 for z in Equations 1 and 3.

$x + y + 2(3) = 11$

$x + 2y - (3) = 5$

Simplify:

$\quad x + y = 5 \quad\quad\quad$ Equation 4

$\quad x + 2y = 8 \quad\quad\quad$ Equation 5

Solve Equations 4 and 5 for x and y by multiplying Equation 5 by -1 and adding the resulting equation to Equation 4.

$\quad\quad x + y = 5$

$\quad \underline{-x - 2y = -8\;}$

$\quad\quad\quad -y = -3$

$\quad\quad\quad\quad y = 3$

Substitute 3 for z and 3 for y in Equation 2 and solve for x.

$x + 3 + 3(3) = 14$

$\quad\;\; x + 12 = 14$

$\quad\quad\quad\; x = 2$

The solution set is $\{(2, 3, 3)\}$.

7. $4x - y + 2z = 11$

$\quad\quad x + 2y - z = -1$

$\quad\quad 2x + 2y - 3z = -1$

Eliminate y from Equation 1 and 2 by multiplying Equation 1 by 2 and adding the resulting equation to Equation 2 and 3.

$\quad 8x - 2y + 4z = 22$

$\quad \underline{\;\;x + 2y - z = -1\;\;}$

$\quad\quad 9x + 3z = 21 \quad\quad$ Equation 4

Eliminate y from Equations 1 and 3 by multiplying Equation 1 by 2 and adding the resulting equation to Equation 3.

$\quad 8x - 2y + 4z = 22$

$\quad \underline{2x + 2y - 3z = -1\;}$

$\quad\quad 10x + z = 21 \quad\quad$ Equation 5

Solve Equations 4 and 5 for x and z by multiplying Equation 5 by -3 and adding the resulting equation to Equation 4.

$\quad\quad 9x + 3z = 21$

$\quad \underline{-30x - 3z = -63\;}$

$\quad\quad -21x = -42$

$\quad\quad\quad\;\; x = 2$

Substitute 2 for x in Equation 5 and solve for z. $10(2) + z = 21$

$\quad\quad 20 + z = 21$

$\quad\quad\quad\quad z = 1$

Substitute 2 for x and 1 for z in Equation 2 and solve for y.

$2 + 2y - 1 = -1$

$\quad\; 2y + 1 = -1$

$\quad\quad\; 2y = -2$

$\quad\quad\quad y = -1$

The solution set is $\{(2, -1, 1)\}$.

9. $3x + 2y - 3z = -2$
$2x - 5y + 2z = -2$
$4x - 3y + 4z = 10$
Eliminate z from Equations 1 and 2 by multiplying Equation 1 by 2 and Equation 2 by 3. Add the resulting equations.
$6x + 4y - 6z = -4$
$\underline{6x - 15y + 6z = -6}$
$12x - 11y = -10$ Equation 4
Eliminate z from Equations 2 and 3 by multiplying Equation 2 by -2.
$-4x + 10y - 4z = 4$
$\underline{4x - 3y + 4z = 10}$
$7y = 14$ Equation 5
Solve Equation 5 for y
$7y = 14$
$y = 2$
Solve for x by substituting 7 for y in Equation 4.
$12x - 11y = -10$
$12x - 11(2) = -10$
$12x - 22 = -10$
$12x = 12$
$x = 1$
Substitute 2 for y and 1 for x in Equation 2 and solve for z.
$2x - 5y + 2z = -2$
$2(1) - 5(2) + 2z = -2$
$2 - 10 + 2z = -2$
$2z = 6$
$z = 3$
The solution set is $\{(1, 2, 3)\}$.

11. $2x - 4y + 3z = 17$
$x + 2y - z = 0$
$4x - y - z = 6$
Eliminate z from Equations 1 and 2 by multiplying Equation 2 by 3 and adding the resulting equation to Equation 1.
$2x - 4y + 3z = 17$
$\underline{3x + 6y - 3z = 0}$
$5x + 2y = 17$ Equation 4
Eliminate z from Equations 2 and 3 by multiplying Equation 2 by -1 and adding the resulting equation to Equation 3.
$-x - 2y + z = 0$
$\underline{4x - y - z = 6}$
$3x - 3y = 6$ Equation 5

Solve Equations 4 and 5 for x and y by multiplying Equation 5 by $\frac{2}{3}$ and adding the resulting equation to Equation 4.
$5x + 2y = 17$
$\underline{2x - 2y = 4}$
$7x = 21$
$x = 3$
Substitute 3 for x in Equation 4 and solve for y.
$5(3) + 2y = 17$
$15 + 2y = 17$
$2y = 2$
$y = 1$
Substitute 3 for x and 1 for y in Equation 2 and solve for z.
$3 + 2(1) - z = 0$
$3 + 2 - z = 0$
$5 - z = 0$
$5 = z$
The solution set is $\{(3, 1, 5)\}$.

13. $2x + y = 2$
$x + y - z = 4$
$3x + 2y + z = 0$
Eliminate z from Equations 2 and 3 by adding Equation 2 and Equation 3.
$x + y - z = 4$
$\underline{3x + 2y + z = 0}$
$4x + 3y = 4$ Equation 4
Solve Equations 1 and 4 for x and y by multiplying Equation 1 by -3 and adding the resulting equation to Equation 4.
$-6x - 3y = -6$
$\underline{4x + 3y = 4}$
$-2x = -2$
$x = 1$
Substitute 1 for x in Equation 1 and solve for y.
$2(1) + y = 2$
$2 + y = 2$
$y = 0$
Substitute 1 for x and 0 for y in Equation 2 and solve for z.
$1 + 0 - z = 4$
$1 - z = 4$
$-z = 3$
$z = -3$
The solution set is $\{(1, 0, -3)\}$.

354

15.
$$x + y = -4$$
$$y - z = 1$$
$$2x + y + 3z = -21$$

Eliminate y from Equations 1 and 2 by multiplying Equation 1 by -1 and adding the resulting equation to Equation 2.

$$-x - y = 4$$
$$\underline{y - z = 1}$$
$$-x - z = 5 \quad \text{Equation 4}$$

Eliminate y from Equations 2 and 3 by multiplying Equation 2 by -1 and adding the resulting equation to Equation 3.

$$-y + z = -1$$
$$\underline{2x + y + 3z = -21}$$
$$2x + 4z = -22 \quad \text{Equation 5}$$

Solve Equations 4 and 5 for x and z by multiplying Equation 4 by 2 and adding the resulting equation to Equation 5.

$$-2x - 2z = 10$$
$$\underline{2x + 4z = -22}$$
$$2z = -12$$
$$z = -6$$

Substitute -6 for z in Equation 2 and solve for y.
$$y - (-6) = 1$$
$$y + 6 = 1$$
$$y = -5$$

Substitute -5 for y in Equation 1 and solve for x
$$x + (-5) = -4$$
$$x = 1$$

The solution set is $\{(1, -5, -6)\}$.

17.
$$3(2x + y) + 5z = -1$$
$$2(x - 3y + 4z) = -9$$
$$4(1 + x) = -3(z - 3y)$$

Simplify each equation.
$$6x + 3y + 5z = -1 \quad \text{Equation 4}$$
$$2x - 6y + 8z = -9 \quad \text{Equation 5}$$
$$4 + 4x = -3z + 9y$$
$$4x - 9y + 3z = -4 \quad \text{Equation 6}$$

Eliminate x from Equations 4 and 5 by multiplying Equation 5 by -3 and adding the resulting equation to Equation 4.

$$-6x + 3y + 5z = -1$$
$$\underline{-6x + 18y - 24z = 27}$$
$$21y - 19z = 26 \quad \text{Equation 7}$$

Eliminate x from Equations 5 and 6 by multiplying Equation 5 by -2 and adding the resulting equation to Equation 6.

$$-4x + 12y - 16z = 18$$
$$\underline{4x - 9y + 3z = -4}$$
$$3y - 13z = 14 \quad \text{Equation 8}$$

Solve Equations 7 and 8 for y and z by multiplying Equation 8 by -7 and adding the resulting equation to Equation 7.

$$21y - 19z = 26$$
$$\underline{-21y + 91z = -98}$$
$$72z = -72$$
$$z = -1$$

Substitute -1 for z in Equation 8 and solve for y.
$$3y - 13(-1) = 14$$
$$3y + 13 = 14$$
$$3y = 1$$
$$y = \frac{1}{3}$$

Substitute $\frac{1}{3}$ for y and -1 for z in Equation 5 and solve for x.
$$2x - 6\left(\frac{1}{3}\right) + 8(-1) = -9$$
$$2x - 2 - 8 = -9$$
$$2x - 10 = -9$$
$$2x = 1$$
$$x = \frac{1}{2}$$

The solution set is $\left\{\left(\frac{1}{2}, \frac{1}{3}, -1\right)\right\}$.

19. $(-1, 6), (1, 4), (2, 9)$

$y = ax^2 + bx + c$

Substitute -1 for x and 6 for y in

$y = ax^2 + bx + c$.

$6 = a(-1)^2 + b(-1) + c$

$6 = a - b + c$ Equation 1

Substitute 1 for x and 4 for y in $y = ax^2 + bx + c$.

$4 = a(1)^2 + b(1) + c$

$4 = a + b + c$ Equation 2

Substitute 2 for x and 9 for y in

$y = ax^2 + bx + c$.

$9 = a(2)^2 + b(2) + c$

$9 = 4a + 2b + c$ Equation 3

Eliminate b from Equations 1 and 2 by adding Equation 1 and Equation 2.

$6 = a - b + c$

$4 = a + b + c$

$10 = 2a + 2c$ Equation 4

Eliminate b from Equations 1 and 3 by multiplying Equation 1 by 2 and adding the resulting equation to Equation 3.

$12 = 2a - 2b + 2c$

$9 = 4a + 2b + c$

$21 = 6a + 3c$ Equation 5

Solve Equations 4 and 5 for a and c by multiplying Equation 4 by -3 and adding the resulting equation to Equation 5.

$-30 = -6a - 6c$

$21 = 6a + 3c$

$-9 = -3c$

$c = 3$

Substitute 3 for c in Equation 4 and solve for a.

$10 = 2a + 2(3)$

$10 = 2a + 6$

$4 = 2a$

$a = 2$

Substitute 2 for a and 3 for c in Equation 2 and solve for b.

$4 = 2 + b + 3$

$4 = b + 5$

$b = -1$

Substituting 2 for a, -1 for b, and 3 for c in the quadratic equation $y = ax^2 + bx + c$ gives

$y = 2x^2 - x + 3$.

21. $(-1, -4), (1, -2), (2, 5)$

Substitute -1 for x and -4 for y in

$y = ax^2 + bx + c$.

$-4 = a(-1)^2 + b(-1) + c$

$-4 = a - b + c$ Equation 1

Substitute 1 for x and -2 for y in

$y = ax^2 + bx + c$.

$-2 = a(1)^2 + b(1) + c$

$-2 = a + b + c$ Equation 2

Substitute 2 for x and 5 for y in $y = ax^2 + bx + c$.

$5 = a(2)^2 + b(2) + c$

$5 = 4a + 2b + c$ Equation 3

Eliminate a and b from Equations 1 and 2 by multiplying Equation 1 by -1 and adding the resulting equation to Equation 2.

$4 = -a + b - c$

$-2 = a + b + c$

$2 = 2b$

$b = 1$

Eliminate c from Equations 1 and 3 by multiplying Equation 1 by -1 and adding the resulting equation to Equation 3.

$4 = -a + b - c$

$5 = 4a + 2b + c$

$9 = 3a + 3b$ Equation 4

Substitute 1 for b in Equation 4 and solve for a.

$9 = 3a + 3(1)$

$9 = 3a + 3$

$6 = 3a$

$a = 2$

Substitute 2 for a and 1 for b in Equation 2 and solve for c.

$-2 = 2 + 1 + c$

$-2 = c + 3$

$c = -5$

Substituting 2 for a, 1 for b, and -5 for c in quadratic equation $y = ax^2 + bx + c$ gives

$y = 2x^2 + x - 5$.

23. $x + y + z = 16$
$2x + 3y + 4z = 46$
$5x - y = 31$

Eliminate z from Equations 1 and 2 by multiplying Equation 1 by -4 and adding the resulting equation to Equation 2.

$-4x - 4y - 4z = -64$
$\underline{2x + 3y + 4z = 46}$
$-2x - y = -18$ Equation 4

Solve Equations 3 and 4 for x and y by multiplying Equation 4 by -1 and adding the resulting equation to Equation 3.

$5x - y = 31$
$\underline{2x + y = 18}$
$7x = 49$
$x = 7$

Substitute 7 for x in Equation 3 and solve for y.

$5(7) - y = 31$
$35 - y = 31$
$-y = -4$
$y = 4$

Substitute 7 for x and 4 for y in Equation 1 and solve for z.

$7 + 4 + z = 16$
$z + 11 = 16$
$z = 5$

The numbers are 7, 4 and 5.

25.
$$\frac{x+2}{6} - \frac{y+4}{3} + \frac{z}{2} = 0$$
$$6\left(\frac{x+2}{6} - \frac{y+4}{3} + \frac{z}{2}\right) = 6(0)$$
$$(x+2) - 2(y+4) + 3z = 0$$
$$x + 2 - 2y - 8 + 3z = 0$$
$$x - 2y + 3z = 6$$

$$\frac{x+1}{2} + \frac{y-1}{2} - \frac{z}{4} = \frac{9}{2}$$
$$4\left(\frac{x+1}{2} + \frac{y-1}{2} - \frac{z}{4}\right) = 4\left(\frac{9}{2}\right)$$
$$2(x+1) + 2(y-1) - z = 18$$
$$2x + 2 + 2y - 2 - z = 18$$
$$2x + 2y - z = 18$$

$$\frac{x-5}{4} + \frac{y+1}{3} + \frac{z-2}{2} = \frac{19}{4}$$
$$12\left(\frac{x-5}{4} + \frac{y+1}{3} + \frac{z-2}{2}\right) = 12\left(\frac{19}{4}\right)$$
$$3(x-5) + 4(y+1) + 6(z-2) = 57$$
$$3x - 15 + 4y + 4 + 6z - 12 = 57$$
$$3x + 4y + 6z = 80$$

We need to solve the equivalent system:
$x - 2y + 3z = 6$
$2x + 2y - z = 18$
$3x + 4y + 6z = 80$

Add the first two equations together.
$x - 2y + 3z = 6$
$\underline{2x + 2y - z = 18}$
$3x + 2z = 24$

Multiply the second equation by -2 and add it to the third equation.

$-4x - 4y + 2z = -36$
$\underline{3x + 4y + 6z = 80}$
$-x + 8z = 44$

Using the two reduced equations, we solve the system
$3x + 2z = 24$
$-x + 8z = 44$

Multiply the second equation by 3 and add the equations.

$3x + 2z = 24$
$\underline{-3x + 24z = 132}$
$26z = 156$
$z = 6$

Back-substitute to find x.
$-x + 8(6) = 44$
$-x + 48 = 44$
$-x = -4$
$x = 4$

Back substitute to find y.
$x - 2y + 3z = 6$
$4 - 2y + 3(6) = 6$
$-2y = -16$
$y = 8$

The solution is $(4, 8, 6)$.

27. Selected points may vary, but the equation will be the same.

$$y = ax^2 + bx + c$$

Use the points $(2, -2)$, $(4, 1)$, and $(6, -2)$ to get the system

$4a + 2b + c = -2$
$16a + 4b + c = 1$
$36a + 6b + c = -2$

Multiply the first equation by -1 and add to the second equation.

$-4a - 2b - c = 2$
$\underline{16a + 4b + c = 1}$
$12a + 2b = 3$

Multiply the first equation by -1 and add to the third equation.

$-4a - 2b - c = 2$
$\underline{36a + 6b + c = -2}$
$32a + 4b = 0$

Using the two reduced equations, we get the system

$12a + 2b = 3$
$32a + 4b = 0$

Multiply the first equation by -2 and add to the second equation.

$-24a - 4b = -6$
$\underline{32a + 4b = 0}$
$8a = -6$

$$a = -\frac{3}{4}$$

Back-substitute to solve for b.

$12a + 2b = 3$

$12\left(-\frac{3}{4}\right) + 2b = 3$

$-9 + 2b = 3$
$2b = 12$
$b = 6$

Back-substitute to solve for c.

$4a + 2b + c = -2$

$4\left(-\frac{3}{4}\right) + 2(6) + c = -2$

$-3 + 12 + c = -2$
$c = -11$

The equation is:

$$y = -\frac{3}{4}x^2 + 6x - 11$$

29. $ax - by - 2cz = 21$
$ax + by + cz = 0$
$2ax - by + cz = 14$

Add the first two equations.

$ax - by - 2cz = 21$
$\underline{ax + by + cz = 0}$
$2ax - cz = 21$

Multiply the first equation by -1 and add to the third equation.

$-ax + by + 2cz = -21$
$\underline{2ax - by + cz = 14}$
$ax + 3cz = -7$

Use the two reduced equations to get the following system:

$2ax - cz = 21$
$ax + 3cz = -7$

Multiply the second equation by -2 and add the equations.

$2ax - cz = 21$
$\underline{-2ax - 6cz = 14}$
$-7cz = 35$

$$z = -\frac{5}{c}$$

Back-substitute to solve for x.

$ax + 3cz = -7$

$ax + 3c\left(-\frac{5}{c}\right) = -7$

$ax - 15 = -7$
$ax = 8$

$$x = \frac{8}{a}$$

Back-substitute to solve for y.

$ax + by + cz = 0$

$a\left(\frac{8}{a}\right) + by + c\left(-\frac{5}{c}\right) = 0$

$8 + by - 5 = 0$
$by = -3$

$$y = -\frac{3}{b}$$

The solution is $\left(\dfrac{8}{a}, -\dfrac{3}{b}, -\dfrac{5}{c}\right)$.

31. a. 2000: $(0, 2.5)$
2002: $(2, 4.1)$
2003: $(3, 3.5)$

b. $y = ax^2 + bx + c$
$a(0)^2 + b(0) + c = 2.5$
$c = 2.5$ Equation 1
$y = ax^2 + bx + c$
$a(2)^2 + b(2) + c = 4.1$
$4a + 2b + c = 4.1$ Equation 2
$y = ax^2 + bx + c$
$a(3)^2 + b(3) + c = 3.5$
$9a + 3b + c = 3.5$ Equation 3
System:
$$c = 2.5$$
$$4a + 2b + c = 4.1$$
$$9a + 3b + c = 3.5$$

c. Substitute $c = 2.5$ into equation 2
$4a + 2b + 2.5 = 4.1$
$\quad 4a + 2b = 1.6$ Equation 4
Substitute $c = 2.5$ into equation 2
$9a + 3b + 2.5 = 3.5$
$\quad 9a + 3b = 1$ Equation 5
Solve the system of two equations using equations 4 and 5.
$4a + 2b = 1.6$ Mult by 3 → $\quad 12a + 6b = 4.8$
$9a + 3b = 1$ Mult by -2 → $\quad \underline{-18a - 6b = -2}$
$\qquad\qquad\qquad\qquad\quad -6a = 2.8$
$\qquad\qquad\qquad\qquad\quad a \approx -0.4667$
$\qquad\qquad\qquad\qquad\quad a \approx -0.47$

Use back-substitution to find b.
$\qquad 4a + 2b = 1.6$
$4(-0.4667) + 2b = 1.6$
$\qquad\qquad b \approx 1.73$
The equation that models steroid use by U.S. high school seniors x years after 2000 is $y = -0.47x^2 + 1.73x + 2.5$

33. a. Substitute the values for x and y into the quadratic form.
$224 = a(1)^2 + b(1) + c$
$a + b + c = 224$

$176 = a(3)^2 + b(3) + c$
$9a + 3b + c = 176$

$104 = a(4)^2 + b(4) + c$
$16a + 4b + c = 104$

Multiply the first equation by -1 and add to both the second and the third equations to obtain 2 new equations with 2 variables.
$-a - b - c = -224$
$\underline{9a + 3b + c = 176}$
$\quad 8a + 2b = -48$

$-a - b - c = -224$
$\underline{16a + 4b + c = 104}$
$\quad 15a + 3b = -120$
Use the two new equations to solve for a and b. Multiply the first equation by -3 and the second equation by 2 and add the results together. Solve for a. Substitute that value in $8a + 2b = -48$ and solve for b.
$-24a - 6b = 144$
$\underline{30a + 6b = -240}$
$\quad 6a = -96$
$\qquad a = -16$

$8(-16) + 2b = -48$
$-128 + 2b = -48$
$\qquad 2b = 80$
$\qquad b = 40$
Substitute -16 for a and 40 for b into the equation $a + b + c = 224$ and solve for c.
$-16 + 40 + c = 224$
$\qquad c = 200$
The equation is $y = -16x^2 + 40x + 200$.

b. $y = -16(5)^2 + 40(5) + 200 = 0$
The ball hit the ground after 5 seconds.

35. $x + y + z = 244$
$x - y = 4$
$y - z = 48$

Multiply the second equation by -1 and add to the first equation.
$x + y + z = 244$
$\underline{-x + y = -4}$
$2y + z = 240$

Add this new equation to equation to the third equation and solve for y.
$y - z = 48$
$\underline{2y + z = 240}$
$3y = 288$
$y = 96$

Substitute 96 for y in the equation $x - y = 4$ and solve for x.
$x - 96 = 4$
$x = 100$

Substitute 96 for y into the equation $y - z = 48$ and solve for z.
$96 - z = 48$
$-z = -48$
$z = 48$

Andrew Carnegie's fortune is worth $100 billion in today's money. Cornelius Vanderbilt's fortune is worth $96 billion and Bill Gates is worth $48 billion.

37. x = number of $8 tickets sold
y = number of $10 tickets sold
z = number of $12 tickets sold
From the given conditions we have the following system of equations.
$x + y + z = 400$
$8x + 10y + 12z = 3700$
$x + y = 7z$ or $x + y - 7z = 0$
Eliminate z from Equations 1 and 2 multiplying Equation 1 by -12 and adding the resulting equation to Equation 2.
$-12x - 12y - 12z = -4800$
$\underline{8x + 10y + 12z = 3700}$
$-4x - 2y = -1100$ Equation 4

Eliminate z from Equations 1 and 3 by multiplying Equation 1 by 7 and adding the resulting equation to Equation 3.
$7x + 7y + 7z = 2800$
$\underline{x + y - 7z = 0}$
$8x + 8y = 2800$ Equation 5

Solve Equations 4 and 5 for x and y by multiplying Equation 4 by 2 and adding the

resulting equation to Equation 5.
$-8x - 4y = -2200$
$\underline{8x + 8y = 2800}$
$4y = 600$
$y = 150$

Substitute 150 for y in Equation 5 and solve for x.
$8x + 8(150) = 2800$
$8x = 2800 - 1200$
$8x = 1600$
$x = 200$

Substitute 200 for x and 150 for y in Equation 1 and solve for z.
$200 + 150 + z = 400$
$350 + z = 400$
$z = 50$

The number of $8 tickets sold was 200.
The number of $10 tickets sold was 150.
The number of $12 tickets sold was 50.

39. x = amount of money invested at 10%
y = amount of money invested at 12%
z = amount of money invested at 15%
$x + y + z = 6700$
$0.08x + 0.10y + 0.12z = 716$
$z = x + y + 300$

Arrange Equation 3 so that variable terms appear on the left and constants appear on the right.
$-x - y + z = 300$ Equation 4

Eliminate x and y from Equations 1 and 4 by adding Equations 1 and 4.
$x + y + z = 6700$
$\underline{-x - y + z = 300}$
$2z = 7000$
$z = 3500$

Substitute 3500 for z in Equation 1 and Equation 2 and simplify.
$x + y + 3500 = 6700$
$x + y = 3200$ Equation 5
$0.08x + 0.10y + 0.12(3500) = 716$
$0.08x + 0.10y + 420 = 716$ S
$0.08x + 10y = 296$ Equation 6

olve Equations 5 and 6 for x and y by multiplying Equation 5 by -0.10 and adding the resulting equation to Equation 6.
$-0.10x - 0.10y = -320$
$\underline{0.08x + 0.10y = 296}$
$-0.02x = 24$
$x = 1200$

Substitute 1200 for x and 3,500 for z in Equation 1 and solve for y.

$$1200 + y + 3500 = 6700$$
$$y + 4700 = 6700$$
$$y = 2000$$

The person invested \$1200 at 8%, \$2000 at 10%, and \$3500 at 12%.

41. $x + y + z = 180$

$$2x - 5 + z = 180$$
$$2x + z = 185$$

$$2x + 5 + y = 180$$
$$2x + y = 175$$

Multiply the second equation by -1 and add to the first equation. Use the new equation and the third equation to solve for x and z.

$$-2x - z = -185$$
$$x + y + z = 180$$
$$-x + y = -5$$

Multiply the new equation by -1.

$$x - y = 5$$
$$2x + y = 175$$
$$3x = 180$$
$$x = 60$$

$$60 - y = 5$$
$$-y = -55$$
$$y = 55$$

Substitute 60 for x and 55 for y in the first equation and solve for z.

$$60 + 55 + z = 180$$
$$z = 65$$

49. $x = $ number of triangles
$y = $ number of rectangles
$z = $ number of pentagons

$$x + y + z = 40$$
$$3x + 4y + 5z = 153$$
$$2y + 5z = 72$$

Eliminate x from Equations 1 and 2 by multiplying Equation 1 by -3 and adding the resulting equation to Equation 2.

$$-3x - 3y - 3z = -120$$
$$\underline{3x + 4y + 5z = 153}$$
$$y + 2z = 33 \qquad \text{Equation 4}$$

Solve for z by multiplying Equation 4 by -2 and adding the resulting equation to Equation 3.

$$2y + 5z = 72$$
$$\underline{-2y - 4z = -66}$$
$$z = 6$$

Substitute 6 for z in Equation 4 and solve for y.

$$y + 2(6) = 33$$
$$y + 12 = 33$$
$$y = 21$$

Substitute 21 for y and 6 for z in Equation 1 and solve for x.

$$x + 21 + 6 = 40$$
$$x + 27 = 40$$
$$x = 13$$

The painting has 13 triangles, 21 rectangles, and 6 pentagons.

Section 5.3

Check Point Exercises

1. $\dfrac{5x-1}{(x-3)(x+4)} = \dfrac{A}{x-3} + \dfrac{B}{x+4}$

   Multiply both sides of the equation by the least common denominator $(x-3)(x+4)$ and divide out common factors.

   $5x-1 = A(x+4) + B(x-3)$

   $5x-1 = Ax + 4A + Bx - 3B$

   $5x-1 = (A+B)x + 4A - 3B$

   Equate coefficients of like powers of x and equate constant terms.

   $A+B = 5$

   $4A - 3B = -1$

   Solving the above system for A and B we find

   $A = 2$ and $B = 3$.

   $\dfrac{5x-1}{(x-3)(x+4)} = \dfrac{2}{x-3} + \dfrac{3}{x+4}$

2. $\dfrac{x+2}{x(x-1)^2} = \dfrac{A}{x} + \dfrac{B}{x-1} + \dfrac{C}{(x-1)^2}$

   Multiply both sides of the equation by the least common denominator $x(x-1)^2$ and divide out common factors.

   $x+2 = A(x-1)^2 + Bx(x-1) + Cx$

   $x+2 = A\left(x^2 - 2x + 1\right) + Bx^2 - Bx + Cx$

   $x+2 = Ax^2 - 2Ax + A + Bx^2 - Bx + Cx$

   $x+2 = Ax^2 + Bx^2 - 2Ax - Bx + Cx + A$

   $x+2 = (A+B)x^2 + (-2A - B + C)x + A$

   Equate coefficients of like powers of x and equate constant terms.

   $A+B = 0$

   $-2A - B + C = 1$

   $A = 2$

   Since $A = 2$, we find that $B = -2$ and $C = 3$ by substitution.

   $\dfrac{x+2}{x(x-1)^2} = \dfrac{2}{x} - \dfrac{2}{x-1} + \dfrac{3}{(x-1)^2}$

3. $\dfrac{8x^2 + 12x - 20}{(x+3)\left(x^2+x+2\right)} = \dfrac{A}{x+3} + \dfrac{Bx+C}{x^2+x+2}$

   Multiply both sides of the equation by the least common denominator $(x+3)\left(x^2+x+2\right)$ and divide out common factors.

   $8x^2 + 12x - 20 = A\left(x^2+x+2\right) + (Bx+C)(x+3)$

   $8x^2 + 12x - 20 = Ax^2 + Ax + 2A + Bx^2 + 3Bx + Cx + 3C$

   $8x^2 + 12x - 20 = Ax^2 + Bx^2 + Ax + 3Bx + Cx + 2A + 3C$

   $8x^2 + 12x - 20 = (A+B)x^2 + (A + 3B + C)x + 2A + 3C$

   Equate coefficients of like powers of x and equate constant terms.

362

$$A + B = 8$$

$$A + 3B + C = 12$$

$$2A + 3C = -20$$

Solving the above system for A, B, and C we find $A = 2$, $B = 6$, and $C = -8$.

$$\frac{8x^2 + 12x - 20}{(x+3)(x^2+x+2)} = \frac{2}{x+3} + \frac{6x-8}{x^2+x+2}$$

4. $\dfrac{2x^3 + x + 3}{(x^2+1)^2} = \dfrac{Ax+B}{x^2+1} + \dfrac{Cx+D}{(x^2+1)^2}$

Multiply both sides of the equation by the common denominator $(x^2+1)^2$ and divide out common factors.

$$2x^3 + x + 3 = (Ax+B)(x^2+1) + Cx + D$$

$$2x^3 + x + 3 = Ax^3 + Bx^2 + Ax + B + Cx + D$$

$$2x^3 + x + 3 = Ax^3 + Bx^2 + Ax + Cx + B + D$$

$$2x^3 + x + 3 = Ax^3 + Bx^2 + (A+C)x + B + D$$

Equate coefficients of like powers of x and equate constant terms.

$$A = 2$$

$$B = 0$$

$$A + C = 1$$

$$B + D = 3$$

Since $A = 2$ and $B = 0$ we find that $C = -1$ and $D = 3$ by substitution.

$$\frac{2x^3 + x + 3}{(x^2+1)^2} = \frac{2x}{x^2+1} + \frac{-x+3}{(x^2+1)^2} = \frac{2x}{x^2+1} - \frac{x-3}{(x^2+1)^2}$$

Exercise Set 5.3

1. $\dfrac{11x - 10}{(x-2)(x+1)} = \dfrac{A}{x-2} + \dfrac{B}{x+1}$

3. $\dfrac{6x^2 - 14x - 27}{(x+2)(x-3)^2} = \dfrac{A}{x+2} + \dfrac{B}{x-3} + \dfrac{C}{(x-3)^2}$

5. $\dfrac{5x^2 - 6x + 7}{(x-1)(x^2+1)} = \dfrac{A}{x-1} + \dfrac{Bx+C}{x^2+1}$

7. $\dfrac{x^3 + x^2}{(x^2+4)^2} = \dfrac{Ax+B}{x^2+4} + \dfrac{Cx+D}{(x^2+4)^2}$

9. $\dfrac{x}{(x-3)(x-2)} = \dfrac{A}{x-3} + \dfrac{B}{x-2}$

Multiply both sides of the equation by the least common denominator $(x-3)(x-2)$ and divide out common factors.

$$x = A(x-2) + B(x-3)$$

$$x = Ax - 2A + Bx - 3B$$

$$x = Ax + Bx - 2A - 3B$$

$$x = (A+B)x - (2A+3B)$$

Equate coefficients of like powers of x, and equate constant terms.

$$A + B = 1$$

$$2A + 3B = 0$$

Solving the above system for A and B, we find $A = 3$ and $B = -2$.

$$\frac{x}{(x-3)(x-2)} = \frac{3}{x-3} - \frac{2}{x-2}$$

11. $\dfrac{3x+50}{(x-9)(x+2)} = \dfrac{A}{x-9} + \dfrac{B}{x+2}$

Multiply both sides of the equation by the least common denominator $(x-9)(x+2)$ and divide out common factors.

$3x+50 = A(x+2) + B(x-9)$

$3x+50 = Ax + 2A + Bx - 9B$

$3x+50 = Ax + Bx + 2A - 9B$

$3x+50 = (A+B)x + (2A-9B)$

Equate coefficients of like powers of x, and equate constant terms.

$A + B = 3$

$2A - 9B = 50$

Solving the above system for A and B, we find $A = 7$ and $B = -4$.

$\dfrac{3x+50}{(x-9)(x+2)} = \dfrac{7}{x-9} - \dfrac{4}{x+2}$

13. $\dfrac{7x-4}{x^2-x-12} = \dfrac{7x-4}{(x-4)(x+3)} = \dfrac{A}{x-4} + \dfrac{B}{x+3}$

Multiply both sides of the last equation by the least common denominator $(x-4)(x-3)$ and divide out common factors.

$7x-4 = A(x+3) + B(x-4)$

$7x-4 = Ax + 3A + Bx - 4B$

$7x-4 = Ax + Bx + 3A - 4B$

$7x-4 = (A+B)x + (3A-4B)$

Equate coefficients of like powers of x, and equate constant terms.

$A + B = 7$

$3A - 4B = -4$

Solving the above system for A and B, we find $A = \dfrac{24}{7}$ and $B = \dfrac{25}{7}$.

$\dfrac{7x-4}{x^2-x-12} = \dfrac{24}{7(x-4)} + \dfrac{25}{7(x+3)}$

15. $\dfrac{4}{(2x+1)(x-3)} = \dfrac{A}{2x+1} + \dfrac{B}{x-3}$

Multiply both sides of the equation by the least common denominator $(2x + 1)(x - 3)$ and divide out common factors.

$4 = A(x-3) + B(2x+1)$

$4 = Ax - A3 + B2x + B$

$4 = (A+2B)x + (-3A+B)$

Equate coefficients of like powers of x and equate the constant terms. Solve for A and B.

$A + 2B = 0$

$-3A + B = 4$

$3A + 6B = 0$

$-3A + B = 4$

$7B = 4$

$B = \dfrac{4}{7}$

$A + 2B = 0$

$6A - 2B = -8$

$7A = -8$

$A = -\dfrac{8}{7}$

$\dfrac{4}{(2x+1)(x-3)} = \dfrac{-8}{7(2x+1)} + \dfrac{4}{7(x-3)}$

17. $\dfrac{4x^2+13x-9}{x(x-1)(x+3)} = \dfrac{A}{x} + \dfrac{B}{x-3} + \dfrac{C}{x+3}$

Multiply both sides of the equation by the least common denominator $x(x-1)(x+3)$ and divide out common factors.

$4x^2+13x-9=A(x\text{-}1)(x+3)+Bx(x+3)+Cx(x-1)$

$4x^2+13x-9=A(x^2+2x-3)+Bx^2+3Bx+Cx^2-Cx$

$4x^2+13x-9=Ax^2+2Ax-3A+Bx^2+3Bx+Cx^2-Cx$

$4x^2+13x-9=Ax^2+Bx^2+Cx^2+2Ax+3Bx-Cx-3A$

$4x^2+13x-9=(A+B+C)x^2+(2A+3B-C)x-3A$

Equate coefficients of like powers of x, and equate constant terms.

$A+B+C=4$

$2A+3B-C=13$

$\qquad -3A=-9$

Solving the above system for A, B, and C, we find $A=3$ and $B=2$, and $C=-1$.

$\dfrac{4x^2+13x-9}{x(x-1)(x+3)} = \dfrac{3}{x} + \dfrac{2}{x-1} - \dfrac{1}{x+3}$

19. $\dfrac{4x^2-7x-3}{x^3-x} = \dfrac{4x^2-7x-3}{x(x+1)(x-1)} = \dfrac{A}{x} + \dfrac{B}{x+1} + \dfrac{C}{x-1}$

Multiply both sides of the last equation by the least common denominator $x(x+1)(x-1)$ and divide out common factors.

$4x^2-7x-3=A(x+1)(x-1)+Bx(x-1)+Cx(x+1)$

$4x^2-7x-3=A(x^2-1)+Bx^2-Bx+Cx^2+Cx$

$4x^2-7x-3=Ax^2-A+Bx^2-Bx+Cx^2+Cx$

$4x^2-7x-3=Ax^2+Bx^2+Cx^2-Bx+Cx-A$

$4x^2-7x-3=(A+B+C)x^2+(-B+C)x-A$

Equate coefficients of like powers of x, and equate constant terms.

$A+B+C=4$

$\quad -B+C=-7$

$\qquad -A=-3$

Solving the above system for A, B, and C, we find $A=3$ and $B=4$, and $C=-3$.

$\dfrac{4x^2-7x-3}{x^3-x} = \dfrac{3}{x} + \dfrac{4}{x+1} - \dfrac{3}{x-1}$

21. $\dfrac{6x-11}{(x-1)^2} = \dfrac{A}{x-1} + \dfrac{B}{(x-1)^2}$

Multiply both sides of the equation by the least common denominator $(x-1)^2$ and divide out common factors.

$6x-11=A(x-1)+B$

$6x-11=Ax-A+B$

Equate coefficients of like powers of x, and equate constant terms.

$\quad A=6$

$-A+B=-11$

Since $A=6$, we find that $B=-5$ by substitution. $\dfrac{6x-11}{(x-1)^2} = \dfrac{6}{x-1} - \dfrac{5}{(x-1)^2}$

23. $$\frac{x^2-6x+3}{(x-2)^3}=\frac{A}{x-2}+\frac{B}{(x-2)^2}+\frac{C}{(x-2)^3}$$

Multiply both sides of the equation by the least common denominator $(x-2)^3$ and divide out common factors.

$x^2-6x+3=A(x-2)^2+B(x-2)+C$

$x^2-6x+3=A(x^2-4x+4)+Bx-2B+C$

$x^2-6x+3=Ax^2-4Ax+4A+Bx-2B+C$

$x^2-6x+3=Ax^2-4Ax+Bx+4A-2B+C$

$x^2-6x+3=Ax^2+(-4A+B)x+4A-2B+C$

Equate coefficients of like powers of x, and equate constant terms.

$$A=1$$
$$-4A+B=-6$$
$$4A-2B+C=3$$

Since $A=1$, we find that $B=-2$ and $C=-5$ by substitution. $\dfrac{x^2-6x+3}{(x-2)^3}=\dfrac{1}{x-2}-\dfrac{2}{(x-2)^2}-\dfrac{5}{(x-2)^3}$

25. $$\frac{x^2+2x+7}{x(x-1)^2}=\frac{A}{x}+\frac{B}{x-1}+\frac{C}{(x-1)^2}$$

Multiply both sides of the equation by the least common denominator $x(x-1)^2$ and divide out common factors.

$x^2+2x+7=A(x-1)^2+Bx(x-1)+Cx$

$x^2+2x+7=A(x^2-2x+1)+Bx^2-Bx+Cx$

$x^2+2x+7=Ax^2-2Ax+A+Bx^2-Bx+Cx$

$x^2+2x+7=Ax^2+Bx^2-2Ax-Bx+Cx+A$

$x^2+2x+7=(A+B)x^2+(-2A-B+C)x+A$

$$A+B=1$$
$$-2A-B+C=2$$
$$A=7$$

Since $A=7$, we find that $B=-6$ and $C=10$ by substitution. $\dfrac{x^2+2x+7}{x(x-1)^2}=\dfrac{7}{x}-\dfrac{6}{x-1}+\dfrac{10}{(x-1)^2}$

27. $$\frac{x^2}{(x+1)(x-1)^2}=\frac{A}{x+1}+\frac{B}{x-1}+\frac{C}{(x-1)^2}$$

Multiply both sides of the equation by the least common denominator $(x+1)(x-1)^2$ and divide out common factors.

$x^2=A(x-1)^2+B(x+1)(x-1)+C(x+1)$

$x^2=x^2A-2xA+A+Bx^2-B+Cx+C$

$x^2=(A+B)x^2+(-2A+C)x+(A-B+C)$

Equate coefficients of like powers of x, and equate constant terms.

$$A+B=1$$
$$-2A+C=0$$
$$A-B+C=0$$

Solving the above system for A, B, and C, we find $A=\dfrac{1}{4}$, $B=\dfrac{3}{4}$, and $C=\dfrac{1}{2}$.

$$\frac{x^2}{(x+1)(x-1)^2}=\frac{1}{4(x+1)}+\frac{3}{4(x-1)}+\frac{1}{2(x-1)^2}$$

29. $\dfrac{5x^2 - 6x + 7}{(x-1)(x^2+1)} = \dfrac{A}{x-1} + \dfrac{Bx+C}{x^2+1}$

Multiply both sides of the equation by the least common denominator $(x-1)(x^2+1)$ and divide out common factors.

$5x^2 - 6x + 7 = A(x^2+1) + (Bx+C)(x-1)$

$5x^2 - 6x + 7 = Ax^2 + A + Bx^2 - Bx + Cx - C$

$5x^2 - 6x + 7 = Ax^2 + Bx^2 - Bx + Cx + A - C$

$5x^2 - 6x + 7 = (A+B)x^2 + (-B+C)x + A - C$

Equate coefficients of like powers of x, and equate constant terms.

$A + B = 5$
$-B + C = -6$
$A - C = 7$

Solving the above system for A, B, and C, we find $A = 3$, $B = 2$, and $C = -4$.

$\dfrac{5x^2 - 6x + 7}{(x-1)(x^2+1)} = \dfrac{3}{x-1} + \dfrac{2x-4}{x^2+1}$

31. $\dfrac{5x^2 + 6x + 3}{(x+1)(x^2+2x+2)} = \dfrac{A}{x+1} + \dfrac{Bx+C}{x^2+2x+2}$

Multiply both sides of the equation by the least common denominator $(x+1)(x^2+2x+2)$ and divide out common factors.

$5x^2 + 6x + 3 = A(x^2+2x+2) + (Bx+C)(x+1)$

$5x^2 + 6x + 3 = Ax^2 + 2Ax + 2A + Bx^2 + Bx + Cx + C$

$5x^2 + 6x + 3 = Ax^2 + Bx^2 + 2Ax + Bx + Cx + 2A + C$

$5x^2 + 6x + 3 = (A+B)x^2 + (2A+B+C)x + 2A + C$

Equate coefficients of like powers of x, and equate constant terms.

$A + B = 5$
$2A + B + C = 6$
$2A + C = 3$

Solving the above system for A, B, and C, we find $A = 2$, $B = 3$, and $C = -1$.

$\dfrac{5x^2 + 6x + 3}{(x+1)(x^2+2x+2)} = \dfrac{2}{x+1} + \dfrac{3x-1}{x^2+2x+2}$

33. $\dfrac{x+4}{x^2(x^2+4)} = \dfrac{A}{x} + \dfrac{B}{x^2} + \dfrac{Cx+D}{x^2+4}$

Multiply both sides of the equation by the least common denominator $x^2(x^2+4)$ and divide out common factors.

$x + 4 = Ax(x^2+4) + B(x^2+4) + (Cx+D)x^2$

$x + 4 = Ax^3 + 4Ax + Bx^2 + 4B + Cx^3 + Dx^2$

$x + 4 = (A+C)x^3 + (B+D)x^2 + 4Ax + 4B$

Equate coefficients of like powers of x, and equate constant terms

$A + C = 0$

$B + D = 0$

$4A = 1$

$4B = 4$

Solving the above system for A, B, and C, we find $A = \frac{1}{4}$, $B = 1$, $C = -\frac{1}{4}$, and $D = -1$.

$$\frac{x+4}{x^2(x^2+4)} = \frac{1}{4x} + \frac{1}{x^2} + \frac{-1x-4}{4\left(x^2+4\right)}$$

35. $\dfrac{6x^2 - x + 1}{x^3 + x^2 + x + 1} = \dfrac{6x^2 - x + 1}{(x+1)(x^2+1)} = \dfrac{A}{x+1} + \dfrac{Bx+C}{x^2+1}$

Multiply both sides of the last equation by the least common denominator $(x+1)(x^2+1)$ and divide out common factors.

$6x^2 - x + 1 = A(x^2+1) + (Bx+C)(x+1)$

$6x^2 - x + 1 = Ax^2 + A + Bx^2 + Bx + Cx + C$

$6x^2 - x + 1 = Ax^2 + Bx^2 + Bx + Cx + A + C$

$6x^2 - x + 1 = (A+B)x^2 + (B+C)x + A + C$

Equate coefficients of like powers of x, and equate constant terms.

$A + B = 6$

$B + C = -1$

$A + C = 1$

Solving the above system for A, B, and C, we find $A = 4$, $B = 2$, and $C = -3$.

$$\frac{6x^2 - x + 1}{x^3 + x^2 + x + 1} = \frac{4}{x+1} + \frac{2x-3}{x^2+1}$$

37. $\dfrac{x^3 + x^2 + 2}{\left(x^2+2\right)^2} = \dfrac{Ax+B}{x^2+2} + \dfrac{Cx+D}{\left(x^2+2\right)^2}$

Multiply both sides of the last equation by the least common denominator $(x^2+2)^2$ and divide out common factors.

$x^3 + x^2 + 2 = \left(Ax+B\right)\left(x^2+2\right) + Cx + D$

$x^3 + x^2 + 2 = Ax^3 + Bx^2 + 2Ax + 2B + Cx + D$

$x^3 + x^2 + 2 = Ax^3 + Bx^2 + 2Ax + Cx + 2B + D$

$x^3 + x^2 + 2 = Ax^3 + Bx^2 + \left(2A+C\right)x + \left(2B+D\right)$

Equate coefficients of like powers of x, and equate constant terms.

$A = 1$

$B = 1$

$2A + C = 0$

$2B + D = 2$

Since $A = 1$ and $B = 1$, we find that $C = -2$ and $D = 0$ by substitution.

$$\frac{x^3 + x^2 + 2}{\left(x^2+2\right)^2} = \frac{x+1}{x^2+2} - \frac{2x}{\left(x^2+2\right)^2}$$

39. $\dfrac{x^3 - 4x^2 + 9x - 5}{(x^2 - 2x + 3)^2} = \dfrac{Ax + B}{x^2 - 2x + 3} + \dfrac{Cx + D}{(x^2 - 2x + 3)^2}$

Multiply both sides of the equation by the least common denominator $(x^2 - 2x + 3)^2$ and divide out common factors.

$x^3 - 4x^2 + 9x - 5 = (Ax + B)(x^2 - 2x + 3) + Cx + D$

$x^3 - 4x^2 + 9x - 5 = Ax^3 - 2Ax^2 + 3Ax + Bx^2 - 2Bx + 3B + Cx + D$

$x^3 - 4x^2 + 9x - 5 = Ax^3 - 2Ax^2 + Bx^2 + 3Ax - 2Bx + Cx + 3B + D$

$x^3 - 4x^2 + 9x - 5 = Ax^3 + (-2A + B)x^2 + (3A - 2B + C)x + 3B + D$

Equate coefficients of like powers of x, and equate constant terms.

$\begin{aligned} A &= 1 \\ -2A + B &= -4 \\ 3A - 2B + C &= 9 \\ 3B + D &= -5 \end{aligned}$

Since $A = 1$, we find that $B = -2$, $C = 2$, and $D = 1$ by substitution.

$\dfrac{x^3 - 4x^2 + 9x - 5}{(x^2 - 2x + 3)^2} = \dfrac{x - 2}{x^2 - 2x + 3} + \dfrac{2x + 1}{(x^2 - 2x + 3)^2}$

41. $\dfrac{4x^2 + 3x + 14}{x^3 - 8} = \dfrac{4x^2 + 3x + 14}{(x - 2)(x^2 + 2x + 4)} = \dfrac{A}{x - 2} + \dfrac{Bx + C}{x^2 + 2x + 4}$

Multiply both sides of the last equation by the least common denominator $(x - 2)(x^2 + 2x + 4)$ and divide out common factors.

$4x^2 + 3x + 14 = A(x^2 + 2x + 4) + (Bx + C)(x - 2)$

$4x^2 + 3x + 14 = A^2 + 2Ax + 4A + Bx^2 - 2Bx + Cx - 2C$

$4x^2 + 3x + 14 = Ax^2 + Bx^2 + 2Ax - 2Bx + Cx + 4A - 2C$

$4x^2 + 3x + 14 = (A + B)x^2 + (2A - 2B + C)x + (4A - 2C)$

Equate coefficients of like powers of x, and equate constant terms.

$A + B = 4$

$2A - 2B + C = 3$

$4A - 2C = 14$

Solving the above system for A, B, and C, we find $A = 3$, $B = 1$, and $C = -1$.

$\dfrac{4x^2 + 3x + 4}{x^3 - 8} = \dfrac{3}{x - 2} + \dfrac{x - 1}{x^2 + 2x + 4}$

43. Divide $x^5 + 2$ by $x^2 - 1$.

$$
\begin{array}{r}
x^3 + x \\
x^2 - 1 \overline{) x^5 + 2} \\
\underline{x^5 - x^3} \\
x^3 \\
\underline{x^3 - x} \\
x + 2
\end{array}
$$

$\dfrac{x^5 + 2}{x^2 - 1} = x^3 + x + \dfrac{x + 2}{x^2 - 1}$

Decompose $\dfrac{x + 2}{x^2 - 1}$.

369

$$\frac{x+2}{x^2-1} = \frac{x+2}{(x+1)(x-1)} = \frac{A}{x+1} + \frac{B}{x-1}$$

$$(x+1)(x-1)\frac{x+2}{(x+1)(x-1)} = (x+1)(x-1)\left(\frac{A}{x+1} + \frac{B}{x-1}\right)$$

$$x+2 = (x-1)A + (x+1)B$$

$$x+2 = Ax - A + Bx + B$$

$$x+2 = (A+B)x + (-A+B)$$

Equate coefficients:

$$A+B=1$$

$$-A+B=2$$

Solving this system results in $A = -\frac{1}{2}$ and $B = \frac{3}{2}$.

$$\frac{x^5+2}{x^2-1} = x^3 + x + \frac{-\frac{1}{2}}{x+1} + \frac{\frac{3}{2}}{x-1} \quad \text{or} \quad x^3 + x + \frac{-1}{2(x+1)} + \frac{3}{2(x-1)}$$

45. Divide $x^4 - x^2 + 2$ by $x^3 - x^2$.

$$
\begin{array}{r}
x+1 \\
x^3 - x^2 \overline{) x^4 - x^2 + 2} \\
\underline{x^4 - x^3} \\
x^3 - x^2 \\
\underline{x^3 - x^2} \\
2
\end{array}
$$

$$\frac{x^4 - x^2 + 2}{x^3 - x^2} = x + 1 + \frac{2}{x^3 - x^2}$$

Decompose $\dfrac{2}{x^3 - x^2}$.

$$\frac{2}{x^3 - x^2} = \frac{2}{x^2(x-1)} = \frac{A}{x} + \frac{B}{x^2} + \frac{C}{x-1}$$

$$x^2(x-1)\frac{2}{x^2(x-1)} = x^2(x-1)\left(\frac{A}{x} + \frac{B}{x^2} + \frac{C}{x-1}\right)$$

$$2 = x(x-1)A + (x-1)B + x^2C$$

$$2 = Ax^2 - Ax + Bx - B + Cx^2$$

$$2 = (A+C)x^2 + (-A+B)x + (-B)$$

Equate coefficients:

$$A+C=0$$

$$-A+B=0$$

$$-B=2$$

Solving this system results in $A = -2$, $B = -2$, and $C = 2$.

$$\frac{x^4 - x^2 + 2}{x^3 - x^2} = x + 1 + \frac{-2}{x} + \frac{-2}{x^2} + \frac{2}{x-1}$$

47. $\dfrac{1}{x^2 - c^2} = \dfrac{1}{(x+c)(x-c)} = \dfrac{A}{x+c} + \dfrac{B}{x-c}$

$$(x+c)(x-c)\dfrac{1}{(x+c)(x-c)} = (x+c)(x-c)\left(\dfrac{A}{x+c} + \dfrac{B}{x-c}\right)$$

$$1 = (x-c)A + (x+c)B$$

$$1 = Ax - Ac + Bx + Bc$$

$$1 = (A+B)x + (-Ac + Bc)$$

Equate coefficients:

$A + B = 0$

$-Ac + Bc = 1$

Solving this system results in $A = \dfrac{-1}{2c}$ and $B = \dfrac{1}{2c}$.

$$\dfrac{1}{x^2 - c^2} = \dfrac{\frac{-1}{2c}}{x+c} + \dfrac{\frac{1}{2c}}{x-c}$$

49. $\dfrac{ax + b}{(x-c)^2} = \dfrac{D}{x-c} + \dfrac{E}{(x-c)^2}$

$$\dfrac{ax + b}{(x-c)^2} = \dfrac{D}{x-c} + \dfrac{E}{(x-c)^2}$$

$$(x-c)^2 \dfrac{ax+b}{(x-c)^2} = (x-c)^2\left(\dfrac{D}{x-c} + \dfrac{E}{(x-c)^2}\right)$$

$$ax + b = (x-c)D + E$$

$$ax + b = Dx - Dc + E$$

$$ax + b = (D)x + (-Dc + E)$$

Equate coefficients:

$D = a$

$-Dc + E = b$

Solving this system results in $D = a$ and $E = ac + b$.

$$\dfrac{ax + b}{(x-c)^2} = \dfrac{a}{x-c} + \dfrac{ac+b}{(x-c)^2}$$

51. $\dfrac{1}{x(x+1)} = \dfrac{A}{x} + \dfrac{B}{x+1}$

Multiply both sides of the equation by the least common denominator $x(x+1)$ and divide out common factors.

$1 = A(x+1) + Bx$

$1 = Ax + A + Bx$

$1 = Ax + Bx + A$

$1 = (A+B)x + A$

Equate coefficients of like powers of x, and equate constant terms.

$A + B = 0$

$\quad A = 1$

Since $A = 1$ we find that $B = -1$ by substitution.

$\dfrac{1}{x(x+1)} = \dfrac{1}{x} - \dfrac{1}{x+1}$

$$\dfrac{1}{1 \cdot 2} + \dfrac{1}{2 \cdot 3} + \dfrac{1}{3 \cdot 4} + \cdots + \dfrac{1}{99 \cdot 100} = \left(\dfrac{1}{1} - \dfrac{1}{2}\right) + \left(\dfrac{1}{2} - \dfrac{1}{3}\right) + \left(\dfrac{1}{3} - \dfrac{1}{4}\right) + \cdots \left(\dfrac{1}{99} - \dfrac{1}{100}\right)$$

$$= \dfrac{1}{1} - \dfrac{1}{100}$$

$$= \dfrac{99}{100}$$

61. $\dfrac{4x^2 + 5x - 9}{x^3 - 6x - 9} = \dfrac{4x^2 + 5x - 9}{(x-3)(x^2 + 3x + 3)} = \dfrac{A}{x-3} + \dfrac{Bx + C}{x^2 + 3x + 3}$

Multiply both sides of the last equation by the common denominator $(x-3)(x^2 + 3x + 3)$ and divide out common factors.

$4x^2 + 5x - 9 = A(x^2 + 3x + 3) + (Bx + C)(x - 3)$

$4x^2 + 5x - 9 = Ax^2 + 3Ax + 3A + Bx^2 - 3Bx + Cx - 3C$

$4x^2 + 5x - 9 = Ax^2 + Bx^2 + 3Ax - 3Bx + Cx + 3A - 3C$

$4x^2 + 5x - 9 = (A + B)x^2 + (3A - 3B + C)x + 3A - 3C$

Equate coefficients of like powers of x and equate constant terms.

$\quad A + B = 4$

$3A - 3B + C = 5$

$\quad 3A - 3C = -9$

Solving the above system for A, B, and C, we find $A = 2$, and $B = 2$, and $C = 5$.

$\dfrac{4x^2 + 5x - 9}{x^3 - 6x - 9} = \dfrac{2}{x-3} + \dfrac{2x+5}{x^2 + 3x + 3}$

Section 5.4

Check Point Exercises

1. $x^2 = y - 1$

$4x - y = -1$

Solve the first equation for y.

$y = x^2 + 1$

Substitute the expression $x^2 + 1$ for y in the second equation and solve for x.

$4x - (x^2 + 1) = -1$

$4x - x^2 - 1 = -1$

$x^2 - 4x = 0$

$x(x - 4) = 0$

$x = 0$ or $x - 4 = 0$

$x = 4$

If $x = 0$, $y = (0)^2 + 1 = 1$.

If $x = 4$, $y = (4)^2 + 1 = 17$.

The solution set is $\{(0, 1), (4, 17)\}$.

2. $x + 2y = 0$

$(x - 1)^2 + (y - 1)^2 = 5$

Solve the first equation for x.

$x = -2y$

Substitute the expression $-2y$ for x in the second equation and solve for y.

$(-2y - 1)^2 + (y - 1)^2 = 5$

$4y^2 + 4y + 1 + y^2 - 2y + 1 = 5$

$5y^2 + 2y - 3 = 0$

$(5y - 3)(y + 1) = 0$

$5y - 3 = 0$ or $y + 1 = 0$

$y = \dfrac{3}{5}$ or $y = -1$

If $y = \dfrac{3}{5}$, $x = -2\left(\dfrac{3}{5}\right) = -\dfrac{6}{5}$.

If $y = -1$, $x = -2(-1) = 2$.

The solution set is $\left\{\left(-\dfrac{6}{5}, \dfrac{3}{5}\right), (2, -1)\right\}$.

3. $3x^2 + 2y^2 = 35$

$4x^2 + 3y^2 = 48$

Eliminate the y^2-term by multiplying the first equation by -3 and the second equation by 2. Add the resulting equations.

$-9x^2 - 6y = -105$

$\underline{8x^2 + 6y^2 = 96}$

$-x^2 = -9$

$x^2 = 9$

$x = \pm 3$

If $x = 3$,

$3(3)^2 + 2y^2 = 35$

$y^2 = 4$

$y = \pm 2$

If $x = -3$,

$3(-3)^2 + 2y^2 = 35$

$y^2 = 4$

$y = \pm 2$

The solution set is $\{(3, 2), (3, -2), (-3, 2), (-3, -2)\}$.

4. $y = x^2 + 5$

$x^2 + y^2 = 25$

Arrange the first equation so that variable terms appear on the left, and constants appear on the right. Add the resulting equations to eliminate the x^2-terms and solve for y.

$-x^2 + y = 5$

$\underline{x^2 + y^2 = 25}$

$y^2 + y = 30$

$y^2 + y - 30 = 0$

$(y + 6)(y - 5) = 0$

$y + 6 = 0$ or $y - 5 = 0$

$y = -6$ or $y = 5$

If $y = -6$,

$x^2 + (-6)^2 = 25$

$x^2 = -11$

no real solution

If $y = 5$,

$x^2 + (5)^2 = 25$

$x^2 = 0$

$x = 0$

The solution set is $\{(0, 5)\}$.

5. $2x + 2y = 20$

$xy = 21$

Solve the second equation for x.

$x = \dfrac{21}{7}$

Substitute the expression $\dfrac{21}{y}$ for x in the first equation and solve for y.

$2\left(\dfrac{21}{y}\right) + 2y = 20$

$\dfrac{42}{y} + 2y = 20$

$y^2 - 10y + 21 = 0$

$(y-7)(y-3) = 0$

$y - 7 = 0$ or $y - 3 = 0$

$y = 7$ or $y = 3$

If $y = 7$, $x = \dfrac{21}{7} = 3$.

If $y = 3$, $x = \dfrac{21}{3} = 7$.

The dimensions are 7 feet by 3 feet.

Exercise Set 5.4

1. $x + y = 2$

$y = x^2 - 4$

Solve the first equation for y. $y = 2 - x$.

Substitute the expression $2 - x$ for y in the second equation and solve for x.

$2 - x = x^2 - 4$

$x^2 + x - 6 = 0$

$(x+3)(x-2) = 0$

$x + 3 = 0$ or $x - 2 = 0$

$x = -3$ or $x = 2$

If $x = -3$, $y = 2 - (-3) = 5$.

If $x = 2$, $y = 2 - 2 = 0$.

The solution set is $\{(-3, 5), (2, 0)\}$.

3. $x + y = 2$

$y = x^2 - 4x + 4$

Substitute the expression $x^2 - 4x + 4$ for y in the first equation and solve for x.

$x + x^2 - 4x + 4 = 2$

$x^2 - 3x + 2 = 0$

$(x-1)(x-2) = 0$

$x - 1 = 0$ or $x - 2 = 0$

$x = 1$ or $x = 2$

Substitute $x = 1$ and then $x = 2$ into the equation $x + y = 2$ and solve for each value of y.

$1 + y = 2$ $\quad 2 + y = 2$

$y = 1$ $\qquad\quad y = 0$

The solution set is $\{(1, 1), (2, 0)\}$.

5. $y = x^2 - 4x - 10$

$y = -x^2 - 2x + 14$

Substitute the expression $x^2 - 4x - 10$ for y in the second equation and solve for x.

$x^2 - 4x - 10 = -x^2 - 2x + 14$

$2x^2 - 2x - 24 = 0$

$x^2 - x - 12 = 0$

$(x-4)(x+3) = 0$

$x - 4 = 0$ or $x + 3 = 0$

$x = 4$ or $x = -3$

If $x = 4$, $y = (4)^2 - 4(4) - 10 = -10$.

If $x = -3$, $y = (-3)^2 - 4(-3) - 10 = 11$.

The solution set is $\{(4, -10), (-3, 11)\}$.

7. $x^2 + y^2 = 25$

$x - y = 1$

Solve the second equation for y. $y = x - 1$

Substitute the expression $x - 1$ for y in the first equation and solve for x.

$x^2 + (x-1)^2 = 25$

$x^2 + x^2 - 2x + 1 = 25$

$2x^2 - 2x - 24 = 0$

$x^2 - x - 12 = 0$

$(x-4)(x+3) = 0$

$x - 4 = 0$ or $x + 3 = 0$

$x = 4$ or $x = -3$

If $x = 4$, $y = 4 - 1 = 3$.

If $x = -3$, $y = -3 - 1 = -4$.

The solution set is $\{(4, 3), (-3, -4)\}$.

9.
$$xy = 6$$
$$2x - y = 1$$
Solve the first equation for y.

$$y = \frac{6}{x}$$

Substitute the expression $\frac{6}{x}$ for y in the second equation and solve for x.

$$2x - \frac{6}{x} = 1$$
$$2x^2 - 6 = x$$
$$2x^2 - x - 6 = 0$$
$$(2x + 3)(x - 2) = 0$$
$$2x + 3 = 0 \quad \text{or} \quad x - 2 = 0$$
$$x = -\frac{3}{2} \quad \text{or} \quad x = 2$$

If $x = -\frac{3}{2}$, $y = \frac{6}{-\frac{3}{2}} = -4$.

If $x = 2$, $y = \frac{6}{2} = 3$.

The solution set is $\left\{ \left(-\frac{3}{2}, -4 \right), (2, 3) \right\}$.

11.
$$y^2 = x^2 - 9$$
$$2y = x - 3$$
Solve the second equation for y.

$$y = \frac{x - 3}{2}$$

Substitute the expression $\frac{x-3}{2}$ for y in the first equation and solve for x.

$$\left(\frac{x-3}{2} \right)^2 = x^2 - 9$$
$$\frac{x^2 - 6x + 9}{4} = x^2 - 9$$
$$x^2 - 6x + 9 = 4x^2 - 36$$
$$3x^2 + 6x - 45 = 0$$
$$x^2 + 2x - 15 = 0$$
$$(x + 5)(x - 3) = 0$$
$$x + 5 = 0 \quad \text{or} \quad x - 3 = 0$$
$$x = -5 \quad \text{or} \quad x = 3$$

If $x = -5$, $y = \frac{-5 - 3}{2} = -4$.

If $x = 3$, $y = \frac{3 - 3}{2} = 0$.

The solution set is $\{ (-5, -4), (3, 0) \}$.

13.
$$xy = 3$$
$$x^2 + y^2 = 10$$
Solve the second equation for y.

$$y = \frac{3}{x}$$

Substitute the expression $\frac{3}{x}$ for y in the second equation and solve for x.

$$x^2 + \left(\frac{3}{x} \right)^2 = 10$$
$$x^2 + \frac{9}{x^2} - 10 = 0$$
$$x^4 - 10x^2 + 9 = 0$$
$$(x^2 - 9)(x^2 - 1) = 0$$
$$(x - 3)(x + 3)(x - 1)(x + 1) = 0$$

$$\text{If } x = 3, y = \frac{3}{3} = 1.$$

$$x - 3 = 0 \quad \text{or} \quad x + 3 = 0 \quad \text{or} \quad x - 1 = 0 \quad \text{or} \quad x + 1 = 0 \qquad \text{If } x = -3, y = \frac{3}{-3} = -1.$$

$$x = 3 \quad \text{or} \qquad x = -3 \quad \text{or} \qquad x = 1 \quad \text{or} \qquad x = -1 \qquad \text{If } x = 1, y = \frac{3}{1} = 3.$$

$$\text{If } x = -1, y = \frac{3}{-1} = -3.$$

The solution set is $\{(3,1),(-3,-1),(1,3),(-1,-3)\}$.

15. $x + y = 1$
$x^2 + xy - y^2 = -5$

Solve the first equation for y. $y = 1 - x$

Substitute the expression $1 - x$ for y in the second equation and solve for x.

$$x^2 + x(1-x) - (1-x)^2 = -5$$
$$x^2 + x - x^2 - (1 - 2x + x^2) = -5$$
$$x - 1 + 2x - x^2 = -5$$
$$x^2 - 3x - 4 = 0$$
$$(x-4)(x+1) = 0$$
$$x - 4 = 0 \quad \text{or} \quad x + 1 = 0$$
$$x = 4 \quad \text{or} \quad x = -1$$

If $x = 4, y = 1 - 4 = -3$.

If $x = -1, y = 1 - (-1) = 2$.

The solution set is $\{(4,-3),(-1,2)\}$.

17. $x + y = 1$
$(x-1)^2 + (y+2)^2 = 10$

Solve the first equation for y.
$y = 1 - x$

Substitute the expression $1 - x$ for y in the second equation and solve for x.

$$(x-1)^2 + (1 - x + 2)^2 = 10$$
$$(x-1)^2 + (3 - x)^2 = 10$$
$$x^2 - 2x + 1 + 9 - 6x + x^2 - 10 = 0$$
$$2x^2 - 8x = 0$$
$$x^2 - 4x = 0$$
$$x(x-4) = 0$$
$$x = 0 \quad \text{or} \quad x - 4 = 0$$
$$x = 4$$

If $x = 0, y = 1 - 0 = 1$.

If $x = 4, y = 1 - 4 = -3$.

The solution set is $\{(0,1),(4,-3)\}$.

19. Eliminate the y^2 –terms by adding the equations.

$$x^2 + y^2 = 13$$
$$\underline{x^2 - y^2 = 5}$$
$$2x^2 = 18$$
$$x^2 = 9$$
$$x = \pm 3$$

If $x = 3$,
$$(3)^2 + y^2 = 13$$
$$y^2 = 4$$
$$y = \pm 2$$

If $x = -3$,
$$(-3)^2 + y^2 = 13$$
$$y^2 = 4$$
$$y = \pm 2$$

The solution set is
$\{(3, 2), (3, -2), (-3, 2), (-3, -2)\}$.

21. $x^2 - 4y^2 = -7$
$3x^2 + y^2 = 31$

Eliminate the x^2 –terms by multiplying the first equation by -3 and adding the resulting equations.

$$-3x^2 + 12y^2 = 21$$
$$\underline{3x^2 + y^2 = 31}$$
$$13y^2 = 52$$
$$y^2 = 4$$
$$y = \pm 2$$

If $y = 2$,
$$x^2 - 4(2)^2 = -7$$
$$x^2 = 9$$
$$x = \pm 3$$
If $y = -2$,
$$x^2 - 4(-2)^2 = -7$$
$$x^2 = 9$$
$$x = \pm 3$$
The solution set is
$$\{(3,2),(3,-2),(-3,2),(-3,-2)\}.$$

23. Arrange the equations so that variable terms appear on the left and constants appear on the right.
$$3x^2 + 4y^2 = 16$$
$$2x^2 - 3y^2 = 5$$

Eliminate the y^2–terms by multiplying the first equation by 3 and the second equation by 4. Add the resulting equations.
$$9x^2 + 12y^2 = 48$$
$$\underline{8x^2 - 12y^2 = 20}$$
$$17x^2 = 68$$
$$x^2 = 4$$
$$x = \pm 2$$
If $x = 2$,
$$3(2)^2 + 4y^2 = 16$$
$$y^2 = 1$$
$$y = \pm 1$$
If $x = -2$,
$$3(-2)^2 + 4y^2 = 16$$
$$y = \pm 1$$
The solution set is
$\{(2, 1), (2, -1), (-2, 1), (-2, -1)\}$.

25.
$$x^2 + y^2 = 25$$
$$(x-8)^2 + y^2 = 41$$

Expand the second equation and eliminate x^2 and y^2–terms by multiplying the first equation by -1 and adding the resulting equations.
$$x^2 - 16x + 64 + y^2 = 41$$
$$\underline{-x^2 - y^2 = -25}$$
$$-16x + 64 = 16$$
$$-16x = -48$$
$$x = 3$$
If $x = 3$,
$$(3)^2 + y^2 = 25$$
$$y^2 = 16$$
$$y = \pm 4$$
The solution set is $\{(3,4),(3,-4)\}$.

27.
$$y^2 - x = 4$$
$$x^2 + y^2 = 4$$

Eliminate the y^2–terms by multiplying the first equation by -1 and adding the resulting equations.
$$x - y^2 = -4$$
$$\underline{x^2 + y^2 = 4}$$
$$x^2 + x = 0$$
$$x(x+1) = 0$$
$$x = 0 \quad \text{or} \quad x + 1 = 0$$
$$x = -1$$
If $x = 0$,
$$y^2 = 4$$
$$y = \pm 2$$
If $x = -1$,
$$y^2 - (-1) = 4$$
$$y^2 = 3$$
$$y = \pm\sqrt{3}$$
The solution set is
$$\left\{(0,2),(0,-2),\left(-1,\sqrt{3}\right),\left(-1,-\sqrt{3}\right)\right\}.$$

29. The addition method is used here to solve the system.

$3x^2 + 4y^2 = 16$

$2x^2 - 3y^2 = 5$

Eliminate the y^2–terms by multiplying the first equation by 3 and the second equation by 4. Add the resulting equations.

$9x^2 + 12y^2 = 48$

$\underline{8x^2 - 12y^2 = 20}$

$\qquad 17x^2 = 68$

$\qquad x^2 = 4$

$\qquad x = \pm 2$

If $x = 2$,

$3(2)^2 + 4y^2 = 16$

$\qquad y^2 = 1$

$\qquad y = \pm 1$

If $x = -2$,

$3(-2)^2 + 4y^2 = 16$

$\qquad y = \pm 1$

The solution set is

$\{(2, 1), (2, -1), (-2, 1), (-2, -1)\}.$

31. The substitution method is used here to solve the system.

$2x^2 + y^2 = 18$

$\qquad xy = 4$

Solve the second equation for y.

$y = \dfrac{4}{x}$

Substitute the expression $\dfrac{4}{x}$ for y in the first equation and solve for x.

$2x^2 + \left(\dfrac{4}{x}\right)^2 = 18$

$2x^2 + \dfrac{16}{x^2} = 18$

$2x^4 + 16 = 18x^2$

$x^4 - 9x^2 + 8 = 0$

$\left(x^2 - 8\right)\left(x^2 - 1\right) = 0$

$x^2 - 8 = 0 \quad \text{or} \quad x^2 - 1 = 0$

$\quad x^2 = 8 \qquad \text{or} \qquad x^2 = 1$

$\quad x = \pm 2\sqrt{2} \quad \text{or} \qquad x = \pm 1$

If $x = 2\sqrt{2}$, $y = \dfrac{4}{2\sqrt{2}} = \sqrt{2}$.

If $x = -2\sqrt{2}, y = \dfrac{4}{-2\sqrt{2}} = -\sqrt{2}$.

If $x = 1$, $y = \dfrac{4}{1} = 4$.

If $x = -1$, $y = \dfrac{4}{-1} = -4$.

The solution set is

$\left\{\left(2\sqrt{2}, \sqrt{2}\right), \left(-2\sqrt{2}, -\sqrt{2}\right), (1, 4), (-1, -4)\right\}.$

33. The substitution method is used here to solve the system.

$x^2 + 4y^2 = 20$

$\quad x + 2y = 6$

Solve the second equation for x.

$x = 6 - 2y$

Substitute the expression $6 - 2y$ for x in the first equation and solve for y.

$(6 - 2y)^2 + 4y^2 = 20$

$36 - 24y + 4y^2 + 4y^2 - 20 = 0$

$8y^2 - 24y + 16 = 0$

$y^2 - 3y + 2 = 0$

$(y - 2)(y - 1) = 0$

$y - 2 = 0 \quad \text{or} \quad y - 1 = 0$

$\quad y = 2 \quad \text{or} \quad\quad y = 1$

If $y = 2, x = 6 - 2(2) = 2$.

If $y = 1, x = 6 - 2(1) = 4$.

The solution set is $\{(2,2),(4,1)\}.$

35. Eliminate y by adding the equations.

$x^3 + y = 0$

$\underline{x^2 - y = 0}$

$x^3 + x^2 = 0$

$x^2(x + 1) = 0$

$x^2 = 0 \quad \text{or} \quad x + 1 = 0$

$\quad x = 0 \quad \text{or} \quad\quad x = -1$

If $x = 0$,

$(0)^3 + y = 0$

$\qquad y = 0$

If $x = -1$,

$(-1)^3 + y = 0$

$\qquad y = 1$

The solution set is $\{(0,0),(-1,1)\}.$

37. The substitution method is used here to solve the system.

$$x^2 + (y-2)^2 = 4$$
$$x^2 - 2y = 0$$

Solve the second equation for x^2.

$$x^2 = 2y$$

Substitute the expression $2y$ for x^2 in the first equation and solve for y.

$$2y + (y-2)^2 = 4$$
$$2y + y^2 - 4y + 4 = 4$$
$$y^2 - 2y = 0$$
$$y(y-2) = 0$$
$$y = 0 \quad \text{or} \quad y - 2 = 0$$
$$y = 2$$

If $y = 0$,
$$x^2 = 2(0)$$
$$x^2 = 0$$
$$x = 0$$

If $y = 2$,
$$x^2 = 2(2)$$
$$x^2 = 4$$
$$x = \pm 2$$

The solution set is $\{(0, 0), (-2, 2), (2, 2)\}$.

39. The substitution method is used here to solve the system.

$$y = (x+3)^2$$
$$x + 2y = -2$$

Solve the first equation for x.

$$x = -2y - 2$$

Substitute the expression $-2y-2$ for x in the first equation and solve for y.

$$y = (-2y - 2 + 3)^2 = (-2y + 1)^2$$
$$y = 4y^2 - 4y + 1$$
$$4y^2 - 5y + 1 = 0$$
$$(4y - 1)(y - 1) = 0$$
$$4y - 1 = 0 \quad \text{or} \quad y - 1 = 0$$
$$y = \frac{1}{4} \quad \text{or} \quad y = 1$$

If $y = \frac{1}{4}$, $x = -2\left(\frac{1}{4}\right) - 2 = -\frac{5}{2}$.

If $y = 1$, $x = -2(1) - 2 = -4$.

The solution set is $\left\{(-4, 1), \left(-\frac{5}{2}, \frac{1}{4}\right)\right\}$.

41. The substitution method is used here to solve the system.

$$x^2 + y^2 + 3y = 22$$
$$2x + y = -1$$

Solve the second equation for y.

$$y = -2x - 1$$

Substitute the expression $-2x-1$ for y in the first equation and solve for x.

$$x^2 + (-2x - 1)^2 + 3(-2x - 1) - 22 = 0$$
$$x^2 + 4x^2 + 4x + 1 - 6x - 3 - 22 = 0$$
$$5x^2 - 2x - 24 = 0$$
$$(5x - 12)(x + 2) = 0$$
$$5x - 12 = 0 \quad \text{or} \quad x + 2 = 0$$
$$x = \frac{12}{5} \quad \text{or} \quad x = -2$$

If $x = \frac{12}{5}$, $y = -2\left(\frac{12}{5}\right) - 1 = -\frac{29}{5}$.

If $x = -2$, $y = -2(-2) - 1 = 3$.

The solution set is $\left\{\left(\frac{12}{5}, -\frac{29}{5}\right), (-2, 3)\right\}$.

43. The substitution method is used here to solve the system.

$$x + y = 10$$
$$xy = 24$$

Solve the first equation for y.

$$y = 10 - x$$

Substitute the expression $10 - x$ for y in the second equation and solve for x.

$$x(10 - x) = 24$$
$$10x - x^2 = 24$$
$$x^2 - 10x + 24 = 0$$
$$(x - 4)(x - 6) = 0$$
$$x - 4 = 0 \quad \text{or} \quad x - 6 = 0$$
$$x = 4 \quad \text{or} \quad x = 6$$

If $x = 4$, $y = 10 - 4 = 6$.

If $x = 6$, $y = 10 - 6 = 4$.

The numbers are 4 and 6.

45. Eliminate the y^2–terms by adding the equations.

$$x^2 - y^2 = 3$$
$$2x^2 + y^2 = 9$$
$$3x^2 = 12$$
$$x^2 = 4$$
$$x = \pm 2$$

If $x = 2$,
$$2(2)^2 + y^2 = 9$$
$$y^2 = 1$$
$$y = \pm 1$$

If $x = -2$,
$$2(-2)^2 + y^2 = 9$$
$$y^2 = 1$$
$$y = \pm 1$$

The numbers are 2 and 1, 2 and –1, –2 and 1, or –2 and –1.

47. $2x^2 + xy = 6$
$x^2 + 2xy = 0$

Multiply the first equation by -2 and add the two equations.

$$-4x^2 - 2xy = -12$$
$$x^2 + 2xy = 0$$
$$-3x^2 = -12$$
$$x^2 = 4$$
$$x = \pm 2$$

Back-substitute these values for x in the second equation and solve for y.

For $x = -2$: $(-2)^2 + 2(-2)y = 0$
$$4 - 4y = 0$$
$$-4y = -4$$
$$y = 1$$

For $x = 2$: $(2)^2 + 2(2)y = 0$
$$4 + 4y = 0$$
$$4y = -4$$
$$y = -1$$

The solution set is $\{(-2,1),(2,-1)\}$.

49. $-4x + y = 12$
$y = x^3 + 3x^2$

Substitute $x^3 + 3x^2$ for y in the first equation and solve for x.
$$-4x + \left(x^3 + 3x^2\right) = 12$$
$$x^3 + 3x^2 - 4x - 12 = 0$$
$$x^2(x+3) - 4(x+3) = 0$$
$$(x+3)(x^2 - 4) = 0$$
$$(x+3)(x-2)(x+2) = 0$$
$$x = -3, \ x = 2, \text{ or } x = -2$$

Substitute these values for x in the second equation and solve for y.

For $x = -3$: $y = (-3)^3 + 3(-3)^2$
$$= -27 + 27$$
$$= 0$$

For $x = 2$: $y = (2)^3 + 3(2)^2$
$$= 8 + 12$$
$$= 20$$

For $x = -2$: $y = (-2)^3 + 3(-2)^2$
$$= -8 + 12$$
$$= 4$$

The solution set is $\{(-3,0),(2,20),(-2,4)\}$.

51.
$$\frac{3}{x^2} + \frac{1}{y^2} = 7$$
$$\frac{5}{x^2} - \frac{2}{y^2} = -3$$

Multiply the first equation by 2 and add the equations.

$$\frac{6}{x^2} + \frac{2}{y^2} = 14$$
$$\frac{5}{x^2} - \frac{2}{y^2} = -3$$
$$\frac{11}{x^2} = 11$$
$$x^2 = 1$$
$$x = \pm 1$$

Back-substitute these values for x in the first equation and solve for y.

For $x = -1$:   For $x = 1$:

$$\frac{3}{(-1)^2} + \frac{1}{y^2} = 7 \qquad \frac{3}{(1)^2} + \frac{1}{y^2} = 7$$

$$3 + \frac{1}{y^2} = 7 \qquad 3 + \frac{1}{y^2} = 7$$

$$\frac{1}{y^2} = 4 \qquad \frac{1}{y^2} = 4$$

$$y^2 = \frac{1}{4} \qquad y^2 = \frac{1}{4}$$

$$y = \pm \frac{1}{2} \qquad y = \pm \frac{1}{2}$$

The solution set is

$$\left\{ \left(-1, -\frac{1}{2}\right), \left(-1, \frac{1}{2}\right), \left(1, -\frac{1}{2}\right), \left(1, \frac{1}{2}\right) \right\}.$$

53.

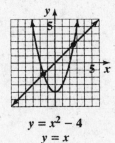

$$y = x^2 - 4$$
$$y = x$$

55. $16x^2 + 4y^2 = 64$
$$y = x^2 - 4$$

Substitute the expression $x^2 - 4$ for y in the first equation and solve for x.

$$16x^2 + 4\left(x^2 - 4\right)^2 = 64$$
$$16x^2 + 4\left(x^4 - 8x^2 + 16\right) = 64$$
$$16x^2 + 4x^4 - 32x^2 + 64 = 64$$
$$4x^4 - 16x^2 = 0$$
$$x^4 - 4x^2 = 0$$
$$x^2\left(x^2 - 4\right) = 0$$
$$x^2 = 0 \quad \text{or} \quad x^2 - 4 = 0$$
$$x = 0 \quad \text{or} \qquad x^2 = 4$$
$$x = \pm 2$$

If $x = 0$, $y = (0)^2 - 4 = -4$.

If $x = 2$, $y = (2)^2 - 4 = 0$.

If $x = -2$, $y = (-2)^2 - 4 = 0$.

It is possible for the comet to intersect the orbiting body at $(0, -4)$, $(-2, 0)$, $(2, 0)$.

57. $2L + 2W = 36$
$$LW = 77$$

Divide each term in the first equation by 2 and solve L.

$$L + W = 18$$
$$L = 18 - W$$

Substitute the expression $18 - W$ for L in the second equation and solve for W.

$$(18 - W)W = 77$$
$$18W - W^2 = 77$$
$$W^2 - 18W + 77 = 0$$
$$(W - 11)(W - 7) = 0$$
$$W - 11 = 0 \quad \text{or} \quad W - 7 = 0$$
$$W = 11 \quad \text{or} \qquad W = 7$$

If $W = 11$, $L = 18 - 11 = 7$.

If $W = 7$, $L = 18 - 7 = 11$.

The dimensions are 11 feet by 7 feet.

59. $L^2 + W^2 = 10^2 = 100$
$$LW = 48$$

Solve the second equation for L. $L = \dfrac{48}{W}$

Substitute the expression $\dfrac{48}{W}$ for L in the first equation and solve for W.

$$\left(\frac{48}{W}\right)^2 + W^2 = 100$$

$$\frac{2304}{W^2} + W^2 - 100 = 0$$

$$2304 + W^4 - 100W^2 = 0$$

$$W^4 - 100W^2 + 2304 = 0$$

$$\left(W^2 - 36\right)\left(W^2 - 64\right) = 0$$

$$W^2 - 36 = 0 \quad \text{or} \quad W^2 - 64 = 0$$
$$W^2 = 36 \quad \text{or} \qquad W^2 = 64$$
$$W = \pm 6 \quad \text{or} \qquad W = \pm 8$$

The width cannot be –6 or –8 inches.

If $W = 6$,
$$L = \frac{48}{6} = 8$$

If $W = 8$,
$$L = \frac{48}{8} = 6$$

The dimensions are 8 inches by 6 inches.

61.
$$x^2 - y^2 = 21$$
$$4x + 2y = 24$$
Divide each term in the second equation by 2 and solve for y.
$$2x + y = 12$$
$$y = 12 - 2x$$
Substitute the expression $12 - 2x$ for y in the first equation and solve for x.
$$x^2 - (12 - 2x)^2 = 21$$
$$x^2 - (144 - 48x + 4x^2) = 21$$
$$3x^2 - 48x + 165 = 0$$
$$x^2 - 16x + 55 = 0$$
$$(x - 5)(x - 11) = 0$$
$$x - 5 = 0 \quad \text{or} \quad x - 11 = 0$$
$$x = 5 \quad \text{or} \quad x = 11$$
If $x = 11$, $y = 12 - 2(11) = -10$.
If $x = 5$, $y = 12 - 2(5) = 2$.
The dimensions of the floor are 5 meters by 5 meters and the dimensions of the square that will accommodate the pool are 2 meters by 2 meters.

63. Substitute $-0.5x^2 + 5.8x + 185.8$ for y in the other equation.

$$5.4x - \overbrace{(-0.5x^2 + 5.8x + 185.8)}^{y} + 146.5 = 0$$
$$5.4x + 0.5x^2 - 5.8x - 185.8 + 146.5 = 0$$
$$0.5x^2 - 0.4x - 39.3 = 0$$
The quadratic formula gives $x = -8.47$ or $x = 9.27$. The negative value for x is rejected because the functions domain is after 1990. Back-substitute $x = 9.27$ into either equation to find y.
$$y = -0.5x^2 + 5.8x + 185.8$$
$$y = -0.5(9.27)^2 + 5.8(9.27) + 185.8$$
$$y \approx 196.58$$
This means that the function predicts that about 9 years after 1990, or 1999, men and women received the same number of science and engineering degrees. The graph shows that the actual time that this occurred was during 1999.

71. First determine the solution to the following system of equations.
$$xy = 20$$
$$x^2 + y^2 = 41$$
Solve the first equation for x.
$$x = \frac{20}{y}$$

Substitute the expression $\frac{20}{y}$ for x in the second equation and solve for in the second equation and solve for y.
$$\left(\frac{20}{y}\right)^2 + y^2 = 41$$
$$\frac{400}{y^2} + y^2 - 41 = 0$$
$$y^4 - 41y^2 + 400 = 0$$
$$(y^2 - 25)(y^2 - 16) = 0$$
$$y^2 - 25 = 0 \quad \text{or} \quad y^2 - 16 = 0$$
$$y^2 = 25 \quad \text{or} \quad y^2 = 16$$
$$y = \pm 5 \quad \text{or} \quad y = \pm 4$$
If $y = 5, x = \frac{20}{5} = 4$.

If $y = -5, x = \frac{20}{-5} = -4$.

If $y = 4, x = \frac{20}{4} = 5$.

If $y = -4, x = \frac{20}{-4} = -5$.

The rectangle formed by joining the points of intersection has sides a and b. The length of a is $\sqrt{(5-4)^2 + (4-5)^2} = \sqrt{2}$. The length of b is $\sqrt{(4-(-5))^2 + (5-(-4))^2} = 9\sqrt{2}$.
The area of the rectangle is
$$a \cdot b = (\sqrt{2})(9\sqrt{2}) = 18 \text{ square units.}$$

73.
$$\log_y x = 3$$
$$\log_y(4x) = 5$$
$$x = y^3$$
$$4x = y^5$$
Substitute y^3 for x in the equation $4x = y^5$ and solve for y.
$$4(y^3) = y^5$$
$$4 = y^2$$
$$y = \pm 2$$
Keep the positive base.
$$x = 2^3 = 8$$
The solution set is $\{(8, 2)\}$.

Mid-Chapter Check Point – Chapter 5

1.
$$x = 3y - 7$$
$$4x + 3y = 2$$

Since the first equation is solved for x already, we will use substitution.
Let $x = 3y - 7$ in the second equation and solve for y.

$$4(3y - 7) + 3y = 2$$
$$12y - 28 + 3y = 2$$
$$15y = 30$$
$$y = 2$$

Substitute this value for y in the first equation.
$$x = 3(2) - 7 = 6 - 7 = -1$$

The solution is $(-1, 2)$.

2.
$$3x + 4y = -5$$
$$2x - 3y = 8$$

Multiply the first equation by 3 and the second equation by 4, then add the equations.

$$9x + 12y = -15$$
$$\underline{8x - 12y = 32}$$
$$17x = 17$$
$$x = 1$$

Back-substitute to solve for y.

$$3x + 4y = -5$$
$$3(1) + 4y = -5$$
$$3 + 4y = -5$$
$$4y = -8$$
$$y = -2$$

The solution is $(1, -2)$.

3.
$$\frac{2x}{3} + \frac{y}{5} = 6$$
$$\frac{x}{6} - \frac{y}{2} = -4$$

Multiply the first equation by 15 and the second equation by 6 to eliminate the fractions.

$$15\left(\frac{2x}{3} + \frac{y}{5}\right) = 15(6)$$
$$10x + 3y = 90$$

$$6\left(\frac{x}{6} - \frac{y}{2}\right) = 6(-4)$$
$$x - 3y = -24$$

We now need to solve the equivalent system
$$10x + 3y = 90$$
$$x - 3y = -24$$

Add the two equations to eliminate y.
$$10x + 3y = 90$$
$$\underline{x - 3y = -24}$$
$$11x = 66$$
$$x = 6$$

Back-substitute to solve for y.
$$x - 3y = -24$$
$$6 - 3y = -24$$
$$-3y = -30$$
$$y = 10$$

The solution is $(6, 10)$.

4.
$$y = 4x - 5$$
$$8x - 2y = 10$$

Since the first equation is already solved for y, we will use substitution.
Let $y = 4x - 5$ in the second equation and solve for x.

$$8x - 2(4x - 5) = 10$$
$$8x - 8x + 10 = 10$$
$$10 = 10$$

This statement is an identity. The system is dependent so there are an infinite number of solutions. The solution set is $\{(x, y) \mid y = 4x - 5\}$.

5. $2x+5y=3$
$3x-2y=1$

Multiply the first equation by 3 and the second equation by -2, then add the equations.
$6x+15y=9$
$\underline{-6x+4y=-2}$
$19y=7$
$y=\dfrac{7}{19}$

Back-substitute to solve for x.
$2x+5y=3$
$2x+5\left(\dfrac{7}{19}\right)=3$
$2x+\dfrac{35}{19}=3$
$2x=\dfrac{22}{19}$
$x=\dfrac{11}{19}$

The solution is $\left(\dfrac{11}{19},\dfrac{7}{19}\right)$.

6. $\dfrac{x}{12}-y=\dfrac{1}{4}$
$4x-48y=16$

Solve the first equation for y.
$\dfrac{x}{12}-y=\dfrac{1}{4}$
$-y=-\dfrac{x}{12}+\dfrac{1}{4}$
$y=\dfrac{x}{12}-\dfrac{1}{4}$

Let $y=\dfrac{x}{12}-\dfrac{1}{4}$ in the second equation and solve for x.
$4x-48\left(\dfrac{x}{12}-\dfrac{1}{4}\right)=16$
$4x-4x+12=16$
$12=16$

This statement is a contradiction. The system is inconsistent so there is no solution. The solution is $\{\ \}$ or $\varnothing$.

7. $2x-y+2z=-8$
$x+2y-3z=9$
$3x-y-4z=3$

Multiply the first equation by 2 and add to the second equation.
$4x-2y+4z=-16$
$\underline{x+2y-3z=9}$
$5x+z=-7$

Multiply the first equation by -1 and add to the third equation.
$-2x+y-2z=8$
$\underline{3x-y-4z=3}$
$x-6z=11$

Use the two reduced equations to get the following system:
$5x+z=-7$
$x-6z=11$

Multiply the first equation by 6 and add to the second equation.
$30x+6z=-42$
$\underline{x-6z=11}$
$31x=-31$
$x=-1$

Back-substitute to solve for z.
$5x+z=-7$
$5(-1)+z=-7$
$-5+z=-7$
$z=-2$

Back-substitute to solve for y.
$2x-y+2z=-8$
$2(-1)-y+2(-2)=-8$
$-2-y-4=-8$
$-y=-2$
$y=2$

The solution is $(-1,2,-2)$.

8. $x\quad-3z=-5$
$2x-y+2z=16$
$7x-3y-5z=19$

Multiply the second equation by -3 and add to the third equation.
$-6x+3y-6z=-48$
$\underline{7x-3y-5z=19}$
$x-11z=-29$

Use this reduced equation and the original first equation to obtain the following system:

$$A+B=1$$
$$3B+C=4$$
$$4A+3C=-23$$

Solving the above system for A, B, and C, we find $A=-2$, $B=3$, and $C=-5$.

$$\frac{x^2+4x-23}{(x+3)(x^2+4)}=\frac{-2}{x+3}+\frac{3x-5}{x^2+4}$$

16. $$\frac{x^3}{(x^2+4)^2}=\frac{Ax+B}{x^2+4}+\frac{Cx+D}{(x^2+4)^2}$$

Multiply both sides of the equation by the least common denominator.

$$(x^2+4)^2\frac{x^3}{(x^2+4)^2}=(x^2+4)^2\left(\frac{Ax+B}{x^2+4}+\frac{Cx+D}{(x^2+4)^2}\right)$$

$$x^3=(x^2+4)(Ax+B)+(Cx+D)$$
$$x^3=x^3A+x^2B+4xA+4B+Cx+D$$
$$x^3=(A)x^3+(B)x^2+(4A+C)x+(4B+D)$$

Equate coefficients of like powers of x, and equate constant terms.

$$A=1$$
$$B=0$$
$$4A+C=0$$
$$4B+D=0$$

Since $A=1$ and $B=0$, we find that $C=-4$ and $D=0$ by substitution.

$$\frac{x^3}{(x^2+4)^2}=\frac{1x+0}{x^2+4}+\frac{-4x+0}{(x^2+4)^2}=\frac{x}{x^2+4}+\frac{-4x}{(x^2+4)^2}$$

17. **a.** $C(x)=400,000+20x$

b. $R(x)=100x$

c. $P(x)=R(x)-C(x)$
$$=100x-(400,000+20x)$$
$$=80x-400,000$$

d. The break even point is the point where cost and revenue are the same. We need to solve the system
$$y=400,000+20x$$
$$y=100x$$

Let $y=400,000+20x$ in the second equation and solve for x.

$$400,000+20x=100x$$
$$400,000=80x$$
$$5000=x$$

Back-substitute to solve for y.
$$y=100x$$
$$=100(5000)$$
$$=500,000$$

Thus, the break-even point is $(5000,\ 500,000)$. The company will break even when it produces and sells 5000 PDAs. At this level, the cost and revenue will both be $500,000.

18. Let x = the number of roses.
Let y = the number of carnations.

$$x + y = 20$$
$$3x + 1.5y = 39$$

Solve the first equation for x.

$$x + y = 20$$
$$x = 20 - y$$

Substitute this expression for x in the second equation and solve for y.

$$3(20 - y) + 1.5y = 39$$
$$60 - 3y + 1.5y = 39$$
$$-1.5y = -21$$
$$y = 14$$

Back-substitute to solve for x.

$$x = 20 - y = 20 - 14 = 6$$

There are 6 roses and 14 carnations in the bouquet.

19. Because the sum of the measures of the angles of any triangle is $180°$,
or
$$x + y + 90 = 180$$
$$x + y = 90.$$
Because the angle with measures x and $(3y + 20)$ are supplementary,
$$x + (3y + 20) = 180.$$
Simplify this equation.
$$x + 3y + 20 = 180$$
$$x + 3y = 160$$
We now have the system
$$x + y = 90$$
$$x + 3y = 160.$$
To solve this system by the addition method, multiply the first equation by -1 and add to the second equation.
$$-x - y = -90$$
$$\underline{x + 3y = 160}$$
$$2y = 70$$
$$y = 35$$
Back-substitute.
$$x + y = 90$$
$$x + 35 = 90$$
$$x = 55$$
Thus, $x = 55°$, $y = 35°$, and $(3y + 20) = 125°$.

20. Using the points $(-1, 0)$, $(1, 4)$, and $(2, 3)$ in the equation $y = ax^2 + bx + c$, we get the following system of equations:
$$a - b + c = 0$$
$$a + b + c = 4$$
$$4a + 2b + c = 3$$
Add the first two equations.
$$a - b + c = 0$$
$$\underline{a + b + c = 4}$$
$$2a + 2c = 4$$
Multiply the first equation by 2 and add to the third equation.
$$2a - 2b + 2c = 0$$
$$\underline{4a + 2b + c = 3}$$
$$6a + 3c = 3$$
Using the two reduced equations, we get the following system of equations:
$$2a + 2c = 4$$
$$6a + 3c = 3$$
Multiply the first equation by -3 and add to the second equation.
$$-6a - 6c = -12$$
$$\underline{6a + 3c = 3}$$
$$-3c = -9$$
$$c = 3$$
Back-substitute to solve for a.
$$2a + 2c = 4$$
$$2a + 2(3) = 4$$
$$2a + 6 = 4$$
$$2a = -2$$
$$a = -1$$
Back-substitute to solve for b.
$$a + b + c = 4$$
$$-1 + b + 3 = 4$$
$$b = 2$$
The equation is $y = -x^2 + 2x + 3$.

21. $2l + 2w = 21$
$lw = 20$

Solving $lw = 20$ for l gives $l = \dfrac{20}{w}$.

Substitute into the other equation:

$$2\overset{l}{\overbrace{\left(\frac{20}{w}\right)}} + 2w = 21$$

$$\frac{40}{w} + 2w = 21$$

$$w\left(\frac{40}{w} + 2w\right) = w(21)$$

$$40 + 2w^2 = 21w$$

$$2w^2 - 21w + 40 = 0$$

$$(2w - 5)(w - 8) = 0$$

$$w = \frac{5}{2} \text{ or } w = 8.$$

Back-substitute to find l.

When $w = \dfrac{5}{2}$, $l = \dfrac{20}{\frac{5}{2}} = 8$.

When $w = 8$, $l = \dfrac{20}{8} = \dfrac{5}{2}$.

The dimensions of the rectangle are $\dfrac{5}{2}$ m by 8 m.

Section 5.5

Check Point Exercises

1. $4x - 2y \geq 8$

Graph the equation $4x - 2y = 8$ as a solid line.
Choose a test point that is not on the line.

$\underline{\text{Test } (0,0)}$

$$4x - 2y \geq 8$$

$$4(0) - 2(0) \geq 8$$

$$0 \geq 8, \text{ false}$$

Since the statement is false, shade the other half-plane.

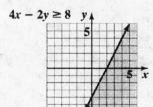

2. $y > -\dfrac{3}{4}x$

Graph the equation $y = -\dfrac{3}{4}x$ as a dashed line.

Choose a test point that is not on the line.

$\underline{\text{Test } (1,1)}$

$$y > -\frac{3}{4}x$$

$$1 > -\frac{3}{4}(1)$$

$$1 > -\frac{3}{4}, \text{ true}$$

Since the statement is true, shade the half-plane containing the point.

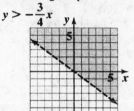

3. **a.** $y > 1$

Graph the equation $y = 1$ as a dashed line.
Choose a test point that is not on the line.

$\underline{\text{Test } (0,0)}$

$$y > 1$$

$$0 > 1, \text{ false}$$

Since the statement is false, shade the other half-plane.

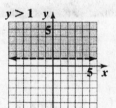

b.   Graph the equation $x = -2$ as a solid line.
Choose a test point that is not on the line.

Test $(0, 0)$

$x \le -2$

$0 \le -2$, false

Since the statement is false, shade the other half-plane.

$x \le -2$

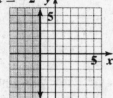

4.   Graph $x^2 + y^2 = 16$ as a solid circle with radius 4 and center (0, 0).

Test $(0, 0)$

$x^2 + y^2 \ge 16$

$(0)^2 + (0)^2 \ge 16$

$0 \ge 16$, false

Shade the region not containing (0, 0).

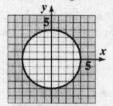

$x^2 + y^2 \ge 16$

5.   Graph the equation $x - 3y = 6$ as a dashed line.

Test $(0, 0)$

$x - 3y < 6$

$(0) - 3(0) < 6$

$0 < 6$, true

Since the statement is true, shade the half-plane containing the point.
Graph the equation $2x + 3y = -6$ as a solid line.

Test $(0, 0)$

$2x + 3y \ge -6$

$2(0) + 3(0) \ge -6$

$0 \ge -6$, true

Since the statement is true, shade the half-plane containing the point.
For the solution graph, place an open circle at the point of intersection and shade the region that satisfies both inequalities.

$x - 3y < 6$
$2x + 3y \ge -6$

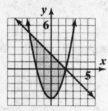

6.   Begin by graphing $y = x^2 - 4$ as a solid parabola with vertex (0, –4) and x-intercepts (–2, 0) and (2, 0). Since (0, 0) makes the inequality $y \ge x^2 - 4$ true, shade the region containing (0, 0). Graph $x + y = 2$ as a solid line by using its x-intercept, (2, 0), and its y-intercept (0, 2). Since (0, 0) makes the inequality $x + y \le 2$ true, shade the region containing (0, 0).

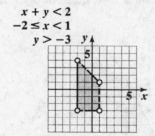

$y \ge x^2 - 4$
$x + y \le 2$

7.   Graph the lines $x + y = 2$, $x = 1$, and $y = -3$ with dashed lines.
Graph the line $x = -2$ with a solid line.
Test points indicate that the solution contains the region to the right of –2, to the left of 1, above –3, and below the line $x + y = 2$. The corner points are represented as open circles because none satisfy all three inequalities.

$x + y < 2$
$-2 \le x < 1$
$y > -3$

8. Test $T = 60$ and $P = 20$ in each inequality.

$T \geq 35$

$60 \geq 35$ True

$5T - 7P \geq 70$

$5(60) - 7(20) \geq 70$

$160 \geq 70$ True

$3T - 35P \leq -140$

$3(60) - 35(20) \leq -140$

$-520 \leq -140$ True

The point (60, 20) checks in all three equations.

Exercise Set 5.5

1. Graph $x + 2y = 8$ as a solid line using its
x-intercept, (8, 0), and its y-intercept, (0, 4).
Test (0, 0):
$0 + 2(0) \leq 8$?
$0 \leq 8$ true
Shade the half-plane containing (0, 0).

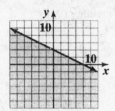

$x + 2y \leq 8$

3. Graph $x - 2y = 10$ as a dashed line using its x-intercept, (10, 0), and its y-intercept,
(0, –5).
Test (0, 0):
$0 - 2(0) > 10$?
$0 > 10$ false
Shade the half-plane not containing (0, 0).

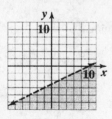

$x - 2y > 10$

5. Graph $y = \dfrac{1}{3}x$ as a solid line using its slope, $\dfrac{1}{3}$,
and its y-intercept (0, 0).
Test (1, 1):
$1 \leq \dfrac{1}{3}(1)$?
$1 \leq \dfrac{1}{3}$ false
Shade the half-plane not containing (1, 1).

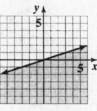

$y \leq \dfrac{1}{3}x$

7. Graph $y = 2x - 1$ as a dashed line using its
x-intercept, $\left(\dfrac{1}{2}, 0 \right)$ and its y-intercept,
(0, –1).
Test (0,0):
$0 > 2(0) - 1$?
$0 > -1$ true
Shade the half-plane containing (0, 0).

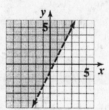

$y > 2x - 1$

9. Graph $x = 1$ as a solid vertical line.
Test (0, 0):
$0 \leq 1$ true
Shade the half-plane containing (0, 0).

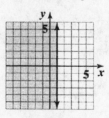

$x \leq 1$

11. Graph $y = 1$ as a dashed horizontal line.
Test $(0, 0)$:
$0 > 1$ false
Shade the half-plane not containing $(0, 0)$.

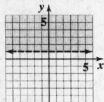

$$y > 1$$

13. Graph $x^2 + y^2 = 1$ as a solid circle with radius 1
and center $(0, 0)$.
Test $(0, 0)$:
$(0)^2 + (0)^2 \leq 1?$

$0 \leq 1$ true
Shade the region containing $(0, 0)$.

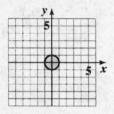

$$x^2 + y^2 \leq 1$$

15. Graph $x^2 + y^2 = 25$ as a dashed circle with
radius 5 and center $(0, 0)$.
Test $(0, 0)$:
$(0)^2 + (0)^2 > 25?$

$0 > 25$ false
Shade the region not containing $(0, 0)$.

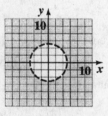

$$x^2 + y^2 > 25$$

17. Graph $(x - 2)^2 + (y + 1)^2 = 9$ as a dashed circle.
Test $(0, 0)$
$(x - 2)^2 + (y + 1)^2 < 9$
$(0 - 2)^2 + (0 + 1)^2 < 9$
$5 < 9,$ true
Shade the region containing $(0, 0)$.

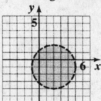

$$(x - 2)^2 + (y + 1)^2 < 9$$

19. Graph $y = x^2 - 1$ as a dashed parabola with
vertex $(0, -1)$ and x-intercepts $(1, 0)$ and
$(-1, 0)$.
Test $(0, 0)$:
$0 < (0)^2 - 1?$

$0 < -1$ false
Shade the region not containing $(0, 0)$.

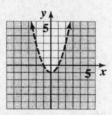

$$y < x^2 - 1$$

21. Graph $y = x^2 - 9$ as a solid parabola with vertex
$(0, -9)$ and x-intercepts $(3, 0)$ and
$(-3, 0)$.
Test $(0, 0)$:
$0 \geq (0)^2 - 9?$

$0 \geq -9$ true
Shade the region containing $(0, 0)$.

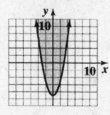

$$y \geq x^2 - 9$$

23. Graph $y = 2^x$ as a dashed exponential function with base 2 that passes through the point $(0, 1)$.
Test $(0, 0)$:

$0 > 2^0$?

$0 > 1$ false

Shade the region not containing $(0, 0)$.

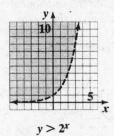

$$y > 2^x$$

25. Graph $y = \log_2(x + 1)$ as a solid logarithmic function.
Test $(0, 0)$:

$y \geq \log_2(x + 1)$

$0 \geq \log_2(0 + 1)$

$0 \geq 0$,   true

Shade the region containing $(0, 0)$.

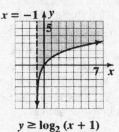

$$y \geq \log_2 (x + 1)$$

27. Begin by graphing $3x + 6y = 6$ as a solid line using its x-intercept, $(2, 0)$, and its y-intercept, $(0, 1)$. Since $(0, 0)$ makes the inequality $3x + 6y \leq 6$ true, shade the half-plane containing $(0, 0)$. Graph $2x + y = 8$ as a solid line using its x-intercept, $(4, 0)$, and its y-intercept, $(0, 8)$. Since $(0, 0)$ makes the inequality $2x + y \leq 8$ true, shade the half-plane containing $(0, 0)$. The solution set of the system is the intersection of the above shaded half-planes, and is shown as the shaded region in the following graph.

$3x + 6y \leq 6$
$2x + y \leq 8$

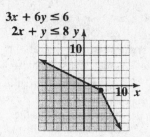

29. Begin by graphing $2x - 5y = 10$ as a solid line using its x-intercept, $(5, 0)$, and its y-intercept, $(0, -2)$. Since $(0, 0)$ makes the inequality $2x - 5y \leq 10$ true, shade the half-plane containing $(0, 0)$. Graph $3x - 2y = 6$ as a dashed line using its x-intercept, $(2, 0)$, and its y-intercept, $(0, -3)$. Since $(0, 0)$ makes the inequality $3x - 2y > 6$ false, shade the half-plane containing $(0, 0)$. The solution set of the system is the intersection of the above shaded half-planes, and is shown as the shaded region in the following graph.

$2x - 5y \leq 10$
$3x - 2y > 6$

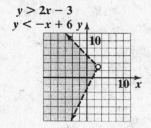

31. Begin by graphing $y = 2x - 3$ as a dashed line using its slope, 2, and its y-intercept, $(0, -3)$. Since $(0, 0)$ makes the inequality $y > 2x - 3$ true, shade the half-plane containing $(0, 0)$. Graph $y = -x + 6$ as a dashed line using its slope, -1, and its y-intercept, $(0, 6)$. Since $(0, 0)$ makes the inequality $y < -x + 6$ true, shade the half-plane containing $(0, 0)$. The solution set of the system is the intersection of the above shaded half-planes, and is shown as the shaded region in the following graph.

$y > 2x - 3$
$y < -x + 6$

393

33. Begin by graphing $x + 2y = 4$ as a solid line using its x-intercept, $(4, 0)$, and its y-intercept, $(0, 2)$. Since $(0, 0)$ makes the inequality $x + 2y \leq 4$ true, shade the half-plane containing $(0, 0)$. Graph $y = x - 3$ as a solid line using its slope, 1, and its y-intercept, $(0, -3)$. Since $(0, 0)$ makes the inequality $y \geq x - 3$ true, shade the half-plane containing $(0, 0)$. The solution set of the system is the intersection of the above shaded half-planes, and is shown as the shaded region in the following graph.

$$x + 2y \leq 4$$
$$y \geq x - 3$$

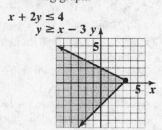

35. Begin by graphing $x = 2$ as a solid vertical line. Since $(0, 0)$ makes the inequality $x \leq 2$ true, shade the half-plane containing $(0, 0)$. Graph $y = 1$ as a solid horizontal line. Since $(0, 0)$ makes the inequality $y \geq -1$ true, shade the half-plane containing $(0, 0)$. The solution set of the system is the intersection of the above shaded half-planes, and is shown as the shaded region in the following graph.

$$x \leq 2$$
$$y \geq -1$$

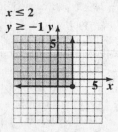

37. Graph $x = -2$ as a solid vertical line and $x = 5$ as a dashed vertical line. Since $(0, 0)$ makes the inequality $-2 \leq x < 5$ true, shade the region between the two lines.

$$-2 \leq x < 5$$

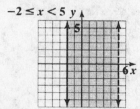

39. Begin by graphing $x - y = 1$ as a solid line using its x-intercept, $(1, 0)$, and its y-intercept $(0, -1)$. Since $(0, 0)$ makes the inequality $x - y \leq 1$ true, shade the half-plane containing $(0, 0)$. Graph $x = 2$ as a solid horizontal line. Since $(0, 0)$ makes the inequality $x \geq 2$ false, shade the half-plane not containing $(0, 0)$. The solution set of the system is the intersection of the above shaded half-planes, and is shown as the shaded region in the following graph.

$$x - y \leq 1$$
$$x \geq 2$$

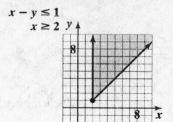

41.
$$x + y > 4$$
$$x + y < -1$$

Begin by graphing $x + y = 4$ as a dashed line using its x-intercept, $(4, 0)$, and its y-intercept $(0, 4)$. Since $(0, 0)$ makes the inequality $x + y > 4$ false, shade the half-plane not containing $(0, 0)$. Graph $x + y = -1$ as a dashed line using its x-intercept, $(-1, 0)$, and its y-intercept, $(0, -1)$. Since $(0, 0)$ makes the inequality $x + y < -1$ false, shade the half-plane not containing $(0, 0)$. Since these half-planes do not intersect the system has no solution.

43. Begin by graphing $x + y = 4$ as a dashed line using its x-intercept, $(4, 0)$, and its y-intercept, $(0, 4)$. Since $(0, 0)$ makes the inequality $x + y > 4$ false, shade the half-plane not containing $(0, 0)$. Graph $x + y = -1$ as a dashed line using its x-intercept, $(-1, 0)$, and its y-intercept, $(0, -1)$. Since $(0, 0)$ makes the inequality $x + y > -1$ true, shade the half-plane containing $(0, 0)$. The solution set of the system is the intersection of the above half-planes, and is shown as the shaded region in the following graph.

$$x + y > 4$$
$$x + y > -1$$

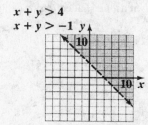

394

45. Begin by graphing $y = x^2 - 1$ as a solid parabola with vertex $(0, -1)$ and x-intercepts, $(-1, 0)$, and $(1, 0)$. Since $(0, 0)$ makes the inequality $y \geq x^2 - 1$ true, shade the half-plane containing $(0, 0)$. Graph $x - y = -1$ as a solid line using its x-intercept, $(-1, 0)$, and its y-intercept, $(0, 1)$. Since $(0, 0)$ makes the inequality $x - y \geq -1$ true, shade the half-plane containing $(0, 0)$. The solution set of the system is the intersection of the above half-planes, and is shown as the shaded region in the following graph.

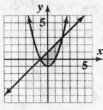

$$y \geq x^2 - 1$$
$$x - y \geq -1$$

47. Begin by graphing $x^2 + y^2 = 16$ as a solid circle with radius 4 and center, $(0, 0)$. Since $(0, 0)$ makes the inequality $x^2 + y^2 \leq 16$ true, shade the half-plane containing $(0, 0)$. Graph $x + y = 2$ as a dashed line using its x-intercept, $(2, 0)$, and its y-intercept, $(0, 2)$. Since $(0, 0)$ makes the inequality $x + y > 2$ false, shade the half-plane not containing $(0, 0)$. The solution set of the system is the intersection of the above half-planes, and is shown as the shaded region in the following graph.

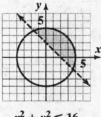

$$x^2 + y^2 \leq 16$$
$$x + y > 2$$

49. Begin by graphing $x^2 + y^2 = 1$ as a dashed circle with radius 1 and center, $(0, 0)$. Since $(0, 0)$ makes the inequality $x^2 + y^2 > 1$ false, shade the half-plane not containing $(0, 0)$. Graph $x^2 + y^2 = 4$ as a dashed circle with radius 2 and center $(0, 0)$. Since $(0, 0)$ makes the inequality $x^2 + y^2 < 4$ true, shade the half-plane containing $(0, 0)$. The solution set of the system is the intersection of the above half-planes, and is shown as the shaded region in the following graph.

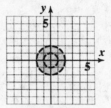

$$x^2 + y^2 > 1$$
$$x^2 + y^2 < 4$$

51.

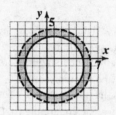

$$(x - 1)^2 + (y + 1)^2 < 25$$
$$(x - 1) + (y + 1)^2 \geq 16$$

53.

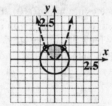

$$x^2 + y^2 \leq 1$$
$$y - x^2 > 0$$

55.

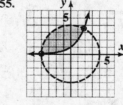

$$x^2 + y^2 < 16$$
$$y \geq 2^x$$

57. Begin by graphing $x - y = 2$ as a solid line using its x-intercept, (2, 0), and its y-intercept, (0, –2). Since (0, 0) makes the inequality $x - y \leq 2$ true, shade the half-plane containing (0, 0). Graph $x = -2$ as a solid vertical line. Since (0, 0) makes the inequality $x \geq -2$ true, shade the half-plane containing (0, 0). Graph $y = 3$ as a solid horizontal line. Since (0, 0) makes the inequality $y \leq 3$ true, shade the half-plane containing (0, 0). The solution set of the system is the intersection of the above half-planes, and is shown as the shaded region in the following graph.

$x - y \leq 2$
$\quad x > -2$
$\quad y \leq 3$

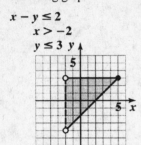

59. Since $x \geq 0$ and $y \geq 0$ the solution to the system lies in the first quadrant. Graph $2x + 5y = 10$ as a solid line using its x-intercept, (5, 0), and its y-intercept, (0, 2). Since (0, 0) makes the inequality $2x + 5y \leq 10$ true, shade the half-plane containing (0, 0). Graph $3x + 4y = 12$ as a solid line by using its x-intercept, (4, 0), and its y-intercept, (0, 3). Since (0, 0) makes the inequality $3x + 4y \leq 12$ true, shade the half-plane containing (0, 0). The solution set of the system is the intersection of the above half-planes which lies in the first quadrant, and is shown as the shaded region in the following graph.

$\quad\quad x \geq 0$
$\quad\quad y \geq 0$
$2x + 5y < 10$
$3x + 4y \leq 12$

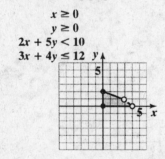

61. Begin by graphing $3x + y = 6$ as a solid line using its x-intercept, (2, 0), and its y-intercept, (0, 6). Since (0, 0) makes the inequality $3x + y \leq 6$ true, shade the half-plane containing (0, 0). Graph $2x - y = -1$ as a solid line using its x-intercept, $\left(-\dfrac{1}{2}, 0\right)$, and its y-intercept, (0, 1). Since (0, 0) makes the inequality $2x - y \leq -1$ false, shade the half-plane not containing (0, 0). Graph $x = -2$ as a solid vertical line. Since (0, 0) makes the inequality $x \geq -2$ true, shade the half-plane containing (0, 0). Graph $y = 4$ as a solid horizontal line. Since (0, 0) makes the inequality $y \leq 4$ true, shade the half-plane containing (0, 0). The solution set of the system is the intersection of the above half-planes, and is shown as the shaded region in the following graph.

$3x + y \leq 6$
$2x - y \leq -1$
$\quad\quad x > -2$
$\quad\quad y < 4$

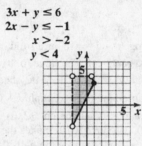

63. $y \geq -2x + 4$

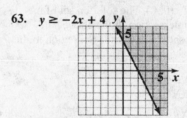

65. $x + y \leq 4$
$3x + y \leq 6$

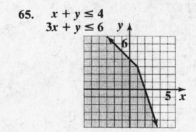

67.

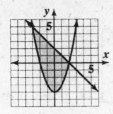

$$x + y \le 2$$
$$y \ge x^2 - 4$$

69. $-2 \le x \le 2$
$-3 \le y \le 3$

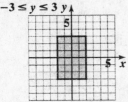

71. Find the union of solutions of
$$y > \frac{3}{2}x - 2 \text{ and } y < 4.$$

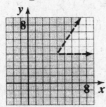

73. The system $\begin{array}{c} 3x + 3y < 9 \\ 3x + 3y > 9 \end{array}$ has no solution.

The number $3x + 3y$ cannot both be less than 9 and greater than 9 at the same time.

75. The system has an infinite number of solutions. The solution is the set of points that make up the circle $(x + 4)^2 + (y - 3)^2 = 9$

77. **a.** The coordinates of point A are $(20, 150)$.

This means that a 20 year-old person with a pulse rate of 150 beats per minute falls within the target zone.

b. $10 \le a \le 70$
$10 \le 20 \le 70$
    True
$150 \ge 0.7(220 - 20)$
    True
$150 \le 0.8(220 - 20)$
    True

Since point *A* makes all three inequalities true, it is a solution of the system.

79. $10 \le a \le 70$
$H \ge 0.6(220 - a)$
$H \le 0.7(220 - a)$

81. **a.** $50x + 150y > 2000$

b. Graph $50x + 150y$ as a dashed line using its *x*-intercept, (40, 0), and its *y*-intercept, $\left(0, \dfrac{40}{3}\right)$.

Test (0, 0):
$50(0) + 150(0) > 2000?$
$\qquad\qquad 0 > 2000$ false
Shade the half-plane not containing (0, 0).

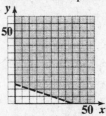

$$50x + 150y > 2000$$

c. Ordered pairs may vary.

83. **a.** $y \ge 0$
$x + y \ge 5$
$x \ge 1$
$200x + 100y \le 700$

b. $y \ge 0$
$x + y \ge 5$
$x \ge 1$
$200x + 100y \le 700$

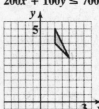

c. 2 nights

85. **a.** $\text{BMI} = \dfrac{703W}{H^2} = \dfrac{703(200)}{72^2} \approx 27.1$

b. A 20 year old man with a BMI of 27.1 is classified as overweight.

97.

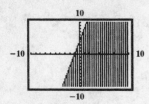

99. $y \geq x^2 - 4$

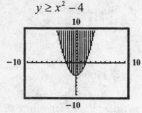

101. $2x + y \leq 6$

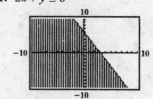

107. $y > x - 3$

   $y \leq x$

109. $x + 2y \leq 6$ or $2x + y \leq 6$

111. $y \geq nx + b$ $(n < 0,\ b > 0)$

   $y \leq mx + b$ $(m > 0,\ b > 0)$

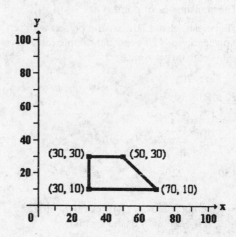

Section 5.6

Check Point Exercises

1. The total profit is 25 times the number of bookshelves, x, plus 55 times the number of desks, y. The objective function is $z = 25x + 55y$

2. Not more than a total of 80 bookshelves and desks can be manufactured per day. This is represented by the inequality $x + y \leq 80$.

3. Objective function: $z = 25x + 55y$
    Constraints: $x + y \leq 80$
    $\qquad\qquad 30 \leq x \leq 80$
    $\qquad\qquad 10 \leq y \leq 30$

4. Graph the constraints and find the corners, or vertices, of the region of intersection.

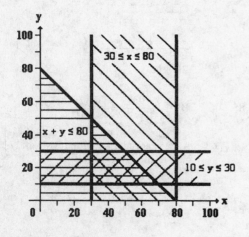

Find the value of the objective function at each corner of the graphed region.

Corner (x, y)	Objective Function $z = 25x + 55y$ z
(30, 10)	$z = 25(30) + 55(10)$ $= 750 + 550 = 1300$
(30, 30)	$z = 25(30) + 55(30)$ $= 750 + 1650 = 2400$
(50, 30)	$z = 25(50) + 55(30)$ $= 1250 + 1650 = 2900 \leftarrow$ Maximum
(70, 10)	$z = 25(70) + 55(10)$ $= 1750 + 550 = 2300$

The maximum value of z is 2900 and it occurs at the point (50, 30).
In order to maximize profit, 50 bookshelves and 30 desks must be produced each day for a profit of $2900.

Exercise Set 5.6

5. objective function: $z = 3x + 5y$
    constraints: $x \geq 0, \ y \geq 0$
    $$x + y \geq 1$$
    $$x + y \leq 6$$

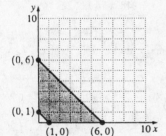

Evaluate the objective function at the four vertices of the region shown:

$(1, 0): 3(1) + 5(0) = 3$

$(0, 1): 3(0) + 5(1) = 5$

$(0, 6): 3(0) + 5(6) = 30$

$(6, 0): 3(6) + 5(0) = 18$

The maximum value of z is 30 and this occurs when $x = 0$ and $y = 6$.

1. $z = 5x + 6y$
    (1, 2): $5(1) + 6(2) = 5 + 12 = 17$
    (2, 10): $5(2) + 6(10) = 10 + 60 = 70$
    (7, 5): $5(7) + 6(5) = 35 + 30 = 65$
    (8, 3): $5(8) + 6(3) = 40 + 18 = 58$
    The maximum value is $z = 70$; the minimum value is $z = 17$.

3. $z = 40x + 50y$
    (0, 0): $40(0) + 50(0) = 0 + 0 = 0$
    (0, 8): $40(0) + 50(8) = 0 + 400 = 400$
    (4, 9): $40(4) + 50(9) = 160 + 450 = 610$
    (8, 0): $40(8) + 50(0) = 320 + 0 = 320$
    The maximum value is $z = 610$; the minimum value is $z = 0$.

5. $z = 3x + 2y$
    $x \geq 0, y \geq 0$
    $2x + y \leq 8$
    $x + y \geq 4$

    a.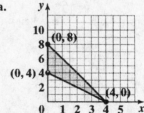

    b. $(0, 8): z = 3(0) + 2(8) = 16$
        $(0, 4): z = 3(0) + 2(4) = 8$
        $(4, 0): z = 3(4) + 2(0) = 12$

    c. The maximum value is 16 at $x = 0$ and $y = 8$.

399

7. $z = 4x + y$
    $x \ge 0, y \ge 0$
    $2x + 3y \le 12$
    $x + y \ge 3$

    a.
    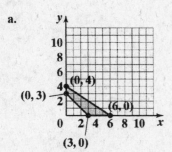

    b. $(0, 4)$: $z = 4(0) + 4 = 4$
        $(0, 3)$: $z = 4(0) + 3 = 3$
        $(3, 0)$: $z = 4(3) + 0 = 12$
        $(6, 0)$: $z = 4(6) + 0 = 24$

    c. The maximum value is 24 at $x = 6$ and $y = 0$.

9. $z = 3x - 2y$
    $1 \le x \le 5$
    $y \ge 2$
    $x - y \ge -3$

    a.
    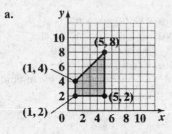

    b. $(1, 2)$: $z = 3(1) - 2(2) = -1$
        $(1, 4)$: $z = 3(1) - 2(4) = -5$
        $(5, 8)$: $z = 3(5) - 2(8) = -1$
        $(5, 2)$: $z = 3(5) - 2(2) = 11$

    c. Maximum value is 11 at $x = 5$ and $y = 2$.

11. $z = 4x + 2y$
    $x \ge 0, y \ge 0$
    $2x + 3y \le 12$
    $3x + 2y \le 12$
    $x + y \ge 2$

    a.
    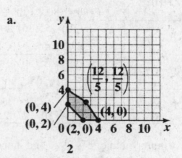

    b. $(0, 4)$: $z = 4(0) + 2(4) = 8$
        $(0, 2)$: $z = 4(0) + 2(2) = 4$
        $(2, 0)$: $z = 4(2) + 2(0) = 8$
        $(4, 0)$: $z = 4(4) + 2(0) = 16$
        $\left(\dfrac{12}{5}, \dfrac{12}{5}\right)$: $z = 4\left(\dfrac{12}{5}\right) + 2\left(\dfrac{12}{5}\right)$
        $\qquad = \dfrac{48}{5} + \dfrac{24}{5} = \dfrac{72}{5}$

    c. The maximum value is 16 at $x = 4$ and $y = 0$.

13. $z = 10x + 12y$
    $x \ge 0, y \ge 0$
    $x + y \le 7$
    $2x + y \le 10$
    $2x + 3y \le 18$

    a.
    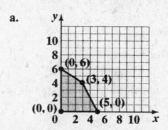

    b. $(0, 6)$: $z = 10(0) + 12(6) = 72$
        $(0, 0)$: $z = 10(0) + 12(0) = 0$
        $(5, 0)$: $z = 10(5) + 12(0) = 50$
        $(3, 4)$: $z = 10(3) + 12(4)$
        $\qquad = 30 + 48 = 78$

    c. The maximum value is 78 at $x = 3$ and $y = 4$.

15. **a.** $z = 125x + 200y$

b. $x \le 450$
$y \le 200$
$600x + 900y \le 360,000$

c. Simplify the third inequality by dividing by 300 to get $2x + 3y \le 1200$.

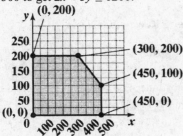

d. $(0, 0)$: $125(0) + 200(0) = 0 + 0 = 0$
$(0, 200)$: $125(0) + 200(200)$
$\qquad = 0 + 40,000 = 40,000$
$(300, 200)$: $125(300) + 200(200)$
$\qquad = 37,500 + 40,000 = 77,500$
$(450, 100)$: $125(450) + 200(100)$
$\qquad = 56,250 + 20,000 = 76,250$
$(450, 0)$: $125(450) + 200(0)$
$\qquad = 56,250 + 0 = 56,250$

e. The television manufacturer will make the greatest profit by manufacturing 300 console televisions each month and 200 wide-screen televisions each month. The maximum monthly profit is $77,500.

17. Let x = number of model A bicycles and y = number of model B bicycles.
The constraints are
$5x + 4y \le 200$
$2x + 3y \le 108$
Graph these inequalities in the first quadrant, since x and y cannot be negative.

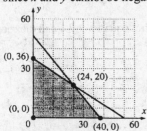

The quantity to be maximized is the profit, which is $25x + 15y$.
$(0, 0)$: $25(0) + 15(0) = 0 + 0 = 0$
$(0, 36)$: $25(0) + 15(36) = 0 + 540 = 540$
$(24, 20)$: $25(24) + 15(20) = 600 + 300 = 900$
$(40, 0)$: $25(40) + 15(0) = 1000 + 0 = 1000$

40 model A bicycles and no model B bicycles should be produced.

19. Let x = the number of cartons of food and y = the number of cartons of clothing.
The constraints are:
$20x + 10y \le 8,000$ or $2x + y \le 8000$
$50x + 20y \le 19,000$ or $5x + 2y \le 1900$
Graph these inequalities in the first quadrant, since x and y cannot be negative.

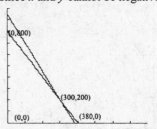

The quantity to be maximized is the number of people helped, which is $12x + 5y$.
$(0, 0)$: $12(0) + 5(0) = 0 + 0 = 0$
$(0, 800)$: $12(0) + 5(800) = 0 + 4000 = 4000$
$(300, 200)$: $12(300) + 5(200) = 4600$
$(380, 0)$: $12(380) + 5(0) = 4500$
300 cartons of food and 200 cartons of clothing should be shipped. This will help 4600 people.

21. Let x = number of students attending and y = number of parents attending.
The constraints are
$x + y \le 150$
$\quad 2x \ge y$
or
$x + y \le 150$
$2x - y \ge 0$
Graph these inequalities in the first quadrant, since x and y cannot be negative.

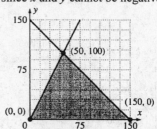

The quantity to be maximized is the amount of money raised, which is $x + 2y$.
$(0, 0)$: $0 + 2(0) = 0 + 0 = 0$
$(50, 100)$: $50 + 2(100) = 50 + 200 = 250$
$(150, 0)$: $150 + 2(0) = 150 + 0 = 150$
50 students and 100 parents should attend.

23. Let x = number of Boeing 727s, y = number of Falcon 20s.
Maximize $z = x + y$ with the following constraints:
$1400x + 500y \le 35,000$ or $14x + 5y \le 350$
$42,000x + 6000y \ge 672,000$ or $7x + y \ge 112$
$x \le 20$
$x \ge 0, y \ge 0$

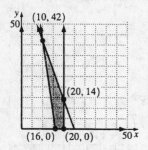

$(16,0): z = 16$

$(20,0): z = 20$

$(20,14): z = 34$

$(10,42): z = 52$

Federal Express should have purchased 10 Boeing 727s and 42 Falcon 20s.

29. Let x = amount invested in stocks and y = amount invested in bonds.
The constraints are:
$x + y \le 10,000$
$\quad y \ge 3000$
$\quad x \ge 2000$
$\quad y \ge x$
Graph these inequalities in the first quadrant, since x and y cannot be negative.

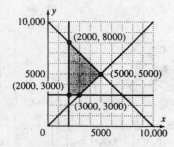

The quantity to be maximized is the return on the investment, which is $0.12x + 0.08y$.
(2000, 3000):
$0.12(2000) + 0.08(3000) = 240 + 240 = 480$
(2000, 8000):
$0.12(2000) + 0.08(8000) = 240 + 640 = 880$

(5000, 5000):
$0.12(5000) + 0.08(5000) = 600 + 400 = 1000$
(3000, 3000):
$0.12(3000) + 0.08(3000) = 360 + 240 = 600$
The greatest return occurs when \$5000 is invested in stocks and \$5000 is invested in bonds.

Chapter 5 Review Exercises

1.
$$y = 4x + 1$$
$$3x + 2y = 13$$
Substitute $4x + 1$ for y in the second equation:
$$3x + 2(4x + 1) = 13$$
$$3x + 8x + 2 = 13$$
$$11x = 11$$
$$x = 1$$
$$y = 4(1) + 1 = 5$$
The solution set is $\{(1,5)\}$.

2. $x + 4y = 14$
$2x - y = 1$
Multiply the second equation by 4 and add to the first equation.
$$x + 4y = 14$$
$$\underline{8x - 4y = 4}$$
$$9x = 18$$
$$x = 2$$
$$2(2) - y = 1$$
$$-y = -3$$
$$y = 3$$
The solution set is $\{(2,3)\}$.

3. $5x + 3y = 1$
$3x + 4y = -6$
Multiply the first equation by 4 and the second equation by -3.
Then add.
$$20x + 12y = 4$$
$$\underline{-9x - 12y = 18}$$
$$11x = 22$$
$$x = 2$$
$$5(2) + 3y = 1$$
$$3y = -9$$
$$y = -3$$
The solution set is $\{(2,-3)\}$.

4. $2y - 6x = 7$
$3x - y = 9$
The second equation can be written as $y = 3x - 9$.
Substitute:
$2(3x - 9) - 6x = 7$
$6x - 18 - 6x = 7$
$-18 = 7$
Since this is false, the system has no solution. The solution set is the empty set, $\varnothing$.

5. $4x - 8y = 16$
$3x - 6y = 12$
Divide the first equation by 4 and the second equation by 3.
$x - 2y = 4$
$x - 2y = 4$
Since these equations are identical, the system has an infinite number of solutions.
The solution set is $\{(x, y) \mid 3x - 6y = 12\}$.

6. a. $C(x) = 60,000 + 200x$

b. $R(x) = 450x$

c. $450x = 60000 + 200x$
$250x = 60000$
$x = 240$
$450(240) = 108,000$
The company must make 240 desks at a cost of \$108,000 to break even.

7. Let x = the number of years of healthy life expectancy of people in Japan.
Let y = the number of years of healthy life expectancy of people in Switzerland.

The system to solve is
$x + y = 146.4$
$x - y = 0.8$
Add the two equations:
$x + y = 146.4$
$\underline{x - y = 0.8}$
$2x = 147.2$
$x = 73.6$
Back substitute to find y:
$x + y = 146.4$
$73.6 + y = 146.4$
$y = 72.8$
The number of years of healthy life expectancy in Japan is 73.6 years and in Switzerland is 72.8 years.

8. Let l = the length of the table
Let w = the width of the table
$2l + 2w = 34$
$4l - 3w = 33$
Multiply the first equation by –2 and solve by addition.
$-4l - 4w = -68$
$\underline{4l - 3w = 33}$
$-7w = -35$
$w = 5$
Back-substitute 5 for w to find l.
$2l + 2w = 34$
$2l + 2(5) = 34$
$2l + 10 = 34$
$2l = 24$
$l = 12$
The dimensions of the table are 12 feet by 5 feet.

9. Let x = the cost of the hotel
y = the cost of the car
$3x + 2y = 360$
$4x + 3y = 500$
Solve the system.
$12x + 8y = 1440$
$\underline{-12x - 9y = -1500}$
$-y = -60$
$y = 60$

$3x + 2(60) = 360$
$3x = 240$
$x = 80$
The room costs \$80 a day and the car rents for \$60 a day.

10. x = number of apples
y = number of avocados
$100x + 350y = 1000$
$24x + 14y = 100$
$100x + 350y = 1000$
$\underline{-600x - 350y = -2500}$
$-500x = -1500$
$x = 3$
$100(3) + 350y = 1000$
$350y = 700$
$y = 2$
3 apples and 2 avocados supply 1000 calories and 100 grams of carbohydrates.

11. $2x - y + z = 1\,(1)$
$3x - 3y + 4z = 5\,(2)$
$4x - 2y + 3z = 4\,(3)$
Eliminate y from (1) and (2) by multiplying (1)
by -3 and adding the result to (2).
$-6x + 3y - 3z = -3$
$\underline{3x - 3y + 4z = 5}$
$-3x + z = 2$ (4)

Eliminate y from (1) and (3) by multiplying (1)
by -2 and adding the result to (3).
$-4x + 2y - 2z = -2$
$\underline{4x - 2y + 3z = 4}$
$z = 2$

Substituting $z = 2$ into (4), we get:
$-3x + 2 = 2$
$-3x = 0$
$x = 0$
Substituting $x = 0$ and $z = 2$ into (1), we have:
$2(0) - y + 2 = 1$
$-y = -1$
$y = 1$
The solution set is $\{(0, 1, 2)\}$.

12. $x + 2y - z = 5$ (1)
$2x - y + 3z = 0$ (2)
$2y + z = 1$ (3)
Eliminate x from (1) and (2) by multiplying (1)
by -2 and adding the result to (2).
$-2x - 4y + 2z = -10$
$\underline{2x - y + 3z = 0}$
$-5y + 5z = -10$
$y - z = 2$ (4)

Adding (3) and (4), we get:
$2y + z = 1$
$\underline{y - z = 2}$
$3y = 3$
$y = 1$
Substituting $y = 1$ into (3), we have:
$2(1) + z = 1$
$z = -1$
Substituting $y = 1$ and $z = -1$ into (1), we obtain:
$x + 2(1) - (-1) = 5$
$x + 3 = 5$
$x = 2$
The solution set is $\{(2, 1, -1)\}$.

13. $y = ax^2 + bx + c$

$(1,4): 4 = a + b + c$ (1)
$(3,20): 20 = 9a + 3b + c$ (2)
$(-2,25): 25 = 4a - 2b + c$ (3)

Multiply (1) by -1 and add to (2).
$20 = 9a + 3b + c$
$\underline{-4 = -a - b - c}$
$16 = 8a + 2b$
$8 = 4a + b$

$8 = 4a + b$ (4)
Multiply (1) by -1 and add to (3).
$25 = 4a - 2b + c$
$\underline{-4 = -a - b - c}$
$21 = 3a - 3b$

$7 = a - b$ (5)
Add (4) and (5).
$8 = 4a + b$
$\underline{7 = a - b}$
$15 = 5a$

$a = 3$

$8 = 4(3) + b$
$b = -4$

$3 - 4 + c = 4$
$c = 5$
Hence, the quadratic function is
$y = 3x^2 - 4x + 5$.

14.   **a.** $(0, 3.5)\ (15, 5.0)\ (33, 3.8)$

b.   Substitute point values into the equation
$y = ax^2 + bx + c$.
$3.5 = a(0)^2 + b(0) + c$
$3.5 = c$

$5.0 = a(15)^2 + b(15) + c$
$5.0 = 225a + 15b + c$

$3.8 = a(33)^2 + b(33) + c$
$3.8 = 1089a + 33b + c$

15. Model the given information as a system of equations.

$x - (y + z) = 48$

or $x - y - z = 48$ Equation 1

$x - 3z = 9$ Equation 2

$x + y + z = 246$ Equation 3

Add equation 1 and 3 and solve for x.

$x - y - z = 48$

$\underline{x + y + z = 246}$

$2x = 294$

$x = 147$

Back-substitute into equation 2 to find z.

$x - 3z = 9$

$147 - 3z = 9$

$-3z = -138$

$z = 46$

Back-substitute into equation 3 to find y.

$147 + y + 46 = 246$

$y = 53$

The registrations for Labs was 147 thousand, for Golden retrievers 53 thousand, and for German shepherds 46 thousand.

16. $\dfrac{x}{(x-3)(x+2)} = \dfrac{A}{x-3} + \dfrac{B}{x+2}$

$x = A(x+2) + B(x-3)$

$= (A+B)x + (2A - 3B)$

$A + B = 1$

$2A - 3B = 0$

Multiply first equation by 3, then add to second equation.

$3A + 3B = 3$

$\underline{2A - 3B = 0}$

$5A = 3$

$A = \dfrac{3}{5}, \ B = \dfrac{2}{5}$

$\dfrac{x}{(x-3)(x+2)} = \dfrac{3}{5(x-3)} + \dfrac{2}{5(x+2)}$

17. $\dfrac{11x-2}{x^2 - x - 12} = \dfrac{11x-2}{(x-4)(x+3)} = \dfrac{A}{x-4} + \dfrac{B}{x+3}$

$11x - 2 = A(x+3) + B(x-4)$

$= Ax + 3A + Bx - 4B$

$= (A+B)x + (3A - 4B)$

$A + B = 11$

$3A - 4B = -2$

Multiply first equation by 4, then add to second

equation.

$3A - 4B = -2$

$\underline{4A + 4B = 44}$

$7A = 42$

$A = 6, \ B = 5$

$\dfrac{11x-2}{x^2 - x - 12} = \dfrac{6}{x-4} + \dfrac{5}{x+3}$

18. $\dfrac{4x^2 - 3x - 4}{x^3 + x^2 - 2x} = \dfrac{4x^2 - 3x - 4}{x(x+2)(x-1)}$

$= \dfrac{A}{x} + \dfrac{B}{x+2} + \dfrac{C}{x-1}$

$4x^2 - 3x - 4 = A(x+2)(x-1) + Bx(x-1) + Cx(x+2)$

$= A(x^2 + x - 2) + Bx^2 - Bx + Cx^2 + 2Cx$

$= Ax^2 + Ax - 2A + Bx^2 - Bx + Cx^2 + 2Cx$

$= (A+B+C)x^2 + (A - B + 2C)x - 2A$

$A + B + C = 4$

$A - B + 2C = -3$

$-2A = -4$

$A = 2$

$B + C = 2$

$-B + 2C = -5$

$3C = -3$

$C = -1$

$B - 1 = 2$

$B = 3$

$\dfrac{4x^2 - 3x - 4}{x^3 + x^2 - 2x} = \dfrac{2}{x} + \dfrac{3}{x+2} - \dfrac{1}{x-1}$

19. $\dfrac{2x+1}{(x-2)^2} = \dfrac{A}{x-2} + \dfrac{B}{(x-2)^2}$

$2x + 1 = A(x-2) + B = Ax - 2A + B$

$A = 2$

$-2A + B = 1$

$-2(2) + B = 1$

$B = 5$

$\dfrac{2x+1}{(x-2)^2} = \dfrac{2}{x-2} + \dfrac{5}{(x-2)^2}$

20. $\dfrac{2x-6}{(x-1)(x-2)^2} = \dfrac{A}{x-1} + \dfrac{B}{x-2} + \dfrac{C}{(x-2)^2}$

$2x-6 = A(x-2)^2 + B(x-1)(x-2) + C(x-1)$

$\qquad = A(x^2-4x+4) + B(x^2-3x+2) + C(x-1)$

$\qquad = Ax^2 - 4Ax + 4A + Bx^2 - 3Bx + 2B + Cx - C$

$\qquad = (A+B)x^2 + (-4A-3B+C)x + (4A+2B-C)$

$\quad A+B = 0$

$-4A - 3B + C = 2$

$\underline{\ 4A + 2B - C = -6\ }$

$\qquad -B = -4$

$\qquad\quad B = 4$

$\qquad\quad\ \ A = -4$

$4(-4) + 2(4) - C = -6$

$\quad -16 + 8 - C = -6$

$\qquad\quad -C - 8 = -6$

$\qquad\qquad -C = 2$

$\qquad\qquad\ \ C = -2$

$\dfrac{2x-6}{(x-1)(x-2)^2} = -\dfrac{4}{x-1} + \dfrac{4}{x-2} - \dfrac{2}{(x-2)^2}$

21. $\dfrac{3x}{(x-2)(x^2+1)} = \dfrac{A}{x-2} + \dfrac{Bx+C}{x^2+1}$

$3x = A(x^2+1) + (Bx+C)(x-2)$

$\quad = Ax^2 + A + Bx^2 - 2Bx + Cx - 2C$

$\quad = (A+B)x^2 + (-2B+C)x - (2C-A)$

$\quad A+B = 0$

$-2B + C = 3$

$\ 2C - A = 0$

$\qquad\ A = 2C$

$\ B + 2C = 0$

$\underline{4B - 2C = -6\ }$

$\qquad 5B = -6$

$\qquad\ \ B = -\dfrac{6}{5}$

$\qquad\ \ A = \dfrac{6}{5}$

$\qquad\ \ C = \dfrac{6}{10} = \dfrac{3}{5}$

$\dfrac{3x}{(x-2)(x^2+1)} = \dfrac{6}{5(x-2)} + \dfrac{-6x+3}{5(x^2+1)}$

22. $\dfrac{7x^2-7x+23}{(x-3)(x^2+4)} = \dfrac{A}{x-3} + \dfrac{Bx+C}{x^2+4}$

$7x^2-7x+23 = A(x^2+4) + (Bx+C)(x-3)$

$\qquad\qquad = Ax^2 + 4A + Bx^2 - 3Bx + Cx - 3C$

$\qquad\qquad = (A+B)x^2 + (-3B+C)x + (4A-3C)$

$\quad A+B = 7$

$-3B + C = -7$

$\ 4A - 3C = 23$

$\ 3A + 3B = 21$

$\underline{-3B + C = -7\ }$

$\ 3A + C = 14$

$\ 9A + 3C = 42$

$\underline{4A - 3C = 23\ }$

$\ 13A = 65$

$\qquad A = 5$

$\ 5 + B = 7$

$\qquad B = 7 - 5 = 2$

$-3(2) + C = -7$

$\qquad\quad C = -7 + 6 = -1$

$\dfrac{7x^2-7x+23}{(x-3)(x^2+4)} = \dfrac{5}{x-3} + \dfrac{2x-1}{x^2+4}$

23. $\dfrac{x^3}{(x^2+4)^2} = \dfrac{Ax+B}{x^2+4} + \dfrac{Cx+D}{(x^2+4)^2}$

$x^3 = (Ax+B)(x^2+4) + Cx + D$

$\quad = Ax^3 + 4Ax + Bx^2 + 4B + Cx + D$

$\quad = Ax^3 + Bx^2 + (4A+C)x + (4B+D)$

$\quad A = 1$

$\quad B = 0$

$4A + C = 0$

$4B + D = 0$

$\qquad C = -4$

$0 + D = 0, D = 0$

$\dfrac{x^2}{(x^2+4)^2} = \dfrac{x}{x^2+4} - \dfrac{4x}{(x^2+4)^2}$

24. $\dfrac{4x^3 + 5x^2 + 7x - 1}{(x^2 + x + 1)^2} = \dfrac{Ax + B}{x^2 + x + 1} + \dfrac{Cx + D}{(x^2 + x + 1)^2}$

$4x^3 + 5x^2 + 7x - 1$

$= (Ax + B)(x^2 + x + 1) + Cx + D$

$= Ax^3 + Ax^2 + Ax + Bx^2 + Bx + B + Cx + D$

$= Ax^3 + (A + B)x^2(A + B + C)x + (B + D)$

$$A = 4$$

$$A + B = 5$$

$$A + B + C = 7$$

$$B + D = -1$$

$$4 + B = 5, B = 1$$

$$4 + 1 + C = 7, C = 2$$

$$1 + D = -1, D = -2$$

$\dfrac{4x^3 + 5x^2 + 7x - 1}{(x^2 + x + 1)^2} = \dfrac{4x + 1}{x^2 + x + 1} + \dfrac{2x - 2}{(x^2 + x + 1)^2}$

25.
$$5y = x^2 - 1$$
$$x - y = 1$$
$$y = x - 1$$
$$5(x - 1) = x^2 - 1$$
$$5x - 5 = x^2 - 1$$
$$x^2 - 5x + 4 = 0$$
$$(x - 4)(x - 1) = 0$$
$$x = 4, 1$$

If $x = 4, y = 4 - 1 = 3$.

If $x = 1, y = 1 - 1 = 0$.

The solution set is $\{(4, 3), (1, 0)\}$.

26. $y = x^2 + 2x + 1$
$$x + y = 1$$
$$y = 1 - x$$
$$1 - x = x^2 + 2x + 1$$
$$x^2 + 3x = 0$$
$$x(x + 3) = 0$$
$$x = 0, -3$$

If $x = 0, y = 1 - 0 = 1$.

If $x = -3, y = 1 - (-3) = 4$.

The solution set is $\{(0, 1), (-3, 4)\}$.

27.
$$x^2 + y^2 = 2$$
$$x + y = 0$$
$$x = -y$$
$$(-y)^2 + y^2 = 2$$
$$2y^2 = 2$$
$$y^2 = 1$$
$$y = 1, -1$$

If $y = 1, x = -1$.

If $y = -1, x = 1$.

The solution set is $\{(1, -1), (-1, 1)\}$.

28.
$$2x^2 + y^2 = 24$$
$$x^2 + y^2 = 15$$

$$\begin{array}{r} 2x^2 + y^2 = 24 \\ -x^2 - y^2 = -15 \\ \hline x^2 = 9 \end{array}$$

$$x = 3, -3$$

If $x = 3, 3^2 + y^2 = 15, y^2 = 6$ and $y = \pm\sqrt{6}$.

If $x = -3, y = \pm\sqrt{6}$.

The solution set is

$\left\{ \left(3, \sqrt{6}\right), \left(3, -\sqrt{6}\right), \left(-3, \sqrt{6}\right), \left(-3, -\sqrt{6}\right) \right\}$.

29. $xy - 4 = 0$
$$y - x = 0$$
$$y = x$$
$$xy = 4$$
$$x^2 = 4$$
$$x = 2, -2$$

If $x = 2, y = 2$.

If $x = -2, y = -2$.

The solution set is $\{(2, 2), (-2, -2)\}$.

30.
$$y^2 = 4x$$
$$x - 2y + 3 = 0$$
$$x = \frac{y^2}{4}$$
$$\frac{y^2}{4} - 2y + 3 = 0$$
$$y^2 - 8y + 12 = 0$$
$$(y - 6)(y - 2) = 0$$
$$y = 6, 2$$

If $y = 6, x = \dfrac{36}{4} = 9$.

If $y = 2, x = \dfrac{4}{4} = 1$.

The solution set is $\{(9, 6), (1, 2)\}$.

31. $x^2 + y^2 = 10$
$$y = x + 2$$
$$x^2 + (x + 2)^2 = 10$$
$$x^2 + x^2 + 4x + 4 - 10 = 0$$
$$2x^2 + 4x - 6 = 0$$
$$x^2 + 2x - 3 = 0$$
$$(x + 3)(x - 1) = 0$$
$$x = -3, 1$$

If $x = -3, y = -3 + 2 = -1$.

If $x = 1, y = 1 + 2 = 3$.

The solution set is $\{(-3, -1), (1, 3)\}$.

32. $xy = 1$
$$y = 2x + 1$$
$$x(2x + 1) = 1$$
$$2x^2 + x - 1 = 0$$
$$(2x - 1)(x + 1) = 0$$
$$x = \frac{1}{2}, -1$$

If $x = \dfrac{1}{2}, y = 2\left(\dfrac{1}{2}\right) + 1 = 2$.

If $x = -1, y = 2(-1) + 1 = -1$.

The solution set is $\left\{\left(\dfrac{1}{2}, 2\right), (-1, -1)\right\}$.

33.
$$x + y + 1 = 0$$
$$x^2 + y^2 + 6y - x = -5$$
$$x = -y - 1$$
$$(-y - 1)^2 + y^2 + 6y - (-y - 1) + 5 = 0$$
$$y^2 + 2y + 1 + y^2 + 6y + y + 1 + 5 = 0$$
$$2y^2 + 9y + 7 = 0$$
$$(2y + 7)(y + 1) = 0$$
$$y = -\frac{7}{2}, -1$$

If $y = -\dfrac{7}{2}, x = \dfrac{7}{2} - 1 = \dfrac{5}{2}$.

If $y = -1, x = 1 - 1 = 0$.

The solution set is $\left\{\left(\dfrac{5}{2}, -\dfrac{7}{2}\right), (0, -1)\right\}$.

34. $x^2 + y^2 = 13$
$$x^2 - y = 7$$
$$x^2 + y^2 = 13$$
$$\underline{-x^2 + y = -7}$$
$$y^2 + y = 6$$
$$y^2 + y - 6 = 0$$
$$(y + 3)(y - 2) = 0$$
$$y = -3, 2$$

If $y = -3, x^2 + 3 = 7$

$x^2 = 4, x = 2, -2$

If $y = 2, x^2 - 2 = 7, x^2 = 9, x = 3, -3$.

The solution set is
$\{(2, -3), (-2, -3), (3, 2), (-3, 2)\}$.

35.
$$2x^2 + 3y^2 = 21$$
$$3x^2 - 4y^2 = 23$$
$$8x^2 + 12y^2 = 84$$
$$\underline{9x^2 - 12y^2 = 69}$$
$$17x^2 = 153$$
$$x^2 = \frac{153}{17} = 9$$
$$x = 3, -3$$

If $x = 3, 2(3)^2 + 3y^2 = 21$.

$3y^2 = 21 - 18 = 3$

$y^2 = 1, y = 1, -1$

If $x = -3, y = 1, -1$.

The solution set is
$\{(3, 1), (3, -1), (-3, 1), (-3, -1)\}$.

36. $2L + 2W = 26$

$LW = 40$

$L = \dfrac{40}{W}$

$2\left(\dfrac{40}{W}\right) + 2W = 26$

$\dfrac{80}{W} + 2W = 26$

$80 + 2W^2 = 26W$

$2W^2 - 26W + 80 = 0$

$W^2 - 13W + 40 = 0$

$(W - 8)(W - 5) = 0$

$W = 8, 5$

If $W = 5, L = \dfrac{40}{5} = 8$

The dimensions are 8 m by 5 m.

37. $xy = 6$

$y = \dfrac{6}{x}$

$2x + y = 8$

$2x + \dfrac{6}{x} = 8$

$2x^2 + 6 = 8x$

$2x^2 - 8x + 6 = 0$

$x^2 - 4x + 3 = 0$

$(x - 1)(x - 3) = 0$

$x = 1, 3$

If $x = 1, y = 6$.

If $x = 3, y = 2$.

The solution set is $\{(1, 6), (3, 2)\}$.

38. $x^2 + y^2 = 2900$

$4x + 2y = 240$

$2x + y = 120$

$y = 120 - 2x$

$x^2 + (120 - 2x)^2 = 2900$

$x^2 + 14,400 - 480x + 4x^2 - 2900 = 0$

$5x^2 - 480x + 11,500 = 0$

$x^2 - 96x + 2300 = 0$

$(x - 46)(x - 50) = 0$

$x = 46, 50$

If $x = 46, y = 120 - 2(46) = 28$.

If $x = 50, y = 120 - 2(50) = 20$.

$x = 46$ ft and $y = 28$ ft   or

$x = 50$ ft   and $y = 20$ ft

39.

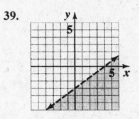

$3x - 4y > 12$

40.

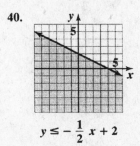

$y \le -\dfrac{1}{2}\,x + 2$

41.

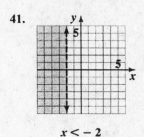

$x < -2$

42.

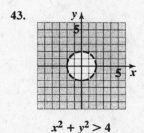

$y \ge 3$

43.

$x^2 + y^2 > 4$

44.

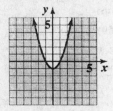

$$y \le x^2 - 1$$

45.

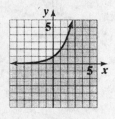

$$y \le 2^x$$

46.

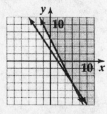

$$3x + 2y \ge 6$$
$$2x + y \ge 6$$

47.

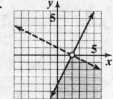

$$2x - y \ge 4$$
$$x + 2y < 2$$

48.

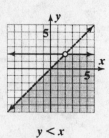

$$y < x$$
$$y \le 2$$

49.

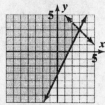

$$x + y \le 6$$
$$y \ge 2x - 3$$

50.

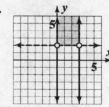

$$0 \le x \le 3$$
$$y > 2$$

51. No solution

52.

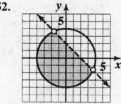

$$x^2 + y^2 \le 16$$
$$x + y < 2$$

53.

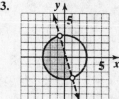

$$x^2 + y^2 \le 9$$
$$y < -3x + 1$$

410

54.

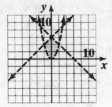
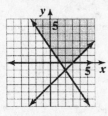

$$y > x^2$$
$$x + y < 6$$
$$y < x + 6$$

55.

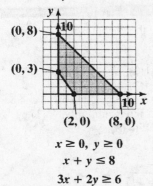

$$y \geq 0$$
$$3x + 2y \geq 4$$
$$x - y \leq 3$$

56.　$z = 2x + 3y$

$(2,2): z = 2(2) + 3(2) = 10$
$(4,0): z = 2(4) + 3(0) = 8$
$\left(\frac{1}{2}, \frac{1}{2}\right): z = 2\left(\frac{1}{2}\right) + 3\left(\frac{1}{2}\right) = \frac{5}{2}$
$(1,0): z = 2(1) + 3(0) = 2$

The maximum value is 10 and the minimum value is 2.

57.　$z = 2x + 3y$

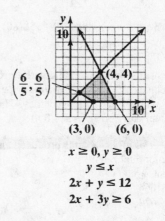

$$x \geq 0, \ y \geq 0$$
$$x + y \leq 8$$
$$3x + 2y \geq 6$$

$(0,8): z = 2(0) + 3(8) = 24$
$(8,0): z = 2(8) + 3(0) = 16$
$(0,3): z = 2(0) + 3(3) = 9$
$(2,0): z = 2(2) + 3(0) = 6$
Maximum value is 24 at (0, 8).

58.　$z = x + 4y$

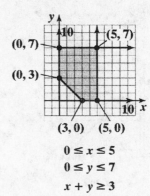

$$0 \leq x \leq 5$$
$$0 \leq y \leq 7$$
$$x + y \geq 3$$

$(0,3): z = 0 + 4(3) = 12$
$(3,0): z = 3 + 4(0) = 3$
$(0,7): z = 0 + 4(7) = 28$
$(5,0): z = 5 + 4(0) = 5$
$(5,7): z = 5 + 4(7) = 33$
Maximum value is 33 at (5,7).

59.　$z = 5x + 6y$

$(3,0): z = 5(3) + 6(0) = 15$
$(6,0): z = 5(6) + 6(0) = 30$
$\left(\frac{6}{5}, \frac{6}{5}\right): z = 5\left(\frac{6}{5}\right) + 6\left(\frac{6}{5}\right) = \frac{66}{5} = 13.2$
$(4,4): 5(4) + 6(4) = 44$
The maximum value is 44.

$$x \geq 0, \ y \geq 0$$
$$y \leq x$$
$$2x + y \leq 12$$
$$2x + 3y \geq 6$$

411

60. a. $z = 500x + 350y$

   b. $x + y \le 200$
            $x \ge 10$
            $y \ge 80$

   c.

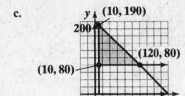

$$x + y \le 200$$
$$x \ge 10, \ y \ge 80$$

   d.   Vertex   Objective Function

                              $z = 500x + 350y$

        $(10, 80)$ $z = 500(10) + 350(80)$
                           $= 33,000$

        $(10, 190)$ $z = 500(10) + 350(190)$
                           $= 71,500$

        $(120, 80)$ $z = 500(120) + 350(80)$
                           $= 88,000$

   e.   The company will make the greatest profit by producing 120 units of writing paper and 80 units of newsprint each day. The maximum daily profit is $88,000.

61. Let x = number of model *A* tents produced and y = number of model *B* tents produced. The constraints are:
$$0.9x + 1.8y \le 864$$
$$0.8x + 1.2y \le 672$$
$$x \ge 0$$
$$y \ge 0$$

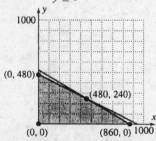

The vertices of the region are $(0, 0)$, $(0, 480)$, $(480, 240)$, and $(840, 0)$.
The objective is to maximize $25x + 40y$.
$(0, 0)$: $25(0) + 40(0) = 0 + 0 = 0$

$(0, 480)$: $25(0) + 40(480) = 0 + 19,200 = 19,200$
$(480, 240)$: $25(480) + 40(240) = 12,000 + 9600$
                    $= 21,600$
$(840, 0)$: $25(840) + 40(0) = 21,000 + 0 = 21,000$
The manufacturer should make 480 of model *A* and 240 of model *B*.

Chapter 5 Test

1. $x = y + 4$
     $3x + 7y = -18$
   Substitute $y + 4$ for x into second equation.
     $3(y + 4) + 7y = -18$
     $3y + 12 + 7y = -18$
           $10y = -30$
              $y = -3$
            $x = -3 + 4 = 1$
   The solution set to the system is $\{(1, -3)\}$.

2. $2x + 5y = -2$
     $3x - 4y = 20$
   Multiply the first equation by 3 and the second equation by –2 and add the result.
     $6 + 15y = -6$
     $\underline{-6x + 8y = -40}$
          $23y = -46$
             $y = -2$
   Substitute $y = -2$ into the first equation:
     $2x + 5(-2) = -2$
       $2x - 10 = -2$
          $2x = 8$
           $x = 4$
   The solution to the system is $\{(4, -2)\}$.

3. $x + y + z = 6 \, (1)$
    $3x + 4y - 7z = 1 \, (2)$
    $2x - y + 3z = 5 \, (3)$
   Eliminate x by multiplying (1) by –3 and adding the result to (2) and by multiplying (1) by –2 and adding the result to (3).
    $-3x - 3y - 3z = -18$
    $\underline{3x + 4y - 7z = 1}$
         $y - 10z = -17 \, (4)$

    $-2x - 2y - 2z = -12$
    $\underline{2x - y + 3z = 5}$
         $-3y + z = -7 \, (5)$

   Multiply (4) by 3 and add the result to (5) to eliminate y.

$3y - 30z = -51$

$\underline{-3y + z = -7}$

$-29z = -58$

$z = 2$

Substitute $z = 2$ into (5).

$-3y + 2 = -7$

$-3y = -9$

$y = 3$

Substitute $z = 2$ and $y = 3$ into (1).

$x + 3 + 2 = 6$

$x = 1$

The solution to the system is $\{(1, 3, 2)\}$.

4. $x^2 + y^2 = 25$

$x + y = 1$

$y = 1 - x$

Substitute $1 - x$ for y in the first equation.

$x^2 + (1 - x)^2 = 25$

$x^2 + 1 - 2x + x^2 = 25$

$2x^2 - 2x - 24 = 0$

$x^2 - x - 12 = 0$

$(x - 4)(x + 3) = 0$

$x = 4, -3$

If $x = 4, y = 1 - 4 = -3$.

If $x = -3, y = 1 - (-3) = 4$.

The solution set is $\{(4, -3), (-3, 4)\}$.

5. $2x^2 - 5y^2 = -2$

$3x^2 + 2y^2 = 35$

Multiply first equation by 2 and the second equation by 5. Then add.

$4x^2 - 10y^2 = -4$

$\underline{15x^2 + 10y^2 = 175}$

$19x^2 = 171$

$x^2 = 9$

$x = 3, -3$

If $x = 3, 2(3)^2 - 5y^2 = -2$.

$18 - 5y^2 = -2$

$-5y^2 = -20$

$y^2 = 4$

$y = 2, -2$

If $x = -3, y = -2$.

The solution to the system is

$\{(3, 2), (3, -2), (-3, 2), (-3, -2)\}$.

6. $\dfrac{x}{(x+1)(x^2+9)} = \dfrac{A}{x+1} + \dfrac{Bx+C}{x^2+9}$

$x = A(x^2 + 9) + (Bx + C)(x + 1)$

$= Ax^2 + 9A + Bx^2 + Bx + Cx + C$

$= (A + B)x^2 + (B + C)x + (9A + C)$

$A + B = 0 \rightarrow A = -B$

$B + C = 1$

$9A + C = 0$

$-9B + C = 0$

$9B - C = 0$

$\underline{B + C = 1}$

$10B = 1$

$B = \dfrac{1}{10}$

$A = -\dfrac{1}{10}$

$\dfrac{1}{10} + C = 1, \ C = \dfrac{9}{10}$

$\dfrac{x}{(x+1)(x^2+9)} = \dfrac{-1}{10(x+1)} + \dfrac{x+9}{10(x^2+9)}$

7.

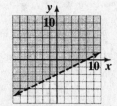

$x - 2y < 8$

8.

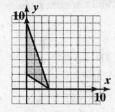

$x \geq 0, \ y \geq 0$

$3x + y \leq 9$

$2x + 3y \geq 6$

9.

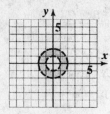

$$x^2 + y^2 > 1$$
$$x^2 + y^2 < 4$$

10.

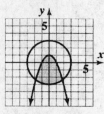

$$y \leq 1 - x^2$$
$$x^2 + y^2 \leq 9$$

11.　$z = 3x + 5y$
$$x \geq 0, y \geq 0$$
$$x + y \leq 6$$
$$x \geq 2$$

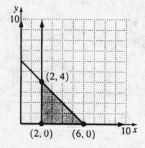

$(2, 0) : z = 3(2) + 5(0) = 6$
$(6, 0) : z = 3(6) + 5(0) = 18$
$(2, 4) : z = 3(2) + 5(4) = 26$
Maximum value is 26.

12.　$x = $ mg of cholesterol in one ounce of shrimp
$y = $ mg of cholesterol in one ounce of scallops
$3x + 2y = 156$
$5x + 3y = 255$
Multiply the first equation by -3 and multiply the second equation by 2.
Add the resulting equations together.

$$-9x - 6y = -468$$
$$\underline{10x + 6y = \ \ 510}$$
$$x = \ \ 42$$

$3(42) + 2y = 156$
$126 + 2y = 156$
$2y = 30$
$y = 15$
$3(42) + 2y = 156$
$126 + 2y = 156$
$2y = 30$
$y = 15$

Shrimp: 42 mg of cholesterol per ounce
Scallops: 15 mg of cholesterol per ounce

13.　**a.**　$C(x) = 360,000 + 850x$

　　　b.　$R(x) = 1150x$

　　　c.　$1150x = 360000 + 850x$
　　　　　　$300x = 360000$
　　　　　　　$x = 1200$
　　　　　　$1150(1200) = 1,380,000$
　　　　　　1200 computers need to be sold to make
　　　　　　$1,380,00 for the company to break even.

14.　$y = ax^2 + bx + c$
$(-1, -2) : -2 = a - b + c$
$(2, 1) : 1 = 4a + 2b + c$
$(-2, 1) : 1 = 4a - 2b + c$
$$4a + 2b + c = 1$$
$$\underline{-4a + 2b - c = -1}$$
$$4b = 0$$
$$b = 0$$
$$a + c = -2$$
$$4a + c = 1$$
$$\underline{-a - c = 2}$$
$$3a = 3$$
$$a = 1$$
$$a + c = -2$$
$$c = -3$$
The quadratic function is $y = x^2 - 3$.

15. $2x + y = 39$
$xy = 180$
$y = 39 - 2x$

$\quad x(39 - 2x) = 180$
$\quad 39x - 2x^2 = 180$
$2x^2 - 39x + 180 = 0$
$(2x - 15)(x - 12) = 0$

$$x = \frac{15}{2}, 12$$

If $x = \dfrac{15}{2}, \dfrac{15}{2} y = 180$ and $y = 24$.
If $x = 12, 12y = 180$ and $y = 15$.
The dimensions are 7.5 ft by 24 ft
or 12 ft by 15 ft

16. Let x = regular, y = deluxe.
objective function: $z = 200x + 250y$
constraints: $x \geq 50, y \geq 75$
$$x + y \leq 150$$

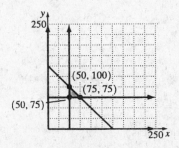

$(50, 75): z = 200(50) + 250(75) = 28,750$
$(50, 100): z = 200(50) + 250(100) = 35,000$
$(75, 75): z = 200(75) + 250(75) = 33,750$
For a maximum profit of \$35,000 a week, the
company should manufacture 50 regular and 100
deluxe jet skis.

Cumulative Review Exercises (Chapters 1–5)

1. Domain: $(-\infty, \infty)$ Range: $[-\infty, 3)$

2. -1 and 1 are both zeros with a minimum
multiplicity of 1.

3. The relative maximum is $y = 3$ and it occurs at
$x = 0$.

4. $f(x)$ is decreasing on the interval $(0, 2)$.

5. At $x = -0.7$, the curve is above the x-axis and
thus $f(x)$ is positive.

6. $(f \circ f)(-1) = f(f(-1)) = f(0) = 3$

7. $f(x) \to -\infty$ as $x \to -2^+$ or as $x \to 2^-$.

8. $f(-x) = f(x)$ thus the function is even.

9. The graph of $g(x) = f(x + 2) - 1$ can be
obtained by shifting $f(x)$ 2 units left and 1 unit
down.

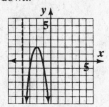

$g(x) = f(x + 2) - 1$

10. The graph of $h(x) = \frac{1}{2} f\left(\frac{1}{2} x\right)$ can be obtained
by shrinking the graph of $f(x)$ horizontally by
a factor of $\frac{1}{2}$ and vertically by a factor of $\frac{1}{2}$.

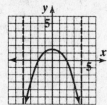

$h(x) = \dfrac{1}{2} f(\dfrac{1}{2} x)$

11. $\quad\quad \sqrt{x^2 - 3x} = 2x - 6$
$\quad\quad x^2 - 3x = 4x^2 - 24x + 36$
$3x^2 - 21x + 36 = 0$
$\quad x^2 - 7x + 12 = 0$
$(x - 3)(x - 4) = 0$
$\quad\quad\quad x = 3, 4$
The solution set is $\{3, 4\}$.

12.
$$4x^2 = 8x - 7$$
$$4x^2 - 8x + 7 = 0$$
$$x = \frac{8 \pm \sqrt{64 - 112}}{8} = \frac{8 \pm \sqrt{-48}}{8}$$
$$= \frac{8 \pm 4\sqrt{3}i}{8} = \frac{2 \pm \sqrt{3}i}{2}$$

The solution set is $\left\{ \dfrac{2 + i\sqrt{3}}{2}, \dfrac{2 - i\sqrt{3}}{2} \right\}$.

13. $\left| \dfrac{x}{3} + 2 \right| < 4$

$$-4 < \frac{x}{3} + 2 < 4$$
$$-6 < \frac{x}{3} < 2$$
$$-18 < x < 6$$

The solution is $\left\{ x \mid -18 < x < 6 \right\}$ or $(-18, 6)$.

14.
$$\frac{x + 5}{x - 1} > 2$$
$$\frac{x + 5}{x - 1} - 2 > 0$$
$$\frac{x + 5 - 2(x - 1)}{x - 1} > 0$$
$$\frac{x + 5 - 2x + 2}{x - 1} > 0$$
$$\frac{-x + 7}{x - 1} > 0$$

$\dfrac{-x + 7}{x - 1} = 0$ when $x = 7$ and is undefined when

$x = 1$.
Test $x = 0$:
$$\frac{0 + 5}{0 - 1} > 2?$$
$$\frac{5}{-1} > 2?$$
$$-5 \not> 2$$
Test $x = 2$:
$$\frac{2 + 5}{2 - 1} > 2?$$
$$\frac{7}{1} > 2?$$
$$7 > 2$$

Test $x = 8$:
$$\frac{8 + 5}{8 - 1} > 2?$$
$$\frac{13}{7} > 2?$$
$$\frac{13}{7} \geq \frac{14}{7}$$

The solution is $\left\{ x \mid 1 < x < 7 \right\}$ or $(1, 7)$.

15. $2x^3 + x^2 - 13x + 6 = 0$

$f(x) = 2x^3 + x^2 - 13x + 6$ has 2 sign changes: 2 or 0 positive real roots.

$f(-x) = -2x^3 + x^2 + 13x + 6$ has 1 sign change: 1 negative real root.

p: $\pm 1, \pm 2, \pm 3, \pm 6$

q: $\pm 1, \pm 2$

$\dfrac{p}{q}$: $\pm 1, \pm \dfrac{1}{2}, \pm 2, \pm 3, \pm \dfrac{3}{2}, \pm 6$

$$
\begin{array}{r|rrrr}
-3 & 2 & 1 & -13 & 6 \\
   &   & -6 & 15 & -6 \\
\hline
   & 2 & -5 & 2 & 0
\end{array}
$$

$$2x^3 + x^2 - 13x + 6 = (x + 3)(2x^2 - 5x + 2)$$
$$= (x + 3)(2x - 1)(x - 2)$$

$$x = -3, \; x = \frac{1}{2}, \; x = 2$$

The solution set is $\left\{ -3, \frac{1}{2}, 2 \right\}$.

16.
$$6x - 3(5x + 2) = 4(1 - x)$$
$$6x - 15x - 6 = 4 - 4x$$
$$-9x - 6 = 4 - 4x$$
$$-5x = 10$$
$$x = -2$$
The solution set is $\{-2\}$.

17.
$$\log(x + 3) + \log x = 1$$
$$\log x(x + 3) = 1$$
$$x(x + 3) = 10$$
$$x^2 + 3x - 10 = 0$$
$$(x + 5)(x - 2) = 0$$
$$x = -5 \text{ or } x = 2$$
$$x = -5 \text{ is extraneous.}$$
$$x = 2$$
The solution set is $\{2\}$.

18. $3^{x+2} = 11$

$\log_3 3^{x+2} = \log_3 11$

$x + 2 = \log_3 11$

$x = -2 + \log_3 11$

$x = -2 + \dfrac{\log 11}{\log 3} \approx 0.18$

The solution set is $\{-2 + \log_3 11\}$.

19. $x^{\frac{1}{2}} - 2x^{\frac{1}{4}} - 15 = 0$

$\sqrt[4]{x}^2 - 2\sqrt[4]{x} - 15 = 0$

$\left(\sqrt[4]{x} + 3\right)\left(\sqrt[4]{x} - 5\right) = 0$

$\sqrt[4]{x} + 3 = 0 \qquad\qquad \sqrt[4]{x} - 5 = 0$

$\sqrt[4]{x} = -3 \qquad\text{or}\qquad \sqrt[4]{x} = 5$

$x = (-3)^4 \qquad\qquad\qquad x = 5^4$

$x = 81 \qquad\qquad\qquad\quad x = 625$

81 does not check. The solution set is $\{625\}$.

20. $3x - y = -2$

$2x^2 - y = 0$

Solve the first equation for y.

$3x - y = -2$

$y = 3x + 2$

Use this equation to substitute into the other equation.

$2x^2 - (\overset{y}{\overbrace{3x + 2}}) = 0$

$2x^2 - 3x - 2 = 0$

$(2x + 1)(x - 2) = 0$

$x = -\dfrac{1}{2} \ \text{ or } \ x = 2.$

Back-substitute to find y.

$y = 3x + 2 \qquad \text{or} \qquad y = 3x + 2$

$y = 3(2) + 2 \qquad\qquad\qquad y = 3\left(-\dfrac{1}{2}\right) + 2$

$y = 8$

$\qquad\qquad\qquad\qquad\qquad y = \dfrac{1}{2}$

$y = 3x + 2$

The solution set is $\left\{ (2, 8), \left(-\dfrac{1}{2}, \dfrac{1}{2}\right) \right\}$.

21. $x + 2y + 3z = -2$

$3x + 3y + 10z = -2$

$2y - 5z = 6$

Multiply equation 1 by -3 and add to equation 2.

$-3x - 6y - 9z = 6$

$\underline{3x + 3y + 10z = -2}$

$\qquad -3y + z = 4 \quad$ Equation 4

Multiply equation 4 by 5 and add to equation 3 and solve for y.

$-15y + 5z = 20$

$\underline{2y - 5z = 6}$

$\qquad -13y = 26$

$\qquad\quad y = -2$

Back-substitute to find z.

$-3y + z = 4$

$-3(-2) + z = 4$

$\qquad\quad z = -2$

Back-substitute to find x.

$x + 2y + 3z = -2$

$x + 2(-2) + 3(-2) = -2$

$\qquad\qquad\qquad x = 8$

The solution set is $\{8, -2, -2\}$.

22. vertex: $(-2, -4)$

y-intercept:

$\qquad f(0) = (0 + 2)^2 - 4 = 0$

x-intercepts:

$\qquad (x + 2)^2 - 4 = 0$

$\qquad x^2 + 4x + 4 - 4 = 0$

$\qquad\qquad x^2 + 4x = 0$

$\qquad\qquad x(x + 4) = 0$

$x = 0, x - 4$

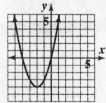

$f(x) = (x + 2)^2 - 4$

23.

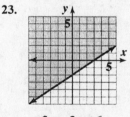

$2x - 3y \le 6$

417

24.

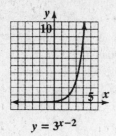

$$y = 3^{x-2}$$

25. vertical asymptote: $x = -1$
horizontal asymptote: $m > n$, none
x-intercepts:

$$x^2 - x - 6 = 0$$
$$(x - 3)(x + 2) = 0$$
$$x = 3, x = -2$$

y-intercept:

$$f(0) = \frac{0^2 - 0 - 6}{0 + 1} = -6$$

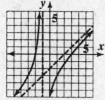

$$f(x) = \frac{x^2 - x - 6}{x + 1}$$

26.

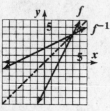

$$f(x) = 2x - 4$$
$$f^{-1}(x) = \frac{x + 4}{2}$$

27.

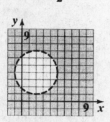

$$(x - 2)^2 + (y - 4)^2 > 9$$

28.

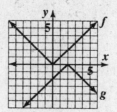

$$f(x) = |x|$$
$$g(x) = -|x - 2|$$

29.
$$(f \circ g)(x) = f(g(x))$$
$$= 2(1 - x)^2 - (1 - x) - 1$$
$$= 2x^2 - 3x$$
$$(g \circ f) = g(f(x))$$
$$= 1 - (2x^2 - x - 1)$$
$$= 1 - 2x^2 + x + 1$$
$$= -2x^2 + x + 2$$

30. $$\frac{f(x + h) - f(x)}{h}$$

$$= \frac{\left[2(x + h)^2 - (x + h) - 1\right] - \left[2x^2 - x - 1\right]}{h}$$

$$= \frac{2x^2 + 4hx + 2h^2 - x - h - 1 - 2x^2 + x + 1}{h}$$

$$= \frac{4hx + 2h^2 - h}{h}$$

$$= 4x + 2h - 1$$

31. Find slope: $m = \dfrac{4 - (-2)}{2 - 4} = \dfrac{6}{-2} = -3$

Use point slope form to find an equation.
$$y - y_1 = m(x - x_1)$$
$$y - 4 = -3(x - 2)$$

Put in slope-intercept form.
$$y - 4 = -3(x - 2)$$
$$y - 4 = -3x + 6$$
$$y = -3x + 10$$

32. Find the slope of the perpendicular line by putting in slope-intercept form.

$$x + 3y - 6 = 0$$
$$3y = -x + 6$$
$$y = -\frac{1}{3}x + 2$$

The slope of the perpendicular line is $-\frac{1}{3}$ so the slope of the desired line is the negative reciprocal, or 3.

Use point slope form to find an equation.

$$y - y_1 = m(x - x_1)$$
$$y - 0 = 3(x + 1)$$

Put in slope-intercept form.

$$y - 0 = 3(x + 1)$$
$$y = 3x + 3$$

33. Let x = the amount invested at 12%
Let $4000 - x$ = the amount invested at 14%

$$0.12x + 0.14(4000 - x) = 508$$
$$0.12x + 560 - 0.14x = 508$$
$$-0.02x = -52$$
$$x = \frac{-52}{-0.02}$$
$$x = 2600$$
$$4000 - x = 4000 - 2600 = 1400$$

Thus, $2600 was invested at 12% and $1400 was invested at 14%.

34.
$$L = 2W + 1$$
$$LW = 36$$
$$W(2W + 1) = 36$$
$$2W^2 + W - 36 = 0$$
$$(2W + 9)(W - 4) = 0$$
$$W = -\frac{9}{2} \text{ or } 4$$

Length cannot be negative. If $W = 4$, $4L = 36$, $L = 9$. The dimensions are 4 m by 9 m.

35.
$$A = Pe^{rt}$$
$$18,000 = 6000e^{10r}$$
$$3 = e^{10r}$$
$$\ln 3 = \ln e^{10r}$$
$$\ln 3 = 10r$$
$$r = \frac{\ln 3}{10} \approx 0.1099$$
10.99%

419

Chapter 6

Check Point Exercises

1. $\begin{bmatrix} 1 & -1 & 1 & | & 8 \\ 0 & 1 & -12 & | & -15 \\ 0 & 0 & 1 & | & 1 \end{bmatrix} \rightarrow \begin{matrix} 1x - 1y + 1z = 8 \\ 0x + 1y - 12z = -15 \\ 0x + 0y + 1z = 1 \end{matrix}$

   $x - y + z = 8$

   $y - 12z = -15$

   $z = 1$

   Solve for y by back-substitution.

   $y - 12(1) = -15$

   $y - 12 = -15$

   $y = -3$

   Use back substitution for x.

   $x - (-3) + 1 = 8$

   $x + 4 = 8$

   $x = 4$

   The solution set for the system is $\{(4, -3, 1)\}$.

2. **a.** The notation $R_1 \leftrightarrow R_2$ means to interchange the elements in row 1 and row 2. This results in the row-equivalent matrix

   $\begin{bmatrix} 1 & 6 & -3 & | & 7 \\ 4 & 12 & -20 & | & 8 \\ -3 & -2 & 1 & | & -9 \end{bmatrix}$.

   b. The notation $\frac{1}{4} R_1$ means to multiply each element in row 1 by $\frac{1}{4}$. This results in the row-equivalent matrix

   $\begin{bmatrix} \frac{1}{4}(4) & \frac{1}{4}(12) & \frac{1}{4}(-20) & | & \frac{1}{4}(8) \\ 1 & 6 & -3 & | & 7 \\ -3 & -2 & 1 & | & -9 \end{bmatrix} = \begin{bmatrix} 1 & 3 & -5 & | & 2 \\ 1 & 6 & -3 & | & 7 \\ -3 & -2 & 1 & | & -9 \end{bmatrix}$

   c. The notation $3R_2 + R_3$ means to add 3 times the elements in row 2 to the corresponding elements in row 3. Replace the elements in row 3 by these sums. First, we find 3 times the elements in row 2: $3(1) = 3, 3(6) = 18, 3(-3) = -9, 3(7) = 21$. Now we add these products to the corresponding elements in row 3. This results in the row equivalent matrix

   $\begin{bmatrix} 4 & 12 & -20 & | & 8 \\ 1 & 6 & -3 & | & 7 \\ -3+3=0 & -2+18=16 & 1-9=-8 & | & -9+21=12 \end{bmatrix} = \begin{bmatrix} 4 & 12 & -20 & | & 8 \\ 1 & 6 & -3 & | & 7 \\ 0 & 16 & -8 & | & 12 \end{bmatrix}$.

3.
$$\begin{aligned} 2x+y+2z &= 18 \\ x-y+2z &= 9 \\ x+2y-z &= 6 \end{aligned} \rightarrow \begin{bmatrix} 2 & 1 & 2 & | & 18 \\ 1 & -1 & 2 & | & 9 \\ 1 & 2 & -1 & | & 6 \end{bmatrix}$$

Interchange row 1 with row 2 to get 1 in the top position of the first column.

$$\begin{bmatrix} 1 & -1 & 2 & | & 9 \\ 2 & 1 & 2 & | & 18 \\ 1 & 2 & -1 & | & 6 \end{bmatrix}$$

Multiply the first row by –2 and add these products to row 2.

$$\begin{bmatrix} 1 & -1 & 2 & | & 9 \\ 2+-2=0 & 1+2=3 & 2+-4=-2 & | & -18+18=0 \\ 1 & 2 & -1 & | & 6 \end{bmatrix} = \begin{bmatrix} 1 & -1 & 2 & | & 9 \\ 0 & 3 & -2 & | & 0 \\ 1 & 2 & -1 & | & 6 \end{bmatrix}$$

Next, multiply the top row by –1 and add these products to row 3.

$$\begin{bmatrix} 1 & -1 & 2 & | & 9 \\ 0 & 3 & -2 & | & 0 \\ 1+-1=0 & 2+1=3 & -1-2=-3 & | & 6-9=-3 \end{bmatrix} = \begin{bmatrix} 1 & -1 & 2 & | & 9 \\ 0 & 3 & -2 & | & 0 \\ 0 & 3 & -3 & | & -3 \end{bmatrix}$$

Next, to obtain a 1 in the second row, second column, multiply 3 by its reciprocal, $\frac{1}{3}$. Therefore, we multiply all the numbers in the second row by $\frac{1}{3}$ to get

$$\begin{bmatrix} 1 & -1 & 2 & | & 9 \\ 0 & 1 & -\frac{2}{3} & | & 0 \\ 0 & 3 & -3 & | & -3 \end{bmatrix}.$$

Next, to obtain a 0 in the third row, second column, multiply the second row by –3 and add the products to row three. The resulting matrix is

$$\begin{bmatrix} 1 & -1 & 2 & | & 9 \\ 0 & 1 & -\frac{2}{3} & | & 0 \\ 0 & 0 & -1 & | & -3 \end{bmatrix}.$$

To get 1 in the third row, third column, multiply –1 by its reciprocal, –1. Multiply all numbers in the third row by –1 to obtain the resulting matrix

$$\begin{bmatrix} 1 & -1 & 2 & | & 9 \\ 0 & 1 & -\frac{2}{3} & | & 0 \\ 0 & 0 & 1 & | & 3 \end{bmatrix}.$$

The system represented by this matrix is:
$$x-y+2z = 9$$
$$y-\frac{2}{3}z = 0$$
$$z = 3$$

Use back substitution to find y and x.

$$y-\frac{2}{3}(3) = 0 \qquad x-2+6 = 9$$
$$y-2 = 0 \qquad\quad x+4 = 9$$
$$y = 2 \qquad\qquad x = 5$$

The solution set for the original system is $\{(5, 2, 3)\}$.

4.
$$w - 3x - 2y + z = -3$$
$$2w - 7x - y + 2z = 1$$
$$3w - 7x - 3y + 3z = -5$$
$$5w + x + 4y - 2z = 18$$

The augmented matrix is

$$\begin{bmatrix} 1 & -3 & -2 & 1 & | & -3 \\ 2 & -7 & -1 & 2 & | & 1 \\ 3 & -7 & -3 & 3 & | & -5 \\ 5 & 1 & 4 & -2 & | & 18 \end{bmatrix}.$$

Multiply the top row by –2 and add the products to the second row. Multiply the top row by –3 and add the products to the third row. Multiply the top row by –5 and add the products to the fourth row. The resulting matrix is

$$\begin{bmatrix} 1 & -3 & -2 & 1 & | & -3 \\ 0 & -1 & 3 & 0 & | & 7 \\ 0 & 2 & 3 & 0 & | & 4 \\ 0 & 16 & 14 & -7 & | & 33 \end{bmatrix}.$$

Next, multiply the second row by –1 to obtain a 1 in the second row, second column.

$$\begin{bmatrix} 1 & -3 & -2 & 1 & | & -3 \\ 0 & 1 & -3 & 0 & | & -7 \\ 0 & 2 & 3 & 0 & | & 4 \\ 0 & 16 & 14 & -7 & | & 33 \end{bmatrix}.$$

Next, multiply the second row by –2 and add the products to the third row. Multiply the second row by –16 and add the products to the fourth row. The resulting matrix is

$$\begin{bmatrix} 1 & -3 & -2 & 1 & | & -3 \\ 0 & 1 & -3 & 0 & | & -7 \\ 0 & 0 & 9 & 0 & | & 18 \\ 0 & 0 & 62 & -7 & | & 145 \end{bmatrix}.$$

Next, multiply the third row by $\frac{1}{9}$ to obtain a 1 in the third row, third column. The resulting matrix is

$$\begin{bmatrix} 1 & -3 & -2 & 1 & | & -3 \\ 0 & 1 & -3 & 0 & | & -7 \\ 0 & 0 & 1 & 0 & | & 2 \\ 0 & 0 & 62 & -7 & | & 145 \end{bmatrix}.$$

Multiply the third row by –62 and add the products to the fourth row to obtain the resulting matrix

$$\begin{bmatrix} 1 & -3 & -2 & 1 & | & -3 \\ 0 & 1 & -3 & 0 & | & -7 \\ 0 & 0 & 1 & 0 & | & 2 \\ 0 & 0 & 0 & -7 & | & 21 \end{bmatrix}.$$

Multiply the fourth row by $-\frac{1}{7}$, the reciprocal of –7. The resulting matrix is

$$\begin{bmatrix} 1 & -3 & -2 & 1 & | & -3 \\ 0 & 1 & -3 & 0 & | & -7 \\ 0 & 0 & 1 & 0 & | & 2 \\ 0 & 0 & 0 & 1 & | & -3 \end{bmatrix}.$$

The system of linear equations corresponding to the resulting matrix is

$$w - 3x - 2y + z = -3$$
$$x - 3y = -7$$
$$y = 2$$
$$z = -3$$

Using back-substitution solve for x and w.

$$x - 3(2) = -7$$
$$x = -1$$

$$w - 3(-1) - 2(2) - 3 = -3$$
$$w - 4 = -3$$
$$w = 1$$

The solution set is $\{(1, -1, 2, -3)\}$.

5. The matrix obtained in 3 will be the starting point.

$$\begin{bmatrix} 1 & -1 & 2 & 9 \\ 0 & 1 & -\frac{2}{3} & 0 \\ 0 & 0 & 1 & 3 \end{bmatrix}$$

Next, multiply the third row by $\dfrac{2}{3}$ and add the products to the second row. Multiply the third row by 2 and add the products to the first row. The resulting matrix is

$$\begin{bmatrix} 1 & -1 & 0 & 3 \\ 0 & 1 & 0 & 2 \\ 0 & 0 & 1 & 3 \end{bmatrix}.$$

Add the second row to the first row and replace the first row.

$$\begin{bmatrix} 1 & 0 & 0 & 5 \\ 0 & 1 & 0 & 2 \\ 0 & 0 & 1 & 3 \end{bmatrix}$$

This matrix corresponds to $x = 5$, $y = 2$ and $z = 3$. The solution set is $\{(5, 2, 3)\}$.

Exercise Set 6.1

1. $$\begin{bmatrix} 2 & 1 & 2 & 2 \\ 3 & -5 & -1 & 4 \\ 1 & -2 & -3 & -6 \end{bmatrix}$$

3. $$\begin{bmatrix} 1 & -1 & 1 & 8 \\ 0 & 1 & -12 & -15 \\ 0 & 0 & 1 & 1 \end{bmatrix}$$

5. $$\begin{bmatrix} 5 & -2 & -3 & 0 \\ 1 & 1 & 0 & 5 \\ 2 & 0 & -3 & 4 \end{bmatrix}$$

7. $$\begin{bmatrix} 2 & 5 & -3 & 1 & 2 \\ 0 & 3 & 1 & 0 & 4 \\ 1 & -1 & 5 & 0 & 9 \\ 5 & -5 & -2 & 0 & 1 \end{bmatrix}$$

9. $$5x + 3z = -11$$
$$y - 4z = 12$$
$$7x + 2y = 3$$

11. $$w + x + 4y + z = 3$$
$$-w + x - y = 7$$
$$12w + 5z = 11$$
$$12y + 4z = 5$$

13.
$$x - 4z = 5$$
$$y - 12z = 13$$
$$z = -\frac{1}{2}$$

$$y - 12\left(-\frac{1}{2}\right) = 13$$
$$y + 6 = 13$$
$$y = 7$$

$$x - 4\left(-\frac{1}{2}\right) = 5$$
$$x + 2 = 5$$
$$x = 3$$

The solution set is $\left\{\left(3, 7, -\frac{1}{2}\right)\right\}$.

15.
$$\begin{bmatrix} 1 & \frac{1}{2} & 1 & \Big| & \frac{11}{2} \\ 0 & 1 & \frac{3}{2} & \Big| & 7 \\ 0 & 0 & 1 & \Big| & 4 \end{bmatrix}$$

$$x + \frac{1}{2}y + z = \frac{11}{2}$$
$$y + \frac{3}{2}z = 7$$
$$z = 4$$

$$y + \frac{3}{2}(4) = 7$$
$$y + 6 = 7$$
$$y = 1$$

$$x + \frac{1}{2}(1) + 4 = \frac{11}{2}$$
$$x + \frac{9}{2} = \frac{11}{2}$$
$$x = \frac{11}{2} - \frac{9}{2}$$
$$x = 1$$

The solution set is $\{(1, 1, 4)\}$.

17.
$$\begin{bmatrix} 1 & -1 & 1 & 1 & \Big| & 3 \\ 0 & 1 & -2 & -1 & \Big| & 0 \\ 0 & 0 & 1 & 6 & \Big| & 17 \\ 0 & 0 & 0 & 1 & \Big| & 3 \end{bmatrix}$$
$$w - x + y + z = 3$$
$$x - 2y - z = 0$$
$$y + 6z = 17$$
$$z = 3$$

$$y + 6(3) = 17$$
$$y + 18 = 17$$
$$y = -1$$

$$x - 2(-1) - 3 = 0$$
$$x - 1 = 0$$
$$x = 1$$

$$w - 1 + (-1) + 3 = 3$$
$$w + 1 = 3$$
$$w = 2$$
The solution set is $\{(2, 1, -1, 3)\}$.

19.
$$\begin{bmatrix} 2\left(\frac{1}{2}\right) & -6\left(\frac{1}{2}\right) & 4\left(\frac{1}{2}\right) & \Big| & 10\left(\frac{1}{2}\right) \\ 1 & 5 & -5 & \Big| & 0 \\ 3 & 0 & 4 & \Big| & 7 \end{bmatrix} \frac{1}{2}R_1$$

$$\begin{bmatrix} 1 & -3 & 2 & \Big| & 5 \\ 1 & 5 & -5 & \Big| & 0 \\ 3 & 0 & 4 & \Big| & 7 \end{bmatrix}$$

21.
$$\begin{bmatrix} 1 & -3 & 2 & \Big| & 0 \\ -3(1)+3 & -3(-3)+1 & -3(2)+-1 & \Big| & -3(0)+7 \\ 2 & -2 & 1 & \Big| & 3 \end{bmatrix} -3R_1 + R_2$$

$$\begin{bmatrix} 1 & -3 & 2 & \Big| & 0 \\ 0 & 10 & -7 & \Big| & 7 \\ 2 & -2 & 1 & \Big| & 3 \end{bmatrix}$$

23. $\begin{bmatrix} 1 & -1 & 1 & 1 & | & 3 \\ 0 & 1 & -2 & -1 & | & 0 \\ 2 & 0 & 3 & 4 & | & 11 \\ 5 & 1 & 2 & 4 & | & 6 \end{bmatrix} \begin{matrix} \\ \\ -2R_1 + R_3 \\ -5R_1 + R_4 \end{matrix}$

$\begin{bmatrix} 1 & -1 & 1 & 1 & | & 3 \\ 0 & 1 & -2 & -1 & | & 0 \\ -2(1)+2 & -2(-1)+0 & -2(1)+3 & -2(1)+4 & | & -2(3)+11 \\ -5(1)+5 & -5(-1)+1 & -5(1)+2 & -5(1)+4 & | & -5(3)+6 \end{bmatrix} = \begin{bmatrix} 1 & -1 & 1 & 1 & | & 3 \\ 0 & 1 & -2 & -1 & | & 0 \\ 0 & 2 & 1 & 2 & | & 5 \\ 0 & 6 & -3 & -1 & | & -9 \end{bmatrix}$

25. $\begin{bmatrix} 1 & -1 & 1 & | & 8 \\ 2 & 3 & -1 & | & -2 \\ 3 & -2 & -9 & | & 9 \end{bmatrix}$

$\begin{bmatrix} 1 & -1 & 1 & | & 8 \\ -2(1)+2 & -2(-1)+3 & -2(1)-1 & | & -2(8)-2 \\ -3(1)+3 & -3(-1)-2 & -3(1)-9 & | & -3(8)+9 \end{bmatrix}$

$\begin{bmatrix} 1 & -1 & 1 & | & 8 \\ 0 & 5 & \boxed{-3} & | & \boxed{-18} \\ 0 & 1 & \boxed{-12} & | & \boxed{-15} \end{bmatrix}$

$\begin{bmatrix} 1 & -1 & 1 & | & 8 \\ 0(\frac{1}{5}) & 1(\frac{1}{5}) & -3(\frac{1}{5}) & | & -18(\frac{1}{5}) \\ 0 & 1 & -12 & | & -15 \end{bmatrix}$

$\begin{bmatrix} 1 & -1 & 1 & | & 8 \\ 0 & 1 & \boxed{-\frac{3}{5}} & | & \boxed{-\frac{18}{5}} \\ 0 & 1 & \boxed{-12} & | & \boxed{-15} \end{bmatrix}$

27.
$$x + y - z = -2$$
$$2x - y + z = 5$$
$$-x + 2y + 2z = 1$$

$\begin{bmatrix} 1 & 1 & -1 & | & -2 \\ 2 & -1 & 1 & | & 5 \\ -1 & 2 & 2 & | & 1 \end{bmatrix} \begin{matrix} \\ -2R_1 + R_2 \\ \\ \end{matrix}$

$\begin{bmatrix} 1 & 1 & -1 & | & -2 \\ 0 & -3 & 3 & | & 9 \\ -1 & 2 & 2 & | & 1 \end{bmatrix} 1R_1 + R_3$

$\begin{bmatrix} 1 & 1 & -1 & | & -2 \\ 0 & -3 & 3 & | & 9 \\ 0 & 3 & 1 & | & -1 \end{bmatrix} -\frac{1}{3}R_2$

$\begin{bmatrix} 1 & 1 & -1 & | & -2 \\ 0 & 1 & -1 & | & -3 \\ 0 & 3 & 1 & | & -1 \end{bmatrix} -3R_2 + R_3$

$= \begin{bmatrix} 1 & 1 & -1 & | & -2 \\ 0 & 1 & -1 & | & -3 \\ 0 & 0 & 4 & | & 8 \end{bmatrix}$

$$4z = 8$$
$$z = 2$$
$$y - z = -3$$
$$y - 2 = -3$$
$$y = -1$$
$$x + y - z = -2$$
$$x - 1 - 2 = -2$$
$$x - 3 = -2$$
$$x = 1$$

The solution set is $\{(1, -1, 2)\}$.

29.

$$x + 3y = 0$$
$$x + y + z = 1$$
$$3x - y - z = 11$$

$$\begin{bmatrix} 1 & 3 & 0 & | & 0 \\ 1 & 1 & 1 & | & 1 \\ 3 & -1 & -1 & | & 11 \end{bmatrix} -1R_1 + R_2$$

$$\begin{bmatrix} 1 & 3 & 0 & | & 0 \\ 0 & -2 & 1 & | & 1 \\ 3 & -1 & -1 & | & 11 \end{bmatrix} -3R_1 + R_3$$

$$\begin{bmatrix} 1 & 3 & 0 & | & 0 \\ 0 & -2 & 1 & | & 1 \\ 0 & -10 & -1 & | & 11 \end{bmatrix} -\frac{1}{2}R_2$$

$$\begin{bmatrix} 1 & 3 & 0 & | & 0 \\ 0 & 1 & -\frac{1}{2} & | & -\frac{1}{2} \\ 0 & -10 & -1 & | & 11 \end{bmatrix} 10R_2 + R_3$$

$$\begin{bmatrix} 1 & 3 & 0 & | & 0 \\ 0 & 1 & -\frac{1}{2} & | & -\frac{1}{2} \\ 0 & 0 & -6 & | & 6 \end{bmatrix} -\frac{1}{6}R_3$$

$$\begin{bmatrix} 1 & 3 & 0 & | & 0 \\ 0 & 1 & -\frac{1}{2} & | & -\frac{1}{2} \\ 0 & 0 & 1 & | & -1 \end{bmatrix}$$

$$z = -1$$

$$y - \frac{1}{2}z = -\frac{1}{2}$$

$$y - \frac{1}{2}(-1) = -\frac{1}{2}$$

$$y + \frac{1}{2} = -\frac{1}{2}$$

$$y = -1$$

Interchange row one and row two.

$$x + 3y = 0$$
$$x + 3(-1) = 0$$
$$x = 3$$

The solution set is $\{(3, -1, -1)\}$.

31.

$$2x - y - z = 4$$
$$x + y - 5z = -4$$
$$x - 2y = 4$$

$$\begin{bmatrix} 2 & -1 & -1 & 4 \\ 1 & 1 & -5 & -4 \\ 1 & -2 & 0 & 4 \end{bmatrix}$$

Interchange rows one and two.

$$\begin{bmatrix} 1 & 1 & -5 & -4 \\ 2 & -1 & -1 & 4 \\ 1 & -2 & 0 & 4 \end{bmatrix}$$

Replace row two with $-2R_1 + R_2$.
Replace row three with $-R_1 + R_3$.

$$\begin{bmatrix} 1 & 1 & -5 & -4 \\ 0 & -3 & 9 & 12 \\ 0 & -3 & 5 & 8 \end{bmatrix}$$

Replace row two with $-\frac{1}{3}R_2$.

$$\begin{bmatrix} 1 & 1 & -5 & -4 \\ 0 & 1 & -3 & -4 \\ 0 & -3 & 5 & 8 \end{bmatrix}$$

Replace row three with $3R_2 + R_3$.

$$\begin{bmatrix} 1 & 1 & -5 & -4 \\ 0 & 1 & -3 & -4 \\ 0 & 0 & -4 & -4 \end{bmatrix}$$

Replace row three with $-\frac{1}{4}R_3$.

$$\begin{bmatrix} 1 & 1 & -5 & -4 \\ 0 & 1 & -3 & -4 \\ 0 & 0 & 1 & 1 \end{bmatrix}$$

$$z = 1$$

$$y - 3z = -4$$
$$y - 3(1) = -4$$
$$y = -1$$

$$x + y - 5z = -4$$
$$x - 1 - 5(1) = -4$$
$$x - 6 = -4$$
$$x = 2$$

The solution set is $\{(2, -1, 1)\}$.

33. $x + y + z = 4$
$x - y - z = 0$
$x - y + z = 2$

$$\begin{bmatrix} 1 & 1 & 1 & 4 \\ 1 & -1 & -1 & 0 \\ 1 & -1 & 1 & 2 \end{bmatrix}$$

Replace row two with $-R_1 + R_2$.
Replace row three with $-R_1 + R_3$.

$$\begin{bmatrix} 1 & 1 & 1 & 4 \\ 0 & -2 & -2 & -4 \\ 0 & -2 & 0 & -2 \end{bmatrix}$$

Replace row two with $-\dfrac{1}{2} R_2$.

$$\begin{bmatrix} 1 & 1 & 1 & 4 \\ 0 & 1 & 1 & 2 \\ 0 & -2 & 0 & -2 \end{bmatrix}$$

Replace row 3 with $2R_2 + R_3$.

$$\begin{bmatrix} 1 & 1 & 1 & 4 \\ 0 & 1 & 1 & 2 \\ 0 & 0 & 2 & 2 \end{bmatrix}$$

Replace row 3 with $\dfrac{1}{2} R_3$.

$$\begin{bmatrix} 1 & 1 & 1 & 4 \\ 0 & 1 & 1 & 2 \\ 0 & 0 & 1 & 1 \end{bmatrix}$$

$z = 1$
$y + 1 = 2$
$y = 1$
$x + 1 + 1 = 4$
$x = 2$

The solution set is $\{(2, 1, 1)\}$.

35. Write the equations in standard form.
$x + 2y - z = -1$
$x - y + z = 4$
$x + y - 3z = -2$

$$\begin{bmatrix} 1 & 2 & -1 & -1 \\ 1 & -1 & 1 & 4 \\ 1 & 1 & -3 & -2 \end{bmatrix}$$

Replace row two with $-R_1 + R_2$.
Replace row three with $-R_1 + R_3$.

$$\begin{bmatrix} 1 & 2 & -1 & -1 \\ 0 & -3 & 2 & 5 \\ 0 & -1 & -2 & -1 \end{bmatrix}$$

Replace row two with $-R_3$.
Replace row three with R_2.

$$\begin{bmatrix} 1 & 2 & -1 & -1 \\ 0 & 1 & 2 & 1 \\ 0 & -3 & 2 & 5 \end{bmatrix}$$

Replace row 3 with $3R_2 + R_3$.

$$\begin{bmatrix} 1 & 2 & -1 & -1 \\ 0 & 1 & 2 & 1 \\ 0 & 0 & 8 & 8 \end{bmatrix}$$

Replace row 3 with $\dfrac{1}{8} R_3$.

$$\begin{bmatrix} 1 & 2 & -1 & -1 \\ 0 & 1 & 2 & 1 \\ 0 & 0 & 1 & 1 \end{bmatrix}$$

$z = 1$
$y + 2(1) = 1$
$y = -1$
$x + 2(-1) - 1 = -1$
$x = 2$

The solution set is $\{(2, -1, 1)\}$.

37. $3a - b - 4c = 3$
$2a - b + 2c = -8$
$a + 2b - 3c = 9$

Interchange equations 1 and 3.

$$\begin{bmatrix} 1 & 2 & -3 & 9 \\ 2 & -1 & 2 & -8 \\ 3 & -1 & -4 & 3 \end{bmatrix}$$

Replace row two with $-2R_1 + R_2$.
Replace row three with $-3R_1 + R_3$.

$$\begin{bmatrix} 1 & 2 & -3 & 9 \\ 0 & -5 & 8 & -26 \\ 0 & -7 & 5 & -24 \end{bmatrix}$$

Replace row two with $-\dfrac{1}{5}R_2$

$$\begin{bmatrix} 1 & 2 & -3 & 9 \\ 0 & 1 & -\dfrac{8}{5} & \dfrac{26}{5} \\ 0 & -7 & 5 & -24 \end{bmatrix}$$

Replace row three with $7R_2 + R_3$.

$$\begin{bmatrix} 1 & 2 & -3 & 9 \\ 0 & 1 & -\dfrac{8}{5} & \dfrac{26}{5} \\ 0 & 0 & -\dfrac{31}{5} & \dfrac{62}{5} \end{bmatrix}$$

Replace row 3 with $-\dfrac{5}{31}R_3$.

$$\begin{bmatrix} 1 & 2 & -3 & 9 \\ 0 & 1 & -\dfrac{8}{5} & \dfrac{26}{5} \\ 0 & 0 & 1 & -2 \end{bmatrix}$$

$z = -2$

$$y - \frac{8}{5}(-2) = \frac{26}{5}$$
$$y + \frac{16}{5} = \frac{26}{5}$$
$$y = 2$$
$$x + 2(2) - 3(-2) = 9$$
$$x + 4 + 6 = 9$$
$$x = -1$$

The solution set is $\{(-1, 2, -2)\}$.

39. $2x + 2y + 7z = -1$
$2x + y + 2z = 2$
$4x + 6y + z = 15$

$$\begin{bmatrix} 2 & 2 & 7 & -1 \\ 2 & 1 & 2 & 2 \\ 4 & 6 & 1 & 15 \end{bmatrix} \tfrac{1}{2}R_1$$

$$\begin{bmatrix} 1 & 1 & \dfrac{7}{2} & -\dfrac{1}{2} \\ 2 & 1 & 2 & 2 \\ 4 & 6 & 1 & 15 \end{bmatrix} -2R_1 + R_2$$

$$\begin{bmatrix} 1 & 1 & \dfrac{7}{2} & -\dfrac{1}{2} \\ 0 & -1 & -5 & 3 \\ 4 & 6 & 1 & 15 \end{bmatrix} -4R_1 + R_3$$

$$\begin{bmatrix} 1 & 1 & \dfrac{7}{2} & -\dfrac{1}{2} \\ 0 & -1 & -5 & 3 \\ 0 & 2 & -13 & 17 \end{bmatrix} -1R_2$$

$$\begin{bmatrix} 1 & 1 & \dfrac{7}{2} & -\dfrac{1}{2} \\ 0 & 1 & 5 & -3 \\ 0 & 2 & -13 & 17 \end{bmatrix} -2R_2 + R_3$$

$$\begin{bmatrix} 1 & 1 & \dfrac{7}{2} & -\dfrac{1}{2} \\ 0 & 1 & 5 & -3 \\ 0 & 0 & -23 & 23 \end{bmatrix} -\tfrac{1}{23}R_3$$

$$\begin{bmatrix} 1 & 1 & \dfrac{7}{2} & -\dfrac{1}{2} \\ 0 & 1 & 5 & -3 \\ 0 & 0 & 1 & -1 \end{bmatrix}$$

$z = -1$
$$y + 5z = -3$$
$$y + 5(-1) = -3$$
$$y - 5 = -3$$
$$y = 2$$

$$x + y + \frac{7}{2}z = -\frac{1}{2}$$
$$x + 2 + \frac{7}{2}(-1) = -\frac{1}{2}$$
$$x - \frac{3}{2} = -\frac{1}{2}$$
$$x = 1$$

The solution set is $\{(1, 2, -1)\}$.

41.
$$w + x + y + z = 4$$
$$2w + x - 2y - z = 0$$
$$w - 2x - y - 2z = -2$$
$$3w + 2x + y + 3z = 4$$

$$\begin{bmatrix} 1 & 1 & 1 & 1 & | & 4 \\ 2 & 1 & -2 & -1 & | & 0 \\ 1 & -2 & -1 & -2 & | & -2 \\ 3 & 2 & 1 & 3 & | & 4 \end{bmatrix} -2R_1 + R_2$$

$$\begin{bmatrix} 1 & 1 & 1 & 1 & | & 4 \\ 0 & -1 & -4 & -3 & | & -8 \\ 1 & -2 & -1 & -2 & | & -2 \\ 3 & 2 & 1 & 3 & | & 4 \end{bmatrix} -1R_1 + R_3$$

$$\begin{bmatrix} 1 & 1 & 1 & 1 & | & 4 \\ 0 & -1 & -4 & -3 & | & -8 \\ 0 & -3 & -2 & -3 & | & -6 \\ 3 & 2 & 1 & 3 & | & 4 \end{bmatrix} -3R_1 + R_4$$

$$\begin{bmatrix} 1 & 1 & 1 & 1 & | & 4 \\ 0 & -1 & -4 & -3 & | & -8 \\ 0 & -3 & -2 & -3 & | & -6 \\ 0 & -1 & -2 & 0 & | & -8 \end{bmatrix} -1R_2$$

$$\begin{bmatrix} 1 & 1 & 1 & 1 & | & 4 \\ 0 & 1 & 4 & 3 & | & 8 \\ 0 & -3 & -2 & -3 & | & -6 \\ 0 & -1 & -2 & 0 & | & -8 \end{bmatrix} 3R_2 + R_3$$

$$\begin{bmatrix} 1 & 1 & 1 & 1 & | & 4 \\ 0 & 1 & 4 & 3 & | & 8 \\ 0 & 0 & 10 & 6 & | & 18 \\ 0 & -1 & -2 & 0 & | & -8 \end{bmatrix} 1R_2 + R_4$$

$$\begin{bmatrix} 1 & 1 & 1 & 1 & | & 4 \\ 0 & 1 & 4 & 3 & | & 8 \\ 0 & 0 & 10 & 6 & | & 18 \\ 0 & 0 & 2 & 3 & | & 0 \end{bmatrix} \tfrac{1}{10}R_3$$

$$\begin{bmatrix} 1 & 1 & 1 & 1 & | & 4 \\ 0 & 1 & 4 & 3 & | & 8 \\ 0 & 0 & 1 & \frac{3}{5} & | & \frac{9}{5} \\ 0 & 0 & 2 & 3 & | & 0 \end{bmatrix} -2R_3 + R_4$$

$$\begin{bmatrix} 1 & 1 & 1 & 1 & | & 4 \\ 0 & 1 & 4 & 3 & | & 8 \\ 0 & 0 & 1 & \frac{3}{5} & | & \frac{9}{5} \\ 0 & 0 & 0 & \frac{9}{5} & | & -\frac{18}{5} \end{bmatrix} \tfrac{5}{9}R_4$$

$$\begin{bmatrix} 1 & 1 & 1 & 1 & | & 4 \\ 0 & 1 & 4 & 3 & | & 8 \\ 0 & 0 & 1 & \frac{3}{5} & | & \frac{9}{5} \\ 0 & 0 & 0 & 1 & | & -2 \end{bmatrix}$$

$$z = -2$$
$$y + \frac{3}{5}z = \frac{9}{5}$$
$$y + \frac{3}{5}(-2) = \frac{9}{5}$$
$$y - \frac{6}{5} = \frac{9}{5}$$
$$y = 3$$
$$x + 4y + 3z = 8$$
$$x + 4(3) + 3(-2) = 8$$
$$x + 6 = 8$$
$$x = 2$$
$$w + x + y + z = 4$$
$$w + 2 + 3 - 2 = 4$$
$$w + 3 = 4$$
$$w = 1$$

The solution set is $\{(1, 2, 3, -2)\}$.

43.
$$3w - 4x + y + z = 9$$
$$w + x - y - z = 0$$
$$2w + x + 4y - 2z = 3$$
$$-w + 2x + y - 3z = 3$$

$$\begin{bmatrix} 3 & -4 & 1 & 1 & | & 9 \\ 1 & 1 & -1 & -1 & | & 0 \\ 2 & 1 & 4 & -2 & | & 3 \\ -1 & 2 & 1 & -3 & | & 3 \end{bmatrix} R_1 \leftrightarrow R_2$$

$$\begin{bmatrix} 1 & 1 & -1 & -1 & | & 0 \\ 3 & -4 & 1 & 1 & | & 9 \\ 2 & 1 & 4 & -2 & | & 3 \\ -1 & 2 & 1 & -3 & | & 3 \end{bmatrix} -3R_1 + R_2$$

$$\begin{bmatrix} 1 & 1 & -1 & -1 & | & 0 \\ 0 & -7 & 4 & 4 & | & 9 \\ 2 & 1 & 4 & -2 & | & 3 \\ -1 & 2 & 1 & -3 & | & 3 \end{bmatrix} -2R_1 + R_3$$

$$\begin{bmatrix} 1 & 1 & -1 & -1 & | & 0 \\ 0 & -7 & 4 & 4 & | & 9 \\ 0 & -1 & 6 & 0 & | & 3 \\ -1 & 2 & 1 & -3 & | & 3 \end{bmatrix} 1R_1 + R_4$$

$$\begin{bmatrix} 1 & 1 & -1 & -1 & | & 0 \\ 0 & -7 & 4 & 4 & | & 9 \\ 0 & -1 & 6 & 0 & | & 3 \\ 0 & 3 & 0 & -4 & | & 3 \end{bmatrix} R_2 \leftrightarrow R_3$$

$$\begin{bmatrix} 1 & 1 & -1 & -1 & | & 0 \\ 0 & -1 & 6 & 0 & | & 3 \\ 0 & -7 & 4 & 4 & | & 9 \\ 0 & 3 & 0 & -4 & | & 3 \end{bmatrix} -R_2$$

$$\begin{bmatrix} 1 & 1 & -1 & -1 & | & 0 \\ 0 & 1 & -6 & 0 & | & -3 \\ 0 & -7 & 4 & 4 & | & 9 \\ 0 & 3 & 0 & -4 & | & 3 \end{bmatrix} 7R_2 + R_3$$

$$\begin{bmatrix} 1 & 1 & -1 & -1 & | & 0 \\ 0 & 1 & -6 & 0 & | & -3 \\ 0 & 0 & -38 & 4 & | & -12 \\ 0 & 3 & 0 & -4 & | & 3 \end{bmatrix} -3R_2 + R_4$$

$$\begin{bmatrix} 1 & 1 & -1 & -1 & | & 0 \\ 0 & 1 & -6 & 0 & | & -3 \\ 0 & 0 & -38 & 4 & | & -12 \\ 0 & 0 & 18 & -4 & | & 12 \end{bmatrix} -\frac{1}{38}R_3$$

$$\begin{bmatrix} 1 & 1 & -1 & -1 & | & 0 \\ 0 & 1 & -6 & 0 & | & -3 \\ 0 & 0 & 1 & -\frac{2}{19} & | & \frac{6}{19} \\ 0 & 0 & 18 & -4 & | & 12 \end{bmatrix} -18R_3 + R_4$$

$$\begin{bmatrix} 1 & 1 & -1 & -1 & | & 0 \\ 0 & 1 & -6 & 0 & | & -3 \\ 0 & 0 & 1 & -\frac{2}{19} & | & \frac{6}{19} \\ 0 & 0 & 0 & -\frac{40}{19} & | & \frac{120}{19} \end{bmatrix} -\frac{19}{40}R_4$$

$$\begin{bmatrix} 1 & 1 & -1 & -1 & | & 0 \\ 0 & 1 & -6 & 0 & | & -3 \\ 0 & 0 & 1 & -\frac{2}{19} & | & \frac{6}{19} \\ 0 & 0 & 0 & 1 & | & -3 \end{bmatrix}$$

$z = -3$

$$y - \frac{2}{19}z = \frac{6}{19}$$

$$y - \frac{2}{19}(-3) = \frac{6}{19}$$

$$y + \frac{6}{19} = \frac{6}{19}$$

$$y = 0$$

$x - 6y = -3$

$x - 6(0) = -3$

$x = -3$

$w + x - y - z = 0$

$w - 3 + 0 + 3 = 0$

$w = 0$

The solution set is $\{(0, -3, 0, -3)\}$.

45. $f(x) = ax^2 + bx + c$

Use the given function values to find three equations in terms of a, b, and c.

$f(-2) = a(-2)^2 + b(-2) + c = -4$

$4a - 2b + c = -4$

$f(1) = a(1)^2 + b(1) + c = 2$

$a + b + c = 2$

$f(2) = a(2)^2 + b(2) + c = 0$

$4a + 2b + c = 0$

System of equations:

$4a - 2b + c = -4$

$a + b + c = 2$

$4a + 2b + c = 0$

Matrix:

$$\begin{bmatrix} 4 & -2 & 1 & | & -4 \\ 1 & 1 & 1 & | & 2 \\ 4 & 2 & 1 & | & 0 \end{bmatrix}$$

This gives $a = -1$, $b = 1$, and $c = 2$.

Thus, $f(x) = -x^2 + x + 2$.

47. $f(x) = ax^3 + bx^2 + cx + d$

Use the given function values to find four equations in terms of a, b, c, and d.

$f(-1) = a(-1)^3 + b(-1)^2 + c(-1) + d = 0$

$-a + b - c + d = 0$

$f(1) = a(1)^3 + b(1)^2 + c(1) + d = 2$

$a + b + c + d = 2$

$f(2) = a(2)^3 + b(2)^2 + c(2) + d = 3$

$8a + 4b + 2c + d = 3$

$f(3) = a(3)^3 + b(3)^2 + c(3) + d = 12$

$27a + 9b + 3c + d = 12$

System of equations:

$-a + b - c + d = 0$

$a + b + c + d = 2$

$8a + 4b + 2c + d = 3$

$27a + 9b + 3c + d = 12$

Matrix:

$$\begin{bmatrix} -1 & 1 & -1 & 1 & | & 0 \\ 1 & 1 & 1 & 1 & | & 2 \\ 8 & 4 & 2 & 1 & | & 3 \\ 27 & 9 & 3 & 1 & | & 12 \end{bmatrix}$$

This gives $a = 1$, $b = -2$, $c = 0$, and $d = 3$.

Thus, $f(x) = x^3 - 2x^2 + 3$.

49. Let $A = \ln w$, $B = \ln x$, $C = \ln y$, and $D = \ln z$.

System of equations:

$2A + B + 3C - 2D = -6$

$4A + 3B + C - D = -2$

$A + B + C + D = -5$

$A + B - C - D = 5$

Matrix:

$$\begin{bmatrix} 2 & 1 & 3 & -2 & | & -6 \\ 4 & 3 & 1 & -1 & | & -2 \\ 1 & 1 & 1 & 1 & | & -5 \\ 1 & 1 & -1 & -1 & | & 5 \end{bmatrix}$$

This gives $A = -1$, $B = 1$, $C = -3$, and $D = -2$.

Substitute back to find w, x, y, and z.

$A = -1$	$B = 1$
$\ln w = -1$	$\ln x = 1$
$w = e^{-1}$	$x = e^1$
$w \approx 0.37$	$x \approx 2.72$
$C = -3$	$D = -2$
$\ln y = -3$	$\ln z = -2$
$y = e^{-3}$	$z = e^{-2}$
$y \approx 0.05$	$z \approx 0.14$

51. a. $s(t) = \dfrac{1}{2}at^2 + v_0 t + s_0$

Use the given function values to find three equations in terms of a, v_0, and s_0.

$s(1) = \dfrac{1}{2}a(1)^2 + v_0(1) + s_0 = 40$

$\dfrac{1}{2}a + v_0 + s_0 = 40$

$s(2) = \dfrac{1}{2}a(2)^2 + v_0(2) + s_0 = 48$

$2a + 2v_0 + s_0 = 48$

$s(3) = \dfrac{1}{2}a(3)^2 + v_0(3) + s_0 = 24$

$\dfrac{9}{2}a + 3v_0 + s_0 = 24$

System of equations:

$\dfrac{1}{2}a + v_0 + s_0 = 40$

$2a + 2v_0 + s_0 = 48$

$\dfrac{9}{2}a + 3v_0 + s_0 = 24$

Matrix:

$$\begin{bmatrix} \dfrac{1}{2} & 1 & 1 & | & 40 \\ 2 & 2 & 1 & | & 48 \\ \dfrac{9}{2} & 3 & 1 & | & 24 \end{bmatrix}$$

This gives $a = -32$, $v_0 = 56$, and $s_0 = 0$.

Thus, $s(t) = \dfrac{1}{2}(-32)t^2 + (56)t + (0)$

$s(t) = -16t^2 + 56t$

b. $s(t) = -16t^2 + 56t$

$s(3.5) = -16(3.5)^2 + 56(3.5) = 0$

This is the point $(3.5, 0)$.

The ball's height is 0 feet after 3.5 seconds. This is the point $(3.5, 0)$.

c. The maximum occurs when $x = -\dfrac{b}{2a}$.

$x = -\dfrac{b}{2a} = -\dfrac{v_0}{2a} = -\dfrac{56}{2(-16)} = 1.75$

$s(1.75) = -16(1.75)^2 + 56(1.75) = 49$

At 1.75 seconds the ball will reach its maximum height of 49 feet.

53. Let x = those who said yes
Let y = those who said no
Let z = those who are not sure
$x + y + z = 100$
$y = x + z + 22$
$2x = y + 7$
Write the equations in standard form.
$x + y + z = 100$
$-x + y - z = 22$
$2x - y = 7$

$$\begin{bmatrix} 1 & 1 & 1 & | & 100 \\ -1 & 1 & -1 & | & 22 \\ 2 & -1 & 0 & | & 7 \end{bmatrix}$$

Replace row two with $R_1 + R_2$.
Replace row three with $-2R_1 + R_3$.

$$\begin{bmatrix} 1 & 1 & 1 & | & 100 \\ 0 & 2 & 0 & | & 122 \\ 0 & -3 & -2 & | & -193 \end{bmatrix}$$

Replace row two with $\frac{1}{2}R_2$.

$$\begin{bmatrix} 1 & 1 & 1 & | & 100 \\ 0 & 1 & 0 & | & 61 \\ 0 & -3 & -2 & | & -193 \end{bmatrix}$$

Replace row three with $3R_2 + R_3$.

$$\begin{bmatrix} 1 & 1 & 1 & | & 100 \\ 0 & 1 & 0 & | & 61 \\ 0 & 0 & -2 & | & -10 \end{bmatrix}$$

Replace row three with $-\frac{1}{2}R_3$.

$$\begin{bmatrix} 1 & 1 & 1 & | & 100 \\ 0 & 1 & 0 & | & 61 \\ 0 & 0 & 1 & | & 5 \end{bmatrix}$$

$z = 5$
$y = 61$
$x + y + z = 100$
$x + 61 + 5 = 100$
$\qquad x = 34$
34% of single women said yes, 61% said no, 5% did not know.

55. Let x = Food A
Let y = Food B
Let z = Food C
$40x + 200y + 400z = 660$
$5x + 2y + 4z = 25$
$30x + 10y + 300z = 425$
$2x + 10y + 20z = 33$
$5x + 2y + 4z = 25$
$6x + 2y + 60z = 85$

$$\begin{bmatrix} 2 & 10 & 20 & | & 33 \\ 5 & 2 & 4 & | & 25 \\ 6 & 2 & 60 & | & 85 \end{bmatrix} \frac{1}{2}R_1$$

$$\begin{bmatrix} 1 & 5 & 10 & | & \frac{33}{2} \\ 5 & 2 & 4 & | & 25 \\ 6 & 2 & 60 & | & 85 \end{bmatrix} -5R_1 + R_2$$

$$\begin{bmatrix} 1 & 5 & 10 & | & \frac{33}{2} \\ 0 & -23 & -46 & | & -\frac{115}{2} \\ 6 & 2 & 60 & | & 85 \end{bmatrix} -6R_1 + R_3$$

$$\begin{bmatrix} 1 & 5 & 10 & | & \frac{33}{2} \\ 0 & -23 & -46 & | & -\frac{115}{2} \\ 0 & -28 & 0 & | & -14 \end{bmatrix} -\frac{1}{23}R_2$$

$$\begin{bmatrix} 1 & 5 & 10 & | & \frac{33}{2} \\ 0 & 1 & 2 & | & \frac{5}{2} \\ 0 & -28 & 0 & | & -14 \end{bmatrix} 28R_2 + R_3$$

$$\begin{bmatrix} 1 & 5 & 10 & | & \frac{33}{2} \\ 0 & 1 & 2 & | & \frac{5}{2} \\ 0 & 0 & 56 & | & 56 \end{bmatrix} \frac{1}{56}R_3$$

$$\begin{bmatrix} 1 & 5 & 10 & | & \frac{33}{2} \\ 0 & 1 & 2 & | & \frac{5}{2} \\ 0 & 0 & 1 & | & 1 \end{bmatrix}$$

$z = 1$
$y + 2z = \dfrac{5}{2}$
$y + 2 = \dfrac{5}{2}$
$2y + 4 = 5$
$2y = 1$
$y = \dfrac{1}{2}$

$$x + 5y + 10z = \frac{33}{2}$$

$$x + \frac{5}{2} + 10 = \frac{33}{2}$$

$$2x + 5 + 20 = 33$$

$$2x + 25 = 33$$

$$2x = 8$$

$$x = 4$$

4 ounces of Food A

$\frac{1}{2}$ ounce of Food B

1 ounce of Food C

65. Statement **d.** is true.

Statement **a.** is false. Multiplying a row by a negative fraction is permitted.

Statement **b.** is false because there are three variables in the system. The augmented matrix should be:

$$\begin{bmatrix} 1 & -3 & 0 & | & 5 \\ 0 & 1 & -2 & | & 7 \\ 2 & 0 & 1 & | & 4 \end{bmatrix}$$

Statement **c.** is false. When solving a system of three equations in three variables, we use row operations to obtain ones along the diagonal and zeros below the ones.

Section 6.2

Check Point Exercises

1.
$$\begin{array}{l} x - 2y - z = 5 \\ 2x - 3y - z = 0 \\ 3x - 4y - z = 1 \end{array} \rightarrow \begin{bmatrix} 1 & -2 & -1 & | & -5 \\ 2 & -3 & -1 & | & 0 \\ 3 & -4 & -1 & | & 1 \end{bmatrix}$$

$$\begin{bmatrix} 1 & -2 & -1 & | & -5 \\ 2 & -3 & -1 & | & 0 \\ 3 & -4 & -1 & | & 1 \end{bmatrix} \begin{array}{l} -2R_1 + R_2 \\ -3R_1 + R_3 \end{array}$$

$$\begin{bmatrix} 1 & -2 & -1 & | & -5 \\ 0 & 1 & 1 & | & 10 \\ 0 & 2 & 2 & | & 16 \end{bmatrix} -2R_2 + R_3$$

$$\begin{bmatrix} 1 & -2 & -1 & | & -5 \\ 0 & 1 & -1 & | & -10 \\ 0 & 0 & 0 & | & -4 \end{bmatrix}$$

$0x + 0y + 0z = -4$ This equation can never be a true statement. Consequently, the system has no solution. The solution set is $\varnothing$, the empty set.

2.
$$\begin{array}{l} x - 2y - z = 5 \\ 2x - 5y + 3z = 16 \\ x - 3y + 4z = 1 \end{array} \rightarrow \begin{bmatrix} 1 & -2 & -1 & | & 5 \\ 2 & -5 & 3 & | & 6 \\ 1 & -3 & 4 & | & 1 \end{bmatrix}$$

$$\begin{bmatrix} 1 & -2 & -1 & | & 5 \\ 2 & -5 & 3 & | & 6 \\ 1 & -3 & 4 & | & 1 \end{bmatrix} \begin{array}{l} -2R_1 + R_2 \\ -1R_1 + R_3 \end{array}$$

$$\begin{bmatrix} 1 & -2 & -1 & | & 5 \\ 0 & -1 & 5 & | & -4 \\ 0 & -1 & 5 & | & -4 \end{bmatrix} -1R_2$$

$$\begin{bmatrix} 1 & -2 & -1 & | & 5 \\ 0 & 1 & -5 & | & 4 \\ 0 & -1 & 5 & | & -4 \end{bmatrix} 1R_2 + R_3$$

$$\begin{bmatrix} 1 & -2 & -1 & | & 5 \\ 0 & 1 & -5 & | & 4 \\ 0 & 0 & 0 & | & 0 \end{bmatrix}$$

$0x + 0y + 0z = 0$ or $0 = 0$

This equation, $0x + 0y + 0z = 0$ is *dependent* on the other two equations. Thus, it can be dropped from the system which can now be expressed in the form

$$\begin{bmatrix} 1 & -2 & -1 & | & 5 \\ 0 & 1 & -5 & | & 4 \end{bmatrix}$$

The original system is equivalent to the system
$$x - 2y - z = 5$$
$$y - 5z = 4$$

Solve for x and y in terms of z.
$$y = 5z + 4$$

Use back-substitution for y in the previous equation.
$$x - 2(5z + 4) - z = 5$$
$$x - 10z - 8 - z = 5$$
$$x = 11z + 13$$

Finally, letting $z = t$ (or any letter of your choice), the solutions to the system are all of the form $x = 11t + 13$, $y = 5t + 4$, $z = t$, where t is a real number. The solution set of the system with dependent equations can be written as $\{(11t + 13, 5t + 4, t)\}$.

3. $\quad \begin{aligned} x+2y+3z &= 70 \\ x+y+z &= 60 \end{aligned} \rightarrow \begin{bmatrix} 1 & 2 & 3 & | & 70 \\ 1 & 1 & 1 & | & 60 \end{bmatrix}$

$\begin{bmatrix} 1 & 2 & 3 & | & 70 \\ 1 & 1 & 1 & | & 60 \end{bmatrix} \; -1R_1 + R_2$

$\begin{bmatrix} 1 & 2 & 3 & | & 70 \\ 0 & -1 & -2 & | & -10 \end{bmatrix} \; -1R_2$

$\begin{bmatrix} 1 & 2 & 3 & | & 70 \\ 0 & 1 & 2 & | & 10 \end{bmatrix} \rightarrow \begin{aligned} x+2y+3z &= 70 \\ y+2z &= 10 \end{aligned}$

Express x and y in terms of z using back-substitution.

$y = -2z + 10$

$x + 2(-2z + 10) + 3z = 70$

$x - 4z + 20 + 3z = 70$

$x = z + 50$

With $z = t$, the ordered solution (x, y, z) enables us to express the system's solution set as $\{(t + 50, -2t + 10, t)\}$.

4. **a.** I^1: $10 + 5 = 15$ cars enter I^1, and $w + z$ cars leave I_1, then $w + z = 15$.
I^2: $20 + 10 = 30$ cars enter I^2 and $w + x$ cars leave I^2, then $w + x = 30$.
I^3: $15 + 30 = 45$ cars enter I_3 and $x + y$ cars leave I^3, then $x + y = 45$.
I^4: $10 + 20 = 30$ cars enter I_4 and $y + z$ cars leave I^4, then $y + z = 30$.
The system of equations that describes this situation is given by

$w + z = 15$

$w + x = 30$

$x + y = 45$

$y + z = 30$

b. $\begin{bmatrix} 1 & 0 & 0 & 1 & | & 15 \\ 1 & 1 & 0 & 0 & | & 30 \\ 0 & 1 & 1 & 0 & | & 45 \\ 0 & 0 & 1 & 1 & | & 30 \end{bmatrix} \; -1R_1 + R_2$

$\begin{bmatrix} 1 & 0 & 0 & 1 & | & 15 \\ 0 & 1 & 0 & -1 & | & 15 \\ 0 & 1 & 1 & 0 & | & 45 \\ 0 & 0 & 1 & 1 & | & 30 \end{bmatrix} \; -1R_2 + R_3$

$\begin{bmatrix} 1 & 0 & 0 & 1 & | & 15 \\ 0 & 1 & 0 & -1 & | & 15 \\ 0 & 0 & 1 & 1 & | & 30 \\ 0 & 0 & 1 & 1 & | & 30 \end{bmatrix} \; -1R_3 + R_4$

$\begin{bmatrix} 1 & 0 & 0 & 1 & | & 15 \\ 0 & 1 & 0 & -1 & | & 15 \\ 0 & 0 & 1 & 1 & | & 30 \\ 0 & 0 & 0 & 0 & | & 0 \end{bmatrix}$

$x + w = 15$

$y - w = 15$

$z + w = 30$

The last row of the matrix shows that the system has dependent equations and infinitely many solutions.
Let z be any real number.
Express w, x and y in terms of z:

$w = 15 - z$

$x = 15 + z$

$y = 30 - z$

With $w = t$, the ordered solution (w, x, y, z) enables us to express the system's solution set as $\{(-t + 15, t + 15, -t + 30, t)\}$

Exercise Set 6.2

1. $\begin{bmatrix} 5 & 12 & 1 & | & 10 \\ 2 & 5 & 2 & | & -1 \\ 1 & 2 & -3 & | & 5 \end{bmatrix} \; R_1 \leftrightarrow R_3$

$\begin{bmatrix} 1 & 2 & -3 & | & 5 \\ 2 & 5 & 2 & | & -1 \\ 5 & 12 & 1 & | & 10 \end{bmatrix} \; \begin{matrix} -2R_1 + R_2 \\ -5R_1 + R_3 \end{matrix}$

$\begin{bmatrix} 1 & 2 & -3 & | & 5 \\ 0 & 1 & 8 & | & -11 \\ 0 & 2 & 16 & | & -15 \end{bmatrix} \; -2R_2 + R_3$

$\begin{bmatrix} 1 & 2 & 3 & | & 5 \\ 0 & 1 & 8 & | & -11 \\ 0 & 0 & 0 & | & 7 \end{bmatrix}$

From the last row, we see that the system has no solution. The solution set is $\varnothing$, the empty set.

3. $\begin{bmatrix} 5 & 8 & -6 & | & 14 \\ 3 & 4 & -2 & | & 8 \\ 1 & 2 & -2 & | & 3 \end{bmatrix} \; R_1 \leftrightarrow R_3$

$\begin{bmatrix} 1 & 2 & -2 & | & 3 \\ 3 & 4 & -2 & | & 8 \\ 5 & 8 & -6 & | & 14 \end{bmatrix} \; \begin{matrix} -3R_1 + R_2 \\ -5R_1 + R_3 \end{matrix}$

$$\begin{bmatrix} 1 & 2 & -2 & | & 3 \\ 0 & -2 & 4 & | & -1 \\ 0 & -2 & 4 & | & -1 \end{bmatrix} -1R_2 + R_3$$

$$\begin{bmatrix} 1 & 2 & -2 & | & 3 \\ 0 & -2 & 4 & | & -1 \\ 0 & 0 & 0 & | & 0 \end{bmatrix} -\frac{1}{2}R_2$$

$$\begin{bmatrix} 1 & 2 & -2 & | & 3 \\ 0 & 1 & -2 & | & \frac{1}{2} \\ 0 & 0 & 0 & | & 0 \end{bmatrix}$$

$$x + 2y - 2z = 3$$

The system $\begin{array}{c} x + 2y - 2z = 3 \\ y - 2z = \frac{1}{2} \end{array}$ has no unique

solution. Express x and y in terms of z:

$$y = 2z + \frac{1}{2}$$

$$x + 2\left(2z + \frac{1}{2}\right) - 2z = 3$$

$$x + 4z + 1 - 2z = 3$$

$$x + 2z + 1 = 3$$

$$x = -2z + 2$$

With $z = t$, the complete solution to the system is

$$\left\{\left(-2t + 2,\ 2t + \frac{1}{2},\ t\right)\right\}.$$

5. $$\begin{bmatrix} 3 & 4 & 2 & | & 3 \\ 4 & -2 & -8 & | & -4 \\ 1 & 1 & -1 & | & 3 \end{bmatrix} R_1 \leftrightarrow R_3$$

$$\begin{bmatrix} 1 & 1 & -1 & | & 3 \\ 4 & -2 & -8 & | & -4 \\ 3 & 4 & 2 & | & 3 \end{bmatrix} \begin{array}{l} -4R_1 + R_2 \\ -3R_1 + R_3 \end{array}$$

$$\begin{bmatrix} 1 & 1 & -1 & | & 3 \\ 0 & -6 & -4 & | & -16 \\ 0 & 1 & 5 & | & -6 \end{bmatrix} R_2 \leftrightarrow R_3$$

$$\begin{bmatrix} 1 & 1 & -1 & | & 3 \\ 0 & 1 & 5 & | & -6 \\ 0 & -6 & -4 & | & -16 \end{bmatrix} 6R_2 + R_3$$

$$\begin{bmatrix} 1 & 1 & 1 & | & 3 \\ 0 & 1 & 5 & | & -6 \\ 0 & 0 & 26 & | & -52 \end{bmatrix} \frac{1}{26}R_3$$

$$\begin{bmatrix} 1 & 1 & -1 & | & 3 \\ 0 & 1 & 5 & | & -6 \\ 0 & 0 & 1 & | & -2 \end{bmatrix}$$

This corresponds to the system
$$x + y - z = 3$$

$$y + 5z = -6$$
$$z = -2$$
Use back-substitution to find the values of x and y:
$$y + 5(-2) = -6$$
$$y - 10 = -6$$
$$y = 4$$
$$x + 4 + 2 = 3$$
$$x + 6 = 3$$
$$x = -3$$
The solution to the system is $\{(-3, 4, -2)\}$.

7. $$\begin{bmatrix} 8 & 5 & 11 & | & 30 \\ -1 & -4 & 2 & | & 3 \\ 2 & -1 & 5 & | & 12 \end{bmatrix} R_1 \leftrightarrow R_2$$

$$\begin{bmatrix} -1 & -4 & 2 & | & 3 \\ 8 & 5 & 11 & | & 30 \\ 2 & -1 & 5 & | & 12 \end{bmatrix} -1R_1$$

$$\begin{bmatrix} 1 & 4 & -2 & | & -3 \\ 8 & 5 & 11 & | & 30 \\ 2 & -1 & 5 & | & 12 \end{bmatrix} \begin{array}{l} -8R_1 + R_2 \\ -2R_1 + R_3 \end{array}$$

$$\begin{bmatrix} 1 & 4 & -2 & | & -3 \\ 0 & -27 & 27 & | & 54 \\ 0 & -9 & 9 & | & 18 \end{bmatrix} -\frac{1}{27}R_2$$

$$\begin{bmatrix} 1 & 4 & -2 & | & -3 \\ 0 & 1 & -1 & | & -2 \\ 0 & -9 & 9 & | & 18 \end{bmatrix} 9R_2 + R_3$$

$$\begin{bmatrix} 1 & 4 & -2 & | & -3 \\ 0 & 1 & -1 & | & -2 \\ 0 & 0 & 0 & | & 0 \end{bmatrix}$$

The system $\begin{array}{c} x + 4y - 2z = -3 \\ y - z = -2 \end{array}$ has no unique

solution. Express x and y in terms of z:
$$y = -2 + z$$
$$x + 4(-2 + z) - 2z = -3$$
$$x - 8 + 4z - 2z = -3$$
$$x - 8 + 2z = -3$$
$$x = 5 - 2z$$
With $z = t$, the complete solution to the system is
$$\{(5 - 2t, -2 + t, t)\}.$$

9.
$$\begin{bmatrix} 1 & -2 & -1 & -3 & | & -9 \\ 1 & 1 & -1 & 0 & | & 0 \\ 3 & 4 & 0 & 1 & | & 6 \\ 0 & 2 & -2 & 1 & | & 3 \end{bmatrix} \begin{matrix} \\ -1R_1 + R_2 \\ -3R_1 + R_3 \\ \\ \end{matrix}$$

$$\begin{bmatrix} 1 & -2 & -1 & -3 & | & -9 \\ 0 & 3 & 0 & 3 & | & 9 \\ 0 & 10 & 3 & 10 & | & 33 \\ 0 & 2 & -2 & 1 & | & 3 \end{bmatrix} \tfrac{1}{3}R_2$$

$$\begin{bmatrix} 1 & -2 & -1 & -3 & | & -9 \\ 0 & 1 & 0 & 1 & | & 3 \\ 0 & 10 & 3 & 10 & | & 33 \\ 0 & 2 & -2 & 1 & | & 3 \end{bmatrix} \begin{matrix} \\ \\ -10R_2 + R_3 \\ -2R_2 + R_4 \end{matrix}$$

$$\begin{bmatrix} 1 & -2 & -1 & -3 & | & -9 \\ 0 & 1 & 0 & 1 & | & 3 \\ 0 & 0 & 3 & 0 & | & 3 \\ 0 & 0 & -2 & -1 & | & -3 \end{bmatrix} \tfrac{1}{3}R_3$$

$$\begin{bmatrix} 1 & -2 & -1 & -3 & | & -9 \\ 0 & 1 & 0 & 1 & | & 3 \\ 0 & 0 & 1 & 0 & | & 1 \\ 0 & 0 & -2 & -1 & | & -3 \end{bmatrix} 2R_3 + R_4$$

$$\begin{bmatrix} 1 & -2 & -1 & -3 & | & -9 \\ 0 & 1 & 0 & 1 & | & 3 \\ 0 & 0 & 1 & 0 & | & 1 \\ 0 & 0 & 0 & -1 & | & -1 \end{bmatrix} -1R_4$$

$$\begin{bmatrix} 1 & -2 & -1 & -3 & | & -9 \\ 0 & 1 & 0 & 1 & | & 3 \\ 0 & 0 & 1 & 0 & | & 1 \\ 0 & 0 & 0 & 1 & | & 1 \end{bmatrix}$$

This corresponds to the system
$$w - 2x - y - 3z = -9$$
$$x + z = 3$$
$$y = 1$$
$$z = 1$$

Use back-substitution to find the values of w and x:
$$x + 1 = 3$$
$$x = 2$$
$$w - 2(2) - 1 - 3(1) = -9$$
$$w - 4 - 1 - 3 = -9$$
$$w - 8 = -9$$
$$w = -1$$

The solution to the system is $\{(-1, 2, 1, 1)\}$.

11.
$$\begin{bmatrix} 2 & 1 & -1 & 0 & | & 3 \\ 1 & -3 & 2 & 0 & | & -4 \\ 3 & 1 & -3 & 1 & | & 1 \\ 1 & 2 & -4 & -1 & | & -2 \end{bmatrix} R_1 \leftrightarrow R_2$$

$$\begin{bmatrix} 1 & -3 & 2 & 0 & | & -4 \\ 2 & 1 & -1 & 0 & | & 3 \\ 3 & 1 & -3 & 1 & | & 1 \\ 1 & 2 & -4 & -1 & | & -2 \end{bmatrix} \begin{matrix} \\ -2R_1 + R_2 \\ -3R_1 + R_3 \\ -1R_1 + R_4 \end{matrix}$$

$$\begin{bmatrix} 1 & -3 & 2 & 0 & | & -4 \\ 0 & 7 & -5 & 0 & | & 11 \\ 0 & 10 & -9 & 1 & | & 13 \\ 0 & 5 & -6 & -1 & | & 2 \end{bmatrix} \tfrac{1}{7}R_2$$

$$\begin{bmatrix} 1 & -3 & 2 & 0 & | & -4 \\ 0 & 1 & -\tfrac{5}{7} & 0 & | & \tfrac{11}{7} \\ 0 & 10 & -9 & 1 & | & 13 \\ 0 & 5 & -6 & -1 & | & 2 \end{bmatrix} \begin{matrix} \\ \\ -10R_2 + R_3 \\ -5R_2 + R_4 \end{matrix}$$

$$\begin{bmatrix} 1 & -3 & 2 & 0 & | & -4 \\ 0 & 1 & -\tfrac{5}{7} & 0 & | & \tfrac{11}{7} \\ 0 & 0 & -\tfrac{13}{7} & 1 & | & -\tfrac{19}{7} \\ 0 & 0 & -\tfrac{17}{7} & -1 & | & -\tfrac{41}{7} \end{bmatrix} -\tfrac{7}{13}R_3$$

$$\begin{bmatrix} 1 & -3 & 2 & 0 & | & -4 \\ 0 & 1 & -\tfrac{5}{7} & 0 & | & \tfrac{11}{7} \\ 0 & 0 & 1 & -\tfrac{7}{13} & | & \tfrac{19}{13} \\ 0 & 0 & -\tfrac{17}{7} & -1 & | & -\tfrac{41}{7} \end{bmatrix} \tfrac{17}{7}R_3 + R_4$$

$$\begin{bmatrix} 1 & -3 & 2 & 0 & | & -4 \\ 0 & 1 & -\tfrac{5}{7} & 0 & | & \tfrac{11}{7} \\ 0 & 0 & 1 & -\tfrac{7}{13} & | & \tfrac{19}{13} \\ 0 & 0 & 0 & -\tfrac{30}{13} & | & -\tfrac{30}{13} \end{bmatrix} -\tfrac{13}{30}R_4$$

$$\begin{bmatrix} 1 & -3 & 2 & 0 & | & -4 \\ 0 & 1 & -\tfrac{5}{7} & 0 & | & \tfrac{11}{7} \\ 0 & 0 & 1 & -\tfrac{7}{13} & | & \tfrac{19}{13} \\ 0 & 0 & 0 & 1 & | & 1 \end{bmatrix}$$

This corresponds to the system
$$w - 3x + 2y = -4$$
$$x - \frac{5}{7}y = \frac{11}{7}$$
$$y - \frac{7}{13}z = \frac{19}{13}$$
$$z = 1$$

Use back-substitution to find the values of
w, x, and y:

$$y - \frac{7}{13}z = \frac{19}{13}$$

$$y - \frac{7}{13}(1) = \frac{19}{13}$$

$$y = 2$$

$$x - \frac{5}{7}(2) = \frac{11}{7}$$

$$x - \frac{10}{7} = \frac{11}{7}$$

$$x = 3$$

$$w - 3(3) + 2(2) = -4$$

$$w - 9 + 4 = -4$$

$$w - 5 = -4$$

$$w = 1$$

The solution to the system is $\{(1, 3, 2, 1)\}$.

13.
$$\begin{bmatrix} 1 & -3 & 1 & -4 & | & 4 \\ -2 & 1 & 2 & 0 & | & -2 \\ 3 & -2 & 1 & -6 & | & 2 \\ -1 & 3 & 2 & -1 & | & -6 \end{bmatrix} \begin{matrix} 2R_1 + R_2 \\ -3R_1 + R_3 \\ R_1 + R_4 \end{matrix}$$

$$\begin{bmatrix} 1 & -3 & 1 & -4 & | & 4 \\ 0 & -5 & 4 & -8 & | & 6 \\ 0 & 7 & -2 & 6 & | & -10 \\ 0 & 0 & 3 & -5 & | & -2 \end{bmatrix} -\frac{1}{5}R_2$$

$$\begin{bmatrix} 1 & -3 & 1 & -4 & | & 4 \\ 0 & 1 & -\frac{4}{5} & \frac{8}{5} & | & -\frac{6}{5} \\ 0 & 7 & -2 & 6 & | & -10 \\ 0 & 0 & 3 & -5 & | & -2 \end{bmatrix} -7R_2 + R_3$$

$$\begin{bmatrix} 1 & -3 & 1 & -4 & | & 4 \\ 0 & 1 & -\frac{4}{5} & \frac{8}{5} & | & -\frac{6}{5} \\ 0 & 0 & \frac{18}{5} & -\frac{26}{5} & | & -\frac{8}{5} \\ 0 & 0 & 3 & -5 & | & -2 \end{bmatrix} \frac{5}{18}R_3$$

$$\begin{bmatrix} 1 & -3 & 1 & -4 & | & 4 \\ 0 & 1 & -\frac{4}{5} & \frac{8}{5} & | & -\frac{6}{5} \\ 0 & 0 & 1 & -\frac{13}{9} & | & -\frac{4}{9} \\ 0 & 0 & 3 & -5 & | & -2 \end{bmatrix} -3R_3 + R_4$$

$$\begin{bmatrix} 1 & -3 & 1 & -4 & | & 4 \\ 0 & 1 & -\frac{4}{5} & \frac{8}{5} & | & -\frac{6}{5} \\ 0 & 0 & 1 & -\frac{13}{9} & | & -\frac{4}{9} \\ 0 & 0 & 0 & -\frac{2}{3} & | & -\frac{2}{3} \end{bmatrix} -\frac{3}{2}R_4$$

$$\begin{bmatrix} 1 & -3 & 1 & -4 & | & 4 \\ 0 & 1 & -\frac{4}{5} & \frac{8}{5} & | & -\frac{6}{5} \\ 0 & 0 & 1 & -\frac{13}{9} & | & -\frac{4}{9} \\ 0 & 0 & 0 & 1 & | & 1 \end{bmatrix}$$

This corresponds to the system

$$w - 3x + y - 4z = 4$$

$$x - \frac{4}{5}y + \frac{8}{5}z = -\frac{6}{5}$$

$$y - \frac{13}{9}z = -\frac{4}{9}$$

$$z = 1$$

Use back-substitution to find the values of w, z, and y:

$$y - \frac{13}{9}(1) = -\frac{4}{9}$$

$$y = 1$$

$$x - \frac{4}{5}(1) + \frac{8}{5}(1) = -\frac{6}{5}$$

$$x + \frac{4}{5} = -\frac{6}{5}$$

$$x = -2$$

$$w - 3(-2) + 1 - 4 = 4$$

$$w + 6 - 3 = 4$$

$$w = 1$$

The solution to the system is $\{(1, -2, 1, 1)\}$.

15.
$$\begin{bmatrix} 2 & 1 & -1 & | & 2 \\ 3 & 3 & -2 & | & 3 \end{bmatrix} \frac{1}{2}R_1 \quad \begin{bmatrix} 1 & \frac{1}{2} & -\frac{1}{2} & | & 1 \\ 3 & 3 & -2 & | & 3 \end{bmatrix} -3R_1 + R_2$$

$$\begin{bmatrix} 1 & \frac{1}{2} & -\frac{1}{2} & | & 1 \\ 0 & \frac{3}{2} & -\frac{1}{2} & | & 0 \end{bmatrix} \frac{2}{3}R_2$$

$$\begin{bmatrix} 1 & \frac{1}{2} & -\frac{1}{2} & | & 1 \\ 0 & 1 & -\frac{1}{3} & | & 0 \end{bmatrix}$$

The system $x + \frac{1}{2}y - \frac{1}{2}z = 1$ has no unique

$$y - \frac{1}{3}z = 0$$

solution. Express x and y in terms of z:

$$y = \frac{1}{3}z$$

$$x + \frac{1}{2}\left(\frac{1}{3}z\right) - \frac{1}{2}z = 1$$

$$x + \frac{1}{6}z - \frac{1}{2}z = 1$$

$$x - \frac{1}{3}z = 1$$

$$x = 1 + \frac{1}{3}z$$

With $z = t$, the complete solution to the system is

$$\left\{\left(1 + \frac{1}{3}t, \frac{1}{3}t, t\right)\right\}.$$

17. The system $\begin{array}{c}x+2y+3z=5\\ y-5z=0\end{array}$ has no unique

solution. Express x and y in terms of z:

$y = 5z$

$x + 2(5z) + 3z = 5$

$x + 10z + 3z = 5$

$x = -13z + 5$

With $z = t$, the complete solution to the system is

$\{(-13t + 5, 5t, t)\}$.

19. $\begin{bmatrix}1 & 1 & -2 & | & 2\\ 3 & -1 & -6 & | & -7\end{bmatrix}-3R_1+R_2$

$\begin{bmatrix}1 & 1 & -2 & | & 2\\ 0 & -4 & 0 & | & -13\end{bmatrix}-\frac{1}{4}R_2$

$\begin{bmatrix}1 & 1 & -2 & | & 2\\ 0 & 1 & 0 & | & \frac{13}{4}\end{bmatrix}$

$\begin{array}{c}x+y-2z=2\\ y=\frac{13}{4}\end{array}$

The system $\qquad$ has no unique

solution. Express x in terms of z:

$x + \frac{13}{4} - 2z = 2$

$x = 2z - \frac{5}{4}$

With $z = t$, the complete solution to the system is

$\left\{\left(2t - \frac{5}{4}, \frac{13}{4}, t\right)\right\}$.

21. $\begin{bmatrix}1 & 1 & -1 & 1 & | & -2\\ 2 & -1 & 2 & -1 & | & 7\\ -1 & 2 & 1 & 2 & | & -1\end{bmatrix}\begin{array}{c}-2R_1+R_2\\ 1R_1+R_3\end{array}$

$\begin{bmatrix}1 & 1 & -1 & 1 & | & -2\\ 0 & -3 & 4 & -3 & | & 11\\ 0 & 3 & 0 & 3 & | & -3\end{bmatrix}R_2\leftrightarrow R_3$

$\begin{bmatrix}1 & 1 & -1 & 1 & | & -2\\ 0 & 3 & 0 & 3 & | & -3\\ 0 & -3 & 4 & -3 & | & 11\end{bmatrix}\frac{1}{3}R_2$

$\begin{bmatrix}1 & 1 & -1 & 1 & | & -2\\ 0 & 1 & 0 & 1 & | & -1\\ 0 & -3 & 4 & -3 & | & 11\end{bmatrix}3R_2+R_3$

$\begin{bmatrix}1 & 1 & -1 & 1 & | & -2\\ 0 & 1 & 0 & 1 & | & -1\\ 0 & 0 & 4 & 0 & | & 8\end{bmatrix}\frac{1}{4}R_3$

$\begin{bmatrix}1 & 1 & -1 & 1 & | & -2\\ 0 & 1 & 0 & 1 & | & -1\\ 0 & 0 & 1 & 0 & | & 2\end{bmatrix}$

The system $\begin{array}{c}x+y-z+w=-2\\ x+z=-1\\ y=2\end{array}$ has no unique

solution. Let $z = t$ and use back substitution to find remaining variables. The complete solution to the system is $\{(1, -t - 1, 2, t)\}$.

23. $\begin{bmatrix}1 & 2 & 3 & -1 & | & 7\\ 0 & 2 & -3 & 1 & | & 4\\ 1 & -4 & 1 & 0 & | & 3\end{bmatrix}-1R_1+R_3$

$\begin{bmatrix}1 & 2 & 3 & -1 & | & 7\\ 0 & 2 & -3 & 1 & | & 4\\ 0 & -6 & -2 & 1 & | & -4\end{bmatrix}\frac{1}{2}R_2$

$\begin{bmatrix}1 & 2 & 3 & -1 & | & 7\\ 0 & 1 & -\frac{3}{2} & \frac{1}{2} & | & 2\\ 0 & -6 & -2 & 1 & | & -4\end{bmatrix}6R_2+R_3$

$\begin{bmatrix}1 & 2 & 3 & -1 & | & 7\\ 0 & 1 & -\frac{3}{2} & \frac{1}{2} & | & 2\\ 0 & 0 & -11 & 4 & | & 8\end{bmatrix}-\frac{1}{11}R_3$

$\begin{bmatrix}1 & 2 & 3 & -1 & | & 7\\ 0 & 1 & -\frac{3}{2} & \frac{1}{2} & | & 2\\ 0 & 0 & 1 & -\frac{4}{11} & | & -\frac{8}{11}\end{bmatrix}$

The system has no unique solution. Let $z = t$ and use back substitution to find remaining variables. The complete solution to the system is $\left\{\left(-\frac{2}{11}t + \frac{81}{11}, \frac{1}{22}t + \frac{10}{11}, \frac{4}{11}t - \frac{8}{11}, t\right)\right\}$.

25. a. System of equations:
$$4w - 2x + 2y - 3z = 0$$
$$7w - x - y - 3z = 0$$
$$w + x - y - z = 0$$

b. Reduced system:
$$w - 0.5z = 0$$
$$x = 0$$
$$y - 0.5z = 0$$
Find w and y in terms of z.
$$w - 0.5z = 0$$
$$w = 0.5z$$
$$y - 0.5z = 0$$
$$y = 0.5z$$
The complete solution to the system is
$$\{(0.5z, 0, 0.5z, z)\}.$$

27. a. System of equations:
$$w + 2x + 5y + 5z = 3$$
$$w + x + 3y + 4z = -1$$
$$w - x - y + 2z = 3$$

b. Reduced system:
$$w + y + 3z = 1$$
$$x + 2y + z = -2$$
Find w and x in terms of y and z.
$$w + y + 3z = 1$$
$$w = 1 - y - 3z$$
$$x + 2y + z = -2$$
$$x = -2 - 2y - z$$
The complete solution to the system is
$$\{(1 - y - 3z, -2 - 2y - z, y, z)\}.$$

29. $z + 12 = x + 6$

31. $x - y = 4$
$$x - z = 6$$
$$y - z = 2$$

$$\begin{bmatrix} 1 & -1 & 0 & 4 \\ 1 & 0 & -1 & 6 \\ 0 & 1 & -1 & 2 \end{bmatrix} \begin{matrix} -1R_1 + R_2 \\ \\ \end{matrix}$$

$$\begin{bmatrix} 1 & -1 & 0 & 4 \\ 0 & -1 & 1 & -2 \\ 0 & 1 & -1 & 2 \end{bmatrix} -1R_2$$

$$\begin{bmatrix} 1 & -1 & 0 & 4 \\ 0 & 1 & -1 & 2 \\ 0 & 1 & -1 & 2 \end{bmatrix} \begin{matrix} \\ -1R_2 + R_3 \\ 1R_2 + R_1 \end{matrix}$$

$$\begin{bmatrix} 1 & 0 & -1 & 6 \\ 0 & 1 & -1 & 2 \\ 0 & 0 & 0 & 0 \end{bmatrix}$$

The system has no unique solution. Express x and y in terms of z:
$$x - z = 6$$
$$y - z = 2$$
$$x = z + 6$$
$$y = z + 2$$
With $z = t$, the complete solution to the system is $\{(t + 6, t + 2, t)\}$.

33. a. From left to right along Palm Drive, then along Sunset Drive, we get the equations
$$w + z = 200 + 180 = 380;$$
$$w + x = 400 + 200 = 600;$$
$$z + 70 = y + 20 \text{ or } y - z = 50;$$
$$y + 200 = x + 30 \text{ or } x - y = 170.$$
The system is
$$w + z = 380$$
$$w + x = 600$$
$$y - z = 50$$
$$x - y = 170$$

b.
$$\begin{bmatrix} 1 & 0 & 0 & 1 & 380 \\ 0 & 1 & 0 & -1 & 220 \\ 0 & 0 & 1 & -1 & 50 \\ 0 & 1 & -1 & 0 & 170 \end{bmatrix} \begin{matrix} \\ \\ -1R_2 + R_4 \\ \end{matrix}$$

$$\begin{bmatrix} 1 & 0 & 0 & 1 & 380 \\ 0 & 1 & 0 & -1 & 220 \\ 0 & 0 & 1 & -1 & 50 \\ 0 & 0 & -1 & 1 & -50 \end{bmatrix} \begin{matrix} \\ \\ 1R_3 + R_4 \\ \end{matrix}$$

$$\begin{bmatrix} 1 & 0 & 0 & 1 & 380 \\ 0 & 1 & 0 & -1 & 220 \\ 0 & 0 & 1 & -1 & 50 \\ 0 & 0 & 0 & 0 & 0 \end{bmatrix}$$

The system has no unique solution. Express x and y and z in terms of z:
$$w = 380 - z$$
$$x = 220 + z$$
$$y = 50 + z$$
With $z = t$, the complete solution to the system is $\{(380 - t, 220 + t, 50 + t, t)\}$.

c. Letting $z = 50$, the solution is
$w = 380 - 50 = 330$
$x = 220 + 50 = 270$
$y = 50 + 50 = 100$

35. Let $x =$ the amount of Food 1,
$y =$ the amount of Food 2, and
$z =$ the amount of Food 3, in ounces.
The amount of vitamin A is $20x + 30y + 10z$; the amount of iron is $20x + 10y + 10z$; the amount of calcium is $10x + 10y + 30z$.

a. Not having Food 1 means that all x terms are left out. The vitamin A requirement can then be represented by $30y + 10z = 220$; the iron requirement is $10y + 10z = 180$; the calcium requirement is $10y + 30z = 340$. The corresponding system is
$30y + 10z = 220$
$10y + 10z = 180$
$10y + 30z = 340$.
Dividing all of the numbers by 10, the matrix for this system is

$$\begin{bmatrix} 3 & 1 & | & 22 \\ 1 & 1 & | & 18 \\ 1 & 3 & | & 34 \end{bmatrix} R_1 \leftrightarrow R_2$$

$$\begin{bmatrix} 1 & 1 & | & 18 \\ 3 & 1 & | & 22 \\ 1 & 3 & | & 34 \end{bmatrix} \begin{matrix} \\ -3R_1 + R_2 \\ -1R_1 + R_3 \end{matrix}$$

$$\begin{bmatrix} 1 & 1 & | & 18 \\ 0 & -2 & | & -32 \\ 0 & 2 & | & 16 \end{bmatrix} 1R_2 + R_3$$

$$\begin{bmatrix} 1 & 1 & | & 18 \\ 0 & -2 & | & -32 \\ 0 & 0 & | & -16 \end{bmatrix}.$$

From the last row, we see that the system has no solution, so there is no way to satisfy these dietary requirements with no Food 1 available.

b. With Food 1 available, and dropping the vitamin A requirement, the system is
$20x + 10y + 10z = 180$
$10x + 10y + 30z = 340$.
Dividing all of the numbers by 10, the matrix for this system is

$$\begin{bmatrix} 2 & 1 & 1 & | & 18 \\ 1 & 1 & 3 & | & 34 \end{bmatrix} R_1 \leftrightarrow R_2$$

$$\begin{bmatrix} 1 & 1 & 3 & | & 34 \\ 2 & 1 & 1 & | & 18 \end{bmatrix} -2R_1 + R_2$$

$$\begin{bmatrix} 1 & 1 & 3 & | & 34 \\ 0 & -1 & -5 & | & -50 \end{bmatrix} -1R_2$$

$$\begin{bmatrix} 1 & 1 & 3 & | & 34 \\ 0 & 1 & 5 & | & 50 \end{bmatrix}.$$

The system $\begin{aligned} x + y + 3z &= 34 \\ y + 5z &= 50 \end{aligned}$ has no unique solution. Express x and y in terms of z:
$y = -5z + 50$
$x + (-5z + 50) + 3z = 34$
$x - 2z + 50 = 34$
$x = 2z - 16$
Now we can choose a value for z, i.e., an amount of Food 3, and find the corresponding values of x and y. Note that negative amounts of food are not realistic, so $z \geq 0$, $y = -5z + 50 \geq 0$, and $x = 2z - 16 \geq 0$. These conditions are equivalent to $8 \leq z \leq 10$.
Using $z = 8$ and $z = 10$, two possibilities are 0 ounces of Food 1, 10 ounces of Food 2, and 8 ounces of Food 3 or 4 ounces of Food 1, 0 ounces of Food 2, and 10 ounces of Food 3. (Other answers are possible.)

41.
$$\begin{bmatrix} 1 & 3 & 1 & | & a^2 \\ 2 & 5 & 2a & | & 0 \\ 1 & 1 & a^2 & | & -9 \end{bmatrix} \begin{matrix} \\ -2R_1 + R_2 \\ -1R_1 + R_3 \end{matrix}$$

$$\begin{bmatrix} 1 & 3 & 1 & | & a^2 \\ 0 & -1 & 2a-2 & | & -2a^2 \\ 0 & -2 & a^2-1 & | & -9-a^2 \end{bmatrix} -1R_2$$

$$\begin{bmatrix} 1 & 3 & 1 & | & a^2 \\ 0 & 1 & 2-2a & | & 2a^2 \\ 0 & -2 & a^2-1 & | & -9-a^2 \end{bmatrix} 2R_2 + R_3$$

$$\begin{bmatrix} 1 & 3 & 1 & | & a^2 \\ 0 & 1 & 2-2a & | & 2a^2 \\ 0 & 0 & a^2-4a+3 & | & -9+3a^2 \end{bmatrix}$$

The system will be inconsistent when $a^2 - 4a + 3 = 0$ but $-9 + 3a^2 \neq 0$.
$a^2 - 4a + 3 = (a-1)(a-3) = 0$ when $a = 1$ or $a = 3$. $-9 + 3a^2 = 0$ when $a = \pm\sqrt{3}$.
Thus, the system is inconsistent when $a = 1$ or $a = 3$.

Section 6.3

Check Point Exercises

1.　**a.**　The matrix $A = \begin{bmatrix} 5 & -2 \\ -3 & \pi \\ 1 & 6 \end{bmatrix}$ has 3 rows and

　　2 columns, so it is of order 3×2.

　b.　The element a_{12} is in the first row and second column. Thus, $a_{12} = -2$. The element a_{31} is in the third row and first column. Thus, $a_{31} = 1$.

2.　**a.**　$\begin{bmatrix} -4 & 3 \\ 7 & -6 \end{bmatrix} + \begin{bmatrix} 6 & -3 \\ 2 & -4 \end{bmatrix}$

　　$= \begin{bmatrix} -4+6 & 3+(-3) \\ 7+2 & -6+(-4) \end{bmatrix} = \begin{bmatrix} 2 & 0 \\ 9 & -10 \end{bmatrix}$

　b.　$\begin{bmatrix} 5 & 4 \\ -3 & 7 \\ 0 & 1 \end{bmatrix} - \begin{bmatrix} -4 & 8 \\ 6 & 0 \\ -5 & 3 \end{bmatrix}$

　　$= \begin{bmatrix} 5-(-4) & 4-8 \\ -3-6 & 7-0 \\ 0-(-5) & 1-3 \end{bmatrix}$

　　$= \begin{bmatrix} 9 & -4 \\ -9 & 7 \\ 5 & -2 \end{bmatrix}$

3.　**a.**　$-6B = -6\begin{bmatrix} -1 & -2 \\ 8 & 5 \end{bmatrix}$

　　$= \begin{bmatrix} -6(-1) & -6(-2) \\ -6(8) & -6(5) \end{bmatrix}$

　　$= \begin{bmatrix} -6 & 12 \\ -48 & -30 \end{bmatrix}$

　b.　$3A + 2B = \begin{bmatrix} -4 & 1 \\ 3 & 0 \end{bmatrix} + 2\begin{bmatrix} -1 & -2 \\ 8 & 5 \end{bmatrix}$

　　$= \begin{bmatrix} 3(-4) & 3(1) \\ 3(3) & 3(0) \end{bmatrix} + \begin{bmatrix} 2(-1) & 2(-2) \\ 2(8) & 2(5) \end{bmatrix}$

　　$= \begin{bmatrix} -12 & 3 \\ 9 & 0 \end{bmatrix} + \begin{bmatrix} -2 & -4 \\ 16 & 10 \end{bmatrix}$

　　$= \begin{bmatrix} -12+(-2) & 3+(-4) \\ 9+16 & 0+10 \end{bmatrix}$

　　$= \begin{bmatrix} -14 & -1 \\ 25 & 10 \end{bmatrix}$

4.　$3X + A = B$
　$3X = B - A$

　$X = \frac{1}{3}(B - A)$

　$X = \frac{1}{3}\left(\begin{bmatrix} -10 & 1 \\ -9 & 17 \end{bmatrix} - \begin{bmatrix} 2 & -8 \\ 0 & 4 \end{bmatrix} \right)$

　$X = \frac{1}{3}\begin{bmatrix} -12 & 9 \\ -9 & 13 \end{bmatrix}$

　$X = \begin{bmatrix} -4 & 3 \\ -3 & \frac{13}{3} \end{bmatrix}$

5.　Given $A = \begin{bmatrix} 1 & 3 \\ 2 & 5 \end{bmatrix}$ and $B = \begin{bmatrix} 4 & 6 \\ 1 & 0 \end{bmatrix}$,

　$AB = \begin{bmatrix} 1 & 3 \\ 2 & 5 \end{bmatrix} \cdot \begin{bmatrix} 4 & 6 \\ 1 & 0 \end{bmatrix} = \begin{bmatrix} 1(4)+3(1) & 1(6)+3(0) \\ 2(4)+5(1) & 2(6)+5(0) \end{bmatrix}$

　$= \begin{bmatrix} 7 & 6 \\ 13 & 12 \end{bmatrix}$

6. If $A = \begin{bmatrix} 2 & 0 & 4 \end{bmatrix}$ and $B = \begin{bmatrix} 1 \\ 3 \\ 7 \end{bmatrix}$, then

$$AB = \begin{bmatrix} 2 & 0 & 4 \end{bmatrix} \begin{bmatrix} 1 \\ 3 \\ 7 \end{bmatrix}$$

$$= \begin{bmatrix} 2(1) + 0(3) + 4(7) \end{bmatrix}$$

$$= \begin{bmatrix} 2 + 0 + 28 \end{bmatrix}$$

$$= \begin{bmatrix} 30 \end{bmatrix}$$

and $BA = \begin{bmatrix} 1 \\ 3 \\ 7 \end{bmatrix} \begin{bmatrix} 2 & 0 & 4 \end{bmatrix} = \begin{bmatrix} 1(2) & 1(0) & 1(4) \\ 3(2) & 3(0) & 3(4) \\ 7(2) & 7(0) & 7(4) \end{bmatrix} = \begin{bmatrix} 2 & 0 & 4 \\ 6 & 0 & 12 \\ 14 & 0 & 28 \end{bmatrix}.$

7. a.
$$\begin{bmatrix} 1 & 3 \\ 0 & 2 \end{bmatrix} \cdot \begin{bmatrix} 2 & 3 & -1 & 6 \\ 0 & 5 & 4 & 1 \end{bmatrix}$$

$$= \begin{bmatrix} 1(2) + 3(0) & 1(3) + 3(5) & 1(-1) + 3(4) & 1(6) + 3(1) \\ 0(2) + 2(0) & 0(3) + 2(5) & 0(-1) + 2(4) & 0(6) + 2(1) \end{bmatrix}$$

$$= \begin{bmatrix} 2 & 18 & 11 & 9 \\ 0 & 10 & 8 & 2 \end{bmatrix}$$

b.
$$\begin{bmatrix} 2 & 3 & -1 & 6 \\ 0 & 5 & 4 & 1 \end{bmatrix} \begin{bmatrix} 1 & 3 \\ 0 & 2 \end{bmatrix}$$

The number of columns in the first matrix does not equal the number of rows in the second matrix. Thus, the product of these two matrices is undefined.

8. Because the L is dark gray and the background is light gray, the digital photograph can be represented by the matrix
$$\begin{bmatrix} 2 & 1 & 1 \\ 2 & 1 & 1 \\ 2 & 2 & 1 \end{bmatrix}$$

We can make the L light gray by decreasing each 2 in the above matrix to 1. We can make the background black by increasing each 1 in the matrix to 3. This is accomplished using the following matrix addition.
$$\begin{bmatrix} 2 & 1 & 1 \\ 2 & 1 & 1 \\ 2 & 2 & 1 \end{bmatrix} + \begin{bmatrix} -1 & 2 & 2 \\ -1 & 2 & 2 \\ -1 & -1 & 2 \end{bmatrix} = \begin{bmatrix} 1 & 3 & 3 \\ 1 & 3 & 3 \\ 1 & 1 & 3 \end{bmatrix}$$

9. a.
$$\begin{bmatrix} 0 & 3 & 4 \\ 0 & 5 & 2 \end{bmatrix} + \begin{bmatrix} -3 & -3 & -3 \\ -1 & -1 & -1 \end{bmatrix} = \begin{bmatrix} -3 & 0 & 1 \\ -1 & 4 & 1 \end{bmatrix}$$

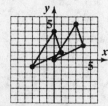

b. $2\begin{bmatrix} 0 & 3 & 4 \\ 0 & 5 & 2 \end{bmatrix} = \begin{bmatrix} 0 & 6 & 8 \\ 0 & 10 & 4 \end{bmatrix}$

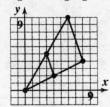

c. $\begin{bmatrix} 1 & 0 \\ 0 & -1 \end{bmatrix}\begin{bmatrix} 0 & 3 & 4 \\ 0 & 5 & 2 \end{bmatrix} = \begin{bmatrix} (-1)(0)+0(0) & (-1)(3)+0(5) & (-1)(4)+0(2) \\ 0(0)+1(0) & 0(3)+1(5) & 0(4)+1(2) \end{bmatrix}$

$\qquad = \begin{bmatrix} 0 & -3 & -4 \\ 0 & 5 & 2 \end{bmatrix}$

Multiplication with $\begin{bmatrix} 1 & 0 \\ 0 & -1 \end{bmatrix}$ reflects the triangle over the x-axis.

Exercise Set 6.3

1. **a.** 2×3

    b. a_{32} does not exist (A only has 2 rows).

       $a_{23} = -1$

3. **a.** 3×4

    b. $a_{32} = \dfrac{1}{2};\ a_{23} = -6$

5. $\begin{bmatrix} x \\ 4 \end{bmatrix} = \begin{bmatrix} 6 \\ y \end{bmatrix}$

    $x = 6$

    $y = 4$

7. $\begin{bmatrix} x & 2y \\ z & 9 \end{bmatrix} = \begin{bmatrix} 4 & 12 \\ 3 & 9 \end{bmatrix}$

    $x = 4$

    $2y = 12$

    $y = 6$

    $z = 3$

9. **a.** $A + B = \begin{bmatrix} 4+5 & 1+9 \\ 3+0 & 2+7 \end{bmatrix} = \begin{bmatrix} 9 & 10 \\ 3 & 9 \end{bmatrix}$

    b. $A - B = \begin{bmatrix} 4-5 & 1-9 \\ 3-0 & 2-7 \end{bmatrix} = \begin{bmatrix} -1 & -8 \\ 3 & -5 \end{bmatrix}$

    c. $-4A = \begin{bmatrix} -16 & -4 \\ -12 & -8 \end{bmatrix}$

d. $3A+2B=\begin{bmatrix}12+10 & 3+18\\9+0 & 6+14\end{bmatrix}=\begin{bmatrix}22 & 21\\9 & 20\end{bmatrix}$

11. a. $A+B=\begin{bmatrix}1+2 & 3+(-1)\\3+3 & 4+(-2)\\5+0 & 6+1\end{bmatrix}=\begin{bmatrix}3 & 2\\6 & 2\\5 & 7\end{bmatrix}$

b. $A-B=\begin{bmatrix}1-2 & 3-(-1)\\3-3 & 4-(-2)\\5-0 & 6-1\end{bmatrix}=\begin{bmatrix}-1 & 4\\0 & 6\\5 & 5\end{bmatrix}$

c. $-4A=\begin{bmatrix}-4 & -12\\-12 & -16\\-20 & -24\end{bmatrix}$

d. $3A+2B=\begin{bmatrix}3+4 & 9-2\\9+6 & 12-4\\15+0 & 18+2\end{bmatrix}=\begin{bmatrix}7 & 7\\15 & 8\\15 & 20\end{bmatrix}$

13. a. $A+B=\begin{bmatrix}2+(-5)\\-4+3\\1+(-1)\end{bmatrix}=\begin{bmatrix}-3\\-1\\0\end{bmatrix}$

b. $A-B=\begin{bmatrix}2-(-5)\\-4-3\\1-(-1)\end{bmatrix}=\begin{bmatrix}7\\-7\\2\end{bmatrix}$

c. $-4A=\begin{bmatrix}-8\\16\\-4\end{bmatrix}$

d. $3A+2B=\begin{bmatrix}6-10\\-12+6\\3-2\end{bmatrix}=\begin{bmatrix}-4\\-6\\1\end{bmatrix}$

15. a. $A+B=\begin{bmatrix}2+6 & -10+10 & -2+(-2)\\14+0 & 12+(-12) & 10+(-4)\\4+(-5) & -2+2 & 2+(-2)\end{bmatrix}$

$=\begin{bmatrix}8 & 0 & -4\\14 & 0 & 6\\-1 & 0 & 0\end{bmatrix}$

b. $A - B = \begin{bmatrix} 2-6 & -10-10 & -2-(-2) \\ 14-0 & 12-(-12) & 10-(-4) \\ 4-(-5) & -2-2 & 2-(-2) \end{bmatrix}$

$\qquad\quad = \begin{bmatrix} -4 & -20 & 0 \\ 14 & 24 & 14 \\ 9 & -4 & 4 \end{bmatrix}$

c. $-4A = \begin{bmatrix} -8 & 40 & 8 \\ -56 & -48 & -40 \\ -16 & 8 & -8 \end{bmatrix}$

d. $3A + 2B = \begin{bmatrix} 6+12 & -30+20 & -6-4 \\ 42+0 & 36-24 & 30-8 \\ 12-10 & -6+4 & 6-4 \end{bmatrix}$

$\qquad\qquad\quad = \begin{bmatrix} 18 & -10 & -10 \\ 42 & 12 & 22 \\ 2 & -2 & 2 \end{bmatrix}$

17. $X - A = B$

$\qquad X = A + B$

$\qquad X = \begin{bmatrix} -3 & -7 \\ 2 & -9 \\ 5 & 0 \end{bmatrix} + \begin{bmatrix} -5 & -1 \\ 0 & 0 \\ 3 & -4 \end{bmatrix} = \begin{bmatrix} -8 & -8 \\ 2 & -9 \\ 8 & -4 \end{bmatrix}$

19. $2X + A = B$

$\qquad 2X = B - A$

$\qquad X = \dfrac{1}{2}(B - A)$

$\qquad X = \dfrac{1}{2}\left(\begin{bmatrix} -5 & -1 \\ 0 & 0 \\ 3 & -4 \end{bmatrix} - \begin{bmatrix} -3 & -7 \\ 2 & -9 \\ 5 & 0 \end{bmatrix} \right) = \dfrac{1}{2}\begin{bmatrix} -2 & 6 \\ -2 & 9 \\ -2 & -4 \end{bmatrix} = \begin{bmatrix} -1 & 3 \\ -1 & \dfrac{9}{2} \\ -1 & -2 \end{bmatrix}$

21. $3X + 2A = B$

$\qquad 3X = B - 2A$

$\qquad X = \dfrac{1}{3}(B - 2A)$

$\qquad X = \dfrac{1}{3}\left(\begin{bmatrix} -5 & -1 \\ 0 & 0 \\ 3 & -4 \end{bmatrix} - 2\begin{bmatrix} -3 & -7 \\ 2 & -9 \\ 5 & 0 \end{bmatrix} \right) = \dfrac{1}{3}\begin{bmatrix} 1 & 13 \\ -4 & 18 \\ -7 & -4 \end{bmatrix} = \begin{bmatrix} \dfrac{1}{3} & \dfrac{13}{3} \\ -\dfrac{4}{3} & 6 \\ -\dfrac{7}{3} & -\dfrac{4}{3} \end{bmatrix}$

23.
$$B - X = 4A$$
$$B - 4A = X$$

$$X = \begin{bmatrix} -5 & -1 \\ 0 & 0 \\ 3 & -4 \end{bmatrix} - 4 \begin{bmatrix} -3 & -7 \\ 2 & -9 \\ 5 & 0 \end{bmatrix} = \begin{bmatrix} -5 & -1 \\ 0 & 0 \\ 3 & -4 \end{bmatrix} + \begin{bmatrix} 12 & 28 \\ -8 & 36 \\ -20 & 0 \end{bmatrix} = \begin{bmatrix} 7 & 27 \\ -8 & 36 \\ -17 & -4 \end{bmatrix}$$

25.
$$4A + 3B = -2X$$
$$-\frac{1}{2}(4A + 3B) = X$$

$$X = -\frac{1}{2}\left(4\begin{bmatrix} -3 & -7 \\ 2 & -9 \\ 5 & 0 \end{bmatrix} + 3\begin{bmatrix} -5 & -1 \\ 0 & 0 \\ 3 & -4 \end{bmatrix} \right) = -\frac{1}{2}\left(\begin{bmatrix} -12 & -28 \\ 8 & -36 \\ 20 & 0 \end{bmatrix} + \begin{bmatrix} -15 & -3 \\ 0 & 0 \\ 9 & -12 \end{bmatrix} \right) = -\frac{1}{2}\begin{bmatrix} -27 & -31 \\ 8 & -36 \\ 29 & -12 \end{bmatrix} = \begin{bmatrix} \frac{27}{2} & \frac{31}{2} \\ -4 & 18 \\ -\frac{29}{2} & 6 \end{bmatrix}$$

27. a.
$$AB = \begin{bmatrix} 1 & 3 \\ 5 & 3 \end{bmatrix}\begin{bmatrix} 3 & -2 \\ -1 & 6 \end{bmatrix} = \begin{bmatrix} (1)(3)+(3)(-1) & (1)(-2)+(3)(6) \\ (5)(3)+(3)(-1) & (5)(-2)+(3)(6) \end{bmatrix} = \begin{bmatrix} 3-3 & -2+18 \\ 15-3 & -10+18 \end{bmatrix} = \begin{bmatrix} 0 & 16 \\ 12 & 8 \end{bmatrix}$$

b.
$$BA = \begin{bmatrix} 3 & -2 \\ -1 & 6 \end{bmatrix}\begin{bmatrix} 1 & 3 \\ 5 & 3 \end{bmatrix} = \begin{bmatrix} (3)(1)+(-2)(5) & (3)(3)+(-2)(3) \\ (-1)(1)+(6)(5) & (-1)(3)+(6)(3) \end{bmatrix} = \begin{bmatrix} 3-10 & 9-6 \\ -1+30 & -3+18 \end{bmatrix} = \begin{bmatrix} -7 & 3 \\ 29 & 15 \end{bmatrix}$$

29. a.
$$AB = \begin{bmatrix} 1 & 2 & 3 & 4 \end{bmatrix}\begin{bmatrix} 1 \\ 2 \\ 3 \\ 4 \end{bmatrix} = [(1)(1)+(2)(2)+(3)(3)+(4)(4)] = [1+4+9+16] = [30]$$

b.
$$BA = \begin{bmatrix} 1 \\ 2 \\ 3 \\ 4 \end{bmatrix}\begin{bmatrix} 1 & 2 & 3 & 4 \end{bmatrix} = \begin{bmatrix} (1)(1) & (1)(2) & (1)(3) & (1)(4) \\ (2)(1) & (2)(2) & (2)(3) & (2)(4) \\ (3)(1) & (3)(2) & (3)(3) & (3)(4) \\ (4)(1) & (4)(2) & (4)(3) & (4)(4) \end{bmatrix} = \begin{bmatrix} 1 & 2 & 3 & 4 \\ 2 & 4 & 6 & 8 \\ 3 & 6 & 9 & 12 \\ 4 & 8 & 12 & 16 \end{bmatrix}$$

31. a.
$$AB = \begin{bmatrix} 1 & -1 & 4 \\ 4 & -1 & 3 \\ 2 & 0 & -2 \end{bmatrix}\begin{bmatrix} 1 & 1 & 0 \\ 1 & 2 & 4 \\ 1 & -1 & 3 \end{bmatrix}$$

$$= \begin{bmatrix} (1)(1)+(-1)(1)+(4)(1) & (1)(1)+(-1)(2)+(4)(-1) & (1)(0)+(-1)(4)+(4)(3) \\ (4)(1)+(-1)(1)+(3)(1) & (4)(1)+(-1)(2)+(3)(-1) & (4)(0)+(-1)(4)+(3)(3) \\ (2)(1)+(0)(1)+(-2)(1) & (2)(1)+(0)(2)+(-2)(-1) & (2)(0)+(0)(4)+(-2)(3) \end{bmatrix}$$

$$= \begin{bmatrix} 1-1+4 & 1-2-4 & 0-4+12 \\ 4-1+3 & 4-2-3 & 0-4+9 \\ 2+0-2 & 2+0+2 & 0+0-6 \end{bmatrix} = \begin{bmatrix} 4 & -5 & 8 \\ 6 & -1 & 5 \\ 0 & 4 & -6 \end{bmatrix}$$

b. $BA = \begin{bmatrix} 1 & 1 & 0 \\ 1 & 2 & 4 \\ 1 & -1 & 3 \end{bmatrix} \begin{bmatrix} 1 & -1 & 4 \\ 4 & -1 & 3 \\ 2 & 0 & -2 \end{bmatrix}$

$= \begin{bmatrix} (1)(1)+(1)(4)+(0)(2) & (1)(-1)+(1)(-1)+(0)(0) & (1)(4)+(1)(3)+(0)(-2) \\ (1)(1)+(2)(4)+(4)(2) & (1)(-1)+(2)(-1)+(4)(0) & (1)(4)+(2)(3)+(4)(-2) \\ (1)(1)+(-1)(4)+(3)(2) & (1)(-1)+(-1)(-1)+(3)(0) & (1)(4)+(-1)(3)+(3)(-2) \end{bmatrix}$

$= \begin{bmatrix} 1+4+0 & -1-1+0 & 4+3+0 \\ 1+8+8 & -1-2+0 & 4+6-8 \\ 1-4+6 & -1+1+0 & 4-3-6 \end{bmatrix} = \begin{bmatrix} 5 & -2 & 7 \\ 17 & -3 & 2 \\ 3 & 0 & -5 \end{bmatrix}$

33. a. $AB = \begin{bmatrix} 4 & 2 \\ 6 & 1 \\ 3 & 5 \end{bmatrix} \begin{bmatrix} 2 & 3 & 4 \\ -1 & -2 & 0 \end{bmatrix} = \begin{bmatrix} (4)(2)+(2)(-1) & (4)(3)+(2)(-2) & (4)(4)+(2)(0) \\ (6)(2)+(1)(-1) & (6)(3)+(1)(-2) & (6)(4)+(1)(0) \\ (3)(2)+(5)(-1) & (3)(3)+(5)(-2) & (3)(4)+(5)(0) \end{bmatrix}$

$= \begin{bmatrix} 8-2 & 12-4 & 16+0 \\ 12-1 & 18-2 & 24+0 \\ 6-5 & 9-10 & 12+0 \end{bmatrix} = \begin{bmatrix} 6 & 8 & 16 \\ 11 & 16 & 24 \\ 1 & -1 & 12 \end{bmatrix}$

b. $BA = \begin{bmatrix} 2 & 3 & 4 \\ -1 & -2 & 0 \end{bmatrix} \begin{bmatrix} 4 & 2 \\ 6 & 1 \\ 3 & 5 \end{bmatrix} = \begin{bmatrix} (2)(4)+(3)(6)+(4)(3) & (2)(2)+(3)(1)+(4)(5) \\ (-1)(4)+(-2)(6)+(0)(3) & (-1)(2)+(-2)(1)+(0)(5) \end{bmatrix}$

$= \begin{bmatrix} 8+18+12 & 4+3+20 \\ -4-12+0 & -2-2+0 \end{bmatrix} = \begin{bmatrix} 38 & 27 \\ -16 & -4 \end{bmatrix}$

35. a. $AB = \begin{bmatrix} 2 & -3 & 1 & -1 \\ 1 & 1 & -2 & 1 \end{bmatrix} \begin{bmatrix} 1 & 2 \\ -1 & 1 \\ 5 & 4 \\ 10 & 5 \end{bmatrix} = \begin{bmatrix} (2)(1)+(-3)(-1)+(1)(5)+(-1)(10) & (2)(2)+(-3)(1)+(1)(4)+(-1)(5) \\ (1)(1)+(1)(-1)+(-2)(5)+(1)(10) & (1)(2)+(1)(1)+(-2)(4)+(1)(5) \end{bmatrix}$

$= \begin{bmatrix} 2+3+5-10 & 4-3+4-5 \\ 1-1-10+10 & 2+1-8+5 \end{bmatrix} = \begin{bmatrix} 0 & 0 \\ 0 & 0 \end{bmatrix}$

37. $4B - 3C = \begin{bmatrix} 20 & 4 \\ -8 & -8 \end{bmatrix} - \begin{bmatrix} 3 & -3 \\ -3 & 3 \end{bmatrix} = \begin{bmatrix} 20-3 & 4-(-3) \\ -8-(-3) & -8-3 \end{bmatrix} = \begin{bmatrix} 17 & 7 \\ -5 & -11 \end{bmatrix}$

39. $BC + CB = \begin{bmatrix} 5-1 & -5+1 \\ -2+2 & 2-2 \end{bmatrix} + \begin{bmatrix} 5+2 & 1+2 \\ -5-2 & -1-2 \end{bmatrix} = \begin{bmatrix} 4 & -4 \\ 0 & 0 \end{bmatrix} + \begin{bmatrix} 7 & 3 \\ -7 & -3 \end{bmatrix} = \begin{bmatrix} 11 & -1 \\ -7 & -3 \end{bmatrix}$

41. $A - C$ is not defined because A is 3 x 2 and C is 2 x 2.

43. $A(BC) = \begin{bmatrix} 4 & 0 \\ -3 & 5 \\ 0 & 1 \end{bmatrix} \begin{bmatrix} 5-1 & -5+1 \\ -2+2 & 2-2 \end{bmatrix} = \begin{bmatrix} 4 & 0 \\ -3 & 5 \\ 0 & 1 \end{bmatrix} \begin{bmatrix} 4 & -4 \\ 0 & 0 \end{bmatrix} = \begin{bmatrix} 16+0 & -16+0 \\ -12+0 & 12+0 \\ 0+0 & 0+0 \end{bmatrix} = \begin{bmatrix} 16 & -16 \\ -12 & 12 \\ 0 & 0 \end{bmatrix}$

45. $(A+B)(C-D) = \left(\begin{bmatrix} 1 & 0 \\ 0 & 1 \end{bmatrix} + \begin{bmatrix} 1 & 0 \\ 0 & -1 \end{bmatrix} \right) \left(\begin{bmatrix} -1 & 0 \\ 0 & 1 \end{bmatrix} - \begin{bmatrix} -1 & 0 \\ 0 & -1 \end{bmatrix} \right) = \left(\begin{bmatrix} 2 & 0 \\ 0 & 0 \end{bmatrix} \right) \left(\begin{bmatrix} 0 & 0 \\ 0 & 2 \end{bmatrix} \right) = \begin{bmatrix} 0 & 0 \\ 0 & 0 \end{bmatrix}$

49. $BZ = \begin{bmatrix} 1 & 0 \\ 0 & -1 \end{bmatrix}\begin{bmatrix} x \\ y \end{bmatrix} = \begin{bmatrix} x \\ -y \end{bmatrix}$ This reflects the graphic about the *x*-axis because all *y*-coordinates are negated.

51. **a.** $\begin{bmatrix} 1 & 3 & 1 \\ 3 & 3 & 3 \\ 1 & 3 & 1 \end{bmatrix}$

b. $\begin{bmatrix} 1 & 3 & 1 \\ 3 & 3 & 3 \\ 1 & 3 & 1 \end{bmatrix} + \begin{bmatrix} -1 & -1 & -1 \\ -1 & -1 & -1 \\ -1 & -1 & -1 \end{bmatrix} = \begin{bmatrix} 0 & 2 & 0 \\ 2 & 2 & 2 \\ 0 & 2 & 0 \end{bmatrix}$

c. $\begin{bmatrix} 1 & 3 & 1 \\ 3 & 3 & 3 \\ 1 & 3 & 1 \end{bmatrix} + \begin{bmatrix} 1 & -2 & 1 \\ -2 & -2 & -2 \\ 1 & -2 & 1 \end{bmatrix} = \begin{bmatrix} 2 & 1 & 2 \\ 1 & 1 & 1 \\ 2 & 1 & 2 \end{bmatrix}$

53. $\begin{bmatrix} 0 & 3 & 3 & 1 & 1 & 0 \\ 0 & 0 & 1 & 1 & 5 & 5 \end{bmatrix} + \begin{bmatrix} -2 & -2 & -2 & -2 & -2 & -2 \\ -3 & -3 & -3 & -3 & -3 & -3 \end{bmatrix} = \begin{bmatrix} -2 & 1 & 1 & -1 & -1 & -2 \\ -3 & -3 & -2 & -2 & 2 & 2 \end{bmatrix}$

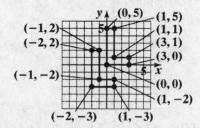

55. $0.5\begin{bmatrix} 0 & 3 & 3 & 1 & 1 & 0 \\ 0 & 0 & 1 & 1 & 5 & 5 \end{bmatrix} + \begin{bmatrix} 0 & 0 & 0 & 0 & 0 & 0 \\ 1 & 1 & 1 & 1 & 1 & 1 \end{bmatrix} = \begin{bmatrix} 0 & 1.5 & 1.5 & 0.5 & 0.5 & 0 \\ 0 & 0 & 0.5 & 0.5 & 2.5 & 2.5 \end{bmatrix} + \begin{bmatrix} 0 & 0 & 0 & 0 & 0 & 0 \\ 1 & 1 & 1 & 1 & 1 & 1 \end{bmatrix}$

$= \begin{bmatrix} 0 & 1.5 & 1.5 & 0.5 & 0.5 & 0 \\ 1 & 1 & 1.5 & 1.5 & 3.5 & 3.5 \end{bmatrix}$

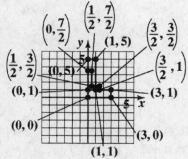

57. a. $AB = \begin{bmatrix} 1 & 0 \\ 0 & -1 \end{bmatrix} \cdot \begin{bmatrix} 0 & 3 & 3 & 1 & 1 & 0 \\ 0 & 0 & 1 & 1 & 5 & 5 \end{bmatrix} = \begin{bmatrix} 0 & 3 & 3 & 1 & 1 & 0 \\ 0 & 0 & -1 & -1 & -5 & -5 \end{bmatrix}$

b.

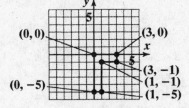

Rotated L about the *x*-axis.

59. a. $AB = \begin{bmatrix} 0 & -1 \\ 1 & 0 \end{bmatrix} \cdot \begin{bmatrix} 0 & 3 & 3 & 1 & 1 & 0 \\ 0 & 0 & 1 & 1 & 5 & 5 \end{bmatrix} = \begin{bmatrix} 0 & 0 & -1 & -1 & -5 & -5 \\ 0 & 3 & 3 & 1 & 1 & 0 \end{bmatrix}$

b.

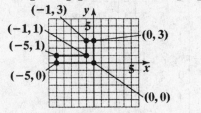

Rotated L 90° counterclockwise about the origin.

61. a. $A = \begin{bmatrix} 61 & 24 \\ 33 & 47 \\ 6 & 29 \end{bmatrix}$

b. $B = \begin{bmatrix} 67 & 23 \\ 28 & 44 \\ 5 & 33 \end{bmatrix}$

c. $B - A = \begin{bmatrix} 67 & 23 \\ 28 & 44 \\ 5 & 33 \end{bmatrix} - \begin{bmatrix} 61 & 24 \\ 33 & 47 \\ 6 & 29 \end{bmatrix} = \begin{bmatrix} 6 & -1 \\ -5 & -3 \\ -1 & 4 \end{bmatrix}$

$B - A$ represents the percent change from 2000 to 2004.

63. a.   System 1: The midterm and final both count for 50% of the course grade.
System 2: The midterm counts for 30% of the course grade and the final counts for 70%

b. $AB = \begin{bmatrix} 84 & 87.2 \\ 79 & 81 \\ 90 & 88.4 \\ 73 & 68.6 \\ 69 & 73.4 \end{bmatrix}$.

System 1 grades are listed first (if different).
Student 1: B; Student 2: C or B; Student 3: A or B; Student 4: C or D; Student 5: D or C

79. $AB = \begin{bmatrix} 0 & -1 \\ 1 & 0 \end{bmatrix} \begin{bmatrix} 1 & 0 \\ 0 & -1 \end{bmatrix} = \begin{bmatrix} 0 & 1 \\ 1 & 0 \end{bmatrix}$

$-BA = \begin{bmatrix} 1 & 0 \\ 0 & -1 \end{bmatrix} \begin{bmatrix} 0 & -1 \\ 1 & 0 \end{bmatrix} = -\begin{bmatrix} 0 & -1 \\ -1 & 0 \end{bmatrix} = \begin{bmatrix} 0 & 1 \\ 1 & 0 \end{bmatrix}$

$AB = -BA$ so they are anticommutative.

Mid-Chapter 6 Check Point

1. $\begin{bmatrix} 1 & 2 & -3 & | & -7 \\ 3 & -1 & 2 & | & 8 \\ 2 & -1 & 1 & | & 5 \end{bmatrix} \begin{matrix} \\ -3R_1 + R_2 \\ -2R_1 + R_3 \end{matrix}$

$\begin{bmatrix} 1 & 2 & -3 & | & -7 \\ 0 & -7 & 11 & | & 29 \\ 0 & -5 & 7 & | & 19 \end{bmatrix} \begin{matrix} \\ -\frac{1}{7}R_2 \\ -\frac{1}{5}R_3 \end{matrix}$

$\begin{bmatrix} 1 & 2 & -3 & | & -7 \\ 0 & 1 & -\frac{11}{7} & | & -\frac{29}{7} \\ 0 & 1 & -\frac{7}{5} & | & -\frac{19}{5} \end{bmatrix} \begin{matrix} \\ \\ -R_2 + R_3 \end{matrix}$

$\begin{bmatrix} 1 & 2 & -3 & | & -7 \\ 0 & 1 & -\frac{11}{7} & | & -\frac{29}{7} \\ 0 & 0 & \frac{6}{35} & | & \frac{12}{35} \end{bmatrix} \frac{35}{6}R_3$

$\begin{bmatrix} 1 & 2 & -3 & | & -7 \\ 0 & 1 & -\frac{11}{7} & | & -\frac{29}{7} \\ 0 & 0 & 1 & | & 2 \end{bmatrix}$

Back-substitute to find y.

$y - \frac{11}{7}z = -\frac{29}{7}$

$y - \frac{11}{7}(2) = -\frac{29}{7}$

$y - \frac{22}{7} = -\frac{29}{7}$

$y = -\frac{7}{7}$

$y = -1$

Back-substitute to find x.

$x + 2y - 3z = -7$

$x + 2(-1) - 3(2) = -7$

$x - 2 - 6 = -7$

$x - 8 = -7$

$x = 1$

The solution is $\{(1, -1, 2)\}$.

2. $\begin{bmatrix} 2 & 4 & 5 & | & 2 \\ 1 & 1 & 2 & | & 1 \\ 3 & 5 & 7 & | & 4 \end{bmatrix} R_1 \leftrightarrow R_3$

$\begin{bmatrix} 1 & 1 & 2 & | & 1 \\ 2 & 4 & 5 & | & 2 \\ 3 & 5 & 7 & | & 4 \end{bmatrix} \begin{matrix} \\ -2R_1 + R_2 \\ -3R_1 + R_3 \end{matrix}$

$\begin{bmatrix} 1 & 1 & 2 & | & 1 \\ 0 & 2 & 1 & | & 0 \\ 0 & 2 & 1 & | & 1 \end{bmatrix} \begin{matrix} \\ \\ -R_2 + R_3 \end{matrix}$

$\begin{bmatrix} 1 & 1 & 2 & | & 1 \\ 0 & 2 & 1 & | & 0 \\ 0 & 0 & 0 & | & 1 \end{bmatrix}$

The third row of the matrix is equivalent to $0x + 0y + 0z = 1$ which is false.
The solution is $\varnothing$.

3. $\begin{bmatrix} 1 & -2 & 2 & | & -2 \\ 2 & 3 & -1 & | & 1 \end{bmatrix} -2R_1 + R_2$

$\begin{bmatrix} 1 & -2 & 2 & | & -2 \\ 0 & 7 & -5 & | & 5 \end{bmatrix} \frac{1}{7}R_2$

$\begin{bmatrix} 1 & -2 & 2 & | & -2 \\ 0 & 1 & -\frac{5}{7} & | & \frac{5}{7} \end{bmatrix}$

Back-substitute to find y in terms of z.

$y - \frac{5}{7}z = \frac{5}{7}$

$y = \frac{5}{7}z + \frac{5}{7}$

Back-substitute to find x in terms of z.

$x - 2y + 2z = -2$

$x - 2\left(\frac{5}{7}z + \frac{5}{7}\right) + 2z = -2$

$x - \frac{10}{7}z - \frac{10}{7} + 2z = -2$

$x + \frac{4}{7}z - \frac{10}{7} = -2$

$x = -\frac{4}{7}z - \frac{4}{7}$

The solution is $\left\{\left(-\frac{4}{7}z - \frac{4}{7}, \frac{5}{7}z + \frac{5}{7}, z\right)\right\}$.

4.

$$\begin{bmatrix} 1 & 1 & 1 & 1 & | & 6 \\ 1 & -1 & 3 & 1 & | & -14 \\ 1 & 2 & 0 & -3 & | & 12 \\ 2 & 3 & 6 & 1 & | & 1 \end{bmatrix}\begin{matrix} \\ -R_1+R_2 \\ -R_1+R_3 \\ -2R_1+R_4 \end{matrix}$$

$$\begin{bmatrix} 1 & 1 & 1 & 1 & | & 6 \\ 0 & -2 & 2 & 0 & | & -20 \\ 0 & 1 & -1 & -4 & | & 6 \\ 0 & 1 & 4 & -1 & | & -11 \end{bmatrix}R_2\leftrightarrow R_3$$

$$\begin{bmatrix} 1 & 1 & 1 & 1 & | & 6 \\ 0 & 1 & -1 & -4 & | & 6 \\ 0 & -2 & 2 & 0 & | & -20 \\ 0 & 1 & 4 & -1 & | & -11 \end{bmatrix}\begin{matrix} \\ \\ 2R_2+R_3 \\ -R_2+R_4 \end{matrix}$$

$$\begin{bmatrix} 1 & 1 & 1 & 1 & | & 6 \\ 0 & 1 & -1 & -4 & | & 6 \\ 0 & 0 & 0 & -8 & | & -8 \\ 0 & 0 & 5 & 3 & | & -17 \end{bmatrix}R_3\leftrightarrow R_4$$

$$\begin{bmatrix} 1 & 1 & 1 & 1 & | & 6 \\ 0 & 1 & -1 & -4 & | & 6 \\ 0 & 0 & 5 & 3 & | & -17 \\ 0 & 0 & 0 & -8 & | & -8 \end{bmatrix}\begin{matrix} \\ \\ \frac{1}{5}R_3 \\ -\frac{1}{8}R_4 \end{matrix}$$

$$\begin{bmatrix} 1 & 1 & 1 & 1 & | & 6 \\ 0 & 1 & -1 & -4 & | & 6 \\ 0 & 0 & 1 & \frac{3}{5} & | & -\frac{17}{5} \\ 0 & 0 & 0 & 1 & | & 1 \end{bmatrix}$$

Back-substitute to find y in terms of z.

$$y+\frac{3}{5}z=-\frac{17}{5}$$
$$y+\frac{3}{5}(1)=-\frac{17}{5}$$
$$y+\frac{3}{5}=-\frac{17}{5}$$
$$y=-\frac{20}{5}$$
$$y=-4$$

Back-substitute to find x in terms of z.
$$x-y-4z=6$$
$$x-(-4)-4(1)=6$$
$$x+4-4=6$$
$$x=6$$

Back-substitute to find w in terms of z.
$$w+x+y+z=6$$
$$w+(6)+(-4)+(1)=6$$
$$w+3=6$$
$$w=3$$

The solution is $\{(3,6,-4,1)\}$.

5.

$$\begin{bmatrix} 2 & -2 & 2 & | & 5 \\ 1 & -1 & 1 & | & 2 \\ 2 & 1 & -1 & | & 1 \end{bmatrix}\begin{matrix} -R_2+R_1 \\ \\ -R_1+R_3 \end{matrix}$$

$$\begin{bmatrix} 1 & -1 & 1 & | & 3 \\ 1 & -1 & 1 & | & 2 \\ 0 & 3 & -3 & | & -4 \end{bmatrix}-R_1+R_2$$

$$\begin{bmatrix} 1 & -1 & 1 & | & 3 \\ 0 & 0 & 0 & | & -1 \\ 0 & 3 & -3 & | & -4 \end{bmatrix}$$

The second row of the matrix is equivalent to $0x+0y+0z=-1$ which is false.

The solution is $\varnothing$.

6. $2C-\frac{1}{2}B$

$$=2\begin{bmatrix} -1 & 0 \\ 0 & 1 \end{bmatrix}-\frac{1}{2}\begin{bmatrix} 4 & 1 \\ -6 & -2 \end{bmatrix}$$

$$=\begin{bmatrix} -2 & 0 \\ 0 & 2 \end{bmatrix}-\begin{bmatrix} 2 & \frac{1}{2} \\ -3 & -1 \end{bmatrix}$$

$$=\begin{bmatrix} -4 & -\frac{1}{2} \\ 3 & 3 \end{bmatrix}$$

7. $A(B+C)$

$$=\begin{bmatrix} 0 & 2 \\ -1 & 3 \\ 1 & 0 \end{bmatrix}\left(\begin{bmatrix} 4 & 1 \\ -6 & -2 \end{bmatrix}+\begin{bmatrix} -1 & 0 \\ 0 & 1 \end{bmatrix}\right)$$

$$=\begin{bmatrix} 0 & 2 \\ -1 & 3 \\ 1 & 0 \end{bmatrix}\left(\begin{bmatrix} 3 & 1 \\ -6 & -1 \end{bmatrix}\right)$$

$$=\begin{bmatrix} -12 & -2 \\ -21 & -4 \\ 3 & 1 \end{bmatrix}$$

8. $A(BC)$

$$=\begin{bmatrix} 0 & 2 \\ -1 & 3 \\ 1 & 0 \end{bmatrix}\left(\begin{bmatrix} 4 & 1 \\ -6 & -2 \end{bmatrix}\cdot\begin{bmatrix} -1 & 0 \\ 0 & 1 \end{bmatrix}\right)$$

$$=\begin{bmatrix} 0 & 2 \\ -1 & 3 \\ 1 & 0 \end{bmatrix}\left(\begin{bmatrix} -4 & 1 \\ 6 & -2 \end{bmatrix}\right)$$

$$=\begin{bmatrix} 12 & -4 \\ 22 & -7 \\ -4 & 1 \end{bmatrix}$$

9. The operation is not defined. Matrices must have the same dimensions in order to be added.

10. $2X - 3C = B$

$$2X = B + 3C$$
$$X = \tfrac{1}{2}(B + 3C)$$
$$= \tfrac{1}{2}\left(\begin{bmatrix} 4 & 1 \\ -6 & -2 \end{bmatrix} + 3\begin{bmatrix} -1 & 0 \\ 0 & 1 \end{bmatrix}\right)$$
$$= \tfrac{1}{2}\left(\begin{bmatrix} 4 & 1 \\ -6 & -2 \end{bmatrix} + \begin{bmatrix} -3 & 0 \\ 0 & 3 \end{bmatrix}\right)$$
$$= \tfrac{1}{2}\left(\begin{bmatrix} 1 & 1 \\ -6 & 1 \end{bmatrix}\right)$$
$$= \begin{bmatrix} \tfrac{1}{2} & \tfrac{1}{2} \\ -3 & \tfrac{1}{2} \end{bmatrix}$$

Section 6.4

Check Point Exercises

1. We must show that: $AB = I_2 = \begin{bmatrix} 1 & 0 \\ 0 & 1 \end{bmatrix}$, and

$$BA = I_2 = \begin{bmatrix} 1 & 0 \\ 0 & 1 \end{bmatrix}.$$
$$AB = \begin{bmatrix} 2 & 1 \\ 1 & 1 \end{bmatrix}\begin{bmatrix} 1 & -1 \\ -1 & 2 \end{bmatrix}$$
$$= \begin{bmatrix} 2(1)+1(-1) & 2(-1)+1(2) \\ 1(1)+1(-1) & 1(-1)+1(2) \end{bmatrix}$$
$$= \begin{bmatrix} 1 & 0 \\ 0 & 1 \end{bmatrix}$$
$$BA = \begin{bmatrix} 1 & -1 \\ -1 & 2 \end{bmatrix}\begin{bmatrix} 2 & 1 \\ 1 & 1 \end{bmatrix}$$
$$= \begin{bmatrix} 1(2)+-1(1) & 1(1)+-1(1) \\ -1(2)+2(1) & -1(1)+2(1) \end{bmatrix}$$
$$= \begin{bmatrix} 1 & 0 \\ 0 & 1 \end{bmatrix}$$

Both products (AB and BA) give the multiplicative identity matrix, I_2. Thus, B is the multiplicative inverse of A.

2. Let us denote the multiplicative inverse of A by $A^{-1} = \begin{bmatrix} w & x \\ y & z \end{bmatrix}$. Because A is a 2×2 matrix, we use the equation $AA^{-1} = I_2$ to find values for w, x, y and z.

$$\begin{bmatrix} 5 & 7 \\ 2 & 3 \end{bmatrix}\begin{bmatrix} w & x \\ y & z \end{bmatrix} = \begin{bmatrix} 1 & 0 \\ 0 & 1 \end{bmatrix}$$
$$\begin{bmatrix} 5w+7y & 5x+7z \\ 2w+3y & 2x+3z \end{bmatrix} = \begin{bmatrix} 1 & 0 \\ 0 & 1 \end{bmatrix}$$

$5w+7y=1 \qquad 5x+7z=0$

$2w+3y=0 \qquad 2x+3z=1$

Each of these systems can be solved using the addition method.

Multiply by –2: $5w+7y=1 \rightarrow -10w-14y=-2$

Multiply by 5: $2w+3y=0 \rightarrow 10w+15y=0$

Use back substitution: $w=3, y=-2$

Multiply by –2: $5x+7z=0 \rightarrow -10x-14z=0$

Multiply by 5: $2x+3z=1 \rightarrow 10x+15z=5$

Use back substitution: $x=-7, z=5$

Using these values, we have

$$A^{-1} = \begin{bmatrix} 3 & -7 \\ -2 & 5 \end{bmatrix}.$$

3. $A^{-1} = \dfrac{1}{ad-bc}\begin{bmatrix} d & -b \\ -c & a \end{bmatrix}$

$$= \frac{1}{3(1)-(-2)(-1)}\begin{bmatrix} 1 & -(-2) \\ -(-1) & 3 \end{bmatrix}$$
$$= \frac{1}{3-2}\begin{bmatrix} 1 & 2 \\ 1 & 3 \end{bmatrix}$$
$$= \frac{1}{1}\begin{bmatrix} 1 & 2 \\ 1 & 3 \end{bmatrix}$$
$$= \begin{bmatrix} 1 & 2 \\ 1 & 3 \end{bmatrix}$$

4. The augmented matrix $[A \mid I_3]$ is

$$\begin{bmatrix} 1 & 0 & 2 & | & 1 & 0 & 0 \\ -1 & 2 & 3 & | & 0 & 1 & 0 \\ 1 & -1 & 0 & | & 0 & 0 & 1 \end{bmatrix}.$$

Perform row transformations on $[A \mid I_3]$ to obtain a matrix of the form $[I_3 \mid B]$.

$$\begin{bmatrix} 1 & 0 & 2 & | & 1 & 0 & 0 \\ -1 & 2 & 3 & | & 0 & 1 & 0 \\ 1 & -1 & 0 & | & 0 & 0 & 1 \end{bmatrix} 1R_1/R_2$$

$$= \begin{bmatrix} 1 & 0 & 2 & | & 1 & 0 & 0 \\ 0 & 2 & 5 & | & 1 & 1 & 0 \\ 1 & -1 & 0 & | & 0 & 0 & 1 \end{bmatrix} -1R_3$$

$$= \begin{bmatrix} 1 & 0 & 2 & | & 1 & 0 & 0 \\ 0 & 2 & 5 & | & 1 & 1 & 0 \\ -1 & 1 & 0 & | & 0 & 0 & -1 \end{bmatrix} R_1 + R_3$$

$$= \begin{bmatrix} 1 & 0 & 2 & | & 1 & 0 & 0 \\ 0 & 2 & 5 & | & 1 & 1 & 0 \\ 0 & 1 & 2 & | & 1 & 0 & -1 \end{bmatrix} \frac{1}{2} R_2$$

$$= \begin{bmatrix} 1 & 0 & 2 & | & 1 & 0 & 0 \\ 0 & 1 & \frac{5}{2} & | & \frac{1}{2} & \frac{1}{2} & 0 \\ 0 & 1 & 2 & | & 1 & 0 & -1 \end{bmatrix} -1R_2 + R_3$$

$$= \begin{bmatrix} 1 & 0 & 2 & | & 1 & 0 & 0 \\ 0 & 1 & \frac{5}{2} & | & \frac{1}{2} & \frac{1}{2} & 0 \\ 0 & 0 & -\frac{1}{2} & | & \frac{1}{2} & -\frac{1}{2} & -1 \end{bmatrix} -2R_3$$

$$= \begin{bmatrix} 1 & 0 & 2 & | & 1 & 0 & 0 \\ 0 & 1 & \frac{5}{2} & | & \frac{1}{2} & \frac{1}{2} & 0 \\ 0 & 0 & 1 & | & -1 & 1 & 2 \end{bmatrix} \begin{matrix} -2R_3 + R_1 \\ -\frac{5}{2}R_3 + R_2 \end{matrix}$$

$$= \begin{bmatrix} 1 & 0 & 0 & | & 3 & -2 & -4 \\ 0 & 1 & 0 & | & 3 & -2 & -5 \\ 0 & 0 & 1 & | & 1 & 1 & 2 \end{bmatrix}$$

Thus, the multiplicative inverse of A is

$$A^{-1} = \begin{bmatrix} 3 & -2 & -4 \\ 3 & -2 & -5 \\ -1 & 1 & 2 \end{bmatrix}.$$

5. The linear system can be written as $AX = B$.

$$\begin{bmatrix} 1 & 0 & 2 \\ -1 & 2 & 3 \\ 1 & -1 & 0 \end{bmatrix} \begin{bmatrix} x \\ y \\ z \end{bmatrix} = \begin{bmatrix} 6 \\ -5 \\ 6 \end{bmatrix}.$$

$$X = A^{-1}B = \begin{bmatrix} 3 & -2 & -4 \\ 3 & -2 & -5 \\ -1 & 1 & 2 \end{bmatrix} \begin{bmatrix} 6 \\ -5 \\ 6 \end{bmatrix}$$

$$= \begin{bmatrix} 3(6) + -2(-5) + -4(6) \\ 3(6) + -2(-5) + -5(6) \\ -1(6) + 1(-5) + 2(6) \end{bmatrix}$$

$$= \begin{bmatrix} 18 + 10 - 24 \\ 18 + 10 - 30 \\ -6 - 5 + 12 \end{bmatrix} = \begin{bmatrix} 4 \\ -2 \\ 1 \end{bmatrix}$$

Thus, $x = 4$, $y = -2$, and $z = 1$. The solution set is $\{(4, -2, 1)\}$.

6. The numerical representation of the word BASE is 2, 1, 19, 5. The 2×2 matrix formed is $\begin{bmatrix} 2 & 19 \\ 1 & 5 \end{bmatrix}$.

$$\begin{bmatrix} -2 & -3 \\ 3 & 4 \end{bmatrix} \begin{bmatrix} 2 & 19 \\ 1 & 5 \end{bmatrix}$$

$$= \begin{bmatrix} -2(2) + -3(1) & -2(19) + -3(5) \\ 3(2) + 4(1) & 3(19) + 4(5) \end{bmatrix}$$

$$= \begin{bmatrix} -4 - 3 & -38 - 15 \\ 6 + 4 & 57 + 20 \end{bmatrix} = \begin{bmatrix} -7 & -53 \\ 10 & 77 \end{bmatrix}$$

The encoded message is $-7, 10, -53, 77$.

7. Use the multiplicative inverse of the coding matrix. It is $\begin{bmatrix} 4 & 3 \\ -3 & -2 \end{bmatrix}$.

$$\begin{bmatrix} 4 & 3 \\ -3 & -2 \end{bmatrix} \begin{bmatrix} -7 & -53 \\ 10 & 77 \end{bmatrix}$$

$$= \begin{bmatrix} 4(-7) + 3(10) & 4(-53) + 3(77) \\ -3(-7) + -2(10) & -3(-53) + -2(77) \end{bmatrix}$$

$$= \begin{bmatrix} -28 + 30 & -212 + 231 \\ 21 - 20 & 159 - 154 \end{bmatrix} = \begin{bmatrix} 2 & 19 \\ 1 & 5 \end{bmatrix}$$

The numbers are 2, 1, 19, and 5. Using letters, the decoded message is BASE.

Exercise Set 6.4

1. $A = \begin{bmatrix} 4 & -3 \\ -5 & 4 \end{bmatrix} \quad B = \begin{bmatrix} 4 & 3 \\ 5 & 4 \end{bmatrix}$

$$AB = \begin{bmatrix} 16 - 15 & 12 - 12 \\ -20 + 20 & -15 + 16 \end{bmatrix} = \begin{bmatrix} 1 & 0 \\ 0 & 1 \end{bmatrix}$$

$$BA = \begin{bmatrix} 16 - 15 & -12 + 12 \\ 20 - 20 & -15 + 16 \end{bmatrix} = \begin{bmatrix} 1 & 0 \\ 0 & 1 \end{bmatrix}$$

Since $AB = I_2$, $BA = I_2$, $B = A^{-1}$.

3. $AB = \begin{bmatrix} 8 + 0 & -16 + 0 \\ -2 + 0 & 4 + 3 \end{bmatrix} = \begin{bmatrix} 8 & -16 \\ -2 & 7 \end{bmatrix}$

$$BA = \begin{bmatrix} 8 + 4 & 0 + 12 \\ 0 + 1 & 0 + 3 \end{bmatrix} = \begin{bmatrix} 12 & 12 \\ 1 & 3 \end{bmatrix}$$

If B is the multiplicative inverse of A, both products (AB and BA) will be the multiplicative identity matrix, I_2. Therefore, B is not the multiplicative inverse of A. That is, $B \neq A^{-1}$.

453

5. $AB = \begin{bmatrix} -2+3 & -4+4 \\ \frac{3}{2}-\frac{3}{2} & 3-2 \end{bmatrix} = \begin{bmatrix} 1 & 0 \\ 0 & 1 \end{bmatrix}$

$BA = \begin{bmatrix} -2+3 & 1-1 \\ -6+6 & 3-2 \end{bmatrix} = \begin{bmatrix} 1 & 0 \\ 0 & 1 \end{bmatrix}$

Since $AB = I_2$ and $BA = I_2$, $B = A^{-1}$.

7. $A = \begin{bmatrix} 0 & 1 & 0 \\ 0 & 0 & 1 \\ 1 & 0 & 0 \end{bmatrix}$ $B = \begin{bmatrix} 0 & 0 & 1 \\ 1 & 0 & 0 \\ 0 & 1 & 0 \end{bmatrix}$

$AB = \begin{bmatrix} 0+1+0 & 0+0+0 & 0+0+0 \\ 0+0+0 & 0+0+1 & 0+0+0 \\ 0+0+0 & 0+0+0 & 1+0+0 \end{bmatrix} = \begin{bmatrix} 1 & 0 & 0 \\ 0 & 1 & 0 \\ 0 & 0 & 1 \end{bmatrix}$

$BA = \begin{bmatrix} 0+0+1 & 0+0+0 & 0+0+0 \\ 0+0+0 & 1+0+0 & 0+0+0 \\ 0+0+0 & 0+0+0 & 0+1+0 \end{bmatrix} = \begin{bmatrix} 1 & 0 & 0 \\ 0 & 1 & 0 \\ 0 & 0 & 1 \end{bmatrix}$

Since $AB = I_3$ and $BA = I_3$, $B = A^{-1}$.

9. $AB = \begin{bmatrix} \frac{7}{2}-1-\frac{3}{2} & -3+0+3 & \frac{1}{2}+1-\frac{3}{2} \\ \frac{7}{2}-\frac{3}{2}-2 & -3+0+4 & \frac{1}{2}+\frac{3}{2}-2 \\ \frac{7}{2}-2-\frac{3}{2} & -3+0+3 & \frac{1}{2}+2-\frac{3}{2} \end{bmatrix} = \begin{bmatrix} 1 & 0 & 0 \\ 0 & 1 & 0 \\ 0 & 0 & 1 \end{bmatrix}$

$BA = \begin{bmatrix} \frac{7}{2}-3+\frac{1}{2} & 7-9+2 & \frac{21}{2}-12+\frac{3}{2} \\ -\frac{1}{2}+0+\frac{1}{2} & -1+0+2 & -\frac{3}{2}+0+\frac{3}{2} \\ -\frac{1}{2}+1-\frac{1}{2} & -1+3-2 & -\frac{3}{2}+4-\frac{3}{2} \end{bmatrix} = \begin{bmatrix} 1 & 0 & 0 \\ 0 & 1 & 0 \\ 0 & 0 & 1 \end{bmatrix}$

Since $AB = I_3$ and $BA = I_3$, $B = A^{-1}$.

11. $AB = \begin{bmatrix} 0+0+0+1 & 0+0-2+2 & 0+0+0+0 & 0+0-2+2 \\ -1+0+0+1 & -2+0+1+2 & 0+0+0+0 & -3+0+1+2 \\ 0+0+0+0 & 0+1-1+0 & 0+1+0+0 & 0+1-1+0 \\ 1+0+0-1 & 2+0+0-2 & 0+0+0+0 & 3+0+0-2 \end{bmatrix} = \begin{bmatrix} 1 & 0 & 0 & 0 \\ 0 & 1 & 0 & 0 \\ 0 & 0 & 1 & 0 \\ 0 & 0 & 0 & 1 \end{bmatrix}$

$BA = \begin{bmatrix} 0-2+0+3 & 0+0+0+0 & -2+2+0+0 & 1+2+0-3 \\ 0-1+0+1 & 0+0+1+0 & 0+1-1+0 & 0+1+0-1 \\ 0-1+0+1 & 0+0+0+0 & 0+1+0+0 & 0+1+0-1 \\ 0-2+0+2 & 0+0+0+0 & -2+2+0+0 & 1+2+0-2 \end{bmatrix} = \begin{bmatrix} 1 & 0 & 0 & 0 \\ 0 & 1 & 0 & 0 \\ 0 & 0 & 1 & 0 \\ 0 & 0 & 0 & 1 \end{bmatrix}$

Since $AB = I_4$ and $BA = I_4$, $B = A^{-1}$.

13. $ad - bc = (2)(2) - (3)(-1) = 4 + 3 = 7$

$A^{-1} = \frac{1}{7}\begin{bmatrix} 2 & -3 \\ 1 & 2 \end{bmatrix} = \begin{bmatrix} \frac{2}{7} & -\frac{3}{7} \\ \frac{1}{7} & \frac{2}{7} \end{bmatrix}$

$AA^{-1} = \begin{bmatrix} \frac{4}{7}+\frac{3}{7} & -\frac{6}{7}+\frac{6}{7} \\ -\frac{2}{7}+\frac{2}{7} & \frac{3}{7}+\frac{4}{7} \end{bmatrix} = \begin{bmatrix} 1 & 0 \\ 0 & 1 \end{bmatrix}$ and $A^{-1}A = \begin{bmatrix} \frac{4}{7}+\frac{3}{7} & \frac{6}{7}-\frac{6}{7} \\ \frac{2}{7}-\frac{2}{7} & \frac{3}{7}+\frac{4}{7} \end{bmatrix} = \begin{bmatrix} 1 & 0 \\ 0 & 1 \end{bmatrix}$

15. $ad - bc = (3)(2) - (-1)(-4) = 6 - 4 = 2$

$$A^{-1} = \frac{1}{2}\begin{bmatrix} 2 & 1 \\ 4 & 3 \end{bmatrix} = \begin{bmatrix} 1 & \frac{1}{2} \\ 2 & \frac{3}{2} \end{bmatrix}$$

$$AA^{-1} = \begin{bmatrix} 3-2 & \frac{3}{2}-\frac{3}{2} \\ -4+4 & -\frac{4}{2}+\frac{6}{2} \end{bmatrix} = \begin{bmatrix} 1 & 0 \\ 0 & 1 \end{bmatrix} \text{ and } A^{-1}A = \begin{bmatrix} 3-\frac{4}{2} & -1+\frac{2}{2} \\ 6-\frac{12}{2} & -2+\frac{6}{2} \end{bmatrix} = \begin{bmatrix} 1 & 0 \\ 0 & 1 \end{bmatrix}$$

17. $ad - bc = (10)(1) - (-2)(-5) = 10 - 10 = 0$

Since division by zero is undefined, A does not have an inverse.

For Problems 19–24, verification that $AA^{-1} = I$ and $A^{-1}A = I$ is left to the student.

For Problems 19–23, verification that $AA^{-1} = I$ and $A^{-1}A = I$ is left to the student.

19. $\begin{bmatrix} 2 & 0 & 0 & 1 & 0 & 0 \\ 0 & 4 & 0 & 0 & 1 & 0 \\ 0 & 0 & 6 & 0 & 0 & 1 \end{bmatrix}$

Divide row 1 by 2, divide row 2 by 4 and divide row 4 by 6.

$$\begin{bmatrix} 1 & 0 & 0 & \frac{1}{2} & 0 & 0 \\ 0 & 1 & 0 & 0 & \frac{1}{4} & 0 \\ 0 & 0 & 1 & 0 & 0 & \frac{1}{6} \end{bmatrix}$$

$$A^{-1} = \begin{bmatrix} \frac{1}{2} & 0 & 0 \\ 0 & \frac{1}{4} & 0 \\ 0 & 0 & \frac{1}{6} \end{bmatrix}$$

21. $\begin{bmatrix} 1 & 2 & -1 & 1 & 0 & 0 \\ -2 & 0 & 1 & 0 & 1 & 0 \\ 1 & -1 & 0 & 0 & 0 & 1 \end{bmatrix}$

Replace row 2 with $2R_1 + R_2$.
Replace row 3 with $R_1 - R_3$.

$$\begin{bmatrix} 1 & 2 & -1 & 1 & 0 & 0 \\ 0 & 4 & -1 & 2 & 1 & 0 \\ 0 & 3 & -1 & 1 & 0 & -1 \end{bmatrix}$$

Replace row 1 with $R_2 - 2R_1$.
Replace row 3 with $-3R_2 + 4R_3$.

$$\begin{bmatrix} -2 & 0 & 1 & 0 & 1 & 0 \\ 0 & 4 & -1 & 2 & 1 & 0 \\ 0 & 0 & -1 & -2 & -3 & -4 \end{bmatrix}$$

Replace row 1 with $R_3 + R_1$.
Replace row 2 with $R_2 - R_3$.
Replace row 3 with $-R_3$.

$$\begin{bmatrix} -2 & 0 & 0 & -2 & -2 & -4 \\ 0 & 4 & 0 & 4 & 4 & 4 \\ 0 & 0 & 1 & 2 & 3 & 4 \end{bmatrix}$$

Divide row 1 by –2 and divide row 2 by 4.

$$\begin{bmatrix} 1 & 0 & 0 & 1 & 1 & 2 \\ 0 & 1 & 0 & 1 & 1 & 1 \\ 0 & 0 & 1 & 2 & 3 & 4 \end{bmatrix}$$

$$A^{-1} = \begin{bmatrix} 1 & 1 & 2 \\ 1 & 1 & 1 \\ 2 & 3 & 4 \end{bmatrix}$$

23. $\begin{bmatrix} 2 & 2 & -1 & | & 1 & 0 & 0 \\ 0 & 3 & -1 & | & 0 & 1 & 0 \\ -1 & -2 & 1 & | & 0 & 0 & 1 \end{bmatrix} R_1 \leftrightarrow R_3$

$\begin{bmatrix} -1 & -2 & 1 & | & 0 & 0 & 1 \\ 0 & 3 & -1 & | & 0 & 1 & 0 \\ 2 & 2 & -1 & | & 1 & 0 & 0 \end{bmatrix} -1R_1$

$\begin{bmatrix} 1 & 2 & -1 & | & 0 & 0 & -1 \\ 0 & 3 & -1 & | & 0 & 1 & 0 \\ 2 & 2 & -1 & | & 1 & 0 & 0 \end{bmatrix} -2R_1 + R_3$

$\begin{bmatrix} 1 & 2 & -1 & | & 0 & 0 & -1 \\ 0 & 3 & -1 & | & 0 & 1 & 0 \\ 0 & -2 & 1 & | & 1 & 0 & 2 \end{bmatrix} \frac{1}{3}R_2$

$\begin{bmatrix} 1 & 2 & -1 & | & 0 & 0 & -1 \\ 0 & 1 & -\frac{1}{3} & | & 0 & \frac{1}{3} & 0 \\ 0 & -2 & 1 & | & 1 & 0 & 2 \end{bmatrix} \begin{matrix} -2R_2 + R_1 \\ 2R_2 + R_3 \end{matrix}$

$\begin{bmatrix} 1 & 0 & -\frac{1}{3} & | & 0 & -\frac{2}{3} & -1 \\ 0 & 1 & -\frac{1}{3} & | & 0 & \frac{1}{3} & 0 \\ 0 & 0 & \frac{1}{3} & | & 1 & \frac{2}{3} & 2 \end{bmatrix} \begin{matrix} 1R_3 + R_1 \\ 1R_2 + R_1 \end{matrix}$

$\begin{bmatrix} 1 & 0 & 0 & | & 1 & 0 & 1 \\ 0 & 1 & 0 & | & 1 & 1 & 2 \\ 0 & 0 & \frac{1}{3} & | & 1 & \frac{2}{3} & 2 \end{bmatrix} 3R_3$

$\begin{bmatrix} 1 & 0 & 0 & | & 1 & 0 & 1 \\ 0 & 1 & 0 & | & 1 & 1 & 2 \\ 0 & 0 & 1 & | & 3 & 2 & 6 \end{bmatrix}$

$A^{-1} = \begin{bmatrix} 1 & 0 & 1 \\ 1 & 1 & 2 \\ 3 & 2 & 6 \end{bmatrix}$

25. $\begin{bmatrix} 5 & 0 & 2 & | & 1 & 0 & 0 \\ 2 & 2 & 1 & | & 0 & 1 & 0 \\ -3 & 1 & -1 & | & 0 & 0 & 1 \end{bmatrix} \frac{1}{5}R_1$

$\begin{bmatrix} 1 & 0 & \frac{2}{5} & | & \frac{1}{5} & 0 & 0 \\ 2 & 2 & 1 & | & 0 & 1 & 0 \\ -3 & 1 & -1 & | & 0 & 0 & 1 \end{bmatrix} \begin{matrix} -2R_1 + R_2 \\ 3R_1 + R_3 \end{matrix}$

$\begin{bmatrix} 1 & 0 & \frac{2}{5} & | & \frac{1}{5} & 0 & 0 \\ 0 & 2 & \frac{1}{5} & | & -\frac{2}{5} & 1 & 0 \\ 0 & 1 & \frac{1}{5} & | & \frac{3}{5} & 0 & 1 \end{bmatrix} R_2 \leftrightarrow R_3$

$\begin{bmatrix} 1 & 0 & \frac{2}{5} & | & \frac{1}{5} & 0 & 0 \\ 0 & 1 & \frac{1}{5} & | & \frac{3}{5} & 0 & 1 \\ 0 & 2 & \frac{1}{5} & | & -\frac{2}{5} & 1 & 0 \end{bmatrix} -2R_2 + R_3$

$\begin{bmatrix} 1 & 0 & \frac{2}{5} & | & \frac{1}{5} & 0 & 0 \\ 0 & 1 & \frac{1}{5} & | & \frac{3}{5} & 0 & 1 \\ 0 & 0 & -\frac{1}{5} & | & -\frac{8}{5} & 1 & -2 \end{bmatrix} \begin{matrix} 2R_3 + R_1 \\ 1R_3 + R_2 \end{matrix}$

$\begin{bmatrix} 1 & 0 & 0 & | & -3 & 2 & -4 \\ 0 & 1 & 0 & | & -1 & 1 & -1 \\ 0 & 0 & -\frac{1}{5} & | & -\frac{8}{5} & 1 & -2 \end{bmatrix} -5R_3$

$\begin{bmatrix} 1 & 0 & 0 & | & -3 & 2 & -4 \\ 0 & 1 & 0 & | & -1 & 1 & -1 \\ 0 & 0 & 1 & | & 8 & -5 & 10 \end{bmatrix}$

$A^{-1} = \begin{bmatrix} -3 & 2 & -4 \\ -1 & 1 & -1 \\ 8 & -5 & 10 \end{bmatrix}$

27. $\begin{bmatrix} 1 & 0 & 0 & 0 & | & 1 & 0 & 0 & 0 \\ 0 & -1 & 0 & 0 & | & 0 & 1 & 0 & 0 \\ 0 & 0 & 3 & 0 & | & 0 & 0 & 1 & 0 \\ 1 & 0 & 0 & 1 & | & 0 & 0 & 0 & 1 \end{bmatrix} -1R_1 + R_4$

$\begin{bmatrix} 1 & 0 & 0 & 0 & | & 1 & 0 & 0 & 0 \\ 0 & -1 & 0 & 0 & | & 0 & 1 & 0 & 0 \\ 0 & 0 & 3 & 0 & | & 0 & 0 & 1 & 0 \\ 0 & 0 & 0 & 1 & | & -1 & 0 & 0 & 1 \end{bmatrix} -1R_2$

$\begin{bmatrix} 1 & 0 & 0 & 0 & | & 1 & 0 & 0 & 0 \\ 0 & 1 & 0 & 0 & | & 0 & -1 & 0 & 0 \\ 0 & 0 & 3 & 0 & | & 0 & 0 & 1 & 0 \\ 0 & 0 & 0 & 1 & | & -1 & 0 & 0 & 1 \end{bmatrix} \frac{1}{3}R_3$

$\begin{bmatrix} 1 & 0 & 0 & 0 & | & 1 & 0 & 0 & 0 \\ 0 & 1 & 0 & 0 & | & 0 & -1 & 0 & 0 \\ 0 & 0 & 1 & 0 & | & 0 & 0 & \frac{1}{3} & 0 \\ 0 & 0 & 0 & 1 & | & -1 & 0 & 0 & 1 \end{bmatrix}$

$A^{-1} = \begin{bmatrix} 1 & 0 & 0 & 0 \\ 0 & -1 & 0 & 0 \\ 0 & 0 & \frac{1}{3} & 0 \\ -1 & 0 & 0 & 1 \end{bmatrix}$

29. $\begin{bmatrix} 6 & 5 \\ 5 & 4 \end{bmatrix} \begin{bmatrix} x \\ y \end{bmatrix} = \begin{bmatrix} 13 \\ 10 \end{bmatrix}$

31. $\begin{bmatrix} 1 & 3 & 4 \\ 1 & 2 & 3 \\ 1 & 4 & 3 \end{bmatrix} \begin{bmatrix} x \\ y \\ z \end{bmatrix} = \begin{bmatrix} -3 \\ -2 \\ -6 \end{bmatrix}$

33. $4x - 7y = -3$
$2x - 3y = 1$

35. $2x - z = 6$
$3y = 9$
$x + y = 5$

37. a.
$$\begin{bmatrix} 2 & 6 & 6 \\ 2 & 7 & 6 \\ 2 & 7 & 7 \end{bmatrix}\begin{bmatrix} x \\ y \\ z \end{bmatrix} = \begin{bmatrix} 8 \\ 10 \\ 9 \end{bmatrix}$$

$$\begin{bmatrix} \frac{7}{2} & 0 & -3 \\ -1 & 1 & 0 \\ 0 & -1 & 1 \end{bmatrix}\begin{bmatrix} 8 \\ 10 \\ 9 \end{bmatrix} = \begin{bmatrix} 28+0-27 \\ -8+10+0 \\ 0-10+9 \end{bmatrix} = \begin{bmatrix} 1 \\ 2 \\ -1 \end{bmatrix}$$

The solution to the system is $\{(1, 2, -1)\}$.

39. a.
$$\begin{bmatrix} 1 & -1 & 1 \\ 0 & 2 & -1 \\ 2 & 3 & 0 \end{bmatrix}\begin{bmatrix} x \\ y \\ z \end{bmatrix} = \begin{bmatrix} 8 \\ -7 \\ 1 \end{bmatrix}$$

b.
$$\begin{bmatrix} 3 & 3 & -1 \\ -2 & -2 & 1 \\ -4 & -5 & 2 \end{bmatrix}\begin{bmatrix} 8 \\ -7 \\ 1 \end{bmatrix}$$

$$= \begin{bmatrix} 24-21-1 \\ -16+14+1 \\ -32+35+2 \end{bmatrix} = \begin{bmatrix} 2 \\ -1 \\ 5 \end{bmatrix}$$

The solution to the system is
$\{(2, -1, 5)\}$.

41. a.
$$\begin{bmatrix} 1 & -1 & 2 & 0 \\ 0 & 1 & -1 & 1 \\ -1 & 1 & -1 & 2 \\ 0 & -1 & 1 & -2 \end{bmatrix}\begin{bmatrix} w \\ x \\ y \\ z \end{bmatrix} = \begin{bmatrix} -3 \\ 4 \\ 2 \\ -4 \end{bmatrix}$$

b.
$$\begin{bmatrix} 0 & 0 & -1 & -1 \\ 1 & 4 & 1 & 3 \\ 1 & 2 & 1 & 2 \\ 0 & -1 & 0 & -1 \end{bmatrix}\begin{bmatrix} -3 \\ 4 \\ 2 \\ -4 \end{bmatrix}$$

$$= \begin{bmatrix} 0+0-2+4 \\ -3+16+2-12 \\ -3+8+2-8 \\ 0-4+0+4 \end{bmatrix} = \begin{bmatrix} 2 \\ 3 \\ -1 \\ 0 \end{bmatrix}$$

The solution to the system is
$\{(2, 3, -1, 0)\}$.

43. $A = \begin{bmatrix} e^x & e^{3x} \\ -e^{3x} & e^{5x} \end{bmatrix}$

$A^{-1} = \dfrac{1}{ad-bc}\begin{bmatrix} d & -b \\ -c & a \end{bmatrix}$

$A^{-1} = \dfrac{1}{(e^x)(e^{5x})-(e^{3x})(-e^{3x})}\begin{bmatrix} e^{5x} & -e^{3x} \\ -(-e^{3x}) & e^x \end{bmatrix}$

$A^{-1} = \dfrac{1}{e^{6x}+e^{6x}}\begin{bmatrix} e^{5x} & -e^{3x} \\ e^{3x} & e^x \end{bmatrix}$

$A^{-1} = \dfrac{1}{2e^{6x}}\begin{bmatrix} e^{5x} & -e^{3x} \\ e^{3x} & e^x \end{bmatrix}$

$A^{-1} = \begin{bmatrix} \frac{e^{5x}}{2e^{6x}} & \frac{-e^{3x}}{2e^{6x}} \\ \frac{e^{3x}}{2e^{6x}} & \frac{e^x}{2e^{6x}} \end{bmatrix}$

$A^{-1} = \begin{bmatrix} \frac{1}{2e^x} & -\frac{1}{2e^{3x}} \\ \frac{1}{2e^{3x}} & \frac{1}{2e^{5x}} \end{bmatrix}$ or $\begin{bmatrix} \frac{e^{-x}}{2} & -\frac{e^{-3x}}{2} \\ \frac{e^{-3x}}{2} & \frac{e^{-5x}}{2} \end{bmatrix}$

Check:

$$\begin{bmatrix} e^x & e^{3x} \\ -e^{3x} & e^{5x} \end{bmatrix}\cdot\begin{bmatrix} \frac{1}{2e^x} & -\frac{1}{2e^{3x}} \\ \frac{1}{2e^{3x}} & \frac{1}{2e^{5x}} \end{bmatrix} = \begin{bmatrix} 1 & 0 \\ 0 & 1 \end{bmatrix}$$

45. $A = \begin{bmatrix} 8 & -5 \\ -3 & 2 \end{bmatrix}$

$I - A = \begin{bmatrix} 1 & 0 \\ 0 & 1 \end{bmatrix} - \begin{bmatrix} 8 & -5 \\ -3 & 2 \end{bmatrix} = \begin{bmatrix} -7 & 5 \\ 3 & -1 \end{bmatrix}$

$(I-A)^{-1} = \dfrac{1}{(-7)(-1)-(5)(3)}\begin{bmatrix} -1 & -(5) \\ -(3) & -7 \end{bmatrix}$

$(I-A)^{-1} = \dfrac{1}{7-15}\begin{bmatrix} -1 & -5 \\ -3 & -7 \end{bmatrix}$

$(I-A)^{-1} = \dfrac{1}{-8}\begin{bmatrix} -1 & -5 \\ -3 & -7 \end{bmatrix}$

$(I-A)^{-1} = \begin{bmatrix} \frac{-1}{-8} & \frac{-5}{-8} \\ \frac{-3}{-8} & \frac{-7}{-8} \end{bmatrix}$

$(I-A)^{-1} = \begin{bmatrix} \frac{1}{8} & \frac{5}{8} \\ \frac{3}{8} & \frac{7}{8} \end{bmatrix}$

47. $A = \begin{bmatrix} 2 & 1 \\ 3 & 1 \end{bmatrix}$ $B = \begin{bmatrix} 4 & 7 \\ 1 & 2 \end{bmatrix}$

$A^{-1} = \begin{bmatrix} -1 & 1 \\ 3 & -2 \end{bmatrix}$ $B^{-1} = \begin{bmatrix} 2 & -7 \\ -1 & 4 \end{bmatrix}$

$AB = \begin{bmatrix} 2 & 1 \\ 3 & 1 \end{bmatrix}\begin{bmatrix} 4 & 7 \\ 1 & 2 \end{bmatrix} = \begin{bmatrix} 9 & 16 \\ 13 & 23 \end{bmatrix}$

$(AB)^{-1} = \left(\begin{bmatrix} 9 & 16 \\ 13 & 23 \end{bmatrix}\right)^{-1} = \begin{bmatrix} -23 & 16 \\ 13 & -9 \end{bmatrix}$

$A^{-1}B^{-1} = \begin{bmatrix} -1 & 1 \\ 3 & -2 \end{bmatrix}\begin{bmatrix} 2 & -7 \\ -1 & 4 \end{bmatrix} = \begin{bmatrix} -3 & 11 \\ 8 & -29 \end{bmatrix}$

$B^{-1}A^{-1} = \begin{bmatrix} 2 & -7 \\ -1 & 4 \end{bmatrix}\begin{bmatrix} -1 & 1 \\ 3 & -2 \end{bmatrix} = \begin{bmatrix} -23 & 16 \\ 13 & -9 \end{bmatrix}$

Observe that $(AB)^{-1} = B^{-1}A^{-1}$.

49. $\begin{bmatrix} a & 0 & 0 \\ 0 & b & 0 \\ 0 & 0 & c \end{bmatrix}\begin{bmatrix} \frac{1}{a} & 0 & 0 \\ 0 & \frac{1}{b} & 0 \\ 0 & 0 & \frac{1}{c} \end{bmatrix}$

$= \begin{bmatrix} (a)(\frac{1}{a})+(0)(0)+(0)(0) & (a)(0)+(0)(\frac{1}{b})+(0)(0) & (a)(0)+(0)(0)+(0)(\frac{1}{c}) \\ (0)(\frac{1}{a})+(b)(0)+(0)(0) & (0)(0)+(b)(\frac{1}{b})+(0)(0) & (0)(0)+(b)(0)+(0)(\frac{1}{c}) \\ (0)(\frac{1}{a})+(0)(0)+(c)(0) & (0)(0)+(0)(\frac{1}{b})+(c)(0) & (0)(0)+(0)(0)+(c)(\frac{1}{c}) \end{bmatrix}$

$= \begin{bmatrix} \frac{a}{a}+0+0 & 0+0+0 & 0+0+0 \\ 0+0+0 & 0+\frac{b}{b}+0 & 0+0+0 \\ 0+0+0 & 0+0+0 & 0+0+\frac{c}{c} \end{bmatrix} = \begin{bmatrix} 1 & 0 & 0 \\ 0 & 1 & 0 \\ 0 & 0 & 1 \end{bmatrix}$

51. The numerical equivalent of HELP is
8, 5, 12, 16.

$\begin{bmatrix} 4 & -1 \\ -3 & 1 \end{bmatrix}\begin{bmatrix} 8 \\ 5 \end{bmatrix} = \begin{bmatrix} 27 \\ -19 \end{bmatrix}$,

$\begin{bmatrix} 4 & -1 \\ -3 & 1 \end{bmatrix}\begin{bmatrix} 12 \\ 16 \end{bmatrix} = \begin{bmatrix} 32 \\ -20 \end{bmatrix}$

The encoded message is 27, –19, 32, –20.

$\begin{bmatrix} 1 & 1 \\ 3 & 4 \end{bmatrix}\begin{bmatrix} 27 \\ -19 \end{bmatrix} = \begin{bmatrix} 8 \\ 5 \end{bmatrix}$, $\begin{bmatrix} 1 & 1 \\ 3 & 4 \end{bmatrix}\begin{bmatrix} 32 \\ -20 \end{bmatrix} = \begin{bmatrix} 12 \\ 16 \end{bmatrix}$

The decoded message is 8, 5, 12, 16 or HELP.

53. $\begin{bmatrix} 1 & -1 & 0 \\ 3 & 0 & 2 \\ -1 & 0 & -1 \end{bmatrix}\begin{bmatrix} 19 & 4 & 1 \\ 5 & 0 & 19 \\ 14 & 3 & 8 \end{bmatrix}$

$= \begin{bmatrix} 19-5+0 & 4+0+0 & 1-19+0 \\ 57+0+28 & 12+0+6 & 3+0+16 \\ -19+0-14 & -4+0-3 & -1+0-8 \end{bmatrix}$

$= \begin{bmatrix} 14 & 4 & -18 \\ 85 & 18 & 19 \\ -33 & -7 & -9 \end{bmatrix}$

The encoded message is 14, 85, –33, 4, 18, –7, –18, 19, –9.

$\begin{bmatrix} 0 & 1 & 2 \\ -1 & 1 & 2 \\ 0 & -1 & -3 \end{bmatrix}\begin{bmatrix} 14 & 4 & -18 \\ 85 & 18 & 19 \\ -33 & -7 & -9 \end{bmatrix}$

$$= \begin{bmatrix} 0+85-66 & 0+18-14 & 0+19-18 \\ -14+85-66 & -4+18-14 & 18+19-18 \\ 0-85+99 & 0-18+21 & 0-19+27 \end{bmatrix}$$

$$= \begin{bmatrix} 19 & 4 & 1 \\ 5 & 0 & 19 \\ 14 & 3 & 8 \end{bmatrix}$$

The decoded message is 19, 5, 14, 4, 0, 3, 1, 19,
8 or SEND_CASH

65. Enter the matrix $\begin{bmatrix} 3 & -1 \\ -2 & 1 \end{bmatrix}$ as [A], then use $[A]^{-1}$.

$$[A]^{-1} = \begin{bmatrix} 1 & 1 \\ 2 & 3 \end{bmatrix}$$

Verify this result by showing that $[A][A]^{-1} = I_2$ and $[A]^{-1}[A] = I_2$.

67. Enter the matrix $\begin{bmatrix} -2 & 1 & -1 \\ -5 & 2 & -1 \\ 3 & -1 & 1 \end{bmatrix}$ as [A], then use $[A]^{-1}$.

$$[A]^{-1} = \begin{bmatrix} 1 & 0 & 1 \\ 2 & 1 & 3 \\ -1 & 1 & 1 \end{bmatrix}$$

Verify this result by showing that $[A][A]^{-1} = I_3$ and $[A]^{-1}[A] = I_3$.

69. Enter the matrix $\begin{bmatrix} 7 & -3 & 0 & 2 \\ -2 & 1 & 0 & -1 \\ 4 & 0 & 1 & -2 \\ -1 & 1 & 0 & -1 \end{bmatrix}$ as [A], then use $[A]^{-1}$. $[A]^{-1} = \begin{bmatrix} 0 & -1 & 0 & 1 \\ -1 & -5 & 0 & 3 \\ -2 & -4 & 1 & -2 \\ -1 & -4 & 0 & 1 \end{bmatrix}$

Verify this result by showing that $[A][A]^{-1} = I_4$ and $[A]^{-1}[A] = I_4$.

71. The system is $AX = B$ where

$A = \begin{bmatrix} 1 & -1 & 1 \\ 4 & 2 & 1 \\ 4 & -2 & 1 \end{bmatrix}$, $X = \begin{bmatrix} x \\ y \\ z \end{bmatrix}$, and $B = \begin{bmatrix} -6 \\ 9 \\ -3 \end{bmatrix}$. $X = \begin{bmatrix} 2 \\ 3 \\ -5 \end{bmatrix}$, so the solution to the system is $\{(2, 3, -5)\}$.

73. The system is $AX = B$ where $A = \begin{bmatrix} 3 & -2 & 1 \\ 4 & -5 & 3 \\ 2 & -1 & 5 \end{bmatrix}$, $X = \begin{bmatrix} x \\ y \\ z \end{bmatrix}$, and $B = \begin{bmatrix} -2 \\ -9 \\ -5 \end{bmatrix}$.

$X = \begin{bmatrix} 1 \\ 2 \\ -1 \end{bmatrix}$ so the solution to the system is $\{(1, 2, -1)\}$.

75. The system is $AX = B$ where $A = \begin{bmatrix} 1 & 0 & -3 & 0 & 1 \\ 0 & 1 & 0 & 1 & 0 \\ 0 & 0 & 1 & 0 & 1 \\ 1 & 1 & -1 & 4 & 0 \\ 1 & 1 & 1 & 1 & 1 \end{bmatrix}$, $X = \begin{bmatrix} v \\ w \\ x \\ y \\ z \end{bmatrix}$ and $B = \begin{bmatrix} -3 \\ -1 \\ 7 \\ -8 \\ 8 \end{bmatrix}$. $X = \begin{bmatrix} 2 \\ 1 \\ 3 \\ -2 \\ 4 \end{bmatrix}$, so the solution to

the system is $\{(2, 1, 3, -2, 4)\}$.

79. a. False; only square matrices have inverses.

    b. False; $\begin{bmatrix} 3 & 6 \\ 2 & 4 \end{bmatrix}$ does not have an inverse since $(3)(4) - (6)(2) = 12 - 12 = 0$ and division by zero is
undefined.

    c. True; $\begin{bmatrix} 1 & 2 \\ 2 & 3 \end{bmatrix} + \begin{bmatrix} 2 & 4 \\ 0 & 1 \end{bmatrix} = \begin{bmatrix} 3 & 6 \\ 2 & 4 \end{bmatrix}$ and $\begin{bmatrix} 1 & 2 \\ 2 & 3 \end{bmatrix}^{-1} = \begin{bmatrix} -3 & 2 \\ 2 & -1 \end{bmatrix}$,

    $\begin{bmatrix} 2 & 4 \\ 0 & 1 \end{bmatrix}^{-1} = \begin{bmatrix} \frac{1}{2} & -2 \\ 0 & 1 \end{bmatrix}$ while $\begin{bmatrix} 3 & 6 \\ 2 & 4 \end{bmatrix}$ does not have an inverse. [See part (b).]

    d. False; to solve the matrix equation for X, multiply the inverse of A and B $(A^{-1}B)$ provided the inverse of A
exists.

    (c) is true.

83. Using the statement before problems 9–14, we want to find values for a such that
$(1)(4) - (a + 1)(a - 2) = 0$.
$(1)(4) - (a + 1)(a - 2) = 4 - (a^2 - a - 2)$
$\qquad = -a^2 + a + 6$
$0 = -a^2 + a + 6$
$0 = a^2 - a - 6$
$0 = (a - 3)(a + 2)$
$a = 3, -2$

Section 6.5

Check Point Exercises

1. a. $\begin{vmatrix} 10 & 9 \\ 6 & 5 \end{vmatrix} = 10 \cdot 5 - 6 \cdot 9 = 50 - 54 = -4$

    b. $\begin{vmatrix} 4 & 3 \\ -5 & -8 \end{vmatrix} = 4 \cdot (-8) - (-5) \cdot (3)$
$\qquad\qquad = -32 + 15 = -17$

2. $5x + 4y = 12$
$3x - 6y = 24$

$$D = \begin{vmatrix} 5 & 4 \\ 3 & -6 \end{vmatrix} = 5 \cdot (-6) - 3 \cdot 4$$

$$= -30 - 12 = -42$$

$$D_x = \begin{vmatrix} 12 & 4 \\ 24 & -6 \end{vmatrix} = 12(-6) - 24(4)$$

$$= -72 - 96 = -168$$

$$D_y = \begin{vmatrix} 5 & 12 \\ 3 & 24 \end{vmatrix} = 5(24) - 3(12)$$

$$= 120 - 36 = 84$$

Thus, $x = \dfrac{D_x}{D} = \dfrac{-168}{-42} = 4$

$$y = \dfrac{D_y}{D} = \dfrac{84}{-42} = -2$$

The solution set is $\{(4, -2)\}$.

3. $\begin{bmatrix} 2 & 1 & 7 \\ -5 & 6 & 0 \\ -4 & 3 & 1 \end{bmatrix}$

The minor for 2 is $\begin{vmatrix} 6 & 0 \\ 3 & 1 \end{vmatrix}$.

The minor for -5 is $\begin{vmatrix} 1 & 7 \\ 3 & 1 \end{vmatrix}$.

The minor for -4 is $\begin{vmatrix} 1 & 7 \\ 6 & 0 \end{vmatrix}$.

$$\begin{bmatrix} 2 & 1 & 7 \\ -5 & 6 & 0 \\ -4 & 3 & 1 \end{bmatrix} = 2\begin{vmatrix} 6 & 0 \\ 3 & 1 \end{vmatrix} - (-5)\begin{vmatrix} 1 & 7 \\ 3 & 1 \end{vmatrix} - 4\begin{vmatrix} 1 & 7 \\ 6 & 0 \end{vmatrix}$$

$$= 2(6 \cdot 1 - 3 \cdot 0) + 5(1 \cdot 1 - 3 \cdot 7) - 4(1 \cdot 0 - 6 \cdot 7)$$

$$= 2(6 - 0) + 5(1 - 21) - 4(0 - 42)$$

$$= 12 - 100 + 168$$

$$= 80$$

4. $\begin{vmatrix} 6 & 4 & 0 \\ -3 & -5 & 3 \\ 1 & 2 & 0 \end{vmatrix} = 0\begin{vmatrix} -3 & -5 \\ 1 & 2 \end{vmatrix} - 3\begin{vmatrix} 6 & 4 \\ 1 & 2 \end{vmatrix} + 0\begin{vmatrix} 6 & 4 \\ -3 & -5 \end{vmatrix}$

$$= 0 - 3(6 \cdot 2 - 1 \cdot 4) + 0$$

$$= -3(12 - 4)$$

$$= -3(8)$$

$$= -24$$

5.

$3x - 2y + z = 16$

$2x + 3y - z = -9$

$x + 4y + 3z = 2$

$$D = \begin{vmatrix} 3 & -2 & 1 \\ 2 & 3 & -1 \\ 1 & 4 & 3 \end{vmatrix}; \quad D_x = \begin{vmatrix} 16 & -2 & 1 \\ -9 & 3 & -1 \\ 2 & 4 & 3 \end{vmatrix}; \quad D_y = \begin{vmatrix} 3 & 16 & 1 \\ 2 & -9 & -1 \\ 1 & 2 & 3 \end{vmatrix}; \quad D_z = \begin{vmatrix} 3 & -2 & 16 \\ 2 & 3 & -9 \\ 1 & 4 & 2 \end{vmatrix}$$

$$D = \begin{vmatrix} 3 & -2 & 1 \\ 2 & 3 & -1 \\ 1 & 4 & 3 \end{vmatrix} = 3\begin{vmatrix} 3 & -1 \\ 4 & 3 \end{vmatrix} - 2\begin{vmatrix} -2 & 1 \\ 4 & 3 \end{vmatrix} + 1\begin{vmatrix} -2 & 1 \\ 3 & -1 \end{vmatrix}$$

$= 3[(3) \cdot 3 - 4 \cdot (-1)] - 2[(-2) \cdot 3 - 4 \cdot 1] + 1[(-2) \cdot (-1) - (3) \cdot 1]$

$= 3(9 + 4) - 2(-6 - 4) + 1(2 - 3)$

$= 39 + 20 - 1$

$= 58$

$$D_x = \begin{vmatrix} 16 & -2 & 1 \\ -9 & 3 & -1 \\ 2 & 4 & 3 \end{vmatrix} = 1\begin{vmatrix} -9 & 3 \\ 2 & 4 \end{vmatrix} - (-1)\begin{vmatrix} 16 & -2 \\ 2 & 4 \end{vmatrix} + 3\begin{vmatrix} 16 & -2 \\ -9 & 3 \end{vmatrix}$$

$= 1[(-9) \cdot 4 - 2 \cdot (3)] + 1[16 \cdot 4 - 2(-2)] + 3[16 \cdot (3) - (-9) \cdot (-2)]$

$= 1(-36 - 6) + 1(64 + 4) + 3(48 - 18)$

$= -42 + 68 + 90$

$= 116$

$$D_y = \begin{vmatrix} 3 & 16 & 1 \\ 2 & -9 & -1 \\ 1 & 2 & 3 \end{vmatrix} = 3\begin{vmatrix} -9 & -1 \\ 2 & 3 \end{vmatrix} - 2\begin{vmatrix} 16 & 1 \\ 2 & 3 \end{vmatrix} + 1\begin{vmatrix} 16 & 1 \\ -9 & -1 \end{vmatrix}$$

$= 3[(-9) \cdot 3 - 2 \cdot (-1)] - 2[16 \cdot 3 - 2 \cdot 1] + 1[16(-1) - (-9) \cdot 1]$

$= 3(-27 + 2) - 2(48 - 2) + 1(-16 + 9)$

$= -75 - 92 - 7$

$= -174$

$$D_z = \begin{vmatrix} 3 & -2 & 16 \\ 2 & 3 & -9 \\ 1 & 4 & 2 \end{vmatrix} = 3\begin{vmatrix} 3 & -9 \\ 4 & 2 \end{vmatrix} - 2\begin{vmatrix} -2 & 16 \\ 4 & 2 \end{vmatrix} + 1\begin{vmatrix} -2 & 16 \\ 3 & -9 \end{vmatrix}$$

$= 3[(3)2 - 4(-9)] - 2[(-2)2 - 4 \cdot 16] + 1[(-2)(-9) - (3) \cdot 16]$

$= 3(6 + 36) - 2(-4 - 64) + 1(18 - 48)$

$= 126 + 136 - 30$

$= 232$

$x = \dfrac{D_x}{D} = \dfrac{116}{58} = 2$

$y = \dfrac{D_y}{D} = \dfrac{-174}{58} = -3$

$z = \dfrac{D_z}{D} = \dfrac{232}{58} = 4$

The solution to the system is $\{(2, -3, 4)\}$.

6. $|A| = \begin{vmatrix} 0 & 4 & 0 & -3 \\ -1 & 1 & 5 & 2 \\ 1 & -2 & 0 & 6 \\ 3 & 0 & 0 & 1 \end{vmatrix} = (-1)^{2+3} 5 \begin{vmatrix} 0 & 4 & -3 \\ 1 & -2 & 6 \\ 3 & 0 & 1 \end{vmatrix} = -5 \begin{vmatrix} 0 & 4 & -3 \\ 1 & -2 & 6 \\ 3 & 0 & 1 \end{vmatrix}$

Evaluate the third-order determinant to get $|A| = -5(50) = -250$.

Exercise Set 6.5

1. $\begin{vmatrix} 5 & 7 \\ 2 & 3 \end{vmatrix} = 5 \cdot 3 - 2 \cdot 7 = 15 - 14 = 1$

3. $\begin{vmatrix} -4 & 1 \\ 5 & 6 \end{vmatrix} = (-4)6 - 5 \cdot 1 = -24 - 5 = -29$

5. $\begin{vmatrix} -7 & 14 \\ 2 & -4 \end{vmatrix} = (-7)(-4) - 2(14) = 28 - 28 = 0$

7. $\begin{vmatrix} -5 & -1 \\ -2 & -7 \end{vmatrix} = (-5)(-7) - (-2)(-1) = 35 - 2 = 33$

9. $\begin{vmatrix} \frac{1}{2} & \frac{1}{2} \\ \frac{1}{8} & -\frac{3}{4} \end{vmatrix} = \frac{1}{2}\left(-\frac{3}{4}\right) - \frac{1}{8} \cdot \frac{1}{2} = -\frac{3}{8} - \frac{1}{16} = -\frac{7}{16}$

11. $D = \begin{vmatrix} 1 & 1 \\ 1 & -1 \end{vmatrix} = -1 - 1 = -2$

$D_x = \begin{vmatrix} 7 & 1 \\ 3 & -1 \end{vmatrix} = -7 - 3 = -10$

$D_y = \begin{vmatrix} 1 & 7 \\ 1 & 3 \end{vmatrix} = 3 - 7 = -4$

$x = \dfrac{D_x}{D} = \dfrac{-10}{-2} = 5$

$y = \dfrac{D_y}{D} = \dfrac{-4}{-2} = 2$

The solution set is $\{(5, 2)\}$.

13. $D = \begin{vmatrix} 12 & 3 \\ 2 & -3 \end{vmatrix} = -36 - 6 = -42$

$D_x = \begin{vmatrix} 15 & 3 \\ 13 & -3 \end{vmatrix} = -45 - 39 = -84$

$D_y = \begin{vmatrix} 12 & 15 \\ 2 & 13 \end{vmatrix} = 156 - 30 = 126$

$x = \dfrac{D_x}{D} = \dfrac{-84}{-42} = 2$

$y = \dfrac{D_y}{D} = \dfrac{126}{-42} = -3$

The solution set is $\{(2, -3)\}$.

15. $D = \begin{vmatrix} 4 & -5 \\ 2 & 3 \end{vmatrix} = 12 - (-10) = 22$

$D_x = \begin{vmatrix} 17 & -5 \\ 3 & 3 \end{vmatrix} = 51 - (-15) = 66$

$D_y = \begin{vmatrix} 4 & 17 \\ 2 & 3 \end{vmatrix} = 12 - 34 = -22$

$x = \dfrac{D_x}{D} = \dfrac{66}{22} = 3$

$y = \dfrac{D_y}{D} = \dfrac{-22}{22} = -1$

The solution set is $\{(3, -1)\}$.

17. $D = \begin{vmatrix} 1 & 2 \\ 5 & 10 \end{vmatrix} = 10 - 10 = 0$

$D_x = \begin{vmatrix} 3 & 2 \\ 15 & 10 \end{vmatrix} = 30 - 30 = 0$

$D_y = \begin{vmatrix} 1 & 3 \\ 5 & 15 \end{vmatrix} = 15 - 15 = 0$

Because all 3 determinants equal zero, the system is dependent.

19. $D = \begin{vmatrix} 3 & -4 \\ 2 & 2 \end{vmatrix} = 6 - (-8) = 14$

$D_x = \begin{vmatrix} 4 & -4 \\ 12 & 2 \end{vmatrix} = 8 - (-48) = 56$

$D_y = \begin{vmatrix} 3 & 4 \\ 2 & 12 \end{vmatrix} = 36 - 8 = 28$

$x = \dfrac{D_x}{D} = \dfrac{56}{14} = 4$

$y = \dfrac{D_y}{D} = \dfrac{28}{14} = 2$

The solution set is $\{(4, 2)\}$.

21. $D = \begin{vmatrix} 2 & -3 \\ 5 & 4 \end{vmatrix} = 8 - (-15) = 23$

$D_x = \begin{vmatrix} 2 & -3 \\ 51 & 4 \end{vmatrix} = 8 - (-153) = 161$

$D_y = \begin{vmatrix} 2 & 2 \\ 5 & 51 \end{vmatrix} = 102 - 10 = 92$

$x = \dfrac{D_x}{D} = \dfrac{161}{23} = 7$

$y = \dfrac{D_y}{D} = \dfrac{92}{23} = 4$

The solution set is $\{(7, 4)\}$.

23. $D = \begin{vmatrix} 3 & 3 \\ 2 & 2 \end{vmatrix} = 6 - 6 = 0$

$D_x = \begin{vmatrix} 2 & 3 \\ 3 & 2 \end{vmatrix} = 4 - 9 = -5$

$D_y = \begin{vmatrix} 3 & 2 \\ 2 & 3 \end{vmatrix} = 9 - 4 = 5$

Because $D = 0$ but D_x or $D_y \neq 0$, the system is inconsistent.

25. Write the equations in standard form.

$3x + 4y = 16$

$6x + 8y = 32$

$D = \begin{bmatrix} 3 & 4 \\ 6 & 8 \end{bmatrix} = 24 - 24 = 0$

$D_x = \begin{bmatrix} 16 & 4 \\ 32 & 8 \end{bmatrix} = 128 - 128 = 0$

$D_y = \begin{bmatrix} 3 & 16 \\ 6 & 32 \end{bmatrix} = 96 - 69 = 0$

Since all determinants are zero, the system is dependent.

27. $\begin{vmatrix} 3 & 0 & 0 \\ 2 & 1 & -5 \\ -2 & 5 & -1 \end{vmatrix} = 3 \begin{vmatrix} 1 & -5 \\ 5 & -1 \end{vmatrix} - 0 \begin{vmatrix} 2 & -5 \\ -2 & -1 \end{vmatrix} + 0 \begin{vmatrix} 2 & 1 \\ -2 & 5 \end{vmatrix}$

$= 3[(1)(-1) - (5)(-5)]$

$= 3(-1 + 25) = 3(24)$

$= 72$

29.
$$\begin{vmatrix} 3 & 1 & 0 \\ -3 & 4 & 0 \\ -1 & 3 & -5 \end{vmatrix} = 0\begin{vmatrix} -3 & 4 \\ -1 & 3 \end{vmatrix} - 0\begin{vmatrix} 3 & 1 \\ -1 & 3 \end{vmatrix} + (-5)\begin{vmatrix} 3 & 1 \\ -3 & 4 \end{vmatrix}$$
$$= -5[3\cdot4 - (-3)(1)]$$
$$= -5(12+3) = -5(15)$$
$$= -75$$

31.
$$\begin{vmatrix} 1 & 1 & 1 \\ 2 & 2 & 2 \\ -3 & 4 & -5 \end{vmatrix} -2R_1 + R_2$$
$$\begin{vmatrix} 1 & 1 & 1 \\ 0 & 0 & 0 \\ -3 & 4 & -5 \end{vmatrix} = 0$$

33. $D = \begin{vmatrix} 1 & 1 & 1 \\ 2 & -1 & 1 \\ -1 & 3 & -1 \end{vmatrix}$
$$= \begin{vmatrix} -1 & 1 \\ 3 & -1 \end{vmatrix} - \begin{vmatrix} 2 & 1 \\ -1 & -1 \end{vmatrix} + \begin{vmatrix} 2 & -1 \\ -1 & 3 \end{vmatrix}$$
$$= (1-3) - [-2-(-1)] + (6-1)$$
$$= -2 - (-1) + 5 = -2 + 1 + 5 = 4$$
$$D_x = \begin{vmatrix} 0 & 1 & 1 \\ -1 & -1 & 1 \\ -8 & 3 & -1 \end{vmatrix} = (-1)\begin{vmatrix} -1 & 1 \\ -8 & -1 \end{vmatrix} + \begin{vmatrix} -1 & -1 \\ -8 & 3 \end{vmatrix}$$
$$= (-1)[1-(-8)] + (-3-8) = (-1)(9) - 11$$
$$= -20$$
$$D_y = \begin{vmatrix} 1 & 0 & 1 \\ 2 & -1 & 1 \\ -1 & -8 & -1 \end{vmatrix} = \begin{vmatrix} -1 & 1 \\ -8 & -1 \end{vmatrix} + \begin{vmatrix} 2 & -1 \\ -1 & -8 \end{vmatrix}$$
$$= 1 - (-8) + (-16-1) = 1 + 8 - 17 = -8$$
$$D_z = \begin{vmatrix} 1 & 1 & 0 \\ 2 & -1 & -1 \\ -1 & 3 & -8 \end{vmatrix} = 1\begin{vmatrix} -1 & -1 \\ 3 & -8 \end{vmatrix} - 1\begin{vmatrix} 2 & -1 \\ -1 & -8 \end{vmatrix}$$
$$= 8 - (-3) - 1(-16-1) = 11 + 17 = 28$$
$$x = \frac{D_x}{D} = \frac{-20}{4} = -5$$
$$y = \frac{D_y}{D} = \frac{-8}{4} = -2$$
$$z = \frac{D_z}{D} = \frac{28}{4} = 7$$
The solution to the system is $\{(-5, -2, 7)\}$.

35. $D = \begin{vmatrix} 4 & -5 & -6 \\ 1 & -2 & -5 \\ 2 & -1 & 0 \end{vmatrix} = 2\begin{vmatrix} -5 & -6 \\ -2 & -5 \end{vmatrix} - (-1)\begin{vmatrix} 4 & -6 \\ 1 & -5 \end{vmatrix}$
$$= 2(25-12) + [-20-(-6)] = 2(13) + (-14)$$
$$= 26 - 14 = 12$$
$$D_x = \begin{vmatrix} -1 & -5 & -6 \\ -12 & -2 & -5 \\ 7 & -1 & 0 \end{vmatrix}$$
$$= 7\begin{vmatrix} -5 & -6 \\ -2 & -5 \end{vmatrix} - (-1)\begin{vmatrix} -1 & -6 \\ -12 & -5 \end{vmatrix}$$
$$= 7(25-12) + (5-72) = 7(13) - 67$$
$$= 91 - 67 = 24$$
$$D_y = \begin{vmatrix} 4 & -1 & -6 \\ 1 & -12 & -5 \\ 2 & 7 & 0 \end{vmatrix} = 2\begin{vmatrix} -1 & -6 \\ -12 & -5 \end{vmatrix} - 7\begin{vmatrix} 4 & -6 \\ 1 & -5 \end{vmatrix}$$
$$= 2(5-72) - 7[-20-(-6)]$$
$$= 2(-67) - 7(-14) = -134 + 98 = -36$$
$$D_z = \begin{vmatrix} 4 & -5 & -1 \\ 1 & -2 & -12 \\ 2 & -1 & 7 \end{vmatrix}$$
$$= 4\begin{vmatrix} -2 & -12 \\ -1 & 7 \end{vmatrix} - (-5)\begin{vmatrix} 1 & -12 \\ 2 & 7 \end{vmatrix} + (-1)\begin{vmatrix} 1 & -2 \\ 2 & -1 \end{vmatrix}$$
$$= 4(-14-12) + 5[7-(-24)] - [-1-(-4)]$$
$$= 4(-26) + 5(31) - (3) = -104 + 155 - 3 = 48$$
$$x = \frac{D_x}{D} = \frac{24}{12} = 2, \ y = \frac{D_y}{D} = \frac{-36}{12} = -3,$$
$$z = \frac{D_z}{D} = \frac{48}{12} = 4$$
The solution set is $\{(2, -3, 4)\}$.

37.
$$D = \begin{vmatrix} 1 & 1 & 1 \\ 1 & -2 & 1 \\ 1 & 3 & 2 \end{vmatrix} = 1\begin{vmatrix} -2 & 1 \\ 3 & 2 \end{vmatrix} - 1\begin{vmatrix} 1 & 1 \\ 1 & 2 \end{vmatrix} + 1\begin{vmatrix} 1 & -2 \\ 1 & 3 \end{vmatrix}$$
$$= -4 - 3 - (2-1) + [3-(-2)]$$
$$= -7 - 1 + 5 = -3$$

$$D_x = \begin{vmatrix} 4 & 1 & 1 \\ 7 & -2 & 1 \\ 4 & 3 & 2 \end{vmatrix} = 4\begin{vmatrix} -2 & 1 \\ 3 & 2 \end{vmatrix} - 1\begin{vmatrix} 7 & 1 \\ 4 & 2 \end{vmatrix} + 1\begin{vmatrix} 7 & -2 \\ 4 & 3 \end{vmatrix}$$
$$= 4(-4-3) - (14-4) + [21-(-8)]$$
$$= 4(-7) - 10 + 29 = -28 + 19 = -9$$

$$D_y = \begin{vmatrix} 1 & 4 & 1 \\ 1 & 7 & 1 \\ 1 & 4 & 2 \end{vmatrix} = 1\begin{vmatrix} 7 & 1 \\ 4 & 2 \end{vmatrix} - 1\begin{vmatrix} 4 & 1 \\ 4 & 2 \end{vmatrix} + 1\begin{vmatrix} 4 & 1 \\ 7 & 1 \end{vmatrix}$$
$$= 14 - 4 - (8-4) + (4-7) = 10 - 4 - 3 = 3$$

$$D_z = \begin{vmatrix} 1 & 1 & 4 \\ 1 & -2 & 7 \\ 1 & 3 & 4 \end{vmatrix} = 1\begin{vmatrix} -2 & 7 \\ 3 & 4 \end{vmatrix} - 1\begin{vmatrix} 1 & 4 \\ 3 & 4 \end{vmatrix} + 1\begin{vmatrix} 1 & 4 \\ -2 & 7 \end{vmatrix}$$
$$= -8 - 21 - (4-12) + [7-(-8)]$$
$$= -29 + 8 + 15 = -6$$

$$x = \frac{D_x}{D} = \frac{-9}{-3} = 3,\ y = \frac{D_y}{D} = \frac{3}{-3} = -1,$$
$$z = \frac{D_z}{D} = \frac{-6}{-3} = 2$$
The solution set is {3, −1, 2}.

39.
$$D = \begin{vmatrix} 1 & 0 & 2 \\ 0 & 2 & -1 \\ 2 & 3 & 0 \end{vmatrix} = \begin{vmatrix} 2 & -1 \\ 3 & 0 \end{vmatrix} + 2\begin{vmatrix} 0 & 2 \\ 2 & 3 \end{vmatrix}$$
$$= 0 - (-3) + 2(0-4) = 3 - 8 = -5$$

$$D_x = \begin{vmatrix} 4 & 0 & 2 \\ 5 & 2 & -1 \\ 13 & 3 & 0 \end{vmatrix} = 4\begin{vmatrix} 2 & -1 \\ 3 & 0 \end{vmatrix} + 2\begin{vmatrix} 5 & 2 \\ 13 & 3 \end{vmatrix}$$
$$= 4[0-(-3)] + 2(15-26)$$
$$= 4(3) + 2(-11) = 12 - 22 = -10$$

$$D_y = \begin{vmatrix} 1 & 4 & 2 \\ 0 & 5 & -1 \\ 2 & 13 & 0 \end{vmatrix} = \begin{vmatrix} 5 & -1 \\ 13 & 0 \end{vmatrix} + 2\begin{vmatrix} 4 & 2 \\ 5 & -1 \end{vmatrix}$$
$$= 0 - (-13) + 2(-4-10)$$
$$= 13 + 2(-14) = 13 - 28 = -15$$

$$D_z = \begin{vmatrix} 1 & 0 & 4 \\ 0 & 2 & 5 \\ 2 & 3 & 13 \end{vmatrix} = \begin{vmatrix} 2 & 5 \\ 3 & 13 \end{vmatrix} + 4\begin{vmatrix} 0 & 2 \\ 2 & 3 \end{vmatrix}$$
$$= 26 - 15 + 4(0-4) = 11 + 4(-4)$$
$$= 11 - 16 = -5$$

$$x = \frac{D_x}{D} = \frac{-10}{-5} = 2,\ y = \frac{D_y}{D} = \frac{-15}{-5} = 3,$$
$$z = \frac{D_z}{D} = \frac{-5}{-5} = 1$$
The solution set is {(2, 3, 1)}.

41.
$$\begin{vmatrix} 4 & 2 & 8 & -7 \\ -2 & 0 & 4 & 1 \\ 5 & 0 & 0 & 5 \\ 4 & 0 & 0 & -1 \end{vmatrix} = -2\begin{vmatrix} -2 & 4 & 1 \\ 5 & 0 & 5 \\ 4 & 0 & -1 \end{vmatrix} + 0\begin{vmatrix} 4 & 8 & -7 \\ 5 & 0 & 5 \\ 4 & 0 & -1 \end{vmatrix} - 0\begin{vmatrix} 4 & 8 & -7 \\ -2 & 4 & 1 \\ 4 & 0 & -1 \end{vmatrix} + 0\begin{vmatrix} 4 & 8 & -7 \\ -2 & 4 & 1 \\ 5 & 0 & 5 \end{vmatrix}$$
$$= (-2)\left[(-4)\begin{vmatrix} 5 & 5 \\ 4 & -1 \end{vmatrix} + 0\begin{vmatrix} -2 & 1 \\ 4 & -1 \end{vmatrix} - 0\begin{vmatrix} -2 & 1 \\ 5 & 5 \end{vmatrix}\right] = (-2)(-4)[5(-1) - 4 \cdot 5] = 8(-5-20) = 8(-25) = -200$$

43.
$$\begin{vmatrix} -2 & -3 & 3 & 5 \\ 1 & -4 & 0 & 0 \\ 1 & 2 & 2 & -3 \\ 2 & 0 & 1 & 1 \end{vmatrix} = -1\begin{vmatrix} -3 & 3 & 5 \\ 2 & 2 & -3 \\ 0 & 1 & 1 \end{vmatrix} + (-4)\begin{vmatrix} -2 & 3 & 5 \\ 1 & 2 & -3 \\ 2 & 1 & 1 \end{vmatrix} - 0\begin{vmatrix} -2 & -3 & 5 \\ 1 & 2 & -3 \\ 2 & 0 & 1 \end{vmatrix} + 0\begin{vmatrix} -2 & -3 & 3 \\ 1 & 2 & 2 \\ 2 & 0 & 1 \end{vmatrix}$$
$$= (-1)\left[0\begin{vmatrix} 3 & 5 \\ 2 & -3 \end{vmatrix} - 1\begin{vmatrix} -3 & 5 \\ 2 & -3 \end{vmatrix} + 1\begin{vmatrix} -3 & 3 \\ 2 & 2 \end{vmatrix}\right] - 4\left[2\begin{vmatrix} 3 & 5 \\ 2 & -3 \end{vmatrix} - 1\begin{vmatrix} -2 & 5 \\ 1 & -3 \end{vmatrix} + 1\begin{vmatrix} -2 & 3 \\ 1 & 2 \end{vmatrix}\right]$$
$$= (-1)\{(-1)[(-3)(-3) - 2 \cdot 5] + [(-3)(2) - 2 \cdot 3]\} - 4\{2[3(-3) - 2 \cdot 5] - [(-2)(-3) - 1 \cdot 5] + [(-2)(2) - 1 \cdot 3]\} = 195$$

45.
$$\begin{Vmatrix} \begin{vmatrix} 3 & 1 \\ -2 & 3 \end{vmatrix} & \begin{vmatrix} 7 & 0 \\ 1 & 5 \end{vmatrix} \\ \begin{vmatrix} 3 & 0 \\ 0 & 7 \end{vmatrix} & \begin{vmatrix} 9 & -6 \\ 3 & 5 \end{vmatrix} \end{Vmatrix} = \begin{vmatrix} 3(3)-(-2)(1) & 7(5)-1(0) \\ 3(7)-0(0) & 9(5)-3(-6) \end{vmatrix} = \begin{vmatrix} 9+2 & 35-0 \\ 21-0 & 45+18 \end{vmatrix} = \begin{vmatrix} 11 & 35 \\ 21 & 63 \end{vmatrix}$$

$$= 11(63) - 21(35) = 693 - 735 = -42$$

47.

From $D = \begin{vmatrix} 2 & -4 \\ 3 & 5 \end{vmatrix}$ we obtain the coefficients of the variables in our equations:

$2x - 4y = c_1$

$3x + 5y = c_2$

From $D_x = \begin{vmatrix} 8 & -4 \\ -10 & 5 \end{vmatrix}$ we obtain the constant coefficients: 8 and -10

$2x - 4y = 8$

$3x + 5y = -10$

49.
$$\begin{vmatrix} -2 & x \\ 4 & 6 \end{vmatrix} = 32$$

$-2(6) - 4(x) = 32$

$-12 - 4x = 32$

$-4x = 44$

$x = -11$

The solution is -11.

51.
$$\begin{vmatrix} 1 & x & -2 \\ 3 & 1 & 1 \\ 0 & -2 & 2 \end{vmatrix} = -8$$

$$0\begin{vmatrix} x & -2 \\ 1 & 1 \end{vmatrix} - (-2)\begin{vmatrix} 1 & -2 \\ 3 & 1 \end{vmatrix} + 2\begin{vmatrix} 1 & x \\ 3 & 1 \end{vmatrix} = -8$$

$$2[1(1) - 3(-2)] + 2[1(1) - 3(x)] = -8$$

$$2(1+6) + 2(1-3x) = -8$$

$$2(7) + 2(1-3x) = -8$$

$$14 + 2 - 6x = -8$$

$$-6x = -24$$

$$x = 4$$

The solution is 4.

53. $\text{Area} = \pm\dfrac{1}{2}\begin{vmatrix} 3 & -5 & 1 \\ 2 & 6 & 1 \\ -3 & 5 & 1 \end{vmatrix} = \pm\dfrac{1}{2}\begin{vmatrix} 3 & -5 & 1 \\ -1 & 11 & 0 \\ -6 & 10 & 0 \end{vmatrix} = \pm\dfrac{1}{2}\begin{vmatrix} -1 & 11 \\ -6 & 10 \end{vmatrix} = \pm\dfrac{1}{2}[-10-(-66)] = \pm\dfrac{1}{2}(56) = 28$

The area is 28 square units.

The slope of the line through $(3, -5)$ and $(-3, 5)$ is $m = \dfrac{5-(-5)}{-3-3} = \dfrac{10}{-6} = -\dfrac{5}{3}$.

The equation of the line is $y-(-5) = -\dfrac{5}{3}(x-3)$ or $y = -\dfrac{5}{3}x$.

The line perpendicular to $y = -\dfrac{5}{3}x$ through $(2, 6)$ has equation $y-6 = \dfrac{3}{5}(x-2)$ or $y = \dfrac{3}{5}x + \dfrac{24}{5}$.

These lines intersect where $-\dfrac{5}{3}x = \dfrac{3}{5}x + \dfrac{24}{5}$.

$-\dfrac{36}{17} = x$ and $-\dfrac{24}{5} = \dfrac{34}{15}x$ $y = -\dfrac{5}{3}\left(-\dfrac{36}{17}\right) = \dfrac{60}{17}$

Using the side connecting $(3, -5)$ and $(-3, 5)$ as the base, the height is the distance from $(2, 6)$ to $\left(-\dfrac{36}{17}, \dfrac{60}{17}\right)$.

$b = \sqrt{[3-(-3)]^2 + (-5-5)^2}$

$= \sqrt{36+100} = \sqrt{136} = 2\sqrt{34}$

$h = \sqrt{\left[2-\left(-\dfrac{36}{17}\right)\right]^2 + \left(6-\dfrac{60}{17}\right)^2}$

$= \sqrt{\dfrac{4900}{289} + \dfrac{1764}{289}} = \dfrac{14\sqrt{34}}{17}$

$\dfrac{1}{2}bh = \dfrac{1}{2}\left(2\sqrt{34}\right)\left(\dfrac{14\sqrt{34}}{17}\right) = \dfrac{14(34)}{17}$

$= 14(2) = 28$ square units

55. $\begin{vmatrix} 3 & -1 & 1 \\ 0 & -3 & 1 \\ 12 & 5 & 1 \end{vmatrix} = \begin{vmatrix} 3 & -1 & 1 \\ -3 & -2 & 0 \\ 9 & 6 & 0 \end{vmatrix} = \begin{vmatrix} -3 & -2 \\ 9 & 6 \end{vmatrix}$

$= -18 - (-18) = 0$

Yes, the points are collinear.

57. $\begin{vmatrix} x & y & 1 \\ 3 & -5 & 1 \\ -2 & 6 & 1 \end{vmatrix} = x\begin{vmatrix} -5 & 1 \\ 6 & 1 \end{vmatrix} - y\begin{vmatrix} 3 & 1 \\ -2 & 1 \end{vmatrix} + \begin{vmatrix} 3 & -5 \\ -2 & 6 \end{vmatrix} = x(-5-6) - y[3-(-2)] + (18-10)$

$= -11x - 5y + 8$

The equation of the line is $-11x - 5y + 8 = 0$. The equation of the line in slope-intercept form is $y = -\dfrac{11}{5}x + \dfrac{8}{5}$.

69. Input the matrix as $[A]$, then use $\det[A]$ to find the determinant.

$$\begin{vmatrix} 8 & 2 & 6 & -1 & 0 \\ 2 & 0 & -3 & 4 & 7 \\ 2 & 1 & -3 & 6 & -5 \\ -1 & 2 & 1 & 5 & -1 \\ 4 & 5 & -2 & 3 & -8 \end{vmatrix} = 13,200$$

In exercise 71, expansions are all done about the first column of the matrix and the resulting products of 0 and a determinant are not shown.

71. a. $\begin{vmatrix} a & a \\ 0 & a \end{vmatrix} = a^2 - 0 = a^2$

b. $\begin{vmatrix} a & a & a \\ 0 & a & a \\ 0 & 0 & a \end{vmatrix} = a\begin{vmatrix} a & a \\ 0 & a \end{vmatrix} - 0 + 0$

$\qquad = a(a^2) = a^3$

c. $\begin{vmatrix} a & a & a & a \\ 0 & a & a & a \\ 0 & 0 & a & a \\ 0 & 0 & 0 & a \end{vmatrix} = a\begin{vmatrix} a & a & a \\ 0 & a & a \\ 0 & 0 & a \end{vmatrix} - 0 + 0 - 0$

$\qquad = a(a^3) = a^4$

d.   Each determinant has zeros below the main diagonal and a's everywhere else.

e.   Each determinant equals a raised to the power equal to the order of the determinant.

73. The sign of the value is changed when 2 columns are interchanged in a 2nd order determinant.

75. Evaluate the determinate and write the equation in slope intercept form.

$$\begin{vmatrix} x & y & 1 \\ x_1 & y_1 & 1 \\ x_2 & y_2 & 1 \end{vmatrix} = 0$$

$$x\begin{vmatrix} y_1 & 1 \\ y_2 & 1 \end{vmatrix} - y\begin{vmatrix} x_1 & 1 \\ x_2 & 1 \end{vmatrix} + 1\begin{vmatrix} x_1 & y_1 \\ x_2 & y_2 \end{vmatrix} = 0$$

$$x(y_1 - y_2) - y(x_1 - x_2) + x_1 y_2 - x_2 y_1 = 0$$

$$-y(x_1 - x_2) = -x(y_1 - y_2) + x_2 y_1 - x_1 y_2$$

$$y(x_2 - x_1) = x(y_2 - y_1) + x_2 y_1 - x_1 y_2$$

$$y = \frac{y_2 - y_1}{x_2 - x_1} x + \frac{x_2 y_1 - x_1 y_2}{x_2 - x_1}$$

$$m = \frac{y_2 - y_1}{x_2 - x_1} \qquad b = \frac{x_2 y_1 - x_1 y_2}{x_2 - x_1}$$

Write the slope-point equation of the line the in point slope form.

$$y - y_1 = \frac{y_2 - y_1}{x_2 - x_1}(x - x_1)$$

$$y - y_1 = \frac{y_2 - y_1}{x_2 - x_1}x + \frac{-x_1 y_2 + x_1 y_1}{x_2 - x_1}$$

$$y = \frac{y_2 - y_1}{x_2 - x_1}x + \frac{-x_1 y_2 + x_1 y_1}{x_2 - x_1} + y_1$$

$$y = \frac{y_2 - y_1}{x_2 - x_1}x + \frac{-x_1 y_2 + x_1 y_1}{x_2 - x_1} + \frac{x_2 y_1 - x_1 y_1}{x_2 - x_1}$$

$$y = \frac{y_2 - y_1}{x_2 - x_1}x + \frac{x_2 y_1 - x_1 y_2}{x_2 - x_1}$$

$$m = \frac{y_2 - y_1}{x_2 - x_1} \qquad b = \frac{x_2 y_1 - x_1 y_2}{x_2 - x_1}$$

Since both forms give the same slope and y-intercept, the determinant does give the equation of the line.

Chapter 6 Review Exercises

1.
$$x + y + 3z = 12$$
$$y - 2z = -4$$
$$z = 3$$

$$y - 2(3) = -4$$
$$y - 6 = -4$$
$$y = 2$$

$$x + 2 + 3(3) = 12$$
$$x + 11 = 12$$
$$x = 1$$

The solution to the system is $\{(1, 2, 3)\}$.

2.
$$w - 2y + 2z = 1$$
$$x + y - z = 0$$
$$y - \frac{7}{3}x = -\frac{1}{3}$$
$$z = 1$$

$$y - \frac{7}{3}(1) = -\frac{1}{3}$$
$$y - \frac{7}{3} = -\frac{1}{3}$$
$$y = \frac{6}{3}$$
$$y = 2$$

$$x + 2 - 1 = 0$$
$$x + 1 = 0$$
$$x = -1$$

$$w - 2(2) + 2(1) = 1$$
$$w - 2 = 1$$
$$w = 3$$

The solution to the system is $\{(3, -1, 2, 1)\}$.

3.
$$\begin{bmatrix} 1 & 2 & 2 & | & 2 \\ 0 & 1 & -1 & | & 2 \\ 0 & 5 & 4 & | & 1 \end{bmatrix} -5R_2 + R_3$$

$$\begin{bmatrix} 1 & 2 & 2 & | & 2 \\ 0 & 1 & -1 & | & 2 \\ 0 & 0 & 9 & | & -9 \end{bmatrix}$$

4. $\begin{bmatrix} 2 & -2 & 1 & | & -1 \\ 1 & 2 & -1 & | & 2 \\ 6 & 4 & 3 & | & 5 \end{bmatrix} \frac{1}{2}R_1$

$\begin{bmatrix} 1 & -1 & \frac{1}{2} & | & -\frac{1}{2} \\ 1 & 2 & -1 & | & 2 \\ 6 & 4 & 3 & | & 5 \end{bmatrix}$

5. $\begin{bmatrix} 1 & 2 & 3 & | & -5 \\ 2 & 1 & 1 & | & 1 \\ 1 & 1 & -1 & | & 8 \end{bmatrix} \begin{matrix} -2R_1 + R_2 \\ -1R_1 + R_3 \end{matrix}$

$\begin{bmatrix} 1 & 2 & 3 & | & -5 \\ 0 & -3 & -5 & | & 11 \\ 0 & -1 & -4 & | & 13 \end{bmatrix} R_2 \leftrightarrow R_3$

$\begin{bmatrix} 1 & 2 & 3 & | & -5 \\ 0 & -1 & -4 & | & 13 \\ 0 & -3 & -5 & | & 11 \end{bmatrix} -1R_2$

$\begin{bmatrix} 1 & 2 & 3 & | & -5 \\ 0 & 1 & 4 & | & -13 \\ 0 & -3 & -5 & | & 11 \end{bmatrix} 3R_2 + R_3$

$\begin{bmatrix} 1 & 2 & 3 & | & -5 \\ 0 & 1 & 4 & | & -13 \\ 0 & 0 & 7 & | & -28 \end{bmatrix} \frac{1}{7}R_3$

$\begin{bmatrix} 1 & 2 & 3 & | & -5 \\ 0 & 1 & 4 & | & -13 \\ 0 & 0 & 1 & | & -4 \end{bmatrix} -2R_2 + R_1$

$\begin{bmatrix} 1 & 0 & -5 & | & 21 \\ 0 & 1 & 4 & | & -13 \\ 0 & 0 & 1 & | & -4 \end{bmatrix} \begin{matrix} 5R_3 + R_1 \\ -4R_3 + R_2 \end{matrix}$

$\begin{bmatrix} 1 & 0 & 0 & | & 1 \\ 0 & 1 & 0 & | & 3 \\ 0 & 0 & 1 & | & -4 \end{bmatrix}$

The solution set is $\{(1, 3, -4)\}$.

6. $\begin{bmatrix} 1 & -2 & 1 & | & 0 \\ 0 & 1 & -3 & | & -1 \\ 0 & 2 & 5 & | & -2 \end{bmatrix} -2R_2 + R_3$

$\begin{bmatrix} 1 & -2 & 1 & | & 0 \\ 0 & 1 & -3 & | & -1 \\ 0 & 0 & 11 & | & 0 \end{bmatrix} \frac{1}{11}R_3$

$\begin{bmatrix} 1 & -2 & 1 & | & 0 \\ 0 & 1 & -3 & | & -1 \\ 0 & 0 & 1 & | & 0 \end{bmatrix} 2R_2 + R_1$

$\begin{bmatrix} 1 & 0 & -5 & -2 \\ 0 & 1 & -3 & -1 \\ 0 & 0 & 1 & 0 \end{bmatrix} \begin{matrix} 3R_3 + R_2 \\ 5R_3 + R_1 \end{matrix}$

$\begin{bmatrix} 1 & 0 & 0 & -2 \\ 0 & 1 & 0 & -1 \\ 0 & 0 & 1 & 0 \end{bmatrix}$

$x = -2; y = -1; z = 0$
The solution set is $\{(-2, -1, 0)\}$.

7. $\begin{bmatrix} 3 & 5 & -8 & 5 & | & -8 \\ 1 & 2 & -3 & 1 & | & -7 \\ 2 & 3 & -7 & 3 & | & -11 \\ 4 & 8 & -10 & 7 & | & -10 \end{bmatrix} R_1 \leftrightarrow R_2$

$\begin{bmatrix} 1 & 2 & -3 & 1 & | & -7 \\ 3 & 5 & -8 & 5 & | & -8 \\ 2 & 3 & -7 & 3 & | & -11 \\ 4 & 8 & -10 & 7 & | & -10 \end{bmatrix} \begin{matrix} -3R_1 + R_2 \\ -2R_1 + R_3 \\ -4R_1 + R_4 \end{matrix}$

$\begin{bmatrix} 1 & 2 & -3 & 1 & | & -7 \\ 0 & -1 & 1 & 2 & | & 13 \\ 0 & -1 & -1 & 1 & | & 3 \\ 0 & 0 & 2 & 3 & | & 18 \end{bmatrix} -1R_2$

$\begin{bmatrix} 1 & 2 & -3 & 1 & | & -7 \\ 0 & 1 & -1 & -2 & | & -13 \\ 0 & -1 & -1 & 1 & | & 3 \\ 0 & 0 & 2 & 3 & | & 18 \end{bmatrix} \begin{matrix} -2R_2 + R_1 \\ 1R_2 + R_3 \end{matrix}$

$\begin{bmatrix} 1 & 0 & -1 & 5 & | & 19 \\ 0 & 1 & -1 & -2 & | & -13 \\ 0 & 0 & -2 & -1 & | & -10 \\ 0 & 0 & 2 & 3 & | & 18 \end{bmatrix} -\frac{1}{2}R_3$

$\begin{bmatrix} 1 & 0 & -1 & 5 & | & 19 \\ 0 & 1 & -1 & -2 & | & -13 \\ 0 & 0 & 1 & \frac{1}{2} & | & 5 \\ 0 & 0 & 2 & 3 & | & 18 \end{bmatrix} \begin{matrix} 1R_3 + R_1 \\ 1R_3 + R_2 \\ -2R_3 + R_4 \end{matrix}$

$\begin{bmatrix} 1 & 0 & 0 & \frac{11}{2} & | & 24 \\ 0 & 1 & 0 & -\frac{3}{2} & | & -8 \\ 0 & 0 & 1 & \frac{1}{2} & | & 5 \\ 0 & 0 & 0 & 2 & | & 8 \end{bmatrix} \frac{1}{2}R_4$

$\begin{bmatrix} 1 & 0 & 0 & \frac{11}{2} & | & 24 \\ 0 & 1 & 0 & -\frac{3}{2} & | & -8 \\ 0 & 0 & 1 & \frac{1}{2} & | & 5 \\ 0 & 0 & 0 & 1 & | & 4 \end{bmatrix} \begin{matrix} -\frac{11}{2}R_4 + R_1 \\ \frac{3}{2}R_4 + R_2 \\ -\frac{1}{2}R_4 + R_3 \end{matrix}$

$$\begin{bmatrix} 1 & 0 & 0 & 0 & | & 2 \\ 0 & 1 & 0 & 0 & | & -2 \\ 0 & 0 & 1 & 0 & | & 3 \\ 0 & 0 & 0 & 1 & | & 4 \end{bmatrix}$$

The solution set is $\{(2, -2, 3, 4)\}$.

8. a. The function must satisfy:
$$98 = 4a = 2b + c$$
$$138 = 16a + 4b + c$$
$$162 = 100a + 10b + c.$$

$$\begin{bmatrix} 4 & 2 & 1 & | & 98 \\ 16 & 4 & 1 & | & 138 \\ 100 & 10 & 1 & | & 162 \end{bmatrix} \frac{1}{4}R_1$$

$$\begin{bmatrix} 1 & \frac{1}{2} & \frac{1}{4} & | & \frac{49}{2} \\ 16 & 4 & 1 & | & 138 \\ 100 & 10 & 1 & | & 162 \end{bmatrix} \begin{matrix} -16R_1 + R_2 \\ -100R_1 + R_3 \end{matrix}$$

$$\begin{bmatrix} 1 & \frac{1}{2} & \frac{1}{4} & | & \frac{49}{2} \\ 0 & -4 & -3 & | & -254 \\ 0 & -40 & -24 & | & -2288 \end{bmatrix} -\frac{1}{4}R_2$$

$$\begin{bmatrix} 1 & \frac{1}{2} & \frac{1}{4} & | & \frac{49}{2} \\ 0 & 1 & \frac{3}{4} & | & \frac{127}{2} \\ 0 & -40 & -24 & | & -2288 \end{bmatrix} 40R_2 + R_3$$

$$\begin{bmatrix} 1 & \frac{1}{2} & \frac{1}{4} & | & \frac{49}{2} \\ 0 & 1 & \frac{3}{4} & | & \frac{127}{2} \\ 0 & 0 & 6 & | & 252 \end{bmatrix} \frac{1}{6}R_3$$

$$\begin{bmatrix} 1 & \frac{1}{2} & \frac{1}{4} & | & \frac{49}{2} \\ 0 & 1 & \frac{3}{4} & | & \frac{127}{2} \\ 0 & 0 & 1 & | & 42 \end{bmatrix} \begin{matrix} -\frac{1}{4}R_3 + R_1 \\ -\frac{3}{4}R_3 + R_2 \end{matrix}$$

$$\begin{bmatrix} 1 & \frac{1}{2} & 0 & | & 14 \\ 0 & 1 & 0 & | & 32 \\ 0 & 0 & 1 & | & 42 \end{bmatrix} -\frac{1}{2}R_3 + R_1$$

$$\begin{bmatrix} 1 & 0 & 0 & | & -2 \\ 0 & 1 & 0 & | & 32 \\ 0 & 0 & 1 & | & 42 \end{bmatrix}$$

The function is $y = -2x^2 + 32x + 42$ and $a = -2$, $b = 32$ and $c = 42$.

b. $y = -2x^2 + 32x + 42$ is a parabola.
The maximum occurs when
$$x = \frac{-32}{2(-2)} = \frac{-32}{-4} = 8.$$

The air pollution level is a maximum 8 hours after 6 A.M., which is 2 P.M.
When $x = 8$, $y = -2(64) + 32(8) + 42$
$$= -128 + 256 + 42.$$
$$= 170.$$
The maximum level is 170 parts per million at 2 P.M.

9.
$$\begin{bmatrix} 2 & -3 & 1 & | & 1 \\ 1 & -2 & 3 & | & 2 \\ 3 & -4 & -1 & | & 1 \end{bmatrix} R_1 \leftrightarrow R_2$$

$$\begin{bmatrix} 1 & -2 & 3 & | & 2 \\ 2 & -3 & 1 & | & 1 \\ 3 & -4 & -1 & | & 1 \end{bmatrix} \begin{matrix} -2R_1 + R_2 \\ -3R_1 + R_3 \end{matrix}$$

$$\begin{bmatrix} 1 & -2 & 3 & | & 2 \\ 0 & 1 & -5 & | & -3 \\ 0 & 2 & -10 & | & -5 \end{bmatrix} -2R_2 + R_3$$

$$\begin{bmatrix} 1 & -2 & 3 & | & 2 \\ 0 & 1 & -5 & | & -3 \\ 0 & 0 & 0 & | & 1 \end{bmatrix}$$

From the last line, we see that the system has no solution. Thus, the solution set is $\varnothing$.

10.
$$\begin{bmatrix} 1 & -3 & 1 & | & 1 \\ -2 & 1 & 3 & | & -7 \\ 1 & -4 & 2 & | & 0 \end{bmatrix} \begin{matrix} 2R_1 + R_2 \\ -1R_1 + R_3 \end{matrix}$$

$$\begin{bmatrix} 1 & -3 & 1 & | & 1 \\ 0 & -5 & 5 & | & -5 \\ 0 & -1 & 1 & | & -1 \end{bmatrix} -\frac{1}{5}R_2$$

$$\begin{bmatrix} 1 & -3 & 1 & | & 1 \\ 0 & 1 & -1 & | & 1 \\ 0 & -1 & 1 & | & -1 \end{bmatrix} 1R_2 + R_3$$

$$\begin{bmatrix} 1 & -3 & 1 & | & 1 \\ 0 & 1 & -1 & | & 1 \\ 0 & 0 & 0 & | & 0 \end{bmatrix}$$

The system $\begin{matrix} x - 3y + z = 1 \\ y - z = 1 \end{matrix}$ has no unique

solution.
Express x and y in terms of z:
$y = z + 1$
$x - 3(z + 1) + z = 1$
$\quad x - 3z - 3 + z = 1$
$\quad\quad\quad\quad\quad x = 2z + 4$
With $z = t$, the complete solution to the system is
$\{(2t + 4,\ t + 1,\ t)\}$.

11. $\begin{bmatrix} 1 & 4 & 3 & -6 & | & 5 \\ 1 & 3 & 1 & -4 & | & 3 \\ 2 & 8 & 7 & -5 & | & 11 \\ 2 & 5 & 0 & -6 & | & 4 \end{bmatrix} \begin{matrix} -1R_1 + R_2 \\ -2R_1 + R_3 \\ -2R_1 + R_4 \end{matrix}$

$\begin{bmatrix} 1 & 4 & 3 & -6 & | & 5 \\ 0 & -1 & -2 & 2 & | & -2 \\ 0 & 0 & 1 & 7 & | & 1 \\ 0 & -3 & -6 & 6 & | & -6 \end{bmatrix} -1R_2$

$\begin{bmatrix} 1 & 4 & 3 & -6 & | & 5 \\ 0 & 1 & 2 & -2 & | & 2 \\ 0 & 0 & 1 & 7 & | & 1 \\ 0 & -3 & -6 & 6 & | & -6 \end{bmatrix} 3R_2 + R_4$

$\begin{bmatrix} 1 & 4 & 3 & -6 & | & 5 \\ 0 & 1 & 2 & -2 & | & 2 \\ 0 & 0 & 1 & 7 & | & 1 \\ 0 & 0 & 0 & 0 & | & 0 \end{bmatrix}$

The system $\begin{matrix} x_1 + 4x_2 + 3x_3 - 6x_4 = 5 \\ x_2 + 2x_3 - 2x_4 = 2 \\ x_3 + 7x_4 = 1 \end{matrix}$
does not have a unique solution.
Express x_1, x_2, and x_3 in terms of x_4 :
$x_3 = -7x_4 + 1$
$x_2 + 2(-7x_4 + 1) - 2x_4 = 2$
$\quad x_2 - 14x_4 + 2 - 2x_4 = 2$
$\quad\quad\quad\quad\quad\quad x_2 = 16x_4$
$x_1 + 4(16x_4) + 3(-7x_4 + 1) - 6x_4 = 5$
$\quad x_1 + 64x_4 - 21x_4 + 3 - 6x_4 = 5$
$\quad\quad\quad\quad\quad\quad\quad\quad x_1 = -37x_4 + 2$
With $x_4 = t$, the complete solution to the system
is $\{(-37t + 2,\ 16t,\ -7t + 1,\ t)\}$.

12. $\begin{bmatrix} 2 & 3 & -5 & | & 15 \\ 1 & 2 & -1 & | & 4 \end{bmatrix} R_1 \leftrightarrow R_2$

$\begin{bmatrix} 1 & 2 & -1 & | & 4 \\ 2 & 3 & -5 & | & 15 \end{bmatrix} -2R_1 + R_2$

$\begin{bmatrix} 1 & 2 & -1 & | & 4 \\ 0 & -1 & -3 & | & 7 \end{bmatrix} -1R_2$

$\begin{bmatrix} 1 & 2 & -1 & | & 4 \\ 0 & 1 & 3 & | & -7 \end{bmatrix}$

The system $\begin{matrix} x + 2y - z = 4 \\ y + 3z = -7 \end{matrix}$ has no unique

solution. Express x and y in terms of z:
$y = -3z - 7$
$x + 2(-3z - 7) - z = 4$
$\quad x - 6z - 14 - z = 4$
$\quad\quad\quad\quad\quad x = 7z + 18$
With $z = t$, the complete solution to the system is
$\{(7t + 18,\ -3t - 7,\ t)\}$.

13. **a.** $350 + 400 = x + z$
         $450 + z = y + 700$
         $x + y = 300 + 200$
         or
         $x + z = 750$
         $y - z = -250$
         $x + y = 500$

   b. $\begin{bmatrix} 1 & 0 & 1 & | & 750 \\ 0 & 1 & -1 & | & -250 \\ 1 & 1 & 0 & | & 500 \end{bmatrix} -1R_1 + R_3$

$\begin{bmatrix} 1 & 0 & 1 & | & 750 \\ 0 & 1 & -1 & | & -250 \\ 0 & 1 & -1 & | & -250 \end{bmatrix} -1R_2 + R_3$

$\begin{bmatrix} 1 & 0 & 1 & | & 750 \\ 0 & 1 & -1 & | & -250 \\ 0 & 0 & 0 & | & 0 \end{bmatrix}$

The system $\begin{matrix} x + z = 750 \\ y - z = -250 \end{matrix}$ has no unique

solution.
Express x and y in terms of z:
$y = z - 250$
$x = -z + 750$
With $z = t$, the complete solution to the
system is $\{(-t + 750,\ t - 250,\ t)\}$.

   c. $x = -400 + 750 = 350$
         $y = 400 - 250 = 150$

14.

$$2x = -10$$
$$x = -5$$
$$y + 7 = 13$$
$$y = 6$$
$$z = 6$$
$$x = -5; \; y = 6; \; z = 6$$

15. $A + D = \begin{bmatrix} 2-2 & -1+3 & 2+1 \\ 5+3 & 3-2 & -1+4 \end{bmatrix} = \begin{bmatrix} 0 & 2 & 3 \\ 8 & 1 & 3 \end{bmatrix}$

16. $2B = \begin{bmatrix} 2(0) & 2(-2) \\ 2(3) & 2(2) \\ 2(1) & 2(-5) \end{bmatrix} = \begin{bmatrix} 0 & -4 \\ 6 & 4 \\ 2 & -10 \end{bmatrix}$

17. $D - A = \begin{bmatrix} -2-2 & 3+1 & 1-2 \\ 3-5 & -2-3 & 4+1 \end{bmatrix}$

$$= \begin{bmatrix} -4 & 4 & -1 \\ -2 & -5 & 5 \end{bmatrix}$$

18. Not possible since B is 3×2 and C is 3×3.

19. $3A + 2D = \begin{bmatrix} 6 & -3 & 6 \\ 15 & 9 & -3 \end{bmatrix} + \begin{bmatrix} -4 & 6 & 2 \\ 6 & -4 & 8 \end{bmatrix}$

$$= \begin{bmatrix} 2 & 3 & 8 \\ 21 & 5 & 5 \end{bmatrix}$$

20.

$$-2A + 4D$$

$$= \begin{bmatrix} -4 & 2 & -4 \\ -10 & -6 & 2 \end{bmatrix} + \begin{bmatrix} -8 & 12 & 4 \\ 12 & -8 & 16 \end{bmatrix}$$

$$= \begin{bmatrix} -12 & 14 & 0 \\ 2 & -14 & 18 \end{bmatrix}$$

21.

$$-5(A + D) = -5\left(\begin{bmatrix} 0 & 2 & 3 \\ 8 & 1 & 3 \end{bmatrix} \right)$$

$$= \begin{bmatrix} 0 & -10 & -15 \\ -40 & -5 & -15 \end{bmatrix}$$

22. $AB = \begin{bmatrix} 0-3+2 & -4-2-10 \\ 0+9-1 & -10+6+5 \end{bmatrix} = \begin{bmatrix} -1 & -16 \\ 8 & 1 \end{bmatrix}$

23. $BA = \begin{bmatrix} 0-10 & 0-6 & 0+2 \\ 6+10 & -3+6 & 6-2 \\ 2-25 & -1-15 & 2+5 \end{bmatrix} = \begin{bmatrix} -10 & -6 & 2 \\ 16 & 3 & 4 \\ -23 & -16 & 7 \end{bmatrix}$

24. $BD = \begin{bmatrix} 0-6 & 0+4 & 0-8 \\ -6+6 & 9-4 & 3+8 \\ -2-15 & 3+10 & 1-20 \end{bmatrix} = \begin{bmatrix} -6 & 4 & -8 \\ 0 & 5 & 11 \\ -17 & 13 & -19 \end{bmatrix}$

25. $DB = \begin{bmatrix} 0+9+1 & 4+6-5 \\ 0-6+4 & -6-4-20 \end{bmatrix} = \begin{bmatrix} 10 & 5 \\ -2 & -30 \end{bmatrix}$

26. Not possible since AB is 2 x 2 and BA is 3 x 3.

27. $(A - D)C = \begin{bmatrix} 4 & -4 & 1 \\ 2 & 5 & -5 \end{bmatrix} \begin{bmatrix} 1 & 2 & 3 \\ -1 & 1 & 2 \\ -1 & 2 & 1 \end{bmatrix} = \begin{bmatrix} 4+4-1 & 8-4+2 & 12-8+1 \\ 2-5+5 & 4+5-10 & 6+10-5 \end{bmatrix} = \begin{bmatrix} 7 & 6 & 5 \\ 2 & -1 & 11 \end{bmatrix}$

28. $B(AC) = \begin{bmatrix} 0 & -2 \\ 3 & 2 \\ 1 & -5 \end{bmatrix} \begin{bmatrix} 2+1-2 & 4-1+4 & 6-2+2 \\ 5-3+1 & 10+3-2 & 15+6-1 \end{bmatrix}$

$= \begin{bmatrix} 0 & -2 \\ 3 & 2 \\ 1 & -5 \end{bmatrix} \begin{bmatrix} 1 & 7 & 6 \\ 3 & 11 & 20 \end{bmatrix}$

$= \begin{bmatrix} 0-6 & 0-22 & 0-40 \\ 3+6 & 21+22 & 18+40 \\ 1-15 & 7-55 & 6-100 \end{bmatrix}$

$= \begin{bmatrix} -6 & -22 & -40 \\ 9 & 43 & 58 \\ -14 & -48 & -94 \end{bmatrix}$

29. $3X + A = B$

$3X = B - A$

$X = \frac{1}{3}(B - A)$

$X = \frac{1}{3}\left(\begin{bmatrix} -2 & -12 \\ 4 & 1 \end{bmatrix} - \begin{bmatrix} 4 & 6 \\ -5 & 0 \end{bmatrix} \right)$

$X = \frac{1}{3} \begin{bmatrix} -6 & -18 \\ 9 & 1 \end{bmatrix}$

$X = \begin{bmatrix} -2 & -6 \\ 3 & \frac{1}{3} \end{bmatrix}$

30. $\begin{bmatrix} 2 & 2 & 2 \\ 1 & 2 & 1 \\ 1 & 2 & 1 \end{bmatrix}$

31. $\begin{bmatrix} 2 & 2 & 2 \\ 1 & 2 & 1 \\ 1 & 2 & 1 \end{bmatrix} + \begin{bmatrix} 1 & 1 & 1 \\ -1 & 1 & -1 \\ -1 & 1 & -1 \end{bmatrix} = \begin{bmatrix} 3 & 3 & 3 \\ 0 & 3 & 0 \\ 0 & 3 & 0 \end{bmatrix}$

$B = \begin{bmatrix} 3 & 3 & 3 \\ 0 & 3 & 0 \\ 0 & 3 & 0 \end{bmatrix}$

32. $\begin{bmatrix} 0 & 2 & 2 \\ 0 & 0 & -4 \end{bmatrix} + \begin{bmatrix} -2 & -2 & -2 \\ 1 & 1 & 1 \end{bmatrix} = \begin{bmatrix} -2 & 0 & 0 \\ 1 & 1 & -3 \end{bmatrix}$

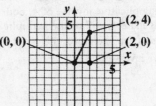

33. $\frac{1}{2} \begin{bmatrix} 0 & 2 & 2 \\ 0 & 0 & -4 \end{bmatrix} + \begin{bmatrix} 0 & 0 & 0 \\ -2 & -2 & -2 \end{bmatrix} = \begin{bmatrix} -2 & -1 & -1 \\ -2 & -2 & -4 \end{bmatrix}$

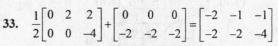

34. $\begin{bmatrix} 1 & 0 \\ 0 & -1 \end{bmatrix} \begin{bmatrix} 0 & 2 & 2 \\ 0 & 0 & -4 \end{bmatrix} = \begin{bmatrix} 0 & 2 & 2 \\ 0 & 0 & 4 \end{bmatrix}$

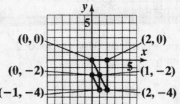

The triangle is reflected about the *x*-axis.

475

35. $\begin{bmatrix} -1 & 0 \\ 0 & 1 \end{bmatrix} \begin{bmatrix} 0 & 2 & 2 \\ 0 & 0 & -4 \end{bmatrix} = \begin{bmatrix} 0 & -2 & -2 \\ 0 & 0 & -4 \end{bmatrix}$

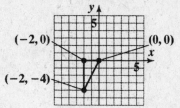

The triangle is reflected about the y-axis.

36. $\begin{bmatrix} 0 & -1 \\ 1 & 0 \end{bmatrix} \begin{bmatrix} 0 & 2 & 2 \\ 0 & 0 & -4 \end{bmatrix} = \begin{bmatrix} 0 & 0 & 4 \\ 0 & 2 & 2 \end{bmatrix}$

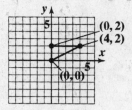

The triangle is rotated 90° counterclockwise about the origin.

37. $\begin{bmatrix} 2 & 0 \\ 0 & 1 \end{bmatrix} \begin{bmatrix} 0 & 2 & 2 \\ 0 & 0 & -4 \end{bmatrix} = \begin{bmatrix} 0 & 4 & 4 \\ 0 & 0 & -4 \end{bmatrix}$

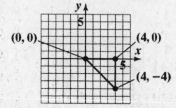

The triangle is stretched by a factor of 2 horizontally.

38. $AB = \begin{bmatrix} 8-7 & -14+21 \\ 4-4 & -7+12 \end{bmatrix} = \begin{bmatrix} 1 & 7 \\ 0 & 5 \end{bmatrix}$

$BA = \begin{bmatrix} 8-7 & 28-28 \\ -2+3 & -7+12 \end{bmatrix} = \begin{bmatrix} 1 & 0 \\ 1 & 5 \end{bmatrix}$

If B is the multiplicative inverse of A, both products (AB and BA) will be the multiplicative identity matrix, I_2. Therefore, B is not the multiplicative inverse of A.

39. $AB = \begin{bmatrix} 1 & 0 & 0 \\ 0 & 2 & -7 \\ 0 & -1 & 4 \end{bmatrix} \begin{bmatrix} 1 & 0 & 0 \\ 0 & 4 & 7 \\ 0 & 1 & 2 \end{bmatrix} = \begin{bmatrix} 1 & 0 & 0 \\ 0 & 1 & 0 \\ 0 & 0 & 1 \end{bmatrix}$

$BA = \begin{bmatrix} 1 & 0 & 0 \\ 0 & 4 & 7 \\ 0 & 1 & 2 \end{bmatrix} \begin{bmatrix} 1 & 0 & 0 \\ 0 & 2 & -7 \\ 0 & -1 & 4 \end{bmatrix} = \begin{bmatrix} 1 & 0 & 0 \\ 0 & 1 & 0 \\ 0 & 0 & 1 \end{bmatrix}$

If B is the multiplicative inverse of A, both products (AB and BA) will be the multiplicative identity matrix, I_3. Therefore, B is the multiplicative inverse of A.

40. $A^{-1} = \dfrac{1}{3-2} \begin{bmatrix} 3 & 1 \\ 2 & 1 \end{bmatrix} = \begin{bmatrix} 3 & 1 \\ 2 & 1 \end{bmatrix}$

$AA^{-1} = \begin{bmatrix} 1 & -1 \\ -2 & 3 \end{bmatrix} \begin{bmatrix} 3 & 1 \\ 2 & 1 \end{bmatrix}$

$= \begin{bmatrix} 3-2 & 1-1 \\ -6+6 & -2+3 \end{bmatrix}$

$= \begin{bmatrix} 1 & 0 \\ 0 & 1 \end{bmatrix}$

$A^{-1}A = \begin{bmatrix} 3 & 1 \\ 2 & 1 \end{bmatrix} \begin{bmatrix} 1 & -1 \\ -2 & 3 \end{bmatrix}$

$= \begin{bmatrix} 3-2 & 3+3 \\ 2-2 & -2+3 \end{bmatrix}$

$= \begin{bmatrix} 1 & 0 \\ 0 & 1 \end{bmatrix}$

41. $A^{-1} = \dfrac{1}{0-5} \begin{bmatrix} 3 & -1 \\ -5 & 0 \end{bmatrix}$

$= \dfrac{-1}{5} \begin{bmatrix} 3 & -1 \\ -5 & 0 \end{bmatrix}$

$= \begin{bmatrix} -\frac{3}{5} & \frac{1}{5} \\ 1 & 0 \end{bmatrix}$

$AA^{-1} = \begin{bmatrix} 0 & 1 \\ 5 & 3 \end{bmatrix} \begin{bmatrix} -\frac{3}{5} & \frac{1}{5} \\ 1 & 0 \end{bmatrix}$

$= \begin{bmatrix} 0+1 & 0+0 \\ -3+3 & 1+0 \end{bmatrix}$

$= \begin{bmatrix} 1 & 0 \\ 0 & 1 \end{bmatrix}$

$$A^{-1}A = \begin{bmatrix} -\frac{3}{5} & \frac{1}{5} \\ 1 & 0 \end{bmatrix}\begin{bmatrix} 0 & 1 \\ 5 & 3 \end{bmatrix}$$

$$= \begin{bmatrix} 0+1 & -\frac{3}{5}+\frac{3}{5} \\ 0+0 & 1+0 \end{bmatrix}$$

$$= \begin{bmatrix} 1 & 0 \\ 0 & 1 \end{bmatrix}$$

42.
$$\left[\begin{array}{ccc|ccc} 1 & 0 & -2 & 1 & 0 & 0 \\ 2 & 1 & 0 & 0 & 1 & 0 \\ 1 & 0 & -3 & 0 & 0 & 1 \end{array}\right] \begin{array}{c} \\ -2R_1+R_2 \\ -1R_1+R_3 \end{array}$$

$$\left[\begin{array}{ccc|ccc} 1 & 0 & -2 & 1 & 0 & 0 \\ 0 & 1 & 4 & -2 & 1 & 0 \\ 0 & 0 & -1 & -1 & 0 & 1 \end{array}\right] -1R_3$$

$$\left[\begin{array}{ccc|ccc} 1 & 0 & -2 & 1 & 0 & 0 \\ 0 & 1 & 4 & -2 & 1 & 0 \\ 0 & 0 & 1 & 1 & 0 & -1 \end{array}\right] \begin{array}{c} 2R_3+R_1 \\ \\ -4R_3+R_2 \end{array}$$

$$\left[\begin{array}{ccc|ccc} 1 & 0 & 0 & 3 & 0 & -2 \\ 0 & 1 & 0 & -6 & 1 & 4 \\ 0 & 0 & 1 & 1 & 0 & -1 \end{array}\right]$$

$$A^{-1} = \begin{bmatrix} 3 & 0 & -2 \\ -6 & 1 & 4 \\ 1 & 0 & -1 \end{bmatrix}$$

$$AA^{-1} = \begin{bmatrix} 1 & 0 & -2 \\ 2 & 1 & 0 \\ 1 & 0 & -3 \end{bmatrix}\begin{bmatrix} 3 & 0 & -2 \\ -6 & 1 & 4 \\ 1 & 0 & -1 \end{bmatrix}$$

$$= \begin{bmatrix} 3+0-2 & 0+0+0 & -2+0+2 \\ 6-6+0 & 0+1+0 & -4+4+0 \\ 3+0-3 & 0+0+0 & -2+0+3 \end{bmatrix}$$

$$= \begin{bmatrix} 1 & 0 & 0 \\ 0 & 1 & 0 \\ 0 & 0 & 1 \end{bmatrix}$$

$$A^{-1}A = \begin{bmatrix} 3 & 0 & -2 \\ -6 & 1 & 4 \\ 1 & 0 & -1 \end{bmatrix}\begin{bmatrix} 1 & 0 & -2 \\ 2 & 1 & 0 \\ 1 & 0 & -3 \end{bmatrix}$$

$$= \begin{bmatrix} 3+0-2 & 0+0+0 & -6+0+6 \\ -6+2+4 & 0+1+0 & 12+0-12 \\ 1+0-1 & 0+0+0 & -2+0+3 \end{bmatrix}$$

$$= \begin{bmatrix} 1 & 0 & 0 \\ 0 & 1 & 0 \\ 0 & 0 & 1 \end{bmatrix}$$

43.
$$\left[\begin{array}{ccc|ccc} 1 & 3 & -2 & 1 & 0 & 0 \\ 4 & 13 & -7 & 0 & 1 & 0 \\ 5 & 16 & -8 & 0 & 0 & 1 \end{array}\right] \begin{array}{c} -4R_1 + R_2 \\ -5R_1 + R_3 \end{array}$$

$$\left[\begin{array}{ccc|ccc} 1 & 3 & -2 & 1 & 0 & 0 \\ 0 & 1 & 1 & -4 & 1 & 0 \\ 0 & 1 & 2 & -5 & 0 & 1 \end{array}\right] \begin{array}{c} -1R_2 + R_3 \\ -3R_2 + R_1 \end{array}$$

$$\left[\begin{array}{ccc|ccc} 1 & 0 & -5 & 13 & -3 & 0 \\ 0 & 1 & 1 & -4 & 1 & 0 \\ 0 & 0 & 1 & -1 & -1 & 1 \end{array}\right] \begin{array}{c} -1R_3 + R_2 \\ 5R_3 + R_1 \end{array}$$

$$\left[\begin{array}{ccc|ccc} 1 & 0 & 0 & 8 & -8 & 5 \\ 0 & 1 & 0 & -3 & 2 & -1 \\ 0 & 0 & 1 & -1 & -1 & 1 \end{array}\right]$$

$$A^{-1} = \begin{bmatrix} 8 & -8 & 5 \\ -3 & 2 & -1 \\ -1 & -1 & 1 \end{bmatrix}$$

$$AA^{-1} = \begin{bmatrix} 1 & 3 & -2 \\ 4 & 13 & -7 \\ 5 & 16 & -8 \end{bmatrix}\begin{bmatrix} 8 & -8 & 5 \\ -3 & 2 & -1 \\ -1 & -1 & 1 \end{bmatrix} = \begin{bmatrix} 8-9+2 & -8+6+2 & 5-3-2 \\ 32-39+7 & -32+26+7 & 20-13-7 \\ 40-48+8 & -40+32+8 & 25-16-8 \end{bmatrix} = \begin{bmatrix} 1 & 0 & 0 \\ 0 & 1 & 0 \\ 0 & 0 & 1 \end{bmatrix}$$

$$A^{-1}A = \begin{bmatrix} 8 & -8 & 5 \\ -3 & 2 & -1 \\ -1 & -1 & -1 \end{bmatrix}\begin{bmatrix} 1 & 3 & -2 \\ 4 & 13 & -7 \\ 5 & 16 & -8 \end{bmatrix} = \begin{bmatrix} 8-32+25 & 24-104+80 & -16+56-40 \\ -3+8-5 & -9+26-16 & 6-14+8 \\ -1-4+5 & -3-13+16 & 2+7-8 \end{bmatrix} = \begin{bmatrix} 1 & 0 & 0 \\ 0 & 1 & 0 \\ 0 & 0 & 1 \end{bmatrix}$$

44. a.
$$\begin{bmatrix} 1 & 1 & 2 \\ 0 & 1 & 3 \\ 3 & 0 & -2 \end{bmatrix}\begin{bmatrix} x \\ y \\ z \end{bmatrix} = \begin{bmatrix} 7 \\ -2 \\ 0 \end{bmatrix}.$$

b.
$$A^{-1}B = \begin{bmatrix} -2 & 2 & 1 \\ 9 & -8 & -3 \\ -3 & 3 & 1 \end{bmatrix}\begin{bmatrix} 7 \\ -2 \\ 0 \end{bmatrix} = \begin{bmatrix} -14-4+0 \\ 63+16+0 \\ -21-6+0 \end{bmatrix} = \begin{bmatrix} -18 \\ 79 \\ -27 \end{bmatrix}$$

The solution to the system is $\{(-18, 79, -27)\}$.

45. a.
$$\begin{bmatrix} 1 & -1 & 2 \\ 0 & 1 & -1 \\ 1 & 0 & 2 \end{bmatrix}\begin{bmatrix} x \\ y \\ z \end{bmatrix} = \begin{bmatrix} 12 \\ -5 \\ 10 \end{bmatrix}$$

b.
$$A^{-1}B = \begin{bmatrix} 2 & 2 & -1 \\ -1 & 0 & 1 \\ -1 & -1 & 1 \end{bmatrix}\begin{bmatrix} 12 \\ -5 \\ 10 \end{bmatrix} = \begin{bmatrix} 24-10-10 \\ -12+10 \\ -12+5+10 \end{bmatrix} = \begin{bmatrix} 4 \\ -2 \\ 3 \end{bmatrix}$$

The solution to the system is $\{(4, -2, 3)\}$.

478

46.   R U L E has a numerical equivalent of 18, 21, 12, 5.

$$\begin{bmatrix} 3 & 2 \\ 4 & 3 \end{bmatrix} \begin{bmatrix} 18 & 12 \\ 21 & 5 \end{bmatrix} = \begin{bmatrix} 54+42 & 36+10 \\ 72+63 & 48+15 \end{bmatrix} = \begin{bmatrix} 96 & 46 \\ 135 & 63 \end{bmatrix}$$

The encoded message is 96, 135, 46, 63.

$$\begin{bmatrix} 3 & -2 \\ -4 & 3 \end{bmatrix} \begin{bmatrix} 96 & 46 \\ 135 & 63 \end{bmatrix} = \begin{bmatrix} 288-270 & 138-126 \\ -384+405 & -184+189 \end{bmatrix} = \begin{bmatrix} 18 & 12 \\ 21 & 5 \end{bmatrix}$$

The decoded message is 18, 21, 12, 5 or RULE.

47. $\begin{vmatrix} 3 & 2 \\ -1 & 5 \end{vmatrix} = 15 - (-2) = 17$

48. $\begin{vmatrix} -2 & -3 \\ -4 & -8 \end{vmatrix} = 16 - 12 = 4$

49. $\begin{vmatrix} 2 & 4 & -3 \\ 1 & -1 & 5 \\ -2 & 4 & 0 \end{vmatrix} = -2 \begin{vmatrix} 4 & -3 \\ -1 & 5 \end{vmatrix} - 4 \begin{vmatrix} 2 & -3 \\ 1 & 5 \end{vmatrix} + 0 \begin{vmatrix} 2 & 4 \\ 1 & -1 \end{vmatrix}$

$$= -2(20-3) - 4[10-(-3)] + 0$$
$$= -2(17) - 4(13)$$
$$= -34 - 52$$
$$= -86$$

50. $\begin{vmatrix} 4 & 7 & 0 \\ -5 & 6 & 0 \\ 3 & 2 & -4 \end{vmatrix} = 4 \begin{vmatrix} 6 & 0 \\ 2 & -4 \end{vmatrix} + 5 \begin{vmatrix} 7 & 0 \\ 2 & -4 \end{vmatrix} + 3 \begin{vmatrix} 7 & 0 \\ 6 & 0 \end{vmatrix}$

$$= 4(-24-0) + 5(-28-0) + 3(0-0)$$
$$= 4(-24) + 5(-28) + 0$$
$$= -236$$

51. $\begin{vmatrix} 1 & 1 & 0 & 2 \\ 0 & 3 & 2 & 1 \\ 0 & -2 & 4 & 0 \\ 0 & 3 & 0 & 1 \end{vmatrix} = \begin{vmatrix} 3 & 2 & 1 \\ -2 & 4 & 0 \\ 3 & 0 & 1 \end{vmatrix}$

$$= 3 \begin{vmatrix} 2 & 1 \\ 4 & 0 \end{vmatrix} + \begin{vmatrix} 3 & 2 \\ -2 & 4 \end{vmatrix}$$
$$= 3(0-4) + [12-(-4)]$$
$$= 3(-4) + 16$$
$$= -12 + 16$$
$$= 4$$

52.
$$\begin{vmatrix} 2 & 2 & 2 & 2 \\ 0 & 2 & 2 & 2 \\ 0 & 0 & 2 & 2 \\ 0 & 0 & 0 & 2 \end{vmatrix} = 2\begin{vmatrix} 2 & 2 & 2 \\ 0 & 2 & 2 \\ 0 & 0 & 2 \end{vmatrix}$$

$$= 2(2)\begin{vmatrix} 2 & 2 \\ 0 & 2 \end{vmatrix}$$

$$= 2(2)(4)$$

$$= 16$$

53. $D = \begin{vmatrix} 1 & -2 \\ 3 & 2 \end{vmatrix} = 2 - (-6) = 2 + 6 = 8$

$D_x = \begin{vmatrix} 8 & -2 \\ -1 & 2 \end{vmatrix} = 16 - 2 = 14$

$D_y = \begin{vmatrix} 1 & 8 \\ 3 & -1 \end{vmatrix} = -1 - 24 = -25$

$x = \dfrac{D_x}{D} = \dfrac{14}{8} = \dfrac{7}{4},\ y = \dfrac{D_y}{D} = \dfrac{-25}{8} = -\dfrac{25}{8}$

The solution to the system is $\left\{\left(\dfrac{7}{4}, -\dfrac{25}{8}\right)\right\}$.

54. $D = \begin{vmatrix} 7 & 2 \\ 2 & 1 \end{vmatrix} = 7 - 4 = 3$

$D = \begin{vmatrix} 7 & 2 \\ 2 & 1 \end{vmatrix} = 7 - 4 = 3$

$D_x = \begin{vmatrix} 0 & 2 \\ -3 & 1 \end{vmatrix} = 0 - (-6) = 6$

$D_y = \begin{vmatrix} 7 & 0 \\ 2 & -3 \end{vmatrix} = -21 - 0 = -21$

$x = \dfrac{D_x}{D} = \dfrac{6}{3} = 2$

$y = \dfrac{D_y}{D} = \dfrac{-21}{3} = -7$

The solution to the system is $\{(2, -7)\}$.

55. $D = \begin{vmatrix} 1 & 2 & 2 \\ 2 & 4 & 7 \\ -2 & -5 & -2 \end{vmatrix}$

$= \begin{vmatrix} 1 & 2 & 2 \\ 0 & 0 & 3 \\ 0 & -1 & 2 \end{vmatrix}$

$= \begin{vmatrix} 0 & 3 \\ -1 & 2 \end{vmatrix}$

$= 0 - (-3)$

$= 3$

$D_x = \begin{vmatrix} 5 & 2 & 2 \\ 19 & 4 & 7 \\ 8 & -5 & -2 \end{vmatrix}$

$= 5\begin{vmatrix} 4 & 7 \\ -5 & -2 \end{vmatrix} - 2\begin{vmatrix} 19 & 7 \\ 8 & -2 \end{vmatrix} + 2\begin{vmatrix} 19 & 4 \\ 8 & -5 \end{vmatrix}$

$= 5[-8 - (-35)] - 2(-38 - 56) + 2(-95 - 32)$

$= 5(27) - 2(-94) - 2(127)$

$= 135 + 188 - 254$

$= 69$

$D_y = \begin{vmatrix} 1 & 5 & 2 \\ 2 & 19 & 7 \\ -2 & 8 & -2 \end{vmatrix}$

$= \begin{vmatrix} 1 & 5 & 2 \\ 0 & 9 & 3 \\ 0 & 18 & 2 \end{vmatrix}$

$= \begin{vmatrix} 9 & 3 \\ 18 & 2 \end{vmatrix}$

$= 18 - 54$

$= -36$

$D_z = \begin{vmatrix} 1 & 2 & 5 \\ 2 & 4 & 19 \\ -2 & -5 & 8 \end{vmatrix}$

$= \begin{vmatrix} 1 & 2 & 5 \\ 0 & 0 & 9 \\ 0 & -1 & 18 \end{vmatrix}$

$= \begin{vmatrix} 0 & 9 \\ -1 & 18 \end{vmatrix}$

$= 0 - (-9)$

$= 9$

$x = \dfrac{D_x}{D} = \dfrac{69}{3} = 23,\ y = \dfrac{D_y}{D} = \dfrac{-36}{3} = -12,$

$z = \dfrac{D_z}{D} = \dfrac{9}{3} = 3$

The solution to the system is $\{(23, -12, 3)\}$.

56.

$$D = \begin{vmatrix} 2 & 1 & 0 \\ 0 & 1 & -2 \\ 3 & 0 & -2 \end{vmatrix}$$

$$= 2\begin{vmatrix} 1 & -2 \\ 0 & -2 \end{vmatrix} + 3\begin{vmatrix} 1 & 0 \\ 1 & -2 \end{vmatrix}$$

$$= 2(-2-0) + 3(-2-0)$$

$$= 2(-2) + 3(-2)$$

$$= -4 - 6$$

$$= -10$$

$$D_x = \begin{vmatrix} -4 & 1 & 0 \\ 0 & 1 & -2 \\ -11 & 0 & -2 \end{vmatrix}$$

$$= -1\begin{vmatrix} 0 & -2 \\ -11 & -2 \end{vmatrix} + 1\begin{vmatrix} -4 & 0 \\ -11 & -2 \end{vmatrix}$$

$$= -1(0-22) + 1(8-0)$$

$$= 22 + 8$$

$$= 30$$

$$D_y = \begin{vmatrix} 2 & -4 & 0 \\ 0 & 0 & -2 \\ 3 & -11 & -2 \end{vmatrix}$$

$$= 2\begin{vmatrix} 0 & -2 \\ -11 & -2 \end{vmatrix} + 3\begin{vmatrix} -4 & 0 \\ 0 & -2 \end{vmatrix}$$

$$= 2(0-22) + 3(8-0)$$

$$= 2(-22) + 3(8)$$

$$= -44 + 24$$

$$= -20$$

$$D_z = \begin{vmatrix} 2 & 1 & -4 \\ 0 & 1 & 0 \\ 3 & 0 & -11 \end{vmatrix}$$

$$= 2\begin{vmatrix} 1 & 0 \\ 0 & -11 \end{vmatrix} + 3\begin{vmatrix} 1 & -4 \\ 1 & 0 \end{vmatrix}$$

$$= 2(-11-0) + 3(0+4)$$

$$= 2(-11) + 3(+4) = -22 + 12$$

$$= -10$$

$$x = \frac{D_x}{D} = \frac{30}{-10} = -3$$

$$y = \frac{D_y}{D} = \frac{-20}{-10} = 2$$

$$z = \frac{D_z}{D} = \frac{-10}{-10} = 1$$

The solution to the system is $\{(-3, 2, 1)\}$.

57. The quadratic function must satisfy

$$f(20) = 400 = 400a + 20b + c$$
$$f(40) = 150 = 1600a + 40b + c$$
$$f(60) = 400 = 3600a + 60b + c$$

$$D = \begin{vmatrix} 400 & 20 & 1 \\ 1600 & 40 & 1 \\ 3600 & 60 & 1 \end{vmatrix}$$

$$= (400)(20)\begin{vmatrix} 1 & 1 & 1 \\ 4 & 2 & 1 \\ 9 & 3 & 1 \end{vmatrix}$$

$$= 8000\begin{vmatrix} 1 & 1 & 1 \\ 3 & 1 & 0 \\ 8 & 2 & 0 \end{vmatrix} = 8000\begin{vmatrix} 3 & 1 \\ 8 & 2 \end{vmatrix}$$

$$= 8000(6-8)$$

$$= 8000(-2)$$

$$= -16,000$$

$$D_a = \begin{vmatrix} 400 & 20 & 1 \\ 150 & 40 & 1 \\ 400 & 60 & 1 \end{vmatrix}$$

$$= (50)(20)\begin{vmatrix} 8 & 1 & 1 \\ 3 & 2 & 1 \\ 8 & 3 & 1 \end{vmatrix}$$

$$= 1000\begin{vmatrix} 8 & 1 & 1 \\ -5 & 1 & 0 \\ 0 & 2 & 0 \end{vmatrix}$$

$$= 1000\begin{vmatrix} -5 & 1 \\ 0 & 2 \end{vmatrix}$$

$$= 1000(-10-0)$$

$$= -10,000$$

$$D_b = \begin{vmatrix} 400 & 400 & 1 \\ 1600 & 150 & 1 \\ 3600 & 400 & 1 \end{vmatrix}$$

$$= (400)(50)\begin{vmatrix} 1 & 8 & 1 \\ 4 & 3 & 1 \\ 9 & 8 & 1 \end{vmatrix}$$

$$= 20,000\begin{vmatrix} 1 & 8 & 1 \\ 3 & -5 & 0 \\ 8 & 0 & 0 \end{vmatrix}$$

$$= 20,000\begin{vmatrix} 3 & -5 \\ 8 & 0 \end{vmatrix}$$

481

$= 20,000[0 - (-40)]$

$= 20,000(40)$

$= 800,000$

$$D_c = \begin{vmatrix} 400 & 20 & 400 \\ 1600 & 40 & 150 \\ 3600 & 60 & 400 \end{vmatrix}$$

$$= (400)(20)(50)\begin{vmatrix} 1 & 1 & 8 \\ 4 & 2 & 3 \\ 9 & 3 & 8 \end{vmatrix}$$

$$= 400,000\begin{vmatrix} 1 & 0 & 0 \\ 4 & -2 & -29 \\ 2 & -6 & -64 \end{vmatrix}$$

$$= 400,000\begin{vmatrix} -2 & -29 \\ -6 & -64 \end{vmatrix}$$

$= 400,000(128 - 174)$

$= 400,000(-46)$

$= -18,400,000$

$a = \dfrac{D_a}{D} = \dfrac{-10,000}{-16,000} = \dfrac{5}{8},$

$b = \dfrac{D_b}{D} = \dfrac{800,000}{-16,000} = -50,$

$c = \dfrac{D_c}{D} = \dfrac{-18,400,000}{-16,000} = 1150$

The model is $f(x) = \dfrac{5}{8}x^2 - 50x + 1150$.

$f(30) = \dfrac{5}{8}(900) - 50(30) + 1150$

$\qquad = 562.5 - 1500 + 1150$

$\qquad = 212.5$

$f(50) = \dfrac{5}{8}(2500) - 50(50) + 1150$

$\qquad = 1562.8 - 2500 + 1150$

$\qquad = 212.5$

30- and 50-year-olds are involved in an average of 212.5 automobile accidents per day.

Chapter 6 Test

1. $\begin{bmatrix} 1 & 2 & -1 & | & -3 \\ 2 & -4 & 1 & | & -7 \\ -2 & 2 & -3 & | & 4 \end{bmatrix} \begin{matrix} -2R_1 + R_2 \\ \\ 2R_1 + R_3 \end{matrix}$

$\begin{bmatrix} 1 & 2 & -1 & | & -3 \\ 0 & -8 & 3 & | & -1 \\ 0 & 6 & -5 & | & -2 \end{bmatrix} -\frac{1}{8}R_2$

$\begin{bmatrix} 1 & 2 & -1 & | & -3 \\ 0 & 1 & -\frac{3}{8} & | & \frac{1}{8} \\ 0 & 6 & -5 & | & -2 \end{bmatrix} -6R_2 + R_3$

$\begin{bmatrix} 1 & 2 & -1 & | & -3 \\ 0 & 1 & -\frac{3}{8} & | & \frac{1}{8} \\ 0 & 0 & -\frac{11}{4} & | & -\frac{11}{4} \end{bmatrix} -\frac{4}{11}R_3$

$\begin{bmatrix} 1 & 2 & -1 & | & -3 \\ 0 & 1 & -\frac{3}{8} & | & \frac{1}{8} \\ 0 & 0 & 1 & | & 1 \end{bmatrix}$

$x + 2y - z = -3$

$\qquad y - \dfrac{3}{8}z = \dfrac{1}{8}$

$\qquad\qquad z = 1$

Using back substitution,

$y - \dfrac{3}{8}(1) = \dfrac{1}{8}$ and $x + 2\left(\dfrac{1}{2}\right) - 1 = -3$.

$\qquad y = \dfrac{1}{2} \qquad\qquad x + 1 - 1 = -3$

$\qquad\qquad\qquad\qquad\qquad x = -3$

The solution to the system is $\left\{\left(-3, \dfrac{1}{2}, 1\right)\right\}$.

2. $\begin{bmatrix} 1 & -2 & 1 & | & 2 \\ 2 & -1 & -1 & | & 1 \end{bmatrix} -2R_1 + R_2$

$\begin{bmatrix} 1 & -2 & 1 & | & 2 \\ 0 & 3 & -3 & | & -3 \end{bmatrix} \frac{1}{3}R_2$

$\begin{bmatrix} 1 & -2 & 1 & | & 2 \\ 0 & 1 & -1 & | & -1 \end{bmatrix}$

The system $\begin{array}{l} x - 2y + z = 2 \\ \quad\;\; y - z = -1 \end{array}$ has no unique

solution. Express x and y in terms of z:

$y = z - 1$

$x - 2(z - 1) + z = 2$

$\quad x - 2z + 2 + z = 2$

$\qquad\qquad\qquad x = z$

With $z = t$, the complete solution to the system is $\{(t, t - 1, t)\}$.

3. $2B + 3C = \begin{bmatrix} 2 & -2 \\ 4 & 2 \end{bmatrix} + \begin{bmatrix} 3 & 6 \\ -3 & 9 \end{bmatrix} = \begin{bmatrix} 5 & 4 \\ 1 & 11 \end{bmatrix}$

4. $AB = \begin{bmatrix} 3+2 & -3+1 \\ 1+0 & -1+0 \\ 2+2 & -2+1 \end{bmatrix} = \begin{bmatrix} 5 & -2 \\ 1 & -1 \\ 4 & -1 \end{bmatrix}$

5. $C^{-1} = \dfrac{1}{(1)(3)-(2)(-1)} \begin{bmatrix} 3 & -2 \\ 1 & 1 \end{bmatrix}$

$= \dfrac{1}{3+2} \begin{bmatrix} 3 & -2 \\ 1 & 1 \end{bmatrix} = \begin{bmatrix} \frac{3}{5} & -\frac{2}{5} \\ \frac{1}{5} & \frac{1}{5} \end{bmatrix}$

6. $BC = \begin{bmatrix} 1+1 & 2-3 \\ 2-1 & 4+3 \end{bmatrix} = \begin{bmatrix} 2 & -1 \\ 1 & 7 \end{bmatrix}$

$BC - 3B = \begin{bmatrix} 2 & -1 \\ 1 & 7 \end{bmatrix} - \begin{bmatrix} 3 & -3 \\ 6 & 3 \end{bmatrix} = \begin{bmatrix} -1 & 2 \\ -5 & 4 \end{bmatrix}$

7. $AB = \begin{bmatrix} -3+14-10 & 2-8+6 & 0+2-2 \\ -6+21-15 & 4-12+9 & 0+3-3 \\ -3-7+10 & 2+4-6 & 0-1+2 \end{bmatrix}$

$= \begin{bmatrix} 1 & 0 & 0 \\ 0 & 1 & 0 \\ 0 & 0 & 1 \end{bmatrix} = I_3$

$BA = \begin{bmatrix} -3+4+0 & -6+6+0 & -6+6+0 \\ 7-8+1 & 14-12-1 & 14-12-2 \\ -5+6-1 & -10+9+1 & -10+9+2 \end{bmatrix}$

$= \begin{bmatrix} 1 & 0 & 0 \\ 0 & 1 & 0 \\ 0 & 0 & 1 \end{bmatrix} = I_3$

10. $D = \begin{vmatrix} 3 & 1 & -2 \\ 2 & 7 & 3 \\ 4 & -3 & -1 \end{vmatrix} = 3\begin{vmatrix} 7 & 3 \\ -3 & -1 \end{vmatrix} - 1\begin{vmatrix} 2 & 3 \\ 4 & -1 \end{vmatrix} - 2\begin{vmatrix} 2 & 7 \\ 4 & -3 \end{vmatrix}$

$= 3[-7-(-9)] - 1(-2-12) - 2(-6-28)$

$= 3(2) - 1(-14) - 2(-34)$

$= 6 + 14 + 68$

$= 88$

$D_x = \begin{vmatrix} -3 & 1 & -2 \\ 9 & 7 & 3 \\ 7 & -3 & -1 \end{vmatrix} = -3\begin{vmatrix} 7 & 3 \\ -3 & -1 \end{vmatrix} - 1\begin{vmatrix} 9 & 3 \\ 7 & -1 \end{vmatrix} - 2\begin{vmatrix} 9 & 7 \\ 7 & -3 \end{vmatrix}$

$= -3[-7-(-9)] - 1(-9-21) - 2(-27-49)$

$= -3(2) - 1(-30) - 2(-76)$

$= -6 + 30 + 152$

$= 176$

$x = \dfrac{D_x}{D} = \dfrac{176}{88} = 2$

8. **a.** $\begin{bmatrix} 3 & 5 \\ 2 & -3 \end{bmatrix} \begin{bmatrix} x \\ y \end{bmatrix} = \begin{bmatrix} 9 \\ -13 \end{bmatrix}$

b. $A^{-1} = \dfrac{1}{(3)(-3)-(5)(2)} \begin{bmatrix} -3 & -5 \\ -2 & 3 \end{bmatrix}$

$= \dfrac{1}{-19} \begin{bmatrix} -3 & -5 \\ -2 & 3 \end{bmatrix} = \begin{bmatrix} \frac{3}{19} & \frac{5}{19} \\ \frac{2}{19} & -\frac{3}{19} \end{bmatrix}$

c. $A^{-1}B = \begin{bmatrix} \frac{3}{19} & \frac{5}{19} \\ \frac{2}{19} & -\frac{3}{19} \end{bmatrix} \begin{bmatrix} 9 \\ -13 \end{bmatrix} = \begin{bmatrix} \frac{27}{19} - \frac{65}{19} \\ \frac{18}{19} + \frac{39}{19} \end{bmatrix} = \begin{bmatrix} -2 \\ 3 \end{bmatrix}$

The solution to the system is $\{(-2, 3)\}$.

9. $\begin{vmatrix} 4 & -1 & 3 \\ 0 & 5 & -1 \\ 5 & 2 & 4 \end{vmatrix} = 4\begin{vmatrix} 5 & -1 \\ 2 & 4 \end{vmatrix} + 5\begin{vmatrix} -1 & 3 \\ 5 & -1 \end{vmatrix}$

$= 4[20-(-2)] + 5(1-15)$

$= 4(22) + 5(-14)$

$= 88 - 70$

$= 18$

Cumulative Review Exercises (Chapters 1–6)

1. $2x^2 = 4 - x$

$2x^2 + x - 4 = 0$

$x = \dfrac{-1 \pm \sqrt{1^2 - 4(2)(-4)}}{2(2)}$

$x = \dfrac{-1 \pm \sqrt{1 - 32}}{4}$

$x = \dfrac{-1 \pm \sqrt{33}}{4}$

The solution set is $\left\{ \dfrac{-1 + \sqrt{33}}{4}, \dfrac{-1 - \sqrt{33}}{4} \right\}$.

2. $5x + 8 \le 7(1 + x)$

$5x + 8 \le 7 + 7x$

$-2x \le -1$

$x \ge \dfrac{1}{2}$

The solution set is $\left\{ x \mid x \ge \dfrac{1}{2} \right\}$ or $\left[\dfrac{1}{2}, \infty \right)$.

3. $\sqrt{2x + 4} - \sqrt{x + 3} - 1 = 0$

$\sqrt{2x + 4} = \sqrt{x + 3} + 1$

$2x + 4 = x + 3 + 2\sqrt{x + 3} + 1$

$x = 2\sqrt{x + 3}$

$x^2 = 4(x + 3)$

$x^2 = 4x + 12$

$x^2 - 4x - 12 = 0$

$(x - 6)(x + 2) = 0$

$x = 6$ or $x = -2$

$x = -2$ does not check. The solution set is $\{6\}$.

4. $3x^3 + 8x^2 - 15x + 4 = 0$

$p = 61, 62, 64$

$q = 61, 63$

$\dfrac{p}{q} = 61, 6\dfrac{1}{3}, 62, 6\dfrac{2}{3}, 64, 6\dfrac{4}{3}$

$$\begin{array}{r|rrrr} -4 & 3 & 8 & -15 & 4 \\ & & -12 & 16 & -4 \\ \hline & 3 & -4 & 1 & 0 \end{array}$$

$(x + 4)(3x^2 - 4x + 1) = 0$

$(x + 4)(3x - 1)(x - 1) = 0$

$x = -4, \ x = \dfrac{1}{3}, \ x = 1$

The solution set is $\left\{ -4, \dfrac{1}{3}, 1 \right\}$.

5. $e^{2x} - 14e^x + 45 = 0 \quad le + t = e^x$

$t^2 - 14t + 45 = 0$

$(t - 5)(t - 9) = 0$

$t = 5 \quad t = 9$

$e^x = 5 \quad e^x = 9$

$\ln e^x = \ln 5 \quad \ln e^x = \ln 9$

$x = e^x = \ln 5 \quad x = \ln 9$

The solution set is $\{\ln 5, \ln 9\}$.

6. $\log_3 x + \log_3 (x + 2) = 1$

$\log_3 x^2 + 2x = 1$

$3^1 = x^2 + 2x$

$x^2 + 2x - 3 = 0$

$(x - 1)(x + 3) = 0$

$x = 1, \ x = -3$

$x = -3$ does not check. The solution set is $\{1\}$.

7. $\left[\begin{array}{rrr|r} 1 & -1 & 1 & 17 \\ 2 & 3 & 1 & 8 \\ -4 & 1 & 5 & -2 \end{array} \right] \begin{array}{l} -2R_1 + R_2 \\ 4R_1 + R_3 \end{array}$

$\left[\begin{array}{rrr|r} 1 & -1 & 1 & 17 \\ 0 & 5 & -1 & -26 \\ 0 & -3 & 9 & 66 \end{array} \right] -\dfrac{1}{3}R_3$

$\left[\begin{array}{rrr|r} 1 & -1 & 1 & 17 \\ 0 & 1 & -3 & -22 \\ 0 & 5 & -1 & -26 \end{array} \right] \begin{array}{l} -5R_2 + R_3 \\ 1R_2 + R_1 \end{array}$

$\left[\begin{array}{rrr|r} 1 & 0 & -2 & -5 \\ 0 & 1 & -3 & -22 \\ 0 & 0 & 14 & 84 \end{array} \right] \dfrac{1}{14}R_3$

$\left[\begin{array}{rrr|r} 1 & 0 & -2 & -5 \\ 0 & 1 & -3 & -22 \\ 0 & 0 & 1 & 6 \end{array} \right] \begin{array}{l} 3R_3 + R_2 \\ 2R_3 + R_1 \end{array}$

$\left[\begin{array}{rrr|r} 1 & 0 & 0 & 7 \\ 0 & 1 & 0 & -4 \\ 0 & 0 & 1 & 6 \end{array} \right]$

$x = 7 \quad y = -4 \quad z = 6$

The solution set is $\{(7, -4, 6)\}$.

8. $D = \begin{vmatrix} 1 & -2 & 1 \\ 2 & 1 & -1 \\ 3 & 2 & -2 \end{vmatrix}$

$= 1\begin{vmatrix} 1 & -1 \\ 2 & -2 \end{vmatrix} - 2\begin{vmatrix} -2 & 1 \\ 2 & -2 \end{vmatrix} + 3\begin{vmatrix} -2 & 1 \\ 1 & 1 \end{vmatrix}$

$= 1(-2+2) - 2(4-2) + 3(2-1)$

$= 0 - 4 + 3$

$= -1$

$D_y = \begin{vmatrix} 1 & 7 & 1 \\ 2 & 0 & -1 \\ 3 & -2 & -2 \end{vmatrix} = 7\begin{vmatrix} 2 & -1 \\ 3 & -2 \end{vmatrix} - 2\begin{vmatrix} 1 & 1 \\ 2 & -1 \end{vmatrix}$

$= 7(-4+3) - 2(-1-2)$

$= -7 + 6 = 1$

$y = \dfrac{D_y}{D} = \dfrac{1}{-1} = -1$

$y = -1$

9. $y = \sqrt{4x-7}$

$x = \sqrt{4y-7}$

$x^2 = 4y-7$

$x^2 + 7 - 4y$

$\dfrac{x^2+7}{4} = y$

$f^{-1}(x) = \dfrac{x^2+7}{4} \ (x \ge 0)$

10. $f(x) = \dfrac{x}{x^2-16}$

$f(0) = \dfrac{0}{-16} = 0$

y-intercept at 0

$0 = \dfrac{x}{x^2-16}$

$0 = x$

x-intercept at 0

$f(x) = \dfrac{x}{(x+4)(x-4)}$

vertical asymptotes at 4, –4
horizontal asymptote at 0

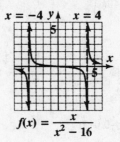

$f(x) = \dfrac{x}{x^2-16}$

11. $f(x) = 4x^4 - 4x^3 - 25x^2 + x + 6$

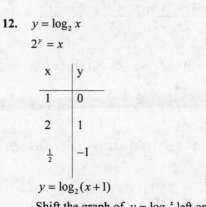

$f(x) = (x+2)(x-3)(4x^2-1)$

$f(x) = (x+2)(x-3)(2x+1)(2x-1)$

12. $y = \log_2 x$

$2^y = x$

x	y
1	0
2	1
$\frac{1}{2}$	-1

$y = \log_2(x+1)$

Shift the graph of $y = \log_2{}^x$ left one unit.

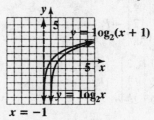

13. a.

$$A = A_0 e^{kt}$$

$$450 = 900e^{k(40)}$$

$$\frac{1}{2} = e^{40k}$$

$$\ln\left(\frac{1}{2}\right) = \ln\left(e^{40k}\right)$$

$$\ln\left(\frac{1}{2}\right) = 40k$$

$$k = \frac{\ln\left(\frac{1}{2}\right)}{40} \approx -0.017$$

$$A = 900e^{-0.017t}$$

b.

$$A = 900e^{-0.017(10)}$$

$$A = 900e^{-0.17}$$

$$A \approx 759.30 \text{ grams}$$

14.

$$\begin{bmatrix} 1 & -1 & 0 \\ 2 & 1 & 3 \end{bmatrix} \begin{bmatrix} 4 & -1 \\ 2 & 0 \\ 1 & 1 \end{bmatrix} = \begin{bmatrix} 4-2+0 & -1+0+0 \\ 8+2+3 & -2+0+3 \end{bmatrix}$$

$$= \begin{bmatrix} 2 & -1 \\ 13 & 1 \end{bmatrix}$$

15.

$$\frac{3x^2+17x-38}{(x-3)(x-2)(x+2)} = \frac{A}{x-3} + \frac{B}{x-2} + \frac{C}{x+2}$$

$$3x^2+17x-38$$

$$= A(x^2-4) + B(x^2-x-6) + C(x^2-5x+6)$$

$$3x^2+17x-38$$

$$= Ax^2 - 4A + Bx^2 - Bx - 6B + Cx^2 - 5Cx + 6c$$

$$3x^2+17x-38$$

$$= (A+B+C)x^2 + (-B-5C)x - (4A+6B-6C)$$

$$A+B+C = 3$$

$$-B-5C = 17$$

$$4A+6B-6C = 38$$

$$\begin{bmatrix} 1 & 1 & 1 & | & 3 \\ 0 & -1 & -5 & | & 17 \\ 4 & 6 & -6 & | & 38 \end{bmatrix} \begin{matrix} \\ \\ -4R_1 + R_3 \end{matrix}$$

$$\begin{bmatrix} 1 & 1 & 1 & | & 3 \\ 0 & -1 & -5 & | & 17 \\ 0 & 2 & -10 & | & 26 \end{bmatrix} \begin{matrix} \\ -1R_2 \\ \end{matrix}$$

$$\begin{bmatrix} 1 & 1 & 1 & | & 3 \\ 0 & 1 & 5 & | & -17 \\ 0 & 2 & -10 & | & 26 \end{bmatrix} \begin{matrix} \\ -2R_2 + R_3 \\ -1R_2 + R_1 \end{matrix}$$

$$\begin{bmatrix} 1 & 0 & -4 & | & 20 \\ 0 & 1 & 5 & | & -17 \\ 0 & 0 & -20 & | & 60 \end{bmatrix} \begin{matrix} \\ \\ -\frac{1}{20}R_3 \end{matrix}$$

$$\begin{bmatrix} 1 & 0 & -4 & | & 20 \\ 0 & 1 & 5 & | & -17 \\ 0 & 0 & 1 & | & -3 \end{bmatrix} \begin{matrix} \\ -5R_3 + R_2 \\ 4R_3 + R_1 \end{matrix}$$

$$\begin{bmatrix} 1 & 0 & 0 & | & 8 \\ 0 & 1 & 0 & | & -2 \\ 0 & 0 & 1 & | & -3 \end{bmatrix}$$

$$A = 8, \quad B = -2, \quad C = -3$$

$$\frac{3x^2+17x-38}{(x-3)(x-2)(x+2)} = \frac{8}{x-3} + \frac{-2}{x-2} + \frac{-3}{x+2}$$

16. $y = -\dfrac{2}{3}x - 1$

x	y
0	−1
3	−3
−3	1

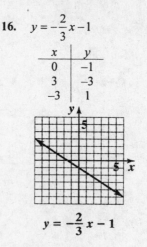

$$y = -\frac{2}{3}x - 1$$

17. $3x - 5y < 15$

$$-5y < -3x + 15$$

$$y > \frac{3}{5}x - 3$$

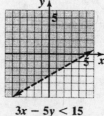

$$3x - 5y < 15$$

18. $f(x) = x^2 - 2x - 3$

$f(x) = (x^2 - 2x + 1) - 3 - 1$

$f(x) = (x-1)^2 - 4$

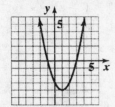

$f(x) = x^2 - 2x - 3$

19. $(x-1)^2 + (y+1)^2 = 9$
center $(1, -1)$
radius = 3

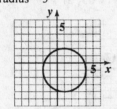

$(x-1)^2 + (y+1)^2 = 9$

20.

$$\begin{array}{r|rrrr} 2 & 1 & 0 & -6 & 4 \\ & & 2 & 4 & -4 \\ \hline & 1 & 2 & -2 & 0 \end{array}$$

$$\frac{x^3 - 6x + 4}{x - 2} = x^2 + 2x - 2$$

Chapter 7

Section 7.1

Check Point Exercises

1. $a^2 = 36, a = 6$

$b^2 = 9, b = 3$

$c^2 = a^2 - b^2 = 36 - 9 = 27$

$c = \sqrt{27} = 3\sqrt{3}$

The foci are located at $(-3\sqrt{3}, 0)$ and $(3\sqrt{3}, 0)$.

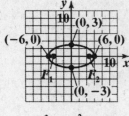

$$\frac{x^2}{36} + \frac{y^2}{9} = 1$$

2. $\frac{16x^2}{144} + \frac{9y^2}{144} = \frac{144}{144}$

$\frac{x^2}{9} + \frac{y^2}{16} = 1$

$a^2 = 16, a = 4$

$b^2 = 9, b = 3$

$c^2 = a^2 - b^2 = 16 - 9 = 7$

$c = \sqrt{7}$

The foci are located at $(0, -\sqrt{7})$ and $(0, \sqrt{7})$.

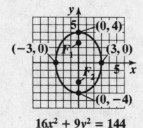

$$16x^2 + 9y^2 = 144$$

3. $c^2 = 4, a^2 = 9$

$b^2 = a^2 - c^2 = 9 - 4 = 5$

$\frac{x^2}{9} + \frac{y^2}{5} = 1$

4. $a^2 = 9, a = 3$

$b^2 = 4, b = 2$

center at $(-1, 2)$

$c^2 = a^2 - b^2$

$c^2 = 9 - 4$

$c^2 = 5$

$c = \sqrt{5}$

The foci are located at

$(-1-\sqrt{5}, 2)$ and $(-1+\sqrt{5}, 2)$.

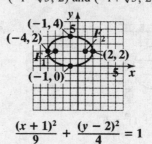

$$\frac{(x + 1)^2}{9} + \frac{(y - 2)^2}{4} = 1$$

5. $\frac{x^2}{20^2} + \frac{y^2}{10^2} = 1$

$\frac{x^2}{400} + \frac{y^2}{100} = 1$

Since the truck is 12 feet wide, substitute $x = 6$ into the equation to find y.

$$\frac{6^2}{400} + \frac{y^2}{100} = 1$$

$$400\left(\frac{36}{400} + \frac{y^2}{100}\right) = 400(1)$$

$$36 + 4y^2 = 400$$

$$4y^2 = 364$$

$$y^2 = 91$$

$$y = \sqrt{91}$$

$$y \approx 9.54$$

6 feet from the center, the height of the archway is 9.54 feet. Since the truck's height is 9 feet, it will fit under the archway.

488

Exercise Set 7.1

1. $\dfrac{x^2}{16} + \dfrac{y^2}{4} = 1$

   $a^2 = 16,\ a = 4$

   $b^2 = 4,\ b = 2$

   $c^2 = a^2 - b^2 = 16 - 4 = 12$

   $c = \sqrt{12} = 2\sqrt{3}$

   The foci are located at $(-2\sqrt{3},\ 0)$ and $(2\sqrt{3},\ 0)$.

   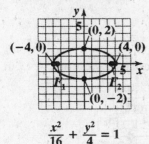

   $$\dfrac{x^2}{16} + \dfrac{y^2}{4} = 1$$

3. $a^2 = 36,\ a = 6$

   $b^2 = 9,\ b = 3$

   $c^2 = a^2 - b^2 = 36 - 9 = 27$

   $c = \sqrt{27} = 3\sqrt{3}$

   The foci are located at $(0,\ -3\sqrt{3})$ and $(0,\ 3\sqrt{3})$.

   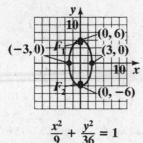

   $$\dfrac{x^2}{9} + \dfrac{y^2}{36} = 1$$

5. $a^2 = 64,\ a = 8$

   $b^2 = 25,\ b = 5$

   $c^2 = a^2 - b^2 = 64 - 25 = 39$

   $c = \sqrt{39}$

The foci are located at $(0,\ -\sqrt{39})$ and $(0,\ \sqrt{39})$.

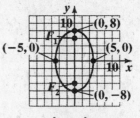

$$\dfrac{x^2}{25} + \dfrac{y^2}{64} = 1$$

7. $a^2 = 81,\ a = 9$

   $b^2 = 49,\ b = 7$

   $c^2 = a^2 - b^2 = 81 - 49 = 32$

   $c = \sqrt{32} = 4\sqrt{2}$

   The foci are located at $(0,\ -4\sqrt{2})$ and $(0,\ 4\sqrt{2})$.

   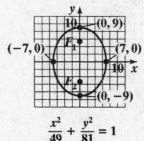

   $$\dfrac{x^2}{49} + \dfrac{y^2}{81} = 1$$

9. $\dfrac{x^2}{\dfrac{9}{4}} + \dfrac{y^2}{\dfrac{25}{4}} = 1$

   $c^2 = \dfrac{25}{4} - \dfrac{9}{4}$

   $c^2 = \dfrac{16}{4}$

   $c^2 = 4$

   $c = 2$

   The foci are located at $(0, 2)$ and $(0, -2)$.

   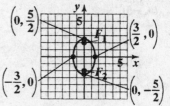

11. $x^2 = 1 - 4y^2$

$x^2 + 4y^2 = 1$

$x^2 + \dfrac{y^2}{\frac{1}{4}} = 1$

$c^2 = 1 - \dfrac{1}{4}$

$c^2 = \dfrac{3}{4}$

$c = \pm\dfrac{\sqrt{3}}{2}$

$c \approx \pm 0.9$

The foci are located at $\left(\dfrac{\sqrt{3}}{2}, 0\right)$ and $\left(-\dfrac{\sqrt{3}}{2}, 0\right)$.

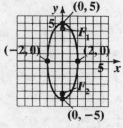

13. $25x^2 + 4y^2 = 100$

$\dfrac{25x^2}{100} + \dfrac{4y^2}{100} = \dfrac{100}{100}$

$\dfrac{x^2}{4} + \dfrac{y^2}{25} = 1$

$a^2 = 25,\ a = 5$

$b^2 = 4,\ b = 2$

$c^2 = a^2 = b^2 = 25 - 4 = 21$

The foci are located at $(0, -\sqrt{21})$ and

$(0, \sqrt{21})$.

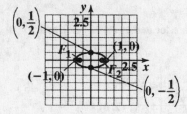

15. $4x^2 + 16y^2 = 64$

$\dfrac{x^2}{16} + \dfrac{y^2}{4} = 1$

$a^2 = 16,\ a = 4$

$b^2 = 4,\ b = 2$

$c^2 = 16 - 4$

$c^2 = 12$

$c = \pm\sqrt{12}$

$c = \pm 2\sqrt{3}$

$c \approx \pm 3.5$

The foci are located at $(2\sqrt{3}, 0)$ and $(-2\sqrt{3}, 0)$.

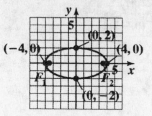

17. $7x^2 = 35 - 5y^2$

$7x^2 + 5y^2 = 35$

$\dfrac{x^2}{5} + \dfrac{y^2}{7} = 1$

$a^2 = 7,\ a = \sqrt{7}$

$b^2 = 5,\ b = \sqrt{5}$

$c^2 = 7 - 5$

$c^2 = 2$

$c = \pm\sqrt{2}$

$c \approx \pm 1.4$

The foci are located at $(0, \sqrt{2})$ and $(0, -\sqrt{2})$.

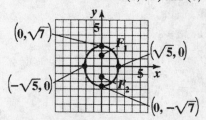

19. $a^2 = 4$, $b^2 = 1$, center at $(0, 0)$

$$\frac{x^2}{4} + \frac{y^2}{1} = 1$$

$$c^2 = a^2 - b^2 = 4 - 1 = 3$$

$$c = \sqrt{3}$$

The foci are at $(-\sqrt{3}, 0)$ and $(\sqrt{3}, 0)$.

21. $a^2 = 4$, $b^2 = 1$,

center: $(0, 0)$

$$\frac{x^2}{1} + \frac{y^2}{4} = 1$$

$$c^2 = a^2 - b^2 = 4 - 1 = 3$$

$$c = \sqrt{3}$$

The foci are at $(0, \sqrt{3})$ and $(0, -\sqrt{3})$.

23. $\dfrac{(x+1)^2}{4} + \dfrac{(y-1)^2}{1} = 1$

$$a^2 = 4, \quad b^2 = 1$$

$$c^2 = 4 - 1$$

$$c^2 = 3$$

$$c = \pm\sqrt{3}$$

The foci are located at

$(-1+\sqrt{3}, 1)$ and $(-1-\sqrt{3}, 1)$.

25. $c^2 = 25$, $a^2 = 64$

$$b^2 = a^2 - c^2 = 64 - 25 = 39$$

$$\frac{x^2}{64} + \frac{y^2}{39} = 1$$

27. $c^2 = 16$, $a^2 = 49$

$$b^2 = a^2 - c^2 = 49 - 16 = 33$$

$$\frac{x^2}{33} + \frac{y^2}{49} = 1$$

29. $c^2 = 4$, $b^2 = 9$

$$a^2 = b^2 + c^2 = 9 + 4 = 13$$

$$\frac{x^2}{13} + \frac{y^2}{9} = 1$$

31. $2a = 8$, $a = 4$, $a^2 = 16$

$$2b = 4, b = 2, b^2 = 4$$

$$\frac{x^2}{16} + \frac{y^2}{4} = 1$$

33. $2a = 10$, $a = 5$, $a^2 = 25$

$$2b = 4, \ b = 2, \ b^2 = 4$$

$$\frac{(x+2)^2}{4} + \frac{(y-3)^2}{25} = 1$$

35. length of the major axis = $9 - 3 = 6$

$2a = 6$, $a = 3$ major axis is vertical

length of the minor axis = $9 - 5 = 4$

$2b = 4$, $b = 2$

Center is at $(7, 6)$.

$$\frac{(x-7)^2}{4} + \frac{(y-6)^2}{9} = 1$$

37. $a^2 = 9$, $a = 3$

$$b^2 = 4, b = 2$$

center: $(2, 1)$

$$c^2 = a^2 - b^2 = 9 - 4 = 5$$

$$c = \sqrt{5}$$

The foci are at $(2-\sqrt{5}, 1)$ and $(2+\sqrt{5}, 1)$.

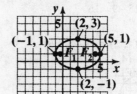

$$\frac{(x-2)^2}{9} + \frac{(y-1)^2}{4} = 1$$

39. $\dfrac{(x+3)^2}{16} + \dfrac{4(y-2)^2}{16} = \dfrac{16}{16}$

$\dfrac{(x+3)^2}{16} + \dfrac{(y-2)^2}{4} = 1$

$a^2 = 16,\ a = 4$

$b^2 = 4,\ b = 2$

center: $(-3, 2)$

$c^2 = a^2 - b^2 = 16 - 4 = 12$

$c = \sqrt{12} = 2\sqrt{3}$

The foci are at $(-3 - 2\sqrt{3},\ 2)$ and

$(-3 + 2\sqrt{3},\ 2)$.

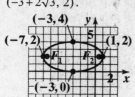

$(x + 3)^2 + 4(y - 2)^2 = 16$

41. $a^2 = 25,\ a = 5$

$b^2 = 9,\ b = 3$

center: $(4, -2)$

$c^2 = a^2 - b^2 = 25 - 9 = 16$

$c = 4$

The foci are at $(4, 2)$ and $(4, -6)$.

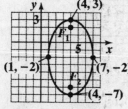

$\dfrac{(x - 4)^2}{9} + \dfrac{(y + 2)^2}{25} = 1$

43. $a^2 = 36,\ a = 6$

$b^2 = 25,\ b = 5$

center: $(0, 2)$

$c^2 = a^2 - b^2 = 36 - 25 = 11$

$c = \sqrt{11}$

The foci are at $(0, 2+\sqrt{11})$ and $(0, 2-\sqrt{11})$.

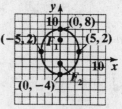

$\dfrac{x^2}{25} + \dfrac{(y - 2)^2}{36} = 1$

45. $a^2 = 9,\ a = 3$

$b^2 = 1,\ b = 1$

center: $(-3, 2)$

$c^2 = a^2 - b^2 = 9 - 1 = 8$

$c = \sqrt{8} = 2\sqrt{2}$

The foci are at $(-3 - 2\sqrt{2},\ 2)$ and

$(-3 + 2\sqrt{2},\ 2)$.

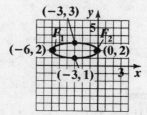

$\dfrac{(x + 3)^2}{9} + (y - 2)^2 = 1$

47. $c^2 = 5 - 2$

$c^2 = 3$

$c = \pm\sqrt{3}$

$c \approx \pm 1.7$

The foci are located at $(1, -3+\sqrt{3})$ and

$(1, -3-\sqrt{3})$.

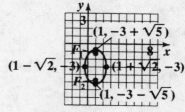

$\dfrac{(x - 1)^2}{2} + \dfrac{(y + 3)^2}{5} = 1$

49.

$$\frac{9(x-1)^2}{36} + \frac{4(y+3)^2}{36} = \frac{36}{36}$$

$$\frac{(x-1)^2}{4} + \frac{(y+3)^2}{9} = 1$$

$a^2 = 9, a = 3$

$b^2 = 4, b = 2$

center: $(1, -3)$

$c^2 = a^2 - b^2 = 9 - 4 = 5$

$c = \sqrt{5}$

The foci are at $(1, -3+\sqrt{5})$ and $(1, -3-\sqrt{5})$.

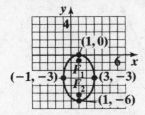

$9(x - 1)^2 + 4(y + 3)^2 = 36$

51.

$$(9x^2 - 36x) + (25y^2 + 50y) = 164$$

$$9(x^2 - 4x) + 25(y^2 + 2y) = 164$$

$$9(x^2 - 4x + 4) + 25(y^2 + 2y + 1)$$

$$= 164 + 36 + 25$$

$$9(x-2)^2 + 25(y+1)^2 = 225$$

$$\frac{9(x-2)^2}{225} + \frac{25(y+1)^2}{225} = \frac{225}{225}$$

$$\frac{(x-2)^2}{25} + \frac{(y+1)^2}{9} = 1$$

center: $(2, -1)$

$a^2 = 25, a = 5$

$b^2 = 9, b = 3$

$c^2 = a^2 - b^2 = 25 - 9 = 16$

$c = 4$

The foci are at $(-2, -1)$ and $(6, -1)$.

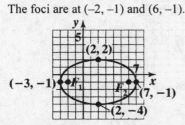

$9x^2 + 25y^2 - 36x + 50y - 164 = 0$

53.

$$(9x^2 - 18x) + (16y^2 + 64y) = 71$$

$$9(x^2 - 2x) + 16(y^2 + 4y) = 71$$

$$9(x^2 - 2x + 1) + 16(y^2 + 4y + 4)$$

$$= 71 + 9 + 64$$

$$9(x-1)^2 + 16(y+2)^2 = 144$$

$$\frac{9(x-1)^2}{144} + \frac{16(y+2)^2}{144} = \frac{144}{144}$$

$$\frac{(x-1)^2}{16} + \frac{(y+2)^2}{9} = 1$$

center: $(1, -2)$

$a^2 = 16, a = 4$

$b^2 = 9, b = 3$

$c^2 = a^2 - b^2 = 16 - 9 = 7$

$c = \sqrt{7}$

The foci are at

$(1 - \sqrt{7}, -2)$ and $(1+\sqrt{7}, -2)$.

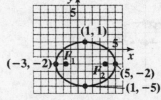

$9x^2 + 16y^2 - 18x + 64y - 71 = 0$

55.

$$(4x^2 + 16x) + (y^2 - 6y) = 39$$

$$4(x^2 + 4x) + (y^2 - 6y) = 39$$

$$4(x^2 + 4x + 4) + (y^2 - 6y + 9) = 39 + 16 + 9$$

$$4(x+2)^2 + (y-3)^2 = 64$$

$$\frac{4(x+2)^2}{64} + \frac{(y-3)^2}{64} = \frac{64}{64}$$

$$\frac{(x+2)^2}{16} + \frac{(y-3)^2}{64} = 1$$

center: $(-2, 3)$

$a^2 = 64, a = 8$

$b^2 = 16, b = 4$

$c^2 = a^2 - b^2 = 64 - 16 = 48$

$c = \sqrt{48} = 4\sqrt{3}$

The foci are at $(-2, 3 + 4\sqrt{3})$ and

$(-2, 3 - 4\sqrt{3})$.

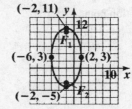

$4x^2 + y^2 + 16x - 6y - 39 = 0$

493

57. $x^2 + y^2 = 1$ $x^2 + 9y^2 = 9$

$$\frac{x^2}{9} + \frac{9y^2}{9} = \frac{9}{9}$$

$$\frac{x^2}{9} + \frac{y^2}{1} = 1$$

The first equation is that of a circle with center at the origin and $r = 1$. The second equation is that of an ellipse with center at the origin, horizontal major axis of length 6 units $(a = 3)$, and vertical minor axis of length 2 units $(b = 1)$.

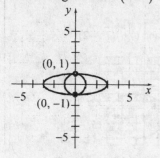

Check each intersection point.

The solution set is $\{(0, -1), (0, 1)\}$.

59. $\frac{x^2}{25} + \frac{y^2}{9} = 1$ $y = 3$

The first equation is for an ellipse centered at the origin with horizontal major axis of length 10 units and vertical minor axis of length 6 units. The second equation is for a horizontal line with a y-intercept of 3.

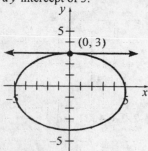

Check the intersection point.

The solution set is $\{(0, 3)\}$.

61. $4x^2 + y^2 = 4$ $2x - y = 2$

$$\frac{4x^2}{4} + \frac{y^2}{4} = \frac{4}{4} \qquad -y = -2x + 2$$

$$\frac{x^2}{1} + \frac{y^2}{4} = 1 \qquad\qquad y = 2x - 2$$

The first equation is for an ellipse centered at the origin with vertical major axis of length 4 units $(b = 2)$ and horizontal minor axis of length 2 units $(a = 1)$. The second equation is for a line with slope 2 and y-intercept -2.

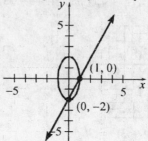

Check the intersection points.

The solution set is $\{(0, -2), (1, 0)\}$.

63.

$$y^2 = \left(-\sqrt{16 - 4x^2}\right)^2$$

$$y^2 = 16 - 4x^2$$

$$4x^2 + y^2 = 16$$

$$\frac{x^2}{4} + \frac{y^2}{16} = 1$$

We want to graph the bottom half of an ellipse centered at the origin with a vertical major axis of length 8 units $(b = 4)$ and horizontal minor axis of length 4 units $(a = 2)$.

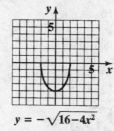

$$y = -\sqrt{16 - 4x^2}$$

65. $a = 15, b = 10$

$$\frac{x^2}{225} + \frac{y^2}{100} = 1$$

Let $x = 4$

$$\frac{4^2}{225} + \frac{y^2}{100} = 1$$

$$900\left(\frac{16}{225} + \frac{y^2}{100}\right) = 900(1)$$

$$64 + 9y^2 = 900$$

$$9y^2 = 836$$

$$y = \sqrt{\frac{836}{9}} \approx 9.64$$

Yes, the truck only needs 7 feet so it will clear.

67. **a.** $a = 48, a^2 = 2304$

$b = 23, b^2 = 529$

$$\frac{x^2}{2304} + \frac{y^2}{529} = 1$$

b. $c^2 = a^2 - b^2 = 2304 - 529 = 1775$

$c = \sqrt{1775} \approx 42.13$

He situated his desk about 42 feet from the center of the ellipse, along the major axis.

79. $a = 6, a^2 = 36$

$$\frac{x^2}{b^2} + \frac{y^2}{36} = 1$$

When $x = 2$ and $y = -4$,

$$\frac{2^2}{b^2} + \frac{(-4)^2}{36} = 1$$

$$\frac{4}{b^2} + \frac{16}{36} = 1$$

$$\frac{4}{b^2} = \frac{5}{9}$$

$$36 = 5b^2$$

$$b^2 = \frac{36}{5}$$

$$\frac{x^2}{\frac{36}{5}} + \frac{y^2}{36} = 1$$

81. The large circle has radius 5 with center $(0, 0)$. Its equation is $x^2 + y^2 = 25$. The small circle has radius 3 with center $(0, 0)$. Its equation is $x^2 + y^2 = 9$.

Section 7.2

Check Point Exercises

1. **a.** $a^2 = 25, a = 5$

vertices: $(5, 0)$ and $(-5, 0)$

$b^2 = 16$

$c^2 = a^2 + b^2 = 25 + 16 = 41$

$c = \sqrt{41}$

The foci are at $(\sqrt{41}, 0)$ and $(-\sqrt{41}, 0)$.

b. $a^2 = 25, a = 5$

vertices: $(0, 5)$ and $(0, -5)$

$b^2 = 16$

$c^2 = a^2 + b^2 = 25 + 16 = 41$

$c = \sqrt{41}$

The foci are at $(0, \sqrt{41})$ and $(0, -\sqrt{41})$.

2. $a = 3, c = 5$

$b^2 = c^2 - a^2 = 25 - 9 = 16$

$$\frac{y^2}{9} - \frac{x^2}{16} = 1$$

3. $a^2 = 36, a = 6$

The vertices are $(6, 0)$ and $(-6, 0)$.

$b^2 = 9, b = 3$

asymptotes: $y = \pm\frac{b}{a}x = \pm\frac{3}{6}x = \pm\frac{1}{2}x$

$c^2 = a^2 + b^2 = 36 + 9 = 45$

$c = \sqrt{45} = 3\sqrt{5}$

The foci are at $(-3\sqrt{5}, 0)$ and $(3\sqrt{5}, 0)$.

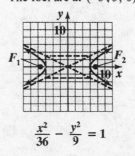

$$\frac{x^2}{36} - \frac{y^2}{9} = 1$$

4.
$$\frac{y^2}{4} - \frac{4x^2}{4} = \frac{4}{4}$$

$$\frac{y^2}{4} - x^2 = 1$$

$a^2 = 4,\ a = 2$

The vertices are $(0, 2)$ and $(0, -2)$.

$b^2 = 1,\ b = 1$

asymptotes: $y = \pm\dfrac{a}{b}x = \pm 2x$

$c^2 = a^2 + b^2 = 4 + 1 = 5$

$c = \sqrt{5}$

The foci are at $(0, \sqrt{5})$ and $(0, -\sqrt{5})$.

$$y^2 - 4x^2 = 4$$

5. center at $(3, 1)$

$a^2 = 4,\ a = 2$

$b^2 = 1,\ b = 1$

The vertices are $(1, 1)$ and $(5, 1)$.

asymptotes: $y - 1 = \pm\dfrac{1}{2}(x - 3)$

$c^2 = a^2 + b^2 = 4 + 1 = 5$

$c = \sqrt{5}$

The foci are at $(3 - \sqrt{5},\ 1)$ and $(3 + \sqrt{5},\ 1)$.

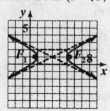

$$\frac{(x-3)^2}{4} - \frac{(y-1)^2}{1} = 1$$

6.
$$4\left(x^2 - 6x \quad\right) - 9\left(y^2 + 10y \quad\right) = 153$$

$$4\left(x^2 - 6x + 9\right) - 9\left(y^2 + 10y + 25\right) = 153 + 36 + (-225)$$

$$4(x-3)^2 - 9(y+5)^2 = -36$$

$$\frac{4(x-3)^2}{-36} - \frac{9(y+5)^2}{-36} = \frac{-36}{-36}$$

$$-\frac{(x-3)^2}{9} + \frac{(y+5)^2}{4} = 1$$

$$\frac{(y+5)^2}{4} - \frac{(x-3)^2}{9} = 1$$

center at $(3, -5)$

$a^2 = 4,\ a = 2$

$b^2 = 9,\ b = 3$

The vertices are $(3, -3)$ and $(3, -7)$.

asymptotes: $y + 5 = \pm\dfrac{2}{3}(x - 3)$

$c^2 = a^2 + b^2 = 4 + 9 = 13$

$c = \sqrt{13}$

The foci are at $(3, -5-\sqrt{13})$ and $(3, -5+\sqrt{13})$.

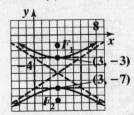

$$4x^2 - 24x - 9y^2 - 90y - 153 = 0$$

7. $c = 5280$

$2a = 3300, a = 1650$

$b^2 = c^2 - a^2 = 5280^2 - 1650^2 = 25,155,900$

The explosion occurred somewhere at the right branch of the hyperbola given by

$$\frac{x^2}{2,722,500} - \frac{y^2}{25,155,900} = 1.$$

Exercise Set 7.2

1. $a^2 = 4, a = 2$

The vertices are $(2, 0)$ and $(-2, 0)$.

$b^2 = 1$

$c^2 = a^2 + b^2 = 4 + 1 = 5$

$c = \sqrt{5}$

The foci are located at $(\sqrt{5}, 0)$ and $(-\sqrt{5}, 0)$.

graph (b)

3. $a^2 = 4, a = 2$

The vertices are $(0, 2)$ and $(0, -2)$.

$b^2 = 1$

$c^2 = a^2 + b^2 = 4 + 1 = 5$

$c = \sqrt{5}$

The foci are located at $(0, \sqrt{5})$ and $(0, -\sqrt{5})$.

graph (a)

5. $a = 1, c = 3$

$b^2 = c^2 - a^2 = 9 - 1 = 8$

$y^2 - \dfrac{x^2}{8} = 1$

7. $a = 3, c = 4$

$b^2 = c^2 - a^2 = 16 - 9 = 7$

$\dfrac{x^2}{9} - \dfrac{y^2}{7} = 1$

9. $2a = 6 - (-6)$

$2a = 12$

$a = 6$

$\dfrac{a}{b} = 2$

$\dfrac{6}{b} = 2$

$6 = 2b$

$3 = b$

Transverse axis is vertical.

$\dfrac{y^2}{36} - \dfrac{x^2}{9} = 1$

11. $a = 2, c = 7 - 4 = 3$

$2^2 + b^2 = 3^2$

$4 + b^2 = 9$

$b^2 = 5$

Transverse axis is horizontal.

$\dfrac{(x-4)^2}{4} - \dfrac{(y+2)^2}{5} = 1$

13. $a^2 = 9, a = 3$

$b^2 = 25, b = 5$

vertices: $(3, 0)$ and $(-3, 0)$

asymptotes: $y = \pm\dfrac{b}{a}x = \pm\dfrac{5}{3}x$

$c^2 = a^2 + b^2 = 9 + 25 = 34$

$c = \sqrt{34}$ on x-axis

The foci are at $(\sqrt{34}, 0)$ and $(-\sqrt{34}, 0)$.

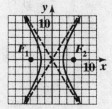

$$\dfrac{x^2}{9} - \dfrac{y^2}{25} = 1$$

15. $a^2 = 100, a = 10$

$b^2 = 64, b = 8$

vertices: $(10, 0)$ and $(-10, 0)$

asymptotes: $y = \pm\dfrac{b}{a}x = \pm\dfrac{8}{10}x$

or $y = \pm\dfrac{4}{5}x$

$c^2 = a^2 + b^2 = 100 + 64 = 164$

$c = \sqrt{164} = 2\sqrt{41}$ on x-axis

The foci are at $(2\sqrt{41}, 0)$ and $(-2\sqrt{41}, 0)$.

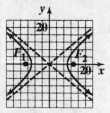

$$\dfrac{x^2}{100} - \dfrac{y^2}{64} = 1$$

17. $a^2 = 16, a = 4$

$b^2 = 36, b = 6$

vertices: $(0, 4)$ and $(0, -4)$

asymptotes: $y = \pm\dfrac{a}{b}x = \pm\dfrac{4}{6}x = \pm\dfrac{2}{3}x$

or $y = \pm\dfrac{2}{3}x$

$c^2 = a^2 + b^2 = 16 + 36 = 52$

$c = \sqrt{52} = 2\sqrt{13}$ on y-axis

The foci are at $(0, 2\sqrt{13})$ and $(0, -2\sqrt{13})$.

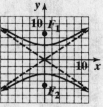

$$\dfrac{y^2}{16} - \dfrac{x^2}{36} = 1$$

19. $\dfrac{y^2}{\frac{1}{4}} - x^2 = 1$

$a^2 = \dfrac{1}{4}, a = \dfrac{1}{2}$

$b^2 = 1, b = 1$

$c^2 = a^2 + b^2$

$c^2 = \dfrac{1}{4} + 1$

$c^2 = \dfrac{5}{4}$

$c = \pm\dfrac{\sqrt{5}}{2}$

$c \approx \pm 1.1$

The foci are located at $\left(0, \dfrac{\sqrt{5}}{2}\right)$ and $\left(0, -\dfrac{\sqrt{5}}{2}\right)$.

asymptotes: $\begin{aligned} y &= \pm\dfrac{\frac{1}{2}}{1}x \\ y &= \pm\dfrac{1}{2}x \end{aligned}$

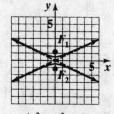

$$4y^2 - x^2 = 1$$

21. $\dfrac{9x^2}{36} - \dfrac{4y^2}{36} = \dfrac{36}{36}$

$\dfrac{x^2}{4} - \dfrac{y^2}{9} = 1$

$a^2 = 4,\ a = 2$

$b^2 = 9,\ b = 3$

vertices: $(2, 0)$ and $(-2, 0)$

asymptotes: $y = \pm\dfrac{b}{a}x = \pm\dfrac{3}{2}x$

$c^2 = a^2 + b^2 = 4 + 9 = 13$

$c = \sqrt{13}$ on x-axis

The foci are at $(\sqrt{13}, 0)$ and $(-\sqrt{13}, 0)$.

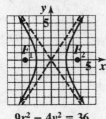

$9x^2 - 4y^2 = 36$

23. $\dfrac{9y^2}{225} - \dfrac{25x^2}{225} = \dfrac{225}{225}$

$\dfrac{y^2}{25} - \dfrac{x^2}{9} = 1$

$a^2 = 25,\ a = 5$

$b^2 = 9,\ b = 3$

vertices: $(0, 5)$ and $(0, -5)$

asymptotes: $y = \pm\dfrac{a}{b}x = \pm\dfrac{5}{3}x$

$c^2 = a^2 + b^2 = 25 + 9 = 34$

$c = \sqrt{34}$ on y-axis

The foci are at $(0, \sqrt{34})$ and $(0, -\sqrt{34})$.

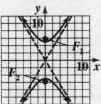

$9y^2 - 25x^2 = 225$

25. $y^2 = x^2 - 2$

$2 = x^2 - y^2$

$1 = \dfrac{x^2}{2} - \dfrac{y^2}{2}$

$a^2 = 2,\ a = \sqrt{2}$

$b^2 = 2,\ b = \sqrt{2}$

$c^2 = 2 + 2$

$c^2 = 4$

$c = 2$

The foci are located at $(2, 0)$ and $(-2, 0)$.

asymptotes: $y = \pm\dfrac{\sqrt{2}}{\sqrt{2}}x$

$y = \pm x$

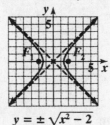

$y = \pm\sqrt{x^2 - 2}$

27. $a = 3,\ b = 5$

$\dfrac{x^2}{9} - \dfrac{y^2}{25} = 1$

29. $a = 2,\ b = 3$

$\dfrac{y^2}{4} - \dfrac{x^2}{9} = 1$

31. Center $(2, -3)$, $a = 2$, $b = 3$

$\dfrac{(x-2)^2}{4} - \dfrac{(y+3)^2}{9} = 1$

33. center: $(-4, -3)$
$a^2 = 9, a = 3$
$b^2 = 16, b = 4$
vertices: $(-7, -3)$ and $(-1, -3)$
asymptotes: $y + 3 = \pm\frac{4}{3}(x+4)$

$c^2 = a^2 + b^2 = 9 + 16 = 25$
$c = \pm 5$ parallel to x-axis
The foci are at $(-9, -3)$ and $(1, -3)$.

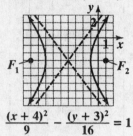

$$\frac{(x+4)^2}{9} - \frac{(y+3)^2}{16} = 1$$

35. center: $(-3, 0)$
$a^2 = 25, a = 5$
$b^2 = 16, b = 4$
vertices: $(2, 0)$ and $(-8, 0)$
asymptotes: $y = \pm\frac{4}{5}(x+3)$

$c^2 = a^2 + b^2 = 25 + 16 = 41$
$c = \sqrt{41}$

The foci are at $(-3+\sqrt{41}, 0)$ and
$(-3-\sqrt{41}, 0)$.

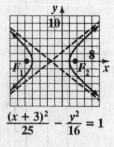

$$\frac{(x+3)^2}{25} - \frac{y^2}{16} = 1$$

37. center: $(1, -2)$
$a^2 = 4, a = 2$
$b^2 = 16, b = 4$
vertices: $(1, 0)$ and $(1, -4)$
asymptotes: $y + 2 = \pm\frac{1}{2}(x-1)$

$c^2 = a^2 + b^2 = 4 + 16 = 20$
$c = \sqrt{20} = 2\sqrt{5}$ parallel to y-axis
The foci are at $(1, -2+2\sqrt{5})$ and
$(1, -2-2\sqrt{5})$.

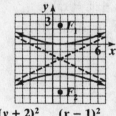

$$\frac{(y+2)^2}{4} - \frac{(x-1)^2}{16} = 1$$

39. $\frac{(x-3)^2}{4} - \frac{4(y+3)^2}{4} = \frac{4}{4}$

$$\frac{(x-3)^2}{4} - (y+3)^2 = 1$$

center: $(3, -3)$
$a^2 = 4, a = 2$
$b^2 = 1, b = 1$
vertices: $(1, -3)$ and $(5, -3)$
asymptotes: $y + 3 = \pm\frac{1}{2}(x-3)$
$c^2 = a^2 + b^2 = 4 + 1 = 5$
$c = \sqrt{5}$
The foci are at $(3+\sqrt{5}, -3)$ and $(3-\sqrt{5}, -3)$.

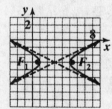

$(x-3)^2 - 4(y+3)^2 = 4$

41. $\dfrac{(x-1)^2}{3}-\dfrac{(y-2)^2}{3}=1$

center: $(1, 2)$

$a^2=3, a=\sqrt{3}$

$b^2=, b=\sqrt{3}$

vertices: $(-1, 2)$ and $(3, 2)$

asymptotes: $y-2=\pm(x-1)$

$c^2=a^2+b^2=3+3=6$

$c=\sqrt{6}$ parallel to y-axis

The foci are at $(1+\sqrt{6},2)$ and $(1-\sqrt{6},2)$.

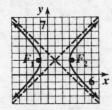

$(x-1)^2-(y-2)^2=3$

43. $(x^2-2x)-(y^2+4y)=4$

$(x^2-2x+1)-(y^2+4y+4)=4+1-4$

$(x-1)^2-(y+2)^2=1$

center: $(1, -2)$

$a^2=1, a=1$

$b^2=1, b=1$

$c^2=a^2+b^2=1+1=2$

$c=\sqrt{2}$

asymptotes: $y+2=\pm(x-1)$

The foci are at $(1+\sqrt{2}, -2)$ and $(1-\sqrt{2}, -2)$.

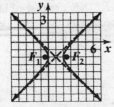

$x^2-y^2-2x-4y-4=0$

45. $(16x^2+64x)-(y^2+2y)=-67$

$16(x^2+4x+4)-(y^2+2y+1)$

$=-67+64-1$

$16(x+2)^2-(y+1)^2=-4$

$\dfrac{16(x+2)^2}{-4}-\dfrac{(y+1)^2}{-4}=\dfrac{-4}{-4}$

$\dfrac{(y+1)^2}{4}-\dfrac{(x+2)^2}{\frac{1}{4}}=1$

center: $(-2, -1)$

$a^2=4, a=2$

$b^2=\dfrac{1}{4}, b=\dfrac{1}{2}$

$c^2=a^2+b^2=4+\dfrac{1}{4}=\dfrac{17}{4}$

$c=\sqrt{\frac{17}{4}}=\sqrt{4.25}$

$(y+1)=\pm\dfrac{2}{\frac{1}{2}}(x+2)$

asymptotes:

$y+1=\pm4(x+2)$

The foci are at $\left(-2, -1+\sqrt{4.25}\right)$ and $\left(-2, -1-\sqrt{4.25}\right)$.

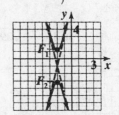

$16x^2-y^2+64x-2y+67=0$

47. $(4x^2-16x)-(9y^2-54y)=101$

$4(x^2-4x+4)-9(y^2-6y+9)$

$=101+16-81$

$4(x-2)^2-9(y-3)^2=36$

$\dfrac{(x-2)^2}{9}-\dfrac{(y-3)^2}{4}=1$

center: $(2, 3)$

$a^2=9, a=3$

$b^2=4, b=2$

$c^2=a^2+b^2=9+4=13$

$c=\sqrt{13}$

asymptotes: $y-3=\pm\dfrac{2}{3}(x-2)$

The foci are at $(2+\sqrt{13}, 3)$ and $(2-\sqrt{13}, 3)$.

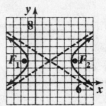

$4x^2-9y^2-16x+5y-101=0$

49.
$$(4x^2 - 32x) - 25y^2 = -164$$
$$4(x^2 - 8x + 16) - 25y^2 = -164 + 64$$
$$4(x-4)^2 - 25y^2 = -100$$
$$\frac{4(x-4)^2}{-100} - \frac{25y^2}{-100} = \frac{-100}{-100}$$
$$\frac{y^2}{4} - \frac{(x-4)^2}{25} = 1$$

center: (4, 0)
$a^2 = 4$, $a = 2$
$b^2 = 25$, $b = 5$
$c^2 = a^2 + b^2 = 4 + 25 = 29$
$c = \sqrt{29}$

asymptotes: $y = \pm\dfrac{2}{5}(x-4)$

The foci are at $(4, \sqrt{29})$ and $(4, -\sqrt{29})$.

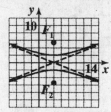

$$4x^2 - 25y^2 - 32x + 164 = 0$$

51. $\dfrac{x^2}{9} - \dfrac{y^2}{16} = 1$

The equation is for a hyperbola in standard form with the transverse axis on the *x*-axis. We have $a^2 = 9$ and $b^2 = 16$, so $a = 3$ and $b = 4$. Therefore, the vertices are at $(\pm a, 0)$ or $(\pm 3, 0)$.

Using a dashed line, we construct a rectangle using the ±3 on the *x*-axis and ±4 on the *y*-axis. Then use dashed lines to draw extended diagonals for the rectangle. These represent the asymptotes of the graph.

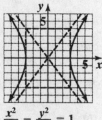

$$\frac{x^2}{9} - \frac{y^2}{16} = 1$$

From the graph we determine the following:
Domain: $\{x \mid x \le -3 \text{ or } x \ge 3\}$ or $(-\infty, -3] \cup [3, \infty)$

Range: $\{y \mid y \text{ is a real number}\}$ or $(-\infty, \infty)$

53. $\dfrac{x^2}{9} + \dfrac{y^2}{16} = 1$

The equation is for an ellipse in standard form with major axis along the y-axis. We have $a^2 = 16$ and $b^2 = 9$, so $a = 4$ and $b = 3$. Therefore, the vertices are $(0, \pm a)$ or $(0, \pm 4)$. The endpoints of the minor axis are $(\pm b, 0)$ or $(\pm 3, 0)$.

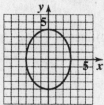

$$\frac{x^2}{9} + \frac{y^2}{16} = 1$$

From the graph we determine the following:
Domain: $\{x \mid -3 \le x \le 3\}$ or $[-3, 3]$

Range: $\{y \mid -4 \le y \le 4\}$ or $[-4, 4]$.

55. $\dfrac{y^2}{16} - \dfrac{x^2}{9} = 1$

The equation is in standard form with the transverse axis on the y-axis. We have $a^2 = 16$ and $b^2 = 9$, so $a = 4$ and $b = 3$. Therefore, the vertices are at $(0, \pm a)$ or $(0, \pm 4)$. Using a dashed line, we construct a rectangle using the ±4 on the y-axis and ±3 on the x-axis. Then use dashed lines to draw extended diagonals for the rectangle. These represent the asymptotes of the graph.

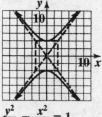

$$\frac{y^2}{16} - \frac{x^2}{9} = 1$$

From the graph we determine the following:
Domain: $\{x \mid x \text{ is a real number}\}$ or $(-\infty, \infty)$

Range: $\{y \mid y \le -4 \text{ or } y \ge 4\}$ or $(-\infty, -4] \cup [4, \infty)$

57. $x^2 - y^2 = 4$
$x^2 + y^2 = 4$

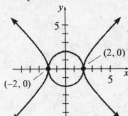

Check $(-2,0)$:

$(-2)^2 - 0^2 = 4$ $(-2)^2 + 0^2 = 4$

$\quad 4 - 0 = 4$ $\quad 4 + 0 = 4$

$\quad\quad 4 = 4$ true $\quad\quad 4 = 4$ true

Check $(2,0)$:

$(2)^2 - 0^2 = 4$ $(2)^2 + 0^2 = 4$

$\quad 4 - 0 = 4$ $\quad 4 + 0 = 4$

$\quad\quad 4 = 4$ true $\quad\quad 4 = 4$ true

The solution set is $\{(-2,0),(2,0)\}$.

59.
$9x^2 + y^2 = 9$ or $\dfrac{x^2}{1} + \dfrac{y^2}{9} = 1$

$y^2 - 9x^2 = 9$ $\dfrac{y^2}{9} - \dfrac{x^2}{1} = 1$

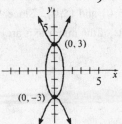

Check $(0,-3)$:

$9(0)^2 + (-3)^2 = 9$ $(-3)^2 - 9(0)^2 = 9$

$\quad 0 + 9 = 9$ $\quad 9 - 0 = 9$

$\quad\quad 9 = 9$ $\quad\quad 9 = 9$

$\quad\quad\quad$ true $\quad\quad\quad$ true

Check $(0,3)$:

$9(0)^2 + (3)^2 = 9$ $(3)^2 - 9(0)^2 = 9$

$\quad 0 + 9 = 9$ $\quad 9 - 0 = 9$

$\quad\quad 9 = 9$ $\quad\quad 9 = 9$

$\quad\quad\quad$ true $\quad\quad\quad$ true

The solution set is $\{(0,-3),(0,3)\}$.

61. $|d_2 - d_1| = 2a = (2\ \text{s})(1100\ \text{ft}/\text{s}) = 2200\ \text{ft}$

$a = 1100\ \text{ft}$

$2c = 5280\ \text{ft},\ c = 2640\ \text{ft}$

$b^2 = c^2 - a^2 = (2640)^2 - (1100)^2$

$\quad = 5{,}759{,}600$

$$\frac{x^2}{(1100)^2} - \frac{y^2}{5{,}759{,}600} = 1$$

$$\frac{x^2}{1{,}210{,}000} - \frac{y^2}{5{,}759{,}600} = 1$$

If M_1 is located 2640 feet to the right of the origin on the x-axis, the explosion is located on the right branch of the hyperbola given by the equation above.

63. $625y^2 - 400x^2 = 250{,}000$

$$\frac{625y^2}{250{,}000} - \frac{400x^2}{250{,}000} = \frac{250{,}000}{250{,}000}$$

$$\frac{y^2}{400} - \frac{x^2}{625} = 1$$

$a^2 = 400,\ a = \sqrt{400} = 20$

$2a = 40$

The houses are 40 yards apart at their closest point.

75. $\dfrac{x^2}{4} - \dfrac{y^2}{9} = 0$

$y^2 = \dfrac{9}{4}x^2$

$y = \pm\dfrac{3}{2}x$

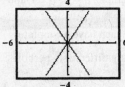

No; in general, the graph is two intersecting lines.

77. $4x^2 - 6xy + 2y^2 - 3x + 10y - 6 = 0$

$2y^2 + (10 - 6x)y + (4x^2 - 3x - 6) = 0$

$y = \dfrac{6x - 10 \pm \sqrt{(10 - 6x)^2 - 8(4x^2 - 3x - 6)}}{4}$

$y = \dfrac{6x - 10 \pm \sqrt{4(x^2 - 24x + 37)}}{4}$

$y = \dfrac{3x - 5 \pm \sqrt{x^2 - 24x + 37}}{2}$

The *xy*-term rotates the hyperbola. Separation of terms into ones containing only *x* or only *y* would not be possible.

79. a. False; one branch of the hyperbola

$\dfrac{x^2}{a^2} - \dfrac{y^2}{b^2} = 1$ will not pass the vertical line test,

so will not define *y* as a function of *x*.

b. False; none of the points on the asymptotes satisfy the hyperbola's equation, since the hyperbola never touches its asymptotes.

c. True; $y = -\dfrac{2}{3}x$ is one of the asymptotes of

the hyperbola and they will not intersect.

d. False; for example, $\dfrac{x^2}{4} - \dfrac{y^2}{4} = 1$ and

$\dfrac{y^2}{4} - \dfrac{x^2}{4} = 1$ each have asymptotes

$y = \pm x$, but are different hyperbolas.

(c) is true.

81. The center is at the midpoint of the line segment joining the vertices, so it is located at (5, 0). The standard form is:

$\dfrac{(y - k)^2}{a^2} - \dfrac{(x - h)^2}{b^2} = 1$

$(h, k) = (5, 0)$, and $a = 6$, so $a^2 = 36$.

$\dfrac{y^2}{36} - \dfrac{(x - 5)^2}{b^2} = 1.$

Substitute $x = 0$ and $y = 9$:

$\dfrac{9^2}{36} - \dfrac{(0 - 5)^2}{b^2} = 1$

$-\dfrac{25}{b^2} = -\dfrac{5}{4}$

$-100 = -5b^2$

$b^2 = 20$

Standard form: $\dfrac{y^2}{36} - \dfrac{(x - 5)^2}{20} = 1$

Mid-Chapter 10 Check Point

1. Center: $(0, 0)$

Because the denominator of the x^2 – term is greater than the denominator of the y^2 – term, the major axis is horizontal. Since $a^2 = 25$, $a = 5$ and the vertices are $(-5, 0)$ and $(5, 0)$. Since $b^2 = 4$, $b = 2$ and endpoints of the minor axis are $(0, -2)$ and $(0, 2)$.

Foci: $\left(\pm\sqrt{21}, 0 \right)$

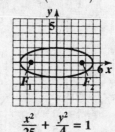

$\dfrac{x^2}{25} + \dfrac{y^2}{4} = 1$

504

2. Divide both sides by 36 to get the standard form:

$$\frac{x^2}{4} + \frac{y^2}{9} = 1$$

Center: $(0,0)$

Because the denominator of the y^2 – term is greater than the denominator of the x^2 – term, the major axis is vertical. Since $a^2 = 9$, $a = 3$ and the vertices are $(0,-3)$ and $(0,3)$. Since $b^2 = 4$, $b = 2$ and endpoints of the minor axis are $(-2,0)$ and $(2,0)$.

Foci: $\left(0, \pm\sqrt{5}\right)$

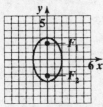

$$9x^2 + 4y^2 = 36$$

3. Center: $(2,-1)$

Because the denominator of the y^2 – term is greater than the denominator of the x^2 – term, the major axis is vertical. We have $a^2 = 25$ and $b^2 = 16$, so $a = 5$ and $b = 4$. The vertices lie 5 units above and below the center. The endpoints of the minor axis lie 4 units to the left and right of the center.

Vertices: $(2,4)$ and $(2,-6)$

Minor endpoints: $(-2,-1)$ and $(6,-1)$

Foci: $(2,2)$, $(2,-4)$

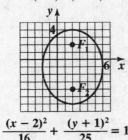

$$\frac{(x-2)^2}{16} + \frac{(y+1)^2}{25} = 1$$

4. Center: $(-2,1)$

Because the denominator of the x^2 – term is greater than the denominator of the y^2 – term, the major axis is horizontal. We have $a^2 = 25$ and $b^2 = 16$, so $a = 5$ and $b = 4$. The vertices lie 5 units to the left and right of the center. The endpoints of the minor axis lie 4 units above and below the center.

Vertices: $(-7,1)$ and $(3,1)$

Minor endpoints: $(-2,5)$ and $(-2,-3)$

Foci: $(-5,1)$, $(1,1)$

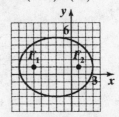

$$\frac{(x+2)^2}{25} + \frac{(y-1)^2}{16} = 1$$

5.
$$x^2 - 4x + 9y^2 + 54y = -49$$
$$\left(x^2 - 4x \right) + 9\left(y^2 + 6y \right) = -49$$
$$\left(x^2 - 4x + 4\right) + 9\left(y^2 + 6y + 9\right) = -49 + 4 + 81$$
$$(x-2)^2 + 9(y+3)^2 = 36$$
$$\frac{(x-2)^2}{36} + \frac{9(y+3)^2}{36} = \frac{36}{36}$$
$$\frac{(x-2)^2}{36} + \frac{(y+3)^2}{4} = 1$$

Center: $(2,-3)$

Foci: $\left(2 \pm 4\sqrt{2}, -3\right)$

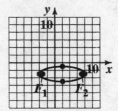

$$x^2 + 9y^2 - 4x + 54y + 49 = 0$$

505

6. The equation is for a hyperbola in standard form with the transverse axis on the x-axis. We have $a^2 = 9$ and $b^2 = 1$, so $a = 3$ and $b = 1$. Therefore, the vertices are at $(\pm a, 0)$ or $(\pm 3, 0)$. Using a dashed line, we construct a rectangle using the ± 3 on the x-axis and ± 1 on the y-axis. Then use dashed lines to draw extended diagonals for the rectangle. These represent the asymptotes of the graph.

Foci: $\left(\pm\sqrt{10}, 0 \right)$

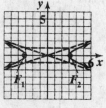

$$\frac{x^2}{9} - y^2 = 1$$

7. The equation is in the form $\dfrac{y^2}{a^2} - \dfrac{x^2}{b^2} = 1$ with $a^2 = 9$, and $b^2 = 1$. We know the transverse axis lies on the y-axis and the vertices are $(0, -3)$ and $(0, 3)$. Because $a^2 = 9$ and $b^2 = 1$, $a = 3$ and $b = 1$. Construct a rectangle using -1 and 1 on the x-axis, and -3 and 3 on the y-axis. Draw extended diagonals to obtain the asymptotes.

Foci: $\left(0, \pm\sqrt{10} \right)$

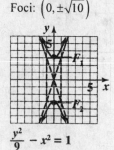

$$\frac{y^2}{9} - x^2 = 1$$

8. $$\frac{y^2}{16} - \frac{x^2}{4} = 1$$

The equation is in the form $\dfrac{y^2}{a^2} - \dfrac{x^2}{b^2} = 1$ with $a^2 = 16$, and $b^2 = 4$. We know the transverse axis lies on the y-axis and the vertices are $(0, -4)$ and $(0, 4)$. Because $a^2 = 16$ and $b^2 = 4$, $a = 4$ and $b = 2$. Construct a rectangle using -2 and 2 on the x-axis, and -4 and 4 on the y-axis. Draw extended diagonals to obtain the asymptotes.

Foci: $\left(0, \pm 2\sqrt{5} \right)$

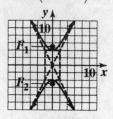

$$y^2 - 4x^2 = 16$$

9. $$\frac{x^2}{49} - \frac{y^2}{4} = 1$$

The equation is for a hyperbola in standard form with the transverse axis on the x-axis. We have $a^2 = 49$ and $b^2 = 4$, so $a = 7$ and $b = 2$. Therefore, the vertices are at $(\pm a, 0)$ or $(\pm 7, 0)$.

Using a dashed line, we construct a rectangle using the ± 7 on the x-axis and ± 2 on the y-axis. Then use dashed lines to draw extended diagonals for the rectangle. These represent the asymptotes of the graph.

Foci: $\left(\pm\sqrt{53}, 0 \right)$

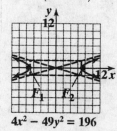

$$4x^2 - 49y^2 = 196$$

10. The equation is for a hyperbola in standard form with center $(2, -2)$. We have $a^2 = 9$ and $b^2 = 16$, so $a = 3$ and $b = 4$.

Asymptotes: $y + 2 = \pm\dfrac{4}{3}(x - 2)$

Foci: $(-3, -2)$, $(7, -2)$

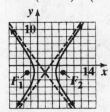

$$\dfrac{(x-2)^2}{9} - \dfrac{(y+2)^2}{16} = 1$$

11. Write the equation for the hyperbola in standard form:

$$4x^2 - y^2 + 8x + 6y + 11 = 0$$
$$4x^2 + 8x \quad - y^2 + 6y \quad = -11$$
$$4\left(x^2 + 2x \quad\right) - \left(y^2 - 6y \quad\right) = -11$$
$$4\left(x^2 + 2x + 1\right) - \left(y^2 - 6y + 9\right) = -11 + 4 - 9$$
$$4(x+1)^2 - (y-3)^2 = -16$$
$$\dfrac{4(x+1)^2}{-16} - \dfrac{(y-3)^2}{-16} = \dfrac{-16}{-16}$$
$$\dfrac{(y-3)^2}{16} - \dfrac{(x+1)^2}{4} = 1$$

Center $(-1, 3)$.

Asymptotes: $y - 3 = \pm 2(x + 1)$

Foci: $\left(-1, 3 \pm 2\sqrt{5}\right)$, $(7, -2)$

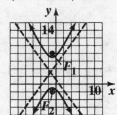

$$4x^2 - y^2 + 8x + 6y + 11 = 0$$

12. This is the equation of a circle centered at the origin with radius $r = \sqrt{4} = 2$.

We can plot points that are 2 units to the left, right, above, and below the origin and then graph the circle. The points are $(-2, 0)$, $(2, 0)$, $(0, 2)$, and $(0, -2)$.

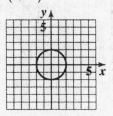

$$x^2 + y^2 = 4$$

13. $x + y = 4$

$y = -x + 4$

This is the equation of a line with slope $m = -1$ and a y-intercept of 4. We can plot the point $(0, 4)$, use the slope to get an additional point, connect the points with a straight line and then extend the line to represent the graph of the equation.

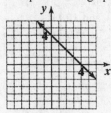

$$x + y = 4$$

14. $x^2 - y^2 = 4$

$$\dfrac{x^2}{4} - \dfrac{y^2}{4} = 1$$

The equation is for a hyperbola in standard form with the transverse axis on the x-axis. We have $a^2 = 4$ and $b^2 = 4$, so $a = 2$ and $b = 2$.

Therefore, the vertices are at $(\pm a, 0)$ or $(\pm 2, 0)$.

Using a dashed line, we construct a rectangle using the ± 2 on the x-axis and ± 2 on the y-axis. Then use dashed lines to draw extended diagonals for the rectangle. These represent the asymptotes of the graph.

Graph the hyperbola.

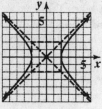

$$x^2 - y^2 = 4$$

15. $x^2 + 4y^2 = 4$

$$\frac{x^2}{4} + \frac{y^2}{1} = 1$$

Center: $(0,0)$

Because the denominator of the x^2- term is greater than the denominator of the y^2- term, the major axis is horizontal. We have $a^2 = 4$ and $b^2 = 1$, so $a = 2$ and $b = 1$. The vertices lie 2 units to the left and right of the center. The endpoints of the minor axis lie 1 unit above and below the center.

Vertices: $(-2,0)$ and $(2,0)$

Minor endpoints: $(0,-1)$ and $(0,1)$

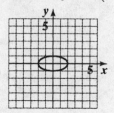

$$x^2 + 4y^2 = 4$$

16.   Center: $(-1,1)$

Radius: $r = \sqrt{4} = 2$

We plot the points that are 2 units to the left, right, above and below the center.

These points are $(-3,1)$, $(1,1)$, $(-1,3)$, and $(-1,-1)$.

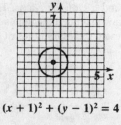

$$(x + 1)^2 + (y - 1)^2 = 4$$

17. $x^2 + 4(y-1)^2 = 4$

$$\frac{x^2}{4} + \frac{(y-1)^2}{1} = 1$$

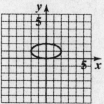

$$x^2 + 4(y - 1)^2 = 4$$

18. $(x-1)^2 - (y-1)^2 = 4$

$$\frac{(x-1)^2}{4} - \frac{(y-1)^2}{4} = 1$$

The equation is for a hyperbola in standard form centered at (1, 1). We have $a^2 = 4$ and $b^2 = 4$, so $a = 2$ and $b = 2$.

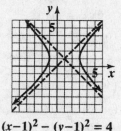

$$(x-1)^2 - (y-1)^2 = 4$$

19.   The foci and vertices show that c is 4 and a is 5.

$$c^2 = a^2 - b^2$$

$$4^2 = 5^2 - b^2$$

$$b^2 = 25 - 16$$

$$b^2 = 9$$

$$\frac{x^2}{25} + \frac{y^2}{9} = 1$$

20.   The endpoints show that the center is (1, 2).

Since $2a = 18$, $a = 9$ and $a^2 = 81$.

Since $2c = 10$, $c = 5$ and $c^2 = 25$.

$$c^2 = a^2 - b^2$$

$$25 = 81 - b^2$$

$$b^2 = 81 - 25$$

$$b^2 = 56$$

$$\frac{(x-1)^2}{81} + \frac{(y-2)^2}{56} = 1$$

21. The foci and vertices show that c is 3 and a is 2.

$$b^2 = c^2 - a^2$$
$$b^2 = 3^2 - 2^2$$
$$b^2 = 9 - 4$$
$$b^2 = 5$$
$$\frac{x^2}{4} - \frac{y^2}{5} = 1$$

22. The endpoints show that the center is $(-1, 5)$.
Since $2a = 4$, $a = 2$ and $a^2 = 4$.
Since $2c = 6$, $c = 3$ and $c^2 = 9$.

$$b^2 = c^2 - a^2$$
$$b^2 = 9 - 4$$
$$b^2 = 5$$
$$\frac{(x+1)^2}{4} + \frac{(y-5)^2}{5} = 1$$

23. $a = 15$, $b = 10$

$$\frac{x^2}{15^2} + \frac{y^2}{10^2} = 1$$
$$\frac{x^2}{225} + \frac{y^2}{100} = 1$$

Since the truck is 10 feet wide, substitute $x = 5$ into the equation to find y.

$$\frac{5^2}{225} + \frac{y^2}{100} = 1$$
$$\frac{25}{225} + \frac{y^2}{100} = 1$$
$$\frac{1}{9} + \frac{y^2}{100} = 1$$
$$900\left(\frac{1}{9} + \frac{y^2}{100}\right) = 900(1)$$
$$100 + 9y^2 = 900$$
$$9y^2 = 800$$
$$y^2 = 88.8889$$
$$y = \sqrt{88.8889}$$
$$y \approx 9.43$$

5 feet from the center, the height of the archway is 9.43 feet. Since the truck's height is 9.5 feet, it will not fit under the archway.

24. Find the distance between the foci.
Since $2a = 40$, $a = 20$ and $a^2 = 400$.
Since $2b = 20$, $b = 10$ and $b^2 = 100$.

$$c^2 = a^2 - b^2$$
$$c^2 = 400 - 100$$
$$c^2 = 300$$
$$c = \sqrt{300}$$
$$= 10\sqrt{3}$$
$$2c = 20\sqrt{3}$$
$$2c \approx 34.64$$

The kidney stone should be 34.64 cm from the electrode that sends the ultrasound waves.

25. a. Since $2c = 6$, $c = 3$ and $c^2 = 9$.
The ranger at the primary station heard the explosion 6 seconds before the other ranger. This means that the explosion occurred $6 \times 0.35 = 2.1$ miles closer to the primary station.
Since $2a = 2.1$, $a = 1.05$ and $a^2 = 1.1025$.

$$b^2 = c^2 - a^2$$
$$b^2 = 9 - 1.1025$$
$$b^2 = 7.8975$$
$$\frac{x^2}{1.1025} - \frac{y^2}{7.8975} = 1$$

b.

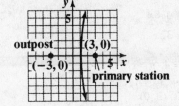

Section 7.3

Check Point Exercises

1. $4p = 8$, $p = 2$
   focus: $(2, 0)$
   directrix: $x = -2$

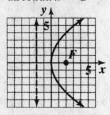

   $y^2 = 8x$

2. $x^2 = -12y$
   $4p = -12$, $p = 3$
   focus: $(0, -3)$
   directrix: $y = 3$

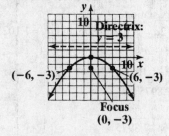

3. $p = 8$
   $y^2 = 4 \cdot 8x$
   $y^2 = 32x$

4. $4p = 4$, $p = 1$
   vertex: $(2, -1)$
   focus: $(2, 0)$
   directrix: $y = -2$

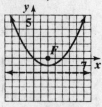

   $(x - 2)^2 = 4(y + 1)$

5. $y^2 + 2y = -4x + 7$
   $y^2 + 2y + 1 = -4x + 7 + 1$
   $(y + 1)^2 = -4(x - 2)$
   $4p = -4$, $p = -1$
   vertex: $(2, -1)$
   focus: $(1, -1)$
   directrix: $x = 3$

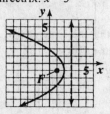

   $y^2 + 2y + 4x - 7 = 0$

6. $x^2 = 4py$
   Let $x = 3$ and $y = 4$.
   $3^2 = 4p \cdot 4$
   $9 = 16p$
   $p = \dfrac{9}{16}$
   $x^2 = \dfrac{9}{4}y$

   The light should be placed at $\left(0, \dfrac{9}{16}\right)$ or $\dfrac{9}{16}$

   inch above the vertex.

Exercise Set 7.3

1. $y^2 = 4x$
   $4p = 4, p = 1$
   vertex: $(0, 0)$
   focus: $(1, 0)$
   directrix: $x = -1$
   graph (c)

3. $x^2 = -4y$
   $4p = -4, p = -1$
   vertex: $(0, 0)$
   focus: $(0, -1)$
   directrix: $y = 1$
   graph (b)

5. $4p = 16, p = 4$
   vertex: $(0, 0)$
   focus: $(4, 0)$
   directrix: $x = -4$

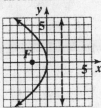

$$y^2 = 16x$$

7. $4p = -8, p = -2$
   vertex: $(0, 0)$
   focus: $(-2, 0)$
   directrix: $x = 2$

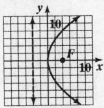

$$y^2 = -8x$$

9. $4p = 12, p = 3$
   vertex: $(0, 0)$
   focus: $(0, 3)$
   directrix: $y = -3$

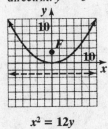

$$x^2 = 12y$$

11. $4p = -16, p = -4$
    vertex: $(0, 0)$
    focus: $(0, -4)$
    directrix: $y = 4$

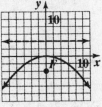

$$x^2 = -16y$$

13. $y^2 = 6x$
    $4p = 6, p = \dfrac{6}{4} = \dfrac{3}{2}$
    vertex: $(0, 0)$
    focus: $\left(\dfrac{3}{2}, 0\right)$
    directrix: $x = -\dfrac{3}{2}$

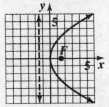

$$y^2 - 6x = 0$$

15. $8x^2 = -4y$
    $x^2 = -\dfrac{1}{2}y$
    $4p = -\dfrac{1}{2}$
    $p = -\dfrac{1}{8}$
    focus: $\left(0, -\dfrac{1}{8}\right)$
    directrix: $y = \dfrac{1}{8}$

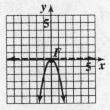

$$8x^2 + 4y = 0$$

17. $p = 7, 4p = 28$
$y^2 = 28x$

19. $p = -5, 4p = -20$
$y^2 = -20x$

21. $p = 15, 4p = 60$
$x^2 = 60y$

23. $p = -25, 4p = -100$
$x^2 = -100y$

25. $p = -5 - (-3) = -2$ Vertex, $(2, -3)$
$(x - 2)^2 = -8(y + 3)$

27. vertex: $(1, 2)$ $p = 2$
$(y - 2)^2 = 8(x - 1)$

29. vertex: $(-3, 3), p = 1$
$(x + 3)^2 = 4(y - 3)$

31. $(y - 1)^2 = 4(x - 1)$
$4p = 4, p = 1$
vertex: $(1, 1)$
focus: $(2, 1)$
directrix: $x = 0$
graph (c)

33. $(x + 1)^2 = -4(y + 1)$
$4p = -4, p = -1$
vertex: $(-1, -1)$
focus: $(-1, -2)$
directrix: $y = 0$
graph (d)

35. $4p = 8, p = 2$
vertex: $(2, 1)$
focus: $(2, 3)$
directrix: $y = -1$

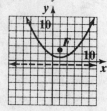

$(x - 2)^2 = 8(y - 1)$

37. $4p = -8, p = -2$
vertex: $(-1, -1)$
focus: $(-1, -3)$
directrix: $y = 1$

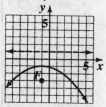

$(x + 1)^2 = -8(y + 1)$

39. $4p = 12, p = 3$
vertex: $(-1, -3)$
focus: $(2, -3)$
directrix: $x = -4$

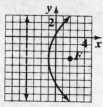

$(y + 3)^2 = 12(x + 1)$

41. $(y + 1)^2 = -8(x - 0)$
$4p = -8, p = -2$
vertex: $(0, -1)$
focus: $(-2, -1)$
directrix: $x = 2$

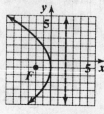

$(y + 1)^2 = -8x$

43.
$$x^2 - 2x + 1 = 4y - 9 + 1$$
$$(x-1)^2 = 4y - 8$$
$$(x-1)^2 = 4(y-2)$$
$4p = 4, p = 1$
vertex: $(1, 2)$
focus: $(1, 3)$
directrix: $y = 1$

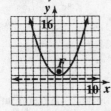

$$x^2 - 2x - 4y + 9 = 0$$

45.
$$y^2 - 2y + 1 = -12x + 35 + 1$$
$$(y-1)^2 = -12x + 36$$
$$(y-1)^2 = -12(x-3)$$
$4p = -12, p = -3$
vertex: $(3, 1)$
focus: $(0, 1)$
directrix: $x = 6$

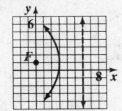

$$y^2 - 2y + 12x - 35 = 0$$

47.
$$x^2 + 6x = 4y - 1$$
$$x^2 + 6x + 9 = 4y - 1 + 9$$
$$(x+3)^2 = 4(y+2)$$
$4p = 4, p = 1$
vertex: $(-3, -2)$
focus: $(-3, -1)$
directrix: $y = -3$

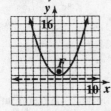

$$x^2 + 6x - 4y + 1 = 0$$

49. The y-coordinate of the vertex is
$$y = -\frac{b}{2a} = -\frac{6}{2(1)} = -3$$
The x-coordinate of the vertex is
$$x = (-3)^2 + 6(-3) + 5$$
$$= 9 - 18 + 5$$
$$= -4$$
The vertex is $(-4, -3)$.
Since the squared term is y and $a > 0$, the graph opens to the right.
Domain: $\{x \mid x \geq -4\}$ or $[-4, \infty)$
Range: $\{y \mid y$ is a real number$\}$ or $(-\infty, \infty)$
The relation is not a function.

51. The x-coordinate of the vertex is
$$x = -\frac{b}{2a} = -\frac{(4)}{2(-1)} = 2$$
The y-coordinate of the vertex is
$$y = -(2)^2 + 4(2) - 3$$
$$= -4 + 8 - 3$$
$$= 1$$
The vertex is $(2, 1)$.
Since the squared term is x and $a < 0$, the graph opens down.
Domain: $\{x \mid x$ is a real number$\}$ or $(-\infty, \infty)$
Range: $\{y \mid y \leq 1\}$ or $(-\infty, 1]$
The relation is a function.

53. The equation is in the form $x = a(y-k)^2 + h$
From the equation, we can see that the vertex is $(3, 1)$.
Since the squared term is y and $a < 0$, the graph opens to the left.
Domain: $\{x \mid x \leq 3\}$ or $(-\infty, 3]$
Range: $\{y \mid y$ is a real number$\}$ or $(-\infty, \infty)$
The relation is not a function.

55.

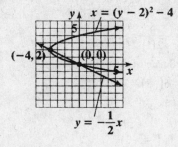

Check $(-4,2)$:

$$-4 = (2-2)^2 - 4 \qquad 2 = -\frac{1}{2}(-4)$$

$$-4 = 0 - 4 \qquad\qquad 2 = 2$$

$$-4 = -4 \qquad\qquad\qquad \text{true}$$

 true

Check $(0,0)$:

$$0 = (0-2)^2 - 4 \qquad 0 = -\frac{1}{2}(0)$$

$$0 = 4 - 4 \qquad\qquad 0 = 0$$

$$0 = 0 \qquad\qquad\qquad \text{true}$$

 true

The solution set is $\{(-4,2),(0,0)\}$.

57.

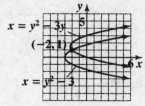

Check $(-2,1)$:

$$-2 = (1)^2 - 3 \qquad -2 = (1)^2 - 3(1)$$

$$-2 = 1 - 3 \qquad\quad -2 = 1 - 3$$

$$-2 = -2 \ \text{true} \qquad -2 = -2 \ \text{true}$$

The solution set is $\{(-2,1)\}$.

59.

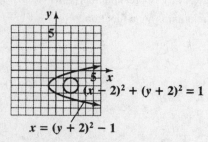

The two graphs do not cross. Therefore, the solution set is the empty set, $\{\ \}$ or $\varnothing$.

61. $x^2 = 4py$

$$2^2 = 4p(1)$$

$$4 = 4$$

$$p = 1$$

The light bulb should be placed 1 inch above the vertex.

63. $x^2 = 4py$

$$6^2 = 4p(2)$$

$$36 = 8p$$

$$p = \frac{36}{8} = \frac{9}{2} = 4.5$$

The receiver should be located 4.5 feet from the base of the dish.

65. $$x^2 = 4py$$

$$(640)^2 = 4p(160)$$

$$p = \frac{(640)^2}{640} = 640$$

$$x = 640 - 200 = 440$$

$$(440)^2 = 4(640)y$$

$$y = \frac{(440)^2}{4(640)} = 75.625$$

The height is 76 meters.

67. $$x^2 = 4py$$

$$\left(\frac{200}{2}\right)^2 = 4p(-50)$$

$$\frac{10,000}{-50} = 4p$$

$$4p = -200$$

$$x^2 = -200y$$

$$(30)^2 = -200y$$

$$y = \frac{900}{-200} = -4.5$$

(height of bridge) $= 50 - 4.5 = 45.5$ feet.
Yes, the boat will clear the arch.

77. $y^2 + 2y - 6x + 13 = 0$

$y^2 + 2y + (-6x + 13) = 0$

$y = \dfrac{-2 \pm \sqrt{2^2 - 4(-6x + 13)}}{2}$

$y = \dfrac{-2 \pm \sqrt{24x - 48}}{2}$

$y = -1 \pm \sqrt{6x - 12}$

79. $16x^2 - 24xy + 9y^2 - 60x - 80y + 100 = 0$

$9y^2 - (24x + 80)y + (16x^2 - 60x + 100) = 0$

$y = \dfrac{24x + 80 \pm \sqrt{(24x + 80)^2 - 36(16x^2 - 60x + 100)}}{18}$

$y = \dfrac{24x + 80 \pm \sqrt{6000x + 2800}}{18}$

$y = \dfrac{24x + 80 \pm 20\sqrt{15x + 7}}{18}$

$y = \dfrac{12x + 40 \pm 10\sqrt{15x + 7}}{9}$

81.   **a.**   False; it opens to the left.

    b.   True; it opens to the right and has a domain $[3, \infty)$.

    c.   False; any parabola that opens to the right will not be a function of x because at least one x-value will be paired with more than 1 y-value.

    d.   False; the graph is a line.

    (b) is true.

83. $y = 4$ is the directrix and $(-1, 0)$ is the focus. The vertex must be located halfway between them at the point $(-1, 2)$. $p = -2$ and the parabola opens down.

$(x + 1)^2 = 4(-2)(y - 2)$

$(x + 1)^2 = -8(y - 2)$

Chapter 7 Review Exercises

1. $a^2 = 36, a = 6$
$b^2 = 25, b = 5$
$c^2 = a^2 - b^2 = 36 - 25 = 11$
$c = \sqrt{11}$
The foci are at $(\sqrt{11}, 0)$ and $(-\sqrt{11}, 0)$

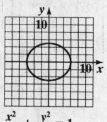

$$\frac{x^2}{36} + \frac{y^2}{25} = 1$$

2. $a^2 = 25, a = 5$
$b^2 = 16, b = 4$
$c^2 = a^2 - b^2$
$c^2 = 25 - 16$
$c^2 = 9$
$c = 3$
The foci are $(0, 3)$ and $(0, -3)$.

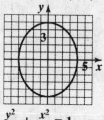

$$\frac{y^2}{25} + \frac{x^2}{16} = 1$$

3. $\dfrac{4x^2}{16} + \dfrac{y^2}{16} = \dfrac{16}{16}$
$\dfrac{x^2}{4} + \dfrac{y^2}{16} = 1$
$b^2 = 4, b = 2$
$a^2 = 16, a = 4$
$c^2 = a^2 - b^2 = 16 - 4 = 12$
$c = \sqrt{12} = 2\sqrt{3}$

The foci are at $(0, 2\sqrt{3})$ and $(0, -2\sqrt{3})$.

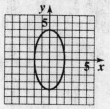

$$4x^2 + y^2 = 16$$

4. $\dfrac{4x^2}{36} + \dfrac{9y^2}{36} = \dfrac{36}{36}$
$\dfrac{x^2}{9} + \dfrac{y^2}{4} = 1$
$a^2 = 9, a = 3$
$b^2 = 4, \ b = 2$
$c^2 = a^2 - b^2 = 9 - 4 = 5, c = \sqrt{5}$
The foci are at $(\sqrt{5}, 0)$ and $(-\sqrt{5}, 0)$.

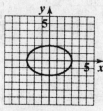

$$4x^2 + 9y^2 = 36$$

5. $a^2 = 16 \ a = 4$
$b^2 = 9 \ b = 3$
$c^2 = 16 - 9 = 7, c = \sqrt{7}$
center: $(1, -2)$
The foci are at $(1 + \sqrt{7}, -2)$ and $(1 - \sqrt{7}, -2)$.

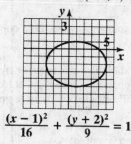

$$\frac{(x-1)^2}{16} + \frac{(y+2)^2}{9} = 1$$

6. $a^2 = 16, a = 4$
$b^2 = 9, b = 3$
$c^2 = a^2 - b^2 = 16 - 9 = 7, c = \sqrt{7}$
center: $(-1, 2)$
The foci are at $(-1, 2 + \sqrt{7})$ and $(-1, 2 - \sqrt{7})$.

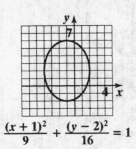

$$\frac{(x+1)^2}{9} + \frac{(y-2)^2}{16} = 1$$

7. $4x^2 + 24x + 9y^2 - 36y = -36$
$4(x^2 + 6x + 9) + 9(y^2 - 4y + 4)$
$= -36 + 36 + 36$
$= 4(x+3)^2 + 9(y-2)^2 = 36$
$$\frac{(x+3)^2}{9} + \frac{(y-2)^2}{4} = 1$$
$c^2 = a^2 - b^2 = 5, c = \sqrt{5}$
center: $(-3, 2)$
The foci are at $(-3 + \sqrt{5}, 2)$ and $(-3 - \sqrt{5}, 2)$.

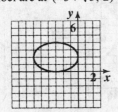

$$4x^2 + 9y^2 + 24x - 36y + 36 = 0$$

8. $9x^2 - 18x + 4y^2 + 8y = 23$
$9(x^2 - 2x + 1) + 4(y^2 + 2y + 1) = 23 + 9 + 4$
$9(x-1)^2 + 4(y+1)^2 = 36$
$$\frac{(x-1)^2}{4} + \frac{(y+1)^2}{9} = 1$$
$c^2 = a^2 - b^2 = 9 - 4 = 5, c = \sqrt{5}$
center: $(1, -1)$
The foci are at $(1, -1 + \sqrt{5})$ and $(1, -1 - \sqrt{5})$.

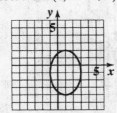

$$9x^2 + 4y^2 - 18x + 8y - 23 = 0$$

9. $c = 4, c^2 = 16$
$a = 5, a^2 = 25$
$b^2 = a^2 - c^2 = 25 - 16 = 9$
$$\frac{x^2}{25} + \frac{y^2}{9} = 1$$

10. $c = 3, c^2 = 9$
$a = 6, a^2 = 36$
$b^2 = a^2 - c^2 = 36 - 9 = 27$
$$\frac{x^2}{27} + \frac{y^2}{36} = 1$$

11. $2a = 12, a = 6, a^2 = 36$
$2b = 4, b = 2, b^2 = 4$
$$\frac{(x+3)^2}{36} + \frac{(y-5)^2}{4} = 1$$

12. $2a = 20, a = 10, a^2 = 100$
$b = 6, b^2 = 36$
$$\frac{x^2}{100} + \frac{y^2}{36} = 1$$

13. $2a = 50, a = 25$
$b = 15$
$$\frac{x^2}{625} + \frac{y^2}{225} = 1$$
Let $x = 14$.
$$\frac{(14)^2}{625} + \frac{y^2}{225} = 1$$
$$y^2 = 225\left(1 - \frac{196}{625}\right)$$
$y \approx 15(0.8285) \approx 12.4 > 12$
Yes, the truck can drive under the archway.

14. The hit ball will collide with the other ball.

15. $c^2 = a^2 + b^2 = 16 + 1 = 17, c = \sqrt{17}$
The foci are at $(\sqrt{17}, 0)$ and $(-\sqrt{17}, 0)$.
Asymptotes: $y = \pm \frac{1}{4}x$

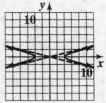

$$\frac{x^2}{16} - y^2 = 1$$

16. $c^2 = a^2 + b^2 = 16 + 1 = 17$
$c = \sqrt{17}$
The foci are at $(0, \sqrt{17})$ and $(0, -\sqrt{17})$.
Asymptotes: $y = \pm 4x$

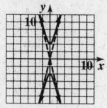

$$\frac{y^2}{16} - x^2 = 1$$

17. $\frac{x^2}{16} - \frac{y^2}{9} = 1$
$c^2 = a^2 + b^2 = 16 + 9 = 25, c = 5$
The foci are at $(5, 0)$ and $(-5, 0)$.

Asymptotes: $y = \pm \frac{3}{4}x$

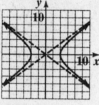

$$9x^2 - 16y^2 = 144$$

18. $\frac{y^2}{4} - \frac{x^2}{16} = 1$
$c^2 = a^2 + b^2 = 4 + 16 = 20$
$c = \sqrt{20} = 2\sqrt{5}$
The foci are at $(0, 2\sqrt{5})$ and $(0, -2\sqrt{5})$.

Asymptotes: $y = \pm \frac{1}{2}x$

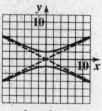

$$4y^2 - x^2 = 16$$

19. $c^2 = a^2 + b^2 = 25 + 16 = 41, c = \sqrt{41}$
center: $(2, -3)$
The foci are at
$(2 + \sqrt{41}, -3)$ and $(2 - \sqrt{41}, -3)$.

Asymptotes: $y + 3 = \pm \frac{4}{5}(x - 2)$

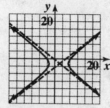

$$\frac{(x-2)^2}{25} - \frac{(y+3)^2}{16} = 1$$

20. $c^2 = a^2 + b^2 = 25 + 16 = 41, c = \sqrt{41}$
center: $(3, -2)$
The foci are at
$(3, -2 + \sqrt{41})$ and $(3, -2 - \sqrt{41})$.

Asymptotes: $y + 2 = \pm \frac{5}{4}(x - 3)$

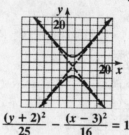

$$\frac{(y+2)^2}{25} - \frac{(x-3)^2}{16} = 1$$

21. $y^2 - 4y - 4x^2 + 8x - 4 = 0$
$(y^2 - 4y + 4) - 4(x^2 - 2x + 1) = 4 + 4 - 4$
$(y - 2)^2 - 4(x - 1)^2 = 4$

$$\frac{(y-2)^2}{4} - (x-1)^2 = 1$$

$c^2 = a^2 + b^2 = 4 + 1 = 5, c = \sqrt{5}$
center: $(1, 2)$
The foci are at $(1, 2 + \sqrt{5})$ and $(1, 2 - \sqrt{5})$.
Asymptotes: $y - 2 = \pm 2(x - 1)$

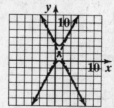

$$y^2 - 4y - 4x^2 + 8x - 4 = 0$$

22. $x^2 - 2x - y^2 - 2y = 1$

$(x^2 - 2x + 1) - (y^2 + 2y + 1) = 1 + 1 - 1$

$(x - 1)^2 - (y + 1)^2 = 1$

$c^2 = a^2 + b^2 = 1 + 1 = 2, \ c = \sqrt{2}$

center: $(1, -1)$

The foci are at $(1 + \sqrt{2}, -1)$ and $(1 - \sqrt{2}, -1)$.

asymptotes: $y + 1 = \pm(x - 1)$

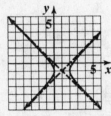

$$x^2 - y^2 - 2x - 2y - 1 = 0$$

23. $c = 4, \ c^2 = 16$

$a = 2, \ a^2 = 4$

$b^2 = c^2 - a^2 = 16 - 4 = 12$

$$\frac{y^2}{4} - \frac{x^2}{12} = 1$$

24. $c = 8, \ c^2 = 64$

$a = 3, \ a^2 = 9$

$b^2 = c^2 - a^2 = 64 - 9 = 55$

$$\frac{x^2}{9} - \frac{y^2}{55} = 1$$

25. If the foci are at $(0, -2)$ and $(0, 2)$, then $c = 2$. If the vertices are at $(0, -3)$ and $(0, 3)$ then $a = 3$. This is not possible since c must be greater than a.

26. foci: $(\pm 100, 0), \ c = 100$

$$\left| d_1 - d_2 \right| = \left(0.186 \frac{\text{mi}}{\mu \text{s}} \right) (500 \mu \text{s}) = 93 \text{ mi} = 2a$$

$$a = \frac{93}{2}$$

$$b^2 = c^2 - a^2 = (100)^2 - \left(\frac{93}{2} \right)^2 = 7837.75$$

$$\frac{x^2}{\left(\frac{93}{2} \right)^2} - \frac{y^2}{7837.75} = 1$$

$$\frac{x^2}{2162.25} - \frac{y^2}{7837.75} = 1$$

27. $4p = 8, \ p = 2$

vertex: $(0, 0)$

focus: $(2, 0)$

directrix: $x = -2$

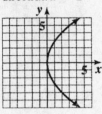

$$y^2 = 8x$$

28. $x^2 + 16y = 0$

$x^2 = -16y$

$4p = -16$

$p = -4$

vertex: $(0, 0)$

focus: $(0, -4)$

directrix: $y = 4$

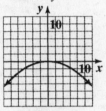

$$x^2 + 16y = 0$$

29. $4p = -16$

$p = -4$

vertex: $(0, 2)$

focus: $(-4, 2)$

directrix: $x = 4$

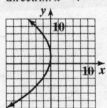

$$(y - 2)^2 = -16x$$

519

30. $4p = 4, p = 1$
vertex: $(4, -1)$
focus: $(4, 0)$
directrix: $y = -2$

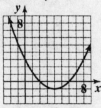

$(x - 4)^2 = 4(y + 1)$

31. $x^2 = -4y + 4$
$x^2 = -4(y - 1)$
$4p = -4, p = -1$
vertex: $(0, 1)$
focus: $(0, 0)$
directrix: $y = 2$

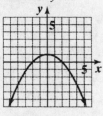

$x^2 + 4y = 4$

32. $y^2 - 10y = 4x - 21$
$y^2 - 10y + 25 = 4x - 21 + 25$
$(y - 5)^2 = 4(x + 1)$
$4p = 4, p = 1$
vertex: $(-1, 5)$
focus: $(0, 5)$
directrix: $x = -2$

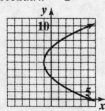

$y^2 - 4x - 10y + 21 = 0$

33. $x^2 - 4x - 2y = 0$
$x^2 - 4x = 2y$
$(x^2 - 4x + 4) = 2y + 4$
$(x - 2)^2 = 2(y + 2)$
$4p = 2, p = \dfrac{1}{2}$
vertex: $(2, -2)$
focus: $\left(2, -\dfrac{3}{2}\right)$
directrix: $y = -\dfrac{5}{2}$

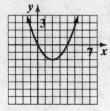

$x^2 - 4x - 2y = 0$

34. $p = 12$
$y^2 = 48x$

35. $p = -11$
$x^2 = -44y$

36. $x^2 = 4py$
$(6)^2 = 4p(3)$
$p = 3$
$x^2 = 12y$
Place the light 3 inches from the vertex at $(0, 3)$.

37. $x^2 = 4py$
$(1750)^2 = 4p(316)$
$4p \approx 9691$
$x^2 = 9691y$
Let $x = 1750 - 1000 = 750$.
$y = \dfrac{x^2}{9691} = \dfrac{(750)^2}{9691} \approx 58$
The height is approximately 58 feet.

38. $x^2 = 4py$
$(150)^2 = 4p(44)$
$22{,}500 = 176p$
$p \approx 128$
The receiver should be placed approximately 128 feet from the base of the dish.

520

Chapter 7 Test

1. $\dfrac{x^2}{4} - \dfrac{y^2}{9} = 1$

$c^2 = a^2 + b^2 = 4 + 9 = 13$, $c = \sqrt{13}$

hyperbola

The foci are at $\left(\sqrt{13}, 0\right)$ and $\left(-\sqrt{13}, 0\right)$.

Asymptotes: $y = \pm\dfrac{3}{2}x$

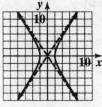

$9x^2 - 4y^2 = 36$

2. $4p = -8$, $p = -2$

parabola

vertex: $(0, 0)$

focus: $(0, -2)$

directrix: $y = 2$

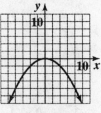

$x^2 = -8y$

3. The center is at $(-2, 5)$.

$c^2 = a^2 - b^2 = 25 - 9 = 16$, $c = 4$

ellipse

The foci are at $(-6, 5)$ and $(2, 5)$.

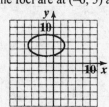

$\dfrac{(x + 2)^2}{25} + \dfrac{(y - 5)^2}{9} = 1$

4. $\quad 4x^2 - y^2 + 8x + 2y + 7 = 0$

$\left(4x^2 + 8x\right) - \left(y^2 - 2y\right) = -7$

$4\left(x^2 + 2x + 1\right) - \left(y^2 - 2y + 1\right) = -7 + 4 - 1$

$4(x+1)^2 - (y-1)^2 = -4$

$(y-1)^2 - 4(x+1)^2 = 4$

$\dfrac{(y-1)^2}{4} - (x+1)^2 = 1$

$c^2 = a^2 + b^2 = 4 + 1 = 5$, $c = \sqrt{5}$

The center is at $(-1, 1)$.

Asymptotes: $y - 1 = \pm 2(x+1)$

hyperbola

The foci are at $\left(-1, 1+\sqrt{5}\right)$ and $\left(-1, 1-\sqrt{5}\right)$.

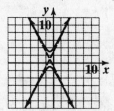

$4x^2 - y^2 + 8x + 2y + 7 = 0$

5. $4p = 8$, $p = 2$

parabola

vertex: $(-5, 1)$

focus: $(-5, 3)$

directrix: $y = -1$

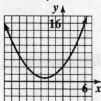

$(x + 5)^2 = 8(y - 1)$

6. $c = 7$, $c^2 = 49$

$a = 10$, $a^2 = 100$

$b^2 = a^2 - c^2 = 100 - 49 = 51$

$\dfrac{x^2}{100} + \dfrac{y^2}{51} = 1$

7. $c = 10$, $c^2 = 100$

$a = 7$, $a^2 = 49$

$b^2 = c^2 - a^2 = 100 - 49 = 51$

$\dfrac{y^2}{49} - \dfrac{x^2}{51} = 1$

521

8. $p = 50$

$y^2 = 4px$

$y^2 = 200x$

9. $b = 24,\ b^2 = 576$

$2a = 80,\ a = 40,\ a^2 = 1600$

$c^2 = a^2 - b^2 = 1600 - 576 = 1024$

$c = \sqrt{1024} = 32$

The two people should each stand 32 feet from the center of the room, along the major axis.

10. a. $x^2 = 4py$

when $x = \pm 3,\ y = 3$

$9 = 4p(3)$

$3 = 4p$

$\dfrac{3}{4} = p$

$x^2 = 3y$

b. focus: $\left(0, \dfrac{3}{4}\right)$

The light is placed $\dfrac{3}{4}$ inch above the vertex.

Cumulative Review Exercises (Chapters 1–7)

1. $2(x - 3) + 5x = 8(x - 1)$

$2x - 6 + 5x = 8x - 8$

$7x - 6 = 8x - 8$

$-x = -2$

$x = 2$

The solution set is $\{2\}$.

2. $-3(2x - 4) > 2(6x - 12)$

$-6x + 12 > 12x - 24$

$-18x > -36$

$x < 2$

The solution set is $\{x \mid x < 2\}$.

3. $x - 5 = \sqrt{x + 7}$

$(x - 5)^2 = x + 7$

$x^2 - 10x + 25 = x + 7$

$x^2 - 11x + 18 = 0$

$(x - 2)(x - 9) = 0$

$x = 2$ or $x = 9$

The solution $x = 2$ is extraneous, so the only solution is $x = 9$.

The solution set is $\{9\}$.

4. $(x - 2)^2 = 20$

$x - 2 = \pm\sqrt{20}$

$x - 2 = \pm 2\sqrt{5}$

$x = 2 \pm 2\sqrt{5}$

The solution set is $\left\{2 + 2\sqrt{5},\ 2 - 2\sqrt{5}\right\}$.

5. $|2x - 1| \geq 7$

$2x - 1 \geq 7$ or $2x - 1 \leq -7$

$2x \geq 8$ $2x \leq -6$

$x \geq 4$ or $x \leq -3$

The solution set is $\{x \mid x \leq -3 \text{ or } x \geq 4\}$

6. $3x^3 + 4x^2 - 7x + 2 = 0$

$p : \pm 1, \pm 2$

$q : \pm 1, \pm 3$

$\dfrac{p}{q} : \pm 1,\ \pm 2,\ \pm\dfrac{1}{3},\ \pm\dfrac{2}{3}$

Let $f(x) = 3x^3 + 4x^2 - 7x + 2$.

Evaluate f at the possible rational zeros to find $f\left(\dfrac{2}{3}\right) = 0$.

$\dfrac{2}{3}$	3	4	−7	2
		2	4	−2
	3	6	−3	0

$\left(x - \dfrac{2}{3}\right)(3x^2 + 6x - 3) = 0$

$(3x - 2)(x^2 + 2x - 1) = 0$

$x = \dfrac{2}{3}$ or $x = \dfrac{-2 \pm \sqrt{(2)^2 - 4(1)(-1)}}{2}$

$x = \dfrac{-2 \pm \sqrt{8}}{2}$

$x = -1 \pm \sqrt{2}$

The solution set is $\left\{\dfrac{2}{3},\ -1 + \sqrt{2},\ -1 - \sqrt{2}\right\}$.

7. $\log_2(x + 1) + \log_2(x - 1) = 3$

$\log_2(x^2 - 1) = 3$

$x^2 - 1 = 2^3$

$x^2 = 9$

$x = \pm 3$

$x = -3$ is not a solution of the original equation.

The solution set is $\{3\}$.

8. $3x + 4y = 2$
          $2x + 5y = -1$

          $6x + 8y = 4$
          $\underline{-6x - 15y = 3}$
          $\qquad -7y = 7$
          $\qquad\quad y = -1$
          $3x + 4(-1) = 2$
          $\qquad\; 3x = 6$
          $\qquad\quad x = 2$
          The solution set is $\{(2, -1)\}$.

9. $2x^2 - y^2 = -8$
          $x - y = 6$

          $x - y = 6$
          $x = y + 6$
          $x^2 = (y + 6)^2 = y^2 + 12y + 36$

          Substitute into first equation.
          $2(y^2 + 12y + 36) - y^2 = -8$
          $2y^2 + 24y + 72 - y^2 = -8$
          $y^2 + 24y + 80 = 0$
          $(y + 4)(y + 20) = 0$
          $\quad y = -4 \text{ or } y = -20$
          $\quad x = 2 \qquad x = -14$
          The solution set is $\{(2, -4), (-14, -20)\}$.

10. Set up the augmented matrix and use Gauss-Jordan reduction.

$$\left[\begin{array}{ccc|c} 1 & -1 & 1 & 17 \\ -4 & 1 & 5 & -2 \\ 2 & 3 & 1 & 8 \end{array}\right]$$

$$\left[\begin{array}{ccc|c} 1 & -1 & 1 & 17 \\ 0 & -3 & 9 & 66 \\ 0 & 5 & -1 & -26 \end{array}\right]\begin{array}{l} \\ 4R_1 + R_2 \\ -2R_1 + R_3 \end{array}$$

$$\left[\begin{array}{ccc|c} 1 & -1 & 1 & 17 \\ 0 & 1 & -3 & -22 \\ 0 & 5 & -1 & -26 \end{array}\right]\begin{array}{l} \\ -\frac{1}{3}R_2 \\ \\ \end{array}$$

$$\left[\begin{array}{ccc|c} 1 & 0 & -2 & -5 \\ 0 & 1 & -3 & -22 \\ 0 & 0 & 14 & 84 \end{array}\right]\begin{array}{l} R_2 + R_1 \\ \\ -5R_2 + R_3 \end{array}$$

$$\left[\begin{array}{ccc|c} 1 & 0 & -2 & -5 \\ 0 & 1 & -3 & -22 \\ 0 & 0 & 1 & 6 \end{array}\right]\begin{array}{l} \\ \\ \frac{1}{14}R_3 \end{array}$$

$$\left[\begin{array}{ccc|c} 1 & 0 & 0 & 7 \\ 0 & 1 & 0 & -4 \\ 0 & 0 & 1 & 6 \end{array}\right]\begin{array}{l} 2R_3 + R_1 \\ 3R_3 + R_2 \\ \\ \end{array}$$

$x = 7, y = -4, z = 6$
The solution set is $\{(7, -4, 6)\}$.

11. Parabola with vertex at $(1, -4)$.

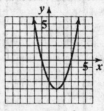

$f(x) = (x - 1)^2 - 4$

12. Ellipse with center at $(0, 0)$ and vertices at $(3, 0)$ and $(-3, 0)$.

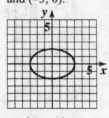

$$\frac{x^2}{9} + \frac{y^2}{4} = 1$$

13. $5x + y \le 10 \qquad\qquad y \ge \frac{1}{4}x + 2$

          $\qquad y \le -5x + 10$
          Graph with solid line $y = -5x + 10$ and

          $y = \frac{1}{4}x + 2$. Shade the region that is below the

          line $y = -5x + 10$ and above the line

          $y = \frac{1}{4}x + 2$. Then dash the solid lines that do

          not contain the solution set.

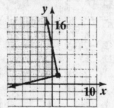

14. a. $p: \pm 1, \pm 3$

$q: \pm 1, \pm 2, \pm 4, \pm 8, \pm 16, \pm 32$

$\dfrac{p}{q}: \pm 1, \pm 3, \pm \dfrac{1}{2}, \pm \dfrac{3}{2}, \pm \dfrac{1}{4}, \pm \dfrac{3}{4}, \pm \dfrac{1}{8},$

$\pm \dfrac{3}{8}, \pm \dfrac{1}{16}, \pm \dfrac{3}{16}, \pm \dfrac{1}{32}, \pm \dfrac{3}{32}$

b. $x = 1$ appears to be a root.

1	32	−52	17	3
		32	−20	−3
	32	−20	−3	0

$32x^3 - 52x^2 + 17x + 3 = 0$

$(x-1)(32x^2 - 20x - 3) = 0$

$(x-1)(4x - 3)(8x + 1) = 0$

$x = 1 \text{ or } x = \dfrac{3}{4} \text{ or } x = -\dfrac{1}{8}$

The solution set is $\left\{ -\dfrac{1}{8}, \dfrac{3}{4}, 1 \right\}$.

15. a.   domain: $(-2, 2)$

range: $[-3, \infty)$

b.   the relative minimum of -3 occurs
at $x = 0$.

c.   increasing: $(0, 2)$

d. $f(-1) - f(0) = 0 - (-3) = 3$

e. $(f \circ f)(1) = f(f(1)) = f(0) = -3$

f. $f(x) \to \infty$ as $x \to -2^+$ or as $x \to 2^-$

g.
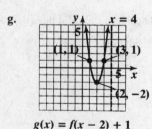

$g(x) = f(x - 2) + 1$

h.
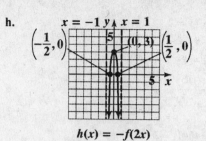

$h(x) = -f(2x)$

16. $f(x) = x^2 - 4, \ g(x) = x + 2$

$(g \circ f)(x) = g(x^2 - 4) = (x^2 - 4) + 2 = x^2 - 2$

17. $\log_5 \dfrac{x^3 \sqrt{y}}{125} = \log_5 x^3 \sqrt{y} - \log_5 125$

$= \log_5 x^3 + \log_5 \sqrt{y} - 3$

$= 3 \log_5 x + \dfrac{1}{2} \log_5 y - 3$

18. $m = \dfrac{y_2 - y_1}{x_2 - x_1} = \dfrac{8 - (-4)}{-5 - 1} = \dfrac{12}{-6} = -2$

$y - y_1 = m(x - x_1)$

$y + 4 = -2(x - 1)$

$y = -2x - 2$

19.   Let R = the cost of a rental at Rent-a-Truck and
let A = the cost of a rental at Ace Truck Rentals.
$R = 39 + 0.16m$
$A = 25 + 0.24m$
where m is the number of miles.
$39 + 0.16m = 25 + 0.24m$
$\qquad\quad 14 = 0.08m$
$\qquad\quad\ m = 175$
$R = 39 + 0.16(175) = 67$
The cost will be the same when the number of
miles driven is 175 miles. The cost will be $67.

20.   Let x = cost of basic cable,
Let y = cost of movie channel.
$\quad x + y = 35$
$\quad x + 2y = 45$
Multiply the first equation by -1 and then add
the two equations.
$\quad -x - y = -35$
$\quad \underline{\ \ x + 2y = 45\ \ }$
$\qquad\qquad y = 10$
Use back-substitution to find x.
$x + 10 = 35$
$\qquad x = 25$
Basic cable costs $25 and one movie channel
costs $10.

Chapter 8

Section 8.1

Check Point Exercises

1. a. $a_n = 2n + 5$

$a_1 = 2(1) + 5 = 7$

$a_2 = 2(2) + 5 = 9$

$a_3 = 2(3) + 5 = 11$

$a_4 = 2(4) + 5 = 13$

The first four terms are 7, 9, 11, and 13.

b. $a_n = \dfrac{(-1)^n}{2^n + 1}$

$a_1 = \dfrac{(-1)^1}{2^1 + 1} = \dfrac{-1}{3} = -\dfrac{1}{3}$

$a_2 = \dfrac{(-1)^2}{2^2 + 1} = \dfrac{1}{5}$

$a_3 = \dfrac{(-1)^3}{2^3 + 1} = \dfrac{-1}{9} = -\dfrac{1}{9}$

$a_4 = \dfrac{(-1)^4}{2^4 + 1} = \dfrac{1}{17}$

The first four terms are $-\frac{1}{3}, \frac{1}{5}, -\frac{1}{9},$
and $\frac{1}{17}$.

2. $a_1 = 3$ and $a_n = 2a_{n-1} + 5$ for $n \geq 2$

$a_2 = 2a_1 + 5$

$\quad = 2(3) + 5 = 11$

$a_3 = 2a_2 + 5$

$\quad = 2(11) + 5 = 27$

$a_4 = 2a_3 + 5$

$\quad = 2(27) + 5 = 59$

The first four terms are 3, 11, 27, and 59.

3. $a_n = \dfrac{20}{(n+1)!}$

$a_1 = \dfrac{20}{(1+1)!} = \dfrac{20}{2!} = 10$

$a_2 = \dfrac{20}{(2+1)!} = \dfrac{20}{3!} = \dfrac{20}{6} = \dfrac{10}{3}$

$a_3 = \dfrac{20}{(3+1)!} = \dfrac{20}{4!} = \dfrac{20}{24} = \dfrac{5}{6}$

$a_4 = \dfrac{20}{(4+1)!} = \dfrac{20}{5!} = \dfrac{20}{120} = \dfrac{1}{6}$

The first four terms are $10, \frac{10}{3}, \frac{5}{6},$ and $\frac{1}{6}$.

4. a. $\dfrac{14!}{2!\,12!} = \dfrac{14 \cdot 13 \cdot 12!}{2!\,12!} = \dfrac{14 \cdot 13}{2 \cdot 1} = 91$

b. $\dfrac{n!}{(n-1)!} = \dfrac{n \cdot (n-1)!}{(n-1)!} = n$

5. a. $\displaystyle\sum_{i=1}^{6} 2i^2$

$= 2(1)^2 + 2(2)^2 + 2(3)^2$

$\quad + 2(4)^2 + 2(5)^2 + 2(6)^2$

$= 2 + 8 + 18 + 32 + 50 + 72$

$= 182$

b. $\displaystyle\sum_{k=3}^{5} \left(2^k - 3\right)$

$= \left(2^3 - 3\right) + \left(2^4 - 3\right) + \left(2^5 - 3\right)$

$= (8 - 3) + (16 - 3) + (32 - 3)$

$= 5 + 13 + 29$

$= 47$

c. $\displaystyle\sum_{i=1}^{5} 4 = 4 + 4 + 4 + 4 + 4 = 20$

6. a. The sum has nine terms, each of the form
i^2, starting at $i = 1$ and ending at $i = 9$.

$1^2 + 2^2 + 3^2 + \cdots + 9^2 = \displaystyle\sum_{i=1}^{9} i^2$

b. The sum has n terms, each of the form $\frac{1}{2^{i-1}}$,
starting at $i = 1$ and ending at $i = n$.

$1 + \dfrac{1}{2} + \dfrac{1}{4} + \dfrac{1}{8} + \cdots + \dfrac{1}{2^{n-1}} = \displaystyle\sum_{i=1}^{n} \dfrac{1}{2^{i-1}}$

Exercise Set 8.1

1. $a_n = 3n + 2$

$a_1 = 3(1) + 2 = 5$

$a_2 = 3(2) + 2 = 8$

$a_3 = 3(3) + 2 = 11$

$a_4 = 3(4) + 2 = 14$

The first four terms are 5, 8, 11, and 14.

3. $a_n = 3^n$

$a_1 = 3^1 = 3$

$a_2 = 3^2 = 9$

$a_3 = 3^3 = 27$

$a_4 = 3^4 = 81$

The first four terms are 3, 9, 27, and 81.

5. $a_n = (-3)^n$

$a_1 = (-3)^1 = -3$

$a_2 = (-3)^2 = 9$

$a_3 = (-3)^3 = -27$

$a_4 = (-3)^4 = 81$

The first four terms are –3, 9, –27, and 81.

7. $a_n = (-1)^n (n+3)$

$a_1 = (-1)^1 (1+3) = -4$

$a_2 = (-1)^2 (2+3) = 5$

$a_3 = (-1)^3 (3+3) = -6$

$a_4 = (-1)^4 (4+3) = 7$

The first four terms are –4, 5, –6, and 7.

9. $a_n = \dfrac{2n}{n+4}$

$a_1 = \dfrac{2(1)}{1+4} = \dfrac{2}{5}$

$a_2 = \dfrac{2(2)}{2+4} = \dfrac{4}{6} = \dfrac{2}{3}$

$a_3 = \dfrac{2(3)}{3+4} = \dfrac{6}{7}$

$a_4 = \dfrac{2(4)}{4+4} = \dfrac{8}{8} = 1$

The first four terms are $\frac{2}{5}, \frac{2}{3}, \frac{6}{7}$, and 1.

11. $a_n = \dfrac{(-1)^{n+1}}{2^n - 1}$

$a_1 = \dfrac{(-1)^{1+1}}{2^1 - 1} = \dfrac{1}{1}\ n = 1$

$a_2 = \dfrac{(-1)^{2+1}}{2^2 - 1} = -\dfrac{1}{3}$

$a_3 = \dfrac{(-1)^{3+1}}{2^3 - 1} = \dfrac{1}{7}$

$a_4 = \dfrac{(-1)^{4+1}}{2^4 - 1} = -\dfrac{1}{15}$

The first four terms are $1, -\frac{1}{3}, \frac{1}{7}$, and $-\frac{1}{15}$.

13. $a_1 = 7$ and $a_n = a_{n-1} + 5$ for $n \geq 2$

$a_2 = a_1 + 5 = 7 + 5 = 12$

$a_3 = a_2 + 5 = 12 + 5 = 17$

$a_4 = a_3 + 5 = 17 + 5 = 22$

The first four terms are 7, 12, 17, and 22.

15. $a_1 = 3$ and $a_n = 4a_{n-1}$ for $n \geq 2$

$a_2 = 4a_1 = 4(3) = 12$

$a_3 = 4a_2 = 4(12) = 48$

$a_4 = 4a_3 = 4(48) = 192$

The first four terms are 3, 12, 48, and 192.

17. $a_1 = 4$ and $a_n = 2a_{n-1} + 3$

$a_2 = 2(4) + 3 = 11$

$a_3 = 2(11) + 3 = 25$

$a_4 = 2(25) + 3 = 53$

The first four terms are 4, 11, 25, and 53.

19. $a_n = \dfrac{n^2}{n!}$

$a_1 = \dfrac{1^2}{1!} = 1$

$a_2 = \dfrac{2^2}{2!} = 2$

$a_3 = \dfrac{3^2}{3!} = \dfrac{9}{6} = \dfrac{3}{2}$

$a_4 = \dfrac{4^2}{4!} = \dfrac{16}{24} = \dfrac{2}{3}$

The first four terms are 1, 2, $\frac{3}{2}$, and $\frac{2}{3}$.

21. $a_n = 2(n+1)!$

$a_1 = 2(1+1)! = 2(2) = 4$

$a_2 = 2(2+1)! = 2(6) = 12$

$a_3 = 2(3+1)! = 2(24) = 48$

$a_4 = 2(4+1)! = 2(120) = 240$

The first four terms are 4, 12, 48, and 240.

23. $\dfrac{17!}{15!} = \dfrac{17 \cdot 16 \cdot 15!}{15!} = 17 \cdot 16 = 272$

25. $\dfrac{16!}{2! \cdot 14!} = \dfrac{16 \cdot 15 \cdot 14!}{2! 14!} = \dfrac{16 \cdot 15}{2 \cdot 1} = \dfrac{8 \cdot 15}{1} = 120$

27. $\dfrac{(n+2)!}{n!} = \dfrac{(n+2)(n+1)n!}{n!} = (n+2)(n+1)$

29. $\displaystyle\sum_{i=1}^{6} 5i = 5 \cdot 1 + 5 \cdot 2 + 5 \cdot 3 + 5 \cdot 4 + 5 \cdot 5 + 5 \cdot 6$

$= 5 + 10 + 15 + 20 + 25 + 30$

$= 105$

31. $\displaystyle\sum_{i=1}^{4} 2i^2 = 2 \cdot 1^2 + 2 \cdot 2^2 + 2 \cdot 3^2 + 2 \cdot 4^2$

$= 2 + 8 + 18 + 32$

$= 60$

33. $\displaystyle\sum_{k=1}^{5} k(k+4) = 1(5) + 2(6) + 3(7) + 4(8) + 5(9)$

$= 5 + 12 + 21 + 32 + 45$

$= 115$

35. $\displaystyle\sum_{i=1}^{4} \left(\dfrac{-1}{2}\right)^i$

$= \left(-\dfrac{1}{2}\right)^1 + \left(-\dfrac{1}{2}\right)^2 + \left(-\dfrac{1}{2}\right)^3 + \left(-\dfrac{1}{2}\right)^4$

$= -\dfrac{1}{2} + \dfrac{1}{4} + -\dfrac{1}{8} + \dfrac{1}{16}$

$= -\dfrac{5}{16}$

37. $\displaystyle\sum_{i=5}^{9} 11 = 11 + 11 + 11 + 11 + 11 = 55$

39. $\displaystyle\sum_{i=0}^{4} \dfrac{(-1)^i}{i!}$

$= \dfrac{(-1)^0}{0!} + \dfrac{(-1)^1}{1!} + \dfrac{(-1)^2}{2!} + \dfrac{(-1)^3}{3!} + \dfrac{(-1)^4}{4!}$

$= 1 - 1 + \dfrac{1}{2} - \dfrac{1}{6} + \dfrac{1}{24}$

$= \dfrac{9}{24} = \dfrac{3}{8}$

41. $\displaystyle\sum_{i=1}^{5} \dfrac{i!}{(i-1)!} = \dfrac{1!}{0!} + \dfrac{2!}{1!} + \dfrac{3!}{2!} + \dfrac{4!}{3!} + \dfrac{5!}{4!}$

$= 1 + 2 + 3 + 4 + 5 = 15$

43. $1^2 + 2^2 + 3^2 + \cdots + 15^2 = \displaystyle\sum_{i=1}^{15} i^2$

45. $2 + 2^2 + 2^3 + 2^4 + \cdots + 2^{11} = \displaystyle\sum_{i=1}^{11} 2^i$

47. $1 + 2 + 3 + \cdots + 30 = \displaystyle\sum_{i=1}^{30} i$

49. $\dfrac{1}{2} + \dfrac{2}{3} + \dfrac{3}{4} + \cdots + \dfrac{14}{14+1} = \displaystyle\sum_{i=1}^{14} \dfrac{i}{i+1}$

51. $4 + \dfrac{4^2}{2} + \dfrac{4^3}{3} + \cdots + \dfrac{4^n}{n} = \displaystyle\sum_{i=1}^{n} \dfrac{4^i}{i}$

53. $1 + 3 + 5 + \cdots + (2n-1) = \displaystyle\sum_{i=1}^{n} (2i-1)$

55. $5 + 7 + 9 + \cdots + 31$

Possible answer: $\displaystyle\sum_{k=1}^{14} (2k+3)$

57. $a + ar + ar^2 + \cdots + ar^{12}$

Possible answer: $\displaystyle\sum_{k=0}^{12} ar^k$

59. $a + (a+d) + (a+2d) + \cdots + (a+nd)$

Possible answer: $\displaystyle\sum_{k=0}^{n} (a+kd)$

61.

$$\sum_{i=1}^{5}(a_i^2 + 1) = \left((-4)^2 + 1\right) + \left((-2)^2 + 1\right) + \left((0)^2 + 1\right) + \left((2)^2 + 1\right) + \left((4)^2 + 1\right)$$

$$= 17 + 5 + 1 + 5 + 17$$

$$= 45$$

63.

$$\sum_{i=1}^{5}(2a_i + b_i) = \left(2(-4) + 4\right) + \left(2(-2) + 2\right) + \left(2(0) + 0\right) + \left(2(2) + (-2)\right) + \left(2(4) + (-4)\right)$$

$$= -4 + (-2) + 0 + 2 + 4 = 0$$

65.

$$\sum_{i=4}^{5}\left(\frac{a_i}{b_i}\right)^2 = \left(\frac{2}{-2}\right)^2 + \left(\frac{4}{-4}\right)^2 = (-1)^2 + (-1)^2 = 1 + 1 = 2$$

67.

$$\sum_{i=1}^{5}a_i^2 + \sum_{i=1}^{5}b_i^2 = \left((-4)^2 + (-2)^2 + 0^2 + 2^2 + 4^2\right) + \left(4^2 + 2^2 + 0^2 + (-2)^2 + (-4)^2\right)$$

$$= (16 + 4 + 0 + 4 + 16) + (16 + 4 + 0 + 4 + 16) = 80$$

69.   **a.**

$$\sum_{i=1}^{8}a_i = 36.4 + 36.5 + 35.6 + 34.5 + 32.3 + 31.6 + 32.9 + 34.6 = 274.4$$

     b.

$$\frac{\sum_{i=1}^{8}a_i}{8} = \frac{274.4}{8} = 34.3$$

From 1995 through 2002, the average number of people living below poverty level each year was approximately 34.3 million.

71.   **a.** $\dfrac{1}{10}\sum_{i=1}^{10}a_i = \dfrac{1}{10}(14.2 + 13.7 + 12.6 + 10.9 + 8.7 + 7.6 + 5.9 + 5.4 + 5.1 + 5.0) = \dfrac{1}{10}(89.1) = 8.91$

From 1994 through 2003, there was an average of 8.91 million Welfare recipients in the US.

     b. $\dfrac{1}{10}\sum_{n=1}^{10}(-1.18n + 15.41)$

$$= \frac{1}{10}\left[(-1.18\cdot1 + 15.41) + (-1.18\cdot2 + 15.41) + (-1.18\cdot3 + 15.41) + (-1.18\cdot4 + 15.41) + (-1.18\cdot5 + 15.41)\right.$$

$$\left. + (-1.18\cdot6 + 15.41) + (-1.18\cdot7 + 15.41) + (-1.18\cdot8 + 15.41) + (-1.18\cdot9 + 15.41) + (-1.18\cdot10 + 15.41)\right]$$

$$= \frac{1}{10}(89.2)$$

$$= 8.92$$

The model is very close to the actual average.

73. $a_n = 6000\left(1 + \dfrac{0.06}{4}\right)^n, n = 1, 2, 3, \cdots$

$$a_{20} = 6000\left(1 + \frac{0.06}{4}\right)^{20} \approx 8081.13$$

After five years, the balance is \$8081.13.

83. Most calculators give error message if the expression is entered directly.
However,
$$\frac{200!}{198!} = \frac{200 \cdot 199 \cdot 198!}{198!} = 200 \cdot 199 = 39,800$$

85. $\dfrac{20!}{300} = 8,109,673,360,588,800$

However, most calculators give a rounded answer in scientific notation.

87. $\dfrac{54!}{(54-3)3!} = 24,804$

91. $a_n = \dfrac{n}{n+1}$

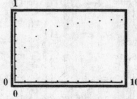

As n gets larger, a_n approaches 1.

93. $a_n = \dfrac{2n^2 + 5n - 7}{n^3}$

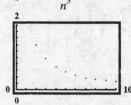

As n gets larger, a_n approaches 0.

95. **a.** False; $\dfrac{n!}{(n-1)!} = \dfrac{n \cdot (n-1)!}{(n-1)!} = n$

b. True

c. False; $\displaystyle\sum_{i=1}^{2} (-1)^i 2^i = -2 + 4 = 2$

d. False; $a_1 b_1 + a_2 b_2 \neq (a_1 + a_2) + (b_1 + b_2)$

(b) is true.

Section 8.2

Check Point Exercises

1. $a_1 = 51.5$
$a_2 = a_1 + 2.18 = 51.5 + 2.18 = 53.68$
$a_3 = a_2 + 2.18 = 53.68 + 2.18 = 55.86$
$a_4 = a_3 + 2.18 = 55.86 + 2.18 = 58.04$
$a_5 = a_4 + 2.18 = 58.04 + 2.18 = 60.22$
The first five terms are 51.5, 53.68, 55.86, 58.04, and 60.22.

2. $a_1 = 6$, $d = -5$
To find the ninth term, a_9, replace n in the formula with 9, a_1 with 6, and d with -5.
$a_n = a_1 + (n-1)d$
$a_9 = 6 + (9-1)(-5)$
$\quad = 6 + 8(-5)$
$\quad = 6 + (-40)$
$\quad = -34$

3. **a.** $a_n = a_1 + (n-1)d = 159,000 + (n-1)9700$
$a_n = 9700n + 149,300$

b. a_1 represents 1995 so a_{16} represents 2010.
$a_n = 9700n + 149,300$
$a_{16} = 9700(16) + 149,300$
$\quad = 304,500$
In 2010, a new one-family house will cost $304,500.

529

4. 3, 6, 9, 12, ...

To find the sum of the first 15 terms, S_{15}, replace n in the formula with 15.

$$S_n = \frac{n}{2}(a_1 + a_n)$$

$$S_{15} = \frac{15}{2}(a_1 + a_{15})$$

Use the formula for the general term of a sequence to find a_{15}. The common difference, d, is 3, and the first term, a_1, is 3.

$$a_n = a_1 + (n-1)d$$
$$a_{15} = 3 + (15-1)(3)$$
$$= 3 + 14(3)$$
$$= 3 + 42$$
$$= 45$$

Thus, $S_{15} = \frac{15}{2}(3 + 45) = \frac{15}{2}(48) = 360$.

5. $\sum_{i=1}^{30}(6i-11) = (6\cdot1-11) + (6\cdot2-11) +$

$$+ (6\cdot3-11) + ... + (6\cdot30-11)$$
$$= -5 + 1 + 7 + ... + 169$$

So the first term, a_1, is -5; the common difference, d, is $1-(-5) = 6$; the last term, a_{30}, is 169. Substitute $n = 30$, $a_1 = -5$, and $a_{30} = 169$ in the formula $S_n = \frac{n}{2}(a_1 + a_n)$.

$$S_{30} = \frac{30}{2}(-5 + 169) = 15(164) = 2460$$

Thus, $\sum_{i=1}^{30}(6i-11) = 2460$

6. $a_n = 1800n + 58,730$

$$a_1 = 1800(1) + 58,730 = 60,530$$
$$a_{10} = 1800(10) + 58,730 = 76,730$$

$$S_n = \frac{n}{2}(a_1 + a_n)$$

$$S_{10} = \frac{10}{2}(a_1 + a_{10})$$

$$= 5(60,530 + 76,730)$$
$$= 5(137,260)$$
$$= \$686,300$$

It would cost \$686,300 for the ten-year period beginning in 2006.

Exercise Set 8.2

1. $a_1 = 200$, $d = 20$
The first six terms are 200, 220, 240, 260, 280, and 300.

3. $a_1 = -7$, $d = 4$
The first six terms are -7, -3, 1, 5, 9, and 13.

5. $a_1 = 300$, $d = -90$
The first six terms are 300, 210, 120, 30, -60, and -150.

7. $a_1 = \frac{5}{2}$, $d = -\frac{1}{2}$

The first six terms are $\frac{5}{2}, 2, \frac{3}{2}, 1, \frac{1}{2}$, and 0.

9. $a_n = a_{n-1} + 6$, $a_1 = -9$
The first six terms are -9, -3, 3, 9, 15, and 21.

11. $a_n = a_{n-1} - 10$, $a_1 = 30$
The first six terms are 30, 20, 10, 0, -10, and -20.

13. $a_n = a_{n-1} - 0.4$, $a_1 = 1.6$
The first six terms are 1.6, 1.2, 0.8, 0.4, 0, and -0.4.

15. $a_1 = 13$, $d = -4$
$$a_n = 13 + (n-1)4$$
$$a_6 = 13 + 5(4) = 13 + 20 = 33$$

17. $a_1 = 7$, $d = 5$
$$a_n = 7 + (n-1)2$$
$$a_{50} = 7 + 49(5) = 252$$

19. $a_1 = -40$, $d = 5$
$$a_n = -40 + (n-1)5$$
$$a_{200} = -40 + (199)5 = 955$$

21. $a_1 = 35$, $d = -3$
$$a_n = 35 - 3(n-1)$$
$$a_{60} = 35 - 3(59) = -142$$

23. 1, 5, 9, 13, ...
$$d = 5 - 1, = 4$$
$$a_n = 1 + (n-1)4 = 1 + 4n - 4$$
$$a_n = 4n - 3$$
$$a_{20} = 4(20) - 3 = 77$$

25. $7, 3, -1, -5, \ldots$
$d = 3 - 7 = -4$
$a_n = 7 + (n-1)(-4) = 7 - 4n + 4$
$a_n = 11 - 4n$
$a_{20} = 11 - 4(20) = -69$

27. $a_1 = 9,\ d = 2$
$a_n = 9 + (n-1)(2)$
$a_n = 7 + 2n$
$a_{20} = 7 + 2(20) = 47$

29. $a_1 = -20,\ d = -4$
$a_n = -20 + (n-1)(-4)$
$a_n = -20 - 4n + 4$
$a_n = -16 - 4n$
$a_{20} = -16 - 4(20) = -96$

31. $a_n = a_{n-1} + 3,\ a_1 = 4$
$d = 3$
$a_n = 4 + (n-1)(3)$
$a_n = 1 + 3n$
$a_{20} = 1 + 3(20) = 61$

33. $a_n = a_{n-1} - 10,\ a_1 = 30,\ d = -10$
$a_n = 30 - 10(n-1) = 30 - 10n + 10$
$a_n = 40 - 10n$
$a_{20} = 40 - 10(20) = -160$

35. $4, 10, 16, 22, \ldots$
$d = 10 - 4 = 6$
$a_n = 4 + (n-1)(6)$
$a_{20} = 4 + (19)(6) = 118$
$S_{20} = \dfrac{20}{2}(4 + 118) = 1220$

37. $-10, -6, -2, 2, \ldots$
$d = -6 - (-10) = -6 + 10 = 4$
$a_n = -10 + (n-1)4$
$a_{50} = -10 + (49)4 = 186$
$S_{50} = \dfrac{50}{2}(-10 + 186) = 4400$

39. $1 + 2 + 3 + 4 + \cdots + 100$
$S_{100} = \dfrac{100}{2}(1 + 100) = 5050$

41. $2 + 4 + 6 + \cdots + 120$
$S_{60} = \dfrac{60}{2}(2 + 120) = 3660$

43. even integers between 21 and 45;
$22 + 24 + 26 + \cdots + 44$

$S_{12} = \dfrac{12}{2}(22 + 44) = 396$

45. $\displaystyle\sum_{i=1}^{17}(5i + 3) = (5+3) + (10+3) + (15+3) + \cdots + (85+3) = 8 + 13 + 18 + \cdots + 88$

$S_{17} = \dfrac{17}{2}(8 + 88) = 816$

47. $\displaystyle\sum_{i=1}^{30}(-3i + 5) = (-3+5) + (-6+5) + (-9+5) + \cdots + (-90+5) = 2 - 1 - 4 - \cdots - 85$

$S_{30} = \dfrac{30}{2}(2 - 85) = -1245$

49. $\displaystyle\sum_{i=1}^{100} 4i = 4 + 8 + 12 + \cdots + 400$

$S_{100} = \dfrac{100}{2}(4 + 400) = 20,200$

51. First find a_{14} and b_{12}:

$a_{14} = a_1 + (n-1)d$

$\quad = 1 + (14-1)(-3-1) = -51$

$b_{12} = b_1 + (n-1)d$

$\quad = 3 + (12-1)(8-3) = 58$

So, $a_{14} + b_{12} = -51 + 58 = 7$.

53. $a_n = a_1 + (n-1)d$

$-83 = 1 + (n-1)(-3-1)$

$-83 = 1 + -4(n-1)$

$-84 = -4n + 4$

$-88 = -4n$

$\quad n = 22$

There are 22 terms.

55. $S_n = \dfrac{n}{2}(a_1 + a_n)$

For $\{a_n\}$: $S_{14} = \dfrac{14}{2}(a_1 + a_{14}) = 7(1 + (-51)) = -350$

For $\{b_n\}$: $S_{14} = \dfrac{14}{2}(b_1 + b_{14}) = 7(3 + 68) = 497$

So $\displaystyle\sum_{n=1}^{14} b_n - \sum_{n=1}^{14} a_n = 497 - (-350) = 847$

57. Two points on the graph are $(1, 1)$ and $(2, -3)$.
 Finding the slope of the line;

$m = \dfrac{y_2 - y_1}{x_2 - x_2} = \dfrac{-3-1}{2-1} = \dfrac{-4}{1} = -4$

Using the point-slope form of an equation of a line;

$y - y_2 = m(x - x_2)$

$y - 1 = -4(x - 1)$

$y - 1 = -4x + 4$

$\quad y = -4x + 5$

Thus, $f(x) = -4x + 5$.

59. Using $a_n = a_1 + (n-1)d$ and $a_2 = 4$:

$a_2 = a_1 + (2-1)d$

$4 = a_1 + d$

And since $a_6 = 16$:

$a_6 = a_1 + (6-1)d$

$16 = a_1 + 5d$

The system of equations is

$4 = a_1 + d$

$16 = a_1 + 5d$

Solving the first equation for a_1:

$a_1 = 4 - d$

Substituting the value into the second equation and solving for d:

$16 = (4 - d) + 5d$

$16 = 4 + 4d$

$12 = 4d$

$\ 3 = d$

Back-substitute:

$a_1 = 4 - d$

$a_1 = 4 - 3)$

$a_1 = 1$

Then $a_n = a_1 + (n-1)d$

$\quad a_n = 1 + (n-1)3$

$\quad a_n = 1 + 3n - 3$

$\quad a_n = 3n - 2$

61. a. $a_n = 23.08 + 0.12n$

b. $a_{40} = 23.08 + 0.12(40) = 27.88$ years old

63. Median age of first marriage for women:
 $a_n = 20.66 + 0.14n$
 $a_{40} = 20.66 + 0.14(40) = 26.26$ years old

Young adults living with parents:
 $a_n = 47.21 + 0.09n$
 $a_{40} = 47.21 + 0.09(40) = 50.81\%$

Number completing four or more years of college:
 $a_n = 10.84 + 1.16n$
 $a_{40} = 10.84 + 1.16(40) = 57.24$ million

65. a. Total cost: $\$7107 + \$7310 + \$7586 + \$8046$
 $\quad\quad\quad\quad\quad = \$30,049$

b. $a_1 = 309(1) + 6739 = 7048$
 $a_2 = 309(2) + 6739 = 7357$
 $a_3 = 309(3) + 6739 = 7666$
 $a_4 = 309(4) + 6739 = 7975$
 Total cost:
 $7048 + 7357 + 7666 + 7975 = \$30,046$
 The model describes the actual sum very well.

67. $a_n = 33,000 + (n-1)(2500)$

$a_{10} = 33,000 + 9(2500) = 55,500$

$S_n = \dfrac{10}{2}(33,000 + 55,500) = 442,500$

The total ten year salary is \$442,500.

69. $a_n = 30 + (n-1)2$

$a_{26} = 30 + (25)2 = 80$

$S_{26} = \dfrac{26}{2}(30 + 80) = 1430$

The theater has 1430 seats.

79. Degree days: 23, 25, 27, …

$a_1 = 23, \ d = 2$

$a_{10} = 23 + 9(2) = 41$

$S_{10} = \dfrac{10}{2}(a_1 + a_{10})$

$S_{10} = \dfrac{10}{2}(23 + 41) = 320$

There are 320 degree-days.

Section 8.3

Check Point Exercises

1. $a_1 = 12, \ r = \dfrac{1}{2}$

$a_2 = 12\left(\dfrac{1}{2}\right)^1 = 6$

$a_3 = 12\left(\dfrac{1}{2}\right)^2 = \dfrac{12}{4} = 3$

$a_4 = 12\left(\dfrac{1}{2}\right)^3 = \dfrac{12}{8} = \dfrac{3}{2}$

$a_5 = 12\left(\dfrac{1}{2}\right)^4 = \dfrac{12}{16} = \dfrac{3}{4}$

$a_6 = 12\left(\dfrac{1}{2}\right)^5 = \dfrac{12}{32} = \dfrac{3}{8}$

The first six terms are $12, \ 6, \ 3, \ \dfrac{3}{2}, \ \dfrac{3}{4},$ and $\dfrac{3}{8}$.

2. $a_1 = 5, \ r = -3$

$a_n = 5r^{n-1}$

$a_7 = 5(-3)^{7-1} = 5(-3)^6 = 5(729) = 3645$

The seventh term is 3645.

3. 3, 6, 12, 24, 48, …

$r = \dfrac{6}{3} = 2, \ a_1 = 3$

$a_n = 3(2)^{n-1}$

$a_8 = 3(2)^{8-1} = 3(2)^7 = 3(128) = 384$

The eighth term is 384.

4. $a_1 = 2, \ r = \dfrac{-6}{2} = -3$

$S_n = \dfrac{a_1(1-r^r)}{1-r}$

$S_9 = \dfrac{2\left(1-(-3)^9\right)}{1-(-3)} = \dfrac{2(19,684)}{4} = 9842$

The sum of the first nine terms is 9842.

5. $\displaystyle\sum_{i=1}^{8} 2 \cdot 3^i$

$a_1 = 2 \cdot (3)^1 = 6, \ r = 3$

$S_n = \dfrac{a_1(1-r^n)}{1-r}$

$S_8 = \dfrac{6\left(1-3^8\right)}{1-3} = \dfrac{6(-6560)}{-2} = 19,680$

Thus, $\displaystyle\sum_{i=1}^{8} 2 \cdot 3^i = 19,680.$

6. $a_1 = 30,000, \ r = 1.06$

$S_n = \dfrac{a_1(1-r^n)}{1-r}$

$S_{30} = \dfrac{30,000\left(1-(1.06)^{30}\right)}{1-1.06} \approx 2,371,746$

The total lifetime salary is \$2,371,746.

7. $A = P\dfrac{\left(1+\frac{r}{n}\right)^{nt} - 1}{\frac{r}{n}}$

$P = 3000, \ r = 0.10, \ n = 1, \ t = 40$

$A = 3000\dfrac{(1+0.10)^{40} - 1}{0.10} \approx 1,327,778$

The value of the IRA will be \$1,327,778.

8. $3 + 2 + \dfrac{4}{3} + \dfrac{8}{9} + \cdots$

$a_1 = 3, r = \dfrac{2}{3}$

$S = \dfrac{a_1}{1 - r}$

$S = \dfrac{3}{1 - \frac{2}{3}} = \dfrac{3}{\frac{1}{3}} = 9$

The sum of this infinite geometric series is 9.

9. $0.\overline{9} = 0.9999\cdots = \dfrac{9}{10} + \dfrac{9}{100} + \dfrac{9}{1000} + \cdots$

$a_1 = \dfrac{9}{10}, r = \dfrac{1}{10}$

$S = \dfrac{\frac{9}{10}}{1 - \frac{1}{10}} = \dfrac{\frac{9}{10}}{\frac{9}{10}} = 1$

An equivalent fraction for $0.\overline{9}$ is 1.

10. $a_1 = 1000(0.8) = 800, \ r = 0.8$

$S = \dfrac{800}{1 - 0.8} = 4000$

The total amount spent is \$4000.

Exercise Set 8.3

1. $a_1 = 5, \ r = 3$
First five terms: 5, 15, 45, 135, 405.

3. $a_1 = 20, \ r = \dfrac{1}{2}$
First five terms: 20, 10, 5, $\frac{5}{2}$, $\frac{5}{4}\frac{5}{4}$.

5. $a_n = -4a_{n-1}, \ a_1 = 10$
First five terms: 10, -40, 160, -640, 2560.

7. $a_n = -5a_{n-1}, \ a_1 = -6$
First five terms: -6, 30, -150, 750, -3750.

9. $a_1 = 6, \ r = 2$
$a_n = 6 \cdot 2^{n-1}$
$a_8 = 6 \cdot 2^7 = 768$

11. $a_1 = 5, \ r = -2$
$a_n = 5 \cdot (-2)^{n-1}$
$a_{12} = 5 \cdot (-2)^{11} = -10,240$

13.
$a_1 = 1000, \ r = -\dfrac{1}{2}$

$a_n = 1000\left(-\dfrac{1}{2}\right)^{n-1}$

$a_{40} = 1000\left(-\dfrac{1}{2}\right)^{39}$

≈ 0.000000002

15. $a_1 = 1,000,000, \ r = 0.1$
$a_n = 1,000,000(0.1)^{n-1}$
$a_8 = 1,000,000(0.1)^7 = 0.1$

17. 3, 12, 48, 192, ...
$r = \dfrac{12}{3} = 4$
$a_n = 3(4)^{n-1}$
$a_7 = 3(4)^6 = 12,288$

19. $19, 6, 2, \dfrac{2}{3}, \cdots$ $r = \dfrac{6}{18} = \dfrac{1}{3}$
$a_n = 18\left(\dfrac{1}{3}\right)^{n-1}$
$a_7 = 18\left(\dfrac{1}{3}\right)^6 = \dfrac{2}{81}$

21. 1.5, -3, 6, -12, ...
$r = \dfrac{6}{-3} = -2$
$a_n = 1.5(-2)^{n-1}$
$a_7 = 1.5(-2)^6 = 96$

23. 0.0004, -0.004, 0.04, -0.4, ...
$r = \dfrac{-0.004}{0.0004} = -10$
$a_n = 0.0004(-10)^{n-1}$
$a_7 = 0.0004(-10)^6 = 400$

25. 2, 6, 18, 54, ...
$r = \dfrac{6}{2} = 3$
$S_{12} = \dfrac{2\left(1 - 3^{12}\right)}{1 - 3} = \dfrac{2(-531,440)}{-2} = 531,440$

27. $3, -6, 12, -24, \ldots$

$$r = \frac{-6}{3} = -2$$

$$S_{11} = \frac{3\left[1 - (-2)^{11}\right]}{1 - (-2)} = \frac{3(2049)}{3} = 2049$$

29. $-\frac{3}{2}, 3, -6, 12, \cdots$

$$r = \frac{3}{\frac{-3}{2}} = -2$$

$$S_{14} = \frac{-\frac{3}{2}\left[1 - (-2)^{14}\right]}{1 - (-2)} = \frac{-\frac{3}{2}(-16,383)}{3} = \frac{16,383}{2}$$

31. $\displaystyle\sum_{i=1}^{8} 3^i$

$r = 3, \quad a_1 = 3$

$$S_8 = \frac{3\left(1 - 3^8\right)}{1 - 3} = \frac{3(-6560)}{-2} = 9840$$

33. $\displaystyle\sum_{i=1}^{10} 5 \cdot 2^i$

$r = 2, \quad a_1 = 10$

$$S_{10} = \frac{10\left(1 - 2^{10}\right)}{1 - 2} = \frac{10(-1023)}{-1} = 10,230$$

35. $\displaystyle\sum_{i=1}^{6} \left(\frac{1}{2}\right)^{i+1}$

$r = \frac{1}{2}, \quad a_1 = \frac{1}{4}$

$$S_6 = \frac{\frac{1}{4}\left(1 - \left(\frac{1}{2}\right)^6\right)}{1 - \frac{1}{2}} = \frac{\frac{1}{4}\left(\frac{63}{64}\right)}{\frac{1}{2}} = \frac{63}{128}$$

37. $r = \frac{1}{3}$

$$S_\infty = \frac{1}{1 - \frac{1}{3}} = \frac{1}{\frac{2}{3}} = \frac{3}{2}$$

39. $r = \frac{1}{4}$

$$S_\infty = \frac{3}{1 - \frac{1}{4}} = \frac{3}{\frac{3}{4}} = 4$$

41. $r = -\frac{1}{2}$

$$S_\infty = \frac{1}{1 - \left(-\frac{1}{2}\right)} = \frac{1}{\frac{3}{2}} = \frac{2}{3}$$

43. $r = -0.3$

$$S_\infty = \frac{8}{1 - (-0.3)} = \frac{8}{1.3} \approx 6.15385$$

45. $r = \frac{1}{10}$

$$S_\infty = \frac{\frac{5}{10}}{1 - \frac{1}{10}} = \frac{\frac{5}{10}}{\frac{9}{10}} = \frac{5}{9}$$

47. $r = \frac{1}{100}$

$$S_\infty = \frac{\frac{47}{100}}{1 - \frac{1}{100}} = \frac{\frac{47}{100}}{\frac{99}{100}} = \frac{47}{99}$$

49. $0.\overline{257} = \frac{257}{1000} + \frac{257}{10^6} + \frac{257}{10^9} + \cdots$

$$r = \frac{1}{1000}$$

$$S_\infty = \frac{\frac{257}{1000}}{1 - \frac{1}{1000}} = \frac{\frac{257}{1000}}{\frac{999}{1000}} = \frac{257}{999}$$

51. $a_n = n + 5$
arithmetic, $d = 1$

53. $a_n = 2^n$
geometric, $r = 2$

55. $a_n = n^2 + 5$
neither

57. First find a_{10} and b_{10}:

$$a_{10} = a_1 r^{n-1}$$

$$= (-5)\left(\frac{10}{-5}\right)^{10-1} = (-5)(-2)^9$$

$$= 2560$$

$$b_{10} = b_1 + (n-1)d$$

$$= 10 + (10-1)(-5-10)$$

$$= 10 + (9)(-15) = -125$$

So,

$$a_{10} + b_{10} = 2560 + (-125) = 2435.$$

59. From Exercise 65, $a_{10} = 2560$ and $b_{10} = -125$.

For $\{a_n\}$, $r = \frac{10}{-5} = -2$ and:

$$S_{10} = \frac{a_1(1-r^n)}{1-r} = \frac{(-5)\left(1-(-2)^{10}\right)}{1-(-2)}$$

$$= \frac{(-5)(-1023)}{3} = 1705$$

For $\{b_n\}$, $\quad S_n = \frac{n}{2}(b_1 + b_n) = \frac{10}{2}(10 + (-125))$

$$= 5(-115) = -575$$

So, $\displaystyle\sum_{n=1}^{10} a_n - \sum_{n=1}^{10} b_n = 1705 - (-575) = 2280$

61. For $\{a_n\}$,

$$S_6 = \frac{a_1(1-r^n)}{1-r} = \frac{(-5)\left(1-(-2)^6\right)}{1-(-2)}$$

$$= \frac{(-5)(-63)}{3} = 105$$

For $\{c_n\}$,

$$S = \frac{a_1}{1-r} = \frac{-2}{1-\frac{1}{-2}} = \frac{-2}{\frac{3}{2}} = -\frac{4}{3}$$

So, $S_6 \cdot S = 105\left(-\frac{4}{3}\right) = -140$

63. It is given that $a_4 = 27$. Using the formula $a_n = a_1 r^{n-1}$ when $n = 4$ we have:

$$27 = 8r^{4-1}$$

$$\frac{27}{8} = r^3$$

$$r = \sqrt[3]{\frac{27}{8}} = \frac{3}{2}$$

Then

$$a_n = a_1 r^{n-1}$$

$$a_2 = 8\left(\frac{3}{2}\right)^{2-1} = 8\left(\frac{3}{2}\right) = 12$$

$$a_3 = 8\left(\frac{3}{2}\right)^{3-1} = 8\left(\frac{3}{2}\right)^2 = 8\left(\frac{9}{4}\right) = 18$$

65. $1, 2, 4, 8, \ldots$

$$r = 2$$

$$a_n = 2^{n-1}$$

$$a_{15} = 2^{14} = \$16,384$$

67. $a_1 = 3,000,000$

$$r = 1.04$$

$$a_n = 3,000,000(1.04)^{n-1}$$

$$a_7 = 3,000,000(1.04)^6 = \$3,795,957$$

69. a. $\dfrac{30.15}{29.76} \approx 1.013$

$\dfrac{30.54}{30.15} \approx 1.013$

$\dfrac{30.94}{30.54} \approx 1.013$

The population is increasing geometrically with $r \approx 1.013$.

b. $a_n = 29.76 \cdot 1.013^{n-1}$

c. $2000 - 1989 = 11$

$$a_{11} = 29.76 \cdot 1.013^{11-1} = 33.86$$

In 2000, the model predicts California population will be 33.86. This is very close to the actual population.

71. $1, 2, 4, 8, \ldots$

$$r = 2$$

$$S_{15} = \frac{1(1-2^{15})}{1-2} = 32,767$$

The total savings is \$32,767.

73. $a_1 = 24,000, \ r = 1.05$

$$S_{20} = \frac{24,000\left[1-(1.05)^{20}\right]}{1-1.05} = 793,582.90$$

The total salary is \$793,583.

75. $r = 0.9$

$$S_{10} = \frac{20(1 - 0.9^{10})}{1 - 0.9} \approx 130.26$$

The total length is 130.26 inches.

77. $A = 2500\dfrac{(1 + 0.09)^{40} - 1}{0.09} \approx 844{,}706.11$

In 40 years, the value is \$844,706.

79. $A = 600\dfrac{\left(1 + \frac{0.08}{4}\right)^{72} - 1}{\frac{0.08}{4}} \approx 94{,}834.21$

After 18 years, the value is \$94,834.

81. $r = 0.6$

$$S_\infty = \frac{6(0.6)}{1 - 0.6} = 9$$

The total economic impact is \$9 million.

83. $r = \frac{1}{4}$

$$S_\infty = \frac{\frac{1}{4}}{1 - \frac{1}{4}} = \frac{1}{4} \cdot \frac{4}{3} = \frac{1}{3}$$

95.

$$f(x) = \frac{2\left[1 - \left(\frac{1}{3}\right)^x\right]}{1 - \frac{1}{3}}$$

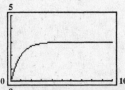

$$S = \frac{2}{1 - \frac{1}{3}} = \frac{2}{\frac{2}{3}} = 2 \div \frac{2}{3} = 2 \cdot \frac{3}{2} = 3$$

The sum of the series is 3 and the asymptote of the function is $y = 3$.

97.   **a.**   False; there is no common ratio.

  b.   False; the sum can be calculated exactly, since the series is geometric $\left(r = \frac{1}{2}\right)$.

  c.   False; $10 - 5 + \dfrac{5}{2} - \dfrac{5}{4} \cdots = \dfrac{10}{1 + \frac{1}{2}}$

  d.   True; $r = 0.5 = \frac{1}{2}$

  (d) is true.

99. $1{,}000{,}000 = P\dfrac{\left(1 + \frac{0.1}{12}\right)^{360} - 1}{\frac{0.1}{12}}$

  $1{,}000{,}000 \approx 2260.49P$

  $P \approx 442.38$

You must deposit \$442 monthly.

Mid-Chapter Check Point

1.
$$a_n = (-1)^{n+1} \frac{n}{(n-1)!}$$

$$a_1 = (-1)^{1+1} \frac{1}{(1-1)!} = (-1)^2 \frac{1}{0!} = 1 \cdot 1 = 1$$

$$a_2 = (-1)^{2+1} \frac{2}{(2-1)!} = (-1)^3 \frac{2}{1!} = (-1)(2) = -2$$

$$a_3 = (-1)^{3+1} \frac{3}{(3-1)!} = (-1)^4 \frac{3}{2!} = 1 \cdot \frac{3}{2} = \frac{3}{2}$$

$$a_4 = (-1)^{4+1} \frac{4}{(4-1)!} = (-1)^5 \frac{4}{3!} = (-1)\frac{4}{6} = -\frac{2}{3}$$

$$a_5 = (-1)^{5+1} \frac{5}{(5-1)!} = (-1)^6 \frac{5}{4!} = 1 \cdot \frac{5}{24} = \frac{5}{24}$$

2. Using $a_n = a_1 + (n-1)d$;

$$a_1 = 5$$

$$a_2 = 5 + (2-1)(-3) = 5 + 1(-3) = 5 - 3 = 2$$

$$a_3 = 5 + (3-1)(-3) = 5 + 2(-3) = 5 - 6 = -1$$

$$a_4 = 5 + (4-1)(-3) = 5 + 3(-3) = 5 - 9 = -4$$

$$a_5 = 5 + (5-1)(-3) = 5 + 4(-3) = 5 - 12 = -7$$

3. Using $a_n = a_1 r^{n-1}$;

$$a_1 = 5$$

$$a_2 = 5(-3)^{2-1} = 5(-3)^1 = 5(-3) = -15$$

$$a_3 = 5(-3)^{3-1} = 5(-3)^2 = 5(9) = 45$$

$$a_4 = 5(-3)^{4-1} = 5(-3)^3 = 5(-27) = -135$$

$$a_5 = 5(-3)^{5-1} = 5(-3)^4 = 5(81) = 405$$

4.
$$a_n = -a_{n-1} + 4$$

$$a_1 = 3$$

$$a_2 = -a_1 + 4 = -3 + 4 = 1$$

$$a_3 = -a_2 + 4 = -1 + 4 = 3$$

$$a_4 = -a_3 + 4 = -3 + 4 = 1$$

$$a_5 = -a_4 + 4 = -1 + 4 = 3$$

5.
$$d = a_2 - a_1 = 6 - 2 = 4$$

$$a_n = a_1 + (n-1)d$$

$$= 2 + (n-1)4$$

$$= 2 + 4n - 4$$

$$= 4n - 2$$

$$a_{20} = 4(20) - 2 = 78$$

6.
$$r = \frac{a_2}{a_1} = \frac{6}{3} = 2$$

$$a_n = a_1 r^{n-1}$$

$$= 3(2)^{n-1}$$

$$a_{10} = 3(2)^{10-1}$$

$$= 3(2)^9$$

$$= 1536$$

7.
$$d = a_2 - a_1 = 1 - \frac{3}{2} = -\frac{1}{2}$$

$$a_n = a_1 + (n-1)d$$

$$= \frac{3}{2} + (n-1)\left(-\frac{1}{2}\right)$$

$$= \frac{3}{2} - \frac{1}{2}n + \frac{1}{2}$$

$$= -\frac{1}{2}n + 2$$

$$a_{30} = -\frac{1}{2}(30) + 2$$

$$= -15 + 2$$

$$= -13$$

8.

$$S_n = \frac{a_1(1-r^n)}{1-r}; \; r = \frac{a_2}{a_1} = \frac{10}{5} = 2$$

$$S_{10} = \frac{5(1-2^{10})}{1-2} = \frac{5(-1023)}{-1} = 5115$$

9. First find a_{10};

$$d = a_2 - a_1 = 0 - (-2) = 2$$

$$a_{50} = a_1 + (n-1)d = -2 + (50-1)(2) = -2 + 49(2) = 96$$

$$S_{50} = \frac{n}{2}(a_1 + a_n) = \frac{50}{2}(-2 + 96) = 25(94) = 2350$$

10. First find a_{10};

$$r = \frac{a_2}{a_1} = \frac{40}{-20} = -2$$

$$a_{10} = a_1 r^{n-1} = -20(2)^{10-1} = -20(2)^9 = -20(512) = -10240$$

$$S_{10} = \frac{a_1(1-r^n)}{1-r} = \frac{-20(-1-(-2)^{10})}{1-(-2)} = \frac{-20(-1023)}{3} = \frac{20460}{3} = 6820$$

11. First find a_{100};

$$d = a_2 - a_1 = -2 - 4 = -6$$

$$a_{100} = a_1 + (n-1)d = 4 + (100-1)(-6) = 4 + 99(-6) = -590$$

$$S_{100} = \frac{n}{2}(a_1 + a_n) = \frac{100}{2}(4 - 590) = 50(-586) = -29,300$$

12.

$$\sum_{i=1}^{4}(i+4)(i-1) = (1+4)(1-1) + (2+4)(2-1) + (3+4)(3-1) + (4+4)(4-1)$$

$$= 5(0) + 6(1) + 7(2) + 8(3) = 0 + 6 + 14 + 24 = 44$$

13.

$$\sum_{i=1}^{50}(3i-2) = (3\cdot1-2) + (3\cdot2-2) + (3\cdot3-3) + ... + (3\cdot50-2)$$

$$= (3-2) + (6-2) + (9-3) + ... + (150-2)$$

$$= 1 + 4 + 6 + ... + 148$$

The sum of this arithmetic sequence is given by $S_n = \frac{n}{2}(a_1 + a_n)$;

$$S_{50} = \frac{50}{2}(1 + 148) = 25(149) = 3725$$

14.

$$\sum_{i=1}^{6}\left(\frac{3}{2}\right)^i = \left(\frac{3}{2}\right)^1 + \left(\frac{3}{2}\right)^2 + \left(\frac{3}{2}\right)^3 + \left(\frac{3}{2}\right)^4 + \left(\frac{3}{2}\right)^5 + \left(\frac{3}{2}\right)^6$$

$$= \frac{3}{2} + \frac{9}{4} + \frac{27}{8} + \frac{81}{16} + \frac{243}{32} + \frac{729}{64} = \frac{1995}{64}$$

15.

$$\sum_{i=1}^{\infty}\left(-\frac{2}{5}\right)^{i-1}=\left(-\frac{2}{5}\right)^{1-1}+\left(-\frac{2}{5}\right)^{2-1}+\left(-\frac{2}{5}\right)^{3-1}+\ldots$$

$$=\left(-\frac{2}{5}\right)^{0}+\left(-\frac{2}{5}\right)^{1}+\left(-\frac{2}{5}\right)^{2}+\ldots$$

$$=1+\left(-\frac{2}{5}\right)+\frac{4}{25}+\ldots$$

This is an infinite geometric sequence with $r=\dfrac{a_2}{a_1}=\dfrac{-\frac{2}{5}}{1}=-\dfrac{2}{5}$.

Using $S=\dfrac{a_1}{1-r}=\dfrac{1}{1-\left(-\frac{2}{5}\right)}=\dfrac{1}{\frac{7}{5}}=\dfrac{5}{7}$

16.

$$0.\overline{45}=\frac{a_1}{1-r}=\frac{\dfrac{45}{100}}{1-\dfrac{1}{100}}=\frac{\dfrac{45}{100}}{\dfrac{99}{100}}$$

$$=\frac{45}{100}\div\frac{99}{100}=\frac{45}{100}\cdot\frac{100}{99}=\frac{45}{99}=\frac{5}{11}$$

17. Answers may vary. An example is $\displaystyle\sum_{i=1}^{18}\frac{i}{i+2}$.

18. The arithmetic sequence is 16, 48, 80, 112, ...
First find a_{15} where $d=a_2-a_1=48-16=32$.
$a_{15}=a_1+(n-1)d=16+(15-1)(32)=16+14(32)=16+448=464$.
The distance the skydiver falls during the 15th second is 464 feet.
$S_{15}=\dfrac{n}{2}(a_1+a_n)=\dfrac{15}{2}(16+464)=7.5(480)=3600$
The total distance the skydiver falls in 15 seconds is 3600 feet.

19. $r=0.10$
$A=P(1+r)^t$
$\quad=120000(1+0.10)^{10}$
$\quad\approx311249$
The value of the house after 10 years is \$311,249.

Section 8.4

Check Point Exercises

1. **a.** $S_1 : 2 = 1(1+1)$

$S_k : 2+4+6+\cdots 2k = k(k+1)$

$S_{k+1} : 2+4+6+\cdots +2(k+1) = (k+1)(k+2)$

   b. $S_1 : 1^3 = \dfrac{1^2(1+1)^2}{4}$

$S_k = 1^3 + 2^3 + 3^3 + \cdots + k^3 = \dfrac{k^2(k+1)^2}{4}$

$S_{k+1} = 1^3 + 2^3 + 3^3 + \cdots + (k+1)^3 = \dfrac{(k+1)^2(k+2)^2}{4}$

2. $S_1 : 2 = 1(1+1)$

$2 = 2$ is true.

$S_k : 2+4+6+\cdots +2k = k(k+1)$

$S_{k+1} : 2+4+6+\cdots +2k+2(k+1) = (k+1)(k+2)$

Add $2(k+1)$ to both sides of S_k :

$2+4+6+\cdots +2k+2(k+1) = k(k+1)+2(k+1)$

Simplify the right-hand side:

$k(k+1)+2(k+1) = (k+1)(k+2)$

If S_k is true, then S_{k+1} is true. The statement is true for all n.

3. $S_1 : 1^3 = \dfrac{1^2(1+1)^2}{4}$

$1 = \dfrac{4}{4}$

$1 = 1$ is true.

$S_k : 1^3 + 2^3 + 3^3 + \cdots + k^3 = \dfrac{k^2(k+1)^2}{4}$

$S_{k+1} : 1^3 + 2^3 + 3^3 + \cdots + k^3 + (k+1)^3 = \dfrac{(k+1)^2(k+2)^2}{4}$

Add $(k+1)^3$ to both sides of S_k :

$1^3 + 2^3 + 3^3 + \cdots + k^3 + (k+1)^3 = \dfrac{k^2(k+1)^2}{4} + (k+1)^3$

Simplify the right hand side:

$$\dfrac{k^2(k+1)^2}{4} + (k+1)^3 = \dfrac{k^2(k+1)^2 + 4(k+1)^3}{4} = \dfrac{(k+1)^2\left[k^2 + 4(k+1)\right]}{4} = \dfrac{(k+1)^2(k^2+4k+4)}{4}$$

$$= \dfrac{(k+1)^2(k+2)^2}{4}$$

If S_k is true, then S_{k+1} is true. The statement is true for all n.

541

4. S_1: 2 is a factor of $1^2 + 1 = 2$, since $2 = 2 \cdot 1$.

   S_k: 2 is a factor of $k^2 + k$

S_{k+1}: 2 is a factor of $(k+1)^2 + (k+1)$

Simplify:

$$(k+1)^2 + (k+1) = k^2 + 2k + 1 + k + 1$$
$$= k^2 + 3k + 2$$
$$= k^2 + k + 2k + 2$$
$$= (k^2 + k) + 2(k+1)$$

Because we assume S_k is true, we know 2 is a factor of $k^2 + k$. Since 2 is a factor of $2(k+1)$, we conclude 2 is a factor of the sum $(k^2 + k) + 2(k+1)$. If S_k is true, then S_{k+1} is true. The statement is true for all n.

Exercise Set 8.4

1. $S_n = 1 + 3 + 5 + \cdots + (n-1) = n^2$

   $S_1 : 1 = 1^2$

   $1 = 1$ true

   $S_2 : 1 + 3 = 2^2$

   $4 = 4$ true

   $S_3 : 1 + 3 + 5 = 3^2$

   $9 = 9$ true

3. S_n : 2 is a factor of $n^2 - n$

   S_1 : 2 is a factor of $1^2 - 1 = 0$

   $0 = 0 \cdot 2$ so 2 is a factor of 0 is true.

   S_2 : 2 is a factor of $2^2 - 2 = 2$

   $2 = 1 \cdot 2$ so 2 is a factor of 2 is true.

   S_3 : 2 is a factor of $3^2 - 3 = 6$

   $6 = 3 \cdot 2$ so 2 is a factor of 6 is true.

5. $S_n : 4 + 8 + 12 + \cdots + 4n = 2n(n+1)$

   $S_k : 4 + 8 + 12 + \cdots + 4k = 2k(k+1)$

$S_{k+1} : 4 + 8 + 12 + \cdots + 4(k+1) = 2(k+1)(k+1+1)$

   $4 + 8 + 12 + \cdots + 4(k+1) = 2(k+1)(k+2)$

7. $S_n : 3 + 7 + 11 + \cdots + (4n-1) = n(2n+1)$

   $S_k : 3 + 7 + 11 + \cdots + (4k-1) = k(2k+1)$

$S_{k+1} : 3 + 7 + 11 + \cdots + [4(k+1) - 1] = (k+1)[2(k+1)+1]$

   $3 + 7 + 11 + \cdots + (4k+3) = (k+1)(2k+3)$

9. S_n : 2 is a factor of $n^2 - n + 2$

S_k : 2 is a factor of $k^2 - k + 2$

S_{k+1} : 2 is a factor of $(k+1)^2 - (k+1) + 2$

$\qquad k^2 + 2k + 1 - k - 1 + 2 = k^2 + k + 2$

S_{k+1} : 2 is a factor of $k^2 + k + 2$.

11. $S_1 : 4 = 2(1)(1+1)$

$4 = 2(2)$

$4 = 4$ is true.

$S_k : 4 + 8 + 12 + \cdots + 4k = 2k(k+1)$

$S_{k+1} : 4 + 8 + 12 + \cdots 4(k+1) = 2(k+1)(k+1+1)$

Add $4(k + 1)$ to both sides of S_k:

$4 + 8 + 12 + \cdots + 4(k+1) = 2k(k+1) + 4(k+1)$

Simplify the right-hand side:

$= 2k(k+1) + 4(k+1) = (2k+4)(k+1)$

$= 2(k+2)(k+1)$

$= 2(k+1)(k+1+1)$

If S_k is true, then S_{k+1} is true. The statement is true for all n.

13. $S_1 : 1 = 1^2$

$1 = 1$ is true.

$S_k : 1 + 3 + 5 + \cdots + (2k-1) = k^2$

$S_{k+1} : 1 + 3 + 5 + \cdots + (2k-1) + [2(k+1) - 1] = (k+1)^2$

$\qquad 1 + 3 + 5 + \cdots + (2k-1) + (2k+1) = (k+1)^2$

Add $(2k + 1)$ to both sides of S_k:

$1 + 3 + 5 + \cdots + (2k-1) + (2k+1) = k^2 + (2k+1)$

Simplify the right-hand side:

$= k^2 + (2k + 1)$

$= (k + 1)^2$

If S_k is true, then S_{k+1} is true. The statement is true for all n.

15. $S_1 : 3 = 1[2(1) + 1)]$

$3 = 3$ is true.

$S_k : 3 + 7 + 11 + \cdots + (4k-1) = k(2k+1)$

$S_{k+1} : 3 + 7 + 11 + \cdots + (4k-1) + [4(k+1) - 1] = (k+1)[2(k+1) + 1]$

$\qquad 3 + 7 + 11 + \cdots + (4k-1) + (4k+3) = (k+1)(2k+3)$

Add $(4k + 3)$ to both sides of S_k:

$3 + 7 + 11 + \ldots + (4k - 1) + (4k + 3) = k(2k+1) + 4(k+3)$

Simplify the right-hand side:

$= k(2k+1) + (4k+3) = 2k^2 + k + 4k + 3$

$= 2k^2 + 5k + 3$

$= (k+1)(2k+3)$

If S_k is true, then S_{k+1} is true. The statement is true for all n.

17. $S_1: 1 = 2^1 - 1$

$\quad\quad 1 = 1$ is true.

$S_k: 1 + 2 + 2^2 + \cdots + 2^{k-1} = 2^k - 1$

$S_{k+1}: 1 + 2 + 2^2 + \cdots + 2^{k-1} + 2^{k+1-1} = 2^{k+1} - 1$

$\quad\quad 1 + 2 + 2^2 + \cdots + 2^{k-1} + 2^k = 2^{k+1} - 1$

Add 2^k to both sides of S_k:

$1 + 2 + 2^2 + \cdots + 2^{k-1} + 2^k = 2^k + 2^k - 1$

Simplify the right-hand side:

$= 2^k + 2^k - 1 = 2(2^k) - 1$

$= 2^{k+1} - 1$

If S_k is true, then S_{k+1} is true. The statement is true for all n.

19. $S_1: 2 = 2^{1+1} - 2$

$\quad\quad 2 = 4 - 2$

$\quad\quad 2 = 2$ is true.

$S_k: 2 + 4 + 8 + \cdots + 2^k = 2^{k+1} - 2$

$S_{k+1}: 2 + 4 + 8 + \cdots + 2^k + 2^{k+1} = 2^{k+2} - 2$

Add 2^{k+1} to both sides of S_k:

$2 + 4 + 8 + \cdots + 2^k + 2^{k+1} = 2^{k+1} + 2^{k+1} - 2$

Simplify the right-hand side:

$= 2^{k+1} + 2^{k+1} - 1 = 2(2^{k+1}) - 2$

$= 2^{k+2} - 2$

If S_k is true, then S_{k+1} is true. The statement is true for all n.

21. $S_1: 1 \cdot 2 = \dfrac{1(1+1)(1+2)}{3}$

$\quad 2 = \dfrac{6}{3}$

$\quad 2 = 2$ is true.

$S_k: 1 \cdot 2 + 2 \cdot 3 + 3 \cdot 4 + \cdots + k(k+1) = \dfrac{k(k+1)(k+2)}{3}$

$S_{k+1}: 1 \cdot 2 + 2 \cdot 3 + 3 \cdot 4 + \cdots + k(k+1) + (k+1)(k+2) = \dfrac{(k+1)(k+2)(k+3)}{3}$

Add $(k+1)(k+2)$ to both sided of S_k:

$1 \cdot 2 + 2 \cdot 3 + 3 \cdot 4 + \cdots + k(k+1) + (k+1)(k+2) = \dfrac{k(k+1)(k+2)}{3} + (k+1)(k+2)$

Simplify the right-hand side:

$= \dfrac{k(k+1)(k+2)}{3} + (k+1)(k+2) = \dfrac{k(k+1)(k+2) + 3(k+1)(k+2)}{3}$

$= \dfrac{(k+1)(k+2)(k+3)}{3}$

If S_k is true, then S_{k+1} is true. The statement is true for all n.

23. $S_1 : \dfrac{1}{1 \cdot 2} = \dfrac{1}{1+1}$

$\dfrac{1}{2} = \dfrac{1}{2}$ is true.

$S_k : \dfrac{1}{1 \cdot 2} + \dfrac{1}{2 \cdot 3} + \dfrac{1}{3 \cdot 4} + \cdots + \dfrac{1}{k(k+1)} = \dfrac{k}{k+1}$

$S_{k+1} : \dfrac{1}{1 \cdot 2} + \dfrac{1}{2 \cdot 3} + \dfrac{1}{3 \cdot 4} + \cdots + \dfrac{1}{k(k+1)} + \dfrac{1}{(k+1)(k+2)} = \dfrac{k+1}{k+2}$

Add $\dfrac{1}{(k+1)(k+2)}$ to both sides of S_k:

$\dfrac{1}{1 \cdot 2} + \dfrac{1}{2 \cdot 3} + \dfrac{1}{3 \cdot 4} + \cdots + \dfrac{1}{k(k+1)} + \dfrac{1}{(k+1)(k+2)} = \dfrac{k}{k+1} + \dfrac{1}{(k+1)(k+2)}$

Simplify the right-hand side:

$\dfrac{k}{(k+1)} + \dfrac{1}{(k+1)(k+2)} = \dfrac{k(k+2)+1}{(k+1)(k+2)}$

$= \dfrac{k^2 + 2k + 1}{(k+1)(k+2)}$

$= \dfrac{(k+1)(k+1)}{(k+1)(k+2)}$

$= \dfrac{k+1}{k+2}$

If S_k is true, then S_{k+1} is true. The statement is true for all n.

25. $S_1 : 2$ is a factor of $1^2 - 1 = 0$, since $0 = 2 \cdot 0$.

$S_k : 2$ is a factor of $k^2 - k$

$S_{k+1} : 2$ is a factor of $(k+1)^2 - (k+1)$

$(k+1)^2 - (k-1) = k^2 + 2k + 1 - k - 1$

$= k^2 + k$

$= k^2 - k + 2k$

$= (k^2 - k) + 2k$

Because we assume S_k is true, we know 2 as a factor of $k^2 - k$. Since 2 is a factor of $2k$, we conclude 2 is factor of the sum $(k^2 + k) + 2k$. If S_k is true, then S_{k+1} is true. The statement is true for all n.

27. $S_1 :$ 6 is a factor of $1(1+1)(1+2) = 6$, since $6 = 6 \cdot 1$.

$S_k :$ 6 is a factor of $k(k+1)(k+2)$

$S_{k+1} :$ 6 is a factor of $(k+1)(k+2)(k+3)$

$(k+1)(k+2)(k+3) = k(k+1)(k+2) + 3(k+1)(k+2)$

Because we assume S_k is true, we know 6 as a factor of $k(k+1)(k+2)$. Since either $k+1$ or $k+2$ must be even, the product $(k+1)(k+2)$ is even. Thus 2 is a factor of $(k+1)(k+2)$, and we can conclude that 6 is factor of $3(k+1)(k+2)$ If S_k is true, then S_{k+1} is true.
The statement is true for all n.

29. $\sum_{i=1}^{n} 5 \cdot 6^i = 6\left(6^n - 1\right)$

Show that S_1 is true: $\sum_{i=1}^{1} 5 \cdot 6^i = 6\left(6^1 - 1\right)$

$$5 \cdot 6^1 = 6(6 - 1)$$
$$5 \cdot 6 = 6 \cdot 5, \text{ True}$$

Show that if S_k is true, then S_{k+1} is true:

Assume $S_k : \sum_{i=1}^{k} 5 \cdot 6^i = 6\left(6^k - 1\right)$ is true. Then,

$$\sum_{i=1}^{k} 5 \cdot 6^i + 5 \cdot 6^{k+1} = 6\left(6^k - 1\right) + 5 \cdot 6^{k+1}$$

$$\sum_{i=1}^{k+1} 5 \cdot 6^i = 6^{k+1} - 6 + 5 \cdot 6^{k+1}$$

$$\sum_{i=1}^{k+1} 5 \cdot 6^i = 6 \cdot 6^{k+1} - 6$$

$$\sum_{i=1}^{k+1} 5 \cdot 6^i = 6\left(6^{k+1} - 1\right)$$

The final statement is S_{k+1}. Thus, by mathematical induction, we have proven that $\sum_{i=1}^{n} 5 \cdot 6^i = 6\left(6^n - 1\right)$.

31. $n + 2 > n$

Show that S_1 is true: $1 + 2 > 1$
$$3 > 1, \text{ True}$$

Show that if S_k is true, then S_{k+1} is true:

Assume $S_k : k + 2 > k$ is true. Then,
$$k + 2 + 1 > k + 1$$
$$(k + 1) + 2 > k + 1$$

The final statement is S_{k+1}. Thus, by mathematical induction, we have proven that $n + 2 > n$.

33. $S_1 : (ab)^1 = a^1 b^1$

$ab = ab$ is true.

$S_k : (ab)^k = a^k b^k$

$S_{k+1} : (ab)^{k+1} = a^{k+1} b^{k+1}$

Multiply both sides of S_k by ab:

$$(ab)^k (ab) = a^k b^k (ab)$$
$$(ab)^{k+1} = a^{k+1} b^{k+1}$$

If S_k is true, then S_{k+1} is true.
The statement is true for all n.

37. $n^2 > 2n + 1$ for $n \geq 3$

$\quad S_3: 3^2 > 2 \cdot 3 + 1$

$\qquad 9 > 7$

$\quad S_k: k^2 > 2k + 1$ for $k \geq 3$

$S_{k+1}: (k+1)^2 > 2k + 3$.

Add $2k + 1$ to both sides of S_k.

$k^2 + (2k+1) > 2k + 1 + (2k+1)$

Write the left side of the inequalities as the square of a binomial and simplify the right side. $(k+1)^2 > 4k + 2$

Since $4k + 2 > 2k + 3$ for $k \geq 3$, we can conclude that $(k+1)^2 > 4k + 2 > 2k + 3$.

By the transitive property,

$(k+1)^2 > 2k + 3$

$(k+1)^2 > 2(k+1) + 1$

If S_k is true, then S_{k+1} is true.

The statement is true for all n.

39. $S_1 = \dfrac{1}{4} = \dfrac{1}{4}$

$S_2 = \dfrac{1}{4} + \dfrac{1}{12} = \dfrac{1}{3}$

$S_3 = \dfrac{1}{4} + \dfrac{1}{12} + \dfrac{1}{24} = \dfrac{3}{8}$

$S_4 = \dfrac{1}{4} + \dfrac{1}{12} + \dfrac{1}{24} + \dfrac{1}{40} = \dfrac{2}{5}$

$S_5 = \dfrac{1}{4} + \dfrac{1}{12} + \dfrac{1}{24} + \dfrac{1}{40} + \dfrac{1}{60} = \dfrac{5}{12}$

$S_n = \dfrac{1}{4} + \dfrac{1}{12} + \dfrac{1}{24} + \cdots + \dfrac{1}{2n(n+1)} = \dfrac{n}{2n+2}$

$S_k = \dfrac{1}{4} + \dfrac{1}{12} + \dfrac{1}{24} + \cdots + \dfrac{1}{2k(k+1)} = \dfrac{k}{2k+2}$

$S_{k+1} = \dfrac{1}{4} + \dfrac{1}{12} + \dfrac{1}{24} + \cdots + \dfrac{1}{2k(k+1)} + \dfrac{1}{2(k+1)(k+2)} = \dfrac{k+1}{2k+4}$

Add $\dfrac{1}{2(k+1)(k+2)}$ to both sides of S_k:

$\dfrac{1}{4} + \dfrac{1}{12} + \dfrac{1}{24} + \cdots + \dfrac{1}{2k(k+1)} + \dfrac{1}{2(k+1)(k+2)} = \dfrac{k}{2k+2} + \dfrac{1}{2(k+1)(k+2)}$

Simplify the right-hand side:

$\dfrac{k}{2k+2} + \dfrac{1}{2(k+1)(k+2)} = \dfrac{k(k+2)+1}{2(k+1)(k+2)} = \dfrac{k^2+2k+1}{2(k+1)(k+2)} = \dfrac{(k+1)^2}{2(k+1)(k+2)} = \dfrac{k+1}{2k+4}$

If S_k is true, then S_{k+1} is true. The conjecture is proven.

Section 8.5

Check Point Exercises

1. a. $\dbinom{6}{3} = \dfrac{6!}{3!(6-3)!} = \dfrac{6!}{3!3!} = \dfrac{5 \cdot 4}{1} = 20$

    b. $\dbinom{6}{0} = \dfrac{6!}{0!(6-0)!} = \dfrac{6!}{6!} = 1$

    c. $\dbinom{8}{2} = \dfrac{8!}{2!(8-2)!} = \dfrac{8!}{2!6!} = \dfrac{8 \cdot 7}{2} = 28$

    d. $\dbinom{3}{3} = \dfrac{3!}{3!(3-3)!} = \dfrac{3!}{3!0!} = \dfrac{3!}{3!} = 1$

2. $(x+1)^4 = \dbinom{4}{0}x^4 + \dbinom{4}{1}x^3 + \dbinom{4}{2}x^2 + \dbinom{4}{1}x + \dbinom{4}{0} = x^4 + 4x^3 + 6x^2 + 4x + 1$

3. $(x-2y)^5 = \dbinom{5}{0}x^5(-2y)^0 + \dbinom{5}{1}x^4(-2y)^1 + \dbinom{5}{2}x^3(-2y)^2 + \dbinom{5}{3}x^2(-2y)^3 + \dbinom{5}{4}x(-2y)^4 + \dbinom{5}{5}x^0(-2y)^5$

    $= x^5 - 5x^4(2y) + 10x^3(4y^2) - 10x^2(8y^3) + 5x(16y^4) - 32y^5$

    $= x^5 - 10x^4 y + 40x^3 y^2 - 80x^2 y^3 + 80xy^4 - 32y^5$

4. $(2x+y)^9$

    fifth term $= \dbinom{9}{4}(2x)^5 y^4 = \dfrac{9!}{4!5!}(32x^5)y^4 = 4032x^5 y^4$

Exercise Set 8.5

1. $\dbinom{8}{3} = \dfrac{8!}{3!(8-3)!} = \dfrac{8 \cdot 7 \cdot 6}{3 \cdot 2 \cdot 1} = 56$

3. $\dbinom{12}{1} = \dfrac{12!}{1!11!} = 12$

5. $\dbinom{6}{6} = \dfrac{6!}{0!6!} = 1$

7. $\dbinom{100}{2} = \dfrac{100!}{2!98!} = \dfrac{100 \cdot 99}{2} = 4950$

9. $(x+2)^3 = \dbinom{3}{0}x^3 + \dbinom{3}{1}2x^2 + \dbinom{3}{2}4x + \dbinom{3}{3}8 = x^3 + 3x^2 \cdot 2 + 3x \cdot 4 + 8 = x^3 + 6x^2 + 12x + 8$

11. $(3x+y)^3 = \dbinom{3}{0}27x^3 + \dbinom{3}{1}9x^2 y + \dbinom{3}{2}3xy^2 + \dbinom{3}{3}y^3 = 27x^3 + 27x^2 y + 9xy^2 + y^3$

13. $(5x-1)^3 = \binom{3}{0}125x^3 - \binom{3}{1}25x^2 + \binom{3}{2}5x - \binom{3}{3} = 125x^3 - 75x^2 + 15x - 1$

15. $(2x+1)^4 = \binom{4}{0}16x^4 - \binom{4}{1}8x^3 + \binom{4}{2}4x^2 + \binom{4}{3}2x + \binom{4}{4} = 16x^4 + 32x^3 + 24x^2 + 8x + 1$

17. $(x^2+2y)^4 = \binom{4}{0}(x^2)^4 + \binom{4}{1}(x^2)^3(2y) + \binom{4}{2}(x^2)^2(2y)^2 + \binom{4}{3}(x^2)^1(2y)^3 + \binom{4}{4}(2y)^4$

$\qquad = 1(x^8) + 4(x^6)(2y) + 6(x^4)(4y^2) + 4x^2(8y^3) + 1(16y^4)$

$\qquad = x^8 + 8x^6 y + 24x^4 y^2 + 32x^2 y^3 + 16y^4$

19. $(y-3)^4 = \binom{4}{0}y^4 + \binom{4}{1}y^3(-3) + \binom{4}{2}y^2(-3)^2 + \binom{4}{3}y(-3)^3 + \binom{4}{4}(-3)^4$

$\qquad = y^4 + 4(y^3)(-3) + 6(y^2)(9) + 4(y)(-27) + 81$

$\qquad = y^4 - 12y^3 + 54y^2 - 108y + 81$

21. $(2x^3-1)^4 = \binom{4}{0}(2x^3)^4 + \binom{4}{1}(2x^3)^3(-1) + \binom{4}{2}(2x^3)^2(-1)^2 + \binom{4}{3}(2x^3)(-1)^3 + \binom{4}{4}(-1)^4$

$\qquad = 16x^{12} - 4(8x^9) + 6(4x^6) - 4(2x^3) + 1$

$\qquad = 16x^{12} - 32x^9 + 24x^6 - 8x^3 + 1$

23. $(c+2)^5 = \binom{5}{0}c^5 + \binom{5}{1}c^4(2) + \binom{5}{2}c^3(2^2) + \binom{5}{3}c^2(2^3) + \binom{5}{4}c(2^4) + \binom{5}{5}(2^5)$

$\qquad = c^5 + 5c^4(2) + 10c^3(4) + 10c^2(8) + 5c(16) + 32$

$\qquad = c^5 + 10c^4 + 40c^3 + 80c^2 + 80c + 32$

25. $(x-1)^5 = \binom{5}{0}x^5 - \binom{5}{1}x^4 + \binom{5}{2}x^3 - \binom{5}{3}x^2 + \binom{5}{4}x - \binom{5}{5} = x^5 - 5x^4 + 10x^3 - 10x^2 + 5x - 1$

27. $(3x-y)^5 = \binom{5}{0}(3x)^5 - \binom{5}{1}(3x)^4 y + \binom{5}{2}(3x)^3 y^2 - \binom{5}{3}(3x)^2 y^3 + \binom{5}{4}3xy^4 - \binom{5}{5}y^5$

$\qquad = (1)243x^5 - 5(81x^4)y + 10(27x^3)y^2 - 10(9x^2)y^3 + 5(3x)y^4 - (1)y^5$

$\qquad = 243x^5 - 405x^4 y + 270x^3 y^2 - 90x^2 y^3 + 15xy^4 - y^5$

29. $(2a+b)^6 = \binom{6}{0}(2a)^6 + \binom{6}{1}(2a)^5 b + \binom{6}{2}(2a)^4 b^2 + \binom{6}{3}(2a)^3 b^3 + \binom{6}{4}(2a)^2 b^4 + \binom{6}{5}(2a)b^5 + \binom{6}{6}b^6$

$\qquad = 64a^6 + 6(32a^5)b + 15(16a^4)b^2 + 20(8a^3)b^3 + 15(4a^2)b^4 + 6(2a)b^5 + b^6$

$\qquad = 64a^6 + 192a^5 b + 240a^4 b^2 + 160a^3 b^3 + 60a^2 b^4 + 12ab^5 + b^6$

31.
$$(x+2)^8 = \binom{8}{0}x^8 + \binom{8}{1}x^7 2 + \binom{8}{3}x^6(2)^2 + \cdots$$
$$= x^8 + 16x^7 + 112x^6 + \cdots$$

33.
$$(x-2y)^{10} = \binom{10}{0}x^{10} - \binom{10}{1}x^9(2y) + \binom{10}{2}x^8(2y)^2 - \cdots$$
$$= x^{10} - 20x^9 y + 180x^8 y^2 - \cdots$$

35.
$$(x^2+1)^{16} = \binom{16}{0}(x^2)^{16} + \binom{16}{1}(x^2)^{15} + \binom{16}{2}(x^2)^{14} + \cdots$$
$$= x^{32} + 16x^{30} + 120x^{28} + \cdots$$

37.
$$(y^3-1)^{20} = \binom{20}{0}(y^3)^{20} - \binom{20}{1}(y^3)^{19} + \binom{20}{2}(y^3)^{18} - \cdots$$
$$= y^{60} - 20y^{57} + 190y^{54} - \cdots$$

39. $(2x+y)^6;$ third term $= \binom{6}{2}(2x)^4(y)^2 = 15(16x^4 y^2) = 240x^4 y^2$

41. $(x-1)^9;$ fifth term $= \binom{9}{4}x^5(-1)^4 = 126x^5$

43. $(x^2+y^3)^8;$ sixth term $= \binom{8}{5}(x^2)^3(y^3)^5 = 56x^6 y^{15}$

45. $(x-\frac{1}{2})^9;$ fourth term $= \binom{9}{3}x^6\left(-\frac{1}{2}\right)^3 = 84x^6\left(-\frac{1}{8}\right) = -\frac{21}{2}x^6$

47. $\binom{22}{14}(x^2)^8 y^{14} = 319,770x^{16} y^{14}$

49.
$$(x^3+x^{-2})^4 = \binom{4}{0}(x^3)^4 + \binom{4}{1}(x^3)^3(x^{-2}) + \binom{4}{2}(x^3)^2(x^{-2})^2 + \binom{4}{3}(x^3)^1(x^{-2})^3 + \binom{4}{4}(x^{-2})^4$$
$$= \frac{4!}{0!(4-0)!}x^{12} + \frac{4!}{1!(4-1)!}x^9 x^{-2} + \frac{4!}{2!(4-2)!}x^6 x^{-4} + \frac{4!}{3!(4-3)!}x^3 x^{-6} + \frac{4!}{4!(4-4)!}x^{-8}$$
$$= \frac{4!}{0! \cdot 4!}x^{12} + \frac{4 \cdot 3!}{1! \cdot 3!}x^7 + \frac{4 \cdot 3 \cdot 2!}{2 \cdot 1 \cdot 2!}x^2 + \frac{4 \cdot 3!}{3! \cdot 1!}x^{-3} + \frac{4!}{4! \cdot 0!}x^{-8}$$
$$= x^{12} + 4x^7 + 6x^2 + \frac{4}{x^3} + \frac{1}{x^8}$$

51.

$$\left(x^{\frac{1}{3}}-x^{-\frac{1}{3}}\right)^3 = \left(x^{\frac{1}{3}}+\left(-x^{-\frac{1}{3}}\right)\right)^3 = \binom{3}{0}\left(x^{\frac{1}{3}}\right)^3 + \binom{3}{1}\left(x^{\frac{1}{3}}\right)^2\left(-x^{-\frac{1}{3}}\right)+$$

$$+\binom{3}{2}\left(x^{\frac{1}{3}}\right)^1\left(-x^{-\frac{1}{3}}\right)^2 + \binom{3}{3}\left(-x^{-\frac{1}{3}}\right)^3$$

$$=\frac{3!}{0!(3-0)!}x^1 + \frac{3!}{1!(3-1)!}x^{\frac{2}{3}}\cdot -x^{-\frac{1}{3}} + \frac{3!}{2!(3-2)!}x^{\frac{1}{3}}x^{-\frac{2}{3}} + \frac{3!}{3!(3-3)!}\cdot -x^{-1}$$

$$=\frac{\cancel{3!}}{0!\cdot\cancel{3!}}x + \frac{3\cdot\cancel{2!}}{1!\cdot\cancel{2!}}\cdot -x^{\frac{1}{3}} + \frac{\cdot 3\cdot\cancel{2!}}{\cancel{2!}\cdot 1!}x^{-\frac{1}{3}} + \frac{\cancel{3!}}{\cancel{3!}\cdot 0!}\cdot -x^{-1}$$

$$=x-3x^{\frac{1}{3}}+\frac{3}{x^{\frac{1}{3}}}-\frac{1}{x}$$

53. $f(x)=x^4+7$;

$$\frac{f(x+h)-f(x)}{h}$$

$$=\frac{(x+h)^4+7-\left(x^4+7\right)}{h}$$

$$=\frac{\binom{4}{0}x^4 + \binom{4}{1}x^3h + \binom{4}{2}x^2h^2 + \binom{4}{3}xh^3 + \binom{4}{4}h^4 + 7 - x^4 - 7}{h}$$

$$=\frac{\frac{4!}{0!(4-0)!}x^4 + \frac{4!}{1!(4-1)!}x^3h + \frac{4!}{2!(4-2)!}x^2h^2 + \frac{4!}{3!(4-3)!}xh^3 + \frac{4!}{4!(4-4)!}h^4 - x^4}{h}$$

$$=\frac{\frac{\cancel{4!}}{0!\cancel{4!}}x^4 + \frac{4\cdot\cancel{3!}}{1!\cancel{3!}}x^3h + \frac{4\cdot 3\cdot\cancel{2!}}{\cancel{2!}\cdot 2\cdot 1}x^2h^2 + \frac{4\cdot\cancel{3!}}{\cancel{3!}1!}xh^3 + \frac{\cancel{4!}}{\cancel{4!}0!}h^4 - x^4}{h}$$

$$=\frac{\cancel{x^4} + 4x^3h + 6x^2h^2 + 4xh^3 + h^4 - \cancel{x^4}}{h}$$

$$=\frac{h(4x^3 + 6x^2h + 4xh^2 + h^3)}{h}$$

$$=4x^3 + 6x^2h + 4xh^2 + h^3$$

55.   We want to find the $(5+1)=6^{th}$ term.

$$\binom{n}{r}a^{n-r}b^r = \binom{10}{5}\left(\frac{3}{x}\right)^{10-5}\left(\frac{x}{3}\right)^5 = \frac{10!}{5!(10-5)!}\left(\frac{3}{x}\right)^5\left(\frac{x}{3}\right)^5$$

$$=\frac{10\cdot 9\cdot 8\cdot 7\cdot 6\cdot\cancel{5!}}{\cancel{5!}\cdot\cancel{5}\cdot 4\cdot 3\cdot\cancel{2}\cdot 1}\left(\frac{3}{x}\right)^5\left(\frac{x}{3}\right)^5 = 252\cdot\frac{3^5}{x^5}\cdot\frac{x^5}{3^5} = 252$$

57.   **a.** $f(x) = -x^3 + 11x^2 + x + 31$

$f(x+3) = -(x+3)^3 + 11(x+3)^2 + (x+3) + 31$

$g(x) = -(x^3 + 9x^2 + 27x + 27) + 11(x^2 + 6x + 9) + x + 3 + 31$

$\quad\quad = -x^3 - 9x^2 - 27x - 27 + 11x^2 + 66x + 99 + x + 3 + 31$

$\quad\quad = -x^3 + 2x^2 + 40x + 106$

     b. $f(3) = -(3)^3 + 11(3)^2 + (3) + 31 = 106$

$g(0) = -(0)^3 + 2(0)^2 + 40(0) + 106 = 106$

These functions model the graph's value of 103 reasonably well.

69. $f_1(x) = (x+1)^4$

$f_2(x) = x^4$

$f_3(x) = x^4 + 4x^3$

$f_4(x) = x^4 + 4x^3 + 6x^2$

$f_5(x) = x^4 + 4x^3 + 6x^2 + 4x$

$f_6(x) = x^4 + 4x^3 + 6x^2 + 4x + 1$

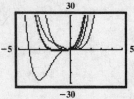

$f_2, f_3, f_4,$ and f_5 are approaching $f_1 = f_6$.

71. $f_1(x) = (x-2)^4$

$= \binom{4}{0}x^4 + \binom{4}{1}x^3(-2) + \binom{4}{2}x^2(-2)^2 + \binom{4}{3}x(-2)^3 + \binom{4}{4}(-2)^4$

$= x^4 + 4x^3(-2) + 6x^2(4) + 4x(-8) + 16$

$= x^4 - 8x^3 + 24x^2 - 32x + 16$

73.   **a.**   False; it contains $n + 1$ terms.

     b.   True

     c.   False; let $a = 1$ and $b = 1$. Thus $\sum_{r=0}^{n}\binom{n}{r}a^{n-r}b^r = \sum_{r=0}^{n}\binom{n}{r} = (1+1)^n = 2^n$.

     d.   False; for example, let $a = 0$ and $b = 0$.

     (b) is true.

75. $\left(x^2 + y^2\right)^5$

Since $\left(x^2\right)^2 = x^4$, the fourth term will contain x^4 : fourth term $= \binom{5}{3}\left(x^2\right)^2\left(y^2\right)^3 = 10x^4 y^6$

77.

$$\binom{n}{r}+\binom{n}{r+1}=\frac{n!}{r!(n-r)!}+\frac{n!}{(r+1)!(n-(r+1))!}$$

$$=\frac{n!}{r!(n-r)!}+\frac{n!}{(r+1)!(n-r-1)!}$$

$$=\frac{n!(r+1)}{(r+1)r!(n-r)!(n-r-1)!}+\frac{(n-r)n!}{(n-r)(r+1)!(n-r-1)!}$$

$$=\frac{n!(r+1)+n!(n-r)}{(r+1)!(n-r)!}$$

$$=\frac{n!(r+1+n-r)}{(r+1)!(n-r)!}$$

$$=\frac{n!(n+1)}{(r+1)!(n-r)!}$$

$$=\frac{(n+1)!}{(r+1)!(n+1-r-1)!}$$

$$=\frac{(n+1)!}{(r+1)!(n+1-(r+1))!}$$

$$=\binom{n+1}{r+1}$$

Section 8.6

Check Point Exercises

1. We use the Fundamental Counting Principal to find the number of ways a one-topping pizza can be ordered.
   Size : Crust : Topping:

   3 × 4 × 6 = 72

   There are 72 different ways of ordering a one-topping pizza.

2. We use the Fundamental Counting Principal to find the number of ways we can answer the questions.
   Question #1: Question #2: Question #3: Question #4: Question #5: Question #6:

   3 × 3 × 3 × 3 × 3 × 3 = 3^6 = 729

   There are 729 ways of answering the questions.

3. We use the Fundamental Counting Principal to find the number of different license plates that can be manufactured. Multiply the number of different letters, 26, for the first two places and the number of different digits, 10, for the next three places. $26\cdot26\cdot10\cdot10\cdot10=26^2\cdot1000=676,000$ plates There are 676,000 different license plates possible.

4. Your group is choosing $r=4$ officers from a group of $n=7$ people. The order in which the officers are chosen matters because the four officers to be chosen have different responsibilities. Thus, we are looking for the number of permutations of 7 things taken 4 at a time.

   We use the formula $_nP_r=\frac{n!}{(n-r)!}$ with $n=7$ and $r=4$. $_7P_4=\frac{7!}{(7-4)!}=\frac{7!}{3!}=840.$

   Thus, there are 840 different ways of filling the four offices.

5. Because you are using all six of your books in every possible arrangement, you are arranging $r = 6$ books from a group of $n = 6$ books. Thus, we are looking for the number of permutations of 6 things taken 6 at a time. We use the formula

$$_n P_r = \frac{n!}{(n-r)!} \text{ with } n = 6 \text{ and } r = 6.$$

$$_6 P_6 = \frac{6!}{(6-6)!} = \frac{6!}{0!} = 6! = 720.$$

There are 720 different possible permutations. Thus, you can arrange the books in 720 ways.

6. **a.** The order does not matter; this is a combination.

    b. Since what place each runner finishes matters, this is a permutation.

7. The order in which the four people are selected does not matter. This is a problem of selecting $r = 4$ people from a group of $n = 10$ people. We are looking for the number of combinations of 10 things taken 4 at a time. We use the formula

$$_n C_r = \frac{n!}{(n-r)! \; r!} \text{ with } n = 10 \text{ and } r = 4.$$

$$_{10} C_4 = \frac{10!}{(10-4)!4!} = \frac{10!}{6!4!} = \frac{10 \cdot 9 \cdot 8 \cdot 7 \cdot 6!}{6! \cdot 4 \cdot 3 \cdot 2 \cdot 1} = \frac{10 \cdot 9 \cdot 8 \cdot 7}{4 \cdot 3 \cdot 2 \cdot 1} = 210$$

Thus, 210 committees of 4 people each can be found from 10 people at the conference on acupuncture.

8. Because the order in which the 4 cards are dealt does not matter, this is a problem involving combinations. We are looking for the number of combinations of $n = 16$ cards drawn $r = 4$ at a time. We use the formula

$$_n C_r = \frac{n!}{(n-r)! \; r!} \text{ with } n = 16 \text{ and } r = 4.$$

$$_{16} C_4 = \frac{16!}{(16-4)!4!} = \frac{16!}{12!4!} = \frac{16 \cdot 15 \cdot 14 \cdot 13 \cdot 12!}{12! \cdot 4 \cdot 3 \cdot 2 \cdot 1} = 1820$$

Thus, there are 1820 different 4-card hands possible.

Exercise Set 8.6

1. $_9 P_4 = \dfrac{9!}{5!} = 3024$

3. $_8 P_5 = \dfrac{8!}{3!} = 8 \cdot 7 \cdot 6 \cdot 5 \cdot 4 = 6720$

5. $_6 P_6 = \dfrac{6!}{0!} = 720$

7. $_8 P_0 = \dfrac{8!}{8!} = 1$

9. $_9 C_5 = \dfrac{9!}{4!5!} = \dfrac{9 \cdot 8 \cdot 7 \cdot 6}{4 \cdot 3 \cdot 2 \cdot 1} = \dfrac{3 \cdot 7 \cdot 6}{1} = 126$

11. $_{11} C_4 = \dfrac{11!}{7!4!} = \dfrac{11 \cdot 10 \cdot 9 \cdot 8}{4 \cdot 3 \cdot 2 \cdot 1} = \dfrac{11 \cdot 10 \cdot 3}{1} = 330$

13. $_7C_7 = \dfrac{7!}{0!7!} = 1$

15. $_5C_0 = \dfrac{5!}{5!0!} = 1$

17. combinations; The order in which the volunteers are chosen does not matter.

19. permutations; The order of the letters matters because ABCD is not the same as BADC.

21. $\dfrac{_7P_3}{3!} - {}_7C_3 = \dfrac{\dfrac{7!}{(7-3)!}}{3!} - \dfrac{7!}{(7-3)!3!} = \dfrac{\dfrac{7!}{4!}}{3!} - \dfrac{7!}{4!3!} = \dfrac{7!}{4!3!} - \dfrac{7!}{4!3!} = 0$

23. $1 - \dfrac{_3P_2}{_4P_3} = 1 - \dfrac{\dfrac{3!}{(3-2)!}}{\dfrac{4!}{(4-3)!}} = 1 - \dfrac{\dfrac{3!}{1!}}{\dfrac{4!}{1!}} = 1 - \dfrac{3!}{4!} = 1 - \dfrac{3!}{4\cdot3!} = 1 - \dfrac{1}{4} = \dfrac{3}{4}$

25. $\dfrac{_7C_3}{_5C_4} - \dfrac{98!}{96!} = \dfrac{\dfrac{7!}{(7-3)!3!}}{\dfrac{5!}{(5-4)!4!}} - \dfrac{98\cdot97\cdot96!}{96!} = \dfrac{\dfrac{7!}{4!3!}}{\dfrac{5!}{1!4!}} - 95067 = \dfrac{\dfrac{7\cdot6\cdot5\cdot4!}{4!3\cdot2\cdot1}}{\dfrac{5\cdot4!}{1!4!}} - 9506 = \dfrac{35}{5} - 9506 = 7 - 9506 = -9499$

27. $\dfrac{_4C_2 \cdot {}_6C_1}{_{18}C_3} = \dfrac{\dfrac{4!}{(4-2)!2!} \cdot \dfrac{6!}{(6-1)!1!}}{\dfrac{18!}{(18-3)!3!}} = \dfrac{\dfrac{4!}{2!2!} \cdot \dfrac{6!}{5!1!}}{\dfrac{18!}{15!3!}} = \dfrac{\dfrac{4\cdot3\cdot2!}{2!2\cdot1} \cdot \dfrac{6\cdot5!}{5!1!}}{\dfrac{18\cdot17\cdot16\cdot15!}{15!3\cdot2\cdot1}} = \dfrac{36}{816} = \dfrac{3}{68}$

29. $9\cdot3 = 27$ ways

31. $2\cdot4\cdot5 = 40$ ways

33. $3^5 = 243$ ways

35. $8\cdot2\cdot9 = 144$ area codes

37. $5\cdot4\cdot3\cdot2\cdot1\cdot1 = 120$ ways

39. $1\cdot3\cdot2\cdot1\cdot1 = 6$ paragraphs

41. $_{10}P_3 = \dfrac{10!}{7!3!} = 10\cdot9\cdot8 = 720$ ways

43. $_{13}P_7 = \dfrac{13!}{6!} = 13\cdot12\cdot11\cdot10\cdot9\cdot8\cdot7$
$= 8,648,640$ ways

45. $_6P_3 = \dfrac{6!}{3!} = 6\cdot5\cdot4 = 120$ ways

47. $_9P_5 = \dfrac{9!}{4!} = 9\cdot8\cdot7\cdot6\cdot5 = 15,120$ lineups

49. $_6C_3 = \dfrac{6!}{3!3!} = \dfrac{6\cdot5\cdot4}{3\cdot2\cdot1} = 20$ ways

51. $_{12}C_4 = \dfrac{12!}{8!4!} = \dfrac{12\cdot11\cdot10\cdot9}{4\cdot3\cdot2\cdot1}$
$= 495$ collections

53. $_{17}C_8 = \dfrac{17!}{9!8!} = \dfrac{17\cdot16\cdot15\cdot14\cdot13\cdot12\cdot11\cdot10}{8\cdot7\cdot6\cdot5\cdot4\cdot3\cdot2\cdot1}$
$= 24,310$ groups

55. $_{53}C_6 = \dfrac{53!}{47!6!} = 22,957,480$ selections

57. $_6P_4 = \dfrac{6!}{2!} = 6\cdot5\cdot4\cdot3 = 360$ ways

59. $_{13}C_6 = \dfrac{13!}{7!6!} = \dfrac{13 \cdot 12 \cdot 11 \cdot 10 \cdot 9 \cdot 8}{6 \cdot 5 \cdot 4 \cdot 3 \cdot 2 \cdot 1}$

$\quad = 1716$ ways

61. $_{20}C_3 = \dfrac{20!}{17!3!} = \dfrac{20 \cdot 19 \cdot 18}{3 \cdot 2 \cdot 1} = 1140$ ways

63. $_7P_4 = \dfrac{7!}{3!} = 840$ passwords

65. $_{15}P_3 = \dfrac{15!}{12!} = 15 \cdot 14 \cdot 13 = 2730$ cones

77. **a.** False; the number of ways is $_{10}C_4$.

    b. False;

$$_nP_r = \frac{n!}{(n-r)!} > \frac{n!}{(n-r)!r!} = {_nC_r} \text{ if } r>1$$

    c. True; $_7P_3 = \dfrac{7!}{4!} = 3!\dfrac{7!}{4!3!} = 3!\, _7C_3$

    d. False;

        the number of ways is $20 \cdot 19 = {_{20}P_2}$.

        (c) is true.

79. $2 \cdot 6 \cdot 6 \cdot 2 = 144$ numbers

Section 8.7

Check Point Exercises

1. **a.** $P(\text{positive test}) = \dfrac{\text{\# women w/positive test}}{\text{total number of women}} = \dfrac{7664}{100,000} = \dfrac{479}{6250} \approx 0.077$

    b. $P(\text{positive test}) = \dfrac{\text{\# women w/breast cancer and positive test}}{\text{total number of women w/breast cancer}} = \dfrac{720}{800} = \dfrac{9}{10} = 0.9$

    c. $P(\text{breast cancer}) = \dfrac{\text{\# women w/breast cancer and positive test}}{\text{total number of women w/positive test}} = \dfrac{720}{7664} = \dfrac{45}{479} = 0.094$

2. The sample space of equally likely outcomes is $S = \{1, 2, 3, 4, 5, 6\}$. There are six outcomes in the sample space, so $n(S) = 6$. The event of getting a number greater than 4 can be represented by $E = \{5, 6\}$. There are two outcomes in this event, so $n(E) = 2$.

The probability of rolling a number greater than 4 is $P(E) = \dfrac{n(E)}{n(S)} = \dfrac{2}{6} = \dfrac{1}{3}$.

3. We have $n(S) = 36$. The phrase "getting a sum of 5" describes the event $E = \{(1,4),(2,3),(3,2),(4,1)\}$. This event has 4 outcomes, so $n(E) = 4$. Thus, the probability of getting a sum of 5 is $P(E) = \dfrac{n(E)}{n(S)} = \dfrac{4}{36} = \dfrac{1}{9}$.

4. Let E be the event of being dealt a king. Because there are 4 kings in the deck, the event of being dealt a king can occur in 4 ways, i.e., $n(E) = 4$. With 52 cards in the deck, $n(S) = 52$.

The probability of being dealt a king is $P(E) = \dfrac{n(E)}{n(S)} = \dfrac{4}{52} = \dfrac{1}{13}$.

5. Because the order of the six numbers does not matter, this is a situation involving combinations. With one lottery ticket, there is only one way of winning so $n(E) = 1$. Using the combinations formula $_nC_r = \dfrac{n!}{(n-r)!r!}$ to find the number of outcomes in the sample space, we are selecting $r = 6$ numbers from a collection of $n = 49$ numbers.

    $_{49}C_6 = \dfrac{49!}{43! \, 6!} = 13,983,816$ So $n(S) = 13,983,816$. If a person bought one lottery ticket, the probability of winning was $P(E) = \dfrac{n(E)}{n(S)} = \dfrac{1}{13,983,816}$

    The probability of winning the state lottery was 0.0000000715.

6. $P(\text{not in Marines}) = 1 - P(\text{in Marines}) = 1 - \dfrac{170+10}{1430} = \dfrac{1250}{1430} = \dfrac{125}{143}$

7. We find the probability that either of these mutually exclusive events will occur by adding their individual probabilities.

    $P(4 \text{ or } 5) = P(4) + P(5) = \dfrac{1}{6} + \dfrac{1}{6} = \dfrac{2}{6} = \dfrac{1}{3}$

    The probability of selecting a 4 or a 5 is $\dfrac{1}{3}$.

8. It is possible for the pointer to land on a number that is odd and less than 5. Two of the numbers , 1 and 3, are odd and less than 5. These events are not mutually exclusive. The probability of landing on a number that is odd and less than 5 is P (odd or less than 5)

    $= P \text{ (odd)} + P \text{ (less than 5)} - P \text{ (odd and less than 5)} = \dfrac{4}{8} + \dfrac{4}{8} - \dfrac{2}{8} = \dfrac{6}{8} = \dfrac{3}{4}$

    The probability that the pointer will stop on an odd number or a number less than 5 is $\dfrac{3}{4}$.

9. $P(\text{Navy or man}) = P(\text{Navy}) + P(\text{man}) - P(\text{both}) = \dfrac{380}{1430} + \dfrac{1210}{1430} - \dfrac{320}{1430} = \dfrac{1270}{1430} = \dfrac{127}{143}$

10. The wheel has 38 equally likely outcomes and 2 are green. Thus, the probability of a green occurring on a play is $\dfrac{2}{38}$, or $\dfrac{1}{19}$. The result that occurs on each play is independent of all previous results. Thus,

    $P \text{ (green and green)} = P \text{ (green)} \cdot P \text{ (green)} = \dfrac{1}{19} \cdot \dfrac{1}{19} = \dfrac{1}{361} \approx 0.00277$.

    The probability of green occurring on two consecutive plays is $\dfrac{1}{361}$.

11. If two or more events are independent, we can find the probability of them all occurring by multiplying the probabilities. The probability of a baby boy is $\dfrac{1}{2}$, so the probability of having four boys in a row is P (4 boys in a row) $= \dfrac{1}{2} \cdot \dfrac{1}{2} \cdot \dfrac{1}{2} \cdot \dfrac{1}{2} = \dfrac{1}{16}$.

557

Exercise Set 8.7

1. $P(\text{female}) = \dfrac{23}{89}$

3. $P(\text{in the Army}) = \dfrac{36}{89}$

5. $P(\text{a woman in the Air Force}) = \dfrac{6}{89}$

7. $P(\text{woman, among Air Force}) = \dfrac{6}{18} = \dfrac{1}{3}$

9. $P(\text{woman in Air Force}) = \dfrac{6}{23}$

11. $P(R) = \dfrac{n(E)}{n(S)} = \dfrac{1}{6}$

13. $P(E) = \dfrac{n(E)}{n(S)} = \dfrac{3}{6} = \dfrac{1}{2}$

15. $P(E) = \dfrac{n(E)}{n(S)} = \dfrac{2}{6} = \dfrac{1}{3}$

17. $P(E) = \dfrac{n(E)}{n(S)} = \dfrac{4}{52} = \dfrac{1}{13}$

19. $P(E) = \dfrac{n(E)}{n(S)} = \dfrac{12}{52} = \dfrac{3}{13}$

21. $P(E) = \dfrac{n(E)}{n(S)} = \dfrac{1}{4}$

23. $P(E) = \dfrac{n(E)}{n(S)} = \dfrac{7}{8}$

25. $P(E) = \dfrac{n(E)}{n(S)} = \dfrac{3}{36} = \dfrac{1}{12}$

27. Buying 1 ticket:
$$P(E) = \frac{n(E)}{n(S)} = \frac{1}{{}_{51}C_6} = \frac{1}{18,009,460}$$
Buying 100 tickets:
$$P(E) = \frac{100}{18,009,460} = \frac{5}{900,473}$$

29. a. $\quad {}_{52}C_5 = \dfrac{52!}{47!5!}$
$$= \frac{52 \cdot 51 \cdot 50 \cdot 49 \cdot 48}{5 \cdot 4 \cdot 3 \cdot 2 \cdot 1} = 2,598,960$$

  b. $\quad {}_{13}C_5 = \dfrac{13!}{8!5!} = \dfrac{13 \cdot 12 \cdot 11 \cdot 10 \cdot 9}{5 \cdot 4 \cdot 3 \cdot 2 \cdot 1} = 1287$

  c. $\quad P(E) = \dfrac{n(E)}{n(S)} = \dfrac{1287}{2,598,960} \approx 0.0005$

31.
$$P(\text{not completed 4 years of college}) = 1 - P(\text{completed 4 years of college}) = 1 - \frac{45}{174} = \frac{43}{58}$$

33. $P(\text{completed H.S. or less than 4 yrs college}) = P(\text{completed H.S}) + P(\text{less than 4 yrs college})$
$$= \frac{56}{174} + \frac{44}{174} = \frac{100}{174} = \frac{50}{87}$$

35. $P(\text{completed 4 yrs H.S. or man}) = P(\text{completed 4 yrs H.S.}) + P(\text{man}) - P(\text{man who completed 4 yrs H.S})$
$$= \frac{56}{174} + \frac{82}{174} - \frac{25}{174} = \frac{113}{174}$$

37. $P(\text{not king}) = 1 - P(\text{king}) = 1 - \dfrac{4}{52} = 1 - \dfrac{1}{13} = \dfrac{12}{13}$

39. $P(2 \text{ or } 3) = P(2) + P(3) = \dfrac{4}{52} + \dfrac{4}{52} = \dfrac{8}{52} = \dfrac{2}{13}$

41. $P(7 \text{ or red card}) = P(7) + P(\text{red card}) - P(7 \text{ and red}) = \dfrac{4}{52} + \dfrac{26}{52} - \dfrac{2}{52} = \dfrac{28}{52} = \dfrac{7}{13}$

43 $P(\text{odd or less than } 6) = P(\text{odd}) + P(\text{less than } 6) - P(\text{odd \# less than } 6) = \dfrac{4}{8} + \dfrac{5}{8} - \dfrac{3}{8} = \dfrac{6}{8} = \dfrac{3}{4}$

45. $P(\text{professor or male}) = P(\text{professor}) + P(\text{male}) - P(\text{male professor}) = \dfrac{19}{40} + \dfrac{22}{40} - \dfrac{8}{40} = \dfrac{33}{40}$

47. $P(2 \text{ and } 3) = P(2) \cdot P(3) = \dfrac{1}{6} \cdot \dfrac{1}{6} = \dfrac{1}{36}$

49. $P(\text{even and greater than } 2) = P(\text{even}) \cdot P(\text{greater than } 2) = \dfrac{3}{6} \cdot \dfrac{4}{6} = \dfrac{1}{3}$

51. $P(\text{all heads}) = \dfrac{1}{2} \cdot \dfrac{1}{2} \cdot \dfrac{1}{2} \cdot \dfrac{1}{2} \cdot \dfrac{1}{2} \cdot \dfrac{1}{2} = \left(\dfrac{1}{2}\right)^6 = \dfrac{1}{64}$

53. a. $P(\text{hit 2 yrs in a row}) = P(\text{hit in 1}^{st} \text{ year and 2}^{nd} \text{ year}) = P(\text{hit 1}^{st} \text{ year}) \cdot P(\text{hit 2}^{nd} \text{ year}) = \dfrac{1}{16} \cdot \dfrac{1}{16} = \dfrac{1}{256}$

b. $P(\text{hit 3 yrs in a row}) = \dfrac{1}{16} \cdot \dfrac{1}{16} \cdot \dfrac{1}{16} = \dfrac{1}{4096}$

c. First find the probability that South Florida will not be hit by a major hurricane in a single year:

$P(\text{not hit}) = 1 - \dfrac{1}{16} = \dfrac{15}{16}$

$P(\text{not hit in next 10 years}) = \left(\dfrac{15}{16}\right)^{10} \approx 0.524$

d. $P(\text{hit at least once}) = 1 - P(\text{hit none}) = 1 - \left(\dfrac{15}{16}\right)^{10} \approx 0.476$

67. a. $P(\text{Democrat who is not a business major})$

$= \dfrac{\text{\# of students who are Democrats but not business majors}}{\text{\# of students}}$

$= \dfrac{29 - 5}{50} = \dfrac{24}{50} = \dfrac{12}{25}$

b. $P(\text{neither Democrat nor business major})$

$= 1 - P(\text{Democrat or business major})$

$= 1 - \big(P(\text{Democrat}) + P(\text{business major}) - P(\text{Democrat and business major})\big)$

$= 1 - \left(\dfrac{29}{50} + \dfrac{11}{50} - \dfrac{5}{50}\right) = 1 - \dfrac{35}{50} = \dfrac{15}{50} = \dfrac{3}{10}$

69. a. The first person can have any birthday in the year. The second person can have all but one birthday.

b. $\dfrac{365}{365} \cdot \dfrac{364}{365} \cdot \dfrac{363}{365} \approx 0.99$

c. $100\% - 99\% = 0.01$

d. $\dfrac{365}{365} \cdot \dfrac{364}{365} \cdot \dfrac{363}{365} \cdots \dfrac{346}{365} \approx 0.59$

$1 - 0.59 = 0.41$

e. With 23 people, the probability that at least two people have the same birthday is

$P(E) = 1 - \dfrac{365}{365} \cdot \dfrac{364}{365} \cdot \dfrac{363}{365} \cdots + \dfrac{342}{365}$

$\approx 1 - 0.4927 \approx 0.5073$

Chapter 8 Review Exercises

1. $a_n = 7n - 4$

$a_1 = 7 - 4 = 3$

$a_2 = 14 - 4 = 10$

$a_3 = 21 - 4 = 17$

$a_4 = 28 - 4 = 24$

First four terms: 3, 10, 17, 24.

2. $a_n = (-1)^n \dfrac{n+2}{n+1}$

$a_1 = (-1)^1 \dfrac{1+2}{1+1} = -\dfrac{3}{2}$

$a_2 = (-1)^2 \dfrac{2+2}{2+1} = \dfrac{4}{3}$

$a_3 = (-1)^3 \dfrac{3+2}{3+1} = -\dfrac{5}{4}$

$a_4 = (-1)^4 \dfrac{4+2}{4+1} = \dfrac{6}{5}$

First four terms: $-\dfrac{3}{2}, \dfrac{4}{3}, -\dfrac{5}{4}, \dfrac{6}{5}$.

3. $a_n = \dfrac{1}{(n-1)!}$

$a_1 = \dfrac{1}{0!} = 1$

$a_2 = \dfrac{1}{1!} = 1$

$a_3 = \dfrac{1}{2!} = \dfrac{1}{2}$

$a_4 = \dfrac{1}{3!} = \dfrac{1}{6}$

First four terms: $1, 1, \dfrac{1}{2}, \dfrac{1}{6}$.

4. $a_n = \dfrac{(-1)^{n+1}}{2^n}$

$a_1 = \dfrac{(-1)^2}{2^1} = \dfrac{1}{2}$

$a_2 = \dfrac{(-1)^3}{2^2} = -\dfrac{1}{4}$

$a_3 = \dfrac{(-1)^4}{2^3} = \dfrac{1}{8}$

$a_4 = \dfrac{(-1)^5}{2^4} = -\dfrac{1}{16}$

First four terms: $\dfrac{1}{2}, -\dfrac{1}{4}, \dfrac{1}{8}, -\dfrac{1}{16}$.

5. $a_1 = 9$ and $a_n = \dfrac{2}{3a_{n-1}}$

$a_1 = 9$

$a_2 = \dfrac{2}{3 \cdot 9} = \dfrac{2}{27}$

$a_3 = \dfrac{2}{3} \cdot \dfrac{27}{2} = \dfrac{54}{6} = 9$

$a_4 = \dfrac{2}{3 \cdot 9} = \dfrac{2}{27}$

First four terms: $9, \dfrac{2}{27}, 9, \dfrac{2}{27}$.

6. $a_1 = 4$ and $a_n = 2a_{n-1} + 3$

$a_1 = 4$

$a_2 = 2 \cdot 4 + 3 = 8 + 3 = 11$

$a_3 = 2 \cdot 11 + 3 = 22 + 3 = 25$

$a_4 = 2 \cdot 25 + 3 = 50 + 3 = 53$

First four terms: 4, 11, 25, and 53.

7. $\dfrac{40!}{4! \cdot 38!} = \dfrac{40 \cdot 39 \cdot 38!}{4 \cdot 3 \cdot 2 \cdot 1 \cdot 38!} = 65$

8. $\displaystyle\sum_{i=1}^{5} (2i^2 - 3) = (2 - 3) + (2 \cdot 2^2 - 3) + (2 \cdot 3^2 - 3) + (2 \cdot 4^2 - 3) + (2 \cdot 5^2 - 3)$

$\qquad\qquad = -1 + 5 + 15 + 29 + 47$

$\qquad\qquad = 95$

9. $\displaystyle\sum_{i=0}^{4} (-1)^{i+1} i! = (-1)^1 0! + (-1)^2 1! + (-1)^3 3! + (-1)^4 4!$

$\qquad\qquad = -1 + 1 - 2 + 6 - 24$

$\qquad\qquad = -20$

10. $\dfrac{1}{3} + \dfrac{2}{4} + \dfrac{3}{5} + \cdots + \dfrac{15}{17} = \displaystyle\sum_{i=1}^{15} \dfrac{i}{i+2}$

11. $4^3 + 5^3 + 6^3 + \cdots + 13^3 = \displaystyle\sum_{i=1}^{10} (i+3)^3$

12. $a_1 = 7, d = 4$

First six terms: 7, 11, 15, 19, 23, 27.

13. $a_1 = -4, d = -5$

First six terms: $-4, -9, -14, -19, -24, -29$.

14. $a_1 = \dfrac{3}{2}, d = -\dfrac{1}{2}$

First six terms: $\dfrac{3}{2}, 1, \dfrac{1}{2}, 0, -\dfrac{1}{2}, -1$.

15. $a_{n+1} = a_n + 5, a_1 = -2$

First six terms: $-2, 3, 8, 13, 18, 23$.

16. $a_1 = 5, d = 3$

$a_n = 5 + (n-1)3$

$a_6 = 5 + (5)3 = 20$

17. $a_1 = -8, d = -2$

$a_n = -8 + (n-1)(-2)$

$a_{12} = -8 + 11(-2) = -30$

18. $a_1 = 14, d = -4$

$a_n = 14 + (n-1)(-4)$

$a_{14} = 14 + (13)(-4) = -38$

19. $-7, -3, 1, 5, \ldots$

$d = -3 - (-7) = 4$

$a_n = -7 + (n-1)(4)$

$a_n = 4n - 11$

$a_{20} = 4(20) - 11$

$a_{20} = 69$

20. $a_1 = 200, d = -20$

$a_n = 200 + (n-1)(-20)$

$a_n = 220 - 20n$

$a_{20} = 220 - 20(20)$

$a_{20} = -180$

561

21. $a_n = a_{n-1} - 5, \ a_1 = 3$
$\quad d = -5$
$\quad a_n = 3 + (n-1)(-5) = 3 - 5n + 5$
$\quad a_n = 8 - 5n$
$\quad a_{20} = 8 - 5(20) = -92$

22. $5, 12, 19, 26, \ldots$
$\quad d = 7$
$\quad a_n = 5 + (n-1)(7)$
$\quad a_{22} = 5 + 21(7) = 152$
$\quad S_{22} = \dfrac{22}{2}(5 + 152) = 1727$

23. $-6, -3, 0, 3, \ldots$
$\quad d = 3$
$\quad a_n = -6 + (n-1)3$
$\quad a_{15} = -6 + (14)3 = 36$
$\quad S_{15} = \dfrac{15}{2}(-6 + 36) = 225$

24. $3 + 6 + 9 + \ldots + 300$
$\quad S_{100} = \dfrac{100}{2}(3 + 300) = 15,150$

25. $\displaystyle\sum_{i=1}^{16}(3i + 2)$
$\quad a_1 = 3 + 2 = 5$
$\quad a_{16} = 3(16) + 2 = 50$
$\quad S_{16} = \dfrac{16}{2}(5 + 50) = 440$

26. $\displaystyle\sum_{i=1}^{25}(-2i + 6)$
$\quad a_1 = -2 + 6 = 4$
$\quad a_{25} = -2(25) + 6 = -44$
$\quad S_{25} = \dfrac{25}{2}(4 - 44) = -500$

27. $\displaystyle\sum_{i=1}^{30} -5i$
$\quad a_1 = -5$
$\quad a_{30} = -5(30) = -150$
$\quad S_{30} = \dfrac{30}{2}(-5 - 150) = -2325$

28. a. $a_1 = 31.5$ and $d = -0.54$
$\quad a_n = a_1 + (n-1)d$
$\quad\quad = 31.5 + (n-1)(-0.54)$
$\quad\quad = 31.5 - 0.54n + 0.54$
$\quad\quad = -0.54n + 32.04$

b. Vegetables:
$\quad a_n = -0.54n + 32.04$
$\quad a_{18} = -0.54(18) + 32.04 = 22.32$

29. $a_n = 31,500 + (n-1)2300$
$\quad a_{10} = 31,500 + (9)2300 = 52,200$
$\quad S_{10} = \dfrac{10}{2}(31,500 + 52,200) = 418,500$
The total salary is \$418, 500.

30. $a_n = 25 + (n-1)$
$\quad a_{35} = 25 + 34 = 59$
$\quad S_{35} = \dfrac{35}{2}(25 + 59) = 1470$
There are 1470 seats.

31. $a_1 = 3, \ r = 2$
First five terms: 3, 6, 12, 24, 48.

32. $a_1 = \dfrac{1}{2}, \ r = \dfrac{1}{2}$
First five terms: $\dfrac{1}{2}, \dfrac{1}{4}, \dfrac{1}{8}, \dfrac{1}{16}, \dfrac{1}{32}$.

33. $a_1 = 16, \ r = -\dfrac{1}{2}$
First five terms: 16, −8, 4, −2, 1.

34. $a_n = -5a_{n-1}, \ a_1 = -1$
First five terms: −1, 5, −25, 125, −625.

35. $a_1 = 2, \ r = 3$
$\quad a_n = 2 \cdot 3^{n-1}$
$\quad a_7 = 2 \cdot 3^6 = 1458$

36. $a_1 = 16, \ r = \dfrac{1}{2}$
$\quad a_n = 16\left(\dfrac{1}{2}\right)^{n-1}$
$\quad a_6 = 16\left(\dfrac{1}{2}\right)^5 = \dfrac{16}{32} = \dfrac{1}{2}$

37. $a_1 = -3$, $r = 2$

$a_n = -3 \cdot 2^{n-1}$

$a_5 = -3 \cdot 2^4 = -48$

38. $1, 2, 4, 8, \ldots$

$a_1 = 1$, $r = \dfrac{2}{1} = 2$

$a_n = 2^{n-1}$

$a_8 = 2^7 = 128$

39. $100, 10, 1, \dfrac{1}{10}, \ldots$

$a_1 = 100$, $r = \dfrac{10}{100} = \dfrac{1}{10}$

$a_n = 100\left(\dfrac{1}{10}\right)^{n-1}$

$a_8 = 100\left(\dfrac{1}{10}\right)^7 = \dfrac{1}{100,000}$

40. $12, -4, \dfrac{4}{3}, -\dfrac{4}{9} \ldots$

$a_1 = 12$, $r = -\dfrac{4}{12} = -\dfrac{1}{3}$

$a_n = 12\left(-\dfrac{1}{3}\right)^{n-1}$

$a_8 = 12\left(-\dfrac{1}{3}\right)^7 = -\dfrac{4}{729}$

41. $5, -15, 45, -135, \ldots$

$r = \dfrac{-15}{5} = -3$

$S_{15} = \dfrac{5\left[1-(-3)^{15}\right]}{1-(-3)} = 17,936,135$

42. $r = \dfrac{1}{2}, a_1 = 8$

$S_{78} = \dfrac{8\left[1-\left(\dfrac{1}{2}\right)^7\right]}{1-\dfrac{1}{2}} = -16\left(1-\dfrac{1}{128}\right)$

$\quad = -16\left(-\dfrac{127}{128}\right) = \dfrac{127}{8}$

43. $S_6 = \dfrac{5\left(1-5^6\right)}{1-5} = \dfrac{5(-15624)}{-4} = 19,530$

44. $\displaystyle\sum_{i=1}^{7} 3(-2)^i$

$a_1 = -6$, $r = -2$

$S_7 = \dfrac{-6\left[1-(-2)^7\right]}{1-(-2)} = \dfrac{-6(129)}{3} = -258$

45. $\displaystyle\sum_{i=1}^{5} 2\left(\tfrac{1}{4}\right)^{i-1}$

$a_1 = 2$, $r = \dfrac{1}{4}$

$S_5 = \dfrac{2\left[1-\left(\tfrac{1}{4}\right)^5\right]}{1-\tfrac{1}{4}} = \dfrac{2\left(\tfrac{1023}{1024}\right)}{\tfrac{3}{4}} = \dfrac{341}{128}$

46. $a_1 = 9$, $r = \dfrac{1}{3}$

$S_\infty = \dfrac{9}{1-\tfrac{1}{3}} = \dfrac{9}{\tfrac{2}{3}} = 9 \cdot \dfrac{3}{2} = \dfrac{27}{2}$

47. $a_1 = 2$, $r = -\dfrac{1}{2}$

$S_\infty = \dfrac{2}{1-\left(-\tfrac{1}{2}\right)} = \dfrac{2}{\tfrac{3}{2}} = \dfrac{4}{3}$

48. $a_1 = -6$, $r = -\dfrac{2}{3}$

$S_\infty = \dfrac{-6}{1-\left(-\tfrac{2}{3}\right)} = \dfrac{-6}{\tfrac{5}{3}} = -\dfrac{18}{5}$

49. $r = 0.8$

$S_\infty = \dfrac{4}{1-0.8} = 20$

50. $0.\overline{6} = 0.6 + 0.06 + 0.006 + \cdots$

$a_1 = \dfrac{6}{10}$, $r = \dfrac{1}{10}$

$S_\infty = \dfrac{\tfrac{6}{10}}{1-\tfrac{1}{10}} = \dfrac{\tfrac{6}{10}}{\tfrac{9}{10}} = \dfrac{6}{9} = \dfrac{2}{3}$

51. $0.\overline{47} = 0.47 + 0.0047 + 0.000047 + \cdots$

$a_1 = \dfrac{47}{100}$, $r = \dfrac{1}{100}$

$S_\infty = \dfrac{\tfrac{47}{100}}{1-\tfrac{1}{100}} = \dfrac{\tfrac{47}{100}}{\tfrac{99}{100}} = \dfrac{47}{99}$

52. a. Divide each value by the previous value:

$$\frac{5.9}{4.2} = 1.405$$

$$\frac{8.3}{5.9} = 1.407$$

$$\frac{11.6}{8.3} = 1.398$$

$$\frac{16.2}{11.6} = 1.397$$

$$\frac{22.7}{16.2} = 1.401$$

The population is increasing geometrically with $r = 1.4$.

b. $a_n = 4.2 \cdot 1.4^n$

c.   2080 is 8 decades after 2000 so $n = 8$.

$$a_n = 4.2 \cdot 1.4^n$$

$$a_8 = 4.2 \cdot 1.4^8 \approx 62.0$$

In 2080, the model predicts the U.S. population, ages 85 and older, will be 62.0 million

53. $a_1 = 32,000, \; r = 1.06$

$a_6 = 32,000(1.06)^5 \approx \$42,823$

The sixth year salary is $42, 823.

$$S_6 = \frac{32,000\left(1 - 1.06^6\right)}{1 - 1.06}$$

$$= \frac{32,000\left(1 - 1.06^6\right)}{-0.06}$$

$$\approx 223,210$$

The total salary paid is $223, 210.

54. $A = 200 \dfrac{\left(1 + \frac{0.1}{12}\right)^{18 \cdot 12} - 1}{\frac{0.1}{12}} \approx 120,113$

You will save $120,113.

55. $4(0.7) + 4(0.7)^2 + \cdots; \; r = 0.7$

$$S_{\infty} = \frac{4(0.7)}{1 - 0.7} = 9.\overline{3}$$

The total spending is $\$9\dfrac{1}{3}$ million.

56. $S_1 : 5 = \dfrac{5(1)(1 + 1)}{2}$

$$5 = \frac{5(2)}{2}$$

$5 = 5$ is true.

$$S_k : 5 + 10 + 15 + \cdots + 5k = \frac{5k(k + 1)}{2}$$

$$S_{k+1} : 5 + 10 + 15 + \cdots + 5k + 5(k + 1)$$

$$= \frac{5(k + 1)(k + 2)}{2}$$

Add $5(k + 1)$ to both sides of S_k:

$$5 + 10 + 15 + \cdots + 5k + 5(k + 1)$$

$$= \frac{5k(k + 1)}{2} + 5k(k + 1)$$

Simplify the right-hand side:

$$\frac{5k(k + 1)}{2} + 5(k + 1) = \frac{5k(k + 1) + 10(k + 1)}{2}$$

$$= \frac{(5k + 10)(k + 1)}{2}$$

$$= \frac{5(k + 1)(k + 2)}{2}$$

If S_k is true, then S_{k+1} is true.

The statement is true for all n.

57. $S_1 : 1 = \dfrac{4^1 - 1}{3}$

$$1 = \frac{3}{3}$$

$1 = 1$ is true.

$$S_k : 1 + 4 + 4^2 + \cdots + 4^{k-1} = \frac{4^k - 1}{3}$$

$$S_{k+1} : 1 + 4 + 4^2 + \cdots + 4^{k-1} + 4^k = \frac{4^{k+1} - 1}{3} \; \text{Ad}$$

d 4^k to both sides of S_k:

$$S_k : 1 + 4 + 4^2 + \cdots + 4^{k-1} = \frac{4^k - 1}{3}$$

$$1 + 4 + 4^2 + \cdots + 4^{k-1} + 4^k = \frac{4^k - 1}{3} + 4^k$$

Simplify the right-hand side:

$$\frac{4^k - 1}{3} + 4^k = \frac{4^k - 1 + 3 \cdot 4^k}{3}$$

$$= \frac{4 \cdot 4^k - 1}{3}$$

$$= \frac{4^{k+1} - 1}{3}$$

If S_k is true, then S_{k+1} is true.

The statement is true for all n.

58. $S_1 : 2 = 2(1)^2$

$2 = 2$ is true.

$S_k : 2 + 6 + 10 + \cdots + (4k - 2) = 2k^2$

$S_{k+1} : 2 + 6 + 10 + \cdots + (4k - 2) + (4k + 2) = 2(k + 1)^2$

Add $(4k + 2)$ to both sides of S_k :

$2 + 6 + 10 + \cdots + (4k - 2) + (4k + 2) = 2k^2 + (4k + 2)$

Simplify the right-hand side:

$2k^2 + 4k + 2 = 2(k^2 + 2k + 1)$

$ = 2(k + 1)^2$

If S_k is true, then S_{k+1} is true. The statement is true for all n.

59. $S_1 : 1 \cdot 3 = \dfrac{1(1+1)[2(1)+7]}{6}$

$3 = \dfrac{2 \cdot 9}{6}$

$3 = \dfrac{18}{6}$

$3 = 3$ is true.

$S_k : 1 \cdot 3 + 2 \cdot 4 + 3 \cdot 5 + \cdots + k(k+2) = \dfrac{k(k+1)(2k+7)}{6}$

$S_{k+1} : 1 \cdot 3 + 2 \cdot 4 + 3 \cdot 5 + \cdots + k(k+2) + (k+1)(k+3) = \dfrac{(k+1)(k+2)(2k+9)}{6}$

Add $(k+1)(k+3)$ to both sides of S_k :

$1 \cdot 3 + 2 \cdot 4 + 3 \cdot 5 + \cdots + k(k+2) + (k+1)(k+3) = \dfrac{k(k+1)(2k+7)}{6} + (k+1)(k+3)$

Simplify the right-hand side:

$= \dfrac{k(k+1)(2k+7)}{6} + (k+1)(k+3)$

$= \dfrac{k(k+1)(2k+7) + 6(k+1)(k+3)}{6}$

$= \dfrac{(k+1)[k(2k+7) + 6(k+3)]}{6}$

$= \dfrac{(k+1)(2k^2 + 13k + 18)}{6}$

$= \dfrac{(k+1)(k+2)(2k+9)}{6}$

If S_k is true, then S_{k+1} is true. The statement is true for all n.

565

60. $S_1 : 2$ is a factor of $1^2 + 5(1) = 6$ since $6 = 2 \cdot 3$.

  $S_k : 2$ is a factor of $k^2 + 5k$.

  $S_{k+1} : 2$ is a factor of $(k+1)^2 + 5(k+1)$.

  $$(k+1)^2 + 5(k+1) = k^2 + 2k + 1 + 5k + 5$$
  $$= k^2 + 7k + 6$$
  $$= k^2 + 5k + 2(k+3)$$
  $$= (k^2 + 5k) + 2(k+3)$$

Because we assume S_k is true, we know 2 is a factor of $k^2 + 5k$. Since 2 is a factor of $2(k+3)$, we conclude 2 is a factor of the sum $(k^2 + 5k) + 2(k+3)$. If S_k is true, then S_{k+1} is true. The statement is true for all n.

61. $\dbinom{11}{8} = \dfrac{11!}{3!8!} = \dfrac{11 \cdot 10 \cdot 9}{3 \cdot 2 \cdot 1} = 165$

62. $\dbinom{90}{2} = \dfrac{90!}{88!2!} = \dfrac{90 \cdot 89}{2 \cdot 1} = 4005$

63. $(2x+1)^3 = \dbinom{3}{0}(2x)^3 + \dbinom{3}{1}(2x)^2 \cdot 1 + \dbinom{3}{2}(2x)1^2 + \dbinom{3}{3}1^3$

  $$= 8x^3 + 3(4x^2) + 3(2x) + 1$$
  $$= 8x^3 + 12x^2 + 6x + 1$$

64. $(x^2 - 1)^4 = \dbinom{4}{0}(x^2)^4 + \dbinom{4}{1}(x^2)^3(-1) + \dbinom{4}{2}(x^2)^2(-1)^2 + \dbinom{4}{3}x^2(-1)^3 + \dbinom{4}{4}(-1)^4$

  $$= x^8 - 4x^6 + 6x^4 - 4x^2 + 1$$

65. $(x+2y)^5 = \dbinom{5}{0}x^5 + \dbinom{5}{1}x^4(2y) + \dbinom{5}{2}x^3(2y)^2 + \dbinom{5}{3}x^2(2y)^3 + \dbinom{5}{4}x(2y)^4 + \dbinom{5}{5}(2y)^5$

  $$= x^5 + 5(2)x^4 y + 10(4)x^3 y^2 + 10(8)x^2 y^3 + 5(16)xy^4 + 32y^5$$
  $$= x^5 + 10x^4 y + 40x^3 y^2 + 80x^2 y^3 + 80xy^4 + 32y^5$$

66. $(x-2)^6 = \dbinom{6}{0}x^6 + \dbinom{6}{1}x^5(-2) + \dbinom{6}{2}x^4(-2)^2 + \dbinom{6}{3}x^3(-2)^3 + \dbinom{6}{4}x^2(-2)^4 + \dbinom{6}{5}x(-2)^5 \dbinom{6}{6}(-2)^6$

  $$= x^6 + 6x^5(-2) + 15x^4(4) + 20x^3(-8) + 15x^2(16) + 6x(-32) + 64$$
  $$= x^6 - 12x^5 + 60x^4 - 160x^3 + 240x^2 - 192x + 64$$

67. $(x^2 + 3)^8 = \dbinom{8}{0}(x^2)^8 + \dbinom{8}{1}(x^2)^7 3 + \dbinom{8}{2}(x^2)^6 3^2 + \cdots$

  $$= x^{16} + 8x^{14} 3 + 28x^{12} 9 + \cdots$$
  $$= x^{16} + 24x^{14} + 252x^{12} + \cdots$$

68. $(x-3)^9 = \binom{9}{0}x^9 + \binom{9}{1}x^8(-3) + \binom{9}{2}x^7(-3)^2 - \cdots$

$= x^9 + 9(-3)x^8 + 36(9)x^7 - \cdots$

$= x^9 - 27x^8 + 324x^7 - \cdots$

69. $(x+2)^5$

fourth term $= \binom{5}{3}x^2(2)^3$

$= 10(8)x^2 = 80x^2$

70. $(2x-3)^6$

fifth term $= \binom{6}{4}(2x)^2(-3)^4$

$= 15(4x^2)(81) = 4860x^2$

71. $_8P_3 = \dfrac{8!}{5!} = 8 \cdot 7 \cdot 6 = 336$

72. $_9P_5 = \dfrac{9!}{4!} = 9 \cdot 8 \cdot 7 \cdot 6 \cdot 5 = 15,120$

73. $_8C_3 = \dfrac{8!}{5!3!} = \dfrac{8 \cdot 7 \cdot 6}{3 \cdot 2 \cdot 1} = 56$

74. $_{13}C_{11} = \dfrac{13!}{2!11!} = \dfrac{13 \cdot 12}{2 \cdot 1} = 78$

75. $4 \cdot 5 = 20$ choices

76. $3^5 = 243$ possibilities

77. $_{15}P_4 = \dfrac{15!}{11!} = 15 \cdot 14 \cdot 13 \cdot 12 = 32,760$ ways

78. $_{20}C_4 = \dfrac{20!}{16!4!} = \dfrac{20 \cdot 19 \cdot 18 \cdot 17}{4 \cdot 3 \cdot 2 \cdot 1} = 4845$ ways

79. $_{20}C_3 = \dfrac{20!}{17!3!} = \dfrac{20 \cdot 19 \cdot 18}{3 \cdot 2 \cdot 1} = 1140$ sets

80. $_{20}P_4 = \dfrac{20!}{16!}$

$= 20 \cdot 19 \cdot 18 \cdot 17$

$= 116,280$ ways

81. $5! = 120$ ways

82. $P(\text{liberal}) = \dfrac{17}{100}$

83. $P(\text{not conservative}) = 1 - P(\text{conservative})$

$= 1 - \dfrac{33}{100} = \dfrac{67}{100}$

84. $P(\text{moderate or conservative})$

$= P(\text{moderate}) + P(\text{conservative})$

$= \dfrac{50}{100} + \dfrac{33}{100} = \dfrac{83}{100}$

85. $P(\text{conservative or attended college})$

$= P(\text{conservative}) + P(\text{attended college})$

$\quad - P(\text{conservative and attended college})$

$= \dfrac{33}{100} + \dfrac{45}{100} - \dfrac{20}{100} = \dfrac{58}{100} = \dfrac{29}{50}$

86. $P(\text{high school only}) = \dfrac{13}{33}$

87. $P(\text{liberal}) = \dfrac{10}{45} = \dfrac{2}{9}$

88. $P(\text{less than 5}) = P(\text{rolling a 1, 2, 3, 4})$

$= \dfrac{4}{6} = \dfrac{2}{3}$

89. $P(\text{less than 3 or greater than 4})$

$= P(\text{less than 3}) + P(\text{greater than 4})$

$= P(\text{rolling a 1, 2}) + P(\text{rolling a 5, 6})$

$= \dfrac{2}{6} + \dfrac{2}{6} = \dfrac{4}{6} = \dfrac{2}{3}$

90. $P(E) = \dfrac{4}{52} + \dfrac{4}{52} = \dfrac{8}{52} = \dfrac{2}{13}$

91. $P(E) = \dfrac{4}{52} + \dfrac{26}{52} - \dfrac{2}{52} = \dfrac{28}{52} = \dfrac{7}{13}$

92. $P(\text{not yellow}) = 1 - P(\text{yellow}) = 1 - \dfrac{1}{6} = \dfrac{5}{6}$

93. $P(\text{red or greater than } 3) = \dfrac{3}{6} + \dfrac{3}{6} - \dfrac{1}{6} = \dfrac{5}{6}$

94. $P(\text{green, then less than } 4) = \dfrac{2}{6} \cdot \dfrac{3}{6} = \dfrac{6}{36} = \dfrac{1}{6}$

95. a. $P(E) = \dfrac{n(E)}{n(S)} = \dfrac{1}{{}_{20}C_5} = \dfrac{1}{15,504}$

b. $P(E) = \dfrac{100}{15,504} = \dfrac{25}{3876}$

96. $P(E) = \left(\dfrac{1}{2}\right)^5 = \dfrac{1}{32}$

97. a. $(0.2)^2 = 0.04$

b. $(0.2)^3 = 0.008$

c. $(1 - 0.2)^4 = (0.8)^4 = 0.4096$

Chapter 8 Test

1. $a_n = \dfrac{(-1)^{n+1}}{n^2}$

$a_1 = \dfrac{(-1)^2}{1^2} = 1$

$a_2 = \dfrac{(-1)^3}{2^2} = -\dfrac{1}{4}$

$a_3 = \dfrac{(-1)^4}{3^2} = \dfrac{1}{9}$

$a_4 = \dfrac{(-1)^5}{4^2} = -\dfrac{1}{16}$

$a_5 = \dfrac{(-1)^6}{5^2} = \dfrac{1}{25}$

First five terms: $1, -\dfrac{1}{4}, \dfrac{1}{9}, -\dfrac{1}{16}, \dfrac{1}{25}$.

2. $\displaystyle\sum_{i=1}^{5} (i^2 + 10) = 11 + 14 + 19 + 26 + 35 = 105$

3. $\displaystyle\sum_{i=1}^{20} (3i - 4)$

$a_1 = 3 - 4 = -1$

$d = 3$

$a_n = -1 + (n-1)3$

$a_{20} = -1 + (19)3 = 56$

$S_{20} = \dfrac{20}{2}(-1 + 56) = 550$

4. $\displaystyle\sum_{i=1}^{15} (-2)^i$

$a_1 = -2,\ r = -2$

$S_{15} = \dfrac{-2\left[1 - (-2)^{15}\right]}{1 - (-2)} = -21,846$

5. $\dbinom{9}{2} = \dfrac{9!}{7!2!} = \dfrac{9 \cdot 8}{2 \cdot 1} = 36$

6. ${}_{10}P_3 = \dfrac{10!}{7!} = 10 \cdot 9 \cdot 8 = 720$

7. ${}_{10}C_3 = \dfrac{10!}{7!3!} = \dfrac{10 \cdot 9 \cdot 8}{3 \cdot 2 \cdot 1} = 120$

8. $\dfrac{2}{3} + \dfrac{3}{4} + \dfrac{4}{5} + \cdots + \dfrac{21}{22} = \displaystyle\sum_{i=1}^{20} \dfrac{i+1}{i+2}$

9. $4, 9, 14, 19, \ldots$

$a_1 = 4,\ d = 5$

$a_n = 4 + (n-1) \cdot 5 = 4 + 5n - 1$

$a_n = 5n - 1$

$a_{12} = 5(12) - 1 = 59$

10. $16, 4, 1, \dfrac{1}{4}, \cdots$

$a_1 = 16,\ r = \dfrac{1}{4}$

$a_n = 16\left(\dfrac{1}{4}\right)^{n-1}$

$a_{12} = 16\left(\dfrac{1}{4}\right)^{11} = \dfrac{1}{262,144}$

11. $7, -14, 28, -56, \ldots$

$a_1 = 7, r = -2$

$$S_{10} = \frac{7\left[1 - (-2)^{10}\right]}{1 - (-2)} = \frac{7(-1023)}{3} = -2387$$

12. $-7, -14, -21, -28, \ldots$

$a_1 = -7, d = -7$

$a_n = -7 + (n-1)(-7)$

$a_{10} = -7 + 9(-7) = -70$

$$S_{10} = \frac{10}{2}(-7 - 70) = -385$$

13. $4 + \dfrac{4}{2} + \dfrac{4}{2^2} + \dfrac{4}{2^3} + \cdots$

$r = \dfrac{1}{2}$

$$S_\infty = \frac{4}{1 - \dfrac{1}{2}} = 8$$

14. $0.\overline{73} = 0.73 + 0.0073 + 0.000073 + \cdots$

$a_1 = \dfrac{73}{100}, r = \dfrac{1}{100}$

$$S_\infty = \frac{\frac{73}{100}}{1 - \frac{1}{100}} = \frac{\frac{73}{100}}{\frac{99}{100}} = \frac{73}{99}$$

15. $a_1 = 30,000, r = 1.04$

$$S_8 = \frac{30,000\left[1 - (1.04)^8\right]}{1 - 1.04} \approx 276,426.79$$

The total salary is \$276,427.

16. $S_1 : 1 = \dfrac{1[3(1) - 1]}{2}$

$1 = \dfrac{2}{2}$

$1 = 1$ is true.

$S_k : 1 + 4 + 7 + \cdots + (3k - 2) = \dfrac{k(3k - 1)}{2}$

$S_{k+1} : 1 + 4 + 7 + \cdots + (3k - 2) + (3k + 1) = \dfrac{(k + 1)(3k + 2)}{2}$

Add $(3k + 1)$ to both sides of S_k:

$$1 + 4 + 7 + \cdots + (3k - 2) + (3k + 1) = \frac{k(3k - 1)}{2} + (3k + 1)$$

Simplify the right-hand side:

$$\frac{k(3k - 1)}{2} + (3k + 1) = \frac{k(3k - 1) + 2(3k + 1)}{2}$$

$$= \frac{3k^2 + 5k + 2}{2}$$

$$= \frac{(k + 1)(3k + 2)}{2}$$

If S_k is true, then S_{k+1} is true. The statement is true for all n.

17. $(x^2 - 1)^5 = \dbinom{5}{0}(x^2)^5 + \dbinom{5}{1}(x^2)^4(-1) + \dbinom{5}{2}(x^2)^3(-1)^2 + \dbinom{5}{3}(x^2)^2(-1)^3 + \dbinom{5}{4}x^2(-1)^4 + \dbinom{5}{5}(-1)^5$

$= x^{10} - 5x^8 + 10x^6 - 10x^4 + 5x^2 - 1$

18. $\left(x+y^2\right)^8$

First Term $\quad\binom{n}{r-1}a^{n-r+1}b^{r-1}=\binom{8}{1-1}x^{8-1+1}\left(y^2\right)^{1-1}=\binom{8}{0}x^8\left(y^2\right)^0=\dfrac{8!}{0!(8-0)!}x^8\cdot 1=\dfrac{\cancel{8!}}{0!\,\cancel{8!}}x^8$

$$=x^8$$

Second Term $\quad\binom{n}{r-1}a^{n-r+1}b^{r-1}=\binom{8}{2-1}x^{8-2+1}\left(y^2\right)^{2-1}=\binom{8}{1}x^7\left(y^2\right)^1=\dfrac{8!}{1!(8-1)!}x^7y^2=\dfrac{8\cdot\cancel{7!}}{1\cdot\cancel{7!}}x^7y^2$

$$=8x^7y^2$$

Third Term $\quad\binom{n}{r-1}a^{n-r+1}b^{r-1}=\binom{8}{3-1}x^{8-3+1}\left(y^2\right)^{3-1}=\binom{8}{2}x^6\left(y^2\right)^2=\dfrac{8!}{2!(8-2)!}x^6y^4=\dfrac{8\cdot 7\cdot\cancel{6!}}{2\cdot 1\cdot\cancel{6!}}x^6y^4$

$$=28x^6y^4$$

$$x^8+8x^7y^2+28x^6y^4+\cdots$$

19. $\;_{11}P_3=\dfrac{11!}{8!}=11\cdot 10\cdot 9=990$ ways

20. $\;_{10}C_4=\dfrac{10!}{6!4!}=\dfrac{10\cdot 9\cdot 8\cdot 7}{4\cdot 3\cdot 2\cdot 1}=210$ sets

21. Four digits are open: $10^4=10,000$

22. $P(\text{not brown eyes})=1-P(\text{brown eyes})$

$$=1-\dfrac{40}{50}$$

$$=\dfrac{60}{100}=\dfrac{3}{5}$$

23. $P(\text{brown eyes or blue eyes})$

$\quad=P(\text{brown eyes})+P(\text{blue eyes})$

$$=\dfrac{40}{100}+\dfrac{38}{100}=\dfrac{78}{100}=\dfrac{39}{50}$$

24. $P(\text{female or green eyes})$

$\quad=P(\text{female})+P(\text{green eyes})$

$\qquad\quad-P(\text{female with green eyes})$

$$=\dfrac{50}{100}+\dfrac{22}{100}-\dfrac{12}{100}=\dfrac{60}{100}=\dfrac{3}{5}$$

25. $P(\text{male, given blue eyes})=\dfrac{18}{38}=\dfrac{9}{19}$

26. $\;_{15}C_6=\dfrac{15!}{9!6!}=\dfrac{15\cdot 14\cdot 13\cdot 12\cdot 11\cdot 10}{6\cdot 5\cdot 4\cdot 3\cdot 2}=5005$

$$P(E)=\dfrac{50}{5005}=\dfrac{10}{1001}$$

27. $P(E)=\dfrac{26}{52}+\dfrac{12}{52}-\dfrac{6}{52}=\dfrac{32}{52}=\dfrac{8}{13}$

28. $P(E)=\dfrac{25}{50}+\dfrac{20}{50}-\dfrac{15}{50}=\dfrac{30}{50}=\dfrac{3}{5}$

29. $P(E)=\left(\dfrac{1}{4}\right)^4=\dfrac{1}{256}$

30. $P(E)=\dfrac{2}{8}\cdot\dfrac{2}{8}=\dfrac{1}{16}$

Cumulative Review Exercises (Chapters 1–8)

1. Domain: $[-4,1)$; Range: $(-\infty,2]$

2. maximum of 2 at $x = -2$

3. decreasing interval: $(-2,1)$

4. neither

5. $f(-3) = 1$ and $f(-1) = 1$

6. $(f \circ f)(-4) = f(f(-4)) = f(0) = 0$

7. $f(x) \to -\infty$ as $x \to 1^-$

8.

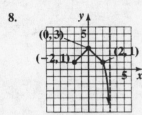

$g(x) = f(x-2) + 1$

9.

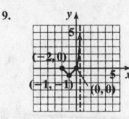

$h(x) = -f(2x)$

10. $-2(x-5) + 10 = 3(x+2)$
$-2x + 10 + 10 = 3x + 6$
$14 = 5x$
$x = \dfrac{14}{5}$

The solution set is $\left\{\dfrac{14}{5}\right\}$.

11. $3x^2 - 6x + 2 = 0$
$$x = \frac{6 \pm \sqrt{36-24}}{6}$$
$$= \frac{6 \pm \sqrt{12}}{6}$$
$$= \frac{6 \pm 2\sqrt{3}}{6}$$
$$= \frac{3 \pm \sqrt{3}}{3}$$

The solution set is $\left\{\dfrac{3+\sqrt{3}}{3}, \dfrac{3-\sqrt{3}}{3}\right\}$.

12. $\log_2 x + \log_2 (2x-3) = 1$
$\log_2 x(2x-3) = 1$
$x(2x-3) = 2$
$2x^2 - 3x - 2 = 0$
$(2x+1)(x-2) = 0$

$2x+1 = 0$ or $x-2 = 0$
$x = -\dfrac{1}{2}$ $x = 2$

$x = -\dfrac{1}{2}$ does not check since $\log_2\left(-\dfrac{1}{2}\right)$ does
not exist.
The solution set is $\{2\}$.

13. $x^{1/2} - 6x^{1/4} + 8 = 0$
Let $t = x^{1/4}$.
$t^2 - 6t + 8 = 0$
$(t-2)(t-4) = 0$
$t-2 = 0$ or $t-4 = 0$
$t = 2$ $t = 4$
$x^{1/4} = 2$ $x^{1/4} = 4$
$x = 16$ $x = 256$
The solution set is $\{16, 256\}$.

14. $\sqrt{2x+4} - \sqrt{x+3} - 1 = 0$

$$\left(\sqrt{2x+4}\right)^2 = \left(\sqrt{x+3}+1\right)^2$$

$$2x+4 = (x+3) + 2\sqrt{x+3} + 1$$

$$x = 2\sqrt{x+3}$$

$$x^2 = 4(x+3)$$

$$x^2 - 4x - 12 = 0$$

$$(x-6)(x+2) = 0$$

$$x - 6 = 0 \quad \text{or} \quad x + 2 = 0$$

$$x = 6 \qquad\qquad x = -2$$

$$x = -2 \text{ does not check.}$$

The solution set is $\{6\}$.

15. $|2x+1| \le 1$

$-1 \le 2x + 1 \le 1$

$-2 \le 2x \le 0$

$-1 \le x \le 0$ or $[-1, 0]$

The solution set is $\{x | -1 \le x \le 0\}$ or $[-1, 0]$.

16. $6x^2 - 6 < 5x$

$6x^2 - 5x - 6 < 0$

$6x^2 - 5x - 6 = 0$

$(3x+2)(2x-3) = 0$

$3x + 2 = 0$ or $2x - 3 = 0$

$x = -\dfrac{2}{3} \qquad x = \dfrac{3}{2}$

The test intervals are $\left(-\infty, -\frac{2}{3}\right), \left(-\frac{2}{3}, \frac{3}{2}\right)$, and $\left(\frac{3}{2}, \infty\right)$. Testing a point in each interval shows that the solution is $\left(-\frac{2}{3}, \frac{3}{2}\right)$.

17. $\dfrac{x-1}{x+3} \le 0$

The test intervals are $(-\infty, -3), (-3, 1)$ and $(1, \infty)$.

Testing a point in each interval shows that the solution is $(-3, 1]$.

18. $30e^{0.7x} = 240$

$e^{0.7x} = 8$

$\ln e^{0.7x} = \ln 8$

$0.7x = \ln 8$

$x = \dfrac{\ln 8}{0.7} \approx 2.9706$

The solution set is $\left\{\dfrac{\ln 8}{0.7}\right\}$ or $\{2.9706\}$.

19. $2x^3 + 3x^2 - 8x + 3 = 0$

$p: \pm 1, \ \pm 3$

$q: \pm 1, \ \pm 2$

$\dfrac{p}{q}: \pm 1, \pm 3, \pm\dfrac{1}{2}, \pm\dfrac{3}{2}$

1	2	3	–8	3
		2	5	–3
	2	5	–3	0

$(x-1)(2x^2 + 5x - 3) = 0$

$(x-1)(2x-1)(x+3) = 0$

$x = 1$ or $x = \dfrac{1}{2}$ or $x = -3$

The solution set is $\left\{-3, \dfrac{1}{2}, 1\right\}$.

20. $4x^2 + 3y^2 = 48$

$3x^2 + 2y^2 = 35$

Multiply equation 1 by –2.

Multiply equation 2 by 3.

$-8x^2 - 6y^2 = -96$

$\underline{9x^2 + 6y^2 = 105}$

Add: $x^2 = 9$

$x = \pm 3$

Let $x = -3$:

$4(-3)^2 + 3y^2 = 48$

$36 + 3y^2 = 48$

$3y^2 = 12$

$y^2 = 4$

$y = \pm 2$

Let $x = 3$:

$4(3)^2 + 3y^2 = 48$

$36 + 3y^2 = 48$

$3y^2 = 12$

$y^2 = 4$

$y = \pm 2$

The solution set is
$\{(3, 2), (3, -2), (-3, 2), (-3, -2)\}$.

21.
$$x - 2y + z = 16$$
$$2x - y - z = 14$$
$$3x + 5y - 4z = -10$$

$$\begin{bmatrix} 1 & -2 & 1 & | & 16 \\ 0 & -1 & -1 & | & 14 \\ 3 & 5 & -4 & | & -10 \end{bmatrix} \begin{matrix} \\ -2R_1 + R_2 \\ -3R_1 + R_3 \end{matrix}$$

$$\begin{bmatrix} 1 & -2 & 1 & | & 16 \\ 0 & 3 & -3 & | & -18 \\ 0 & 11 & -7 & | & -58 \end{bmatrix} \begin{matrix} \\ \frac{1}{3}R_2 \\ \\ \end{matrix}$$

$$\begin{bmatrix} 1 & -2 & 1 & | & 16 \\ 0 & 1 & -1 & | & -6 \\ 0 & 11 & -7 & | & -58 \end{bmatrix} \begin{matrix} \\ 2R_2 + R_1 \\ -11R_2 + R_3 \end{matrix}$$

$$\begin{bmatrix} 1 & 0 & -1 & | & 4 \\ 0 & 1 & -1 & | & -6 \\ 0 & 0 & 4 & | & 8 \end{bmatrix} \begin{matrix} \\ \\ \frac{1}{4}R_3 \end{matrix}$$

$$\begin{bmatrix} 1 & 0 & -1 & | & 4 \\ 0 & 1 & -1 & | & -6 \\ 0 & 0 & 1 & | & 2 \end{bmatrix} \begin{matrix} R_3 + R_1 \\ R_2 + R_1 \\ \\ \end{matrix}$$

$$\begin{bmatrix} 1 & 0 & 0 & | & 6 \\ 0 & 1 & 0 & | & -4 \\ 0 & 0 & 1 & | & 2 \end{bmatrix} \begin{matrix} R_3 + R_1 \\ R_2 + R_1 \\ \\ \end{matrix}$$

The solution set is $\{(6, -4, 2)\}$.

22.
$$x - y = 1$$
$$x^2 - x - y = 1$$

Multiply $x - y = 1$ by -1, then add

$$-x + y = -1$$
$$\underline{x^2 - x - y = 1}$$
$$x^2 - 2x = 0$$
$$x(x - 2) = 0$$

$x = 0$ or $x = 2$
If $x = 0$, $-y = 1$ so $y = -1$.
If $x = 2$, $2 - y = 1$ so $y = 1$.
The solution set is $\{(0, -1), (2, 1)\}$.

23. $100x^2 + y^2 = 25$

$$4x^2 + \frac{y^2}{25} = 1$$

$$\frac{x^2}{\left(\frac{1}{4}\right)} + \frac{y^2}{25} = 1$$

Ellipse
Foci on the y-axis

$a^2 = 25$ and $b^2 = \frac{1}{4}$, so $\frac{1}{4} = 25 - c^2$.

$$c^2 = \frac{99}{4}$$

$$c = \frac{3\sqrt{11}}{2}$$

Foci: $\left(0, -\frac{3\sqrt{11}}{2}\right), \left(0, \frac{3\sqrt{11}}{2}\right)$

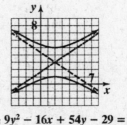

$100x^2 + y^2 = 25$

24. $4x^2 - 9y^2 - 16x + 54y - 29 = 0$

$$4(x^2 - 4x) - 9(y^2 - 6y) = 29$$
$$4(x^2 - 4x + 4) - 9(y^2 - 6y + 9) = 16 - 81 + 29$$
$$4(x - 2)^2 - 9(y - 3)^2 = -36$$
$$\frac{(y - 3)^2}{4} - \frac{(x - 2)^2}{9} = 1$$

Hyperbola with center at $(2, 3)$
Transverse axis vertical
$a^2 = 4$ and $b^2 = 9$, so $9 = c^2 - 4$.

$$c^2 = 13$$
$$c = \sqrt{13}$$

Foci: $\left(2, 3 - \sqrt{13}\right), \left(2, 3 + \sqrt{13}\right)$

$4x^2 - 9y^2 - 16x + 54y - 29 = 0$

573

25. Symmetry:

$$f(-x) = \frac{x^2 - 1}{-x - 2}$$

No symmetry since $f(-x) \neq f(x)$ and $f(-x) \neq -f(-x)$.

x-intercepts:

$$x^2 - 1 = 0$$

$$x = \pm 1$$

y-intercept:

$$f(0) = \frac{1}{2}$$

$$y = \frac{1}{2}$$

Vertical asymptote:

$$x - 2 = 0$$

$$x = 2$$

Horizontal asymptote:

$n > m$, so no horizontal asymptote.

Slant asymptote: $n = m + 1$

$$f(x) = x + 2 + \frac{3}{x - 2}$$

$$y = x + 2$$

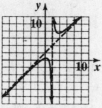

$$f(x) = \frac{x^2 - 1}{x - 2}$$

26.

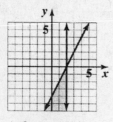

$$2x - y \geq 4$$
$$x \leq 2$$

27. $f(x) = x^2 - 4x - 5$

$$x = \frac{-b}{2a} = \frac{4}{2} = 2$$

$$f(2) = 2^2 - 8 - 5 = -9$$

vertex: $(2, -9)$

x-intercepts:

$$x^2 - 4x - 5 = 0$$

$$(x - 5)(x + 1) = 0$$

$$x = 5, -1$$

y-intercept: $f(0) = -5$

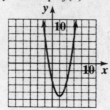

$$f(x) = x^2 - 4x - 5$$

28.

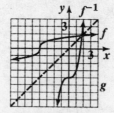

29.

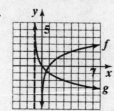

30. $f(x) = -x^2 - 2x + 1$, $g(x) = x - 1$

$$(f \circ g)(x) = f(g(x))$$

$$= -(x - 1)^2 - 2(x - 1) + 1$$

$$= -x^2 + 2x - 1 - 2x + 2 + 1$$

$$= -x^2 + 2$$

$$(g \circ f)(x) = g(f(x))$$

$$= \left(-x^2 - 2x + 1\right) - 1$$

$$= -x^2 - 2x$$

31. $f(x) = -x^2 - 2x + 1$

$$\frac{f(x+h) - f(x)}{h} = \frac{\left(-(x+h)^2 - 2(x+h) + 1\right) - \left(-x^2 - 2x + 1\right)}{h}$$

$$= \frac{-x^2 - 2xh - h^2 - 2x - 2h + 1 + x^2 + 2x - 1}{h}$$

$$= \frac{-2xh - h^2 - 2h}{h}$$

$$= \frac{h(-2x - h - 2)}{h}$$

$$= -2x - h - 2$$

32. $AB - 4A = \begin{bmatrix} 4 & 2 \\ 1 & -1 \\ 0 & 5 \end{bmatrix} \begin{bmatrix} 2 & 4 \\ 3 & 1 \end{bmatrix} - 4 \begin{bmatrix} 4 & 2 \\ 1 & 1 \\ 0 & 5 \end{bmatrix}$

$= \begin{bmatrix} 14 & 18 \\ -1 & 3 \\ 15 & 5 \end{bmatrix} - \begin{bmatrix} 16 & 8 \\ 4 & -4 \\ 0 & 20 \end{bmatrix} = \begin{bmatrix} -2 & 10 \\ -5 & 7 \\ 15 & -15 \end{bmatrix}$

33. $\dfrac{2x^2 - 10x + 2}{(x-2)(x^2 + 2x + 2)} = \dfrac{A}{x-2} + \dfrac{Bx + C}{x^2 + 2x + 2}$

$2x^2 - 10x + 2 = A(x^2 + 2x + 2) + (Bx + C)(x - 2)$

$\qquad\qquad = Ax^2 + 2Ax + 2A + Bx^2 - 2Bx + Cx - 2C$

$\qquad\qquad = (A + B)x^2 + (2A - 2B + C)x + 2A - 2C$

Thus we have the following system of equations.

$\qquad A + B = 2$
$\ 2A - 2B + C = -10$
$\qquad 2A - 2C = 2$

Add twice the first equation to the second equation.

$\qquad 2A + 2B = 4$

$\underline{\ 2A - 2B + C = -10\ }$

$\qquad 4A + C = -6$

Add twice the resulting equation to the third equation.

$\ 8A + 2C = -12$

$\underline{\ 2A - 2C = 2\ }$

$\quad 10A = -10$

$\qquad A = -1$

Back-substitute to find B and C.

$2(-1) - 2C = 2$
$\ \ -2 - 2C = 2$
$\qquad -2C = 4$
$\qquad\quad C = -2$
$-1 + B = 2$
$\quad\ B = 3$

$\dfrac{-1}{x-2} + \dfrac{3x - 2}{x^2 + 2x + 2}$

34. $(x^3 + 2y)^5 = \binom{5}{0}(x^3)^5 + \binom{5}{1}(x^3)^4(2y) + \binom{5}{2}(x^3)^3(2y)^2 + \binom{5}{3}(x^3)^2(2y)^3 + \binom{5}{4}(x^3)(2y)^4 + \binom{5}{5}(2y)^5$

$\qquad = x^{15} + 5x^{12}(2y) + 10x^9(4y^2) + 10x^6(8y^3) + 5x^3(16y^4) + 32y^5$

$\qquad = x^{15} + 10x^{12}y + 40x^9y^2 + 80x^6y^3 + 80x^3y^4 + 32y^5$

35. $\sum\limits_{i=1}^{50}(4i - 25)$

$\qquad a_1 = 4(1) - 25 = -21$

$\qquad a_{50} = 4(50) - 25 = 175$

$\qquad S_{50} = \dfrac{50}{2}(-21 + 175) = 3850$

36. Find slope:

$\qquad m = \dfrac{y_2 - y_1}{x_2 - x_1} = \dfrac{1 - 3}{-2 - 6} = \dfrac{-2}{-8} = \dfrac{1}{4}$

Find equation:

$\qquad y - y_1 = m(x - x_1)$

$\qquad y - 3 = \dfrac{1}{4}(x - 6)$

$\qquad y - 3 = \dfrac{1}{4}x - \dfrac{3}{2}$

$\qquad y = \dfrac{1}{4}x + \dfrac{3}{2}$

37. Find the slope:

$\qquad x - 5y - 20 = 0$

$\qquad\qquad -5y = -x + 20$

$\qquad\qquad \dfrac{-5y}{-5} = \dfrac{-x}{-5} + \dfrac{20}{-5}$

$\qquad\qquad y = \dfrac{1}{5}x - 4$

$\qquad m = -\dfrac{1}{\frac{1}{5}} = -5$

Find the equation:

$\qquad y - y_1 = m(x - x_1)$

$\qquad y - (-2) = -5(x - 0)$

$\qquad y + 2 = -5x$

$\qquad y = -5x - 2$

38. $200 + 0.05x = 0.15x$

$\qquad 200 = 0.1x$

$\qquad 2000 = x$

At \$2000 in sales, the two earnings will be the same.

39. $2L + 2W = 300$
    $\qquad L = W + 50$
    Rearrange the equations and add:
    $L + W = 150$
    $\underline{L - W = 50}$
    $\qquad 2L = 200$
    $\qquad\; L = 100$
    $\qquad W = 50$
    length: 100 yards, width 50 yards

40. $10x + 12y = 42$
    $\;\; 5x + 10y = 29$
    Multiply second equation by -2 and add:
    $\quad 10x + 12y = 42$
    $\underline{-10x - 20y = -58}$
    $\qquad\quad -8y = -16$
    $\qquad\qquad y = 2$
    Back substitute:
    $5x + 10(2) = 29$
    $\qquad\;\; 5x = 9$
    $\qquad\quad x = 1.8$
    pen: \$1.80, pad: \$2

41. $s(t) = -16t^2 + 80t + 96$

   a. $-16t^2 + 80t + 96 = 0$
    $\qquad\quad t^2 - 5t - 6 = 0$
    $\qquad (t + 1)(t - 6) = 0$
    $\qquad\qquad\quad t = -1 \text{ or } t = 6$
    The ball will strike the ground after 6 seconds.

   b. $t = \dfrac{-b}{2a} = \dfrac{-80}{-32} = \dfrac{5}{2} \text{ or } 2.5$
    $S(2.5) = -16(2.5)^2 + 80(2.5) + 96 = 196$
    The ball reaches a maximum height of 196 feet, 2.5 seconds after it is thrown.

42. $I = \dfrac{k}{R}$

   $5 = \dfrac{k}{22}$

   $k = 110$

   $I = \dfrac{110}{10} = 11$

   11 amperes

43.   Let x represent the number of years after 1982.
    The data from 1982 and 2002 are represented as $(0, 179)$ and $(20, 57)$

   Find slope: $m = \dfrac{57 - 179}{20 - 0} = -6.1$

   Thus, $y = -6.1x + 179$

   At this rate there may eventually be no farms growing tobacco in the U.S.